INTERNATIONAL CRITICAL TABLES
OF
NUMERICAL DATA
PHYSICS, CHEMISTRY AND TECHNOLOGY

VOLUME III

INTERNATIONAL CRITICAL TABLES
OF
NUMERICAL DATA,
PHYSICS, CHEMISTRY AND TECHNOLOGY

Prepared under the Auspices of the International
Research Council and the National
Academy of Sciences

BY THE
NATIONAL RESEARCH COUNCIL
OF THE
UNITED STATES OF AMERICA

EDITOR-IN-CHIEF

EDWARD W. WASHBURN, PH.D.
Chief of the Division of Chemistry, National Bureau of Standards

ASSOCIATE EDITORS

CLARENCE J. WEST, PH.D.
Director, Research Information Service
National Research Council

N. ERNEST DORSEY, PH.D.
Formerly Physicist, National Bureau of Standards

ASSISTANT EDITORS

F. R. BICHOWSKY, PH.D.
Naval Research Laboratory
Washington, D. C.

ALFONS KLEMENC, PH.D.
Professor of Chemistry, University of Vienna

VOLUME III

PUBLISHED FOR THE
NATIONAL RESEARCH COUNCIL
BY THE
McGRAW-HILL BOOK COMPANY
NEW YORK AND LONDON
1928

PRINTED IN THE UNITED STATES OF AMERICA

13 14 15 16-MAMB-1
ISBN 07-031840-9 - 31750-x

BOARD OF TRUSTEES

BOARD OF EDITORS

CORRESPONDING EDITORS
AND
ADVISORY COMMITTEES

COOPERATING EXPERTS—VOLUME THREE

ARRANGEMENT OF CHEMICAL SUBSTANCES

Throughout I. C. T., except when otherwise indicated, the tabular arrangement of all chemical substances and of all systems capable of representation by formula is in accordance with a system called the "Standard Arrangement," which will now be explained and which should be learned by every user of I. C. T.

Elementary Substances

All tables containing *only* elementary substances (𝔄-Tables) are arranged in alphabetical order of the symbols of the elements. In tables containing both elements and compounds (𝔄-𝔅-Tables) the elements follow the "standard arrangement," *v. infra.*

Chemical Compounds and Other Systems Represented by Formula

The arrangement is based upon the following table of "Key-numbers" of the elements:

ARRANGEMENT DES SUBSTANCES CHIMIQUES

L'arrangement tabulaire de toutes les substances chimiques et de tous les systèmes susceptibles d'une représentation par formule est, dans les T. C. I., excepté lorsqu'il y a une autre indication, en accord avec un système appelé "arrangement type," (standard arrangement) expliqué ci-dessous, qui devra être appris par chaque personne qui veut utiliser les T. C. I.

Substances Élémentaires

Toutes les tables ne contenant que les substances élémentaires (Tables 𝔄) sont arrangées dans l'ordre alphabétique des symboles des éléments. Dans les tables contenant les éléments et les corps composés (Tables 𝔄-𝔅) les éléments se trouvent suivant "l'arrangement type," *voir infra.*

Composés Chimiques et Autres Systèmes Représentés par Formule

L'arrangement est basé sur la table suivante des "nombres-clés" des éléments:

KEY-NUMBERS OF THE ELEMENTS — NOMBRES-CLÉS DES ÉLÉMENTS

−6	−5	−4	−3	−2	−1	1	2	3	4	5	6	7	8	9	10	11	12	13	14	15	16	17	18	19	20
(He	Ne	A	Kr	Xe	Rn)	O	H	F	Cl	Br	I	(85)	S	Se	Te	N	P	As	Sb	Bi	C	Po	Si	Ti	Ge
						46	47	48	49	50	51	52	53	54	55	56	57	58	59	60	61	62	63	64	65
						Cr	Mo	W	U	V	Cb(Nb)	Ta	Pa	B	Al	Sc	Y	La	Ce	Pr	Nd	(61)	Sa	Eu	Gd

Ac	Ag	Al	As	Au	B	Ba	Be	Bi	Br	C	Ca	Cb	Cd	Ce	Cl	Co	Cr	Cs	Cu	Dy	Er	Eu	F	Fe
74	32	55	13	33	54	79	75	15	5	16	77	51	29	59	4	44	46	85	31	67	69	64	3	43
					Os	P	Pa	Pb	Pd	Po	Pr	Pt	Ra	Rb	Re	Rh	Ru	S	Sa	Sb	Sc	Se	Si	Sn
					35	12	53	23	41	17	60	37	80	84	34	40	39	8	63	14	56	9	18	22

To locate a given compound, first write its "key-formula," neglecting water of crystallization, thus:

Afin de situer un composé donné, il faut d'abord écrire sa "formule-clé," en négligeant l'eau de cristallisation ainsi:

Compound	Composé	Na_2SO_4	$HClO_4.3H_2O$	$Hg(C_{18}H_{33}O_2)_2$	$2Fe_2O_3.P_2O_5.12H_2O$	$Ni_3Pr_2(NO_3)_{12}.24H_2O$	$I_2C_6H_3SO_3H$	$(NH_4)_2CO_3$
Key formula	Formule-clé	82–8–1	4–2–1	30–16–2–1	43–12–1	60–45–11–1	16–8–6–2–1	16–11–2–1

DIE ANORDNUNG DER CHEMISCHEN VERBINDUNGEN

Durch die ganzen I. C. T., ausgenommen es ist etwas anderes angegeben, ist die tabellarische Anordnung aller chemischen Verbindungen und aller durch chemische Zeichen oder Formeln darstellbarer Systeme, nach der "Normal-Anordnung" (standard arrangement), durchgeführt. Sie ist im folgenden dargelegt und soll von jedem Leser der I. C. T. erlernt werden.

Elementare Stoffe

Alle Tafeln, welche *nur* elementare Stoffe (𝔄-Tabellen) enthalten, sind in alphabetischer Reihenfolge nach den Symbolen der Elemente angeordnet. In den Tafeln, welche beides, Elemente und Verbindungen (𝔄-𝔅-Tabellen), enthalten, folgen die Elemente der "Normal-Anordnung." Siehe weiter unten.

Die chemischen Verbindungen und andere durch Formeln darstellbare Systeme

Die Anordnung ist auf der folgenden Tafel begründet, welche die "Schlüsselnummern" der Elemente enthält:

ORDINE DI ELENCAZIONE DELLE SOSTANZE

In tutti i volumi delle T. C. I. l'ordine in cui le sostanze ed i sistemi rappresentabili con formule sono disposti nelle tabelle è (tranne che non sia diversamente indicato) quello "standard" illustrato più avanti. Chiunque voglia servirsi delle T. C. I. deve anzitutto apprendere in che consiste questo sistema "standard."

Sostanze Elementari

Tutte le tabelle contenenti soltanto sostanze elementari (Tabelle 𝔄) sono disposte secondo l'ordine alfabetico dei simboli degli elementi. Nelle tabelle che comprendono elementi e composti (Tabelle 𝔄-𝔅) gli elementi sono ordinati secondo la disposizione "Standard," *v. infra.*

Composti Chimici ed Altri Sistemi Rappresentati da Formule

La disposizione è basata sul quadro seguente di "numeri chiave" degli elementi:

SCHLÜSSELNUMMERN DER ELEMENTE															NUMERI CHIAVE DEGLI ELEMENTI									
21	22	23	24	25	26	27	28	29	30	31	32	33	34	35	36	37	38	39	40	41	42	43	44	45
Zr	Sn	Pb	Th	Ga	In	Tl	Zn	Cd	Hg	Cu	Ag	Au	Re	Os	Ir	Pt	Ma	Ru	Rh	Pd	Mn	Fe	Co	Ni
66	67	68	69	70	71	72	73	74	75	76	77	78	79	80	81	82	83	84	85	86				
Tb	Dy	Ho	Er	Tm	Yb	Lu	Hf	Ac	Be(Gl)	Mg	Ca	Sr	Ba	Ra	Li	Na	K	Rb	Cs	(87)				
Ga	Gd	Ge	Gl	H	Hf	Hg	Ho	I	In	Ir	K	La	Li	Lu	Ma	Mg	Mn	Mo	N	Na	Nb	Nd	Ni	O
25	65	20	75	2	73	30	68	6	26	36	83	58	81	72	38	76	42	47	11	82	51	61	45	1
Sr	Ta	Tb	Te	Th	Ti	Tl	Tm	U	V	W	Y	Yb	Zn	Zr	(61)	(75)	(85)	(87)						
78	52	66	10	24	19	27	70	49	50	48	57	71	28	21	62	34	7	86						

Um eine gegebene Verbindung aufzufinden, hat man zuerst seine Schlüsselformel aufzuschreiben, wobei man das Kristallwasser auslässt. z.B.:

Per trovare il posto di un dato composto bisogna prima scrivere la formula chiave trascurando l'acqua di cristallizzazione, p. es.:

Verbindungen	Composto	Na_2SO_4	$HClO_4.3H_2O$	$Hg(C_{18}H_{33}O_2)_2$	$2Fe_2O_3.P_2O_5.12H_2O$	$Ni_3Pr_2(NO_3)_{12}.24H_2O$	$I_2C_6H_3SO_3H$	$(NH_4)_2CO_3$
Schlüsselformel	Formula chiave	82–8–1	4–2–1	30–16–2–1	43–12–1	60–45–11–1	16–8–6–2–1	16–11–2–1

In writing a key-formula the key-numbers must be written *in descending order.*

All chemical compounds (𝔅-Tables) are arranged in the inverse numerical order of their key-formulae. *Example:* to find the compound $Hg(C_{18}H_{33}O_2)_2$ = 30 − 16 − 2 − 1: First, turn to section 30 of the table. Then follow down the column of chemical formulae until element 16 (C) is first encountered. From this point continue until element 2 (H) is found, and then on until element 1 (O) is reached. At this point will be found all the compounds composed of the four elements Hg, C, H, and O and these compounds are arranged in an obvious manner according to the subscripts in the chemical formula. To facilitate the use of the tables, key-numbers are inserted at frequent intervals either along the top of the page or down the left-hand column or both.

In looking for a chemical compound *always consult the 𝔅-Table,* the scope of which provides for *all* chemical compounds except those of the radioactive elements, of which only compounds of U, Th and Ra are given in the 𝔅-Table. For the others, *see* Vol. I, p. 364. In certain of the 𝔅-Tables, at the point where key-formulae beginning with 16 occur, there will be found frequently only a few of the simpler compounds, and the reader will be referred to a ℭ-Table where the remainder of such compounds will be found listed under a different arrangement known as

The ℭ-Arrangement

In this arrangement the compounds are arranged according to their empirical formulae (*including* water of crystallization), in the order C, H, with the remaining symbols alphabetical, *e.g.,* $C_6H_4I_2O_3S$. The ℭ-Tables, however, will not contain any carbon compound whose key-formula contains a number greater than 16.

SYSTEMS OF MORE THAN ONE COMPONENT

Case I.—The Nature of the A-Component Is Not Specifically Designated

To find a given system: First arrange the components of the system in order according to the arrangement stated for the table (*i.e.,* according to the standard arrangement or the ℭ-arrangement as the case may be).

Example: For the system, sodium chloride, ethyl alcohol, benzene, the standard arrangement would give:

$$A = \underset{16\ 2}{C_6H_6},\ B = \underset{16\ 2\ 1}{C_2H_6O},\ C = \underset{82\ 4}{NaCl}$$

For the system, hydrogen, water, mercuric chloride:

$$A = \underset{2}{H_2},\ B = \underset{2\ 1}{H_2O},\ C = \underset{30\ 4}{HgCl_2}$$

For the system acetic acid, benzene, carbon tetrachloride in the standard arrangement:

$$A = \underset{16\ 2}{C_6H_6},\ B = \underset{16\ 2\ 1}{C_2H_4O_2},\ C = \underset{16\ 4}{CCl_4}$$

In the ℭ-arrangement:

$$A = CCl_4,\ B = C_2H_4O_2,\ C = C_6H_6$$

The systems in the table are arranged in order of their A-components in the arrangement stated. All systems having the same A-component will be found under that component arranged in order of their B-components, etc., for the other components. To facilitate the use of the tables the initial key numbers (for standard arrangement) or the number of carbon atoms (for the ℭ-arrangement) of the A-components are inserted at frequent intervals along the top of the page. By use of these numbers the reader will be able to turn quickly to the page upon which a given system should be found.

Case II.—The A-Component Is Specifically Designated

In Case I it is necessary to make use of the stated arrangement in order to determine the A-component of the system. In many

Lorsqu'on écrit une formule-clé, les nombres-clés doivent être écrits *dans l'ordre des valeurs décroissantes.*

Tous les composés chimiques dans toutes les tables (Tables 𝔅) sont arrangés d'après l'ordre numérique inverse de leurs formules-clés. *Exemple:* Pour trouver le composé $Hg(C_{18}H_{33}O_2)_2$ = 30 − 16 − 2 − 1: Il s'agit premièrement de chercher la section 30 de la table; ensuite de suivre en descendant la colonne des formules chimiques jusqu'à ce qu'on trouve l'élément 16 (C). De ce point, on continue jusqu'à ce qu'on rencontre l'élément 2 (H), et ensuite jusqu'à ce que l'élément 1 (O) soit atteint. On trouvera alors à ce point tous les composés renfermant les quatre éléments Hg, C, H et O et ces composés sont arrangés d'une manière apparente en relation avec les indices de leurs formules chimiques. Afin de faciliter l'usage des tables, les nombres-clés sont inscrits, à de fréquents intervalles, ou au haut de la page ou le long de la colonne gauche, ou aux deux places.

Pour la recherche d'un composé chimique, il s'agit de *consulter toujours la Table 𝔅* dont le but est de renseigner sur *tous* les composés chimiques, à l'exception des éléments radio-actifs, dont seuls ceux de U, Th et Ra sont donnés dans la Table 𝔅. Pour les autres, *voir* Vol. I, p. 364. Dans certaines des Tables 𝔅, au point où les formules-clés commençant par 16 se présentent, on ne trouvera fréquemment qu'un petit nombre de composés plus simples, et le lecteur sera alors renvoyé à une Table ℭ, où le reste de ces composés se trouvera disposé d'une façon différente nommé

L'Arrangement ℭ

Dans cet arrangement, les composés sont disposés en relation avec leurs formules empiriques (l'eau de cristallisation inclusivement) dans l'ordre C, H, les symboles restants venant ensuite dans l'ordre alphabétique; par ex: $C_6H_4I_2O_3S$. Cependant les Tables ℭ ne contiendront aucun composé dont la formule-clé renferme un nombre supérieur à 16.

SYSTÈMES À PLUS D'UN CONSTITUANT

Cas I.—La nature du constituant A n'est pas spécifiquement désignée

Pour trouver un système donné il faut: Premièrement arranger les constituants du système dans l'ordre en accord avec l'arrangement fixé pour la table (*i.e.,* en accord avec l'arrangement type, ou l'arrangement ℭ suivant les cas).

Exemple: Pour le système, chlorure de sodium, alcool éthylique, benzène, l'arrangement type donnera:

$$A = \underset{16\ 2}{C_6H_6},\ B = \underset{16\ 2\ 1}{C_2H_6O},\ C = \underset{82\ 4}{NaCl}$$

Pour le système hydrogène, eau, chlorure mercurique:

$$A = \underset{2}{H_2},\ B = \underset{2\ 1}{H_2O},\ C = \underset{30\ 4}{HgCl_2}$$

Pour le système, acide acétique, benzène, tétrachlorure de carbone on aura suivant l'arrangement type:

$$A = \underset{16\ 2}{C_6H_6},\ B = \underset{16\ 2\ 1}{C_2H_4O_2},\ C = \underset{16\ 4}{CCl_4}$$

Suivant l'arrangement ℭ:

$$A = CCl_4,\ B = C_2H_4O_2,\ C = C_6H_6$$

Dans les tables les systèmes sont arrangés dans l'ordre de leurs constituants A dans l'arrangement fixé. On trouvera tous les systèmes ayant le même constituant A, disposés sous ce constituant, arrangés dans l'ordre de leurs constituants B; etc., pour les autres constituants. Afin de faciliter la recherche, il a été inscrit à de fréquents intervalles au haut de la page, les nombres-clés initiaux (pour l'arrangement type) ou le nombre des atomes de carbone (pour l'arrangement ℭ) des constituants A. Au moyen de ces nombres, le lecteur trouvera rapidement la page à laquelle est mentionné un système donné.

In die Schlüsselformel müssen die Schlüsselnummern in *absteigender* Reihenfolge geschrieben werden.

Alle chemischen Verbindungen (𝔅-Tabellen) sind in der umgekehrten Reihenfolge der Schlüsselformeln angeordnet. Z. B.: um die Verbindung $Hg(C_{18}H_{33}O_2)_2$ = 30–16–2–1 zu finden, hat man zuerst den Abschnitt 30 aufzusuchen. Dann hat man den Kolonnen der chemischen Verbindungen abwärts zu folgen, bis man zuerst das Element 16 (C) antrifft, von da an setzt man weiter fort, bis das Element 2 (H) gefunden ist und dann weiter, bis das Element 1 (O) erreicht ist. Bei dieser Stelle werden alle Verbindungen gefunden werden, welche sich aus den 4 Elementen Hg, C, H, und O zusammensetzen. Diese Verbindungen sind in deutlicher Art, entsprechend der Bezeichnungsweise chemischer Formeln, angeordnet. Um den Gebrauch der Tafeln möglichst zu erleichtern, sind die Schlüsselnummern häufig an verschiedenen Stellen eingefügt. Sie befinden sich entweder am Kopf der Seiten, oder auf der linken Seite unten, oder an beiden Stellen.

Um eine chemische Verbindung zu suchen, *benütze man immer die 𝔅-Tabellen:* die *alle* chemischen Verbindungen enthalten, ausgenommen jene der radioaktiven Elemente. Von diesen sind in den 𝔅-Tabellen nur die Verbindungen des U, Th und Ra enthalten. Für die anderen, *siehe* Bd. I, Seite 364. In einigen 𝔅-Tabellen, dort wo die Schlüsselnummern mit 16 beginnen, findet man häufig nur einige wenige einfache Verbindungen. Der Leser wird dann auf die ℭ-Tabellen verwiesen, wo die restlichen derartigen Verbindungen gefunden werden können. Diese Tabellen sind nach anderen Gesichtspunkten zusammengestellt. Es ist das die

ℭ-Anordnung (ℭ-Arrangement)

Bei dieser Anordnung sind die Verbindungen nach ihrer empirischen Formel gegeben (einschliesslich Kristallwasser) und zwar in der Ordnung C, H, die restlichen Zeichen dann in alphabetischer Ordnung, z.B. $C_6H_4I_2O_3S$. Die ℭ-Tabellen enthalten jedoch keine Kohlenstoffverbindung, in deren Schlüsselformel eine Zahl grösser als 16 vorkommt.

SYSTEME MIT MEHR ALS EINER KOMPONENTE

Fall I.—Die Natur der A-Komponente ist nicht besonders gekennzeichnet

Auffindung eines gegebenen Systems: Man ordne zuerst die Komponenten des Systems nach den diesen Tafeln zugrunde gelegten Anordnung (das ist entweder die Standardanordnung oder die ℭ-Anordnung, wie gerade der Fall vorliegt).

Beispiel: Man hat das System Natriumchlorid, Äthylalkohol, Benzol, von dem die Standardanordnung gibt:

$$A = \underset{16\ 2}{C_6H_6},\ B = \underset{16\ 2\ 1}{C_2H_6O},\ C = \underset{82\ \ 4}{NaCl}$$

Für das System Wasserstoff, Wasser, Merkurichlorid, hat man:

$$A = \underset{2}{H_2},\ B = \underset{2\ 1}{H_2O},\ C = \underset{30\ \ 4}{HgCl_2}$$

Für das System Essigsäure, Benzol, Kohlenstofftetrachlorid erhält man nach dem gleichen System:

$$A = \underset{16\ 2}{C_6H_6},\ B = \underset{16\ 2\ 1}{C_2H_4O_2},\ C = \underset{16\ 4}{CCl_4}$$

Nach der ℭ-Anordnung jedoch:

$$A = CCl_4,\ B = C_2H_4O_2,\ C = C_6H_6$$

In den Tafeln sind die Systeme in der Reihenfolge ihrer A-Komponenten nach der gegebenen Anordnung gereiht. Alle Systeme welche dieselbe A-Komponente besitzen werden unter dieser Komponente gefunden, die nach der B-Komponente gereiht sind. Das gleiche gilt für die anderen Komponenten. Um den Gebrauch der Tafeln zu erleichteren, sind für die Standardanordnung die Schlüsselzahlen, oder für die ℭ-Anordnung die Zahl der Kohlen-

Nella formula chiave, i numeri chiave devono essere scritti *in ordine decrescente.*

Tutti i composti in tutte le tabelle (Tabelle 𝔅) sono disposti nell'ordine numerico inverso delle loro formule chiavi. Supponiamo ad es. di voler trovare il composto $Hg(C_{18}H_{33}O_2)_2$ = 30–16–2–1. Prima si cerca la sezione 30 della tabella, poi si scorre la colonna delle formule fino ad incontrare l'elemento 16 (C). Da questo punto si continua finchè si trova l'elemento 2 (H), e quindi fino a raggiungere l'elemento 1 (O). Qui si trovano tutti i composti risultanti dai quattro elementi Hg, C, H e O ordinati secondo gli indici delle formule. Per facilitare l'uso delle tabelle i numeri chiave sono inseriti ad intervalli frequenti nella testata o lungo il margine sinistro della pagina, o nell'una e nell'altro.

Per cercare un composto bisogna *sempre consultare la Tabella 𝔅* che contiene *tutti* i composti tranne quelli degli elementi radioattivi; di questi sono riportati nella Tabella 𝔅 soltanto i composti di U, Th, Ra. Per gli altri, *vedi* Vol. I, p. 364. In alcune Tabelle 𝔅, laddove si trovano formule chiave che cominciano con 16, si troveranno spesso soltanto pochi composti fra i più semplici e il lettore sarà rimandato a una Tabella ℭ dove si troveranno gli altri disposti con criterio differente che viene chiamato

La Disposizione ℭ

Secondo questa i composti sono disposti in base alle formule empiriche (*compresa* l'acqua di cristallizzazione) nell'ordine C, H e con i rimanenti simboli ordinati alfabeticamente, p. es. $C_6H_4I_2O_3S$. Le Tabelle ℭ non comprendono però composti del carbonio che hanno un numero chiave più grande di 16.

SISTEMI CON PIÙ DI DUE COMPONENTI

Caso I.—La natura del componente A non è specificatamente indicata

Per trovare un dato sistema si dispongono i componenti seguendo l'ordine stabilito per la tabella (cioè l'ordinamento standard o quello ℭ a seconda del caso).

Esempio: Per il sistema cloruro di sodio, alcool etilico, benzolo, l'ordinamento standard sarebbe:

$$A = \underset{16\ 2}{C_6H_6},\ B = \underset{16\ 2\ 1}{C_2H_6O},\ C = \underset{82\ \ 4}{NaCl}$$

Per il sistema idrogeno, acqua, cloruro mercurico:

$$A = \underset{2}{H_2},\ B = \underset{2\ 1}{H_2O},\ C = \underset{30\ \ 4}{HgCl_2}$$

Per il sistema acido acetico, benzolo, tetracloruro di carbonio, nell'ordinamento standard:

$$A = \underset{16\ 2}{C_6H_6},\ B = \underset{16\ 2\ 1}{C_2H_4O_2},\ C = \underset{16\ 4}{CCl_4}$$

Nell'ordinamento ℭ:

$$A = CCl_4,\ B = C_2H_4O_2,\ C = C_6H_6$$

Nella tabella i sistemi sono disposti secondo l'ordine che compete al componente A nell'ordinamento seguito. Tutti i sistemi con lo stesso componente A si trovano sotto quel componente disposti nell'ordine dei componenti B. E così per tutti gli altri componenti. Per facilitare l'uso delle tabelle, i numeri chiave iniziali (per l'ordinamento standard), o il numero di atomi di carbonio del componente A (per l'ordinamento ℭ), sono riportati spesso nella testata della pagina. Con l'uso di questi numeri il lettore potrà arrivare facilmente alla pagina dove deve ricercare un dato sistema.

Caso II.—Il componente A è specificatamente designato

Nel Caso I è necessario servirsi dell'ordinamento stabilito per fissare il componente A del sistema. In molti casi però questo non è necessario, perchè la natura del componente A è spesso designata in modo specifico per certe tabelle. Così nel capitolo

instances this is not necessary, however, since the nature of the A-component is frequently specifically designated for certain tables. Thus for the systems in the section on the solubility of gases in liquids the dissolving gas is designated as the A-component; for the systems in the sections on distribution of a solute between two non-miscible solvents, the distributed substance is designated as the A-component; for certain two-component systems composed of a substance (1) whose key-formula does not begin with 16 and a substance (2) whose key-formula begins with 16, the former (1) is arbitrarily designated as the A-component, etc.

Just as in Case I, the systems with specifically designated A-components are arranged in the order of these A-components according to the arrangement stated at the head of the table.

Example: The density or coefficient of thermal expansion of a liquid solution of 2-hydroxytoluene in benzene under atmospheric pressure is desired.

1. Consult the table of contents, p. xiv. It is evident that the information sought can belong only in the chapter entitled "*P-V-T* Relations for one-phase systems," p. 1.

2. Turn to p. 1 and glance through the main headings and then the appropriate sub-heads until the correct section is located which will obviously be thus:

(*a*) **Systems of more than one component.**
(*b*) *The liquid state under atmospheric pressure.*
(*c*) Non-aqueous solutions.
(*d*) Non-metallic liquids, p. 130.

3. Turn to p. 130, and similarly scan the table of contents there given, locating the appropriate section thus:

(*a*) All components of the system are chemical compounds.
(*b*) All components have key-formulae beginning with 16.
(*c*) Two-component systems, p. 143.

In locating this final section it is necessary first to write the key-formulae of the components of the system, or at least to determine whether one or both key formulae begin or do not begin with 16. In the present example both formulae obviously begin with 16 and we therefore:

4. Turn to p. 143. Here we find a table for which the arrangement stated is the $\mathfrak{C}$-arrangement. With the aid of the name index in Vol. I, p. 280 (or from some other source of formulae for organic compounds) we obtain the empirical formulae of our two components, which when listed in the $\mathfrak{C}$-arrangements give us:

$$A = C_6H_6;\ B = C_7H_8O$$

5. With the aid of the running heads at the tops of the pages we then turn readily to the C_6 and then to the C_6H_6 page (p. 179) and on p. 179 we readily locate C_6H_6 in large bold-face type. We also note carefully that there is given in this type face only one compound of this formula.

6. Under C_6H_6 are listed a series of B-components in the $\mathfrak{C}$-arrangement among which we finally locate (Item No. 889) on p. 179 the desired system, *i.e.*, $B = C_7H_8O$, *o*-Cresol, which name is a synonym for 2-hydroxytoluene.*

*Not infrequently the name in the table may be a synonym of the one sought.

Cas II. Le constituant A est spécifiquement désigné

Dans le Cas I il est nécessaire d'utiliser l'arrangement fixé afin de déterminer le constituant A du système. Dans plusieurs circonstances ceci n'est cependant pas nécessaire, car la nature du constituant A est fréquemment spécifiquement désignée pour certaines tables. Ainsi pour les systèmes dans la section relative à la solubilité des gaz dans les liquides, le gaz dissout est désigné comme constituant A. Pour les systèmes dans la section relative à la distribution d'un corps dissout entre deux dissolvants non miscibles, la substance distribuée est désignée comme constituant A; pour certains systèmes à deux constituants composés d'une substance (1) dont la formule-clé ne commence pas par 16 et d'une substance (2) dont la formule-clé commence par 16, la première (1) est arbitrairement désignée comme constituant A, etc.

De même que dans le Cas I, les systèmes à constituants A spécifiquement désignés, sont arrangés dans l'ordre de ces constituants A en accord avec l'arrangement fixé au début de la table.

Exemple: On désire connaître la densité ou le coëfficient de dilatation thermique d'une solution liquide de 2-hydroxytoluène dans le benzène à la pression atmosphérique.

1. Consulter la table des matières p. xiv. Il est évident que l'information cherchée ne peut se trouver qu'au chapitre intitulé "Relations entre *P-V-T* pour des systèmes à une phase," p. 1.

2. À la page 1 on parcourera des yeux les titres principaux et ensuite les sous-titres appropriés jusqu'à ce qu'on localise la section convenable. C'est ainsi qu'on trouvera:

(*a*) **Systèmes de plus d'un constituant.**
(*b*) *L'état liquide à la pression atmosphérique.*
(*c*) Solutions non-aqueuses.
(*d*) Liquides non-métalliques, p. 130.

3. Chercher la p. 130 et d'une façon similaire parcourir la table des matières qui s'y trouve afin de déterminer la section cherchée, ainsi:

(*a*) Tous les constituants du système sont des composés chimiques.

(*b*) Tous les constituants possèdent une formule-clé commençant par 16.

(*c*) Systèmes à deux constituants, p. 143.

Pour pouvoir localiser cette section finale il est alors nécessaire d'écrire la formule-clé des constituants du système ou au moins de déterminer si la formule-clé de l'un de ceux-ci ou si les deux formules commencent ou non par 16. Dans le présent exemple il est évident que les deux formules commencent par 16.

4. On cherche donc la p. 143. On y trouve une table pour laquelle l'arrangement fixé est l'arrangement $\mathfrak{C}$. Au moyen de l'index des noms dans le Vol. I, p. 280 (ou à partir d'une autre source de formules pour composés organiques) on obtient la formule empirique de nos deux constituants qui disposés suivant l'arrangement $\mathfrak{C}$ donnent:

$$A = C_6H_6;\ B = C_7H_8O$$

5. À l'aide des rappels qui se trouvent au haut des pages, on trouve rapidement C_6 et ensuite la page C_6H_6 (p. 179) et on situe de suite C_6H_6 écrit en gros caractères gras à la page 179. On note soigneusement qu'il n'est imprimé en ce genre de caractères qu'un seul composé de cette formule.

6. Sous C_6H_6, les différents constituants B sont disposés suivant l'arrangement $\mathfrak{C}$ et parmi ceux-ci on trouve finalement (article N° 889) à la p. 179, le système désiré, c'est à dire $B = C_7H_8O$, *o*-crésol dont le nom est un synonyme de 2-hydroxytoluène.*

*Il n'est pas rare que le nom dans la table puisse être un synonyme de celui qu'on cherche.

stoffatome der A-Komponente in kurzen Abständen am Kopfe der Seite angebracht. Beim Gebrauch dieser Zahlen wird der Leser im Stande sein, rasch die Seite aufzuschlagen auf welcher das gesuchte System gefunden werden kann.

Fall II.—Die A-Komponente ist besonders gekennzeichnet

Im Fall I ist es notwendig die Standardanordnung zu gebrauchen, um die A-Komponente des Systems festzulegen. In vielen Fällen ist dies doch nicht notwendig, da die A-Komponente in bestimmten Tafeln besonders gekennzeichnet ist. So ist in dem Abschnitt über die Löslichkeit der Gase in Flüssigkeiten, das sich lösende Gas als A-Komponente angeführt; in dem Abschnitt weiters, über die Verteilung eines gelösten Stoffes zwischen zwei nicht mischbaren Flüssigkeiten, ist der sich verteilende Stoff als A-Komponente angeführt. Ferner ist in gewissen Zwei-Komponenten Systemen die aus einem Stoff (1) bestehen, dessen Schlüsselformel nicht mit 16 beginnt und einem Stoff (2) dessen Schlüsselformel mit 16 beginnt, der Stoff (1) willkürlich als A-Komponente bezeichnet; u.s.w.

Genau so wie im Fall I sind die Systeme mit näher gekennzeichneten A-Komponente, nach der am Kopfe der Tafeln angegebenen Anordnung nach der A-Komponente gereiht.

Beispiel: Es ist die Dichte oder der thermische Ausdehnungskoefficient einer flüssigen Lösung von 2-Hydroxytoluol in Benzol unter Atmosphären Druck aufzufinden.

1. Man sehe zuerst das Inhaltsverzeichnis, S. xiv an. Es ist klar, dass die gesuchte Grösse nur zu dem Kapitel "*P-V-T* Beziehungen für Einphasen-Systeme," S. 1 gehören kann.

2. Man schlage S. 1 auf und sehe die Kopftitel und die dazugehörigen Untertiteln durch, bis der richtige Abschnitt von der folgenden Art festgestellt ist:

(*a*) **Systeme mit mehr als einer Komponente.**
(*b*) *Flüssiger Zustand unter Atmosphären Druck.*
(*c*) Nichtwässrige Lösungen.
(*d*) Nichtmetallische Flüssigkeiten, S. 130.

3. Man schlage S. 130 auf und prüfe in gleicher Weise das hier gegebene Inhaltsverzeichnis nach dem bezüglichen Abschnitt:

(*a*) Alle Komponenten des Systems sind chemische Verbindungen.
(*b*) Die Schlüsselformeln aller Komponenten beginnen mit 16.
(*c*) Zwei-Komponenten Systeme, S. 143.

Um diesen letzten Abschnitt zu bestimmen, ist es notwendig zuerst die Schlüsselformeln der Komponenten des Systems niederzuschreiben, oder mindestens zu bestimmen, ob die Schlüsselformel der einen oder beider Komponenten mit 16 beginnt oder nicht. In dem gegenwärtigen Beispiel beginnen selbstverständlich beide Formeln mit 16 und man wendet sich deshalb:

4. Auf S. 143. Hier findet man eine Tafel für welche die angegebene Anordnung die 𝕮-Anordnung ist. Mit Hilfe des Namen-Verzeichnisses, Band I, S. 280 (oder aus einer andern die Formel der chemischen Verbindung liefernden Quelle) erhält man die empirische Formel unserer zwei Komponenten, die in der 𝕮-Anordnung angeführt lauten:

$$A = C_6H_6;\ B = C_7H_8O$$

5. Mit Hilfe der fortlaufenden Hauptzeichen am Kopfe der Seiten findet man leicht zur C_6 und dann zur C_6H_6 Seite (S. 179). Auf S. 179 kann man leicht C_6H_6 in grossen fettgedruckten Zeichen auffinden. Man stelle mit Vorsicht auch fest, dass in dieser Zeichenart nur eine Komponente dieser Formel vorkommt.

6. Unter C_6H_6 sind eine Serie von B-Komponenten in der 𝕮-Anordnung gereiht, unter denen wir schliesslich (Item No. 889) auf S. 179 das gesuchte System, B = C_7H_8O, *o*-Cresol feststellen, ein für 2-Hydroxytoluol gleiches bezeichnender Name.*

* Es wird nicht selten der in der Tafel vorkommende Namen mit dem gesuchten nicht gleichlauten.

riguardante la solubilità dei gas nei liquidi, il gas che si discioglie è considerato come componente A; nel capitolo riguardante la distribuzione di un soluto fra due solventi non miscibili, la sostanza disciolta è indicata come componente A; per certi sistemi a due componenti risultanti di una sostanza (1) la cui formula chiave non comincia con 16, e una sostanza (2) con formula chiave che comincia con 16, la prima (1) è arbitrariamente designata come componente A, ecc.

Come nel Caso I i sistemi con componenti A indicati in modo specifico sono ordinati secondo questi componenti A in accordo con l'ordinamento stabilito in testa alla tabella.

Esempio: Si desideri la densità o il coefficiente di dilatazione termica di una soluzione liquida di 2-idrossitoluolo in benzolo alla pressione atmosferica.

1. Si consulta l'indice a page xiv. È evidente che la notizia che si cerca si trova solo nel capitolo "Relazioni fra *P-V-T* nei sistemi monofasi," a pag. 1.

2. Si cerca a p. 1 e si guarda tra le intestazioni principali e secondarie fino a trovare il capitolo esatto:

(*a*) **Sistemi con più di un componente.**
(*b*) *Liquidi alla pressione atmosferica.*
(*c*) Soluzioni non acquose.
(*d*) Liquidi non metallici, p. 130.

3. Si cerca a pag. 130 e si esamina l'indice. Si trova:

(*a*) Tutti i componenti del sistema sono composti.
(*b*) La formula chiave di tutti i componenti comincia con 16.
(*c*) Sistemi a due componenti, p. 143.

Per trovare questo capitolo finale è necessario scrivere prima la formula chiave dei componenti o almeno determinare se una sola delle due formule chiave o entrambe cominciano con 16. Nell' esempio di cui si tratta entrambe le formule cominciano con 16 e perciò:

4. Si passa a p. 143. Qui si trova una tabella nella quale l'ordinamento seguito è quello 𝕮. Per mezzo dell'indice dei nomi nel Vol. I, pag. 280 (oppure con un altro elenco di formule di composti organici) si ottengono le formule empiriche dei nostri due componenti, i quali, disposti secondo l'ordinamento 𝕮 ci danno:

$$A = C_6H_6;\ B = C_7H_8O$$

5. Con l'aiuto delle intestazioni a capo delle pagine si passa allora facilmente alla pagina con C_6 e quindi con C_6H_6 (p. 179) e a p. 179 si trova agevolmente C_6H_6 stampato in carattere grosso. In questo carattere è riportato solo un composto di questa formula.

6. Sotto C_6H_6 è elencata una serie di componenti B nell'ordinamento 𝕮, e tra essi alla fine troviamo a pag. 179 il sistema cercato (Item N° 889) cioè B = C_7H_8O *o*-cresolo, sinonimo di 2-idrossitoluolo.*

* Spesso il nome della tabella può essere un sinonimo di quello cercato.

CONTENTS

MATIÈRES

INHALTSVERZEICHNIS

INDICE

INTERNATIONAL CRITICAL TABLES

P-V-T RELATIONS FOR ONE-PHASE SYSTEMS

(DENSITY, SPECIFIC GRAVITY, THERMAL EXPANSION AND COMPRESSIBILITY)

Complete Index

One-Component Systems

* *See also* Vol. I, p. 102.

† This chapter covers only data showing the variation of density or volume with temperature. For additional density data at single temperatures, *see* Vol. I, p. 98–314 and 338–347.

Index Complet

Systèmes à un constituant

* *Voir aussi* Vol. I, p. 102.

† Ce chapitre ne comprend que les données indiquant la variation de la densité ou du volume avec la température. Pour d'autres données de densité à une seule température, *voir* Vol. I, p. 98–314 et 338–347.

Gesamt Index Verzeichnis

Einkomponenten-Systeme

* *Siehe auch* Bd. I, S. 102.

† Dieser Abschnitt enthält nur Angaben über die Änderung der Dichte oder des Volumens mit der Temperatur. Weitere Angaben über Dichten bei einzelnen Temperaturen, *siehe* Bd. I, S. 98–314 und 338–347.

Indice Completo

Sistemi ad un componente

* *Vedi anche* Vol. I, p. 102.

† Questo capitolo contiene solo notizie sulla variazione della densità e del volume in funzione della temperatura. Per ulteriori notizie sulle densità a singole temperature, *vedi* Vol. I, p. 98–314 e 338–347.

INDEX.—(*Continued*)

Systems of More Than One Component

‡ *See also* **Vol. I, p.** 98–314 and 338–347.

MATIÈRES.—(*Suite*)

Systèmes de plus d'un constituant

‡ *Voir aussi* Vol. I, p. 98–314 et 338–347.

INHALTSVERZEICHNIS.—(*Fortsetzung*)

Systeme mit mehr als einer Komponente

‡ *Siehe auch* **Bd. I, S.** 98–314 und 338–347.

INDICE.—(*Continuazione*)

PAGE

Sistemi con più di un componente

‡ *Vedi anche* Vol. I, p. 98–314 e 338–347.

P-V-T RELATIONS IN THE GASEOUS STATE FOR SUBSTANCES WHICH ARE GASES AT 0° AND 1 ATMOSPHERE

S. F. Pickering

PART I. STANDARD DENSITY

$$1 + \lambda = \frac{p_0 v_0(0°, 0_{atm.})}{p_1 v_1(0°, 1A_n)}. \quad v_0 = \frac{M(1+\lambda)}{d_s}$$

Formula	Formula weight, M	d_s, gl^{-1} 0°, 1A$_n$	Lit.	$1 + \lambda$	Lit.	v_0
A-Table.—Elements and Atmospheric Air						
A	39.91	1.7832	(55, 71, 112, 124)	1.0009_0	(54 55, 100)	22.401
Cl_2	70.916	3.214	(61)			
F_2	38.000	1.696	(78)			
H_2	2.0154	0.08988	(42, 92, 93, 131)	0.9993_9	(44, 49, 51, 54, 99, 138)	22.410
He	4.00	0.1785	(16, 42, 50, 131, 140)	0.9995_4	(49, 54, 55, 97)	22.398
Kr	82.9	3.70_8	(91, 139)			
N_2 (chem.)	28.016	1.2505_7	(37, 82, 87, 88, 146)	1.0004_7	(49, 52, 54, 74, 125, 146)	22.413
N_2 (atm.)		1.2568	(107)			
Ne	20.2	0.900_2	(139)	0.999_6	(53, 54, 101)	22.430
O_2	32.00	1.4290_4	(15, 22, 34, 37, 58, 60, 69, 84, 89, 90, 92, 94, 114, 122, 134, 145, 153)	1.0009_4	(10, 44, 52, 59, 67, 74, 145)	22.413_7
Rn	222	9.73	(38)			
Xe	130.2	5.85_1	(91, 139)			
Air		1.2929	(34, 35, 41, 46, 68, 86, 107, 114, 136)	1.0006_1	(54, 55)	

B-Table.—Chemical Compounds

Standard arrangement (*v.* p. viii)

Formula	Formula weight, M	d_s, gl^{-1} 0°, 1A$_n$	Lit.	$1 + \lambda$	Lit.	v_0
Cl_2O	86.916	3.89	(33)			
HCl	36.4657	1.6392	(24, 122)	1.0074	(123)	22.411
HBr	80.9237	3.6445	(80, 120)	1.0092_9	(80, 120)	22.411
HI	127.9397	5.789_1	(30, 148)	1.015	(148)	22.432
SO_2	64.065	2.9269	(40, 122)	1.024_0	(11, 59)	22.414
H_2S	34.0804	1.539	(12)	1.010	(74)	22.369
H_2Se	81.2154	3.670	(23)	1.01_2	(23)	22.391
H_2Te	129.5154	4.49*	(32)			
NO	30.008	1.3402	(37, 45, 122)	1.0011	(5, 9, 59, 123)	22.420
N_2O	44.016	1.977_8	(47, 77, 116)	1.0074	(9, 39, 117)	22.420
NH_3	17.0311	0.7710	(48, 75, 110, 122, 154)	1.015_1	(74)	22.423
NOCl	65.466	2.992	(143)			
PH_3	34.0471	1.529_4	(132)			
PF_5	126.024	5.81	(76)			
POF_3	104.024	4.8	(77)			
AsH_3	77.9831	3.48	(31)			
SbH_3	124.7931	5.30†	(127)			
CO	28.000	1.250_4	(77, 115)	1.0005	(123)	22.404
CO_2	44.000	1.9769	(27, 48, 68, 115, 119)	1.0070_6	(44)	22.414
CH_4	16.0308	0.716_8	(13, 64)	1.0024	(64)	22.418
C_2H_2	26.0154	1.173	(126, 150)	1.010	(57, 150)	22.400
C_2H_4	28.0308	1.260_4	(4)	1.0078_0	(9, 44)	22.413
C_2H_6	30.0462	1.3566	(13, 126)			
C_3H_8	44.0616	2.020	(135)			
iso-C_4H_{10}	58.077	2.673	(106)			
$(CH_3)_2O$	46.0462	2.1098	(6, 11)	1.0254	(7, 9)	22.379
CH_3F	34.0231	1.545_2	(85)	1.018_1	(83)	22.416
CH_3Cl	50.4811	2.3076	(8, 11, 144)	1.0244	(8, 11, 14, 144)	22.410
iso-C_4H_9F	92.5273	2.58‡	(79)			
COS	60.065	2.72	(133)			
CH_3NH_2	31.0465	1.396	(95)			
$(CH_3)_2NH$	45.0619	1.966§	(95)			
$(CH_3)_3N$	59.0773	2.580§	(95)			
SiH_4	32.0908	1.44	(128)			
Si_2H_6	62.1662	2.85	(128)			
SiF_4	104.06	4.684	(36)			
SiH_3Cl	66.5411	3.03	(129)			
$SiH_3(CH_3)$	46.1062	2.08	(129)			
$SiH_2(CH_3)_2$	60.1216	2.73	(129)			
$SiH_2Cl(CH_3)$	80.5565	3.64	(129)			
$SiHCl_2(CH_3)$	115.0068	5.3	(129)			
GeH_4	76.4108	3.420	(26)			
$(CH_3)_3B$	55.8893	2.52	(130)			

* 3°/air 3°. † 15°, 754 mm. ‡ 21°/air 21°. § 17°.

PART II. THERMAL EXPANSION AND COMPRESSIBILITY

$\alpha_{0,t} = \dfrac{v - v_0}{t v_0}$, the coefficient of expansion at constant pressure, p_0, between 0° and t, °C

$\beta_{0,t} = \dfrac{p - p_0}{t p_0}$, the coefficient at constant volume, v_0, between 0° and t, °C

A-Table.—Elementary Substances and Atmospheric Air

A, Argon

p, m Hg	100α (53, 55) 0 to 50°C	0 to 100°C	0 to 150°C	0 to 200°C	0 to 300°C	0 to 400°C
0					0.3660	0.3660
1	0.3678	0.3676	0.3675	0.3673	0.3672	0.3671
5					0.3716	0.3711
10	0.3826	0.3804	0.3793	0.3780	0.3772	0.3761
15					0.3826	0.3811
20	0.4004	0.3955	0.3930	0.3903	0.3881	0.3860
25					0.3934	0.3908
30	0.4176	0.4104	0.4064	0.4026	0.3986	0.3955
35					0.4038	0.4001
40	0.4348	0.4251	0.4195	0.4146	0.4089	0.4047
45					0.4138	0.4091
50	0.4507	0.4390	0.4321	0.4259	0.4187	0.4135
55					0.4235	0.4177
60	0.4662	0.4525	0.4442	0.4369	0.4282	0.4218
65					0.4327	0.4259
70	0.4813	0.4656	0.4556	0.4473	0.4371	0.4298
75	0.4886	0.4720	0.4610	0.4524	0.4415	0.4336
80					0.4456	0.4372

$\frac{1}{v}$	100β (53, 55) 0 to 50°C	0 to 100°C	0 to 150°C	0 to 200°C	0 to 300°C	0 to 400°C
0					0.3660	0.3660
1	0.3676	0.3675	0.3675	0.3674	0.3674	0.3674
5					0.3728	0.3727
10	0.3801	0.3794	0.3796	0.3790	0.3796	0.3794
15					0.3863	0.3860

A, Argon.—(*Continued*)

$\frac{1}{v}$	100β (53, 55) 0 to 50°C	0 to 100°C	0 to 150°C	0 to 200°C	0 to 300°C	0 to 400°C
20	0.3957	0.3940	0.3937	0.3930	0.3931	0.3926
25					0.3998	0.3991
30	0.4109	0.4085	0.4081	0.4070	0.4066	0.4055
35					0.4112	
40	0.4255	0.4228	0.4224	0.4209	0.4158	
50	0.4397	0.4371	0.4360			
60	0.4539					
65	0.4609					

100β = 0.3671, 0 to 20°, p at 0° = 0.76 m (100).

p, kg/cm²	$v_{3000} - v_p$, cm³/g	p, kg/cm²	$v_{3000} - v_p$, cm³/g	p, kg/cm²	$v_{3000} - v_p$, cm³/g	Lit.
2 000	−0.083	6 000	0.112	11 000	0.190	(19, 20)
2 500	−0.034	7 000	0.134	12 000	0.201	
3 000	0.000	8 000	0.152	13 000	0.209	
4 000	+0.049	9 000	0.167	14 000	0.217	
5 000	0.085	10 000	0.180	15 000	0.224	

p in atm.; v = 1.0000 at 0°C and 1 atm.; range, 0 to 100 atm. (53, 54, 55)

−100°C	$pv = 0.6346 - 0.0_2 2872p - 0.0_4 1021p^2 - 0.0_9 130p^4$
− 50°C	$pv = 0.8178 - 0.0_2 1687p + 0.0_6 79p^2 + 0.0_9 100p^4$
0°C	$pv = 1.0010 - 0.0_3 986p + 0.0_5 237p^2$
+ 50°C	$pv = 1.1842 - 0.0_3 492p + 0.0_5 179p^2$
100°C	$pv = 1.3674 - 0.0_3 192p + 0.0_5 161p^2$
150°C	$pv = 1.5506 + 0.0_4 52p + 0.0_5 124p^2$
200°C	$pv = 1.7338 + 0.0_3 208p + 0.0_5 112p^2$
300°C	$pv = 2.1002 + 0.0_3 501p + 0.0_6 46p^2$
400°C	$pv = 2.4666 + 0.0_3 683p$

Leiden Temperature Scale (*v*. Vol. I, p. 54)

v = 1.0000 at 0°C and 1 atm. (100)

p, atm.	pv	p, atm.	pv	p, atm.	pv	p, atm.	pv
+20.39°C		+18.39°C		0.00°C		−57.72°C	
21.783	1.0627	37.264	1.0526	20.576	0.9856	17.872	0.7602
27.320	1.0606	49.586	1.0471	26.070	0.9808	25.228	0.7465
34.487	1.0582	62.489	1.0405	31.572	0.9774	35.127	0.7300
37.673	1.0535			36.743	0.9725	46.209	0.7115
49.604	1.0483			49.871	0.9620	62.079	0.6845
61.741	1.0420			62.230	0.9526		
−87.05°C		−102.51°C		−109.88°C		−113.80°C	
16.178	0.6432	14.864	0.5813	14.443	0.5504	31.001	0.4622
21.651	0.6282	19.790	0.5642	18.653	0.5359	38.005	0.4276
33.296	0.5965	32.394	0.5205	31.515	0.4838	42.682	0.4001
41.094	0.5752	40.976	0.4878	39.166	0.4493	47.655	0.3689
51.533	0.5446	45.088	0.4706	43.718	0.4254	51.752	0.3389
61.830	0.5159	51.398	0.4435	49.515	0.3944	52.188	0.3358
		56.882	0.4194	54.250	0.3658	55.763	0.3062
		62.239	0.3939	59.616	0.3297	55.991	0.3030
						58.898	0.2765
−115.86°C		−115.86°C		−116.62°C		−116.62°C	
31.323	0.4478	53.204	0.2957	13.863	0.5235	46.496	0.3478
37.788	0.4138	57.493	0.2442	17.697	0.5065	50.259	0.3147
41.908	0.3880	61.626	0.1929	30.681	0.4470	50.447	0.3119
46.648	0.3547			37.250	0.4113	54.922	0.2615
50.324	0.3244			41.943	0.3806	60.669	0.1831

p, atm.	pv	p, atm.	pv	p, atm.	pv	p, atm.	pv
−119.20°C		−119.20°C		−120.24°C		−120.24°C	
13.766	0.5123	43.006	0.3441	30.809	0.4242	47.705	0.2877
17.378	0.4970	47.272	0.3023	33.776	0.4078	50.351	0.2438
30.303	0.4299	51.679	0.2321	37.836	0.3812	52.253	0.1864
34.052	0.4090	53.044	0.1929	41.668	0.3516	53.191	0.1569
37.641	0.3887	54.244	0.1610	44.510	0.3265		
37.923	0.3836						
−121.21°C		−130.38°C		−139.62°C		−149.60°C	
13.754	0.5033	12.773	0.4662	11.986	0.4262	11.150	0.3820
17.225	0.4882	15.664	0.4511	14.586	0.4100	12.788	0.3691
30.122	0.4215	22.861	0.4096				
34.070	0.3981	25.519	0.3918				
37.465	0.3734	28.878	0.3711				
45.282	0.3040						
47.094	0.2769						
49.865	0.2130						
50.885	0.1525						

H_2, Hydrogen

p, kg/cm²	$(v_{3000} - v_p)$ cm³/g 30°C	65°C	$\frac{(pv)_{t,p}}{(pv)_{0,1}}$* (19, 20) 30°C	65°C
2 000	−2.25		2.43	
3 000	0.00	0.00	3.04	3.18
4 000	1.12	1.14	3.66	3.84
5 000	1.84	1.88	4.30	4.47
6 000	2.35	2.44	4.85	5.08
7 000	2.77	2.88	5.40	5.66
8 000	3.09	3.21	5.95	6.23
9 000	3.38	3.46	6.47	6.82
10 000	3.63	3.68	6.97	7.38
11 000	3.86	3.88	7.45	7.93
12 000	4.09	4.04	7.89	8.47
13 000	4.32	4.21	8.28	9.00

* Assuming v_{3000} = 11.64 and 12.17 cm³/g at 30 and 65° respectively (Amagat).

p in atm.; v = 1.0000 at 0°C and 1 atm.; range 0 to 100 atm.* (51, 53, 54, 138, 147)

−207.9°C	$pv = 0.2388 - 0.0_2 1077p + 0.0_5 242p^2 + 0.0_6 2704p^3 - 0.0_8 1785p^4$
−183°C	$pv = 0.3299_5 - 0.0_3 247p + 0.0_5 381p^2$
−150°C	$pv = 0.4506_5 + 0.0_3 132p + 0.0_5 200p^2$
−100°C	$pv = 0.6336 + 0.0_3 408p + 0.0_6 90p^2$
− 50°C	$pv = 0.8165 + 0.0_3 540p + 0.0_6 50p^2$
0°C	$pv = 0.99938 + 0.0_3 624p + 0.0_6 20p^2$
+ 20°C	$pv = 1.0726 + 0.0_3 645p + 0.0_6 12p^2$
50°C	$pv = 1.1824 + 0.0_3 676p$
100°C	$pv = 1.3653 + 0.0_3 695p$
200°C	$pv = 1.7310 + 0.0_3 701p$

* At 0 and 20° (138) covers a range from 0 to 200 atm.

Leiden Temperature Scale

v = 1.0000 at 0°C and 1 atm. (105)

p, atm.	pv	p, atm.	pv
−103.57°C		−139.89°C	
38.414	0.6376	29.800	0.4954
45.000	0.6402	35.132	0.4976
51.489	0.6433	40.172	0.4991

p, atm.	pv	p, atm.	pv
−182.74°C		−203.97°C	
20.159	0.3274	16.970	0.2425
22.995	0.3272	19.335	0.2412
23.010	0.3273	21.764	0.2400
26.255	0.3271		
26.281	0.3271		
29.530	0.3270		

Leiden Temperature Scale

H_2, Hydrogen.—(*Continued*)

v = 1.0000 at 0°C and 1 atm. (105).—(*Continued*)

p, atm.	*pv*	*p*, atm.	*pv*
−212.73°C		−217.32°C	
14.571	0.2074	13.288	0.1889
16.539	0.2057	15.052	0.1871
18.443	0.2039	16.812	0.1851
		13.199	0.1890
		14.875	0.1872
		16.558	0.1853
−225.37°C		−231.38°C	
10.898	0.1566	9.472	0.1315
12.424	0.1541	10.291	0.1296
13.685	0.1520	11.402	0.1268
−236.28°C		−238.29°C	
8.298	0.1106	8.083	0.1007
8.663	0.1093	8.310	0.0998
9.496	0.1065	8.715	0.0981
−239.90°C		−241.88°C	
7.512	0.0940	6.821	0.0858
7.843	0.0924	6.820	0.0858
8.155	0.0910	7.117	0.0840

p, atm.	*pv*
−243.88°C	
6.191	0.0767
6.192	0.0767
6.392	0.0752
6.604	0.0735
6.619	0.0734

pv = 1.0000 at 0°C and 1 atm. (29)

p, atm.	*pv*	*p*, atm.	*pv*
−217.33°C		−225.36°C	
34.24	0.1695	28.75	0.1280
36.98	0.1677	33.38	0.1231
40.21	0.1659	36.83	0.1205
44.09	0.1645	38.13	0.1198
48.33	0.1637	39.51	0.1192

pv = 1.0000 at 0°C and 1 atm. (29).—(*Continued*)

p, atm.	*pv*	*p*, atm.	*pv*
−217.33°C		−225.36°C	
53.52	0.1635	43.47	0.1185
56.52	0.1642	48.68	0.1191
		55.85	0.1225
−231.40°C		−236.31°C	
23.44	0.0952	17.91	0.0668
26.40	0.0889	18.62	0.0632
27.43	0.0872	21.89	0.0525
28.54	0.0856	22.45	0.0524
30.28	0.0837	23.00	0.0518
31.11	0.0831	24.11	0.0517
32.29	0.0826	24.83	0.0519
33.38	0.0821	25.98	0.0524
34.64	0.0821	28.12	0.0540
35 79	0.0824	29.65	0.0554
36.18	0.0823	30.00	0.0559
39.42	0.0838	34.77	0.0607
42.37	0.0858	40.64	0.0675
48.60	0.0911		
−238.29°C		−239.91°C	
15.39	0.0542	13.62	0.0288
17.60	0.0401	13.77	0.0286
18.00	0.0391	14.05	0.0286
18.95	0.0390	14.25	0.0286
20.07	0.0395	14.45	0.0286
20.90	0.0402	14.78	0.0288
22.79	0.0420	15.59	0.0294
23.05	0.0421	17.67	0.0317
25.87	0.0453	20.94	0.0357
29.79	0.0499	23.43	0.0388
38.08	0.0598	24.08	0.0396
43.47	0.0665	25.86	0.0419
45.50	0.0690	28.76	0.0455
− 239.92°C		29.25	0.0462
12.96	0.0434	31.62	0.0491
13.01	0.0408	33.05	0.0509
13.03	0.0397	38.38	0.0576
		47.94	0.0693
		51.46	0.0735

Virial Coefficients of Hydrogen

$pv = A + B/v$; Leiden temperature scale; v = 1.00000 at 0°C and 1 atm. (1)

T, °K	A	B
90.23	0.33019	−0.000120
69.86	0.25562	−0.000194
20.55	0.07518	−0.000470
20.53	0.07516	−0.000474
18.16	0.06647	−0.000505
16.65	0.06094	−0.000527
15.64	0.05725	−0.000553
14.50	0.05306	−0.000581
18.22	0.06666	−0.000506

Values of *pv*

Each individual value in this table has been experimentally determined (151, 152, 156)

p, atm.	*pv* 0°	50°	99.85°	198.9°	299.1°	399.3°
1	**1.0000**					
50	1.0330	1.2182	1.4026	1.7684		
100	1.0639	1.2521	1.4359	1.8030	2.1700	2.5141
200	1.1336	1.3272	1.5105	1.8804	2.2502	2.6054
300	1.2045	1.3986	1.5836	1.9556	2.3240	2.6800
400	1.2775	1.4720	1.6563	2.0295	2.3977	2.7625
600	1.4226	1.6160	1.7999	2.1726	2.5394	
800	1.5665	1.7582	1.9415	2.3157	2.6762	
1000	1.7107	1.9006	2.0839	2.4568	2.8125	

p, atm.	*pv* (3) 0°C	15.4°C	47.3°C
1	**1.0000**		
500	1.3565		
1000	1.7260	1.7780	1.8930
1100	1.8007	1.8535	1.9635
1200	1.8690	1.9248	2.0334
1300	1.9383	1.9929	2.1027
1400	2.0048	2.0608	2.1714
1500	2.0700	2.1270	2.2395
1600	2.1352	2.1920	2.3072
1700	2.2006	2.2542	2.3732
1800	2.2644	2.3184	2.4372
1900	2.3275	2.3835	2.5004
2000	2.3890	2.4450	2.5614
2100	2.4496	2.5074	2.6229
2200	2.5102	2.5707	2.6840
2300	2.5714	2.6323	2.7473
2400	2.6340	2.6940	2.8092
2500	2.6950	2.7525	2.8700
2600	2.7547	2.8145	2.9289
2700	2.8134	2.8701	2.9889
2800	2.8686	2.9260	3.0464
2900		2.9812	3.1059
3000		3.0375	

p_0, atm.	100α (142) 0 to +100°C	0 to +20°C	0 to −77°C	0 to −104°C	0 to −147°C
1	0.3661				
5	0.3665	0.3655	0.3658	0.3661	0.3666
10	0.3646	0.3647	0.3652	0.3656	0.3667
15	0.3637	0.3639	0.3646	0.3652	0.3668
20	0.3629	0.3631	0.3640	0.3648	0.3669
25	0.3620	0.3623	0.3635	0.3644	0.3670
30	0.3611	0.3615	0.3629	0.3640	0.3670
35	0.3602	0.3608	0.3623	0.3635	0.3669
40	0.3594	0.3601	0.3618	0.3631	0.3668
45	0.3585	0.3593	0.3613	0.3626	0.3666
50	0.3576	0.3586	0.3608	0.3621	0.3663
55	0.3567	0.3578	0.3602	0.3616	0.3659
60	0.3558	0.3571	0.3596	0.3611	0.3654

H_2, **Hydrogen**.—(*Continued*)

p_0, atm.	100α (142)			
	0 to −183°C	0 to −190°C	0 to −205°C	0 to −212°C
1				
5	0.3674	0.3678	0.3685	0.3691
10	0.3680	0.3685	0.3701	0.3711
15	0.3688	0.3696	0.3717	0.3732
20	0.3697	0.3707	0.3734	0.3754
25	0.3704	0.3716	0.3751	0.3774
30	0.3710	0.3724	0.3766	0.3792
35	0.3715	0.3731	0.3779	0.3808
40	0.3721	0.3738	0.3789	0.3821
45	0.3724	0.3742	0.3796	0.3830
50	0.3727	0.3746	0.3802	0.3835
55	0.3728	0.3748	0.3806	0.3838
60	0.3728	0.3749	0.3808	0.3841

p_0,* atm.	100α (3)			100β (3)		
	0 to 15.4°C	0 to 99.2°C	99.2 to 200.2°C	0 to 15.4°C	0 to 47.3°C	0 to 99.2°C
100	0.360			0.357		0.373
200	0.345	0.332	0.242			0.383
300	0.323	0.314	0.231			0.383
400	0.300	0.295	0.221			0.380
500	0.278	0.278	0.214			0.379
600	0.260	0.261	0.204			0.376
700	0.244	0.249	0.196			0.371
800	0.231	0.237	0.189			
900	0.220	0.226	0.182			
1000	0.210	0.218		0.357	0.347	
1200	0.190			0.346	0.335	
1500	0.176			0.342	0.334	
1800	0.161			0.321	0.318	
2000	0.153			0.321	0.317	
2400	0.141			0.319	0.305	
2500	0.138					
2800	0.131			0.325		
3000	0.128					

* p_0 = constant pressure for α and initial pressure for β.

p, m Hg	100α (49)	100β (49)
	t = 0°C	t = 0°C
ca. 1	$0.36604 - 0.00012p$	$0.36604 + 0.00017p$

p, respectively p_0 = 1 atm. (70)

100α		100β	
0°C	0 to 100°C	0°C	0 to 100°C
0.3660	0.3661	0.3662	0.3663

p, m Hg	100α (51, 53)		
	0 to 50°C	0 to 100°C	0 to 200°C
0	0.3662	0.3662	0.3660
1	0.3660	0.3660	0.3658
5	0.3654	0.3651	0.3648
10	0.3645	0.3641	0.3635
15	0.3636	0.3630	0.3623
20	0.3626	0.3619	0.3610
25	0.3616	0.3608	0.3597
30	0.3606	0.3596	0.3584
35	0.3596	0.3585	0.3572
40	0.3585	0.3573	0.3559
45	0.3574	0.3561	0.3546
50	0.3563	0.3550	0.3532
55	0.3551	0.3538	0.3520
60	0.3539	0.3525	0.3506
65	0.3526	0.3513	0.3493
70	0.3513	0.3501	0.3480
75	0.3500	0.3488	0.3467
76	0.3498	0.3486	
80			0.3453

$\frac{1}{v}$	100β (51, 53)		
	0 to 50°C	0 to 100°C	0 to 200°C
0	0.3662	0.3662	0.3660
1	0.3663	0.3663	0.3661
5	0.3670	0.3668	0.3665
10	0.3678	0.3674	0.3669
15	0.3685	0.3680	0.3673
20	0.3692	0.3686	0.3677
25	0.3698	0.3691	0.3681
30	0.3704	0.3696	0.3684
35	0.3709	0.3701	0.3688
40	0.3714	0.3705	0.3691
45	0.3719	0.3710	0.3694
50	0.3723	0.3714	
55	0.3726		
60	0.3729		

He, Helium (19, 20)

p, kg/cm²	$v_{3000} - v_p$, cm³/g at 65°C	$v_{95°} - v_{30°}$, cm³/g	$v_{65°}$, cm³/g*	$\frac{(pv)_{t,\,p}}{(pv)_{0,\,1}}$, 65°*
3 000	0.00	0.613	5.54	2.88
4 000	0.77	0.598	4.77	3.29
5 000	1.23	0.589	4.31	3.72
6 000	1.54	0.584	4.00	4.15
7 000	1.77	0.581	3.77	4.56
8 000	1.96	0.579	3.59	4.96
9 000	2.10	0.578	3.44	5.34
10 000	2.22	0.576	3.32	5.73
11 000	2.33	0.575	3.21	6.09
12 000	2.41	0.574	3.13	6.49
13 000	2.48	0.572	3.06	6.88
14 000	2.55	0.571	2.99	7.25
15 000	2.60	0.570	2.94	7.61

* Based on the value of v_{3000} obtained by extrapolation from an unpublished equation of Keyes (63.5).

p in atm.; v = 1.0000 at 0°C and 1 atm.; range, 0 to 105 atm. (52, 53, 54, 147)

−258.0°C*	$pv = 0.05558 - 0.0_3797p + 0.0_45437p^2 - 0.0_67513p^3 + 0.0_83796p^4$
−252.8°C*	$pv = 0.07460 - 0.0_31642p + 0.0_41853p^2 - 0.0_61105p^3$
−208.0°C*	$pv = 0.23847 + 0.0_35508p + 0.0_5238p^2 - 0.0_7141p^3$
−183.0°C*	$pv = 0.32992 + 0.0_36229p + 0.0_6735p^2$
−150°C	$pv = 0.4507 + 0.0_3509p + 0.0_6259p^2$
−100°C	$pv = 0.6336 + 0.0_3531p + 0.0_6165p^2$
− 50°C	$pv = 0.81655 + 0.0_3532p + 0.0_794p^2$
0°C	$pv = 0.99945 + 0.0_3529p$
+ 50°C	$pv = 1.18245 + 0.0_3524p$
100°C	$pv = 1.3654 + 0.0_3508p$
200°C	$pv = 1.7312 + 0.0_3494p$
300°C	$pv = 2.0970 + 0.0_3468p$
400°C	$pv = 2.46285 + 0.0_3452p$

* The pressure unit is m Hg.

He, Helium.—*(Continued)*
Leiden Temperature Scale
$pv = 1.0000$ at 0°C and 1 atm. [109]

p, atm.	pv	p, atm.	pv	p, atm.	pv	p, atm.	pv
−205.31°C		−212.06°C		−217.41°C		−252.65°C	
43.987	0.2690	40.113	0.2421	36.351	0.2202	12.411	0.0748
47.605	0.2707	42.770	0.2433	38.669	0.2213	13.196	0.0749
50.301	0.2721	42.749	0.2432	41.026	0.2224	13.903	0.0750
		45.220	0.2444				

p, atm.	pv
−258.33°C	
8.614	0.0513
9.168	0.0511
9.728	0.0510

Leiden Temperature Scale
$pv = 1.0000$ at 0°C and 1 atm. [18]

p atm.	pv	p, atm.	pv
−37.40°C		−70.32°C	
24.46	0.8758	22.82	0.7541
26.87	0.8774	24.89	0.7556
26.88	0.8770	28.77	0.7584
30.24	0.8791	28.78	0.7584
31.35	0.8796	33.92	0.7609
37.43	0.8842	35.29	0.7629
37.44	0.8834	41.13	0.7645
37.55	0.8834	43.39	0.7667
46.55	0.8874	56.27	0.7731
−103.64°C		−142.01°C	
21.34	0.6321	20.54	0.4911
21.54	0.6320	24.58	0.4932
24.12	0.6337	24.88	0.4932
27.66	0.6362	24.88	0.4933
27.69	0.6360	28.20	0.4954
32.40	0.6388	28.76	0.4957
32.62	0.6388	28.77	0.4958
35.31	0.6403	34.06	0.4988
39.52	0.6422	41.52	0.5027
49.96	0.6479	53.06	0.5088
−183.32°C		−201.51°C	
20.61	0.3391	20.10	0.2716
23.21	0.3407	29.69	0.2769
23.22	0.3407		
26.54	0.3426		
30.97	0.3451		
37.02	0.3482		
−225.01°C		−235.91°C	
43.44	0.1952	36.68	0.1498
43.47	0.1951	40.32	0.1515
48.58	0.1976	50.34	0.1562
55.06	0.2008	50.35	0.1561
		55.16	0.1585
−249.87°C		−252.63°C	
25.27	0.0896	22.53	0.0773
26.93	0.0902	23.84	0.0777
26.95	0.0902	25.31	0.0782
28.84	0.0909	26.97	0.0788
31.12	0.0918	28.26	0.0792
32.84	0.0925		

p, atm.	pv	p, atm.	pv
−256.04°C		−258.78°C	
18.74	0.0617	15.43	0.0490
19.61	0.0619	16.01	0.0491
20.63	0.0622	16.65	0.0492
21.70	0.0625	17.30	0.0493
22.50	0.0627	17.78	0.0494

$v = 1.0000$ at 0°C and 1 atm. [97]

p, atm.	pv	p, atm.	pv
−103.57°C		−182.75°C	
20.580	0.6314	13.751	0.3379
24.100	0.6330	16.019	0.3390
29.185	0.6360	18.189	0.3402
33.383	0.6384		

−103.57°

$$pv = 0.6203 + \frac{0.0_3337}{v}.$$

−182.75°

$$pv = 0.3306 + \frac{0.0_3176}{v}.$$

$v = 1.0000$ at 0°C and 1 atm. [98]

p, atm.	pv	p, atm.	pv
−268.88°C		−269.37°C	
0.2709	0.0145	0.1550	0.0129
0.3551	0.0140	0.1616	0.0129
0.3800	0.0140	0.2493	0.0125
0.6624	0.0127	0.2748	0.0123
0.9928	0.0107	0.2757	0.0123
		0.4322	0.0115
		0.5703	0.0107
−269.69°C		−270.52°C	
0.2323	0.0113	0.0308	0.0091
0.2608	0.0110	0.0486	0.0087
0.3531	0.0104	0.0649	0.0086

Virial Coefficients of Helium

$pv = A + B/v$; Leiden temperature scale; $v = 1.00000$ at 0°C and 1 atm. [1]

T, °K	A	B
69.86	0.25572	+0.000100
20.55	0.07520	−0.000004
20.53	0.07516	−0.000009
20.51	0.07508	−0.000009
18.22	0.06669	−0.000024
16.65	0.06096	−0.000024

p, m Hg	100α [52, 53]				
	0 to 50°C	0 to 100°C	0 to 200°C	0 to 300°C	0 to 400°C
0	0.3660	0.3660	0.3660	0.3660	0.3660
1*	0.3658	0.3658	0.3658	0.3658	0.3658
10	0.3635	0.3634	0.3633	0.3632	0.3633
20	0.3609	0.3608	0.3606	0.3605	0.3605
30	0.3584	0.3582	0.3579	0.3578	0.3578
40	0.3558	0.3556	0.3552	0.3551	0.3551
50	0.3532	0.3529	0.3526	0.3524	0.3525
60	0.3506	0.3503	0.3501	0.3498	0.3499
70	0.3481	0.3477	0.3475	0.3473	0.3474
80	0.3455	0.3450	0.3450	0.3447	0.3448

* At *ca.* $p = 1$ m Hg, $100\alpha = 0.3660_4 - 0.00019p$ [49].

$\frac{1}{v}$	100β [52, 53]				
	0 to 50°C	0 to 100°C	0 to 200°C	0 to 300°C	0 to 400°C
0	0.3661	0.3661	0.3661	0.3660	0.3660
1*	0.3661	0.3661	0.3660	0.3660	0.3660
10	0.3660	0.3658	0.3656	0.3655	0.3654
20	0.3658	0.3656	0.3652	0.3649	0.3648
30	0.3656	0.3653	0.3648	0.3643	0.3641
40	0.3655	0.3650	0.3645	0.3638	
50	0.3653	0.3648	0.3640		
60	0.3652	0.3645			

* At *ca.* $p = 1$ m Hg, $100\beta = 0.3660_4 - 0.00004p$ [49].

Kr, Krypton
$v = 1.000$ at 0°C and 1 atm. [113]

p, atm.	pv	p, atm.	pv
11.2°C		237.3°C	
25.88	1.012	50.93	1.882
27.91	1.008	54.82	1.880
30.31	1.000	59.36	1.874
33.15	0.993	65.12	1.868
36.60	0.980	71.20	1.862
40.89	0.968	79.25	1.859
46.29	0.953	89.53	1.856
49.58	0.940	104.09	1.877
53.72	0.937		
57.81	0.918		
63.07	0.901		
69.46	0.884		
72.10	0.863		
87.39	0.841		
101.74	0.821		

N_2, Nitrogen; *v.* p. 17

Ne, Neon

p in atm.; v = 1.0000 at 0°C and 1 atm.; range, 0 to 95 atm. (53, 54, 147)

−207.9°C*	$pv = 0.23885 - 0.0_21231p + 0.0_5177p^2 + 0.0_9894p^3$
−182.5°C	$pv = 0.3318 - 0.0_3365p + 0.0_5225p^2$
−150°C	$pv = 0.45075 + 0.0_54p + 0.0_5136p^2$
−100°C	$pv = 0.6337 + 0.0_3288p + 0.0_650p^2$
− 50°C	$pv = 0.8166 + 0.0_3407p + 0.0_635p^2$
0°C	$pv = 0.9995 + 0.0_3530p$
+100°C	$pv = 1.3653 + 0.0_3584p$
200°C	$pv = 1.7312 + 0.0_3609p$
300°C	$pv = 2.0970 + 0.0_3631p$
400°C	$pv = 2.4629 + 0.0_3607p$

* The pressure unit is m Hg.

Leiden Temperature Scale

v = 1.0000 at 0°C and 1 atm. (28, 101)

p, atm.	pv	p, atm.	pv
+20.00°C		0.00°C	
22.804	1.0835	22.064	1.0089
25.015	1.0852	23.555	1.0103
26.575	1.0863	25.867	1.0121
29.090	1.0872	28.468	1.0135
32.572	1.0897	30.790	1.0147
34.887	1.0902	39.753	1.0168
35.423	1.0917	44.892	1.0196
37.812	1.0928	59.777	1.0265
39.168	1.0928	66.104	1.0307
44.762	1.0955	74.059	1.0359
54.149	1.1003	79.108	1.0392
59.717	1.1026	84.662	1.0408
65.021	1.1059		
77.360	1.1131		
82.545	1.1160		
88.239	1.1186		
93.298	1.1220		
−103.01°C		−141.22°C	
35.558	0.6304	33.840	0.4846
36.697	0.6302	37.707	0.4852
40.610	0.6324	38.581	0.4853
42.107	0.6329	43.319	0.4869
55.136	0.6369	49.881	0.4875
58.583	0.6384	51.916	0.4878
78.110	0.6481	66.471	0.4927
		78.558	0.4970
−182.60°C		−200.08°C	
32.067	0.3210	26.214	0.2494
32.988	0.3208	28.402	0.2483
36.438	0.3205	31.417	0.2469
36.880	0.3205	34.268	0.2451
41.371	0.3196	34.285	0.2451
42.533	0.3194	39.843	0.2425
49.943	0.3189	39.891	0.2423

p, atm.	pv	p, atm.	pv
−182.60°C		−200.08°C	
50.514	0.3186	46.517	0.2394
63.320	0.3179	46.529	0.2392
		47.951	0.2388
		61.657	0.2338
		67.456	0.2317
		73.850	0.2302
		79.923	0.2293
−208.10°C		−213.08°C	
24.071	0.2151	23.086	0.1925
28.844	0.2114	24.810	0.1911
31.948	0.2088	26.673	0.1893
37.856	0.2041	29.365	0.1862
41.798	0.2010	32.441	0.1829
58.472	0.1897	37.418	0.1776
64.451	0.1867	53.896	0.1611
69.692	0.1844	59.769	0.1565
74.532	0.1822	66.271	0.1522
79.228	0.1804	72.858	0.1503
		79.698	0.1491

p, atm.	pv
−217.52°C	
21.349	0.1730
22.997	0.1707
24.686	0.1683
26.848	0.1652
30.042	0.1607
32.795	0.1564
49.930	0.1393
53.528	0.1353
59.618	0.1301
64.975	0.1269
71.649	0.1253
79.417	0.1256

O_2, Oxygen

p, atm.	pv (3) 0°C	15.65°C	99.50°C	199.50°C	p, atm.	pv (3) 0°C	15.6°C
1	**1.0000**				1	**1.0000**	
100	0.9265	1.0045	1.3750		500	1.1570	
200	0.9140	0.9945	1.4000	1.8190	1000	1.7360	1.8000
300	0.9625	1.0420	1.4530	1.8850	1200	1.9620	2.0268
400	1.0515	1.1250	1.5320	1.9610	1400	2.1798	2.2470
500	1.1560	1.2270	1.6220	2.0500	1600	2.3960	2.4640
600	1.2690	1.3370	1.7200	2.1420	1800	2.6073	2.6793
700	1.3855	1.4515	1.8270	2.2415	2000	2.8160	2.8880
800	1.5030	1.5660	1.9340	2.3430	2200	3.0217	3.0932
900	1.6200	1.6820	2.0415	2.4465	2400	3.2244	3.2976
1000	1.7355	1.7980	2.1510		2600	3.4229	3.4996
					2800	3.6176	3.6946
					3000		3.8880

p in atm.; v = 1.0000 at 0°C and 1 atm.; range, 0 to 100 atm. (52, 67)

0°C	$pv = 1.0010 - 0.0_3994p + 0.0_5219p^2$
20°C	$pv = 1.07425 - 0.0_3753p + 0.0_5150p^2$
50°C	$pv = 1.1842 - 0.0_3491p + 0.0_5170p^2$
100°C	$pv = 1.3674 - 0.0_3160p + 0.0_5137p^2$
0°C	$pv = 1.0010 - \frac{0.0_3958}{v} + \frac{0.0_5206}{v^2}$
20°C	$pv = 1.07425 - \frac{0.0_3804}{v} + \frac{0.0_5206}{v^2}$

Leiden Temperature Scale

pv = 1.0000 at 0°C and 1 atm. (96)

p, atm.	pv	p, atm.	pv
−40.01°C		−80.00°C	
5.755	0.8462	6.445	0.6926
7.385	0.8432	7.300	0.6902
8.559	0.8416	7.918	0.6892
9.382	0.8403		
−102.49°C		−109.99°C	
4.759	0.6105	5.594	0.5788
5.783	0.6076	6.218	0.5767
6.507	0.6051	6.684	0.5745
7.029	0.6037		
−113.94°C		−116.01°C	
5.470	0.5642	4.506	0.5594
6.092	0.5613	5.422	0.5557
6.501	0.5597	6.008	0.5534
		6.486	0.5512

p, atm.	pv	p, atm.	pv
−116.03°C		−117.01°C	
3.841	0.5616	4.493	0.5555
4.533	0.5596	5.385	0.5517
		5.965	0.5496
		6.389	0.5478
−118.58°C		−124.95°C	
3.799	0.5520	2.882	0.5316
5.910	0.5433	3.715	0.5276
6.254	0.5421	5.160	0.5213
		5.688	0.5190
		6.013	0.5171
−135.29°C		−145.39°C	
3.550	0.4878	3.375	0.4492
4.838	0.4816	5.007	0.4387
5.599	0.4773		

p, atm.	pv
−152.56°C	
3.251	0.4213
4.636	0.4117
4.854	0.4102

v = 1.0000 at 0°C and 1 atm. (137); Leiden temperature scale

p, atm.	pv	p, atm.	pv	p, atm.	pv
0°C		15.6°C		20°C	
36.20	0.9685	34.10	1.0322	35.61	1.0499
38.77	0.9661	44.19	1.0252	40.49	1.0467
46.90	0.9590	56.70	1.0168	46.10	1.0427
47.15	0.9589			51.38	1.0392
54.74	0.9528			57.04	1.0358
				62.43	1.0329

Leiden Temperature Scale
v = 1.0000 at 0°C and 1 atm. (104)

p, atm.	pv	p, atm.	pv
−40.05°C		−80.03°C	
21.142	0.8218	21.010	0.6550
28.034	0.8112	27.295	0.6388
34.794	0.7992	33.475	0.6221
41.818	0.7898	34.178	0.6213
49.255	0.7806	39.240	0.6086
55.425	0.7713	43.247	0.5976
61.030	0.7642	44.613	0.5949
		50.430	0.5772
		61.880	0.5464
−102.46°C		−109.97°C	
20.118	0.5594	20.010	0.5244
26.932	0.5344	25.330	0.5022
31.601	0.5155	29.977	0.4804
37.564	0.4910	35.427	0.4544
42.513	0.4710	38.979	0.4346
48.720	0.4420	45.687	0.3989
54.588	0.4127	51.130	0.3618
60.474	0.3811	56.200	0.3220
		56.655	0.3174
		60.867	0.2770
−113.97°C		−116.01°C	
20.149	0.5044	22.300	0.4835
24.462	0.4847	27.849	0.4560
28.893	0.4624	32.648	0.4297
33.731	0.4370	37.468	0.4012

p, atm.	pv	p, atm.	pv
−113.97°C		−116.01°C	
33.758	0.4369	43.947	0.3541
37.979	0.4133	50.445	0.2836
43.890	0.3739	50.506	0.2816
48.304	0.3385	52.446	0.2477
51.059	0.3061	53.469	0.2213
52.543	0.2951	54.200	0.1959
54.066	0.2672	54.319	0.1638
56.761	0.2073	54.635	0.1792
58.518	0.1754	55.050	0.1667

p, atm.	pv
−116.99°C	
20.264	0.4891
22.298	0.4783
26.413	0.4579
30.248	0.4371
34.117	0.4144
37.210	0.3958
43.662	0.3458
48.344	0.2936
49.507	0.2790
51.297	0.2388
52.072	0.1745
52.218	0.1671
52.343	0.1989
52.649	0.1776
53.000	0.1587

p_0, atm.	100α (3)			100β (3)	
	0 to 15.6°C	0 to 99.5°C	99.5 to 199.5°C	0 to 15.6°C	0 to 99.5°C
100	0.538	0.486		0.480	0.492
200	0.561	0.534	0.300	0.570	0.613
300	0.528	0.512	0.297	0.641	0.696
400	0.450	0.459	0.280	0.691	0.731
500	0.388	0.405	0.264	0.697	0.740
600	0.341	0.357	0.245	0.737	
700	0.301	0.320	0.226		
800	0.270	0.288	0.212	0.705	
900	0.248	0.261	0.198		
1000	0.233	0.241		0.679	
1200	0.212			0.668	
1500	0.190			0.657	
1800	0.174				
2000	0.165			0.602	
2400	0.148			0.580	
2500	0.145				
2800	0.137			0.538	
3000	0.134				

p, m Hg	100α (52)		$\frac{1}{v}$	100β (52)	
	0 to 50°C	0 to 100°C		0 to 50°C	0 to 100°C
0	0.3660	0.3660	0	0.3660	0.3660
1	0.3679	0.3676	1	0.3677	0.3676
5	0.3752	0.3739	5	0.3739	0.3734
10	0.3842	0.3817	10	0.3817	0.3809
15	0.3932	0.3894	15	0.3894	0.3882
20	0.4019	0.3971	20	0.3970	0.3956
25	0.4107	0.4047	25	0.4044	0.4028
30	0.4193	0.4123	30	0.4117	0.4101
35	0.4279	0.4199	35	0.4190	0.4174
40	0.4364	0.4274	40	0.4262	0.4247
45	0.4446	0.4347	45	0.4337	0.4322
50	0.4530	0.4420	50	0.4411	0.4396
55	0.4614	0.4492	55	0.4488	0.4472
60	0.4696	0.4563	60	0.4565	
65	0.4777	0.4632	65	0.4642	
70	0.4856	0.4701			
75	0.4935	0.4768			

p, respectively p_0 = 1 atm. (70)

100α		100β	
0°C	0 to 100°C	0°C	0 to 100°C
0.3675	0.3672	0.3672	0.3671

Xe, Xenon

v = 1.000 at 0°C and 1 atm. (113)

p, atm.	pv	p, atm.	pv	p, atm.	pv
11.2°C				237.3°C	
25.65	0.697	36.39	0.628	53.53	1.397
26.62	0.691	38.42	0.612	57.97	1.389
27.68	0.685	40.69	0.598	63.21	1.377
28.79	0.677	43.24	0.576	69.62	1.375
30.07	0.670	46.22	0.552	77.54	1.359
31.40	0.659	49.39	0.522	88.15	1.354
32.92	0.650	53.20	0.437	102.55	1.357
34.57	0.640				

Air

p, atm.	pv (3)			
	0°C	15.70°C	99.40°C	200.4°C
1	**1.0000**			
100	0.9730	1.0389	1.4030	
150	0.9840	1.0555	1.4310	1.8430
200	1.0100	1.0855	1.4670	1.8860
250	1.0490	1.1260	1.5110	1.9340
300	1.0975	1.1740	1.5585	1.9865
350	1.1540	1.2250	1.6085	2.0410
400	1.2145	1.2835	1.6625	2.0960
450	1.2765	1.3460	1.7200	2.1530
500	1.3400	1.4110	1.7815	2.2110
550	1.4040	1.4740	1.8440	2.2700
600	1.4700	1.5375	1.9060	2.3300
650	1.5365	1.6015	1.9670	2.3900
700	1.6020	1.6670	2.0300	2.4515
750	1.6690	1.7340	2.0930	2.5130
800	1.7345	1.8000	2.1555	2.5750
850	1.7990	1.8655	2.2180	2.6370
900	1.8640	1.9300	2.2830	2.7000
950	1.9280	1.9960	2.3490	2.7640
1000	1.9920	2.0600	2.4150	2.8280

p, atm.	pv (3)		
	0°C	15.7°C	45.10°C
1	**1.0000**		
500	1.3400		
1000	1.9990	2.0615	2.1765
1100	2.1329	2.1912	2.3067
1200	2.2596	2.3196	2.4360
1300	2.3842	2.4440	2.5610
1400	2.5081	2.5676	2.6838

Air.—(*Continued*)

p, atm.	pv (3)		
	0°C	15.7°C	45.10°C
1500	2.6310	2.6902	2.8072
1600	2.7528	2.8112	2.9320
1700	2.8738	2.9325	3.0540
1800	2.9916	3.0510	3.1725
1900	3.1103	3.1692	3.2927
2000	3.2260	3.2860	3.4100
2100	3.3400	3.4209	3.5248
2200	3.4540	3.5156	3.6388
2300	3.5661	3.6294	3.7547
2400	3.6804	3.7428	3.8688
2500	3.7912	3.8550	3.9837
2600	3.9000	3.9650	4.0963
2700	4.0081	4.0770	4.2052
2800	4.1146	4.1860	4.3148
2900	4.2195	4.2934	4.4225
3000	4.3230	4.3980	4.5285

p in atm.; pv = 1.0000 at 0°C and 1 atm.; range, 0 to 100 atm. (53)

0°C	$pv = 1.0006 - 0.0_3603p + 0.0_5302p^2$
50°C	$pv = 1.1838 - 0.0_3141p + 0.0_5217p^2$
100°C	$pv = 1.3668 + 0.0_3159p + 0.0_5179p^2$
150°C	$pv = 1.5500 + 0.0_3380p + 0.0_5135p^2$
200°C	$pv = 1.7328 + 0.0_3550p + 0.0_5105p^2$

Leiden Temperature Scale

pv = 1.0000 at 0°C and 1 atm. (108)

p, atm.	pv	p, atm.	pv
20.00°C		−70.09°C	
28.548	1.0654	52.810	0.6611
34.103	1.0637	58.860	0.6533
42.747	1.0613		
57.300	1.0598		
61.426	1.0595		
−84.08°C		−103.48°C	
48.031	0.5979	40.760	0.5099
52.753	0.5890	43.411	0.5024
56.250	0.5830	45.017	0.4979
		48.400	0.4882

p atm.	pv	p, atm.	p
−122.03°C		−129.97°C	
34.122	0.4232	30.961	0.3864
36.736	0.4112	33.458	0.3717
39.458	0.3985	35.729	0.3580
−135.00°C		140.00°C	
28.877	0.3627	27.055	0.3374
31.113	0.3476	30.174	0.3106
33.009	0.3337		

p, atm.	pv
−145.05°C	
25.033	0.3126
26.721	0.2947
27.876	0.2805

p, atm.	100α (3)			100β (3)	
	0 to 15.7°C	0 to 99.4°C	99.4 to 200.4°C	0 to 15.7°C	0 to 99.4°C
100		0.444		0.446	0.462
200	0.475	0.455	0.287	0.541	0.552
300	0.436	0.422	0.275	0.616	0.600
400	0.370	0.371	0.261	0.621	0.617
500	0.327	0.331	0.241	0.637	0.617
600	0.294	0.294	0.222	0.616	
700	0.265	0.269	0.207		
800	0.241	0.244	0.194	0.605	
900	0.223	0.226	0.182		
1000	0.206	0.214	0.171	0.567	
1200	0.177			0.504	
1500	0.144			0.467	
1800	0.124			0.439	
2000	0.116			0.417	
2400	0.108			0.403	
2500	0.107				
2800	0.110				
3000	0.110				

p, m Hg	100α (53, 55)			
	0 to 50°C	0 to 100°C	0 to 150°C	0 to 200°C
1	0.3676	0.3674	0.3673	0.3672
10	0.3803	0.3785	0.3769	0.3760
20	0.3943	0.3904	0.3876	0.3855
30	0.4078	0.4019	0.3978	0.3947
40	0.4203	0.4126	0.4072	0.4031
50	0.4315	0.4224	0.4156	0.4106
60	0.4412	0.4309	0.4230	0.4172
70	0.4502	0.4385	0.4295	0.4230
75	0.4543	0.4418	0.4325	0.4255

$\frac{1}{v}$	100β (53, 55)			
	0 to 50°C	0 to 100°C	0 to 150°C	0 to 200°C
1	0.3675	0.3675	0.3674	0.3674
10	0.3798	0.3794	0.3790	0.3788
20	0.3940	0.3932	0.3925	0.3919
30	0.4080	0.4067	0.4056	0.4048
40	0.4216	0.4201	0.4186	0.4178
50	0.4351	0.4337	0.4322	
60	0.4486			
65	0.4557			

p, atm.	100α, constant pressure (141)								
	0 to 100°C	0 to 16°C	0 to −35°C	0 to −78.5°C	0 to −103.5°C	0 to −130°C	0 to −135°C	0 to −140°C	0 to −145°C
10	0.375	0.376							
20	0.383	0.387		0.401	0.410	0.427		0.440	0.450
30	0.392	0.398		0.420	0.434	0.462	0.477	0.492	0.519*
40	0.402	0.408		0.438	0.461	0.508	0.544	0.632	
50	0.410	0.419	0.430	0.457	0.487	0.569	0.619		
60	0.418	0.429	0.442	0.476	0.512	0.610	0.622		
70	0.425	0.438	0.454	0.494	0.536	0.612			
80	0.431	0.446	0.467	0.512	0.557	0.607			
90	0.437	0.452	0.479	0.527	0.572				
100	0.441	0.458	0.489	0.537	0.579				
110	0.445	0.462	0.497	0.545	0.580				
120	0.449	0.465	0.501	0.550	0.577				
130		0.468		0.551	0.571				

* p = 29 atm.

𝔅-Table, Chemical Compounds

Standard arrangement

NO, Nitric Oxide, v. p. 14. **NH_3**, Ammonia (63)

v = 39 cm³/g t, °C	p, atm.	v = 44 cm³/g t, °C	p, atm.	v = 49 cm³/g t, °C	p, atm.	v = 54 cm³/g t, °C	p, atm.	v = 59 cm³/g t, °C	p, atm.
75.14	32.522	69.65	28.992	62.00	25.709	61.96	23.891	55.70	21.597
75.21	32.509	75.86	29.951	69.68	26.750	69.69	24.825	60.31	22.105
80.16	33.371	79.86	30.547	75.81	27.532	75.24	25.475	65.98	23.075
84.73	34.153	89.42	31.863	79.77	28.059	79.69	25.955	73.57	23.553
89.51	34.925	94.03	32.522	84.81	28.689	84.66	26.536	73.83	23.576
93.81	35.628	100.32	33.416	89.37	29.262	84.60	26.511	79.16	24.114
100.32	36.703	104.94	34.057	94.09	29.858	89.35	27.058	79.71	24.172
105.66	37.584	110.81	34.864	100.37	30.638	94.06	27.574	83.22	24.537
110.78	38.397	115.88	35.532	105.02	31.201	100.38	28.274	88.06	25.022
115.95	39.234	121.29	36.261	111.18	31.953	104.88	28.757	92.82	25.514
121.25	40.047	127.01	37.011	115.91	32.508	111.05	29.422	97.61	25.992
				121.14	33.142	115.94	29.938	103.46	26.561
				126.66	33.788	121.21	30.507	109.25	27.125
				131.91	34.384	126.55	31.070	115.10	27.699
						132.00	31.632	119.34	28.084
								123.92	28.526
								128.81	29.016
								134.89	29.549
								140.47	30.079
								146.23	30.629
								152.47	31.203
								158.70	31.780
								164.31	32.292

v is expressed in cm³/g (75)

t, °C \ v	1300	500	300	200	150	115	85.5
	p (kg/cm²)						
−35	0.8935						
−30	0.9110						
−20	0.9512						
−10		2.5017					
0	1.0305	2.6116					
+ 5			4.3267				
10			4.4212				
15				6.573			
25	1.1288	2.8788	4.7000	6.866	8.905		
30					9.105	11.499	
35						11.770	

t, °C \ v	1300	500	300	200	150	115	85.5
	p (kg/cm²)						
50	1.2263	3.1403	5.1504	7.571	9.885	12.566	16.245
100	1.4199	3.6549	6.0256	8.919	11.730	15.051	19.745
150	1.6128	4.1639	6.8854	10.231	13.510	17.419	23.026
200	1.8050	4.6695	7.7376	11.524	15.257	19.733	26.204
250		5.1735	8.5847	12.807	16.986	22.014	29.322
300			9.4291	14.084	18.703	24.278	

p, respectively p_0 = 1 atm. (70)

100α		100β	
0°C	0 to 100°C	0°C	0 to 100°C
0.386	0.380	0.380	0.377

CO_2, Carbon dioxide

p, atm.	Values of pv (3) 0°C	10°C	20°C	30°C	40°C	50°C	60°C	70°C	80°C	90°C
1	**1.0000**									
50	0.1050	0.1145	0.6800	0.7750	0.8500	0.9200	0.9840	1.0430	1.0960	1.1530
75	0.1530	0.1630	0.1800	0.2190	0.6200	0.7470	0.8410	0.9180	0.9880	1.0515
100	0.2020	0.2130	0.2285	0.2550	0.3090	0.4910	0.6610	0.7770	0.8725	0.9535
125	0.2490	0.2620	0.2785	0.3000	0.3350	0.3950	0.5100	0.6430	0.7590	0.8580
150	0.2950	0.3090	0.3260	0.3460	0.3770	0.4190	0.4850	0.5750	0.6805	0.7815
175	0.3405	0.3550	0.3725	0.3930	0.4215	0.4570	0.5055	0.5730	0.6515	0.7410
200	0.3850	0.4010	0.4190	0.4400	0.4675	0.5000	0.5425	0.5955	0.6600	0.7315
225	0.4305	0.4455	0.4655	0.4875	0.5130	0.5425	0.5825	0.6285	0.6815	0.7460
250	0.4740	0.4900	0.5100	0.5335	0.5580	0.5865	0.6250	0.6670	0.7135	0.7690
275	0.5170	0.5340	0.5545	0.5775	0.6040	0.6330	0.6675	0.7070	0.7515	0.8015
300	0.5595	0.5775	0.5985	0.6225	0.6485	0.6765	0.7100	0.7485	0.7900	0.8375
350	0.6445	0.6640	0.6850	0.7090	0.7365	0.7650	0.7980	0.8325	0.8725	0.9135
400	0.7280	0.7475	0.7710	0.7950	0.8230	0.8515	0.8840	0.9180	0.9560	0.9660
450	0.8090	0.8310	0.8550	0.8800	0.9075	0.9365	0.9690	1.0035	1.0400	1.0775
500	0.8905	0.9130	0.9380	0.9630	0.9900	1.0210	1.0540	1.0880	1.1240	1.1610
550	0.9700	0.9935	1.0200	1.0465	1.0740	1.1035	1.1370	1.1720	1.2085	1.2430

CO_2, Carbon dioxide.—(*Continued*)

p, atm.	Values of *pv* (3)									
	0°C	10°C	20°C	30°C	40°C	50°C	60°C	70°C	80°C	90°C
600	1.0495	1.0730	1.0995	1.1275	1.1570	1.1865	1.2190	1.2540	1.2900	1.3265
650	1.1275	1.1530	1.1800	1.2075	1.2375	1.2680	1.3010	1.3360	1.3725	1.4085
700	1.2055	1.2320	1.2590	1.2890	1.3190	1.3500	1.3825	1.4170	1.4535	1.4900
750	1.2815	1.3105	1.3395	1.3700	1.4000	1.4315	1.4640	1.4985	1.5335	1.5705
800	1.3580	1.3870	1.4170	1.4475	1.4790	1.5105	1.5435	1.5780	1.6140	1.6505
850	1.4340	1.4625	1.4935	1.5245	1.5570	1.5885	1.6225	1.6575	1.6925	1.7285
900	1.5090	1.5385	1.5685	1.6000	1.6325	1.6650	1.6995	1.7345	1.7710	1.8075
950	1.5830	1.6115	1.6430	1.6740	1.7065	1.7395	1.7745	1.8100	1.8470	1.8845
1000	1.6560	1.6850	1.7160	1.7480	1.7800	1.8140	1.8475	1.8840	1.9210	1.9590

p, atm.	100°C	137°C	198°C	258°C	*p*, atm.	100°C	137°C	198°C	258°C
50	1.2065	1.3800			450	1.1190	1.2880	1.6160	1.9280
75	1.1180	1.3185	1.6150	1.8670	500	1.2005	1.3620	1.6775	
100	1.0300	1.2590	1.5820	1.8470	550	1.2830	1.4400	1.7450	
125	0.9470	1.2050	1.5530	1.8310	600	1.3655	1.5180	1.8120	
150	0.8780	1.1585	1.5295	1.8180	650	1.4475	1.5960	1.8835	
175	0.8320	1.1230	1.5100	1.8095	700	1.5285	1.6760	1.9560	
200	0.8145	1.0960	1.4960	1.8040	750	1.6100	1.7565	2.0330	
225	0.8175	1.0835	1.4890	1.8035	800	1.6890	1.8355	2.1080	
250	0.8355	1.0810	1.4870	1.8060	850	1.7680	1.9150	2.1860	
275	0.8600	1.0885	1.4875	1.8115	900	1.8460	1.9940	2.2600	
300	0.8900	1.1080	1.4935	1.8200	950	1.9230	2.0720	2.3350	
350	0.9615	1.1565	1.5210	1.8465	1000	1.9990			
400	1.0385	1.2175	1.5630	1.8830					

Compressibility in the Neighborhood of Saturation

p in atm.; *v* = 1.0000 at 0°C and 0 atm. (62)

v	*p*, atm.	*pv*
25.55°C		
0.008573	63.12	0.5411
0.007812	64.36	0.5028
28.15°C		
0.009338	63.44	0.5924
0.008565	65.19	0.5583

v	*p*, atm.	*pv*
28.15°C		
0.007807	66.75	0.5212
0.007030	67.99	0.4780
0.006950	68.19	0.4739
0.006673	68.39	0.4564

Border Curve in the Neighborhood of the Critical Point (62)

Beginning condensation			End condensation		
t, °C	*v*	*p*, atm.	*t*, °C	*v*	*p*, atm.
30.05	0.005594	71.47	30.11	0.003328	71.53
30.82	0.004833	72.725	30.81	0.003725	72.74

Critical temperature = 30.98°C; critical pressure = 72.93 atm.; critical volume = 0.00443; *v* = 1.0000 at 0°C and 0 atm. (62)

v	*p*, atm.	*pv*	*v*	*p*, atm.	*pv*
Critical isothermal (30.98°C)			Critical isothermal (30.98°C)		
0.010068	63.36	0.6379	0.003959	72.96	0.2888
0.009314	65.39	0.6090	0.003656	72.995	0.2669
0.008582	67.22	0.5769	0.003296	73.53	0.2423
0.007809	69.085	0.5395	0.003230	73.89	0.2387
0.007031	70.73	0.4973	0.003051	75.43	0.2302
0.006275	71.95	0.4515	0.002862	79.43	0.2273
0.005483	72.745	0.3988	0.002721	86.10	0.2343
0.005102	72.87	0.3718	0.002593	95.70	0.2482
0.004777	72.93	0.3484	0.002509	106.18	0.2664
0.004403	72.94	0.3211	0.002435	119.35	0.2906
0.004254	72.98	0.3104	0.002362	138.65	0.3275

v	*p*, atm.	*pv*	*v*	*p*, atm.	*pv*
31.89°C			34.02°C		
0.010086	63.87	0.6442	0.010067	65.18	0.6562
0.009314	65.995	0.6147	0.009337	67.295	0.6283
0.008570	67.945	0.5823	0.008560	69.49	0.5948
0.007771	70.03	0.5442	0.007791	71.64	0.5581
0.007017	71.68	0.5030	0.007023	73.65	0.5173
0.006267	73.035	0.4577	0.006255	75.34	0.4712
0.005528	73.94	0.4087	0.005529	76.605	0.4236
0.005117	74.24	0.3799	0.004672	77.575	0.3624
0.004742	74.44	0.3530	0.003971	78.385	0.3113
0.004364	74.56	0.3254	0.003243	81.11	0.2630
0.003942	74.69	0.2944	0.002955	86.16	0.2546
0.003610	75.00	0.2707	0.002746	95.02	0.2609
0.003228	76.20	0.2460	0.002614	105.95	0.2770
0.002883	82.02	0.2365	0.002510	119.53	0.3000
0.002717	89.90	0.2443	0.002426	136.66	0.3316
0.002593	99.77	0.2587			
0.002503	111.45	0.2790			
0.002439	122.79	0.2995			
0.002377	136.71	0.3249			
37.09°C			41.95°C		
0.010863	64.56	0.7013	0.011546	64.85	0.7487
0.010093	66.90	0.6752	0.0107945	67.28	0.7262
0.009339	69.20	0.6471	0.010047	69.81	0.7014
0.008554	71.73	0.6135	0.009211	72.78	0.6704
0.007810	74.11	0.5788	0.008486	75.48	0.6405
0.007059	76.40	0.5394	0.007640	78.57	0.6003
0.006287	78.585	0.4940	0.006915	81.31	0.5622
0.005525	80.47	0.4446	0.006181	84.04	0.5194
0.004770	82.11	0.3917	0.005320	87.18	0.4638
0.004011	83.89	0.3365	0.004530	90.13	0.4082
0.003230	88.89	0.2871	0.003778	94.10	0.3555
0.002799	103.08	0.2885	0.003087	105.01	0.3242
0.002609	119.27	0.3112	0.002817	117.96	0.3323
0.002495	136.01	0.3393	0.002642	134.85	0.3563

v	p, atm.	pv	v	p, atm.	pv
48.10°C			57.75°C		
0.012311	65.20	0.8027	0.013174	66.27	0.8730
0.011572	67.69	0.7833	0.012356	69.20	0.8550
0.010787$_5$	70.52	0.7607	0.011586	72.18	0.8363
0.009970	73.61	0.7339	0.010807	75.42	0.8151
0.009232	76.61	0.7073	0.010009	78.99	0.7906
0.008442	80.07	0.6760	0.009271	82.49	0.7648
0.007678	83.38	0.6402	0.008482	86.62	0.7347
0.006899	87.07	0.6007	0.007668	91.16	0.6990
0.006118	90.90	0.5561	0.006930	95.79	0.6638
0.005380	94.78	0.5099	0.006113	101.32	0.6194
0.004570	99.62	0.4552	0.005372	107.06	0.5751
0.003823	105.50	0.4033	0.004596	114.45	0.5260
0.003129$_5$	119.38	0.3736	0.003795	126.10	0.4786
0.002864	135.56	0.3883	0.003421	135.81	0.4647

NOTE: All tables on p. 12 and 13 based on (62), pv = 1.0000 at 0°C. and 0 atm.

p, m Hg	100α (25)			100β (25)		
	0 to 20°C	0 to 40°C	0 to 100°C	0 to 20°C	0 to 40°C	0 to 100°C
0.518	0.3713	0.3710	0.3707			
0.998	0.3760	0.3754	0.3741	0.3734	0.3730	0.3726
1.377	0.3797	0.3791	0.3770			

p, respectively p_0 = 1 atm. (70)			
100α		100β	
0°C	0 to 100°C	0°C	0 to 100°C
0.3750	0.3722	0.3723	0.3711

VALUES OF pv

v = 1.0000 at 0°C and 0 atm. (62)

$\frac{1}{v}$	25.55°C	28.15°C	30.98°C	31.89°C	34.02°C	37.09°C	41.95°C	48.10°C	57.75°C
80									0.8583
100			0.6355	0.6411	0.6538	0.6719	0.6997	0.7349	0.7903
120		0.5467	0.5653	0.5715	0.5844	0.6036	0.6335	0.6712	0.7285
140		0.4839	0.5037	0.5094	0.5240	0.5440	0.5746	0.6135	0.6743
160			0.4499	0.4566	0.4708	0.4918	0.5237	0.5640	0.6273
180			0.4039	0.4106	0.4254	0.4466	0.4796	0.5212	0.5864
200			0.3646	0.3716	0.3863	0.4081	0.4416	0.4847	0.5521
220			0.3314	0.3387	0.3494	0.3754	0.4094	0.4536	0.5226
240			0.3041	0.3109	0.3226	0.3477	0.3819	0.4264	0.4991
260			0.2806	0.2875	0.3021	0.3243	0.3597	0.4048	0.4812
280			0.2611	0.2680	0.2825	0.3052	0.3423	0.3872	0.4692
300			0.2448	0.2521	0.2677	0.2915	0.3302	0.3763	
320			0.2333	0.2410	0.2590	0.2835	0.3245	0.3737	
340		0.2058	0.2273	0.2321	0.2554	0.2863	0.3255	0.3817	
360	0.1806	0.2043	0.2305	0.2401	0.2588	0.2900	0.3362		
380	0.1886	0.2140	0.2427	0.2530	0.2742	0.3073			
400	0.2084	0.2379	0.2690	0.2800	0.3031	0.3376			
420	0.2442	0.2780	0.3199	0.3230					
440	0.3118								

Values of $\left(\frac{10^5(v_{t_2} - v_{t_1})}{v_{t_1}(t_2 - t_1)}\right)$ at various pressures (3)

p, atm.	0 to 10°C	10 to 20°C	20 to 30°C	30 to 40°C	40 to 50°C	50 to 60°C	60 to 70°C	70 to 80°C	80 to 90°C	90 to 100°C	100 to 137°C	137 to 198°C	198 to 258°C
50	905		1394	1097	823	695	600	508	520	464			
60	800	1259		1557	1081	853	705	604	560	521			
75	654	1043	2166	18310	2048	1258	916	762	643	595	485	369	260
85	637	872	1425	9079	4965	1813	1222	921	753	696			
100	544	728	1159	2128	5899	3462	1755	1229	928	802	601	420	279
125	522	630	772	1666	1791	2911	2608	1804	1304	1037			
150	474	550	613	922	1114	1575	1855	1835	1484	1247	864	525	313
175	423	493	550	728	842	1061	1335	1370	1374	1228	945	565	330
200	416	449	501	625	695	850	977	1083	1083	1134	934	798	343
250	337	408	461	459	511	656	672	697	778	865	794	616	358
300	322	364	401	418	432	495	542	554	601	627	662	570	364
400	268	314	311	352	346	382	384	414	419	426	466	465	341
500	253	274	266	280	313	323	322	330	329	349	364	386	
600	224	247	255	261	255	274	287	287	283	293	302	317	
800	214	216	215	218	223	219	224	228	226	233	234	243	
1000	175	184	180	183	191	184	198	197	198	204	234		

NO, Nitric oxide

p, atm.	pv (21) +9.0°C	−20°C	−40°C	−60°C	−78.6°C
1	**1.000**	**1.000**	**1.000**	**1.000**	**1.000**
30	0.962$_5$	0.9475	0.936$_5$	0.921$_5$	0.893
40	0.950	0.931	0.913$_5$	0.891	0.779
50	0.938	0.913$_5$	0.889$_5$	0.859$_5$	0.779
60	0.926	0.897	0.864$_5$	0.824$_5$	0.709$_5$
70	0.913$_5$	0.880$_5$	0.838$_5$	0.785	0.642
80	0.902$_5$	0.863$_5$	0.812$_5$	0.764$_5$	0.573$_5$
90	0.892	0.845$_5$	0.789	0.707$_5$	0.520
100	0.881$_5$	0.849$_5$	0.768	0.662	0.475$_5$
110	0.862	0.813$_5$	0.747$_5$	0.617	0.441
120	0.862	0.800	0.727	0.576	0.419
130	0.854$_5$	0.787	0.711	0.545	0.424
140	0.854$_5$	0.776	0.692	0.528	0.433$_5$
150	0.843	0.767	0.674$_5$	0.518	0.443$_5$
160	0.837$_5$	0.758	0.659	0.524	0.452$_5$

CH_4, Methane (64)*

v, cm³/g	p, atm. (0°C)	pv	p, atm. (50°C)	pv	p, atm. (100°C)	pv
	1.00	**1.0000**				
35.104	36.37	0.9156	44.55	1.1216	52.63	1.3250
30.089	41.89	0.9040	51.55	1.1124	61.17	1.3200
25.074	49.21	0.8849	61.20	1.1005	72.96	1.3120
20.059	59.85	0.8610	75.35	1.0840	90.56	1.3028
15.045	76.47	0.8251	98.34	1.0611	119.88	1.2935
10.030	107.25	0.7715	143.66	1.0334	179.61	1.2920
9.026	117.08	0.7579	159.21	1.0306	200.51	1.2980
8.024	129.73	0.7465	179.03	1.0303	227.58	1.3096
	150°C		200°C			
35.104	60.70	1.5282	68.66	1.7286		
30.089	70.68	1.5252	80.09	1.7283		
25.074	84.64	1.5220	96.22	1.7303		
20.059	105.63	1.5196	120.42	1.7324		
15.045	140.95	1.5208	161.76	1.7454		
10.030	214.59	1.5436	250.03	1.7985		
9.026	240.62	1.5576	280.55	1.8161		
8.024	275.10	1.5831	321.92	1.8525		

* *See* (155) for revision of this table.

p, m Hg	t	100α	100β	Lit.
0.760	0 to 100°C	0.3683	0.3680	(64)

p, respectively p_0 = 1 atm. (70)

100α 0°C	100α 0 to 100°C	100β 0°C	100β 0 to 100°C
0.369	0.3680	0.368	0.3677

CH_3Cl, Methyl chloride

v = 1.0000 at 0°C and 1 atm. (56, 65)

p, atm.	pv	p, atm.	pv
69.9°C		84.95°C	
15.065	1.0251	16.19	1.0909
15.425	1.0190	16.586	1.0834
15.76	1.0115	17.09	1.0734
16.10	1.0062	17.61	1.0665
16.44	0.9966	18.13	1.0561
		18.74	1.0477
		19.36	1.0368
		19.40	1.0367
		20.00	1.0239
		20.68	1.0106
		21.49	0.9969
		22.24	0.9813
99.95°C		115.0°C	
17.67	1.1519	18.26	1.2231
18.26	1.1438	20.12	1.2000
19.02	1.1338	21.57	1.1805
19.86	1.1210	22.99	1.1627
20.76	1.1108	28.99	1.0785
21.82	1.0902	33.53	0.9499
23.15	1.0698	38.30	0.9172
25.14	1.0361	40.66	0.8665
25.94	1.0220		
26.66	1.0112		
27.55	0.9952		
30.71	0.9309		

At 16.8°C (17)	p (mm)	760	1200	1650	2100	2800
	pv	**1.0000**	0.9796	0.9648	0.9533	0.9335

p, respectively p_0 = 1 atm. (70)

100α 0°C	100α 0 to 100°C	100β 0°C	100β 0 to 100°C
0.403	0.389	0.392	0.385

C_2H_2, Acetylene (150)

p, atm.	pv 0°C	pv 25°C
0.5	1.0057	1.0989
1.0	1.0000	1.0937
2.0	0.9891	1.0841
4.0	.9708	1.0684
6.0	.9530	1.0531
8.0	.9360	1.0385
10.0	.9194	1.0255
12.0	.9026	1.0139

C_2H_4, Ethylene

Values of $\left(\frac{10^5(v_{t_2} - v_{t_1})}{v_{t_1}(t_2 - t_1)}\right)$ at various pressures (3)

p, atm.	0 to 10°C	10 to 20°C	20 to 30°C	30 to 40°C	40 to 50°C	50 to 60°C	60 to 70°C	70 to 80°C	80 to 90°C	90 to 100°C	100 to 137.5°C	137.5 to 198.5°C
50		4976	1622	1135	902	744	671	585	539	502	406	332
75	948	1714	3826	3500	2136	1355	1019	834	743	663	516	387
100	661	893	1195	1427	2040	1790	1407	1109	945	847	641	438
125	533	696	769	967	1122	1252	1353	1171	972	875	728	478
150	420	566	619	689	799	917	925	945	941	883	733	504
175	377	468	539	555	640	679	744	746	746	781	699	517
200	354	419	467	486	508	583	611	614	620	629	643	506
250	306	346	362	382	406	439	461	464	492	493	509	456

C_2H_4, Ethylene.—(*Continued*)

p, atm.	0 to 10°C	10 to 20°C	20 to 30°C	30 to 40°C	40 to 50°C	50 to 60°C	60 to 70°C	70 to 80°C	80 to 90°C	90 to 100°C	100 to 137.5°C	137.5 to 198.5°C
300	267	302	305	336	347	351	376	387	392	409	417	397
350	239	265	273	296	297	303	303	335	354	358	352	344
400	212	241	254	261	263	269	274	304	322	324	303	303
450	199	231	234	241	243	249	250	266	281	284	271	275
500	195	227	226	224	230	232	234	242	240	270	243	251
600	177	177	200	199	199	210	203	207	206	216	212	215
700	152	167	177	178	187	185	184	184	191	193	187	188
800	151	154	159	166	167	167	170	173	172	174	172	164
900	148	149	149	149	149	160	157	159	159	157	165	145
1000	138	142	142	145	145	147	147	146	146	150	157	

p, atm.	Values of *pv* (3)							
	0°C	20°C	40°C	60°C	80°C	100°C	137.5°C	198.5°C
1	**1.0000**							
50	0.1755	0.6290	0.8140	0.9535	1.0770	1.1920	1.3736	1.6520
100	0.3100	0.3600	0.4705	0.6680	0.8465	1.0050	1.2466	1.5800
150	0.4405	0.4850	0.5505	0.6490	0.7760	0.9240	1.1780	1.5400
200	0.5650	0.6095	0.6690	0.7440	0.8380	0.9460	1.1740	1.5368
250	0.6870	0.7325	0.7880	0.8560	0.9370	1.0315	1.2284	1.5690
300	0.8055	0.8520	0.9075	0.9720	1.0475	1.1330	1.3100	1.6276
350	0.9229	0.9690	1.0250	1.0875	1.1580	1.2420	1.4060	1.7010
400	1.0365	1.0840	1.1405	1.2020	1.2725	1.3560	1.5104	1.7900
450	1.1465	1.1975	1.2550	1.3175	1.3865	1.4660	1.6150	1.8858
500	1.2555	1.3075	1.3670	1.4310	1.5000	1.5775	1.7212	1.9846
550	1.3640	1.4165	1.4770	1.5420	1.6115	1.6855	1.8290	2.0868
600	1.4725	1.5250	1.5865	1.6520	1.7215	1.7950	1.9376	2.1910
650	1.5785	1.6325	1.6930	1.7610	1.8305	1.9035	2.0450	2.2950
700	1.6835	1.7375	1.7995	1.8670	1.9365	2.0115	2.1526	2.3990
750	1.7865	1.8420	1.9050	1.9720	2.0420	2.1190	2.2604	2.5030
800	1.8880	1.9460	2.0100	2.0775	2.1495	2.2245	2.3684	2.6060
850	1.9900	2.0495	2.1140	2.1820	2.2555	2.3300	2.4762	2.7104
900	2.0905	2.1530	2.2175	2.2865	2.3595	2.4345	2.5848	2.8104
950	2.1900	2.2535	2.3200	2.3900	2.4635	2.5390	2.6916	
1000	2.2890	2.3535	2.4215	2.4925	2.5660	2.6425	2.7980	

p, atm.	0°C	5°C	7.5°C	10°C	20°C	30°C	40°C	50°C
38	0.5955	0.6490	0.6735					
40	0.5330	0.6155	0.6425	0.6685				
41	0.1610							
42	0.1570	0.5730	0.6085	0.6370	0.7320			
43	0.1580	0.5470						
44	0.1600	0.5150	0.5675	0.6030				
45		0.4770			0.6980			
46	0.1645	0.1890	0.5100	0.5620	0.6840			
47		0.1850	0.4670					
48	0.1695	0.1855	0.3300	0.5075			0.8300	
49		0.1875	0.2150	0.4700				
50	0.1755	0.1900	0.2075	0.4200	0.6290	0.7310	0.8140	0.8865
51				0.2900				
52	0.1810	0.1945	0.2060	0.2400	0.5975			
54			0.2090	0.2290	0.5610	0.6905	0.7810	0.8595
56		0.2050	0.2125	0.2270	0.5235			
58			0.5180	0.2285	0.4805			
60	0.2025	0.2145		0.2315	0.4300	0.6195	0.7285	0.8170
65					0.3310	0.5500	0.6805	
70					0.3110	0.4830	0.6310	0.7430
75	0.2425	0.2535		0.2655	0.3110	0.4300	0.5805	0.7045
80	0.2565			0.2785	0.3165	0.3990	0.5390	0.6660
90					0.3370	0.3915	0.4875	0.6060
100	0.3100			0.3305	0.3600	0.4030	0.4710	0.5665

C_2H_4, Ethylene.—(*Continued*)

p, atm.	*pv* (73)	*p*, atm.	*pv* (73)
24.95°C		24.95°C	
1	**1.0000**	65	0.4681
5	0.9745	70	0.4076
10	0.9443	75	0.3666
15	0.9198	80	0.3493
20	0.8818	85	0.3445
25	0.8495	90	0.3466
30	0.8143	95	0.3524
35	0.7764	100	0.3596
40	0.7364	105	0.3679
45	0.6940	110	0.3774
50	0.6467	115	0.3875
55	0.5949	120	0.3975
60	0.5360	125	0.4081

p, respectively p_0 = 1 atm. (70)

100α		100β	
0°C	0 to 100°C	0°C	0 to 100°C
0.376	0.3734	0.373	0.3721

Coefficients of Expansion of Various Gases as Calculated by Leduc (70)

p, respectively p_0 = 1 atm.

Gas	100α		100β		Experimental values	
					100α	100β
	0°C	0 to 100°C	0°C	0 to 100°C	0 to 100°C	0 to 100°C
CO	0.3674	0.3671	0.3671	0.3672	0.3669*	0.3667*
NO	0.3677	0.3673	0.3673	0.3671		
N_2O	0.3761	0.3731	0.3733	0.3718	0.372*	0.368*
HCl	0.3769	0.3733	0.374	0.3720		
C_2H_2	0.3771	0.3738	0.3740	0.3725		
PH_3	0.379	0.375	0.376	0.374		
H_2S	0.382	0.377	0.378	0.376		
Cl_2	0.390	0.383	0.383	0.380	0.383†	0.381†
C_2N_2	0.396	0.387	0.387	0.383	0.388*	0.383*
SO_2	0.398	0.388	0.389	0.384	0.390*	0.384*
$(CH_3)_2O$	0.400	0.391	0.390	0.387		

* Regnault, 20 to 100°C (118).

† Pier (111).

LITERATURE

(For a key to the periodicals see end of volume)

(1) van Agt and Onnes, *64P*, **28**: 674; 25. *168*, No. **176b**. (2) Amagat, *6*, **19**: 345; 80. (3) Amagat, *6*, **29**: 68; 93. (4) Batuecas, *42*, **16**: 322; 18. (5) Batuecas, *132*, **20**: 441; 22. (6) Batuecas, *34*, **179**: 440; 24. (7) Batuecas, *34*, **179**: 565; 24. (8) Batuecas, *34*, **180**: 1929; 25. **181**: 40; 25. *132*, **23**: 343; 25. (9) Batuecas, *42*, **22**: 101; 25.

(10) Batuecas, Maverick and Schlatter, *42*, **22**: 131; 25. (11) Baume, *42*, **6**: 1; 08. (12) Baume and Perrot, *42*, **6**: 610; 08. (13) Baume and Perrot, *42*, **7**:369; 09. *34*, **148**: 39; 09 (14) Baume and Wourtzel, *42*, **10**: 520; 12. (15) Baxter and Starkweather, *197*, **10**: 479; 24. (16) Baxter and Starkweather, *197*, **11**: 231; 25. (17) Bodareu, *22*, **23 I**: 492; 14. (18) Boks and Onnes, *448*, **1**: 81a; 24. *168*, No. **170a**, 24. (19) Bridgman, *197*, **9**: 370; 23.

(20) Bridgman, *70*, **42**: 568; 23. (21) Briner, Biedermann and Rother, *37*, **8**: 923; 25. (22) Bruylants and Bytebier, *186*, **1912**: 856. (23) Bruylants and Dondeyne, *186*, **8**: 387; 22. (24) Burt and Gray, *135*, **103**: 161, 170; 11. (25) Chappuis, *238*, **13**; 1907. (26) Corey, Laubengayer and Dennis, *1*, **47**: 112; 25. (27) Crafts, *34*, **106**: 1662; 88. (28) Crommelin, Martinez and Onnes, *64P*, **22**: 108; 20. *168*, No. **154a**; 18. (29) Crommelin and Swallow, *448*, **1**: 53a; 24. *168*, No. **172a**; 24.

(30) Cuthbertson and Cuthbertson, *62*, **213**: 1; 13. (31) Dumas, *6*, **33**: 337; 1826. **44**: 288; 1830. *8*, **9**: 293; 1827. (32) Ernyrei, *93*, **25**: 313; 00. (33) Garzarolli-Thurnlackh, and Schacherl, *13*, **230**: 273; 85. (34) Germann, *34*, **157**: 926; 13. *42*, **12**: 66; 14. *50*, **19**: 437; 15. (35) Germann and Booth, *Bull. Western Reserve University*, **19**: 15; 16. (36) Germann and Booth, *50*, **21**: 81; 17. (37) Gray, *4*, **87**: 1601; 05. (38) Gray and Ramsay, *5*, **84**: 536; 11. (39) Guye, *42*, **6**: 769; 08.

(40) Guye, *136*, **36**: 402; 12. (41) Guye, *42*, **15**: 561; 17. (42) Guye, *42*, **16**: 46; 18. (43) Guye and Batuecas, *37*, **5**: 532; 22. (44) Guye and Batuecas, *42*, **20**: 308; 23. (45) Guye and Davila, *34*, **141**: 826; 05. (46) Guye, Kovacs, and Wourtzel, *42*, **10**: 332; 12. (47) Guye and Pintza, *34*, **139**: 677; 04. (48) Guye and Pintza, *34*, **141**: 51; 05. *463*, **35**: 569; 08. (49) Henning and Heuse, *96*, **5**: 285; 21.

(50) Heuse, *26*, **15**: 518; 13. (51) Holborn, *8*, **63**: 674; 20. (52) Holborn and Otto, *96*, **10**: 367; 22. (53) Holborn and Otto, *96*, **23**: 77; 24. (54) Holborn and Otto, *96*, **33**: 1; 25. (55) Holborn and Schultze, *8*, **47**: 1089; 15. (56) Holst, *462*, **6**: 48; 15. *168*, No. **144**: 14. (57) Howarth and Burt, *83*, **20**: 544; 25. (58) Jaquerod and Pintza, *34*, **139**: 129; 04. *463*, **35**: 589; 08. (59) Jaquerod and Scheuer, *34*, **140**: 1384; 05.

(60) Jaquerod and Tourpaian, *149*, **31**: 20; 11. (61) Jaquerod and Tourpaian, *42*, **11**: 3; 13. (62) Keesom, *64V*, **12**: 391, 544, 616, 621; 03. *168*, No. **88**; 03. (63) Keyes, *382*, **7**: 371; 21. (63.5) Keyes, Mass. Inst. Tech., *0*. (64) Keyes, Smith and Joubert, *285*, **1**: 191; 22. (65) Kuenen, *18*, **26**: 354; 93. (66) Kuypers, *448*, **1**: 69a; 24. *168*, No. **169b**: 24. (67) Kuypers and Onnes, *18*, **6**: 277; 23. *168*, No. **165**: 23. (68) Leduc, *6*, **15**: 5; 98. (69) Leduc, *Recherches sur les gaz*. Paris, Gauthier-Villars, 1898. *238*, **16**; 1917.

(70) Leduc, *8*, **5**: 180; 16. (71) Leduc, *34*, **167**: 70; 18. (72) Martinez and Onnes, *18*, **6**: 253; 23. *168*, No. **164**: 23. (73) Masson and Dolley, *5*, **103**: 524; 23. (74) Maverick, *Thesis*, Geneva, 1923. (75) Meyers and Jessup, Bureau of Standards, *0*. (76) Moissan, *34*, **101**: 1490; 85. (77) Moissan, *34*, **102**: 1245; 86. (78) Moissan, *34*, **138**: 728; 04. (79) Moissan and Meslans, *34*, **107**: 1155; 88.

(80) Moles, *42*, **14**: 389; 16. (81) Moles, *42*, **14**: 434; 16. (82) Moles, *42*, **19**: 283; 21. (83) Moles and Batuecas, *42*, **17**: 586; 19. (84) Moles and Batuecas, *132*, **18**: 211; 20. (85) Moles and Batuecas, *42*, **18**: 353; 20. (86) Moles, Batuecas and Paya, *132*, **20**: 34; 22. (87) Moles and Clavera, *132*, **20**: 550; 22. (88) Moles and Clavera, *42*, **21**: 10; 24. (89) Moles and Crespi, *132*, **20**: 190; 22.

(90) Moles and Gonzalez, *42*, **19**: 310; 21. (91) Moore, *4*, **93**: 2181; 08. (92) Morley, *Smithsonian Contributions to Knowledge*, **29**: No. 980; 95. (93) Morley, *11*, **17**: 267; 95. (94) Morley, *7*, **20**: 68; 96. (95) Muller, *6*, **20**: 116; 10. (96) Nijhoff and Keesom, *64P*, **28**: 963; 25. *168*, No. **179b**. (97) Onnes, *64P*, **10**: 445; 08. *168*, No. **102**; 08. (98) Onnes and Boks, *448*, **1**: 189a; 24. *168*, No. **170b**; 24. (99) Onnes and Braak, *64P*, **10**: 204, 413; 08. *168*, No. **100a**; 08.

(100) Onnes and Crommelin, *64P*, **13**: 614; 11. *168*, No. **118**; 11. (101) Onnes and Crommelin, *64P*, **18**: 515; 15. (102) Onnes, Crommelin and Smid, *64P*, **18**: 465; 15. (103) Onnes, Dorsmann and Holst, *64P*, **18**: 458; 15. (104) Onnes and Kuypers, *448*, **1**: 65a; 24. *168*, No. **169a**; 24. (105) Onnes and Penning, *18*, **6**: 277; 23. **7**: 157; 23. *168*, No. **165b**; 23. (106) Ouedinoff, *28*, **23**: 266; 09. (107) Paya and Moles, *132*, **20**: 247; 22. (108) Penning, *18*, **7**: 172; 24. (109) Penning and Onnes, *18*, **7**: 166; 24. *168*, No. **165c**; 23.

(110) Perman and Davies, *5*, **78**: 28; 06. (111) Pier, *7*, **62**: 385; 08. (112) Ramsay and Travers, *5*, **64**: 183; 98. (113) Ramsay and Travers, *62*, **197**: 47; 01. *7*, **38**: 679; 01. (114) Rayleigh, *5*, **53**: 134; 93. (115) Rayleigh, *5*, **62**: 204; 97. (116) Rayleigh, *5*, **74**: 181; 04. (117) Rayleigh, *62*, **204**: 351; 05. (118) Regnault, *6*, **5**: 52; 42. (119) Regnault, *151*, **21**: 107; 47.

(120) Reiman, *42*, **15**: 293; 17. (121) Roth, *8*, **11**: 1; 80. (122) Scheuer, *75*, **123 II A**: 931; 14. (123) Schlatter, *Thesis*, Geneva, 1923. (124) Schultze, *8*, **48**: 269; 15. (125) Smith and Taylor, *1*, **45**: 2107; 23. (126) Stahrfoss, *42*, **16**: 175; 18. (127) Stock and Guttman, *25*, **37**: 885; 04. (128) Stock and Somieski, *25*, **49**: 111; 16. (129) Stock and Somieski, *25*, **52**: 695; 19.

(130) Stock and Zeidler, *25*, **54**: 531; 21. (131) Taylor, *2*, **10**: 653; 17. (132) Ter-Gazarian, *42*, **7**: 337; 09. (133) Than, *6*, **15**: 459; 68. (134) Thomsen, *93*, **12**: 1; 96. (135) Timmermans, *42*, **18**: 133; 20. (136) Treuthardt, *34*, **172**: 1598; 21. (137) van Urk and Nijhoff, *448*, **1**: 73a; 24. *168*, No. **169c**; 24. (138) Verschoyle, *5*, **111**: 552; 26. (139) Watson, *4*, **97**: 810; 10.

(140) Watson, *4*, **97**: 833; 10. (141) Witkowski, *3*, **41**: 288; 96. (142) Witkowski, *180*, **1905**: 305. (143) Wourtzel, *34*, **155**: 152; 12. *42*, **11**: 29; 13. (144) Batuecas, *132*, **24**: 528; 26. (145) Baxter and Starkweather, *65*, **12**: 699; 26. (146) Baxter and Starkweather, *65*, **12**: 703; 26. (147) Holborn and Otto, *96*, **38**: 359; 26. (148) Moles and Miravalles, *132*, **24**: 356; 26. (149) Onnes and van Urk, *168*, No. **169**; 24.

(150) Sameshima, *Bull. Chem. Soc. Japan*, **1**: 41; 26. (151) Bartlett, *1*, **49**: 687; 27. (152) Bartlett, *1*, **49**: 1955; 27. (153) Moles, *36*, **56**: 915; 26. (154) Moles, *132*, **24**: 717; 26. (155) Keyes and Burks, *1*, **49**: 1403; 27. (156) Bartlett, Cupples and Tremearne, Fixed Nitrogen Research Lab., *O*.

P-V-T RELATIONS FOR GAS MIXTURES

Components A	Components B	*t*, range	*p*, range	Lit.
A	O_2	At 24.95°C	Up to 125 atm.	(11)
A	N_2	−200 to −183°C	Up to 1200 mm	(8)
A	C_2H_4	At 24.95°C	Up to 125 atm.	(11)
O_2	N_2	At 20° and −141 to −120°C	32 to 56 atm.	(10)
O_2	CO_2	9 to 25°C	58 to 140 atm.	(9)
O_2	C_2H_4	At 24.95°C	Up to 125 atm.	(11)
H_2	CO_2	15 to 32°C	30 to 120 atm.	(13)
H_2	N_2	0 and 20°C	24 to 205 atm.	(14)
		0–300°C	Up to 1000 atm.	(16, 17)
H_2O	NH_3	98 to 200°C	1 atm.	(15)
H_2O	CO_2	98 to 200°C	1 atm.	(15)
HCl	PH_3	24 to 54°C	Up to 80 atm.	(1)
HCl	CO_2	20 to 52°C	30 to 96 atm.	(6)
HCl	C_2H_6	13 to 53°C	32 to 78 atm.	(12)
SO_2	CH_3Cl			(3)
SO_2	$(CH_3)_2O$	56, 77, 109°C	6 to 37 atm.	(2)
Natural gas		15°C	Up to 40 atm.	(4, 5)
Natural gas		19 to 24°C	Up to 48 atm.	(7)

LITERATURE

(For a key to the periodicals see end of volume)

(1) Briner, *42*, **4**: 476; 06. (2) Briner and Cardoso, *34*, **144**: 911; 07. (3) Brinkman, *Diss.*, Amsterdam, 1904. (4) Burrell and Robertson, *30*, No. **131**: 16. (5) Burrell and Robertson, *30*, No. **158**; 17. (6) Dorsmann, *Diss.*, Amsterdam, 1908. (7) Earhart and Wyer, *122*, **38**: 695; 16. (8) Holst and Hamburger, *64V*, **24**: 798; 15. *64P*, **18**: 872; 16. (9) Keesom, *64P*, **6**: 532; 04. *168*, No. **88**; 03.
(10) Kuenen, Verschoyle and van Urk, *64P*, **26**: 49; 23. *168*, No. **161**: 22. (11) Masson and Dolley, *5*, **103**: 524; 23. (12) Quint Gzn, *7*, **39**: 14; 01. (13) Verschaffelt, *18*, **11**: 403; 06. (14) Verschoyle, *5*, **111**: 552; 26. (15) Maass and Mennie, *5*, **110**: 198; 26. (16) Bartlett, *1*, **49**: 687, 1955; 27. (17) Bartlett, Fixed Nitrogen Research Lab., *O.*

N_2, NITROGEN

Louis Décombe

COMPRESSIBILITY

Low Pressures

At 16°C and between $p = 76$ and 152 cm Hg, $\frac{p_0 v_0}{pv} = 1 + 3 \times 10^{-6}(p - p_0)$ (13).

At 14.9°C and between $p_0 = \frac{1}{2}$ and $p = 1$ atm., $\frac{p_0 v_0}{pv} = 1.00015$ (15).

Between $p = 1$ and 1.4 m Hg and with unit of $v = v$ at 0°C and 1 m Hg, $pv = 1.000571 - 0.000571p$, at 0°C; and $pv = 1.366966 + 0.000347p$, at 100°C (4).

Between $p = 1$ and 27 atm., and 4.1 and 5.2°C, $\frac{pv}{p_0 v_0} = 1 + \mathrm{A}\left(\frac{v_0}{v} - 1\right) + \mathrm{B}\left(\frac{v_0}{v} - 1\right)^2$, where $\log_{10}(-\mathrm{A}) = \bar{4}.8389375$ and $\log_{10} \mathrm{B} = \bar{6}.8476020$ (16).

Unit of v = v at 16° and 1 atm.

p, atm.	*pv*, 16.0°	*p*, atm.	*pv*, 16.0°	*p*, atm.	*pv*, 16.0°	*p*, atm.	*pv*, 16.0°
1	1.0000	65	0.9897	130	1.0050	240	1.0783
5	0.9987	70	0.9900	135	1.0076	250	1.0867
10	0.9971	75	0.9904	140	1.0103	260	1.0954
15	0.9957	80	0.9908	145	1.0131	270	1.1048
20	0.9945	85	0.9914	150	1.0160	280	1.1145
25	0.9933	90	0.9921	160	1.0221	290	1.1243
30	0.9923	95	0.9930	170	1.0284	300	1.1340
35	0.9914	100	0.9941	180	1.0349	320	1.1552
40	0.9907	105	0.9953	190	1.0414	340	1.1765
45	0.9901	110	0.9967	200	1.0483	360	1.1990
50	0.9897	115	0.9984	210	1.0555	380	1.2215
55	0.9895	120	1.0004	220	1.0627	400	1.2445
60	0.9896	125	1.0026	230	1.0703	430	1.2785

High Pressures

Measurements by Amagat (1); *cf.* (19, 20)

Volume unit = v at 0° and 1 atm.

p, atm.	*pv* 0°	*pv* 16.0°	*pv* 43.6°	*p*, atm.	*pv* 0°	*pv* 16.0°	*pv* 43.6°
1	1.0000			1600	2.8456	2.9088	3.0264
100	0.9910			1700	2.9665	3.0328	3.1509
200	1.0390			1800	3.0861	3.1536	3.2715
300	1.1360			1900	3.20815	3.2765	3.3962
400	1.2570			2000	3.3270	3.3980	3.5170
500	1.3900			2100	3.4461	3.5175	3.6361
600	1.5260			2200	3.5640	3.6366	3.7554
700	1.6625			2300	3.6823	3.7536	3.8720
800	1.8016	1.8648		2400	3.8004	3.8724	3.9924
900	1.9368	2.0016	2.1186	2500	3.9200	3.9900	4.1100
1000	2.0700	2.1340	2.2420	2600	4.0378	4.1054	4.2276
1100	2.20385	2.2682	2.3782	2700	4.1553	4.2228	4.3416
1200	2.3352	2.4000	2.5140	2800	4.2700	4.3386	4.4576
1300	2.46545	2.5285	2.6455	2900	4.3558	4.4544	4.5733
1400	2.5942	2.6558	2.7748	3000	4.4970	4.5675	4.6890
1500	2.72025	2.7810	2.8995				

Values of $p_{atm.}$ at Constant v

v, const.	*p*, atm. 0°	*p*, atm. 16.0°	*p*, atm. 43.6°	*v*, const.	*p*, atm. 0°	*p*, atm. 16.03°	*p*, atm. 99.45°	*p*, atm. 199.5°
0.002070	1000	1088	1239	0.009910	100	107	146	192
.001946	1200	1298	1474	.005195	150	162	225	299
.0018135	1500	1613	1812	.004330	200	217	307	414
.0017145	1800	1937	2168	.003786	250	273	392	530
.0016635	2000	2150	2401	.003414	300	328	474	644
.0015835	2400	2572	2858	.003142	350	383	556	758
.001525	2800	2990		.002940	400	439	637	869
				.002780	450	494	718	
				.002652	500	548	797	
				.002543	550	602	875	
					600	656	957	

Measurements by Bartlett (19, 20)

p, atm.	*pv* 0°	*pv* 50°	*pv* 99.85°	*pv* 198.9°	*pv* 299.8°	*pv* 399.3°
1	1.0000					
50	0.9846	1.1888	1.3888	1.7683		
100	0.9846	1.2046	1.4114	1.8071	2.1978	2.5729
200	1.0362	1.2742	1.4958	1.9073	2.3119	2.6944
300	1.1335	1.3711	1.5971	2.0169	2.4279	2.8166
400	1.2557	1.4870	1.7112	2.1407	2.5498	2.9422
600	1.5214	1.7473	1.9650	2.3914	2.8034	3.1949
800	1.7959	2.0155	2.2273	2.6510	3.0615	3.4559
1000	2.0641	2.2825	2.4942	2.9165	3.3195	3.7196

Measurements by Holborn and Otto (11)

Volume unit = v at 0° and 1 m Hg

p, m Hg	pv −130°	−100°	−50°	0°	+50°	100°	150°	200°	300°	400°
0	0.5244$_6$	0.6343$_4$	0.8174$_7$	1.0006$_0$	1.1836$_8$	1.3668$_2$	1.5499$_6$	1.7330$_8$	2.0993$_4$	2.4655$_8$
1	0.5197$_5$	.6312$_9$	.8159$_3$	1.0000$_0$	1.1836$_7$	1.3671$_8$	1.5506$_4$	1.7339$_8$	2.1005$_5$	2.4669$_6$
5				0.9976$_8$	1.1837$_0$	1.3687$_0$	1.5534$_0$	1.7376$_3$	2.1054$_2$	2.4725$_0$
10	0.4749$_6$	.6035$_9$	.8025$_5$	.9950$_5$	1.1839$_1$	1.3707$_4$	1.5569$_5$	1.7422$_5$	2.1115$_4$	2.4794$_7$
15				.9926$_9$	1.1843$_1$	1.3729$_4$	1.5606$_0$	1.7469$_6$	2.1177$_0$	2.4864$_8$
20	0.4182$_6$	.5724$_9$	.7888$_1$	.9906$_0$	1.1849$_0$	1.3752$_9$	1.5643$_6$	1.7517$_4$	2.1238$_9$	2.4935$_2$
25				.9887$_8$	1.1856$_7$	1.3778$_0$	1.5682$_3$	1.7566$_0$	2.1301$_2$	2.5006$_1$
30	0.3516$_4$	.5417$_1$	.7763$_3$	.9872$_3$	1.1866$_4$	1.3804$_7$	1.5722$_0$	1.7615$_4$	2.1363$_9$	2.5077$_3$
35				.9859$_5$	1.1878$_0$	1.3833$_0$	1.5762$_8$	1.7665$_6$	2.1427$_0$	2.5149$_0$
40	0.2806$_6$	.5123$_5$	.7652$_6$	.9849$_4$	1.1891$_5$	1.3862$_9$	1.5804$_7$	1.7716$_6$	2.1490$_5$	2.5221$_1$
45				.9842$_0$	1.1906$_9$	1.3894$_3$	1.5847$_7$	1.7768$_4$	2.1554$_3$	2.5293$_6$
50	0.2343$_6$	.4860$_0$	.7558$_0$	.9837$_4$	1.1924$_1$	1.3927$_3$	1.5891$_7$	1.7820$_9$	2.1618$_5$	2.5366$_4$
55				.9835$_4$	1.1943$_3$	1.3961$_8$	1.5936$_7$	1.7874$_3$	2.1683$_0$	2.5439$_7$
60		.4646$_5$	.7482$_2$	.9836$_1$	1.1964$_4$	1.3998$_0$	1.5982$_9$	1.7928$_4$	2.1748$_0$	2.5513$_4$
65				.9839$_5$	1.1987$_3$	1.4035$_7$	1.6030$_1$	1.7983$_3$	2.1813$_3$	2.5587$_5$
70		.4507$_6$	.7428$_5$	.9845$_7$	1.2012$_2$	1.4075$_0$	1.6078$_4$	1.8039$_0$	2.1879$_0$	2.5662$_0$
75				.9854$_5$	1.2039$_0$	1.4115$_9$	1.6127$_8$	1.8095$_6$	2.1945$_1$	2.5736$_9$
80		.4471$_9$	.7400$_5$	.9866$_2$	1.2067$_6$	1.4158$_4$	1.6178$_2$	1.8152$_8$	2.2011$_5$	2.5815$_2$

Measurements by Kamerlingh Onnes and Urk (14)

Volume unit = v at 0° and 1 pressure unit. Pressure unit = 759.778 mm Hg at 0° at the pavilion of Breteuil

p	pv +20.00°	0.00°	−23.62°	−50.26°	−81.10°	−102.25°	−121.19°	−131.27°	−141.53°	−144.46°	−146.32°
22											0.3400
24								0.4225	0.3605	0.3395	.3260
26							0.4700	.4135	.3470	.3247	.3090
28						0.5590	.4625	.4045	.3332$_5$	.3080	.2895
30					0.6523	.5540	.4550	.3945	.3180	.2892	.2670
32				0.7832	.6489	.5490	.4475	.3845	.3015	.2675	.2385
34	1.0682	0.9890	0.8920	.7812	.6455	.5441	.4400	.3745	.2825	.2400	.1800
36	1.0679	.9883	.8909	.7792	.6422	.5392	.4325	.3635	.2615	.2000	.1063
38	1.0676	.9876$_5$	.8899	.7773	.6389	.5344	.4250	.3525	.2360	.1425	
40	1.0673	.9870	.8890	.7754	.6356	.5296	.4175	.3415	.2065	.1225	
42	1.0670$_5$	.9864$_5$	.8880	.7736	.6324	.5249	.4100	.3300	.1750	.1207	
44	1.0668$_5$	.9859	.8871	.7717	.6293	.5202	.4025	.3175			
46	1.0667	.9853$_5$	.8861	.7699	.6262	.5156		.3055			
48	1.0666	.9848	.8852	.7681	.6232	.5109		.2940			
50	1.0665	.9843$_5$	.8842	.7664	.6202	.5063		.2825			
52	1.0665	.9839	.8833	.7648	.6173			.2715			
54	1.0665$_5$	.9835$_5$	.8824	.7632	.6145			.2610			
56	1.0667	.9832	.8815	.7616	.6118			.2517			
58	1.0668	.9829	.8806	.7600	.6092			.2432			
60	1.0670	.9826	.8796								
62	1.0672										
64	1.0674										

p	−148.58°
28	0.2625
29	0.2502
30	0.2325
30.4	0.2207
30.8	0.1900

Measurements at 68°C by Bridgman (3)

p, kg/cm²	v, cm³/g	pv*	p, kg/cm²	v, cm³/g	pv*
2 500	1.356	4.11	9 000	1.003	10.94
3 000	1.290	4.68	10 000	0.982	11.91
4 000	1.201	5.82	11 000	.964	12.84
5 000	1.138	6.89	12 000	.948	13.78
6 000	1.093	7.95	13 000	.933	14.70
7 000	1.056	8.95	14 000	.920	15.60
8 000	1.026	9.94	15 000	.908	16.50

* Volume unit = v at 0°C and 1 kg/cm².

Empirical Formulae

Formulae of Holborn and Otto (11)

Pressure unit = m Hg. Volume unit = v at 0° and 1 m Hg

$$pv = \mathrm{A} + \mathrm{B}p + \mathrm{C}p^2 + \mathrm{D}p^4 + \mathrm{E}p^6 \quad (1)$$

$$\left(\frac{\partial(pv)}{\partial p}\right)_{p=0} \times 10^5 = \mathrm{B} \times 10^5 = \mathrm{a} + \mathrm{b}\theta + \frac{\mathrm{c}}{\theta} + \frac{\mathrm{e}}{\theta^3} \quad (2)$$

t, °C	A	10^3B	10^6C	10^9D	10^{12}E
−130	0.52446	−4.68594	−24.4699	−20.2026	8.4248
−100	0.63434	−3.04600	− 3.0667	+1.8603	
− 50	0.81747	−1.54934	+ 5.7092	0.2438	

FORMULAE OF HOLBORN AND OTTO [11].—(*Continued*)

t, °C	A	10^3B	10^6C	Equation (2)	
0	1.00060	−0.60716	5.4056	a	357.46
+ 50	1.18368	−0.01514	3.7959	b	− 9.36
100	1.36682	+0.36057	3.1510	c	−1044.84
150	1.54996	0.67717	2.1389	e	− 242.53
200	1.73308	0.90133	1.5778	$\theta = \frac{t + 273}{100}$	
300	2.09934	1.21257	0.7510		
400	2.46558	1.38086	0.8082		

FORMULA OF R. BECKER [2]

Based upon the measurements of Amagat at 0 and 16°C and between 0 and 3000 atm. Holds accurately up to the highest pressures and yields correct values for t_c and d_c.

$$p = \frac{RT}{v}\left(1 + \frac{k}{v}e^{\frac{k}{v}}\right) - \frac{a}{v^2} + \frac{x}{v^{\beta+2}}$$

	R	k	a	x	β
1*	$\frac{1}{273}$	0.001801	0.00250	1.34×10^{-17}	5
2†	8.31×10^7	40.3	1.26×10^{12}	384×10^{17}	5

* For p in atm. and volume unit = v at 0° and 1 atm.
† For 1 g-mole, p in baryes and v in cm^3.

FORMULA OF VERSCHOYLE [18]

Pressure unit = 759.778 mm Hg at 0°C at the pavilion of Breteuil.

Volume unit = v at 0° and 1 pressure unit. $pv = A + Bp + Cp^2$.

For $t = 0°$, $A = 1.00049$, $B = 0.4961 \times 10^{-3}$, $C = 3.334 \times 10^{-6}$.

For $t = 20°$, $A = 1.07370$, $B = -0.2798 \times 10^{-3}$, $C = 2.800 \times 10^{-6}$.

For range, and deviation graph, *see* Fig. 1.

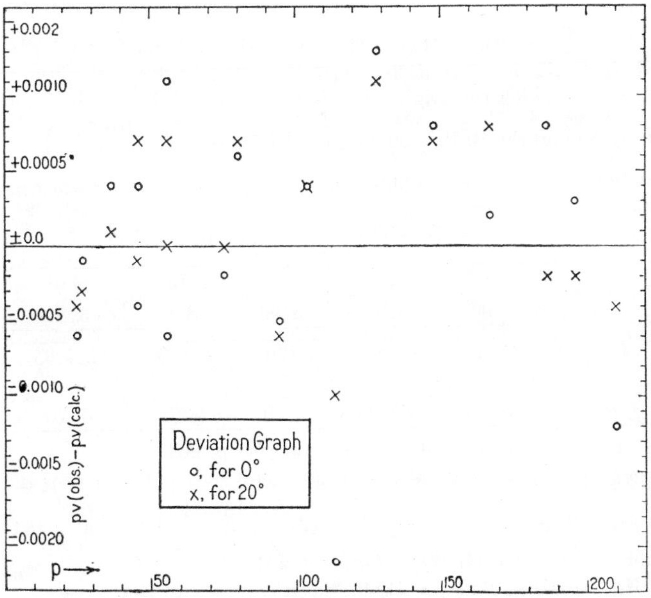

FIG. 1.

Virial Coefficients

$$pv = A\left(1 + \frac{B}{v} + \frac{C}{v^2} + \ldots\right)$$

Pressure unit = 759.778 mm Hg at 0°C, at the pavilion of Breteuil.
Volume unit = v at 0°C and 1 pressure unit

t, °C	A	10^3B	10^6C
Kamerlingh Onnes and Urk [17]			
+ 20	1.07370	−0.24448	2.3284
0	1.00041	−0.40996	2.06556
− 23.62	0.913901	−0.74651	3.057
− 50.26	.816309	−1.10626	2.680
− 81.10	.703330	−1.74585	3.513
−102.25	.625850	−2.34448	4.167
−121.19	.556465	−3.11693	5.367
−131.27	.519539	−3.60025	5.7245
−141.53	.481953	−4.21676	6.455
−144.46	.471218	−4.38627	6.911
−146.32	.464395	−4.54174	6.664
Holborn and Otto [10]			
400	2.46522	1.04930	2.2523
300	2.09903	0.92142	1.7599
200	1.73283	0.68491	2.0487
150	1.54973	0.51457	2.1797
100	1.36662	+0.273995	2.5627
+ 50	1.18368	−0.01150	2.5954
0	1.00045	−0.46137	3.3371
− 50	0.81735	−1.17733	4.0822
−100	0.63425	−2.31462	4.2354
−130	0.52438	−3.56079	5.2703

Thermal Expansion

$$\alpha = \frac{v_2 - v_1}{v_1 t} \text{ at the constant pressure } p_1\text{, cm Hg}$$

$$\beta = \frac{p_2 - p_1}{p_1 t}\text{, at constant volume, the initial pressure being } p_1\text{,}$$

cm Hg

p_1	53.05	79.35	100.19	100.19	100.19	138.68
t, °C	100	100	20	40	100	100
$10^7\alpha$ =			36 770	36 750	36 732	36 778
$10^7\beta$ =	36 685	36 720	36 754	36 752	36 744	(4)

At t = 100° C

p_1	$10^7\beta$	p_1	$10^6\beta$	p_1	$10^7\alpha$	p_1	$10^7\beta$
79.35	36 718	98.5	3 673	79.2	36 701	65.4	36 696
53.3	36 685	74.4	3 670	75.7	36 699		
52.9	36 681	55.0	3 668	41.5	36 659		
39.2	36 677	31.4	3 665	39.5	36 656		
Lit.	(5)	Lit.	(6)	Lit.	(7)	Lit.	(12)

p_1	110.5	51.1	22.0	p_1	110.5	51.1	22.0	Lit.
$10^7\alpha$	36 742	36 679	36 630	$10^7\beta$	36 752	36 675	36 626	(8)

MEASUREMENTS BY AMAGAT [1]

Const. press., atm.	$\frac{10^5}{v}\frac{\Delta v}{\Delta t}$ 0–100°	$\frac{10^5}{v}\frac{\Delta v}{\Delta t}$ 100–200°	Const. press., atm.	$\frac{10^5}{v}\frac{\Delta v}{\Delta t}$ 0–100°	$\frac{10^5}{v}\frac{\Delta v}{\Delta t}$ 100–200°	Const. press., atm.	$\frac{10^5}{v}\frac{\Delta v}{\Delta t}$ 0–16°	$\frac{10^5}{v}\frac{\Delta v}{\Delta t}$ 0–44°
200	433	280	600	282	219	1000	193	191
300	402	267	700	256	204	1500	140	151
400	358	250	800	236	189	2000	133	131
500	315	235	900	218	179	2500	111	108
						3000	98	98

p at 0°, (atm.)	Const. vol.*	$\frac{10^5}{p}\frac{\Delta p}{\Delta t}$ 0–100°	$\frac{10^5}{p}\frac{\Delta p}{\Delta t}$ 100–200°	p at 0°, (atm.)	Const. vol.*	$\frac{10^5}{p}\frac{\Delta p}{\Delta t}$ 0–16°	$\frac{10^5}{p}\frac{\Delta p}{\Delta t}$ 0–44°
100	0.009910	462	315	1000	0.0020700	550	548
200	.005195	537	349	1200	.0019460	510	524
300	.003786	582	359	1500	.0018135	471	477
400	.003142	595	364	1800	.0017145	475	469
500	.002780	596		2000	.0016635	468	460
600	.002543	597		2400	.0015835	448	437
				2800	.0015250	424	

* Volume unit = v at 0° and 1 atm.

Values of $\left(\frac{\partial p}{\partial t}\right)_v$ at 16°C

p, atm.	10	25	50	100	150	200	250	300	350	400	450
$\left(\frac{\partial p}{\partial t}\right)_v$	0.04	0.10	0.21	0.45	0.735	1.073	1.405	1.73	2.05	2.35	2.61

MEASUREMENTS BY HOLBORN AND OTTO (9, 10)

p, m Hg	Values of $10^7(v_t - v_0)/v_0t$ 400°	300°	200°	150°	100°	+50°	−50°	−100°	−130°
0	36604	36604	36604	36604	36603	36602	36604	36604	36604
1	36674	36685	36699	36709	36718	36734	36814	36871	36942
5	36956	37011	37084	37134	37188	37291			
10	37295	37401	37547	37646	37756	37960	38692	39341	40206
15	37619	37776	37993	38140	38305	38607			
20	37930	38135	38418	38614	38834	39228	40741	42208	44444
25	38225	38476	38826	39068	39344	39826			
30	38504	38801	39216	39502	39832	40398	42726	45128	49524
35	38768	39108	39586	39917	40301	40946			
40	39017	39397	39937	40309	40748	41467	44608	47982	55003
45	39249	39668	40268	40682	41174	41960			
50	39464	39919	40578	41029	41575	42424	46342	50597	58598
55	39664	40153	40868	41356	41955	42864			
60	39846	40368	41137	41661	42313	43275	47862	52761	
65	40012	40564	41384	41945	42647	43657			
70	40160	40740	41609	42203	42956	44009	49102	54218	
75	40292	40897	41815	42439	43243	44335			
80							49983	54675	

$\frac{1}{v}$*	Values of $10^7 (p_t - p_0)/p_0t$; const. vol. (9) 400°	300°	200°	150°	100°	50°
0	36604	36604	36604	36604	36603	36602
1	36725	36729	36732	36733	36731	36732
5	37213	37234	37249	37258	37252	37279
10	37823	37863	37894	37911	37904	37960
15	38432	38484	38534	38561	38554	38635
20	39040	39105	39175	39209	39207	39308
25	39648	39724	39811	39854	39860	39975
30	40255	40330	40444	40495	40512	40638
35		40935	41072	41131	41161	41296
40			41696	41765	41812	41950
45			42316	42390	42458	42593
50					43103	43233
55					43735	43864
60						44487
65						45098
70						45709

* Volume unit = v at 0° and 1 m Hg.

LITERATURE

(For a key to the periodicals see end of volume)

(1) Amagat, *6*, **29**: 68; 93. (2) Becker, *96*, **4**: 393; 21. (3) Bridgman, *65*, **59**: 173; 24. (4) Chappuis, *238*, **13**: 1907. (5) Chappuis and Harker, *238*, **12**: 1902. (6) Day and Clement, *12*, **26**: 405; 08. (7) Eumorfopoulas, *5*, **90**: 189; 14. (8) Henning and Heuse, *96*, **5**: 285; 21. (9) Holborn and Otto, *96*, **23**: 77; 24.

(10) Holborn and Otto, *96*, **30**: 320; 24. (11) Holborn and Otto, *96*, **33**: 1; 25. (12) Keyes, Townshend and Young, *285*, **1**: 243; 22. (13) Leduc and Sacerdote, *34*, **125**: 297; 97. (14) Onnes and van Urk, *B60*, p. 69. *168*, No. **169d**; 24. (15) Rayleigh, *7*, **52**: 705; 05. (16) Regnault, *151*, **21**: 329; 47. (17) van Urk, *B60*, p. 79. *168*, No. **169e**; 24. (18) Verschoyle, *5*, **111**: 552; 26. (19) Bartlett, *1*, **49**: 687, 1955; 27. (20) Bartlett, Cupples and Tremearne, Fixed Nitrogen Research Lab., *O*.

DENSITY AND THERMAL EXPANSION OF NON-METALLIC ELEMENTARY SUBSTANCES UNDER ATMOSPHERIC PRESSURE

A. W. PORTER

The values given are density in g/ml = specific gravity, $t/4$ (*in vacuo*) and coefficients of expansion.

I. THE LIQUID STATE*

A.—1.37396 at −183.15° (49). $\frac{10^3}{V}\left(\frac{dV}{dt}\right)_{P=1\,atm.} = 4.65 \pm 0.15$ at −183° (3, 49); *v. further* p. 203.

Br	0°	20°	25°	30°
	3.1875	3.1193	3.1023	3.0848

$\frac{10^3}{V}\left(\frac{dV}{dt}\right)_{0^\circ} = 1.1_1$ (1, 62, 63, 81); *cf.* (18, 66)

Cl.—$d_4^t = [(1.468 - 2.89 \times 10^{-3}t - 5.3 \times 10^{-6}t^2) \pm 1\%]$ between −100 and 144°; liquid under its own vapor pressure above the B. P. (36, 41, 60); *v. further* p. 202.

Δt, °C†	−80 to −33.6	−30 to 0	5–10	15–20	25–30	35–40	50–60	70–80	Lit.
$\frac{10^3}{V}\frac{\Delta V}{\Delta t}$	1.49	1.793	1.978	2.030	2.190	2.260	2.690	3.460	(36)

t, °C	−40	−30	−20	−10	0	+10	20	30
$\frac{10^3}{V}\frac{dV}{dt}$	1.53	1.58	1.65	1.75	1.87	1.99	2.12	2.26

t, °C	40	50	60	70	80	90	100	Lit.
$\frac{10^3}{V}\frac{dV}{dt}$	2.42	2.59	2.78	3.01	3.33	3.76	4.30	(41)

F.—1.14 at −200° (54); 1.108 at B. P., −187°C (24). $\frac{10^3}{V}\frac{\Delta V}{\Delta t}$ = *ca.* 3, between −210 and −187°C (24).

* For orthobaric densities, *v.* p. 202, 203.

† Atmospheric pressure.

H.—$d_4^{T_K} = 0.084404 - 223 \times 10^{-6}\,T_K - 21.83 \times 10^{-6}\,T_K^2$ where T_K is the absolute temperature on the Leiden scale (Vol. I p. 54) on which the triple point is 13.95° and 51.4 mm Hg (d = 0.07709) and the B. P. is 20.35° (d = 0.07085) (58). $\frac{10^3}{V}\left(\frac{\Delta V}{\Delta t}\right)_{P=p}$ = 12.6 between T_K = 13.99° and T_K = 20.39° (58); *v. further* p. 203. The above value at the B. P. is confirmed by Augustin (2).

He.—0.1255 at −268.88°C (56); *v. further* p. 203.

I (24) t, °C	107°	110°	120°	130°	140°
d_4^t	4.004	3.991	3.960	3.929	3.898
t, °C	150°	160°	170°	180°	184.35° B. P.
d_4^t	3.864	3.826	3.796	3.736	3.706

Kr.—2.155 at *ca.* −146°C (70); *v. further* p. 204.

N.—0.8084 ± 0.003 at the B. P., −195.78°C; $d_4^t = 1.1604 - 0.00455\,(t + 273)$ (range −182 to −210°); $\frac{10^3}{V}\frac{\Delta V}{\Delta t}$ between −184 and −205° = 6.0 (3, 50); *v. further* p. 204.

Ne.—1.204 at B. P., −245.92° (15); *v. further* p. 204.

O.—1.1447 at the B. P., −182.95°C; $\frac{10^3}{V}\frac{\Delta V}{\Delta t}$ between −182 and −210° = 4.0 (3, 48).

t, °C	−210	−205	−200	−195
d_4^t	1.2726	1.2489	1.2248	1.2008
t, °C	−190	−185	−182	Lit.
d_4^t	1.1767	1.1527	1.1385	(3)

t, °C	−210.4	−182.0	−154.51	−140.2
d_4^t	1.2746	1.1415	0.9758	0.8742
t, °C	−129.9	−123.3	−120.4	Lit.
d_4^t	0.7781	0.6779	0.6032	(48)

O_3 (Ozone).—1.71 ± 0.05; $\frac{10^3}{V}\frac{dV}{dt} = 2.0$ at −183°; = 2.5 at B. P., −112.4°; $\frac{1}{d_4^t} = 0.512 + 456 \times 10^{-6}\,(t + 273.1) + 3.93 \times 10^{-6}\,(t + 273.1)^2$, from −213 to −83°C (73, 77).

P (28, 32, 59, 69)	t, °C	44.5	100	*ca.* 280 B. P.	40	100	200	280
	d_4^t	1.745	1.69	1.485	1.7492	1.6949	1.6027	1.5287

$\frac{10^5}{V}\frac{\Delta V}{\Delta t} = 5_2$,(50–60°) (64).

Rn.—4.40 at B. P. −62°C (10).

S.—d_4^{113} = 1.8114 (84); d_4^{446} = 1.4579 to 1.5130 (mean 1.480) (68).

t	115.1	122.2	134.0	138.2	145.5
d_4^t	1.8084–1.8094	1.8028	1.7921–1.7938	1.7905	1.7807–1.7846

t	151.5	156.9	158.5	161.0	165.0
d_4^t	1.7761–1.7794	1.7747	1.7710–1.7739	1.7704–1.7733	1.7724

t	171.3	178.3	184.0	210.0	239.5
d_4^t	1.7705	1.7681	1.7632–1.7651	1.7505–1.7511	1.7307–1.7341

t	278.5	357.0	445.0	Lit.
d_4^t	1.7072–1.7119	1.6563–1.6620	1.5994–1.6140	(35)

t	115–134	134–138.2	138.2–145.5	145.5–151.5	151.5–156.9
$\frac{10^6}{V}\frac{\Delta V}{\Delta t}$	430	439	465	487	490

t	156.9–158.5	158.5–161	161–165	165–171.3	171.3–178.3
$\frac{10^6}{V}\frac{\Delta V}{\Delta t}$	282	135	127	170	194

t	178.3–184	184–210	210–239.5
$\frac{10^6}{V}\frac{\Delta V}{\Delta t}$	298	308	344

t	239.5–278.5	278.5–357	357–445	Lit.
$\frac{10^6}{V}\frac{\Delta V}{\Delta t}$	366	366	338	(35); *cf.* (53, 61)

Xe.—3.063 at B. P., −106.9°C (59); *v. further* p. 204.

II. THE CRYSTALLINE STATE

A.—1.65 ± 0.02 at 40°K (from crystal structure) (78).

Br.—Reliable data lacking; Pierre (62) finds *ca.* 6 % decrease in volume on crystallization.

C (Diamond).—d_4^{20} varies with the specimen 3.47 to 3.56 (85). For graphite, *v.* Vol. II, p. 592.

−163.6°	−38°	18°	Room
3.519 (12)	3.510 (12)	3.514 (12)	3.518 (85)

t (26)	20°	40°	50°
$\frac{10^6}{l}\frac{dl}{dt}$	0.89	1.18	1.32

H.—0.08077 at −262.0° (58); 0.0763 at −259.9° (22); the former value implies a contraction of 4.8 % on crystallization.

I.—Iodine.

(40)	(4)	(71)	(6)							
4°	19°	20°	40°	50°	60°	70°	80°	90°	100°	107°
4.933	4.911	4.940	4.918	4.903	4.886	4.871	4.856	4.841	4.830	4.825

N.—1.026$_5$ at −252.5° (22).

O.—1.425$_6$ at −252.5° (22).

P.—Much confusion in results and conclusions of different investigators; *v.* especially (8, 13).

Type	d_4^t	t, °C	Lit.
White: octahedral	1.8177	13	(83)
rhombic	1.8272	13	(83)
P_I	1.83		(44, 45)
Yellow	1.828		(85)
Red: P_{II}	2.34		(44, 45)
light red by heat at 280°	2.16		(44, 45)
pyromorphic	2.18	0	(32)
by heating red at 360°	2.37	0	(32)
	2.296		(85)
	2.28–2.31	18	(13)
Hittorf's metallic	2.33	15.5	(29)
	2.31–2.33		(80)
Metallic	2.19–2.23	18	(13)
Violet (by heating red at 560°)	2.36	20	(46)
Black (by heating metallic to 200° at 12 000 atm.)	2.69	20	(9)

See also (7, 27, 28, 37, 42, 76, 79, 82).

$\frac{10^6}{l}\frac{dl}{dt} = 12_5$, 0 to 40° (64).

S.—Rhombic: $\frac{10^6}{l}\frac{dl}{dt}$ = 64.13 at 40°; mean 0–100° = 67.48 (26). $\frac{10^6}{V}\frac{\Delta V}{\Delta t}$ = 11.52, −188 to 17° (21); *cf.* (39).

Type	d_4^t	t, °C	Lit.
Rhombic	2.0989	−188	(21)
M. P., 112.8°C	2.0522	17	(21)
	2.06		(85)
	2.07		(72)
	2.135		(25)
	2.01–1.99		(61)
Natural	2.0784	0	(63)
	2.070	Rm.	(19)
Crystalline from CS_2	2.063	Rm.	(19)
	2.045		(47)
Monoclinic	1.96	Rm.	(85)
M. P., 119°C	1.94		(61)
Amorphous	1.87		(61)
	1.92–1.93	Rm.	(19)
Soluble in CS_2	1.86	Rm.	(85)
Insoluble in CS_2	1.89	Rm.	(85)

Se.—*See* the literature for details.

Type	d_4^t	t, °C	Lit.
Insoluble in CS_2—metallic	4.80–4.82	17	(14)
	4.80	Rm.	(74)
Insoluble in CS_2—crystalline	4.80		(85)
Soluble in CS_2—crystalline	4.455	17	(14)
	4.46		(61)
	4.47	Rm.	(74)
Amorphous	4.302	17	(14)
	4.26–4.28	Rm.	(74)
	4.29		(61)
	4.28	20	(72)
Heated not higher than necessary for crystallization	4.5–4.6		(39)
Melted	4.80		(39)
Then heated to 125°	4.77		(39)
	4.57	19	(4)

Se.—(*Continued*)

t, °C	$\frac{10^6}{l}\frac{dl}{dt}$	Lit.
0	43.9	(23)
− 40	40.4	(23)
− 80	36.9	(23)
−120	33.5	(23)
−160	32.4	(23)
0 to 100	37.92	(23)
40	36.80	(23)

Te.—Varies with mode of preparation, *v.* (11, 16, 17).

Type	d_4^t	t, °C	Lit.
Amorphous	6.022–6.150	25	(11)
Amorphous	5.85 –5.87		(16, 17)
Amorphous, ppt	5.97 –6.08		(5)
Same, preheated to 430°	6.04 –6.20		(5)
Cast, cooled slowly	6.30 –6.39		(5)
Same, preheated to 430°	6.29 –6.34		(5)
Pptd. from alk. solns	6.07 –6.21		(5)
Pptd. from alk. solns., preheated to 430°	6.06 –6.16		(5)
Cast, quickly cooled	6.10 –6.22		(5)
Pptd. from alk. solns	5.95 –6.06	25	(11)
Crystalline needles	6.310		(16, 17)
Crystalline	6.235	20	(34)
Crystalline	6.281	19	(4)
Crystalline	6.246	18.2	(67)

$\frac{10^6}{l}\frac{dl}{dt}$ = 16.75 at 40°; mean (0–100°) = 17.32 (26).

LITERATURE

(For a key to the periodicals see end of volume)

(1) Andrews and Carlton, *1*, **29**: 688; 07. (2) Augustin, *8*, **46**: 419; 15. (3) Baly and Donnan, *4*, **81**: 907; 02. (4) Beckmann and Faust, *93*, **84**: 103; 13. (5) Beljankin, *136*, **25**: 1002; 01. (6) Billet, *167*, **8**: 46; 55. (7) Boeseken, *70*, **26**: 289; 07. (8) Bridgman, *1*, **36**: 1344; 14. (9) Bridgman, *2*, **3**: 153; 14.

(10) Chaumat, *10*, **1**: 265; 12. (11) Cohen and Kröner, *7*, **82**: 587; 13. (12) Cohen and Olie, *7*, **71**: 385; 10. *168*, No. **113**; 11. (13) Cohen and Olie, *7*, **74**: 10; 10. (14) Coste, *34*, **149**: 674; 09. (15) Crommelin and Onnes, *64P*, **18**: 515; 15. *168*, No. **147d**; 15. (16) Damiens, *6*, **18**: 282; 22. (17) Damiens, *34*, **174**: 1344; 22. (18) Darby, *1*, **40**: 347; 18. (19) Deville, *34*, **25**: 857; 47.

(20) Dewar, *5*, **70**: 237; 02. (21) Dewar, *325*, **17**: 418; 02. (22) Dewar, *5*, **73**: 251; 04. (23) Dorsey, *2*, **27**: 1; 08. (24) Drugmann and Ramsay, *4*, **77**: 1228; 00. (25) Engel, *34*, **112**: 866; 91. (26) Fizeau, *34*, **68**: 1125; 69. (27) Gladstone and Dale, *3*, **18**: 30; 59. (28) Hess, *63*, **6**: 186; 05. (29) Hittorf, *8*, **126**: 193; 65.

(30) Inglis and Coates, *4*, **89**: 886; 06. (31) Johnson and McIntosh, *1*, **31**: 1138; 09. (32) Jolibois, *34*, **289**: 287; 09. (33) Jolibois, *Thesis*, Paris, **10**. *10*, **1**: 4; 12. (34) Kahlbaum, Roth and Siedler, *93*, **29**: 177; 02. (35) Kellas, *4*, **113**: 903; 18. (36) Knietsch, *13*, **259**: 100; 90. (37) Kopp, *13*, **93**: 129; 55. (38) Kruyt, *7*, **64**: 513; 08. (39) Kruyt, *93*, **64**: 305; 09.

(40) Ladenberg, *25*, **35**: 1256; 02. (41) Lange, *92*, **1900**: 683. (42) Leduc, *34*, **113**: 259; 91. (43) Lenher and Morgan, *1*, **22**: 28; 00. (44) Linck, *93*, **56**: 393; 08. (45) Linck and Möller, *25*, **41**: 1404; 08. (46) Marckwald and Helmholz, *93*, **124**: 81; 22. (47) Maquenne, *34*, **100**: 1499; 85. (48) Mathias and Onnes, *64P*, **13**: 939; 11. *168*, No. **113**; 11. (49) Mathias, Onnes, and Crommelin, *64P*, **15**: 667; 12. *168*, No. **131a**; 12.

(50) Mathias, Onnes and Crommelin, *64P*, **17**: 953; 15. *168*, No. **145c**; 15. (51) Mathias, Crommelin and Onnes, *34*, **175**: 933; 22. *168*, No. **162b**; 22. (52) Mathias, Crommelin and Onnes, *6*, **19**: 231; 23. (53) Melcher, *128*, **4**: 431; 14. (54) Moissan and Dewar, *34*, **125**: 505; 97. (55) Onnes, *64P*, **13**: 1093; 11. *168*, No. **119**; 11. (56) Onnes, *0*. (57) Onnes and Boks, *168*, No. **170**: 24. *B60*: 215; 24. (58) Onnes and Crommelin, *168*, No. **137a**. *64V*, **21**: 214; 13. *B60*; 24. (59) Patterson, Cripps and Whytlaw-Gray, *5*, **86**: 579; 12.

(60) Pellaton, *42*, **13**: 426; 15. (61) Petersen, *7*, **8**: 601; 91. (62) Pierre, *6*, **20**: 5; 47. (63) Pisati, *25*, **7**: 361; 74. (64) Pisati and de Franchis, *36*, **4**: 497; 74. (65) van der Plaats, *70*, **5**: 34; 86. (66) Plotnikov and Rokotyan, *7*, **84**: 365; 13. (67) Priwoznik, *Mon. des Museums für Geschichte der Oesterr. Arbeit.*, No. **2**; 1893. *25*, **26**, Pt. **4**: 580; 93. (68) Ramsay, *4*, **35**: 463; 79. (69) Ramsay and Masson, *25*, **13**: 2147; 80.

(70) Ramsay and Travers, *7*, **38**: 641; 01. (71) Richards, *65*, **39**: 579; 04. (72) Richards, Stull and Brink, *152*, No. **76**; 07. (73) Riesenfeld and Schwab, *96*, **11**: 12; 22. (74) Saunders, *50*, **4**: 483; 00. (75) Schrötter, *6*, **24**: 406; 48. (76) Schrötter, *8*, **81**: 299; 50. (77) Schwab, *7*, **110**: 599; 24. (78) Simon and Simson, *96*, **25**: 160; 24. (79) Smits, Meyer and Beck, *87*, **26**: 268; 17.

(80) Stock and Gomolka, *25*, **42**: 4510; 09. (81) Thorpe, *4*, **37**: 172; 80. (82) Troost and Hautefeuille, *25*, **7**: 482; 74. (83) Vernon, *3*, **32**: 365; 91. (84) Vicentini and Omodei, *22*, **4 I**: 718, 805; **4 II**: 19, 39, 75; 88. (85) Wigand, *8*, **22**: 64, 99; 07.

DENSITY AND THERMAL EXPANSION OF INORGANIC COMPOUNDS IN THE LIQUID (INCLUDING VITREOUS) STATE UNDER ONE ATMOSPHERE

G. P. Baxter

B-TABLE

Standard arrangement (*v.* p. viii)

Substance	$d_{t_2}^{t_1} = d_0 + at + bt^2 + \ldots$ (range, °C)	Lit.
2 H_2O	*v.* p. 24	
H_2O_2	$d_4^t = 1.4632 - 0.00117t + 0.0_55t^2$ (−12 to 20)	(48)
HCl	$d_4^t = 0.923 - 0.00318t$ (−104 to −83)	(77)
$HClO_4$	$d_4^t = 1.806 - 0.001927t$ (20 to 50)	(91, 93)
HBr	$d_4^t = 1.549 - 0.00885t$ (−88 to −69)	(77)
HI	$d_4^t = 2.371 - 0.012t$ (−50 to −36)	(77)
ICl	$d_4^t = 3.1822 - 0.002914t - 0.0_761t^2 - 0.0_843t^3$ (24 to 90)	(84)
ICl	$d^t = 3.278 - 0.00327t$ (24 to 100)	(28)
SO_2	$d_4^t = 1.4350 - 0.0025t - 0.0_5112t^2$ (−50 to −10)	(41)
SO_3	$d_4^t = 1.998 - 0.00466t$ (15 to 46)	(72)
SO_3	$d_4^t = 1.9962 - 0.003235t - 0.0_4215t^2$ (15 to 46)	(44)
SO_3	$d_4^t = 1.9982 - 0.003193t - 0.0_4222t^2$ (15 to 46)	(8)
H_2S	$d_4^t = 0.866 - 0.001629t$ (−82 to −63)	(77)
H_2SO_4	$d_4^t = 1.854 - 0.0_398t$ (0 to 76)	(19, 35, 37, 49, 51, 58, 62, 73)
8 S_2Cl_2	$d_4^t = 1.7094 - 0.001596t + 0.0_667t^2 - 0.0_847t^3$ (0 to 136)	(84)
S_2Cl_2	$d_4^t = 1.7055 - 0.001634t + 0.0_514t^2 - 0.0_895t^3$ (12 to 111)	(38)
$SOCl_2$	$d_4^t = 1.6767 - 0.001951t + 0.0_665t^2 - 0.0_7117t^3$ (0 to 69)	(84)
SO_2Cl_2	$d_4^t = 1.7081 - 0.0021t + 0.0_5107t^2 - 0.0_7181t^3$ (0 to 70)	(84)
SO_2Cl_2	$d^t = 1.7045 - 0.00160t$ (0 to 50)	(60)
$S_2O_5Cl_2$	$d_4^t = 1.8585 - 0.001796t - 0.0_631t^2 - 0.0_7225t^3$ (0 to 100)	(84)
$S_2O_5Cl_2$	$d_4^0 = 1.872$; $d_4^{20} = 1.837$	(71)
$S_2O_5Cl_2$	$d_4^0 = 1.873$; $d_4^{18} = 1.839$	(64)
SO_3HCl	$d_4^t = 1.7847 - 0.001615t + 0.0_5121t^2 - 0.0_841t^3$ (0 to 100)	(71, 84)
H_2Se	$d^{-42} = 2.12$	(21)
H_2Te	$d^{-20} = 2.57$	(22)
11 NO	$d^{-150.2} = 1.269$	(1)

𝔅-TABLE.—(*Continued*)

Substance	$d_{t_2}^{t_1} = d_0 + at + bt^2 + \ldots$ (range, °C)	Lit.
11 NO_2	$d_4^t = 1.4903 - 0.00238t - 0.0_648t^2 - 0.0_637t^3$ (0 to 20)	(85)
	$d_4^t = 1.496 - 0.00148t$ (−5 to 15)	(24)
	$d_4^t = 1.490 - 0.00209t$ (0 to 22)	(57)
	$d_4^t = 1.4905 - 0.00204t - 0.0_693t^2$ (0 − 21)	(95)
N_2O	$d_4^{-89.4} = 1.2257$	(26)
N_2O_3	$d_4^t = 1.450 - 0.0017t$ (−8 to 2)	(24)
NH_3	$d_4^t = 0.6386 - 0.00134t - 0.0_41365t^2$ (−78 to −33)	(14, 87)
	$d_4^t = 0.6387 - 0.001365t - 0.0_5163t^2$ (−50 to −33)	(34)
HNO_3	$d_4^t = 1.5300 - 0.0014t$ (0 to 30)	(57)
	$d_4^t = 1.5501 - 0.00203t + 0.0_55t^2$ (4 to 24)	(89)
NOCl	$d_4^t = 1.349 - 0.00242t$ (−48 to 0)	(10)
12 PH_3	$d_4^t = 0.693 - 0.0_36t$ (−106 to −80)	(77)
PCl_3	$d_4^t = 1.6162 - 0.001828t + 0.0_6706t^2 - 0.0_7238t^3$ (−36 to 75)	(61)
	$d_4^t = 1.6128 - 0.001869t + 0.0_6184t^2 - 0.0_8792t^3$ (0 to 76)	(84)
	$d_4^t = 1.6128 - 0.001733t + 0.0_532t^2 + 0.0_7233t^3$ (−80 to 0)	(36)
	$d_4^t = 1.6094 - 0.00134t + 0.0_612t^2$ (−90 to 0)	(87)
$POCl_3$	$d_4^t = 1.7116 - 0.001839t + 0.0_6166t^2 - 0.0_855t^3$ (0 to 105)	(84)
PBr_3	$d_4^t = 2.9249 - 0.002477t + 0.0_675t^2 - 0.0_852t^3$ (0 to 100)	(61)
	$d_4^t = 2.9249 - 0.002415t - 0.0_66t^2 + 0.0_8195t^3$ (100 to 175)	(61)
	$d_4^t = 2.9231 - 0.002458t + 0.0_6378t^2 - 0.0_8281t^3$ (0 to 158)	(84)
$POBrCl_2$	$d_4^t = 2.1207 - 0.002128t + 0.0_688t^2 - 0.0_857t^3$ (12 to 134)	(84)
$PSCl_3$	$d_4^t = 1.6682 - 0.001681t + 0.0_648t^2 - 0.0_848t^3$ (0 to 124)	(84)
13 AsF_3	$d_4^t = 2.6659 - 0.003839t + 0.0_5435t^2$ (0 to 60)	(84)
$AsCl_3$	$d_4^t = 2.2050 - 0.002159t - 0.0_7395t^2 - 0.0_9443t^3$ (−15 to 130)	(61)
	$d_4^t = 2.2050 - 0.002186t + 0.0_6211t^2 - 0.0_8273t^3$ (0 to 129)	(84)
$AsBr_3$	$d_4^t = 3.4694 - 0.002948t + 0.0_5248t^2$ (50 to 100)	(32)
	$d_4^{25} = 3.540$	(66)
SbH_3	$d^{-25} = 2.26$; $d^{-50} = 2.34$	(78)
$SbCl_3$	$d_4^t = 2.8131 - 0.001636t - 0.0_532t^2$ (75 to 150)	(40)
$SbBr_3$	$d_4^{99.5} = 3.845$	(31)
	$d_4^{95} = 3.6926$; $d_4^{100} = 3.6807$	(39)
$BiCl_3$	$d_4^t = 4.438 - 0.00229t$ (250 to 350)	(4, 32, 90)
$BiBr_3$	$d_4^t = 5.248 - 0.0026t$ (272 to 330)	(32)
16 CO	$d_4^t = -0.0052 - 0.0042t$ (−205 to −185)	(7)
CS_2	$d_4^t = 1.2931 - 0.001475t - 0.0_77t^2 - 0.0_7194t^3$ (−35 to 60)	(61)
	$d_4^t = 1.2922 - 0.001487t + 0.0_6217t^2 - 0.0_7182t^3$ (0 to 45)	(84)
	$d_4^t = 1.2918 - 0.00139t + 0.0_64t^2$ (−110 to 0)	(36)
	$d_4^t = 1.2927 - 0.00148t - 0.0_6306t^2$ (−111 to 0)	(76, 87)
	$d_4^t = 1.2931 - 0.001508t$ (0 to 45)	(6, 15, 20, 23, 27, 29, 30, 33, 47, 56, 61, 74, 75, 84, 86, 88, 92)
	$d_4^{-186} = 1.539$	(30)
COS	$d_4^{-87} = 1.24$	(79)
CNCl	$d^t = 1.222 - 0.0018t$ (0 to 45)	(50)
	For other C-compounds, *v.* p. 27	
18 SiO_2	*v.* Vol. IV, p. 19	
SiH_4	$d_4^{-185} = 0.68$	(80)
18 Si_2H_6	$d_4^{-25} = 0.686$	(80)
Si_2H_6O	$d_4^{-80} = 0.881$	(81)
$SiCl_4$	$d_4^t = 1.5237 - 0.001975t - 0.0_6714t^2 - 0.0_749t^3$ (−32 to 59)	(61)
	$d_4^t = 1.5241 - 0.002038t - 0.0_6408t^2 - 0.0_7149t^3$ (0 to 57)	(84)
SiH_2Cl_2	$d_4^{-122} = 1.42$	(82)
SiH_3Cl	$d_4^{-113} = 1.145$	(82)
$SiBr_4$	$d_4^t = 2.8128 - 0.00268t + 0.0_6445t^2 + 0.0_964t^3$	(84)
SiH_3Br	$d_4^{-80} = 1.72$	(81)
Si_3H_9N	$d_4^{-106} = 0.895$	(83)
$TiCl_4$	$d_4^t = 1.7609 - 0.00166t - 0.0_681t^2 + 0.0_8158t^3$ (−22 to 135)	(61)
	$d_4^t = 1.7604 - 0.001729t - 0.0_6654t^2 - 0.0_8578t^3$ (0 to 135)	(84)
GeH_4	$d_4^{-142} = 1.523$	(13)
Ge_2H_6	$d_4^{-109} = 1.98$	(16)
Ge_3H_8	$d_4^{-106} = 2.20$	(16)
22 $SnCl_2$	$d_4^t = 3.674 - 0.001253t$ (290 to 400)	(32)
$SnCl_4$	$d_4^t = 2.2671 - 0.00257t + 0.0_673t^2 - 0.0_7111t^3$ (−19 to 113)	(61)
	$d_4^t = 2.2788 - 0.002643t + 0.0_5137t^2 - 0.0_712t^3$ (0 to 113)	(84)
SnI_4	$d_4^t = 4.145 - 0.00245t$ (145 to 275)	(94)
$PbCl_2$	$d_4^t = 5.627 - 0.00144t$ (522 to 740)	(45)
$PbBr_2$	$d_4^t = 6.175 - 0.00145t$ (600 to 800)	(45)
PbI_2	$d^{383} = 5.625$	(67)
$GaCl_3$	$d^{80} = 2.36$	(42)
$TlNO_3$	$d_4^t = 5.312 - 0.00195t$ (214 to 290)	(32)
$CdCl_2$	$d_4^t = 3.731 - 0.0_3685t$ (600 to 800)	(45)
	$d_4^{600} = 3.299$	(5)
$HgCl_2$	$d_4^t = 5.021 - 0.002218t$ (280 to 335)	(65)
$HgBr_2$	$d_4^t = 5.928 - 0.00338t$ (240 to 340)	(65)
HgI_2	$d_4^t = 6.060 - 0.00322t$ (255 to 355)	(65)
	$d_4^{200} = 5.287$	(67)
32 AgCl	$d^t = 5.267 - 0.0_392t$ (628 to 783)	(46)
	$d^{451} = 4.919$	(67)
$AgClO_3$	$d_4^t = 4.2626 - 0.001742t$ (223 to 247)	(25)
AgBr	$d^t = 6.023 - 0.00103t$ (681 to 819)	(46)
	$d^{427} = 5.595$	(67)
AgI	$d^t = 6.139 - 0.00101t$ (597 to 801)	(46)
	$d^{527} = 5.522$	(67)
$AgNO_3$	$d_4^t = 4.2070 - 0.001112t$ (239 to 410)	(25, 32, 67)
$Fe(CO)_5$	$d_4^t = 1.4937 - 0.001853t$ (0 to 60)	(17)
	$d_4^{18} = 1.4644$	(54)
$Ni(CO)_4$	$d_4^t = 1.3561 - 0.002213t - 0.0_54t^2$ (0 to 36)	(55)
CrO_2Cl_2	$d_4^t = 1.9586 - 0.001908t + 0.0_516t^2 - 0.0_87t^3$ (−47 to 25)	(53)
	$d_4^t = 1.9610 - 0.001880t - 0.0_633t^2 - 0.0_977t^3$ (0 to 116)	(84)
$VOCl_3$	$d_4^t = 1.8653 - 0.0018t - 0.0_72t^2 - 0.0_826t^3$ (0 to 125)	(43, 63, 68, 84)
B_2O_3	$d_4^t = 1.633 - 0.0_3125t$ (900 to 1100)	(2)
	$d_4^t = 1.8766 - 0.00245t + 0.0_528564t^2$ (0 to 80)	(18)
	$d_4^{18} = 1.7955$	(11)
	$\frac{1}{l}\frac{dl}{dt} < 15 \times 10^{-6}$ (below 240°); $> 200 \times 10^{-6}$ (above 240°)	(70)
$AlCl_3$	$d^t = 1.85 - 0.0027t$ (200 to 230)	(9)
$AlBr_3$	$d^t = 2.87 - 0.0023t$ (100 to 225)	(9)
	$d_4^{99.5} = 2.754$	(31)
AlI_3	$d^t = 3.70 - 0.0025t$ (200 to 240)	(9)
77 $CaCl_2$	$d_4^t = 2.37 - 0.0_34t$ (850 to 1000)	(2)
$SrCl_2$	$d_4^t = 3.11 - 0.0_347t$ (850 to 1000)	(2)

B-TABLE.—(*Continued*)

Substance	$d_{t_2}^{t_1} = d_0 + at + bt^2 + \ldots$ (range, °C)	Lit.
79 $BaCl_2$	$d_4^t = 3.72 - 0.0_36t$ (1000 to 1050)	(2)
LiF	$d_4^t = 2.201 - 0.0_3474t$ (887 to 1058)	(32)
LiCl	$d_4^t = 1.762 - 0.0_3432t$ (626 to 985)	(12, 32)
LiBr	$d_4^t = 2.93 - 0.0_37t$ (above 547)	(12)
Li_2SO_4	$d_4^t = 2.346 - 0.0_3402t$ (853 to 1112)	(12, 32)
$LiNO_3$	$d_4^t = 1.919 - 0.0_3547t$ (288 to 546)	(32)
	$d_4^t = 1.930 - 0.0_3549t$ (260 to 309)	(25)
Li_2CO_3	$d_4^t = 2.071 - 0.0_334t$ (800 to 1000)	(12)
82 NaOH	$d_4^t = 2.11 - 0.0_363t$ (340 to 440)	(52)
NaF	$d_4^t = 2.506 - 0.0_3564t$ (1017 to 1214)	(32)
NaCl	$d_4^t = 1.959 - 0.0_352t$ (809 to 1010)	(2, 12, 32, 45)
NaBr	$d_4^t = 2.927 - 0.0_3795t$ (785 to 954)	(12, 32)
NaI	$d_4^t = 3.441 - 0.001061t$ (675 to 724)	(32)
Na_2SO_4	$d_4^t = 2.495 - 0.0_348t$ (900 to 1046)	(12, 32)
$NaNO_3$	$d_4^t = 2.114 - 0.0_367t$ (320 to 550)	(32, 45)
	$d_4^t = 2.134 - 0.0_3702t$ (343 to 492)	(25)
$NaPO_3$	$d_4^t = 2.545 - 0.0_344t$ (905 to 1007)	(2, 32)
Na_2CO_3	$d_4^t = 2.305 - 0.0_34t$ (893 to 1048)	(12)
Na_2MoO_4	$d_4^t = 3.235 - 0.0_363t$ (804 to 1063)	(12)
Na_2WO_4	$d_4^t = 4.409 - 0.0_3795t$ (917 to 1330)	(12)
Na_3AlF_6	$d^t = 0.708 + 0.00152t$ (972 to 995)	(59)
	$d^t = 3.543 - 0.00133t$ (995 to 1083)	(59)
83 KOH	$d_4^t = 2.25 - 0.001t$ (380 to 440)	(52)
KF	$d_4^t = 2.477 - 0.0_3666t$ (913 to 1054)	(32)
KCl	$d_4^t = 1.971 - 0.0_358t$ (785 to 958)	(2, 12, 32, 69)
Carnallite	$d_4^t = 1.945 - 0.0_341t$ (570 to 780)	(3)
KBr	$d_4^t = 2.708 - 0.0_38t$ (751 to 945)	(12, 32, 45)
KI	$d_4^t = 3.159 - 0.00104t$ (700 to 751)	(32)
K_2SO_4	$d_4^t = 2.472 - 0.0_3545t$ (1100 to 1300)	(32)
KNO_3	$d_4^t = 2.097 - 0.0_370t$ (352 to 564)	(25, 32, 45)
KPO_3	$d_4^t = 2.455 - 0.0_343t$ (988 to 1196)	(32)
K_2CO_3	$d_4^t = 2.314 - 0.0_346t$ (911 to 1036)	(12)
$K_2Cr_2O_7$	$d_4^t = 2.564 - 0.0_3698t$ (420 to 497)	(32)
K_2MoO_4	$d_4^t = 2.964 - 0.0_3644t$ (964 to 1324)	(32)
K_2WO_4	$d_4^t = 3.871 - 0.0_376t$ (991 to 1361)	(32)
84 RbF	$d_4^t = 3.707 - 0.00101t$ (820 to 1006)	(12)
RbCl	$d_4^t = 2.701 - 0.000818t$ (734 to 822)	(12)
RbBr	$d_4^t = 3.460 - 0.0011t$ (697 to 780)	(12)
RbI	$d_4^t = 3.577 - 0.00111t$ (700 to 800)	(12)
Rb_2SO_4	$d_4^t = 3.260 - 0.0_3665t$ (1101 to 1307)	(12)
$RbNO_3$	$d_4^t = 2.782 - 0.0_397t$ (348 to 555)	(12)
85 CsF	$d_4^t = 3.611 - 0.00124t$ (720 to 824)	(32)
CsCl	$d_4^t = 3.489 - 0.00108t$ (661 to 741)	(32)
CsBr	$d_4^t = 3.997 - 0.001342t$ (662 to 743)	(32)
CsI	$d_4^t = 3.953 - 0.001215t$ (639 to 701)	(32)
Cs_2SO_4	$d_4^t = 3.867 - 0.0_38t$ (1040 to 1220)	(32)
$CsNO_3$	$d_4^t = 3.270 - 0.001115t$ (445 to 575)	(32)

LITERATURE

(For a key to the periodicals see end of volume)

(1) Adwentowski, *180*, **1909 II**: 742. (2) Arndt and Gessler, *9*, **14**: 665; 08. (3) Arndt and Kunze, *9*, **18**: 994; 12. (4) Aten, *7*, **66**: 641; 09. (5) Aten, *7*, **73**: 578; 10. (6) Aten, *7*, **88**: 321; 14. (7) Baly and Donnan, *4*, **81**: 907; 02. (8) Berthoud, *42*, **20**: 77; 23. (9) Biltz and Voigt, *93*, **126**: 39; 23.

(10) Briner and Pylkoff, *42*, **10**: 640; 12. (11) Briscoe, Robinson and Stephenson, *4*, **1926**: 70. (12) Brunner, *93*, **38**: 350; 04. (13) Corey, Laubengayer and Dennis, *1*, **47**: 112; 25. (14) Cragoe and Harper, *31*, No. **420**: 287; 21. (15) Dawson, *4*, **97**: 1041; 10. (16) Dennis, Corey and Moore, *1*, **46**: 657; 24. (17) Dewar and Jones, *5*, **76**: 558; 05. (18) Ditte, *34*, **85**: 1069; 77. (19) Drucker and Kassel, *7*, **76**: 367; 11.

(20) Faust, *7*, **79**: 97; 12. (21) de Forcrand and Fonzes-Diacon, *34*, **134**: 171; 02. (22) de Forcrand and Fonzes-Diacon, *34*, **134**: 1209; 02. (23) Friedburg, *135*, **47**: 52; 83. (24) Geuther, *13*, **245**: 96; 88. (25) Goodwin and Mailey, *2*, **25**: 469; 07. (26) Grunmach, *8*, **15**: 401; 04. *63*, **5**: 677; 04; *25*, **37**: 1198, 04. (27) Haagen, *13*, **131**: 117; 64. (28) Hannay, *4*, **26**: 815; 73. (29) Hubbard, *7*, **74**: 207; 10. *2*, **30**: 740; 10.

(30) Isnarde, *96*, **9**: 153; 22. (31) Izbekov and Plotnikov, *93*, **71**: 328; 11. (32) Jaeger, *93*, **101**: 16; 17. (33) Jaeger and Kahn, *64P*, **18**: 269; 15. (34) Keyes, *382*, **2**: 20; 16. (35) Knietsch, *25*, **34**: 4069; 01. (36) Körber. *8*, **37**: 1014; 12. (37) Kohlrausch, *8*, **159**: 233, 240; 76. (38) Kopp, *13*, **95**: 307; 55. (39) Kurnakov, Krotkov and Oksman, *53*, **47**: 558; 15.

(40) Kurnakov, Perel'muter and Kanov, *169*, **24**: 399; 15. *10*, **4**: 13; 21. (41) Lange, *92*, **12**: 275; 99. (42) Lecoq de Boisbaudran, *135*, **44**: 166; 81. *34*, **93**: 294, 329, 815; 81. (43) L'Hôte, *34*, **101**: 1151; 85. (44) Lichty, *1*, **34**: 1440; 12. (45) Lorenz, Frei and Jabs, *7*, **61**: 468; 08. (46) Lorenz and Höchberg, *93*, **94**: 288; 16. (47) Lowry, *4*, **105**: 81; 14. (48) Maass and Hatcher, *1*, **42**: 2548; 20. (49) Marignac, *6*, **39**: 184; 53.

(50) Mauguin and Simon, *14*, **15**: 18; 21. (51) Mendelejeff, *25*, **17**: 2536; 84. (52) Meyer and Heck, *7*, **100**: 316; 22. (53) Moles and Gomez, *7*, **80**: 513; 12. (54) Mond and Langer, *4*, **59**: 1090; 91. (55) Mond and Nasini, *7*, **8**: 150; 91. (56) Nasini, *25*, **15**: 2878; 82. (57) Pascal and Garnier, *27*, **25**: 309; 19. (58) Pascal and Garnier, *315*, **20**: 17; 23. (59) Pascal and Jouniaux, *9*, **22**: 71; 16.

(60) Pavlevski, *25*, **30**: 765; 97. (61) Pierre, *6*, **15**: 325; 45. (62) Pound, *4*, **99**: 698; 11. (63) Prandtl and Bleyer, *93*, **65**: 152; 10. (64) Prandtl and Boriniski, *93*, **62**: 24; 09. (65) Prideaux, *4*, **97**: 2032; 10. (66) Retgers, *7*, **11**: 328; 93. (67) Rodwell, *62*, **173**: 1125; 82. (68) Roscoe, *62*, **158**: 1; 68. (69) Sackur, *7*, **83**: 297; 13.

(70) Samsoen, *34*, **181**: 354; 25. (71) Sanger and Riegel, *65*, **47**: 673; 11. (72) Schenck, *13*, **316**: 1; 01. (73) Schertel, *52*, **26**: 246; 82. (74) Schiff, *25*, **14**: 2761; 81. **19**: 560; 86. (75) Schwers, *4*, **101**: 1889; 12. (76) Seitz, Alterthum and Lechner, *8*, **49**: 85; 16. (77) Steele, McIntosh and Archibald, *7*, **55**: 129; 06. (78) Stock and Guttmann, *25*, **37**: 885; 04. (79) Stock and Kuss, *25*, **50**: 159; 17.

(80) Stock and Somieski, *25*, **49**: 111; 16. (81) Stock and Somieski, *25*, **50**: 1739; 17. (82) Stock and Somieski, *25*, **52**: 695; 19. (83) Stock and Somieski, *25*, **54**: 740; 21. (84) Thorpe, *4*, **37**: 327; 80. (85) Thorpe, *4*, **37**: 141; 80. (86) Timmermans, *117*, **13**: 310; 12. (87) Timmermans, *28*, **32**: 299; 23. (88) Tyrer, *4*, **105**: 2534; 14. (89) Veley and Manley, *5*, **62**: 223; 97.

(90) Voigt and Biltz, *93*, **133**: 277; 24. (91) Vorländer and Schilling, *13*, **310**: 369; 00. (92) Wullner, *8*, **133**: 1; 68. (93) van Wyk, *93*, **48**: 1; 05. (94) Dortmann and Hildebrand, *1*, **49**: 737; 27. (95) Mittasch, Kuss and Schlueter, *93*, **159**: 1; 26.

DENSITY AND SPECIFIC VOLUME OF WATER

V. Stott and Philip H. Bigg

1. Density of Water in g per ml between 0°C and 40°C

The values given below are the means of those given by P. Chappuis, *238*, **13**: D 40; 07, and those of M. Thiessen, K. Scheel, and H. Diesselhorst, *89*, **3**: 68; 00. The last column gives the average differences, expressed in units in the seventh decimal place, of the values tabulated in the preceding columns from the values of which they are the mean.

°C	0.0	0.1	0.2	0.3	0.4	0.5	0.6	0.7	0.8	0.9	Diff. × 10⁷
0	0.9998679	0.9998746	0.9998811	0.9998874	0.9998935	0.9998995	0.9999053	0.9999109	0.9999163	0.9999216	1
1	9267	9315	9363	9408	9452	9494	9534	9573	9610	9645	0
2	9679	9711	9741	9769	9796	9821	9844	9866	9887	9905	0
3	9922	9937	9951	9962	9973	9981	9988	9994	9998	*0000	0
4	1.0000000	*9999	*9996	*9992	*9986	*9979	*9970	*9960	*9947	*9934	0
5	0.9999919	0.9999902	0.9999883	0.9999864	0.9999842	0.9999819	0.9999795	0.9999769	0.9999741	0.9999712	1
6	9681	9649	9616	9581	9544	9506	9467	9426	9384	9340	1
7	9295	9248	9200	9150	9099	9046	8992	8936	8879	8821	2
8	8762	8701	8638	8574	8509	8442	8374	8305	8234	8162	3
9	8088	8013	7936	7859	7780	7699	7617	7534	7450	7364	5
10	7277	7189	7099	7008	6915	6820	6724	6627	6529	6428	6
11	6328	6225	6121	6017	5911	5803	5694	5585	5473	5361	2
12	5247	5132	5016	4898	4780	4660	4538	4415	4291	4166	0
13	4040	3913	3784	3655	3524	3391	3258	3123	2987	2850	1
14	2712	2572	2432	2290	2147	2003	1858	1711	1564	1415	1
15	1265	1113	0961	0808	0653	0497	0340	0182	0023	*9862	2
16	0.9989701	0.9989538	0.9989374	0.9989209	0.9989043	0.9988876	0.9988707	0.9988538	0.9988367	0.9988195	6
17	8022	7848	7673	7497	7319	7141	6961	6781	6599	6416	9
18	6232	6046	5861	5673	5485	5295	5105	4913	4720	4526	14
19	4331	4136	3938	3740	3541	3341	3140	2937	2733	2529	18
20	2323	2117	1909	1701	1490	1280	1068	0855	0641	0426	22
21	0210	*9993	*9775	*9556	*9335	*9114	*8892	*8669	*8444	*8219	25
22	0.9977993	0.9977765	0.9977537	0.9977308	0.9977077	0.9976846	0.9976613	0.9976380	0.9976145	0.9975910	27
23	5674	5437	5198	4959	4718	4477	4235	3991	3747	3502	29
24	3256	3009	2760	2511	2261	2010	1758	1505	1250	0995	30
25	0739	0482	0225	*9966	*9706	*9445	*9184	*8921	*8657	*8393	31
26	0.9968128	0.9967861	0.9967594	0.9967326	0.9967057	0.9966786	0.9966515	0.9966243	0.9965970	0.9965696	30
27	5421	5146	4869	4591	4313	4033	3753	3472	3190	2907	29
28	2623	2338	2052	1766	1478	1190	0901	0610	0319	0027	28
29	0.9959735	0.9959440	0.9959146	0.9958850	0.9958554	0.9958257	0.9957958	0.9957659	0.9957359	0.9957059	25
30	6756	6454	6151	5846	5541	5235	4928	4620	4312	4002	23
31	3692	3380	3068	2755	2442	2127	1812	1495	1178	0861	20
32	0542	0222	*9901	*9580	*9258	*8935	*8612	*8286	*7961	*7635	19
33	0.9947308	0.9946980	0.9946651	0.9946321	0.9945991	0.9945660	0.9945328	0.9944995	0.9944661	0.9944327	17
34	3991	3655	3319	2981	2643	2303	1963	1622	1280	0938	16
35	0594	0251	*9906	*9560	*9214	*8867	*8518	*8170	*7820	*7470	16
36	0.9937119	0.9936767	0.9936414	0.9936061	0.9935707	0.9935351	0.9934996	0.9934639	0.9934282	0.9933924	18
37	3565	3206	2846	2484	2123	1760	1397	1032	0668	0302	22
38	0.9929936	0.9929568	0.9929201	0.9928833	0.9928463	0.9928093	0.9927722	0.9927351	0.9926978	0.9926605	28
39	6232	5857	5482	5106	4730	4352	3974	3595	3216	2836	36
40	2455										42

2. Volume, in ml, of 1 g of Water between 0°C and 40°C

Computed from Table 1

°C	0.0	0.1	0.2	0.3	0.4	0.5	0.6	0.7	0.8	0.9
0	1.0001322	1.0001255	1.0001190	1.0001127	1.0001065	1.0001005	1.0000948	1.0000892	1.0000837	1.0000785
1	0734	0685	0637	0592	0548	0506	0466	0427	0390	0355
2	0320	0289	0259	0230	0204	0179	0156	0134	0113	0095
3	0078	0063	0049	0038	0027	0019	0012	0006	0003	0000
4	0000	0001	0004	0008	0014	0022	0030	0040	0053	0067
5	0081	0098	0117	0137	0159	0182	0206	0232	0259	0288
6	0319	0351	0384	0419	0456	0494	0533	0574	0617	0661
7	0706	0753	0801	0851	0902	0954	1008	1064	1121	1179
8	1239	1300	1362	1426	1491	1558	1626	1696	1767	1839
9	1913	1988	2064	2142	2221	2302	2384	2467	2551	2637
10	2724	2813	2905	2993	3086	3181	3278	3374	3473	3573
11	3674	3776	3881	3985	4091	4199	4308	4417	4529	4641
12	4755	4871	4987	5105	5223	5343	5465	5588	5712	5837
13	5963	6091	6219	6349	6480	6613	6747	6882	7018	7155
14	7293	7433	7574	7716	7859	8003	8149	8296	8444	8592
15	8743	8895	9047	9201	9356	9512	9669	9828	9987	*0149
16	1.0010309	1.0010473	1.0010638	1.0010803	1.0010970	1.0011137	1.0011306	1.0011476	1.0011647	1.0011819
17	1993	2167	2343	2519	2697	2876	3056	3237	3419	3603
18	3787	3973	4160	4348	4537	4727	4918	5110	5303	5498

2. Volume, in ml, of 1 g of Water between 0°C and 40°C.—(*Continued*)

°C	0.0	0.1	0.2	0.3	0.4	0.5	0.6	0.7	0.8	0.9
19	1.0015694	1.0015890	1.0016088	1.0016286	1.0016487	1.0016687	1.0016889	1.0017093	1.0017296	1.0017502
20	7708	7916	8124	8333	8544	8756	8968	9182	9397	9612
21	9830	*0048	*0266	*0486	*0708	*0930	*1153	*1377	*1603	*1828
22	1.0022056	1.0022285	1.0022514	1.0022744	1.0022976	1.0023208	1.0023442	1.0023676	1.0023912	1.0024148
23	4386	4624	4864	5104	5346	5589	5832	6077	6322	6569
24	6816	7065	7314	7565	7817	8069	8322	8577	8833	9089
25	9346	9605	9864	*0124	*0387	*0649	*0912	*1176	*1442	*1708
26	1.0031974	1.0032243	1.0032512	1.0032782	1.0033052	1.0033325	1.0033598	1.0033871	1.0034146	1.0034422
27	4699	4976	5255	5535	5815	6097	6379	6662	6947	7232
28	7517	7804	8093	8381	8671	8962	9253	9546	9839	*0134
29	1.0040428	1.0040725	1.0041022	1.0041320	1.0041619	1.0041918	1.0042219	1.0042521	1.0042824	1.0043127
30	3432	3736	4043	4350	4658	4966	5277	5587	5898	6211
31	6523	6838	7153	7469	7786	8104	8422	8741	9062	9382
32	9704	*0028	*0351	*0676	*1001	*1327	*1654	*1983	*2311	*2641
33	1.0052972	1.0053303	1.0053636	1.0053969	1.0054303	1.0054637	1.0054973	1.0055310	1.0055647	1.0055985
34	6324	6664	7005	7346	7688	8032	8376	8711	9067	9413
35	9761	*0109	*0457	*0807	*1158	*1510	*1862	*2215	*2570	*2924
36	1.0063279	1.0063636	1.0063993	1.0064351	1.0064710	1.0065070	1.0065430	1.0065791	1.0066153	1.0066516
37	6879	7244	7609	7975	8341	8709	9077	9447	9817	*0187
38	1.0070559	1.0070932	1.0071304	1.0071678	1.0072052	1.0072428	1.0072804	1.0073181	1.0073559	1.0073938
39	4317	4697	5077	5460	5841	6225	6609	6993	7379	7765
40	8152									

3. Density of Water in g per ml between 40°C and 100°C

The values given are from M. Thiessen, *89*, **4:** 32; 03

°C	0.0	1.0	2.0	3.0	4.0	5.0	6.0	7.0	8.0	9.0
40	0.99224	0.99186	0.99147	0.99107	0.99066	0.99024	0.98982	0.98940	0.98896	0.98852
50	0.98807	0.98762	0.98715	0.98669	0.98621	0.98573	0.98525	0.98475	0.98425	0.98375
60	0.98324	0.98272	0.98220	0.98167	0.98113	0.98059	0.98005	0.97950	0.97894	0.97838
70	0.97781	0.97723	0.97666	0.97607	0.97548	0.97489	0.97429	0.97368	0.97307	0.97245
80	0.97183	0.97121	0.97057	0.96994	0.96930	0.96865	0.96800	0.96734	0.96668	0.96601
90	0.96534	0.96467	0.96399	0.96330	0.96261	0.96192	0.96122	0.96051	0.95981	0.95909
100	0.95838									

4. Volume, in ml, of 1 g of Water, between 40°C and 100°C

Computed from Table 3

°C	0.0	1.0	2.0	3.0	4.0	5.0	6.0	7.0	8.0	9.0
40	1.00782	1.00821	1.00861	1.00901	1.00943	1.00985	1.01028	1.01072	1.01116	1.01161
50	1.01207	1.01254	1.01301	1.01349	1.01398	1.01448	1.01498	1.01548	1.01600	1.01652
60	1.01705	1.01758	1.01813	1.01867	1.01923	1.01979	1.02036	1.02093	1.02154	1.02210
70	1.02270	1.02330	1.02390	1.02452	1.02513	1.02576	1.02639	1.02703	1.02768	1.02833
80	1.02899	1.02965	1.03032	1.03099	1.03168	1.03237	1.03306	1.03376	1.03447	1.03518
90	1.03590	1.03663	1.03736	1.03810	1.03884	1.03959	1.04035	1.04111	1.04188	1.04265
100	1.04343									

5. Density and Specific Volume of Water below 0°C, g/ml and ml/g

J. F. Mohler, *1*, **35:** 236; 12

t, °C	Density	Volume
0	0.9999	1.0001
− 1	0.9998	1.0002
− 2	0.9997	1.0003
− 3	0.9996	1.0004
− 4	0.9994	1.0006
− 5	0.9992	1.0008
− 6	0.9990	1.0011
− 7	0.9987	1.0013
− 8	0.9985	1.0015
− 9	0.9982	1.0018
−10	0.9979	1.0021
−11	0.9976	1.0024
−12	0.9973	1.0027
−13	0.9969	1.0031

6. Effect of Dissolved Air on the Density of Water

Between the temperatures 5°C and 8°C the density of water saturated with air was found to be 0.0000030 g/ml less than the density of air-free water (Chappuis, *238*, **14:** D 63; 10).

DENSITY AND THERMAL EXPANSION OF LIQUID ORGANIC COMPOUNDS UNDER ATMOSPHERIC PRESSURE

ROGER F. BRUNEL✠ AND KATHARINE VAN BIBBER

CONTENTS	MATIÈRES	INHALTSVERZEICHNIS	INDICE	PAGE

UNITS

d = density in g/ml = specific gravity $t/4$ (*in vacuo*). t = °C.

Methyl Alcohol

Klason and Norlin (119) give values for d_4^t as follows: 0°, 0.80999; 10°, 0.80069; 15°, 0.79601; 20°, 0.79134; 30°, 0.78184.

These values are checked by other investigators as follows: At 0° to 0.00001 by Young and Fortey (283), at 15° to 0.00001 by Gyr (86) and Doroshevskii (47); at 10° to 0.00004 and at 20° to 0.00001 by Loomis (137). Values of Dittmar and Fawsitt (42), Young (281), Timmermans (252), and Tyrer (257) are higher, but do not agree with each other.

The following equation reproduces the above values to 0.00002:

$$d_4^t = 0.80999 - 0.0_3 9253t - 0.0_6 41t^2.$$

Extrapolation by this equation to 60° gives values which are probably the best available. They run nearly parallel to those of Dittmar and Fawsitt (42) but about 0.0003 lower.

Timmermans gives for the range −94.5° to +15°:

$$d_4^t = 0.81015 - 0.0_2 10041t - 0.0_5 1802t^2 - 0.0_7 1657t^3.$$

The value at 0° is probably in error, but the values for lower temperatures are the best available.

Ethyl Alcohol

Osborne, McKelvy, and Bearce (166) give the following values for ethyl alcohol saturated with air, which supersede all earlier determinations: 10°, 0.79784; 15°, 0.79360; 20°, 0.78934; 25°, 0.78506; 30°, 0.78075; 35°, 0.77641; 40°, 0.77203.

$$d_4^t = 0.78506 - 0.0_3 8591(t - 25) - 0.0_6 56(t - 25)^2 - 0.0_8 5(t - 25)^3.$$

These values are about 0.00004 lower than those of Winkler (275) and those of Klason and Norlin (119). *See* (166) for an exhaustive review of earlier work.

Rüber (221) has more recently determined the density at 20° as 0.789334 ± 0.000003 (d_4^{20} for water taken as 0.998232).

The following equation reproduces the above values to 0.0001, and then follows the results of Young (281) up to 80° to 0.0002, although this degree of reliability at the higher temperatures cannot be claimed for it:

$$d_4^t = 0.80625 - 0.0_3 8461t + 0.0_6 160t^2 - 0.0_8 85t^3.$$

Timmermans (253) gives the following equation for temperatures below 0° without specifying in the reference quoted the range for which it holds:

$$d_4^t = 0.80625 - 0.0_3 845t + 0.0_6 29t^2.$$

Young's value for d_4^0 is used.

DENSITY-TEMPERATURE EQUATIONS

Table 1 gives the parameters of the equation:

$$d_t = [d_s + 10^{-3}\,\alpha(t - t_s) + 10^{-6}\,\beta(t - t_s)^2 + 10^{-9}\,\gamma(t - t_s)^3] \pm 10^{-4}\,\Delta.$$

Except where indicated by giving t_s as a subscript in Column 3, t_s = 0°C. Where the density at 0°C has not been determined, a value has in many cases been arrived at by extrapolation. Such values are enclosed in parentheses and are given as a basis for calculation only.

Except in the case of a few common compounds which are difficult to investigate or which have been investigated over an unusual temperature range, equations have not been calculated unless there are checks to establish their reliability. Such checks are either determinations by different investigators or determinations on duplicate specimens by the same investigator. Such checks are rarely available over a wide temperature range, but the extent of agreement at particular temperatures indicates at least the probable degree of purity of the material used. The probable limit of error indicated is based upon the degree of concordance of such checks. The values given by the equations are likely in many cases to be more nearly correct than indicated, in the neighborhood of room temperature, less reliable at more remote temperatures. It cannot be safely assumed that specimens of a substance differing even slightly in purity will give parallel density-temperature curves.

Except where the density-temperature curve is practically linear, the equations have been calculated by the method of least squares. Many of them are based upon a composite set of values from different sources where these fall upon a smooth curve. Equations quoted directly from the literature are indicated in the table.

The equations cannot be used with any degree of certainty for values outside of the temperature range upon which they are based.

Equations covering temperatures below the melting points of the substances refer to measurements upon undercooled liquids.

As regards the method of formulating the density-temperature relationship, it may be noted that Körber (121) and Timmermans (253) have shown the possibility of basing calculations on extrapolated values for the density at absolute zero. Albertosi (49) proposes the equation $d_4^t = A - BT$, where T = absolute temperature.

TABLE 1.—DENSITY-TEMPERATURE EQUATIONS BASED ON RELIABLE DATA

Formula	Name	d_s	α	β	γ	Limit of error	Range, °C	Lit.	
								Data employed	Confirmatory
CCl_2O	Carbonyl chloride	1.435	−2.377	−0.7		0.005	−140 to +50	(4)	(66)
CCl_4	Carbon tetrachloride	1.63255	−1.9110	−0.690		.0002¶	0 to 40	(13, 279)	(45, 59)
$CHCl_3$	Chloroform	1.52643	−1.8563	− .5309	− 8.81	.0001¶	−53 to +55	(250, 257)	
CHN	Hydrocyanic acid	0.7205	−1.45			.005	0 to 15	(255)	
CH_2O_2*	Formic acid	1.2441	−1.221	+ .126		.002	0 to 40	(77)	(191, 266)
CH_3I†	Methyl iodide	2.3343	−2.670	−1.77		.002	0 to 40	(44)	(172)
CH_3NO	Formamide	(1.1517)	−0.8405	+0.075		.001	0 to 75	(256)	(267)
CH_3NO_2	Nitromethane	(1.1645)	−1.337	−1.15	+ 3.8	.001	0 to 100	(93)	(185, 264); *cf.* (274)
C_2Cl_4	Tetrachloroethylene	(1.6475)	−1.62			.002	0 to 90	(96)	(229)
$C_2H_2Br_4$	1, 1, 2, 2-Tetrabromoethane	(3.0087)	−2.230	−0.0889		.001	0 to 70	(269)	(172)
$C_2H_2Cl_2O_2$	Dichloroacetic acid	(1.5919)	−1.375			.002	0 to 100	(103, 231)	(188)
$C_2H_2Cl_4$‡	1, 1, 2, 2-Tetrachloroethane	1.5869^{25}	−1.530	− .78	+ 2.5	.001	25 to 90	(268)	(39, 285)
C_2H_3N	Acetonitrile	0.8035	−1.055	− .138	− 6	.0001¶	−45 to +65	(56, 252, 266)	
$C_2H_4Br_2$	Ethylene bromide	(2.2223)	−2.090	− .20		.001¶	0 to 30	(12, 254)	
$C_2H_4Cl_2$	Ethylene chloride	1.28248	−1.4217	− .933	+ 2.29	.0002¶	0 to 74	(257)	(103, 250)
C_2H_4O	Ethylene oxide	0.8968	−1.348	− .32		.001	−50 to +20	(141)	(187)
$C_2H_4O_2$§	Acetic acid	(1.0724)	−1.1229	+ .0058	− 2.0	.001¶	9 to 100	(257)	(163)
$C_2H_4O_2$	Methyl formate	1.00319	−1.4174	− .776	− 8.62	.0005¶	0 to 100	(285)	(183, 250)
C_2H_5Br‖	Ethyl bromide**	1.50138	−2.0644	+ .2673		.003	−119 to +34	(253)	(182, 257)
C_2H_5I†	Ethyl iodide	1.98049	−2.217	−1.55	+ 3.0	.002	0 to 63	(257)	(44, 182, 189)
C_2H_5NO	Acetamide	0.9986^{85}	−0.81			.003	85 to 120	(256)	(14, 54)
C_2H_6	Ethane	0.5612^{-100}	−1.307			.001	−108 to −74	(142)	(143)
$C_2H_6N_2O$	Dimethylnitrosamine	1.0242	−0.867	−1.83		.001	0 to 75	(256, 264)	
$C_2H_6O_2$	Glycol	1.1257	−0.5713	−2.766	+10.9	.001	0 to 136	(232)	(61, 265)
C_2H_6S	Ethylmercaptan	0.8623	−1.077	−2.25		.001	0 to 80	(10)	(161, 259)
C_2H_7N	Ethylamine	0.7057	−1.112	−2.7		.0005¶	0 to 15	(185, 250)	
$C_3H_2N_2$	Malonic nitrile	(1.0850)	−1.124	+2.66	−12.8	.001	33 to 107	(268)	(24)
C_3H_4	Allylene	0.7062^{-50}	−1.245				−55 to −13	(143)	
C_3H_5ClO	α-Epichlorohydrin	1.2031	−1.218	−0.246		.002	0 to 115	(229, 247)	(103)
C_3H_5N	Propionitrile	0.80200**	−1.017	− .483			−90 to 0	(253)	
		0.8020	−0.991	− .553		.0005	0 to 100	(24, 56, 253, 266)	
C_3H_5NO	Lactonitrile	1.0048	− .8438	− .518		.002	0 to 60	(256, 264)	
C_3H_6O††	Acetone	0.81248**	−1.1142	− .315		.0002	−83 to +25	(252)	
		0.81248	−1.100	− .858		.001¶	0 to 50	(183, 239, 252)	
$C_3H_6O_2$	Ethyl formate	0.94802	−1.2506	−1.063	− 0.98	.001¶	0 to 100	(285)	(183)
$C_3H_6O_2$	Methyl acetate	0.95932	−1.2710	−0.405	− 6.09	.001	0 to 100	(285)	(218, 252)
C_3H_7I	*n*-Propyl iodide	1.7844	−1.845	−1.25		.0005¶	0 to 52	(61, 110, 204)	
C_3H_7I	Isopropyl iodide	1.7439	−1.948	−0.80		.001¶	0 to 25	(20, 183, 249)	
C_3H_7N	Allylamine	0.7838	−0.953	−6.2		.001	0 to 25	(185)	(24)
C_3H_7NO	Propionamide	0.9437^{100}	− .8135	−0.42		.005	80 to 120	(256)	(54)
C_3H_8	Propane	0.6259^{-80}	−1.156	+ .15			−78 to −24	(143)	
C_3H_8O‡‡	*n*-Propyl alcohol	0.8201	−0.8183	+1.08	−16.5	.001¶	0 to 100	(274)	(25, 67, 183)
C_3H_8O	Isopropyl alcohol	0.8014	− .809	−0.27		.0005¶	0 to 25	(25, 46, 283)	(134)
$C_3H_8O_3$§§	Glycerol	1.2727	− .5506	−1.016	+ 1.270	.001	0 to 280	(80)	(100, 169)
C_3H_9N	*n*-Propylamine	(0.7344)	− .6133	−8.4		.001	0 to 45	(256)	(103)
$C_4H_4N_2$	Succinonitrile	0.9880^{60}	− .80			.002	60 to 110	(93)	(24, 53, 61)
C_4H_4S	Thiophene	1.08717	−1.124	−0.93		.0005	0 to 50	(120)	(103)
C_4H_7N‖‖	*n*-Butyronitrile**	0.8092	−0.909	− .32		.002	0 to 98	(56)	(85, 89)
$C_4H_8Cl_2S$	Di-(2-chloroethyl) sulfide	(1.2950)	−1.058			.001	15 to 90	(273)	(89)
C_4H_8O	Methyl ethyl ketone	0.82551	−1.022	− .46		.0005¶	0 to 50	(145, 207, 250)	
$C_4H_8O_2$	*n*-Butyric acid	(0.9780)	−0.9831	− .080		.001	25 to 81	(21, 61, 70, 149)	
$C_4H_8O_2$	Isobutyric acid**	0.96820	− .9849	+1.036		.0005¶	−45 to +18	(252)	(61)
$C_4H_8O_2$	Ethyl acetate**	0.92454	−1.168	−1.95	+20	.00005	0 to 40	(261)	
		0.92450	−1.1987	−0.3265		.0001¶	−83 to 0	(252)	
$C_4H_8O_2$	Methyl propionate	0.93871	−1.1891	+ .419	− 0.0106	.001	0 to 100	(285)	(64, 211)
$C_4H_8O_3$	Methyl lactate	1.1160	−1.160			.0015	−75 to +125	(176)	(204)
C_4H_{10}	*n*-Butane	0.601	−1.28	− .6		.005	−24 to +35	(127)	(222)
$C_4H_{10}N_2O$	Nitrosodiethylamine	0.9598	−0.874	− .39		.001	0 to 75	(256)	(24)
$C_4H_{10}O$	*n*-Butyl alcohol	0.82390	− .699	− .32		.0004¶	0 to 47	(3, 26, 214)	(218)
$C_4H_{10}O$	Isobutyl alcohol	0.8169	− .751	− .28	− 8	.0005¶	0 to 50	(160)	(25, 48, 67)
$C_4H_{10}O$	Ether	0.73629**	−1.1044	− .4772		.0001	−120 to 0	(244)	(252)
		0.73629**	−1.1138	−1.237		.0001¶	0 to 70	(244)	(252)
$C_4H_{10}O_4S$	Diethyl sulfate	1.1717	−0.9936	−0.453		.002	0 to 75	(264, 268)	(30)
$C_4H_{10}S$	Diethyl sulfide	0.8563	− .9612	− .668		.001¶	0 to 99	(10)	(25, 161)
$C_5H_4O_2$	Furfural	1.1808	−1.064	− .179		.0005¶	0 to 75	(22, 235, 264)	(144)
C_5H_5N	Pyridine	1.00304	−1.000	+ .355	− 0.50	.0005¶	−45 to +18	(252)	(55, 286)
$C_5H_7NO_2$	Ethyl cyanoacetate	1.0817	−1.022	+ .115		.002	0 to 70	(264, 268)	(24)

TABLE 1.—DENSITY-TEMPERATURE EQUATIONS BASED ON RELIABLE DATA.—(*Continued*)

Formula	Name	d_s	α	β	γ	Limit of error	Range, °C	Lit.	
								Data employed	Confirmatory
$C_5H_8O_2$	Acetylacetone	0.9971	−1.005	+0.40		0.001	0 to 75	(103, 264)	(69)
$C_5H_8O_3$	Levulinic acid	1.1564	−0.85			.002	0 to 75	(103)	(23, 186)
$C_5H_{10}O$	Diethyl ketone	0.8337	− .940	− .662		.001	0 to 53	(32, 61, 78, 233)	
$C_5H_{10}O$¶¶	Methyl propyl ketone	0.8261	− .923	− .766		.0005¶	0 to 54	(157)	(183, 248)
$C_5H_{10}O_2$	Ethyl propionate	0.9124	−1.1223	+0.203	− 7.31	.0005¶	0 to 100	(285)	(13, 146, 229)
$C_5H_{10}O_2$	Methyl *n*-butyrate	0.92006	−1.0704	− .714	+ 1.19	.0002¶	0 to 100	(281)	(218)
$C_5H_{10}O_2$	Methyl isobutyrate	0.91131	−1.0986	− .712	+ 0.37	.0002	0 to 100	(285)	(65)
$C_5H_{10}O_2$	*n*-Propyl acetate	0.90835	−1.094	−0.438		.001	0 to 40	(13)	(211)
$C_5H_{10}O_3$	Ethyl lactate	(1.0553)	−1.126			.0005	7 to 108	(277)	(101)
$C_5H_{11}N$	Piperidine	(0.9791)	−0.9258	+1.512	−22.5	.0005¶	0 to 80	(60, 131, 185)	
C_5H_{12}	2-Methylbutane	0.63943**	− .9719	−0.408			−123 to +15	(252)	
		0.63930	− .9714	− .695	− 7.08	.0003¶	−50 to +100	(252, 281)	
C_5H_{12}	*n*-Pentane	0.64537**	− .9467	− .4495			−123 to +15	(252)	
		0.64539	− .9398	− .6243	− 7.53	.0005¶	−53 to +100	(252, 281)	
C_6H_5Br***	Bromobenzene	1.52231	−1.345	− .24	+ 0.76	.0005¶	0 to 80	(13)	(250, 278)
C_6H_5Cl†††	Chlorobenzene	1.12782	−1.0664	− .2463	− .53	.0005¶	0 to 73	(257)	(13, 278)
		1.12795**	−1.0606	+ .717			−45 to 0	(252)	
C_6H_5F	Fluorobenzene	1.0466	−1.164	−1.074	+ 5.28	.001¶	0 to 90	(150, 278)	(189)
C_6H_5I‡‡‡	Iodobenzene	1.86059	−1.4814	−0.4234		.001¶	0 to 150	(278)	(177, 189)
$C_6H_5NO_2$	Nitrobenzene	(1.22300)	−0.98721	− .09944		.0002¶	0 to 58	(257)	(133, 189, 250)
C_6H_6	Benzene	(0.90005)	−1.0636	− .0376	− 2.213	.0002¶	11 to 72	(13, 281)	
C_6H_6O	Phenol	(1.0920)	−0.8188	− .670		.001	40 to 150	(18, 155, 189)	
C_6H_7N	Aniline	1.03893	− .86534	+ .0929	− 1.90	.0002¶	0 to 99	(257)	(29, 233, 246, 252)
$C_6H_{10}O$	Cyclohexanone	(0.9625)	− .852			.001	8 to 92	(95)	(6, 219)
$C_6H_{10}O_3$	Ethyl acetoacetate	(1.0456)	− .9540	− .7351		.0005¶	17 to 74	(233)	(189, 245)
$C_6H_{10}O_4$	Glycol diacetate	(1.1266)	-1.1_3						
$C_6H_{10}O_4$	Diethyl oxalate	(1.1017)	−1.145	− .416		.0005¶	13 to 95	(233)	(53, 183)
$C_6H_{10}O_6$§§§	Dimethyl *d*-tartrate	1.2925^{60}	−1.044			.002	60 to 135	(151)	(170, 171, 202)
C_6H_{12}	Cyclohexane	0.79707	−0.8879	− .972	+ 1.55	.0003¶	0 to 65	(79)	(6, 219)
$C_6H_{12}O$	Cyclohexanol	(0.9627)	− .7587			.0005¶	16 to 90	(95)	(219)
$C_6H_{12}O_2$	Isobutyl acetate	0.89200	−1.036	− .313		.0003¶	0 to 40	(13)	(64, 65, 218)
$C_6H_{12}O_2$	*sec.*-Butyl acetate	(0.8905)	−0.9024	−2.1		.002	15 to 85	(165)	(38, 198)
$C_6H_{12}O_2$	Ethyl *n*-butyrate	0.8997	−1.031	−0.46		.0003¶	0 to 69	(13)	(65, 70, 130)
$C_6H_{12}O_2$	Ethyl isobutyrate	0.89060	−1.055	− .500		.0005	0 to 40	(13)	(65); *cf.* (218)
C_6H_{14}	Diisopropyl	0.67948	−0.8763	− .5010	− 4.59	.0001¶	0 to 100	(281)	(34)
C_6H_{14}	*n*-Hexane	0.6769	− .8486	−1.084	+ 0.164	.0001¶	0 to 100	(281)	(251)
$C_6H_{15}N$	Di-*n*-propylamine	(0.7553)	− .826	−0.74		.001	0 to 60	(256)	(185)
C_7H_5N	Benzonitrile	1.02279	− .8758	− .14		.001¶	0 to 60	(189, 250, 256, 266)	
C_7H_6O	Benzaldehyde	1.0620	− .875	− .117		.002	0 to 100	(189)	(122)
C_7H_7Br	*p*-Bromotoluene	(1.4313)	−1.25			.0005¶	30 to 100	(158, 189)	
$C_7H_7NO_2$	*m*-Nitrotoluene	(1.1765)	−0.937			.001	17 to 100	(172)	(228)
C_7H_8	Toluene	0.88448**	− .9159	+ .368			−95 to +18	(252)	
		0.88412	− .92248	+ .0152	− 4.223	.0005¶	0 to 99	(257)	(13, 217, 252)
C_7H_8O	Benzyl alcohol	(1.0609)	− .7683	− .459		.001	0 to 100	(189)	(218, 266)
C_7H_8O	*o*-Cresol	1.0654	− .84	− .43		.0005¶	0 to 150	(16)	(19, 218)
C_7H_8O	*m*-Cresol	(1.0495)	− .7639	− .471		.0003¶	9 to 153	(16, 265)	(189, 218)
C_7H_8O	*p*-Cresol	1.0487	− .75	− .3		.0005¶	0 to 100	(19)	(189)
C_7H_9N	Benzylamine	(0.9981)	− .8207	− .432		.001¶	0 to 100	(189)	(256)
C_7H_9N	Methylaniline	1.0027**	− .803	− .242		.0005¶	0 to 158	(57)	(189)
C_7H_9N	*o*-Toluidine	1.0149**	− .833	− .04		.0005¶	11 to 158	(57)	(189)
C_7H_9N	*p*-Toluidine	0.9702^{40}	− .8340	− .410		.001	40 to 175	(18)	(57, 128)
$C_7H_{12}O$	*o*-Methylcyclohexanone	(0.9424)**	− .8640			.001	15 to 90	(95)	(6)
$C_7H_{12}O$	*p*-Methylcyclohexanone	(0.9312)**	− .8028			.001	17 to 90	(95)	(6)
$C_7H_{12}O_4$	Diethyl malonate	1.07593	− .9948	− .705		.001	0 to 100	(272)	(53, 183)
$C_7H_{14}O$	*o*-Hexahydrocresol	(0.9459)**	− .8590			.001	39 to 90	(95)	(6, 225)
$C_7H_{14}O_2$	Heptylic acid	(0.9323)	− .7474	−1.017		.001	0 to 80	(52)	(61, 139)
$C_7H_{14}O_2$	Ethyl isovalerate	0.88540	− .9815	−0.313		.0005	0 to 40	(13)	(65)
$C_7H_{14}O_2$	*d-sec.*-Butyl propionate	(0.8883)	−1.070	+ .07		.002	17 to 125	(198)	(165)
C_7H_{16}	*n*-Heptane	0.70048	−0.8476	+ .1880	− 5.23	.0002¶	0 to 100	(281)	(35, 247)
C_8H_7N	Benzyl cyanide	1.0325	− .794	− .37		.001	0 to 50	(189, 266)	(51, 256)
C_8H_8O	Acetophenone	$1.0267^{21.6}$**	− .8467	− .596		.0002¶	21 to 114	(56)	(189)
C_8H_9NO	Acetanilide	1.0261^{120}	− .820			.003	120 to 160	(256)	(83)
C_8H_{10}	*m*-Xylene	0.88151	− .8515	− .109	− 1.73	.0005¶	0 to 100	(257)	(189, 218)
$C_8H_{10}O$	Phenetole	0.9852	− .9224			.001¶	0 to 80	(18)	(85, 112)
$C_8H_{11}N$	Dimethylaniline	0.9726	− .8140	− .216		.001¶	0 to 177	(19, 57)	(126, 152, 189, 246)
$C_8H_{14}O_5$	Diethyl malate	(1.1480)	− .9227	− .804		.001	20 to 60	(154, 263)	
$C_8H_{14}O_6$	Diethyl *d*-tartrate	1.2254	−1.007			.0005	−23 to +160	(169, 170)	(100)
$C_8H_{14}O_6$	Dimethyl dimethoxysuccinate	1.1305^{60}	−1.052			.02	60 to 153	(179)	(209)
$C_8H_{16}O_2$	*d-sec.*-Butyl butyrate	(0.8861)	−0.877	−1.09		.001	13 to 126	(198)	(262)
C_8H_{18}	*n*-Octane	0.71848	− .8239	+0.4459	− 5.293	.001	0 to 130	(281, 284)	(35, 36)
C_9H_7N	Quinoline‖‖‖	1.1090	− .7542	− .1265	− 0.80	.001¶	0 to 200	(16, 140)	(189, 208)
$C_9H_{10}O_2$	Ethyl benzoate	(1.0651)	− .9046	− .2423		.001¶	4 to 69	(126, 130)	(189, 213)
C_9H_{12}	*n*-Propylbenzene	0.8780	− .8115	− .366		.0003¶	0 to 160	(61, 189, 219, 229)	

TABLE 1.—DENSITY-TEMPERATURE EQUATIONS BASED ON RELIABLE DATA.—(*Continued*)

Formula	Name	d_s	α	β	γ	Limit of error	Range, °C	Lit.	
								Data employed	Confirmatory
C_9H_{12}	Pseudocumene	(0.8923)	−0.8036	−0.170		0.0003	10 to 95	(189)	(13, 23)
$C_9H_{13}N$	Dimethyl-*o*-toluidine	0.9447**	− .828	− .33		.0005	0 to 151	(57)	(189)
C_9H_{20}	*n*-Nonane	0.7333	− .75	− .455		.0005¶	0 to 99	(123)	(37)
$C_9H_{21}N$	Tri-*n*-propylamine	0.7730	− .7660	− .45		.001	0 to 75	(103, 256)	
$C_{10}H_8$	Naphthalene	0.9779^{80}	− .7670	− .755		.001¶	82 to 177	(57, 128, 228)	(2)
$C_{10}H_{14}$	Cymene¶¶¶	0.8734**	− .785	− .275		.001¶	0 to 83	(138)	(22, 189)
$C_{10}H_{14}N_2$	Nicotine	(1.02385)	− .7041	− .964		.001¶	20 to 98	(105)	(206)
$C_{10}H_{14}O$	3-Methyl-2-hydroxyisopropylbenzene	(0.9894)	− .7741	− .224		.001	25 to 70	(164)	(61, 189)
$C_{10}H_{15}N$	Diethylaniline	0.9508	− .785	− .259		.001	0 to 158	(50, 57, 189)	
$C_{10}H_{16}$	*d*-Pinene****	0.8624^{20}	− .83			.002	20 to 93	(151)	(1)
$C_{10}H_{18}O_6$	Dipropyl *d*-tartrate	(1.1563)	− .9391	− .245		.001	15 to 167	(173)	(94, 170)
$C_{10}H_{20}O$	*l*-α-Menthol	0.8840^{40}	− .765			.001	40 to 80	(181, 190)	
$C_{10}H_{22}$	*n*-Decane	0.7455	− .7293	− .371		.0005	0 to 100	(123)	
$C_{10}H_{22}$	2, 6-Dimethyloctane	0.73880	− .7302	− .515		.0005¶	0 to 80	(63, 133)	(64, 69)
$C_{11}H_{12}O_2$	*trans*-Ethyl cinnamate	(1.0667)	− .861			.001	10 to 100	(189)	(103)
$C_{11}H_{24}$	*n*-Undecane	0.7563	− .745	− .05		.001	0 to 100	(123)	(223)
$C_{13}H_{10}O$	α-Benzophenone	1.0800^{57}	− .790	− .12		.001	25 to 100	(57)	(14, 103, 189)
$C_{13}H_{28}$	*n*-Tridecane	0.7716	− .704	− .072		.0005¶	0 to 99	(123)	
$C_{14}H_{15}N$	Dibenzylamine	(1.0428)	− .753	− .35		.002	20 to 75	(256)	(189)
$C_{14}H_{30}$	*n*-Tetradecane	(0.7787)	− .69	− .13		.001	0 to 99	(123)	(124)
$C_{15}H_{32}$	*n*-Pentadecane	(0.7832)	− .70	− .025		.0005¶	10 to 99	(123)	
$C_{16}H_{34}$	*n*-Hexadecane	(0.7879)	− .688			.0005¶	18 to 99	(123)	
$C_{17}H_{36}$	*n*-Heptadecane	(0.7913)	− .639	− .29		.0005¶	22 to 100	(123)	
$C_{18}H_{38}$	*n*-Octadecane	(0.7757^{30})	− .7024	+ .395		.0005¶	28 to 99	(123)	
$C_{20}H_{42}$	*n*-Eicosane	0.7827^{30}	− .666			.0005¶	36 to 99	(123)	

* *v.* (68, 191, 266) for values not agreeing with this equation, but probably less reliable.

† The values recorded in the literature for methyl and ethyl iodides are particularly discordant.

‡ De Pauw (41) gives d_4^{25} 1.5891 for material purified with particular care.

§ The equation given, based on the values of Tyrer, although reproducing his values and those of Nasini and Bresciani (163) with an error in most cases less than 0.0001, is apparently based on values determined with impure acid. The acid of the latter authors melted at 16.1°. Bousfield and Lowry (17) obtained with very pure acid a M. P. of 16.60 ± 0.005° and a density at 18° and 20°, 0.0007 lower than the values given by the equation. These values are probably correct. The following equation:

$$D_t = (1.0695) - 0.0_2 10092t - 0.0_6 339t^2 - 0.0_8 574t^3$$

based on the values of Ramsay and Young (210) gives a value at 20° very close to that of Bousfield and Lowry, but their values do not fall on a smooth curve, and their value at 13.11° determined by pycnometer does not fall on the curve given by the above equation. Subtraction of 0.0007 from the values given by the equation in the above table should be nearly correct in the interval 15-30°.

‖ Tyrer (257) gives values for 0–31° running nearly parallel to those of Timmermans, but 0.003 lower. The values of the latter may be, however, more accurate than is indicated above.

¶ *See* Table 3 for accurate values for the density at particular temperatures.

** Equation quoted from the literature cited.

†† The wide divergence in values given for acetone is probably due to the failure of many investigators to realize the difficulty in drying it; *v.* (25, 252). The two equations given agree and are probably correct to 0.0002 from 0° to 25°.

‡‡ Young's values were used in calculating the equation, but the value of d_4^0 was so altered that the equation gives a value at 25° which is probably more reliable than Young's. This is a questionable procedure, but the equation is probably at least as accurate as indicated.

§§ The equation is based on the values of Gerlach since these are the only ones covering a wide temperature range. Data to be found in (109, 169) may be more reliable over narrower temperature ranges.

‖‖ The data in the confirming references in the table would indicate an accuracy of at least 0.0005 for this equation, but widely divergent values (256) are also to be found.

¶¶ This equation gives a value for 101.7° differing by only 0.0014 from that given by the specific volume equation of Thorpe and Jones (248).

*** Equation accurate to 0.0002 for 0° to 40°.

††† Equation accurate to 0.0001 for 0° to 40°.

‡‡‡ The values of Meyer and Mylius (150) run nearly parallel to those given by the equation, but 0.0005 to 0.001 lower.

§§§ The density of dimethyl racemate runs uniformly about 0.001 lower than that of the *d*-tartrate (151).

‖‖‖ The accuracy of this equation at temperatures up to 40° is probably considerably greater than indicated in the table.

¶¶¶ Values of Bolle and Guye (16) lie about 0.0015 below the equation and run up to 150°.

**** Densities and expansion of *d*-, *l*- and *dl*-pinenes are nearly the same (151). The values of these investigators are higher than those of most others.

Table 2 gives references to data covering a considerable temperature range for which there are either no checks or checks which are not in agreement. The first reference usually indicates the data covering the widest temperature range. Subsequent references refer either to further similar data or to checks at particular temperatures, but no complete list of such checks is attempted. The checks are in all cases unsatisfactory.

Following the table is a list of papers giving additional data for large classes of substances, of which only the simpler representatives have been included in the table.

TABLE 2.—DENSITY-TEMPERATURE EQUATIONS OF UNKNOWN RELIABILITY

Formula	Name	Range, °C	Lit.
$CHBrCl_2$	Bromodichloromethane	25 to 70	(269, 102)
CH_3Cl	Methyl chloride	−40 to +40	(238, 260)
CH_4S	Methylmercaptan	0 to 78	(10)
C_2HBr_3O	Bromal	25 to 100	(58)
C_2HCl_3	Trichloroethylene	17 to 75	(96, 258)
C_2HCl_3O	Chloral	25 to 85	(58, 184, 247)
$C_2HCl_3O_2$	Trichloroacetic acid	75 to 125	(103, 188)
C_2HCl_5	Pentachloroethane	15 to 90	(96, 247)
C_2H_2	Acetylene	−82 to −55	(142, 143, 148)
$C_2H_2Cl_2$	*cis*-1, 2-Acetylene dichloride	15 to 45	(97, 15)
$C_2H_2Cl_2$	*trans*-1, 2-Acetylene dichloride	15 to 45	(97, 15)
$C_2H_3Br_3O_2$	Bromal hydrate	40 to 100	(58)
$C_2H_3ClO_2$	Chloroacetic acid	40 to 125	(83, 103, 158)
C_2H_4	Ethylene	−114 to −69	(142, 143)
C_2H_4O	Acetaldehyde	0 to 50	(141)
C_2H_5BrO	2-Bromoethyl alcohol	0 to 30	(212)
C_2H_5BrO	Bromomethyl methyl ether	0 to 20	(110)
C_2H_5ClO	2-Chloroethyl alcohol	0 to 20	(110)

TABLE 2.—DENSITY-TEMPERATURE EQUATIONS OF UNKNOWN RELIABILITY.—(*Continued*)

Formula	Name	Range, °C	Lit.
C_2H_5ClO	Chloromethyl methyl ether	0 to 20	(110)
C_2H_6O	Methyl ether	−41 to +12	(141)
$C_2H_6O_4S$	Methyl sulfate	16 to 83	(241)
C_2H_6S	Methyl sulfide	0 to 60	(10, 248)
$C_3H_4Br_2O_2$	1, 2-Dibromopropionic acid	50 to 90	(158)
C_3H_6	Propylene	−78 to +19	(143)
$C_3H_6Br_2$	1, 2-Dibromopropane	25 to 81	(61)
C_3H_6O	Allyl alcohol	−120 to +20	(121, 3)
$C_3H_6O_2$	Propionic acid	15 to 96	(188, 149)
C_3H_7Br*	*n*-Propyl bromide	0 to 20	(110)
$C_3H_7ClO_2$	3-Chloro-1, 2-dihydroxypropane	25 to 70	(268)
$C_3H_7NO_2$	Lactamide	80 to 120	(257)
$C_3H_7NO_2$	Urethane	60 to 153	(256, 84)
C_3H_8O	Methylethyl ether	0 to 51	(10)
C_4H_5NS	Allyl isothiocyanate	25 to 80	(130)
$C_4H_6Cl_2O_2$	Methyl 1, 2-dichloropropionate	12 to 68	(75)
$C_4H_6O_3$	Acetic anhydride	0 to 77	(50, 71)
$C_4H_7NO_2$	2-Aminocrotonic acid	11 to 57	(158)
$C_4H_8O_2$	*n*-Propyl formate	0 to 100	(281, 13)
C_4H_9Br*	*n*-Butyl bromide	0 to 20	(110, 136)
$C_4H_9NO_2$	Methyl urethane	56 to 99	(228)
$C_4H_9NO_2$	Butyl nitrite	11 to 45	(241)
$C_4H_{10}O$*	*d-sec.*-Butyl alcohol	16 to 76	(194)
$C_4H_{10}O_3S$	Diethyl sulfite	25 to 80	(268)
$C_4H_{10}O_4$	*dl*-Erythritol	69 to 143	(83)
$C_4H_{10}O_4S$	Diethyl sulfate	12 to 67	(241)
$C_4H_{11}N$	*n*-Butylamine	0 to 40	(103, 159)
$C_4H_{11}N$	Isobutylamine	0 to 50	(103, 185)
$C_4H_{11}N$	*tert.*-Butylamine	0 to 50	(103)
$C_5H_8Cl_2O_2$	Ethyl 1, 2-dichloropropionate	16 to 57	(75)
$C_5H_8O_2$	2, 2-Dimethylacrylic acid	24 to 154	(81)
C_5H_9N	*n*-Valeronitrile	10 to 50	(153)
C_5H_9NS	Isobutyl isothiocyanate	11 to 109	(16)
$C_5H_{10}O_2$	*n*-Valeric acid	20 to 70	(52)
$C_5H_{10}O_2$	Isovaleric acid	18 to 61	(236)
$C_5H_{10}O_2$	*d-sec.*-Butyl formate	21 to 94	(200)
$C_5H_{10}O_2$	Isobutyl formate	0 to 40	(13)
$C_5H_{10}O_3$	Ethyl carbonate	13 to 57	(241)
$C_5H_{10}O_3$	Methyl *l*-1-methoxypropionate	−16 to +130	(176)
$C_5H_{10}O_4$	Glycerol acetate	10 to 70	(153, 268)
$C_5H_{11}NO$	Methylpropylketoxime	16 to 109	(16)
$C_5H_{11}NO_2$	Isoamyl nitrite	13 to 75	(241)
$C_5H_{12}O$*	*d-sec.*-Amyl alcohol	12 to 61	(194)
$C_5H_{12}O$	*tert.*-Amyl alcohol	25 to 80	(58)
$C_5H_{12}O$	*d*-Methyl isopropyl carbinol	15 to 71	(198, 195)
$C_5H_{12}O$	Ethyl propyl ether	0 to 78	(10, 43)
$C_5H_{13}N$	*n*-Amylamine	0 to 50	(103)
$C_5H_{13}N$	Isoamylamine	0 to 60	(103, 256)
$C_5H_{13}N$	*tert.*-Amylamine	0 to 30	(103)
$C_5H_{14}Si$	Trimethyl ethyl silicane	0 to 60	(28)
$C_6H_3ClN_2O_4$	α-4-Chloro-1, 3-dinitrobenzene	75 to 125	(103)
$C_6H_3Cl_2NO_2$	2, 4-Dichloronitrobenzene	75 to 125	(103, 99)
$C_6H_3Cl_2NO_2$	2, 5-Dichloronitrobenzene	75 to 125	(103, 99)
$C_6H_3Cl_2NO_2$	3, 4-Dichloronitrobenzene	75 to 125	(103, 99)
$C_6H_3Cl_3O$	2, 4, 6-Trichlorophenol	75 to 125	(103)
C_6H_4BrCl	*p*-Bromochlorobenzene	71 to 155	(240)
$C_6H_4BrNO_2$	*o*-Bromonitrobenzene	53 to 125	(103, 242)
$C_6H_4BrNO_2$	*m*-Bromonitrobenzene	24 to 125	(83, 103, 242)
$C_6H_4BrNO_2$	*p*-Bromonitrobenzene	133 to 164	(242)
$C_6H_4Br_2$	*p*-Dibromobenzene	100 to 140	(103)
C_6H_4ClI	*p*-Chloroiodobenzene	57 to 151	(240)
$C_6H_4ClNO_2$	*o*-Chloronitrobenzene	45 to 125	(103, 242)
$C_6H_4ClNO_2$	*m*-Chloronitrobenzene	25 to 125	(83, 103, 242)
$C_6H_4ClNO_2$	*p*-Chloronitrobenzene	85 to 135	(103)
$C_6H_4Cl_2$	*p*-Dichlorobenzene	63 to 161	(103, 107)
$C_6H_4FNO_2$	*m*-Fluoronitrobenzene	25 to 75	(103, 9)
$C_6H_4FNO_2$	*p*-Fluoronitrobenzene	30 to 75	(103, 9)
$C_6H_4INO_2$	*o*-Iodonitrobenzene	75 to 125	(103)
$C_6H_4INO_2$	*m*-Iodonitrobenzene	50 to 100	(103)
$C_6H_4N_2O_4$	*o*-Dinitrobenzene	120 to 160	(103)
$C_6H_4N_2O_4$	*m*-Dinitrobenzene	120 to 160	(103)
$C_6H_4N_2O_5$	2, 4-Dinitrophenol	72 to 138	(83)
C_6H_5ClO	*o*-Chlorophenol	10 to 150	(19)
$C_6H_5NO_2$*	Nitrobenzene	*ca.* 210	(106)
$C_6H_5NO_3$	*o*-Nitrophenol	40 to 80	(19)
$C_6H_5NO_3$	*m*-Nitrophenol	100 to 150	(103)
$C_6H_5NO_3$	*p*-Nitrophenol	120 to 160	(103)
$C_6H_5N_3$	Triazobenzene	0 to 50	(31, 189)
C_6H_6ClN	*p*-Chloroaniline	77 to 159	(240)
$C_6H_6N_2O_2$	*m*-Nitroaniline	120 to 160	(103)
C_6H_6S	Thiophenol	25 to 75	(268)
$C_6H_7ClO_4$	Methyl chloromaleate	25 to 75	(268)
$C_6H_7ClO_4$	Methyl chlorofumarate	25 to 75	(268)
$C_6H_8N_2$	Phenylhydrazine	20 to 60	(256)
$C_6H_8O_4$	Dimethyl fumarate	106 to 160	(243)
$C_6H_8O_4$	Dimethyl maleate	20 to 135	(243)
$C_6H_8O_6$	Glyceryl triformate	50 to 100	(103)
$C_6H_{10}O$	Mesityl oxide	5 to 90	(81, 90, 91)
$C_6H_{10}O_4$	Dimethyl succinate	25 to 75	(103, 183)
$C_6H_{10}O_4$	Glycol diacetate	14 to 74	(233)
$C_6H_{10}O_4$	Methyl *l*-1-acetoxypropionate	−7 to +141	(176)
$C_6H_{11}N$	Capronitrile	24 to 75	(103)
$C_6H_{11}N$	Isobutylacetonitrile	20 to 60	(256)
$C_6H_{12}O_2$	Caproic acid	25 to 90	(52, 135)
$C_6H_{12}O_3$	Paraldehyde	15 to 75	(72, 233)
$C_6H_{12}O_3$	*n*-Propyl lactate	2 to 122	(204)
C_6H_{14}	2-Methylpentane (isohexane)	0 to 40	(13, 34)
$C_6H_{14}O$	*l*-Ethylpropyl carbinol	13 to 104	(197)
$C_6H_{14}O$	*d*-Ethylisopropyl carbinol	18 to 63	(195)
$C_6H_{14}O$	*d*-Methylbutyl carbinol	17 to 133	(194)
$C_6H_{14}O$	*d*-Pinacolyl alcohol	16 to 99	(199)
$C_6H_{15}N$	*n*-Hexylamine	0 to 40	(103)
$C_6H_{15}N$	2-Hexylamine	0 to 50	(103)
$C_6H_{15}N$	Triethylamine	0 to 50	(103)
$C_6H_{15}O_4P$	Triethyl phosphate	15 to 83	(241)
$C_6H_{16}Si$	Dimethyldiethylsilicane	0 to 91	(28)
$C_6H_{16}Si$	Trimethylpropylsilicane	0 to 85	(28)
$C_6H_{18}Si_2$	Hexamethylsilicoethane	12 to 94	(28)
C_7H_5NO	Phenyl isocyanate	0 to 50	(31)
C_7H_5NS	Phenyl thiocyanate	25 to 50	(131)
C_7H_7Br	*o*-Bromotoluene	4 to 75	(103, 189)
C_7H_7I	*p*-Iodotoluene	40 to 164	(240)
C_7H_7NO	Benzamide	130 to 170	(256)
C_7H_7NO	Formanilide	60 to 105	(256, 189)
$C_7H_7NO_2$	*o*-Hydroxybenzamide	140 to 170	(256)
$C_7H_7NO_2$	*o*-Nitrotoluene	16 to 101	(172, 242)
$C_7H_7NO_2$	*m*-Nitrotoluene	20 to 121	(242)
$C_7H_7NO_2$	*p*-Nitrotoluene	55 to 125	(103, 189, 230)
$C_7H_7NO_3$	*p*-Nitroanisole	75 to 125	(103)
$C_7H_8N_2O$	Nitrosomethylaniline	20 to 90	(256, 103)
$C_7H_8N_2O_2$	*p*-Nitromethylaniline	160 to 200	(103)
$C_7H_8N_2O_2$	3-Nitro-*o*-toluidine	100 to 140	(103)
$C_7H_8N_2O_2$	5-Nitro-*o*-toluidine	140 to 180	(103)
$C_7H_8N_2O_2$	3-Nitro-*p*-toluidine	120 to 160	(103)
$C_7H_{10}O_4$	Dimethyl citraconate	26 to 78	(243)
$C_7H_{10}O_4$	Dimethyl mesaconate	20 to 80	(243)
$C_7H_{12}Cl_2O_2$	Isobutyl 1, 2-dichloropropionate	16 to 65	(75)
$C_7H_{12}O$	*m*-Methylcyclohexanone	17 to 90	(95, 6, 225)
$C_7H_{14}O$	*m*-Hexahydrocresol	39 to 90	(95, 6, 225)
$C_7H_{14}O$	*p*-Hexahydrocresol	39 to 90	(95, 6)
$C_7H_{14}O_2$	*d*-β-Amyl acetate	18 to 91	(198)
$C_7H_{14}O_2$	Isoamyl acetate	14 to 109	(101)
$C_7H_{16}O$	*d*-Ethylbutyl carbinol	13 to 127	(197)
$C_7H_{16}O$	*d*-Methylamyl carbinol	20 to 64	(194)
$C_7H_{16}O$	*d*-Propylisopropyl carbinol	17 to 74	(195)
$C_7H_{16}Si$	Dimethylcyclopentamethylene-silicane	0 to 80	(28, 27)
$C_7H_{17}N$	*n*-Heptylamine	0 to 40	(103)
$C_7H_{18}Si$	Dimethylethylpropylsilicane	0 to 81	(28)
$C_7H_{18}Si$	Trimethylbutylsilicane	0 to 85	(28)
$C_7H_{18}Si$	Trimethylisobutylsilicane	0 to 49	(28)
$C_8H_4Cl_2O_2$	*o*-Phthalyl dichloride	33 to 181	(167)
C_8H_7N	*o*-Tolunitrile	20 to 95	(256, 189, 242)
C_8H_7N	*m*-Tolunitrile	18 to 80	(256, 242)
C_8H_7N	*p*-Tolunitrile	30 to 176	(57, 189, 242, 256)
C_8H_7NO	Mandelonitrile	20 to 60	(256)
$C_8H_8N_2O_6$	4, 5-Dinitro-1, 2-dimethoxybenzene	140 to 180	(103)
$C_8H_8O_2$	*p*-Methoxybenzaldehyde	25 to 75	(103, 189)
$C_8H_8O_2$	Phenylacetic acid	77 to 130	(53, 230)
C_8H_9NO	Phenylacetamide	160 to 180	(256)
C_8H_9NO	Benz*anti*aldoxime, *O*-methyl ether	14 to 72	(241)
C_8H_9NO	Benz*anti*aldoxime, *N*-methyl ether	103 to 151	(241)
$C_8H_9NO_3$	*p*-Nitrophenetole	75 to 125	(103)
C_8H_{10}†	Ethylbenzene	0 to 40	(13, 189, 215, 220, 271)

TABLE 2.—DENSITY-TEMPERATURE EQUATIONS OF UNKNOWN RELIABILITY.—(*Continued*)

Formula	Name	Range, °C	Lit.
$C_8H_{10}O$	*d*-Methylphenyl carbinol	13 to 80	(194)
$C_8H_{10}O_2$	*o*-Dimethoxybenzene	25 to 75	(103, 61, 189)
$C_8H_{11}ClO_4$	Ethyl chloromaleate	25 to 70	(268)
$C_8H_{11}N$	*n*-Ethylaniline	0 to 158	(57, 189)
$C_8H_{13}BrO_4$	Diethyl bromoisosuccinate	25 to 75	(103)
C_8H_{14}	*n*-Hexylacetylene	25 to 70	(269)
$C_8H_{16}O_2$	*d*-β-Amyl propionate	18 to 96	(198)
$C_8H_{16}O_2$	*d*-β-Hexyl acetate	18 to 125	(198)
$C_8H_{17}Br$	*l*-2-Bromooctane	14 to 53	(194)
C_8H_{18}	2, 5-Dimethylhexane	0 to 276.8	(281, 282)
$C_8H_{18}O$	*d*-Methyl-*n*-hexyl carbinol	25 to 46	(194)
$C_8H_{20}Si$	Trimethylisoamylsilicane	0 to 81	(28)
$C_8H_{20}Si$	Dimethylethylisobutylsilicane	0 to 80	(28)
$C_8H_{20}Si$	Dimethyldi-*n*-propylsilicane	0 to 48	(28)
$C_8H_{20}Si$*	Tetraethylsilicane	0 to 91	(28)
$C_9H_{10}OS$	Ethyl thiobenzoate	0 to 15	(213)
$C_9H_{10}S_2$	Ethyl dithiobenzoate	0 to 25	(213)
$C_9H_{11}NO$	*N*-Methylacetanilide	105 to 145	(256)
$C_9H_{11}NO_2$	*N*-Phenylurethane	60 to 105	(256)
C_9H_{12}‡	Mesitylene	4 to 95	(189, 57, 219)
$C_9H_{12}O$	*l*-Ethylphenyl carbinol	14 to 70	(199)
$C_9H_{14}O_6$	Glycerol triacetate	25 to 75	(103)
$C_9H_{14}Si$	Trimethylphenylsilicane	0 to 66	(28)
$C_9H_{17}BrO_2$	*l*-Amyl bromobutyrate	25 to 90	(269)
$C_9H_{18}O_2$	Pelargonic acid	20 to 50	(52)
$C_9H_{18}O_2$	*d*-β-Amyl *n*-butyrate	18 to 96	(198)
$C_9H_{18}O_2$	*d*-*sec.*-Butyl valerate	13 to 128	(198)
$C_9H_{18}O_2$	*d*-β-Octyl formate	12 to 134	(200)
$C_9H_{22}Si$	Triethyl-*n*-propylsilicane	0 to 67	(28)
$C_{10}H_9BrO_2$	Methyl α (β)-bromocinnamate	20 to 135	(243)
$C_{10}H_9BrO_2$	Methyl α (β)-bromoallocinnamate	20 to 95	(243)
$C_{10}H_{10}O$	Benzylideneacetone	60 to 200	(81, 82, 189)
$C_{10}H_{10}O_2$	Methyl cinnamate	36 to 90	(243)
$C_{10}H_{10}O_2$	Methyl allocinnamate	20 to 80	(243)
$C_{10}H_{12}O$	*p*-Anethole	11 to 99	(163, 228)
$C_{10}H_{12}O$	*d*-1, 2, 3, 4-Tetrahydro-β-naphthol	61 to 155	(196)
$C_{10}H_{12}O_2$	*d*-Methylbenzylcarbinyl formate	22 to 152	(200)
$C_{10}H_{13}NO$	*N*-Ethylacetanilide	60 to 105	(256)
$C_{10}H_{14}$	Trimethylphenylmethane	0 to 90	(27)
$C_{10}H_{14}O$	*d*-Benzylethyl carbinol	0 to 142	(199)
$C_{10}H_{14}O$	Methyl *d*-methylbenzylcarbinyl ether	27 to 132	(192)
$C_{10}H_{14}O$	*l*-Methylphenylethyl carbinol	0 to 136	(199)
$C_{10}H_{14}O_6$	Diallyl tartrate	15 to 168	(173)
$C_{10}H_{16}$	*d*- (*l*, *dl*)-Limonene	10 to 90	(151)
$C_{10}H_{16}O_7$	Diethyl monoacetyl-*d*-tartrate	20 to 71	(147)
$C_{10}H_{16}Si$	Dimethylethylphenylsilicane	0 to 67	(28)
$C_{10}H_{16}Si$	Trimethylbenzylsilicane	0 to 90	(28)
$C_{10}H_{18}Cl_2O_2$	Heptyl 1, 2-dichloropropionate	13 to 79	(75)
$C_{10}H_{18}O$	*l*-Isopulegol	18 to 172	(193)
$C_{10}H_{18}O_6$	Di-*sec.*-propyl tartrate	14 to 150	(173)
$C_{10}H_{20}O$	*l*-Neomenthol	0 to 30	(201)
$C_{10}H_{20}O_2$	*d*-γ-Nonyl formate	20 to 154	(200)
$C_{10}H_{23}N$	Diisoamylamine	0 to 50	(103)
$C_{10}H_{24}Si$	Triethylbutylsilicane	0 to 89	(28)
$C_{10}H_{24}Si$	Triethylisobutylsilicane	0 to 70	(28)
$C_{11}H_{10}O_2$	Ethyl phenylpropiolate	25 to 75	(268)
$C_{11}H_{12}N_2O$	Antipyrine	66 to 140	(83)
$C_{11}H_{12}O$	Benzylidenemethyl ethyl ketone	18 to 200	(81, 5, 82)
$C_{11}H_{14}O_2$	*d*-β-Butyl benzoate	18 to 128	(118)
$C_{11}H_{16}$	Pentamethylbenzene	75 to 197	(57)
$C_{11}H_{16}$	Trimethylbenzylmethane	0 to 92	(27)
$C_{11}H_{20}$	Nonylacetylene	20 to 70	(269)
$C_{11}H_{26}Si$	Triethylisoamylsilicane	0 to 79	(28)
$C_{12}H_{10}N_2O$	Azoxybenzene	44 to 92	(241)
		50 to 100	(103)
$C_{12}H_{10}O$§	Diphenyl ether	30 to 100	(49)
$C_{12}H_{11}N$	Diphenylamine	60 to 125	(18, 103, 256)
$C_{12}H_{12}Cl_6O_8$	Diethyl di-(trichloroacetyl) tartrate	15 to 131	(175)
$C_{12}H_{12}O$	*l*-Methyl-α-naphthyl carbinol	14 to 138	(199)
$C_{12}H_{16}O_2$	Isopropyl hydrocinnamate	25 to 75	(268)
$C_{12}H_{18}$	*l*-Methyl-3-*tert.*-amylbenzene	−20 to +100	(33)
$C_{12}H_{18}O_6$	Triethyl aconitate	25 to 90	(269)
$C_{12}H_{18}O_8$	Diethyl diacetyltartrate	67 to 180	(228, 147)
$C_{12}H_{20}O_2$	Isopulegyl acetate	16 to 132	(193)
$C_{12}H_{20}Si$	Triethylphenylsilicane	0 to 81	(28)
$C_{12}H_{21}ClO_2$	Menthyl chloroacetate	38 to 95	(72)
$C_{12}H_{22}O_2$	*l*-Menthyl acetate	17 to 132	(117)
$C_{12}H_{22}O_6$	Di-*n*-butyl *d*-tartrate	18 to 170	(74)
$C_{12}H_{22}O_6$	Diisobutyl *d*-tartrate	75 to 98	(173)
$C_{12}H_{22}O_6$	Diisobutyl *l*-tartrate	98 to 146	(173)
$C_{12}H_{22}O_{11}$‖	Saccharose	−15 to +115	(234)
$C_{12}H_{24}O_2$	Lauric acid	50 to 90	(52, 61)
$C_{12}H_{26}$	*n*-Dodecane	0 to 99	(123)
$C_{12}H_{27}N$	Triisobutylamine	0 to 50	(103)
$C_{13}H_6Cl_6$	2, 4, 2′, 4′-Tetrachlorobenzophenone chloride	145 to 185	(103)
$C_{13}H_{10}O_3$	Phenyl carbonate	87 to 145	(241)
$C_{13}H_{12}$	Diphenylmethane	54 to 210	(57)
$C_{13}H_{13}N$	*N*-Methyldiphenylamine	10 to 80	(18)
$C_{13}H_{14}O_2$	Isobutyl phenylpropiolate	25 to 75	(268)
$C_{13}H_{16}O$	Benzalpinacolin	60 to 200	(81)
$C_{13}H_{20}$	Triethylphenylmethane	0 to 75	(27)
$C_{13}H_{24}O_4$	Di-*l*-amyl malonate	25 to 75	(268)
$C_{14}H_{10}O_2$	Benzil	40 to 137	(83)
$C_{14}H_{12}O_2$*	Benzyl benzoate	5 to 100	(11, 111)
$C_{14}H_{14}$	Dibenzyl	76 to 210	(57)
$C_{14}H_{14}N_2O$	*o*-Azoxytoluene	74 to 139	(241)
$C_{14}H_{20}O_2$	*l*-Amyl hydrocinnamate	20 to 75	(268)
$C_{14}H_{23}ClO_4$	Di-*l*-amyl chlorofumarate	25 to 75	(268)
$C_{14}H_{23}N$	Diisobutylaniline	25 to 75	(103)
$C_{14}H_{24}O_4$	Di-*l*-amyl maleate	25 to 75	(268)
$C_{14}H_{26}O_4$	Di-*l*-amyl succinate	25 to 70	(268)
$C_{14}H_{26}O_4$	Diethyl sebacate	25 to 90	(269)
$C_{14}H_{26}O_5$	Diamyl malate	30 to 60	(154)
$C_{14}H_{26}O_6$	Diisoamyl tartrate	14 to 175	(173)
$C_{15}H_{26}O_4$	Di-*l*-amyl citraconate	25 to 75	(268)
$C_{15}H_{26}O_4$	Di-*l*-amyl mesaconate	25 to 75	(268)
$C_{15}H_{33}N$	Triisoamylamine	20 to 75	(256)
$C_{16}H_{16}NO_2$	Anisaldazine	173 to 225	(103)
$C_{16}H_{20}O_7$	Diethyl phenylacetyl-*d*-tartrate	36 to 93	(147)
$C_{16}H_{22}Cl_4O_8$	Diisobutyl di-(dichloroacetyl) tartrate	18 to 157	(175)
$C_{16}H_{26}O_8$	Diisobutyl diacetyl-*d*-tartrate	14 to 202	(174)
$C_{16}H_{30}O_6$	Di-*l*-amyl *d*-dimethoxysuccinate	15 to 99	(179)
$C_{16}H_{32}O_2$	Palmitic acid	60 to 80 (?)	(224)
$C_{16}H_{33}I$	*n*-Cetyl iodide	18 to 138	(61)
$C_{17}H_{22}O$	*d*-α-Naphthyl-*n*-hexyl carbinol	31 to 146	(116)
$C_{17}H_{34}O_2$	Margaric acid	60 to 80	(224)
$C_{18}H_{15}As$	Triphenylarsine	48 to 82	(168)
$C_{18}H_{15}O_4P$	Triphenyl phosphate	58 to 89	(241)
$C_{18}H_{15}P$	Triphenylphosphine	50 to 100	(168, 268)
$C_{18}H_{15}Sb$	Triphenylstibine	25 to 100	(168, 268)
$C_{18}H_{18}O_6$	Dibenzyl tartrate	15 to 170	(173)
$C_{18}H_{26}O_4$	Di-*l*-amyl phthalate	25 to 75	(268)
$C_{18}H_{34}O_6$	Di-*n*-heptyl tartrate	41 to 131	(74)
$C_{18}H_{36}O_2$	Stearic acid	60 to 80 (?)	(224)
$C_{19}H_{40}$	*n*-Nondecane	32 to 99	(155)
$C_{20}H_{16}Br_2O_8$¶	Dimethyl di-*o*-bromobenzoyltartrate	15 to 93	(73)
$C_{20}H_{16}Cl_2O_8$¶	Dimethyl di-*o*-chlorobenzoyltartrate	15 to 140	(73)
$C_{20}H_{16}I_2O_8$¶	Dimethyl di-*o*-iodobenzoyltartrate	15 to 140	(73)
$C_{20}H_{38}O_4$	Diisoamyl sebacate	25 to 90	(269)
$C_{20}H_{38}O_6$	Di-*n*-octyl *d*-tartrate	54 to 135	(74)
$C_{20}H_{38}O_6$ **	Di-β-*n*-octyl *d*-tartrate	36 to 100	(173)
$C_{21}H_{21}N$	Tribenzylamine	95 to 135	(256)
$C_{21}H_{23}NO_3$	Ethyl 1-methyl-*p*-ethoxybenzalaminocinnamate	95 to 160	(103)
$C_{21}H_{38}O_6$	Tricaproin	50 to 100	(103)
$C_{21}H_{44}$	Heneicosane	40 to 99	(123, 62)
$C_{22}H_{42}O_3$	Isobutyl ricinoleate	25 to 75	(267)
$C_{22}H_{46}$	*n*-Docosane	44 to 99	(123)
$C_{24}H_{26}O_8$	Diethyl diphenacetyl-*d*-tartrate	15 to 98	(147)
$C_{26}H_{30}O_8$	Diisobutyl dibenzoyl-*d*-tartrate	17 to 100	(178)
$C_{26}H_{54}$	*n*-Hexacosane	91 to 158	(227)
$C_{27}H_{50}O_6$	Tricaprylin	50 to 100	(103)
$C_{30}H_{62}O$	Melissyl alcohol	95 to 158	(227)
$C_{32}H_{64}O_2$	Cetyl palmitate	50 to 65	(255)
$C_{33}H_{62}O_6$	Tricaprin	50 to 100	(103)
$C_{39}H_{74}O_6$	Trilaurin	75 to 125	(103)
$C_{51}H_{98}O_6$	Tripalmitin	75 to 125	(103, 226, 267)
$C_{57}H_{104}O_6$	Triolein	50 to 100	(103)
$C_{57}H_{110}O_6$	Tristearin	75 to 125	(103, 226, 267)
$C_{60}H_{122}$	Hexacontane	115 to 190	(227)

* See Table 3 for accurate values for the density at particular temperatures.

† As may be seen in the articles referred to, there appear to be two sets of values for ethylbenzene differing by about 0.006.

‡ The values in the two references given check each other well, but most values recorded are lower.

§ $\frac{10^6}{V}\frac{\Delta V}{\Delta t}$ (30 to 100°) = 800.

‖ Densities of the undercooled liquid dissolved in paraffin.

¶ Densities of the *m*- and *p*-chloro-, bromo-, and iodo-derivatives over approximately the same temperature ranges are also given by these authors.

** Pickard and Kenyon (194) give densities at 17° for esters of *d*-β-*n*-octanol with *d*-, *l*-, and *dl*-tartaric acids.

Density-Temperature Data for Various Complex Compounds

The following articles contain density determinations over a considerable range of temperature for large numbers of compounds, only part of which, usually the simpler ones, have been listed in Table 2.

Bygden (27). Thirty-one alkyl and aryl substituted silicanes over varying temperature ranges. Where the range exceeds 50°, they have been listed in the table.

Hall (87). Esters of *d*-β-octanol with dibasic acids from oxalic to undecanedicarboxylic, and a few mixed esters with one methyl or ethyl radical.

Hall (88). Esters of *l*-menthol with dibasic acids from malonic to decanedicarboxylic.

Kenyon (113). Esters of *d*-γ-nonanol, acetate to dodecoate, myristate, palmitate, stearate; acetates of active γ-carbinols, hexanol to octadecanol.

Kenyon and Pickard (115). Esters of *d*-methylbenzyl carbinol, acetate to dodecoate, myristate, palmitate, stearate. Esters of *d*-*n*-hexyl-α-naphthyl carbinol, acetate to undecoate (116). Esters of menthol with acetic, oxalic, phenylacetic, and substituted benzoic acids (117). Esters of various active alcohols with benzoic and α- and β-naphthoic acids (118).

Kenyon and McNicol (114). Ethers of *d*-β-octanol with *n*-alkyl radicals, methyl to nonyl.

Phillips (192). Ethers of *d*-methylbenzyl carbinol with *n*-alkyl radicals, methyl to nonyl.

Pickard and Kenyon (194). Alcohols $CH_3.CHOH.R$, R representing *n*-alkyl radicals from ethyl to undecyl, together with some esters and halides. Alcohols, $(CH_3)_2CH.CHOH.R$, R representing *n*-alkyl radicals, methyl to octyl and decyl (195). Six aliphatic esters of 1-*ac*-tetrahydro-2-naphthol (196). Alcohols, $CH_3.CH_2.CHOH.R$, R representing *n*-alkyl radicals, propyl to tridecyl and pentadecyl (197). Many esters of active β-*n*-alkyl alcohols with acids from acetic to stearic, but not complete series (198).

Pickard, Hunter, Lewcock, and de Pennington (193). Esters of *l*-isopulegol with fatty acids, acetate to dodecoate and myristate.

Wood, Such, and Scarf (277). Esters of *l*-lactic acid with *n*-primary alcohols, methyl to nonyl.

Table 3.—Accurate Values for Densities of Liquid Organic Compounds at Particular Temperatures

This table gives densities at particular temperatures which have a probable error of 0.0005 or less. The probable limit of error is based upon the concordance of check determinations as in Table 1. The checking values must in some cases be obtained by interpolation. In the case of some substances, values which have been determined with particular care are included, although not confirmed by other investigators. No limit of error is indicated in such cases.

Table 3 cannot lay claim to any degree of completeness. It contains values which have been found in the course of work upon the temperature coefficients. The complete list would, however, probably not be a long one.

Formula	Name	d_4^t	$10^4\Delta$	Lit.
CCl_4	Carbon tetrachloride	1.6326^{0}	1	(13, 250)
		1.5941^{20}	2	(13, 45)
$CHCl_3$	Chloroform	1.5264^{0}	2	(250, 257)
C_2H_3N	Acetonitrile	0.7770^{25}	1	(56, 252, 266)
$C_2H_4Br_2$	Ethylene bromide	2.1805^{20}	2	(12, 254)
$C_2H_4Cl_2$	1, 1-Dichloroethane	1.1676^{25}	5*	(182, 183)
$C_2H_4Cl_2$	Ethylene chloride	1.28243^{0}	2	(250, 257)
$C_2H_4O_2$	Acetic acid	1.04925^{20}	1	(17)
$C_2H_4O_2$	Methyl formate	1.0032^{0}	2	(250, 289)
C_2H_5BrO	Bromomethyl methyl ether	1.5976^{20}		(110)
C_2H_5IO	Iodomethyl methyl ether	2.0302^{20}		(110)
C_2H_7N	Ethylamine	0.7057^{0}	5	(185, 250)
C_3H_6O	Acetone	0.7958^{15}	2	(183, 252)
		0.7844^{25}	2	(183, 252)
$C_3H_6O_2$	Ethyl formate	0.9161^{25}	5	(183, 285)
C_3H_7Br	*n*-Propyl bromide	1.3626^{15}	3	(110, 189)
C_3H_7I	*n*-Propyl iodide	1.7471^{20}		(110)
C_3H_7I	Isopropyl iodide	1.7149^{15}	5	(20, 183)
C_3H_8O	*n*-Propyl alcohol	0.8001^{25}	1	(25, 67, 183)
C_3H_8O	Isopropyl alcohol	0.7810^{25}	2	(25)
$C_3H_8O_3$	Glycerol	1.2641^{15}	3	(100, 109)
$C_4H_8Br_2$	1, 2-Dibromo-2-methylpropane	1.7730^{15}		(132)
C_4H_8O	Methylethyl ketone	0.82551^{0}		(250)
$C_4H_8O_2$	Isobutyric acid	0.9482^{20}	5	(61, 252)
$C_4H_8O_2$	Ethyl acetate	0.92454^{0}	0.5†	(252, 261)
		0.90056^{20}	0.5	(261)
		0.89446^{25}	0.5	(261)
C_4H_9Br	*n*-Butyl bromide	1.3035^{0}	3	(110, 136)
$C_4H_{10}O$	*n*-Butyl alcohol	0.8097^{20}	3	(108, 214, 218, 287)
		0.8059^{25}	2	(26)
$C_4H_{10}O$	Isobutyl alcohol	0.7979^{25}	1	(25)
$C_4H_{10}O$	*sec.*-Butyl alcohol	0.80254^{25}	1	(25)
$C_4H_{10}O$	Ether	0.73628^{0}	0.1	(244, 252, 280)
		0.71930^{15}	0.5	(244, 252)
		0.71352^{20}	0.5	(244, 280)
		0.70767^{25}	0.5	(244)
$C_4H_{10}S$	Ethyl sulfide	0.8370^{20}	4	(10, 25, 56)
$C_4H_{11}N$	Diethylamine	0.7000^{25}	5	(136, 185)
$C_5H_4O_2$	Furfural	1.1594^{20}	5	(22, 144, 235)
		1.1543^{25}	5	(144, 235, 264)
C_5H_5N	Pyridine	1.00304^{0}		(252)
		0.9781^{25}	2‡	(252, 286)
$C_5H_{10}O$	Methyl propyl ketone	0.8261^{0}	3	(32, 157, 248)
$C_5H_{10}O_2$	Ethyl propionate	0.9125^{0}	2	(252, 284, 285)
$C_5H_{10}O_2$	Methyl *n*-butyrate	0.8983^{20}	5	(218, 281)
$C_5H_{11}N$	Piperidine	0.8565^{25}	3	(131, 185)
C_5H_{12}	2-Methylbutane	0.63936^{0}	1	(252, 281)
C_5H_{12}	*n*-Pentane	0.64538^{0}		(252, 281)
$C_5H_{12}O$	*sec.*-Amyl alcohol	0.8050^{25}		(25)
C_6H_5Br	Bromobenzene	1.52193^{0}	1	(250, 278)
C_6H_5Cl	Chlorobenzene	1.1063^{20}	1	(13, 257, 278)
C_6H_5F	Fluorobenzene	1.0226^{20}	3	(150, 189, 281)
C_6H_5I	Iodobenzene	1.8308^{20}	5	(189, 278)
$C_6H_5NO_2$	Nitrobenzene	1.1229^{0}	2	(250, 257)
		1.2032^{20}	5	(189, 257)
C_6H_6	Benzene	0.8788^{20}	2	(13, 257, 281)
C_6H_7N	Aniline	1.03894^{0}	2	(252, 257)
$C_6H_{10}O_3$	Ethyl acetoacetate	1.02126^{25}	2	(233, 245)
$C_6H_{10}O_4$	Diethyl oxalate	1.0728^{25}	3	(53, 183, 233)
C_6H_{12}	Cyclohexane	0.7790^{20}	5	(79, 219)
$C_6H_{12}O$	Cyclohexanol	0.9325^{40}	3	(95, 219)
$C_6H_{12}O_2$	Isobutyl acetate	0.8711^{20}	2	(13, 218)
$C_6H_{12}O_2$	Ethyl *n*-butyrate	0.8789^{20}	2	(13, 217)
$C_6H_{13}I$	*n*-Hexyl iodide	1.4652^{0}		(43, 110)
C_6H_{14}	Diisopropyl	0.6795^{0}	2	(34, 281)
C_6H_{14}	*n*-Hexane	0.6770^{0}	2	(251, 281)
$C_6H_{14}O$	Methylisobutyl carbinol	0.8027^{25}	1	(25)
C_7H_5N	Benzonitrile	1.0005^{25}	3	(24, 61, 189, 256)
C_7H_5NO	Phenyl isocyanate	1.0948^{20}	5	(24, 31)
C_7H_7Br	*p*-Bromotoluene	1.3813^{40}	5	(158, 189)
C_7H_8	Toluene	0.88448^{0}	2	(13, 252)
		0.8658^{20}	2	(13, 217, 257)
C_7H_8O	*o*-Cresol	1.0482^{20}	5	(19, 218)
C_7H_8O	*m*-Cresol	1.0341^{20}	5	(189, 218, 265)
C_7H_8O	*p*-Cresol	1.0345^{20}	5	(189, 218)
C_7H_8O	Phenyl methyl ether	1.01237^{0}		(252)
C_7H_9N	Methylaniline	0.9825^{25}	3	(57, 189)
C_7H_9N	*o*-Toluidine	0.9940^{25}	3	(57, 189)

TABLE 3.—ACCURATE VALUES FOR DENSITIES OF LIQUID ORGANIC COMPOUNDS AT PARTICULAR TEMPERATURES.—(*Continued*)

Formula	Name	d_4^t	$10^4\Delta$	Lit.
C_7H_{16}	*n*-Heptane	0.6879^{15}	2	(35, 247, 281)
C_8H_8O	Acetophenone	1.02383^{25}	1	(56, 156)
C_8H_{10}	*m*-Xylene	0.8643^{20}	3	(81, 218, 276)
C_8H_{10}	*p*-Xylene	0.8611^{20}	2	(133, 189, 220)
$C_8H_{10}O$	Phenetole	0.9621^{25}	3	(7, 18, 112)
$C_8H_{11}N$	Dimethylaniline	0.9562^{20}	5	(19, 216)
$C_8H_{16}O_2$	Octoic acid	$0.9101^{20.02}$		(76)
		$0.8862^{50.27}$		(57)
$C_8H_{19}N$	Diisobutylamine	0.7444^{20}	5	(89, 185)
$C_8H_{20}Si$	Tetraethylsilicane	$0.76734^{19.93}$	0.5	(104)
C_9H_7N	Quinoline	1.0900^{25}	2	(189, 208, 245)
$C_9H_{10}O_2$	Ethyl benzoate	1.0420^{25}	5	(189, 213)
C_9H_{12}	*n*-Propylbenzene	0.8616^{20}	3	(71, 189, 219)
$C_9H_{18}O_2$	Nonoic acid	$0.8813^{50.17}$		(76)
		0.9087^{15}		
C_9H_{20}	*n*-Nonane	0.7221^{15}	5	(37, 123)
$C_{10}H_8$	Naphthalene	0.9623^{100}	5	(2, 128, 228)
$C_{10}H_{14}$	Cymene	0.8570^{20}	3	(22, 133, 189)
$C_{10}H_{14}N_2$	Nicotine	1.0093^{20}	3	(105, 206)
$C_{10}H_{20}O_2$	Decoic acid	$0.8884^{35.05}$		(76)
		$0.8773^{50.17}$		
$C_{10}H_{22}$	2, 6-Dimethyloctane	0.7239^{20}	2	(64, 133)
$C_{11}H_{22}O_2$	Undecoic acid	0.8889^{30}		(76)
		$0.8741^{50.15}$		
$C_{11}H_{24}$	*n*-Undecane	0.7452^{15}	10	(123, 223)
$C_{12}H_{24}O_2$	Lauric acid	$0.8744^{45.10}$		(76)
		$0.8707^{50.25}$		
$C_{13}H_{28}$	*n*-Tridecane	0.7718^{0}	3	(123)
$C_{14}H_{12}O_2$	Benzyl benzoate§	1.1121^{25}		(111)
$C_{15}H_{32}$	*n*-Pentadecane	0.7761^{10}	3	(123)
$C_{16}H_{34}$	*n*-Hexadecane	0.7757^{18}	2	(123)
$C_{17}H_{36}$	*n*-Heptadecane	$0.7766^{22.5}$	3	(123)
$C_{18}H_{38}$	*n*-Octadecane	0.7770^{28}	3	(123)
$C_{20}H_{42}$	*n*-Eicosane	$0.7780^{36.7}$	3	(123, 124)

* The equation of Thorpe ([247]) with $d_4^0 = 1.2018$ reproduces the values of Perkin ([185]) and Patterson and Thomson ([182]) and is probably accurate to 0.001 or better from 0 to 30°.

† It is possible that the values are more accurate than here indicated.

‡ Hartley, Thomas and Applebey ([92]) give a lower value and claim that higher values arise from presence of water, but Timmermans ([252]) attributes the lower values of well-purified products to presence of homologues. His own values were obtained with synthetic material.

§ No checks are available, but the material had the highest M. P. recorded and should be pure.

LITERATURE

(For a key to the periodicals see end of volume)

([1]) Ahlström and Aschan, *25*, **39**: 1441; 06. ([2]) Alluard, *13*, **113**: 150; 60. ([3]) Atkins and Wallace, *4*, **103**: 1461; 13. ([4]) Atkinson, Heycock and Pope, *4*, **117**: 1410; 20. ([5]) Auwers, *25*, **45**: 2764; 12. ([6]) Auwers, *13*, **410**: 257; 15. ([7]) Baker, *4*, **101**: 1409; 12. ([8]) Baker, *4*, **103**: 1653; 13. ([9]) Beekman, *70*, **23**: 225; 04.

([10]) Berthoud and Bruns, University of Neuchâtel, Neuchâtel, Switzerland, *0*. ([11]) Bingham and Sarver, *1*, **42**: 2011; 20. ([12]) Biron, *53*, **40**: 1609; 08. ([13]) Biron, *53*, **42**: 135; 10. ([14]) Bloch, *7*, **78**: 385; 12. ([15]) Böeseken and Bastet, *70*, **32**: 184; 13. ([16]) Bolle and Guye, *42*, **3**: 38; 05. ([17]) Bousfield and Lowry, *4*, **99**: 1432; 11. ([18]) Bramley, *4*, **109**: 10; 16. ([19]) Bramley, *4*, **109**: 434; 16.

([20]) Brown, *5*, **26**: 238; 77. ([21]) Brühl, *13*, **203**: 1; 80. ([22]) Brühl, *13*, **235**: 1; 86. ([23]) Brühl, *52*, **50**: 119; 94. ([24]) Brühl, *7*, **16**: 193; 95. ([25]) Brunel, *1*, **45**: 1334; 23. ([26]) Brunel, Crenshaw and Tobin, *1*, **43**: 561; 21. ([27]) Bygden, *25*, **48**: 1236; 15. ([28]) Bygden, *Thesis*, Upsala, 16. ([29]) Campbell, *83*, **11**: 91; 15.

([30]) Carius, *52*, **2**: 262; 70. ([31]) Carothers, *1*, **45**: 1734; 23. ([32]) Chancel, *34*, **99**: 1053; 84. ([33]) Charrier, Gallotti and Zappelli, *36*, **52 II**: 317; 22. ([34]) Chavanne and van Risseghem, *28*, **31**: 87; 22. ([35]) Chavanne and Simon, *34*, **168**: 1111; 19. ([36]) Clarke, *1*, **33**: 520; 11. ([37]) Clarke, *1*, **37**: 2536; 15. ([38]) Clough and Johns, *45*, **15**: 1030; 23. ([39]) Cohen, Meester and Moesveld, *70*, **42**: 779; 23.

([40]) Dasannacharya, *1*, **46**: 1627; 24. ([41]) De Pauw, *Diss*, Utrecht, 22. ([42]) Dittmar and Fawsitt, *174*, **33**: 509; 88. ([43]) Dobriner, *13*, **243**: 1; 88. ([44]) Dobriner, *13*, **243**: 23; 88. ([45]) Dobroserdov, *53*, **44**: 679; 12. ([46]) Doroshevskii, *53*, **41**: 958; 09. ([47]) Doroshevskii, *53*, **43**: 46; 11. ([48]) Doroshevskii and Dvirzhanchik, *53*, **40**: 908; 08. ([49]) Dow Chemical Co., Midland, Mich., *0*.

([50]) Drücker and Kassel, *7*, **76**: 367; 11. ([51]) Drücker and Moles, *7*, **75**: 405; 11. ([52]) Dunstan, *4*, **107**: 667; 15. ([53]) Dunstan, Hilditch and Thole, *4*, **103**: 133; 13. ([54]) Dunstan and Mussell, *4*, **97**: 1935; 10. ([55]) Dunstan, Thole and Hunt, *4*, **91**: 1728; 07. ([56]) Dutoit and Friederich, *27*, **19**: 321; 98. ([57]) Dutoit and Friederich, *149*, **9**: 105; 00. ([58]) Efremov, *53*, **50**: 364; 18. ([59]) Egerton and Lee, *5*, **103**: 487; 23.

([60]) Eijkman, *25*, **25**: 3069; 92. ([61]) Eijkman, *70*, **12**: 157; 93. ([62]) Eijkman, *70*, **15**: 52; 96. ([63]) Eijkman, *Oeuvres Posth.*, p. 443. ([64]) Eisenlohr, *7*, **75**: 585; 11. ([65]) Elsässer, *13*, **218**: 302; 83. ([66]) Emmerling and Lengyel, *13*, Supp. **7**: 101; 70. ([67]) English and Turner, *4*, **105**: 1656; 14. ([68]) Ewins, *4*, **105**: 350; 14. ([69]) Falk, *1*, **31**: 86; 09.

([70]) Falk, *1*, **31**: 806; 09. ([71]) Faust, *7*, **79**: 97; 12. ([72]) Frankland and Barrow, *4*, **105**: 990; 14. ([73]) Frankland, Carter and Adams, *4*, **101**: 2470; 12. ([74]) Frankland and Garner, *4*, **115**: 636; 19. ([75]) Frankland and Turnbull, *4*, **105**: 456; 14. ([76]) Garner and Ryder, *4*, **127**: 720; 25. ([77]) Garner, Saxton and Parker, *11*, **46**: 236; 11. ([78]) Gartenmeister, *7*, **6**: 524; 90. ([79]) Gay, *16*, **6**: 36; 16.

([80]) Gerlach, *167*, **38 II**: 2089; 85. ([81]) Getman, *11*, **44**: 145; 10. ([82]) Getman, *11*, **45**: 539; 11. ([83]) Grinakovskii, *53*, **45**: 1210; 13. ([84]) Guye and Baud, *34*, **132**: 1553; 01. ([85]) Guye and Mallet, *149*, **13**: 274; 02. ([86]) Gyr, *25*, **41**: 4322; 08. ([87]) Hall, *4*, **123**: 32; 23. ([88]) Hall, *4*, **123**: 105; 23. ([89]) Harkins, Clark and Roberts, *1*, **42**: 700; 20.

([90]) Harries, *25*, **32**: 1326; 99. ([91]) Harries, *13*, **330**: 185; 04. ([92]) Hartley, Thomas and Applebey, *4*, **93**: 538; 08. ([93]) Henry, *186*, **1906**: 732. ([94]) Hernquist, *Diss.*, Upsala; 14. ([95]) Herz and Bloch, *7*, **110**: 23; 24. ([96]) Herz and Rathmann, *136*, **36**: 1417; 12. ([97]) Herz and Rathmann, *136*, **37**: 621; 13. ([98]) Hofmann, *25*, **22**: 699; 89. ([99]) Holleman, *70*, **23**: 357; 04.

([100]) Holmes, *4*, **103**: 2147; 13. ([101]) Homfray and Guye, *42*, **1**: 505; 04. ([102]) Jacobson and Neumeister, *25*, **15**: 599; 82. ([103]) Jaeger, *93*, **101**: 1; 17. ([104]) Jaeger and Dijkstra, *64P*, **27**: 403; 24. ([105]) Jephcott, *4*, **115**: 104; 19. ([106]) Jezewski, *165*, **1921A**: 110. ([107]) Jungfleisch, *6*, **15**: 186; 68. ([108]) Kahlbaum, *7*, **26**: 577; 98. ([109]) Kailan, *91*, **51**: 81; 12.

([110]) Karvonen, *175*, **3A**: No. **7**; 12. ([111]) Kendall and Monroe, *1*, **43**: 115; 21. ([112]) Kendall and Wright, *1*, **42**: 1776; 20. ([113]) Kenyon, *4*, **105**: 2226; 14. ([114]) Kenyon and McNicol, *4*, **123**: 14; 23. ([115]) Kenyon and Pickard, *4*, **105**: 2262; 14. ([116]) Kenyon and Pickard, *4*, **105**: 2644; 14. ([117]) Kenyon and Pickard, *4*, **107**: 35; 15. ([118]) Kenyon and Pickard, *4*, **107**: 115; 15. ([119]) Klason and Norlin, *167*, **58 II**: 173; 05–8.

([120]) Knops, *13*, **248**: 175; 88. ([121]) Körber, *8*, **37**: 1014; 12. ([122]) Kopp, *13*, **94**: 257; 55. ([123]) Krafft, *25*, **15**: 1687; 82. ([124]) Krafft, *25*, **19**: 2218; 86. ([125]) Krasuskii, *53*, **34**: 287; 02. ([126]) Kremann, Weingast and Gugl, *57*, **35**: 1235; 14. ([127]) Kuenen and Wisser, *168*, No. **136**: 13. *64V*, **21**: 22; 13. ([128]) Kultasev, *Diss.*, Dorpat, 15. ([129]) Kurnakov, Krotkov and Oksman, *53*, **47**: 558; 15.

([130]) Kurnakov, Perel'muter and Kanov, *169*, **24**: 399; 16. ([131]) Kurnakov and Zhemchuzhnui, *169*, **18**: 125; 12. ([132]) Lambrette, *Diss.*, Brussels, 23. ([133]) Landolt and Jahn, *7*, **10**: 289; 92. ([134]) Lebo, *1*, **43**: 1005; 21. ([135]) Lieben and Rossi, *13*, **159**: 70; 71. ([136]) Lievens, *Diss.*, Brussels, *0*. ([137]) Loomis, *7*, **32**: 578; 00. ([138]) Louguinine, *6*, **11**: 453; 67. ([139]) Lumsden, *4*, **87**: 90; 05.

([140]) Lumsden, *4*, **91**: 24; 07. ([141]) Maass and Boomer, *1*, **44**: 1709; 22. ([142]) Maass and McIntosh, *1*, **36**: 737; 14. ([143]) Maass and Wright, *1*, **43**: 1098; 21. ([144]) Mains, *33*, **26**: 779; 22. ([145]) Marshall, *4*, **89**: 1350; 06. ([146]) Mathews and Faville, *50*, **22**: 1; 18. ([147]) McCrae and Patterson, *4*, **77**: 1096; 00. ([148]) McIntosh, *50*, **11**: 306; 07. ([149]) Merry and Turner, *4*, **105**: 748; 14.

([150]) Meyer and Mylius, *7*, **95**: 349; 20. ([151]) Mitchell and Smith, *4*, **103**: 489; 13. ([152]) Morgan, *1*, **33**: 672; 11. ([153]) Morgan and Chazal, *1*, **35**: 1821; 13. ([154]) Morgan and Cramer, *1*, **35**: 1834; 13. ([155]) Morgan and Egloff, *1*, **38**: 844; 16. ([156]) Morgan and Lammert, *1*, **46**: 881; 24. ([157]) Morgan and Stone, *1*, **35**: 1505; 13. ([158]) Müller, *7*, **86**: 177; 14. ([159]) Mussell, Thole and Dunstan, *4*, **101**: 1008; 12.

([160]) Naccari and Pagliani, *427*, **6**: 87; 82. ([161]) Nasini, *25*, **15**: 2878; 82. ([162]) Nasini and Bernheimer, *36*, **13**: 317; 83. ([163]) Nasini and Bresciani, *36*, **43 II**: 281; 13. ([164]) Nasini and Bresciani, *170*, **9**: 341; 13. ([165]) Norris and Green, *11*, **26**: 293; 01. ([166]) Osborne, McKelvy and Bearce, *31A*, **9**: 327; 13. ([167]) Ott, *13*, **392**: 245; 12. ([168]) Pascal, *34*, **156**: 1904; 13. ([169]) Patterson, *4*, **79**: 167; 01.

([170]) Patterson, *4*, **85**: 765; 04. ([171]) Patterson, *4*, **85**: 1116; 04. ([172]) Patterson, *4*, **93**: 1836; 08. ([173]) Patterson, *4*, **103**: 145; 13. ([174]) Patterson, *4*, **109**: 1139; 16. ([175]) Patterson and Davidson, *4*, **101**: 374; 12. ([176]) Patterson and Forsyth, *4*, **103**: 2263; 13. ([177]) Patterson and MacDonald, *4*, **93**: 936; 08. ([178]) Patterson and Moudgill, *68*, **39**: 18; 18. ([179]) Patterson and Patterson, *4*, **107**: 142; 15.

([180]) Patterson and Pollock, *4*, **105**: 2322; 14. ([181]) Patterson and Taylor, *4*, **87**: 33; 05. ([182]) Patterson and Thomson, *4*, **93**: 355; 08. ([183]) Perkin, *4*, **45**: 421; 84. ([184]) Perkin, *4*, **51**: 808; 87. ([185]) Perkin, *4*, **55**: 680; 89. ([186]) Perkin, *4*, **61**: 800; 92. ([187]) Perkin, *4*, **63**: 488; 93. ([188]) Perkin, *4*, **65**: 402; 94. ([189]) Perkin, *4*, **69**: 1025; 96.

([190]) Perkin, *4*, **81**: 292; 02. ([191]) Petterson, *52*, **24**: 293; 81. ([192]) Phillips, *4*, **123**: 22; 23. ([193]) Pickard, Hunter, Lewcock and de Pennington, *4*, **117**: 1248; 20. ([194]) Pickard and Kenyon, *4*, **99**: 45; 11. ([195]) Pickard and Kenyon, *4*, **101**: 620; 12. (196) Pickard and Kenyon, *4*, **101**: 1427; 12. (197) Pickard and Kenyon, *4*, **103**: 1923; 13. (198) Pickard and Kenyon, *4*, **105**: 830; 14. (199) Pickard and Kenyon, *4*, **105**: 1115; 14.

(200) Pickard, Kenyon and Hunter, *4*, **123**: 1; 23. (201) Pickard and Littlebury, *4*, **101**: 109; 12. (202) Pictet, *167*, **35**: 854; 82. (203) Pierre and Puchot, *6*, **22**: 234; 71. (204) Pierre and Puchot, *13*, **163**: 253; 72. (205) Polowzow, *7*, **75**: 513; 11. (206) Pribram and Glücksmann, *57*, **18**: 303; 97. (207) Price, *4*, **115**: 1116; 19. (208) Prilezhaev, *53*, **42**: 1387; 10. (209) Purdie and Irvine, *4*, **79**: 957; 01.

(210) Ramsay and Young, *4*, **49**: 790; 86. (211) Rayman, *Diss.*, Budapest, 06. (212) Read and Hook, *4*, **117**: 1214; 20. (213) Reid, *172*, **25**: 423; 12. (214) Reilly and Ralph, *117*, **15**: 597; 19. (215) Richards and Barry, *1*, **37**: 993; 15. (216) Richards and Carver, *1*, **43**: 827; 21. (217) Richards and Coombs, *1*, **3** : 1656; 15. (218) Richards and Mathews, *1*, **30**: 8; 08. (219) Richards and Shipley, *1*, **38**: 989; 16.

(220) Richards, Stull, Mathews and Speyers, *1*, **34**: 971; 12. (221) Riiber, *9*, **29**: 334; 23. (222) Ronalds, *4*, **18**: 54; 65. (223) Ross and Leather, *173*, **31**: 284; 06. (224) Ruttan, *172*, **25**: 431; 12. (225) Sabatier and Mailhe, *34*, **140**: 350; 05. (226) Scheij, *70*, **18**: 169; 99. (227) Schenck and Kintzinger, *70*, **42**: 759; 23. (228) Scheuer, *7*, **72**: 513; 10. (229) Schiff, *13*, **220**: 71; 83.

(230) Schiff, *13*, **223**: 247; 84. (231) Schreiner, *93*, **122**: 201; 22. (232) Schwers, *186*, **1908**: 814. (233) Schwers, *42*, **9**: 15; 11. (234) Schwers, *4*, **99**: 1478; 11. (235) Schwers, *22*, **20 II**: 398; 11. (236) Schwers, *4*, **101**: 1889; 12. (237) Seubert, *25*, **22**: 2519; 89. (238) Shorthose, *B40*. (239) Squibb, *1*, **17**: 187; 95.

(240) Sugden, *4*, **125**: 1177; 24. (241) Sugden, Reed and Williams, *4*, **127**: 1525; 25. (242) Sugden and Wilkins, *4*, **127**: 2517; 25. (243) Sugden and Whittaker, *4*, **127**: 1868; 25. (244) Taylor and Smith, *1*, **44**: 2450; 22. (245) Thole, *7*, **74**: 683; 10. (246) Thole, *4*, **103**: 317; 13. (247) Thorpe, *4*, **37**: 141; 80. (248) Thorpe and Jones, *4*, **63**: 273; 93. (249) Thorpe and Rodger, *62*, **185A**: 397; 94.

(250) Timmermans, *28*, **24**: 244; 10. (251) Timmermans, *28*, **25**: 300; 11. (252) Timmermans, *117*, **13**: 310; 12. (253) Timmermans, *186*, **32**: 299; 23. (254) Timmermans and Martin, University of Brussels, Belgium, *0*. (255) Tromp, *70*, **41**: 278; 22. (256) Turner and Merry, *4*, **97**: 2069: 10. (257) Tyrer, *4*, **105**: 2534; 14. (258) Veley, *5B*, **82**: 217; 10. (259) Vespignani, *36*, **33 I**: 76; 03.

(260) Vincent and Delachanal, *27*, **31**: 11; 79. (261) Wade and Merriman, *4*, **101**: 2429; 12. (262) Walden *7*, **20**: 569; 96. 263) Walden, *7*, **55**: 1; 06. (264) Walden, *7*, **55**: 207; 06. (265) Walden, *7*, **59**: 385; 07. (266) Walden, *7*, **65**: 129; 08. (267) Walden, *7*, **75**: 555; 11. (268) Walden and Swinne, *7*, **69**: 700; 12. (269) Walden and Swinne, *7*, **82**: 271; 13.

(270) Wallace and Atkins, *4*, **101**: 1958; 12. (271) Weger, *13*, **221**: 61; 83. (272) Wiens, *13*, **253**: 289; 89. (273) Wilkinson and Wernland, *1*, **42**: 1382; 20. (274) Williams, *1*, **47**: 2644; 25. (275) Winkler, *25*, **38**: 3612; 05. (276) Winther, *7*, **41**: 161; 02. (277) Wood, Such and Scarf *4*, **123**: 600; 23. (278) Young, *4*, **55**: 486; 89. (279) Young, *4*, **59**: 911; 91.

(280) Young, *3*, **33**: 153; 92. (281) Young, *117*, **12**: 374; 10. (282) Young and Fortey, *4*, **77**: 1126; 00. (283) Young and Fortey, *4*, **81**: 717; 02. (284) Young and Fortey, *4*, **83**: 45; 03. (285) Young and Thomas, *4*, **63**: 1191; 93. (286) Zawidzki. *136*, **30**: 299; 06. (287) Zoubov, *53*, **30**: 926; 98.

THE LIQUID (INCLUDING VITREOUS) STATE UNDER PRESSURES HIGHER THAN ATMOSPHERIC. (DENSITY, THERMAL EXPANSION AND COMPRESSIBILITY)

LOUIS AND JEAN DÉCOMBE

Except as otherwise noted below, the tables in this section constitute a complete index of substances for this subject.

Abbreviations and Units.—The quantity recorded in the following tables, except as otherwise noted, is $\beta = \frac{-10^6}{V}\left(\frac{\partial V}{\partial p}\right)_T$ or $= \frac{10^6}{V_1}\left(\frac{V_1 - V_2}{p_2 - p_1}\right)_T$, according as a single pressure or a pressure range is given. The pressure unit is the megabarye. (*Cf.* Vol. I, p. 34, "barye.")

To convert megabaryes	Multiply by	To convert "per megabarye"	Multiply by
To atm.	0.987	To per atm.	1.013
To lb./in.^{2}	14.50	To per (lb./in.^{2})	0.0689
To kg/cm^2	1.0197	To per (kg/cm^2)	0.9806

A-TABLE, NON-METALLIC ELEMENTS

For metallic elements, *v.* p. 46

VALUES OF β AT 20° (23)

p_1, p_2	0–100	100–200	200–300	300–400	400–500
Br	(62.5)†	57	54	51	49
Cl*	(116)	(108)	(100)	(89)	(83)

* Estimated; not directly measured. † Extrapolated.

VALUES OF β BETWEEN 1 AND 14 700 MEGABARYES (7)

H, $\beta > 31$ at −260°; He, $\beta > 38$ at −271.6°; N, $\beta > 15$ at −205°.

B-TABLE, INORGANIC COMPOUNDS

Substance	t, °C	p_1, p_2	β	Lit.
H_2O	*v.* page 40.			
H_2SO_4, concd	12.6	1–163	*ca.* 33	(1)
NH_3	12.6	1–224	*ca.* 37	(1)
HNO_3, $d_4^0 = 1.403$	0	1–32	*ca.* 35	(9)
PCl_3	*v.* page 40.			
CO_2	*v.* Tables 1 and 2, p. 37, 38.			

C-TABLE, CARBON COMPOUNDS

CCl_4, Carbon tetrachloride, *cf.* Tables 5 and 9

t, °C	p_1, p_2 megabaryes	β
20° (23)	1–100	90
	100–200	88
	200–300	82
	300–400	74
	400–500	69
24.6° (10)	29.4	99
	98.1	93
	196.2	86
	294.3	79
	392.4	73
	490.5	67
	588.6	62

CO_2, *v.* Tables 1 and 2

CS_2, *v.* p. 41

$CHBr_3$, Bromoform

t, °C	p_1, p_2	β
20° (23)	1–100	(50)*
	100–200	47
	200–300	43
	300–400	41
	400–500	(40)*
20° (22)	100–300	45
	300–500	41
	100–500	43

* Extrapolated.

$CHCl_3$, Chloroform, *v. also* Table 5

t, °C	p_1, p_2	β
20° (23)	1–100	(93)*
	100–200	88
	200–300	79
	300–400	72
	400–500	(67)*

$CHCl_3$.—(*Contd*).

t, °C	p_1, p_2 megabaryes	β
20° (22)	100–300	83
	300–500	70
	100–500	76
100° [B. P. 60°] (2)	8–9	208
	19–36	203
25° (11)	1–6	105
24.6° (10)	29.4	99
	98.1	91.5
	196.2	83
	294.3	77
	392.4	72
	490.5	66
	588.6	61

* Extrapolated.

CH_3I, Methyl iodide, *v.* Table 5

CH_3NO_2, Nitromethane (13)

t, °C	p_1, p_2	β
18.36°	1–9.1	68.5
24.85°	1–9.1	71

CH_4O, Methyl alcohol, *v.* p. 41

C_2Cl_4, Tetrachloroethylene

t, °C	Lit.	p_1, p_2	β
10°	(14)	1–5.3	69
58.5°	(14)	1–5.3	93
98°	(14)	1–5.3	123

C_2H_4, Ethylene, *v.* Table 2

$C_2H_4Br_2$, Ethylene bromide

t, °C	Lit.	p_1, p_2	β
10°	(14)	1–5.3	55
64°	(14)	1–5.3	76
100°	(14)	1–5.3	96

$C_2H_4Br_2$.—(*Continued*)

t, °C	p_1, p_2 mega-baryes	β
20° (23)	100–300	54
	300–500	49
	100–500	52

$C_2H_4Cl_2$, Ethylene chloride, *cf. also* Table 5

10° (14)	1–5.3	67
75° (14)	1–5.3	110
20° (22)	100–300	67.5
	300–500	58
	100–500	63
0° (10)	29.4	76
	98.1	71
	196.2	66
	294.3	61.5
	392.4	58
	490.5	55
	588.6	52.5

$C_2H_4O_2$, Acetic acid, *v.* Table 5

C_2H_5Br, Ethyl bromide, *v.* p. 41

C_2H_5Cl, Ethyl chloride, *v.* p. 41

C_2H_5I, Ethyl iodide, *v.* p. 41

$C_2H_5NO_3$, Ethyl nitrate (9)

0°	1–24	*ca.* 71

C_2H_6O, Ethyl alcohol, *v.* p. 41

$C_2H_6O_2$, Glycol

20° (22)	100–300	34
	300–500	32
	100–500	33

C_3H_6O, Allyl alcohol, *cf.* Table 3

9.6° (3)	1–507	68
	507–1013	50
	1013–1520	42
	1520–2026	36
	2026–2533	31

C_3H_6O, Acetone, *v.* p. 42

$C_3H_6O_2$, Methyl acetate, *cf. also* Table 5

B. P. 58° (2)		
14.3°	8.2–38	95.5
99.7°	8.4–37.5	247
20° (22)	100–300	87.5
	300–500	73
	100–500	80

C_3H_8O, *n*-Propyl alcohol, *v.* p. 42

C_3H_8O, Isopropyl alcohol (24)

5.65°	1–8.1	94
17.85°	1–8.1	102

$C_3H_8O_3$, Glycerol $d_{15}^{16.5} = 1.245$ (17)

t, °C	p_1, p_2 mega-baryes	β
14.9°	1–10.1	22

$C_4H_8O_2$, Ethyl acetate, *cf.* Table 5

20° (22)	100–300	90
	300–500	75
	100–500	83
B. P. = 72° (2)		
13.3°	8.2–37.9	103
99.6°	8.2–37.6	247

$C_4H_8O_2$, Propyl formate

20° (22)	100–300	87
	300–500	72
	100–500	79.5

$C_4H_{10}O$, *n*-Butyl alcohol

3.05° (24)	1–8.1	82
17.4° (24)	1–8.1	89
20° (22)	100–300	76.5
	300–500	64
	100–500	70

$C_4H_{10}O$, Isobutyl alcohol, *v.* p. 42

$C_4H_{10}O$, *tert.*-Butyl alcohol

20° (22)	100–300	89
	300–500	70
	100–500	80

$C_4H_{10}O$, Ethyl ether, *v.* p. 42

C_5H_{10}, Isoamylene (25)

16.7°	0.4–18.2	168
34.7°	0.2–18.2	206.5

$C_5H_{10}O$, Diethyl ketone

20° (21)	100–300	84
	300–500	70
	100–500	77

$C_5H_{10}O_2$, Isobutyl formate

20° (22)	100–300	86
	300–500	72
	100–500	79

$C_5H_{10}O_2$, Ethyl propionate

20° (22)	100–300	87.5
	300–500	72.5
	100–500	80

$C_5H_{10}O_2$, Methyl *n*-butyrate

10° (14)	1–5.3	88
62° (14)	1–5.3	132
20° (22)	100–300	84
	300–500	70
	100–500	77

$C_5H_{10}O_2$, Methyl isobutyrate

20° (22)	100–300	89
	300–500	74
	100–500	81

$C_5H_{10}O_2$, Valeric acid

t, °C	p_1, p_2 mega-baryes	β
20° (22)	100–300	77
	300–500	64
	100–500	70.5

C_5H_{12}, Pentane
B. P. 30–35° (2)

13.1°	9–26	177
13.1°	9–37.5	170
99.4°	9–13.5	532
99.4°	9–38	522

C_5H_{12}, Isopentane, *v.* Tables 4 and 5

$C_5H_{12}O$, Amyl alcohol, *v.* p. 42

$C_5H_{12}O$, Isoamyl alcohol

20° (22)	100–300	84
	300–500	69.5
	100–500	77

C_6H_5Br, Bromobenzene, *v.* Table 9

C_6H_5Cl, Chlorobenzene, *v. also* Tables 5 and 9

13.3° (25)	0.4–18.2	66
35.4° (25)	0.4–18.2	76
100.4° (25)	0.4–18.2	126

C_6H_5F, Fluorobenzene

13.9° (25)	0.4–18.2	87
35.4° (25)	0.4–18.2	101
99.7° (25)	0.4–18.2	187

$C_6H_5NO_2$, Nitrobenzene, *v.* Table 5

C_6H_6, Benzene, *cf. also* Table 5

0° (9)	1–26	*ca.* 72
6° (24)	1–8	82
17.9° (24)	1–8	90.5
12.9° (25)	0.4–18	86
34.9° (25)	2–18	99
99.9° (25)	4.5–19	187
99.3° (2)	8–38	185
20° (20, 21)	100–300	78
	300–500	66.5
	100–500	72
21° (8)	1–51	96
	1–101	94
	1–253	90
	1–507	77
24.6° (10)	29.4	91
	98.1	85
	196.2	79
	294.3	73.5
	392.4	68
	490.5	63
	588.6	60

C_6H_7N, Aniline, *cf. also* Table 5

17.95° (13)	1–9	44
24.74° (13)	1–9	45

$C_6H_{10}O$, Cyclohexanone

t, °C	p_1, p_2 mega-baryes	β
20° (21)	100–300	58
	300–500	51
	100–500	54

$C_6H_{10}O_4$, Ethyl oxalate, *v.* Table 5

C_6H_{12}, Cyclohexane, *cf. also* Table 5

20° (21)	100–200	93

$C_6H_{12}O$, Cyclohexanol

40° (21)	100–300	56
34.16° (21)	100–300	54

$C_6H_{12}O_2$, Isoamyl formate

20° (22)	100–300	80
	300–500	68
	100–500	74

$C_6H_{12}O_2$, Isobutyl acetate

20° (22)	100–300	87
	300–500	72
	100–500	80

$C_6H_{12}O_2$, Ethyl *n*-butyrate

20° (22)	100–300	85
	300–500	71
	100–500	78
10° (14)	1–5.3	92
62.5° (14)	1–5.3	134
97° (14)	1–5.3	182.5

$C_6H_{12}O_2$, Ethyl isobutyrate

20° (23)	100–300	90
	300–500	75
	100–500	82

$C_6H_{12}O_2$, Methyl *n*-valerate

10° (14)	1–5.3	90
63° (14)	1–5.3	132
100° (14)	1–5.3	181

$C_6H_{12}O_2$, Methyl isovalerate

20° (22)	100–300	84
	300–500	70
	100–500	77

$C_6H_{12}O_3$, Paraldehyde

12.13° (13)	1–9.1	81
17.91° (13)	1–9.1	87

C_6H_{14}, Hexane

B. P., 66–72° (2)		
13°	9–38	141
99°	8.6–38	351
B. P., 68°		
23° (5)	$\frac{1}{8}$–1	157
20° (22); *cf.* (2, 5)	100–300	117.5
	300–500	91
	100–500	104

C_6H_{14}, Isohexane

20° (22)	100–300	119
	300–500	93
	100–500	106

C_7H_8, Toluene, *cf. also* Tables 5 and 7

t, °C	p_1, p_2 megabaryes	β
10° (14)	1–5.3	78
66°		113
100°		148.5
0°	100–300	66
0° (20)	300–500	58
20° (21)	100–300	74
	300–500	64
	100–500	69

C_7H_8O, Benzyl alcohol

17.85° (13)	1–9.1	46
25.02°		47
20° (22)	100–300	43
	300–500	38
	100–500	41

C_7H_8O, Phenyl methyl ether, anisole

11.87° (13)	1–9.1	60
17.95°		62

C_7H_8O, *o*-Cresol

20° (22)	100–300	44
	300–500	42
	100–500	43

C_7H_8O, *m*-Cresol

20° (22)	100–300	45.5
	300–500	41.5
	100–500	43.5
17.78° (13)	1–9.1	49
25.29°		50

C_7H_8O, *p*-Cresol

20° (22)	100–300	44
	300–500	42
	100–500	43

C_7H_9N, Methylaniline

20° (22)	100–300	45
	300–500	40.5
	100–500	43

C_7H_9N, *o*-Toluidine

20° (22)	100–300	44
	300–500	39
	100–500	41

C_7H_9N, *m*-Toluidine

20° (22)	100–300	45
	300–500	41
	100–500	43

C_7H_9N, *p*-Toluidine, *v.* Table 8

$C_7H_{12}O_4$, Ethyl malonate, *v.* Table 5

$C_7H_{14}O_2$, Ethyl valerate

10° (14)	1–5.3	94.5
62.5°		137
100°		180

C_7H_{16}, Heptane B. P. = 90–94°

t, °C	p_1, p_2 megabaryes	β
13.8° (2)	8–38	120
99.5°		266

B. P. = 93°

23° (5)	*ca.* 0.07–1	132

C_8H_{10}, Ethylbenzene, *v. also* Table 9

20° (21)	100–300	71
	300–500	61
	100–500	66
17.89° (13)	1–9.1	81
25.28°		84.5

C_8H_{10}, Xylene, *v.* Tables 5, 6, 7

$C_8H_{11}N$, Dimethylaniline

20° (22)	100–300	52
	300–500	45
	100–500	48

$C_8H_{11}N$, Ethylaniline

20° (22)	100–300	50
	300–500	45
	100–500	47

$C_8H_{16}O_2$, Butyl butyrate

10° (14)	1–5.3	89
63°		128
100°		168

C_8H_{18}, Octane

20° (22)	100–300	97.5
	300–500	78
	100–500	88
23° (5)	*ca.* 0.07–1	120*

C_8H_{18}, 2, 5-Dimethylhexane

20° (22)	100–300	105
	300–500	84.5
	100–500	95

C_8H_{18}, 2-Methylheptane

20° (22)	100–300	101
	300–500	82
	100–500	91

C_8H_{18}, 3, 4-Dimethylhexane

20° (22)	100–300	94.5
	300–500	74
	100–500	84

C_8H_{18}, 3-Ethylhexane

20° (22)	100–300	96
	300–500	78
	100–500	87

C_9H_{12}, *n*-Propylbenzene

20° (21)	100–300	69.7
	300–500	60.1
	100–500	64.9

C_9H_{12}, Isopropylbenzene

20° (21)	100–300	70.3
	300–500	60.4
	100–500	65.4

*B. P. = 117°.

C_9H_{12}, Cumene, *v.* Table 7

C_9H_{12}, Pseudocumene, *v. also* Table 9

t, °C	p_1, p_2 megabaryes	β
20° (21)	100–300	64
	300–500	56
	100–500	60

C_9H_{12}, Mesitylene

20° (21)	100–300	67
	300–500	58
	100–500	63

$C_9H_{18}O_2$, Butyl valerate

10° (14)	1–5.3	91
63.5°		128.5
100°		171

$C_9H_{18}O_2$, Amyl butyrate

10° (14)	1–5.3	85
63.5°		121
97°		155

C_9H_{20}, Nonane B. P. = 137° (5)

23°	*ca.* 0.07–1	111

C_9H_{20}, 2, 4-Dimethylheptane

20° (21)	100–300	96
	300–500	79
	100–500	87

C_9H_{20}, 2, 5-Dimethylheptane

20° (21)	100–300	95
	300–500	77
	100–500	86

$C_{10}H_{14}$, *tert.*-Butylbenzene

20° (21)	100–300	68
	300–500	59
	100–500	63

$C_{10}H_{14}O$, Thymol, *v.* Table 8

$C_{10}H_{15}N$, Diethylaniline

20° (22)	100–300	54
	300–500	47.5
	100–500	51

$C_{10}H_{20}O_2$, Amyl valerate

t, °C	p_1, p_2 megabaryes	β
10° (14)	1–5.3	87
62.7°		120
99°		154

$C_{10}H_{20}O_2$, Capric acid, *v.* Table 8

$C_{10}H_{22}$, Decane B. P. = 160° (5)

23°	*ca.* 0.07–1	104

$C_{11}H_{14}O_2$, Butyl benzoate

10° (14)	1–5.3	58
64°		79
100°		97

$C_{11}H_{24}$, Undecane B. P. = 181° (5)

23°	*ca.* 0.07–1	96

$C_{12}H_{11}N$, Diphenylamine, *v.* Table 8

$C_{12}H_{16}O_2$, Isoamyl benzoate

10° (14)	1–5.3	57
65°		76.5
100°		91

$C_{12}H_{26}$, Dodecane B. P. = 199° (5)

23°	*ca.* 0.07–1	90.5

$C_{13}H_{28}$, Tridecane B. P. = 219° (5)

23°	*ca.* 0.07–1	86

$C_{14}H_{30}$, Tetradecane B. P. = 238° (5)

23°	*ca.* 0.05–1	82

$C_{15}H_{32}$, Pentadecane B. P. = 260° (5)

23°	*ca.* 0.07–1	78

$C_{16}H_{32}O_2$, Palmitic acid, *v.* Table 8

$C_{16}H_{34}$, Hexadecane B. P. = 280° (5)

23°	*ca.* 0.07–1	74

TABLE 1.—CO_2. VALUES OF $\beta = \frac{-10^6}{V}\left(\frac{\partial V}{\partial p}\right)_T$ (16)

v. also Table 2

p \ $t°$	−37	−30	−20	−10	0	+5	10	15	20	25	30
13.8	220										
14.5		305									
20.7			550								
27.6		290	490	900							
35.9					1 050						
41.4		275	400	680		1 400					
44.8							1 730				
55.2		260	340	520	830	1 120	1 500	2 360			
56.55									4 060		
63.45										5 940	
69		245	290	400	650	900	1 190	1 740	2 900	5 070	
75.9											16 500
82.8		230	260	320	540	720	940	1 270	1 930	3 200	7 400
89.7											4 900
96.6		215	230	290	430	570	730	910	1 200	1 740	2 750

TABLE 2.—VALUES OF pv

The volume unit is the volume of the gaseous substance at 0° and 1 atm. (4)

	CO_2, *v. also* Table 1				C_2H_4
p, atm.	0°	10°	20°	30°	0°
1	1.0000				1.0000
50	0.1050	0.1145			0.1755
75	0.1530	0.1630	0.1800	0.2190	0.2425
100	0.2020	0.2130	0.2285	0.2550	0.3100
125	0.2490	0.2620	0.2785	0.3000	0.3750
150	0.2950	0.3090	0.3260	0.3460	0.4405
175	0.3405	0.3550	0.3725	0.3930	0.5040
200	0.3850	0.4010	0.4190	0.4400	0.5650
225	0.4305	0.4455	0.4655	0.4875	0.6270
250	0.4740	0.4900	0.5100	0.5335	0.6870
275	0.5170	0.5340	0.5545	0.5775	
300	0.5595	0.5775	0.5985	0.6225	0.8055
350	0.6445	0.6640	0.6850	0.7090	0.9229
400	0.7280	0.7475	0.7710	0.7950	1.0365
450	0.8090	0.8310	0.8550	0.8800	1.1465
500	0.8905	0.9130	0.9380	0.9630	1.2555
550	0.9700	0.9935	1.0200	1.0465	1.3640
600	1.0495	1.0730	1.0995	1.1275	1.4725
650	1.1275	1.1530	1.1800	1.2075	1.5785
700	1.2055	1.2320	1.2590	1.2890	1.6835
750	1.2815	1.3105	1.3395	1.3700	1.7865
800	1.3580	1.3870	1.4170	1.4475	1.8880
850	1.4340	1.4625	1.4935	1.5245	1.9900
900	1.5090	1.5385	1.5685	1.6000	2.0905
950	1.5830	1.6115	1.6430	1.6740	2.1900
1000	1.6560	1.6850	1.7160	1.7480	2.2890

CO_2	
p, atm.	pv
0°	
35	0.0750
37	0.0790
50	0.1050
10°	
45	0.1050
50	0.1145
20°	
57	0.1480
60	0.1520
30°	
71	0.2300
72	0.2230
74	0.2190
75	0.2190
78	0.2205
80	0.2225

C_2H_4, Ethylene		
p, atm.	pv 0°	pv 5°
41	0.1610	
42	0.1570	
43	0.1580	
44	0.1600	
46	0.1645	0.1890
47		0.1850
48	0.1695	0.1855
49		0.1875
50	0.1755	0.1900
52	0.1810	0.1945
56		0.2050
60	0.2025	0.2145
75	0.2425	0.2535
80	0.2565	
100	0.3100	

TABLE 3.—C_3H_6O, ALLYL ALCOHOL

Volume of the liquid in terms of its volume at 0° and 1 atm. taken as unity (4)

p, atm.	9.60°	35.45°	p, atm.	9.60°	35.45°
1	1.0097	1.0371	1500	0.9296	0.9454
100	1.0015		1600	0.9260	0.9415
200	0.9941		1700	0.9225	0.9378
300	0.9872		1800	0.9192	0.9342
400	0.9808	1.0031	1900	0.9159	0.9307
500	0.9748	0.9962	2000	0.9128	0.9273
600	0.9692	0.9898	2100	0.9097	0.9241
700	0.9638	0.9837	2200	0.9068	0.9209
800	0.9588	0.9779	2300	0.9039	0.9178
900	0.9543	0.9725	2400	0.9011	0.9147
1000	0.9499	0.9674	2500	0.8984	0.9118
1100	0.9455	0.9625	2600	0.8957	0.9090
1200	0.9412	0.9579	2700	0.8931	0.9063
1300	0.9372	0.9535	2800		0.9036
1400	0.9334	0.9494			

TABLE 4.—C_5H_{12}, ISOPENTANE

Values of the specific volume (cm³/g) at t, °C and p megabaryes (27); *v.* Table 5

t \ p	$\frac{16}{3}$	$\frac{32}{3}$	16	$\frac{64}{3}$	$\frac{80}{3}$	32	$\frac{112}{3}$	$\frac{128}{3}$	48	$\frac{160}{3}$	$\frac{176}{3}$	64	$\frac{208}{3}$	$\frac{224}{3}$
10	1.5871	1.5854	1.5838	1.5820	1.5806	1.5790	1.5773	1.5757	1.5742	1.5726	1.5711	1.5696	1.5682	1.5667
15.6	1.6012	1.5994	1.5976	1.5959	1.5941	1.5923	1.5906	1.5889	1.5872	1.5856	1.5839	1.5821	1.5806	1.5791
30	1.6388	1.6366	1.6344	1.6322	1.6300	1.6280	1.6260	1.6240	1.6220	1.6202	1.6184	1.6166	1.6149	1.6131
40	1.6681	1.6655	1.6630	1.6605	1.6581	1.6556	1.6533	1.6510	1.6487	1.6465	1.6444	1.6423	1.6402	1.6382
50	1.6984	1.6953	1.6924	1.6896	1.6868	1.6841	1.6814	1.6788	1.6763	1.6739	1.6715	1.6691	1.6668	1.6645
60	1.7312	1.7277	1.7244	1.7210	1.7179	1.7148	1.7116	1.7086	1.7057	1.7027	1.6999	1.6971	1.6944	1.6916
70	1.7666	1.7625	1.7585	1.7547	1.7510	1.7474	1.7440	1.7405	1.7372	1.7339	1.7306	1.7275	1.7244	1.7212
80	1.8038	1.7992	1.7948	1.7904	1.7861	1.7820	1.7780	1.7740	1.7700	1.7663	1.7625	1.7589	1.7552	1.7516
90	1.8477	1.8420	1.8364	1.8309	1.8255	1.8203	1.8154	1.8106	1.8060	1.8014	1.7974	1.7934	1.7893	1.7749
100		1.8896	1.8825	1.8760	1.8695	1.8634	1.8576	1.8516	1.8460	1.8406	1.8356	1.8306	1.8256	1.8008
110		1.9417	1.9334	1.9253	1.9176	1.9102	1.9029	1.8961	1.8895	1.8830	1.8771	1.8710	1.8652	1.8596
120		2.0037	1.9922	1.9815	1.9713	1.9615	1.9527	1.9445	1.9365	1.9287	1.9215	1.9150	1.9083	1.9015
130			2.0630	2.0485	2.0350	2.0230	2.0115	2.0005	1.9910	1.9810	1.9715	1.9630	1.9540	1.9463
140			2.1512	2.1290	2.1105	2.0940	2.0787	2.0650	2.0520	2.0405	2.0287	2.0185	2.0085	1.9987
150				2.2317	2.2035	2.1782	2.1565	2.1385	2.1210	2.1050	2.0912	2.0780	2.0655	2.0537
160					2.3285	2.2900	2.2575	2.2305	2.2062	2.1852	2.1657	2.1485	2.1322	2.1180
170					2.5252	2.4485	2.3882	2.3450	2.3080	2.2777	2.2512	2.2270	2.2057	2.1872
180						2.7230	2.5835	2.5005	2.4405	2.3985	2.3550	2.3245		
185						3.1830	2.7345	2.6050	2.5270	2.4645	2.4165			
187.8	(Critical point)						2.8585	2.6770	2.5790	2.5075	2.4550	2.4115	2.3745	2.3445

Table 5.—Adiabatic Coefficient

In this table is recorded the mean adiabatic coefficient $\left[\alpha = \frac{-10^6}{V}\left(\frac{\Delta V}{\Delta p}\right)_Q\right]$ between 1 and 2 megabaryes, together with the isothermal coefficient $\left[\beta = \frac{-10^6}{V}\left(\frac{\Delta V}{\Delta p}\right)_T\right]$ thermodynamically computed therefrom (12, 26).

t, °C (26)	CCl_4, Carbon tetrachloride		$CHCl_3$, Chloroform		$C_2H_4Cl_2$, Ethylene chloride		$C_2H_4O_2$, Acetic acid		$C_4H_8O_2$, Ethyl acetate	
	α	β	α	β	α	β	α	β	α	β
0	62	90	58	85	48	69			69	95
10	67	97	62	92	51	74	72*	87.5*	75	104
20	72	105	67	100	55	80	75	91	82	113
30	78	113	73	109	59	86	80.5	97	90	124
40	84	122	79.5	118	64	92.5	86	104	99	135
50	92	132	86	129	69	100	93	111	108	148
60	100	145	93.5	141	75	108	100	119	118.5	162
70	108	158			81	118	107	128	132	179
80					89	128	115	137		

* At 15°C.

t, °C (26)	C_6H_5Cl, Chlorobenzene		$C_6H_5NO_2$, Nitrobenzene		C_6H_6, Benzene		C_7H_8, Toluene		C_8H_{10},* *m*-Xylene	
	α	β	α	β	α	β	α	β	α	β
0	49	66	36	44	55	81	58	78	57	74
10	52	70	38	47	60	87	62	84	61	79.5
20	55	74	40	49	65	94.5	67	90	65	85
30	59	79	43	52	71	102	71.5	96	69	90
40	63	84	45	55	77	110	77	103	74.5	96
50	67	89	48	55	84	119	83	111	80	103
60	72	95	50		92	128	90	120	86	110
70	77	101			101	141	97	129.5	92	118
80	82	108			110	154.5	*v. also* Table 7		99	126

* *v. also* Tables 6 and 7.

C_6H_7N, Aniline (26)

t, °C	α	β	t, °C	α	β
0	32.5	41	50	42	53
10	34	43	60	45	56
20	36	45	70	47	60
30	38	48	80	50	63
40	40	50	90	53	67

	t, °C	α	β
CH_3I, Methyl iodide (12)	0.7	54	
	20.9	64	
$C_3H_6O_2$, Methyl acetate (12)	0.3	65	89
	23.2	81	112
C_5H_{12}, Isopentane, *v. also* Table 4	0.4	134	178
	23.3	169	222.5
$C_6H_{10}O_4$, Ethyl oxalate	0.8	49	65
	22.7	56	74
C_6H_{12}, Cyclohexane	25	83	110
$C_7H_{12}O_4$, Ethyl malonate	0.9	48	
	24.8	56.5	

Table 6.—C_8H_{10}, Xylene. β at 20° (22)

v. Tables 5 and 7

p_1, p_2	o-	m-	p-
100–300	66	69.5	72
300–500	57	60	62
100–500	61	65	67

Table 7.—$\beta = \beta_0 (1 + at + bt^2)$; 0 to 100°C; 1–4 Megabaryes

(18)	β_0	a	b
Toluene	76	0.00657	0.0_4174
Xylene	72.4	0.00220	0.0_4644
Cumene	71.6	0.00253	0.0_4521

Table 8.—Values of β (6)

t° / p_1, p_2	C_7H_9N, *p*-Toluidine. M. P. = 43°; B. P. = 198°				
	28	65	100	185	310
20–101	55	66	80	132	360
20–203	55	64	79	125	312
20–304	55	63	78	118	266
20–405	54	61	77	111	223

t° / p_1, p_2	$C_{10}H_{14}O$, Thymol. M. P. = 53.5°; B. P. = 233°				
	28	64	100	185	310
20–101	65	74	95	151	402
20–203	62	70	89	142	334
20–304	59	67	84	133	295
20–405	56	64	79	125	263

t° / p_1, p_2	$C_{10}H_{20}O_2$, Capric acid. M. P. = 30°; B. P. = 269°			
	30	65	100	185
20–101	72	90	112	184
20–203	70	86	106.5	173
20–304	68.5	83	101	161
20–405	67	81	96	149

t° / p_1, p_2	$C_{12}H_{11}N$, Diphenylamine. M. P. = 54°; B. P. = 310°			
	65	100	185	310
0–101	61	63	108	199
0–203	60	62	102	187
0–304	58	62	97	174
0–405	57	61	91	161
0–506.5	56	60	86	148

t° / p_1, p_2	$C_{16}H_{32}O_2$, Palmitic acid. M. P. = 62°; B. P. = 350°	
	100	185
20–101	98	150
20–203	94	142
20–304	90	135
20–405	87	127

Table 9.—Compressibilities According to Biron (6.5)

$v = a + \frac{c}{b + p}$, at 0°C. Pressure unit, the atm. Volume unit = v at 0°C and zero pressure. Author estimates error <0.0001.

Formula	Name	a	b	c	p_1, p_2
CCl_4	Carbon tetrachloride	0.80365	2264.0	444.54	0–314.3
CCl_4	Carbon tetrachloride	0.76862	2728.3	631.10	0–595.7
C_6H_5Cl	Chlorobenzene	0.76671	3625.5	845.78	0–486.4
C_6H_5Br	Bromobenzene	0.84855	2494.0	377.72	0–481.8
C_7H_8	Toluene	0.81950	2268.7	409.51	0–589.6
C_8H_{10}	Ethylbenzene	0.85745	1755.0	250.18	0–494.7
C_9H_{12}	Pseudocumene	0.83285	2408.0	402.50	0–596.0

LITERATURE

(For a key to the periodicals see end of volume)

(1) Aimé, *6*, **8**: 257; 1843. (2) Amagat, *6*, **11**: 520; 77. (3) Amagat, *6*, **29**: 68, 505; 93. (4) Amagat, *6*, **28**: 5; 13. (5) Bartoli, *72*, **28**: 1141; 95. *36*, **26 I**: 466; 96. (6) Barus, *12*, **39**: 478; 90. (6.5) Biron, *53*, **44**: 65; 12. (7) Bridgman, *65*, **59**: 173; 24. (8) Carnazzi, *59*, **9**: 161; 05. (9) Colladon and Sturm, *6*, **36**: 113; 1827.

(10) Dolezalek and Speidel, *7*, **94**: 72; 20. (11) Drecker, *8*, **20**: 870; 83. (12) Gay, *6*, **6**: 36; 16. (13) Hebeisen, *8*, **77**: 216; 25. (14) de Heen, *186*, **9**: 550; 85. (15) Hyde, *5*, **97**: 240; 20. (16) Jenkin, *5*, **98**: 170; 20. (17) de Metz, *8*, **41**: 663; 90. (18) Pagliani and Palazzo, *170*, **19**: 273; 84. (19) Protz, *8*, **31**: 127; 10.

(20) Richards, Bartlett and Hodges, *1*, **43**: 1538; 21. (21) Richards and Shipley, *1*, **38**: 989; 16. (22) Richards, Stull, Mathews and Speyers, *1*, **34**: 971; 12. (23) Richards and Stull, *1*, **26**: 399; 04. (24) Röntgen, *8*, **44**: 1; 91. (25) Suchodski, *7*, **74**: 257; 10. (26) Tyrer, *7*, **87**: 182; 14. (27) Young, *67*, **13**: 602; 95.

THE COMPRESSIBILITIES OF CERTAIN LIQUIDS

P. W. Bridgman

The values recorded below are the relative volumes in terms of the volume at 0° and 1 A_n. The values are nearly all taken from the papers of Bridgman, to which the reader is referred for additional literature references and for the methods by which the data of other observers have been incorporated into the final tables.

Les valeurs données ci-dessous sont les volumes relatifs par rapport au volume à 0° et sous 1 A_n. Les valeurs sont presque toutes tirées des mémoires de Bridgman auxquels le lecteur s'adressera pour connaitre les sources bibliographiques supplémentaires et les méthodes au moyen desquelles les valeurs d'autres observateurs ont été incorporées dans les tables finales.

Die unten angegebenen Werte sind relative Volumina, ausgedrückt in Volumen bei 0° und 1 A_n. Die Werte stammen beinahe alle aus den Arbeiten von Bridgman, wo weitere Literatur und die Methoden zu finden sind, nach welchen die Einfügung fremder Beobachtungen in die Endtabelle erfolgte.

I valori qui sotto riportati sono i volumi relativi, riferiti ai volumi a 0° e a 1 A_n. I valori provengono quasi tutti dai lavori di Bridgman, nei quali si trovano ulteriori notizie sulla letteratura, e la indicazione dei metodi seguiti per riunire i dati degli altri osservatori nelle tabelle finali.

The low temperature data of Seitz and Lechner (4) recorded below do not join smoothly with those of Bridgman at 0°.

Les données de Seitz et Lechner (4) relatives à de basses températures inscrites en bas ne s'accordent pas convenablement avec celles de Bridgman à 0°.

Die von Seitz und Lechner (4) für tiefe Temperaturen angegebenen Zahlen fügen sich denen von Bridgman bei 0° nicht glatt an.

I dati di Seitz e Lechner (4) per le temperature basse non si recollegano bene con quelli di Bridgman a 0°.

H_2O, Water (2)

P, atm.	−15°	−10°	−5°	0°	+10°	20°
0		1.0017	1.0006	**1.0000**	1.0001	1.0016
500	Freezes	0.9788	0.9776	0.9769	0.9778	0.9804
1 000		.9581	.9572	.9566	.9591	.9619
1 500	0.9386	.9399	.9391	.9286	.9424	.9456
2 000	.9215	.9223	.9233	.9223	.9277	.9712
2 500	.9073	.9083	.9096	.9080	.9147	.9183
3 000	.8949	.8962	.8975	.8954	.9028	.9065
3 500	.8840	.8852	.8865	.8842	.8919	.8956
4 000	.8742	.8751	.8763	.8739	.8818	.8855
4 500		.8658	.8670	.8648	.8725	.8762
5 000		.8573	.8585	.8565	.8639	.8675
5 500			.8509	.8491	.8558	.8593
6 000			.8438	.8423	.8481	.8517
6 500		Freezes	.8373	.8361	.8409	.8444
7 000					.8340	.8374
7 500					.8274	.8307
8 000						.8244
8 500						.8185
9 000						.8128
9 500						.8076
10 000						.8027

P, atm.	−20°
2 000	0.9208
2 500	.9064
3 000	.8941

P, atm.	30°	40°	50°	60°	70°	80°
0	1.0041	1.0076	1.0128	1.0168	1.0224	1.0287
500	0.9831	0.9867	0.9915	0.9967	1.0014	1.0071
1 000	.9652	.9689	.9732	.9780	0.9831	0.9884
1 500	.9492	.9529	.9571	.9617	.9667	.9717
2 000	.9347	.9386	.9428	.9472	.9521	.9568
2 500	.9200	.9257	.9300	.9343	.9390	.9437
3 000	.9083	.9139	.9183	.9225	.9270	.9315
3 500	.8974	.9030	.9074	.9115	.9159	.9203
4 000	.8872	.8931	.8974	.9012	.9055	.9097
4 500	.8779	.8838	.8880	.8919	.8959	.9001
5 000	.8692	.8752	.8792	.8832	.8869	.8913
5 500	.8611	.8671	.8710	.8750	.8790	.8830

H_2O, Water (2).—(*Continued*)

P, atm.	30°	40°	50°	60°	70°	80°
6 000	0.8535	0.8595	0.8634	0.8674	0.8713	0.8752
6 500	.8464	.8523	.8562	.8602	.8641	.8679
7 000	.8395	.8456	.8494	.8534	.8572	.8610
7 500	.8331	.8391	.8430	.8469	.8507	.8545
8 000	.8270	.8330	.8369	.8408	.8446	.8481
8 500	.8232	.8273	.8312	.8351	.8389	.8425
9 000	.8177	.8219	.8258	.8297	.8335	.8371
9 500	.8125	.8168	.8207	.8245	.8282	.8318
10 000	.8077	.8119	.8158	.8196	.8233	.8268
10 500	.8030	.8071	.8110	.8148	.8185	.8220
11 000		.8023	.8062	.8101	.8137	.8172
11 500		.7977	.8016	.8055	.8091	.8126
12 000		.7931	.7970	.8009	.8045	.8080

PCl_3, Phosphorus Trichloride (3)

P, atm.	20°	40°	60°	80°
1	1.0234	1.0485	1.0742	1.1039
500	0.9852	1.0029	1.0226	1.0443
1 000	.9577	0.9722	0.9880	1.0040
1 500	.9363	.9488	.9622	0.9758
2 000	.9184	.9297	.9414	.9531
2 500	.9034	.9135	.9242	.9347
3 000	.8902	.8997	.9096	.9192
3 500	.8784	.8873	.8967	.9053
4 000	.8679	.8763	.8853	.8933
4 500	.8585	.8664	.8750	.8825
5 000	.8499	.8574	.8657	.8728
6 000	.8348	.8418	.8494	.8561
7 000	.8218	.8285	.8353	.8420
8 000	.8105	.8167	.8230	.8292
9 000	.7999	.8057	.8120	.8179
10 000	.7902	.7957	.8020	.8077
11 000	.7816	.7867	.7930	.7983
12 000	.7741	.7789	.7849	.7898

CS_2, Carbon Disulfide (3, 4)

P, atm.	20°	40°	60°	80°
1	1.0235	1.0490	1.0774	1.1092
500	0.9854	1.0051	1.0243	1.0458
1 000	.9567	0.9734	0.9887	1.0061
1 500	.9338	.9483	.9615	0.9762
2 000	.9151	.9277	.9397	.9525
2 500	.8994	.9105	.9215	.9327
3 000	.8852	.8953	.9055	.9154
3 500	.8730	.8820	.8916	.9003
4 000	.8620	.8702	.8790	.8870
4 500	.8521	.8596	.8679	.8754
5 000	.8429	.8501	.8578	.8649
6 000	.8265	.8337	.8405	.8468
7 000	.8119	.8196	.8258	.8316
8 000	.7990	.8070	.8130	.8188
9 000	.7875	.7954	.8014	.8071
10 000	.7774	.7844	.7906	.7962
11 000	.7686	.7741	.7802	.7857
12 000	.7609	.7646	.7706	.7758

P, atm.	−100°	−80°	−60°	−40°	−20°	0°
1	0.8994	0.91815	0.93725	0.9571	0.97805	**1.0000**
500	.8830	.8992	.9155	.93225	.94955	0.96725
1 000		.88345	.8980	.9125	.9273	.9425

CH_3OH, Methyl Alcohol (3, 4)

P, atm.	20°	40°	60°	80°
1	1.0238	1.0483	1.0737	1.1005
500	0.9811	0.9987	1.0182	1.0400
1 000	.9494	.9651	0.9808	0.9993
1 500	.9256	.9393	.9526	.9672
2 000	.9064	.9189	.9306	.9429
2 500	.8906	.9019	.9124	.9231
3 000	.8763	.8870	.8966	.9065
3 500	.8636	.8733	.8824	.8915
4 000	.8523	.8613	.8700	.8782
4 500	.8420	.8505	.8587	.8663
5 000	.8325	.8407	.8487	.8559
6 000	.8163	.8240	.8314	.8381
7 000	.8023	.8099	.8163	.8231
8 000	.7907	.7973	.8039	.8102
9 000	.7797	.7859	.7920	.7981
10 000	.7696	.7756	.7816	.7875
11 000	.7605	.7664	.7728	.7785
12 000	.7527	.7587	.7652	.7709

P, atm.	−100°	−80°	−60°	−40°	−20°	0°
1	0.8939	0.91455	0.9352	0.9561	0.9775	**1.0000**
500	.8727	.8904	.9076	.92455	.9418	0.95955
1 000	.8556	.8713	.8865	.90115	.9159	.93085

C_2H_5Br, Ethyl Bromide (3)

P, atm.	20°	40°	60°	80°
1	1.0275	1.0578		
500	0.9776	0.9990		
1 000	.9460	.9624	0.9800	0.9988
1 500	.9216	.9358	.9492	.9626
2 000	.9022	.9151	.9268	.9381
2 500	.8857	.8981	.9088	.9187
3 000	.8714	.8830	.8931	.9020
3 500	.8590	.8697	.8791	.8873
4 000	.8479	.8577	.8666	.8742
4 500	.8380	.8469	.8554	.8625
5 000	.8289	.8372	.8453	.8519
6 000	.8131	.8206	.8276	.8339

C_2H_5Br, Ethyl Bromide (3).—(*Continued*)

P, atm.	20°	40°	60°	80°
7 000	0.7991	0.8064	0.8126	0.8189
8 000	.7868	.7937	.7995	.8056
9 000	.7756	.7820	.7879	.7935
10 000	.7656	.7715	.7775	.7825
11 000	.7568	.7623	.7685	.7730
12 000	.7495	.7546	.7606	.7648

C_2H_5Cl, Ethyl Chloride (3)

P, atm.	20°	40°	60°	80°
500	0.9696	0.9931	1.0179	1.0358
1 000	.9253	.9419	0.9618	0.9797
1 500	.8964	.9107	.9268	.9411
2 000	.8749	.8874	.9010	.9128
2 500	.8569	.8680	.8800	.8904
3 000	.8415	.8515	.8623	.8715
3 500	.8283	.8375	.8475	.8557
4 000	.8167	.8253	.8346	.8422
4 500	.8061	.8143	.8230	.8302
5 000	.7965	.8045	.8125	.8194
6 000	.7796	.7870	.7944	.8008
7 000	.7654	.7726	.7795	.7856
8 000	.7533	.7602	.7666	.7728
9 000	.7423	.7488	.7549	.7611
10 000	.7320	.7382	.7442	.7501
11 000	.7228	.7283	.7344	.7397
12 000	.7148	.7192	.7255	.7301

C_2H_5I, Ethyl Iodide (3)

P, atm.	20°	40°	60°	80°
1	1.0214	1.0438	1.0677	1.0935
500	0.9774	0.9958	1.0156	1.0351
1 000	.9475	.9640	0.9799	0.9946
1 500	.9257	.9390	.9521	.9637
2 000	.9070	.9188	.9298	.9397
2 500	.8913	.9020	.9114	.9202
3 000	.8777	.8873	.8956	.9034
3 500	.8659	.8744	.8819	.8886
4 000	.8555	.8632	.8698	.8760
4 500	.8460	.8530	.8593	.8651
5 000	.8370	.8439	.8500	.8551
6 000	.8207	.8277	.8336	.8381
7 000	.8063	.8135	.8189	.8232
8 000	.7937	.8007	.8057	.8099
9 000	.7825	.7891	.7938	.7981
10 000	.7725	.7785	.7832	.7877
11 000	.7635	.7691	.7742	.7786
12 000	.7554	.7608	.7664	.7706

C_2H_5OH, Ethyl Alcohol (3, 4)

P, atm.	20°	40°	60°	80°
1	1.0212	1.0438	1.0679	1.0934
500	0.9782	0.9943	1.0121	1.0319
1 000	.9479	.9608	0.9760	0.9922
1 500	.9247	.9358	.9482	.9615
2 000	.9059	.9159	.9266	.9380
2 500	.8899	.8991	.9088	.9187
3 000	.8760	.8848	.8935	.9025
3 500	.8634	.8718	.8800	.8884
4 000	.8517	.8599	.8678	.8756
4 500	.8410	.8491	.8567	.8640
5 000	.8314	.8394	.8467	.8536
6 000	.8149	.8225	.8291	.8354
7 000	.8009	.8080	.8139	.8196

C_2H_5OH, Ethyl Alcohol (3, 4).—(*Continued*)

P, atm.	20°	40°	60°	80°
8 000	0.7888	0.7953	0.8005	0.8061
9 000	.7776	.7836	.7884	.7940
10 000	.7671	.7726	.7776	.7830
11 000	.7574	.7626	.7682	.7734
12 000	.7485	.7535	.7600	.7648

P, atm.	−100°	−80°	−60°	−40°	−20°	0°
1	0.90215	0.9212	0.94035	0.9597	0.97945	**1.0000**
500	.8815	.89775	.91385	.92985	.9458	0.96205
1 000	.8652	.87935	.8935	.90765	.9216	.9356

C_3H_7OH, *n*-Propyl Alcohol (3)

P, atm.	20°	40°	60°	80°
1	1.0173	1.0390	1.0612	1.0865
500	0.9770	0.9936	1.0108	1.0305
1 000	.9483	.9624	0.9760	0.9913
1 500	.9280	.9396	.9513	.9634
2 000	.9124	.9222	.9322	.9424
2 500	.8991	.9079	.9167	.9258
3 000	.8876	.8957	.9039	.9120
3 500	.8773	.8849	.8925	.8999
4 000	.8677	.8752	.8824	.8893
4 500	.8588	.8664	.8732	.8796
5 000	.8507	.8582	.8647	.8706
6 000	.8365	.8436	.8495	.8548
7 000	.8243	.8308	.8365	.8414
8 000	.8138	.8196	.8249	.8301
9 000	.8043	.8096	.8148	.8203
10 000	.7958	.8010	.8058	.8114
11 000	.7883	.7931	.7976	.8031
12 000	.7814	.7858	.7899	.7952

C_4H_9OH, Isobutyl Alcohol (3)

P, atm.	20°	40°	60°	80°
1	1.0195	1.0406	1.0625	1.0880
500	0.9740	0.9909	1.0079	1.0262
1 000	.9470	.9601	0.9740	0.9883
1 500	.9253	.9366	.9484	.9607
2 000	.9078	.9180	.9280	.9385
2 500	.8929	.9020	.9111	.9203
3 000	.8798	.8880	.8968	.9052
3 500	.8680	.8756	.8840	.8919
4 000	.8575	.8647	.8728	.8802
4 500	.8480	.8550	.8630	.8697
5 000	.8494	.8462	.8540	.8602
6 000	.8242	.8307	.8375	.8433
7 000	.8113	.8178	.8242	.8298
8 000	.8001	.8065	.8126	.8181
9 000	.7898	.7961	.8021	.8075
10 000	.7802	.7864	.7923	.7976
11 000	.7712	.7773	.7832	.7884
12 000	.7631	.7691	.7750	.7799

LITERATURE

(For a key to the periodicals see end of volume)

(1) Bridgman, *65*, **47**: 345; 11. (2) Bridgman, *65*, **48**: 309; 12. (3) Bridgman, *65*, **49**: 3; 13. (4) Seitz and Lechner, *8*, **49**: 93; 16.

$C_5H_{11}OH$, Amyl Alcohol (3)

P, atm.	20°	40°	60°	80°
1	1.0181	1.0374	1.0583	1.0814
500	0.9788	0.9946	1.0108	1.0288
1 000	.9511	.9643	0.9773	0.9915
1 500	.9307	.9417	.9529	.9644
2 000	.9138	.9237	.9330	.9427
2 500	.8993	.9084	.9166	.9254
3 000	.8869	.8955	.9028	.9110
3 500	.8758	.8840	.8910	.8986
4 000	.8658	.8737	.8807	.8877
4 500	.8568	.8644	.8713	.8780
5 000	.8488	.8560	.8627	.8690
6 000	.8348	.8414	.8475	.8531
7 000	.8225	.8288	.8340	.8396
8 000	.8116	.8173	.8218	.8273
9 000	.8015	.8065	.8108	.8160
10 000	.7918	.7964	.8010	.8060
11 000	.7831	.7874	.7927	.7972
12 000	.7754	.7800	.7860	.7902

$(C_2H_5)_2O$, Ether (3, 4)

P, atm.	20°	40°	60°	80°
1	1.0315	1.0669		
500	0.9668	0.9884	1.0123	1.0369
1 000	.9337	.9498	0.9683	0.9874
1 500	.9070	.9195	.9336	.9484
2 000	.8850	.8952	.9069	.9189
2 500	.8663	.8756	.8860	.8962
3 000	.8503	.8594	.8688	.8776
3 500	.8366	.8454	.8539	.8620
4 000	.8246	.8329	.8407	.8481
4 500	.8139	.8218	.8292	.8360
5 000	.8044	.8121	.8189	.8252
6 000	.7883	.7953	.8017	.8070
7 000	.7743	.7806	.7865	.7917
8 000	.7613	.7670	.7725	.7779
9 000	.7492	.7545	.7597	.7652
10 000	.7380	.7431	.7482	.7535
11 000	.7275	.7325	.7377	.7427
12 000	.7178	.7225	.7280	.7326

P, atm.	−100°	−80°	−60°	−40°	−20°	0°
1	0.8750	0.8969	0.92015	0.94465	0.97105	**1.0000**
500	.85285	.87075	.8888	.90745	.9263	0.9464
1 000	.83565	.85085	.8660	.8812	.8964	.9126

$(CH_3)_2CO$, Acetone (3)

P, atm.	20°	40°	60°	80°
1	1.0279	1.0585	1.0925	
500	0.9818	1.0032	1.0282	
1 000	.9526	0.9706	0.9894	1.0082
1 500	.9286	.9441	.9594	0.9736
2 000	.9076	.9217	.9347	.9467
2 500	.8900	.9028	.9141	.9253
3 000	.8748	.8868	.8968	.9073
3 500	.8619	.8729	.8821	.8920
4 000	.8504	.8607	.8694	.8786
4 500	.8402	.8498	.8583	.8666
5 000	.8309	.8398	.8482	.8558
6 000	.8143	.8225	.8306	.8370
7 000	.7997	.8072	.8148	.8209
8 000	.7866	.7935	.8003	.8066
9 000		.7815	.7876	.7939
10 000		.7707	.7764	.7821
11 000	Freezes	.7607	.7665	.7715
12 000		.7515	.7577	.7617

DENSITY AND THERMAL EXPANSION OF CHEMICAL COMPOUNDS IN THE CRYSTALLINE STATE, UNDER ATMOSPHERIC PRESSURE

J. R. Clarke

I. Inorganic Compounds (𝔅-Table)

This section includes only substances for which density values reliable to four decimal places, or values over a temperature range, are available. For less accurate values at individual temperatures, *v.* Vol. I, p. 106.

Symbols and Abbreviations

The quantities recorded in the table below are the following:

$\alpha^t = \frac{10^6}{l}\frac{dl}{dt}$ at $t°$; or $\alpha = \frac{10^6 \Delta l}{l \Delta t}$ over the range $\Delta t°$.

$\Delta = 10^9 \frac{d\alpha}{dt}\left(\text{resp. } 10^9 \frac{\Delta\alpha}{\Delta t}\right)$, *i.e.*, $10^9 \times$ the rate of change of α with t, at $t°$ (resp. over $\Delta t°$).

d_4^t = the density in g/ml at $t°$ = the specific gravity at $t°$ referred to H_2O at 4°C.

d_4^0, a, b and c, = the parameters of the equation: $d_4^t = d_4^0(1 - 10^{-5}at - 10^{-7}bt^2 - 10^{-9}ct^3)$, valid over the range indicated; b and c are zero when not given.

Arrangement

The compounds are arranged in groups, as follows: I. Oxides; II. Halogen compounds in the order, F, Cl, Br, I; III. Sulfides; IV. Sulfates; V. Nitrates; VI. Carbonates; VII. Metallo-organic compounds; VIII. Various silicates; IX. Other compounds. For organic compounds, *v.* the ℭ-Table, p. 45.

I. OXIDES

H_2O	$d_4^0 = 0.9168 \pm 0.0005$;* For α *see* Fig. 1
H_2O_2	$d_4^{-6} = 1.6436$ (36)
As_2O_3	$d_4^0 = 3.873$, a = 12 (0°–50°) (5); $\alpha^{40} = 41.26$, $\Delta(20°–70°) = 67.9$ (17, 18, 33)
Sb_2O_3: Senarmontite	$\alpha^{40} = 19.63$, $\Delta(20°–70°) = 5.7$ (17, 18, 33)
CO_2	see table below (35.5)
SiO_2	*v.* Vol. IV, p. 19.
TiO_2: Brookite	Values of $\alpha^{17.5}$ ∥ a, b and c axes (a) 14.4939, (b) 19.2029, (c) 22.0489 (44)
Anatase	$\alpha^{40} = 8.19$ ∥, = 4.68 ⊥; and $\Delta(20°–70°) = 31.1$ ∥, = 29.5 ⊥ to opt. axis (33); *cf.* (44)
Rutile	$\alpha^{40} = 7.14$ ⊥, = 9.19 ∥; $\Delta(20°–70°) = 11.0$ ⊥, = 22.5 ∥ to principal axis (17, 18, 33); *cf.* (44)
ZrO_2	(36.5)
SnO_2: Cassiterite	$\alpha^{40} = 3.2$ ⊥, = 3.9 ∥; $\Delta(20°–70°) = 7.6$ ⊥, = 12 ∥ to principal axis (17, 18, 33)
PbO_2	$\alpha(25°–93°) = 7.9 \pm 0.6$ (39)
ThO_2	(36.5)
ZnO: Zincite	$\alpha^{40} = 3.2$ ⊥, = 3.9 ∥; $\Delta(20°–70°) = 7.6$ ⊥, = 12 ∥ to principal axis (17, 18, 33)
Cu_2O: Cuprite	$\alpha^{40} = 0.93$, $\Delta(20°–70°) = 21$. $d_{max.}$ at −43°C (15, 16, 17, 18, 21, 22, 33); *cf.* (43)
Fe_2O_3: Hematite	$\alpha^{40} = 7.61$ ∥ = 7.71 ⊥; $\Delta(5°–80°) = 4.90$ ∥, = 11.4 ⊥ to opt. axis. (3); *cf.* (17, 18, 33)
Fe_3O_4: Magnetite	$\alpha^{40} = 8.46$, $\Delta = 28.9$ (14, 33)
(Fe, Zn, Mn) O.Fe_2O_3: Franklinite	$\alpha^{40} = 8.1$, $\Delta(20°–70°) = 9.4$ (14, 33)
Al_2O_3: Corundum	$\alpha^{40} = 6.2$ ∥; = 5.4 ⊥; and $\Delta(20°–70°) = 20.5$ ∥; = 22.5 ⊥ to principal axis. (14, 16, 33); *cf.* (Vol. II, p. 87)
Al_2O_3.ZnO: Gahnite	$\alpha^{40} = 5.95$, $\Delta(20°–70°) = 18.3$ (14, 15, 16, 33)
$5Al_2O_3.2FeO.4SiO_2.H_2O$: Staurolite	$\alpha^{40} = 7.08$, $\Delta = 31.5$ (14)

CO_2 (35.5):

t, °C	−80	−90	−100	−110	−120	−130	−183
d_4^t	1.565	1.581	1.594	1.607	1.618	1.627	1.665

* Estimate by Howard T. Barnes on basis of critical examination of all available data. For discussion and bibliography *see* (3.5) and his forthcoming book on *The Physics of Ice*.

(Zn, Fe)O.(Al, Fe)$_2$O$_3$: Kreittonite	$\alpha^{40} = 5.96$, $\Delta(20°–70°) = 19.4$ (15, 16, 33)
Al_2O_3.BeO: Chrysoberyl	see table below
MgO	(Prefused) $\alpha = 11.40 + 9.2(t - 120)$, 120° to 270° (24)
Periclase	$\alpha^{40} = 10.43$, $\Delta(20°–70°) = 26.7$ (15, 16, 33)
MgO.Al_2O_3: Spinel	$\alpha^{40} = 5.93$, $\Delta(20°–70°) = 19.5$ (15, 16, 33)
(Mg, Fe)O.Al_2O_3: Pleonaste	$\alpha^{40} = 6.03$, $\Delta(20°–70°) = 19.7$ (15, 16, 33)

Al_2O_3.BeO: Chrysoberyl:

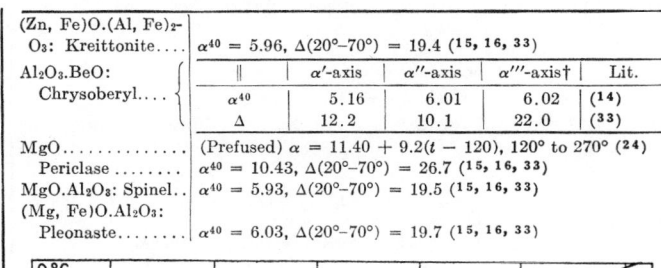

∥	α'-axis	α''-axis	α'''-axis†	Lit.
α^{40}	5.16	6.01	6.02	(14)
Δ	12.2	10.1	22.0	(33)

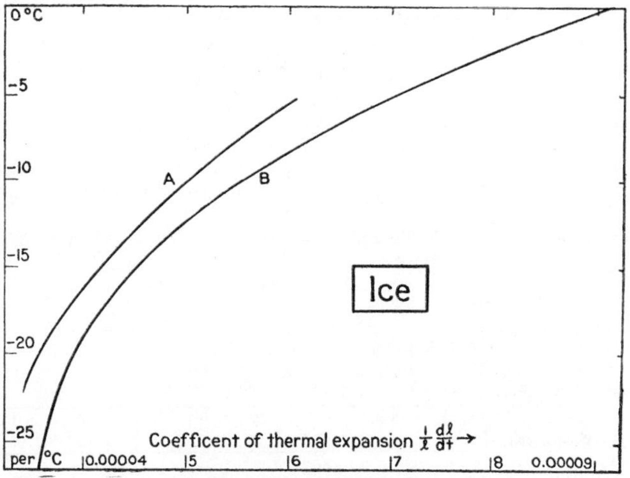

Fig. 1.—Curve A from Sawyer(43.5), *Proc. Marine Soc. Civil Eng.*, **1**: 27; 11. Curve B from Andrews(2.5), 5, **40**: 544; 86.

II. HALOGEN COMPOUNDS

CaF_2: Fluorite (54, 55): $\alpha(50°–60°) = 5.734$ (40); $\alpha^{52} = 19.34$ (56); $\alpha^{40} = 19.11$ and $\Delta(20°–70°) = 28.8$ (21, 22, 33)

T, °K	α
265.7	18.53
255.6	17.58
231.4	16.78
209.8	16.04
186.9	14.65
156.3	13.02
124.9	10.26
94.4	7.17

NH_4Cl	$d_4^{20} = 1.5256$ (26). $\alpha^{40} = 62.55$ and $\Delta(20°–70°) = 297.5$ (19, 20, 33)
$PbCl_2$	(Prefused) $d_4^0 = 5.899$, a = 8.8 (0°–50°) (5); *cf.* (47)
AgCl	$\alpha^{40} = 32.94$, $\Delta(20°–70°) = 122.8$ (19, 20, 33)
$PrCl_3$	$d_4^{25} = 4.0203$ (5)
$MgCl_2.6H_2O$	$d_4^4 = 1.5907$ (28)
$CaCl_2.6H_2O$	$d_4^4 = 1.7182$ (28)
$CaCl_2.2MgCl_2.6H_2O$	$d_4^4 = 1.6655$ (28)
LiCl	$d_4^{20} = 2.0678$ (26)
NaCl	$d_4^0 = 2.1680$, a = 11.2, b = 0.5 (−184° to 50°) (6, 7, 12, 27, 45); *cf.* (19, 20, 33, 40); α (20° to 80°K) = 10.8 (34)
KCl	$d_4^0 = 1.9920$, a = 10.5, b = 0.4 (−184° to 70°) (27); *cf.* (19, 20, 33, 40). $d_4^{30} = 1.9786$ (large crys.) = 1.9841 (small crys.) (29, 30)
RbCl	$d_4^0 = 2.8057$, a = 12.6, b = −6 (0°–50°) (6)
CsCl	$d_4^0 = 3.9887$, a = 15.9, b = −4 (0°–70°) (6)
$KClO_3$	$d_4^0 = 2.3467$, a = 18, b = −3 (0°–44°) (2)
$LiClO_4$	$d_4^{25} = 2.4284$ (42)
$PbBr_2$	$d_4^0 = 6.676$, a = 9.5, (0°–50°) (5)
AgBr	$\alpha^{40} = 34.7$, $\Delta(20°–70°) = 38.8$ (19, 20, 33)
$CaBr_2$	$d_4^{20} = 3.3535$ (41)
NaBr	$d_4^0 = 3.213$, a = 12, b = 0.3 (−184° to 50°) (6, 27)

† α' along bisector of acute angle, α'' along bisector of obtuse angle formed by optic axes, α''' along the normal to the plane of optic axes.

KBr: d_4^0 = 2.756, a = 11.4, b = 0.45 (−184° to 50°) [6, 27], *cf.* [19, 20, 33]

RbBr: d_4^0 = 3.358, a = 11 (0°–50°) [6]

CsBr: d_4^0 = 4.449, a = 14 (0°–50°) [6]

PbI_2: α^{40} = 33.6, Δ(20°–70°) = 58.4 [19, 20]

CdI_2: α^{40} = 29.16, Δ(20°–70°) = 175 [19, 20]

HgI_2: α^{40} = 2.39, Δ(20°–70°) = 200 [19, 20]

AgI: α^{40} = −3.97 ‖; = 0.65 ⊥; and Δ = −42.7 ‖; = 13.8 ⊥ principal axis [19, 20, 31, 33]

NaI: d_4^0 = 3.665, a = 13.55 (0°–50°) [4, 6]; d_4^0 = 3.6587, a = 14.1, b = 2.1 (−184° to 0°) [27]; a = 12.7 (−79° to 0°) [27]

KI: d_4^0 = 3.133, a = 12.6, b = −2.5 (0°–50°) [6]; d_4^0 = 3.1265, a = 12.7, b = 0.4 (−184° to 20°) [27]; a = 11.5 (−79° to 0°) [27]; α^{40} = 42.65, Δ(20°–70°) = 167.6 [19, 20, 33]

RbI: d_4^0 = 3.560, a = 12, b = −4.5 (0°–50°) [6]

CsI: d_4^0 = 4.525, a = 14.6 (0°–50°) [6]

III. SULFIDES

Sb_2S_3: Stibnite: α^{40} = 1.53, Δ(20°–70°) = 21.9 [14]

CS_2: $d_4^{-115.7}$ = 1.5539 [32]

PbS: Galena: α^{40} = 20.14, Δ(20°–70°) = 5.4 [21, 22, 33]

ZnS: Sphalerite: α^{40} = 6.70, Δ(20°–70°) = 12.8 [9, 33]

HgS: Cinnabarite: α^{40} = 21.5‖; Δ(20°–70°) = 15 and α^{40} = 17.9⊥; Δ = 6.3 [9, 33]; Red sublimed: d_4^t = 8.203, a = 42, b = −33 (16°–78°) [46]; Black sublimed: d_4^{17} = 8.0395 [46]

$3Ag_2S.Sb_2S_3$: Pyrargyrite: α^{40} = 0.91‖; Δ(20°–70°) = 105 and α^{40} = 20.1, ⊥; Δ = −23.1 [14, 33]

MnS: Alabandite: α^{40} = 15.2, Δ(20°–70°) = 21.7 [14, 33]

MnS_2: Hauerite: α^{40} = 11.1, Δ(20°–70°) = 88.9 [14, 33]

FeS_2: Pyrite [54, 55]:

°K	268.7	237.4	214.8	155.0	129.7	108.0
α	8.43	7.73	7.09	5.16	3.92	2.95

Also, α^{40} = 9.1 and Δ(20°–70°) = 18 [21, 22, 33]

Pyrrhotite: Fe_5S_6 to $Fe_{16}S_{17}$:

α^{40}	Δ(20°–70°)	Lit.
2.35‖	86.4‖	[14, 33]
31.20⊥	−16.5⊥	

$CuFeS_2$: Chalcopyrite: α^{40} = 17.1, Δ(20°–70°) = 17 [14]

$NiS_2.NiSb_2$: Ullmannite: α^{40} = 11.12, Δ(20°–70°) = −1.5 [14, 33]

(Fe, Co, Ni)S_2 (Co-Ni-pyrite): Kobaltnickelkies: α^{40} = 10.4, Δ(20°–70°) = 15.9 [14, 33]

$5Cu_2S.2(Cu, Fe)S.2Sb_2O_3$: Tetrahedrite: Three samples [14, 33]:

α^{40} =	9.22	8.71	7.33
Δ(20°–70°) =	20.7	22.5	23.4

IV. SULFATES

$(NH_4)_2SO_4$: d_4^{30} = 1.7637 [29] = 1.7716 [52] = 1.7681 [50]

$Sb_2(SO_4)_3$: d_4^4 = 3.6246 [37]

$(NH_4)_2Sb_2(SO_4)_4$: d_4^4 = 3.0948 [37]

$ZnSO_4$: $d_4^{16.2}$ = 1.9661 [1]

$CuSO_4.5H_2O$: d_4^t = 2.2895, a = 9.6 (15°–45°) [1]

$MnSO_4.5H_2O$: $d_4^{14.5}$ = 2.1996 [1]

$FeSO_4.7H_2O$: $d_4^{14.4}$ = 1.8988, $d_4^{37.6}$ = 1.8959 [1]

$MgSO_4.7H_2O$: d_4^t = 1.6812, a = 12 (14°–32°) [1, 2]

$CaSO_4.2H_2O$: Gypsum: α_1^{40} = 41.63 with Δ(20°–70°) = 93.6 ‖ b-axis; α_2^{40} = 1.57, α_3^{40} = 29.33 ‖ to the other two axes of the thermal ellipsoid [21, 22]

$SrSO_4$: α^{40} = 52.62, Δ(20°–70°) = 34.5 [14]

$BaSO_4$: Barite: α^{40} = 54.18, Δ(20°–70°) = 28.5 [14]; d_4^{15} = 4.4662 [10]

$Na_2SO_4.10H_2O$: d_4^t = 1.4697, a = 14, b = −15 (0°–24°) [2]

$Na_2Sb_2(SO_4)_4$: d_4^4 = 3.2298 [37]

K_2SO_4: d_4^{30} = 2.6563 (large crys.); = 2.6574 (small crys.) [29, 30]; d_4^t = 2.6673, a = 10.5, b = 0.7 (20°–60°) [1, 2]

‖	α(0° to 96°) [48, 49]
a-axis	36.16 + 0.0144t
b-axis	32.25 + 0.0141t
c-axis	36.34 + 0.0413t

$K_2Sb_2(SO_4)_4$: d_4^4 = 3.3396 [37]

$K_2Zn(SO_4)_2.6H_2O$: d_4^{20} = 2.2458 [51]

$KAl(SO_4)_2.12H_2O$: Alum. d_4^t = 1.7541, a = 3.8 (13°–56°) [1]

$K_2Mg(SO_4)_2.6H_2O$: d_4^{20} = 2.0337 [51]

Rb_2SO_4: Values of α (0° to 96°), ‖ the three axes [48, 49]

a-axis	33.85 + 0.0214t
b-axis	31.95 + 0.0182t
c-axis	35.90 + 0.0414t

$Rb_2Zn(SO_4)_2.6H_2O$: d_4^{20} = 2.5905 [51]

$Rb_2Mg(SO_4)_2.6H_2O$: d_4^{20} = 2.3859 [51]

$Cs_2Zn(SO_4)_2.6H_2O$: d_4^{20} = 2.8753 [51]

$Cs_2Mg(SO_4)_2.6H_2O$: d_4^{20} = 2.6760 [51]

V. NITRATES

$TlNO_3$: Values for three crystal forms [8]

Form	$t_{Tr.}$	d_0^t	a	b	Range
I	73°	5.5767	17.3	4.2	0°– 70°
II	142.5°	5.5393	11.6	5.5	81°–142°
III		5.5812	35.3	−0.48	144°–200°

$AgNO_3$: Prefused: α(20° to 150°) = 77 [25]

$LiNO_3$: d_4^{20} = 2.3658 [26]

$NaNO_3$: d_4^0 = 2.2663, a = 12 (0°–45°) [2]

KNO_3: d_4^0 = 2.1126, a = 18.1, b = 2.56 (0°–50°) [2]; d_4^0 = 2.1106, a = 18.1, b = 2.56 (0°–122°) [8]; d_4^0 = 2.1106, a = 28.06 (130°–155°) [8]; $t_{Tr.}$ at 127.8°C

$RbNO_3$: d_4^{20} = 3.1119 [26]; d_4^0 = 3.1063, a = 19.3, b = 2.58, c = −0.5 (0°–158°); $t_{Tr.}$ = 161.4°C; Form II, d_4^0 = 3.0979, a = 27.5, b = 2.23 (164°–219°) [8]

$CsNO_3$: d_4^{20} = 3.6432 [26]; d_4^0 = 3.6524, a = 20.5, b = −2.1, c = 1.62 (0°–134°); $t_{Tr.}$ = 151°C; Form II, d_4^0 = 3.6479, a = 28 (151°–172°) [8]

VI. CARBONATES

$2CuCO_3.Cu(OH)_2$: Azurite: α_1^{40} = 12.59 with Δ(20°–70°) = 20.3; α_2^{40} = 20.8; α_3^{40} = −0.98 [21, 22, 23]*

$FeCO_3$: Siderite: α^{40} = 19.2 with Δ(20°–70°) = 25.5 ‖; and α^{40} = 6.05 with Δ(20°–70°) = 917 ⊥ [14, 33]

$MgCO_3$: Magnesite: α^{40} = 21.3 with Δ(20°–70°) = 33.9‖; and α^{40} = 5.99 with Δ(20°–70°) = 24.3⊥ [14, 33]

$CaCO_3$: Calcite: d_4^0 = 2.7710, d_4^{20} = 2.7102 [12]; α(2° to 81°) = 25.1353 + 0.0118t, ‖ opt. axis; and = −5.5782 + 0.00138t, ⊥ opt. axis [9]; α^{40} = 26.21 + 0.0160(t − 40), ‖ opt. axis; and = −5.40 + 0.0087(t − 40), ⊥ opt. axis [21, 22, 23]; a(50° to 60°) = 1.447 [40]

$CaCO_3$: Aragonite: 20°–70°: α_1^{40} = 34.60 + 0.0337t; α_2^{40} = 17.19 + 0.0368t; α_3^{40} = 10.16 + 0.0064t [21, 22, 33]†

$CaMg(CO_3)_2$: Dolomite: α^{40} = 20.60 with Δ(20°–70°) = 36.8 ‖; α^{40} = 4.15 with Δ(20°–70°) = 19.3 ⊥ [33]

K_2CO_3: d_4^{15} = 2.3296 [10]

VII. METALLO-ORGANIC COMPOUNDS

$Sn(C_6H_5)_4$: d_4^t = 1.4922, a = 20, (5°–38°) [11]

$Sn_2(C_6H_5)_6$: $d_4^{13.9}$ = 1.5147, $d_4^{35.7}$ = 1.5098 [11]

$Sn_5(C_6H_5)_{12}$: $d_4^{22.8}$ = 1.6088, $d_4^{44.1}$ = 1.5967 [11]

$ISn(C_6H_5)_3$: $d_4^{30.0}$ = 1.7617, $d_4^{1.6}$ = 1.7665 [11]

$KNaC_4H_4O_6.4H_2O$: Rochelle salt: −10° to +20°: α_1 = 59.9, α_2 = 38.1, α_3 = 44.8 [53]

VIII. VARIOUS SILICATES

$ZrSiO_4$: Zircon: α^{40} = 4.43 with Δ(20°–70°) = 14.1 ‖; α^{40} = 2.33 with Δ(20°–70°) = 19.1 ⊥ [21, 22, 33]

$(AlF)_2SiO_4$: Topaz:

	α_1	α_2	α_3†	Lit.
α^{40}	5.92	4.84	4.44	[9, 21, 22, 33]
Δ(20°–70°)	18.3	15.3	16.8	

$3MnO.Al_2O_3.3SiO_2$: Spessartite: α^{40} = 8.24, Δ(20°–70°) = 21.4 [33]

$3FeO.Al_2O_3.3SiO_2$: Almandite	$\alpha^{40} = 8.37$, $\Delta(20°–70°) = 18.0$ (33)
$HNaAl_3BSi_2O_{11}$: Tourmaline	6° to 320°: ∥ opt. axis, $\alpha = 8.624$, $\Delta(20°–70°) = 5.625$; ⊥ opt. axis, $\alpha = 3.583$, $\Delta(20°–70°) = 4.490$ (35) $\alpha^{40} = 9.05$, with $\Delta(20°–70°) = 32.0$ ∥ $\alpha^{40} = 3.79$, with $\Delta(20°–70°) = 18.3$ ⊥ (33)

Compound					Lit.
$2BeO.SiO_2$: Phenacite	α^{40}	3.79 ∥	2.99 ⊥		(14)
	$\Delta(20°–70°)$	21.3 ∥	23.0 ⊥		

$Be_3Al_2(SiO_3)_6$: Beryl	∥ opt. axis, $\alpha^{40} = -1.348$, $\Delta(2°–80°) = 4.12$ ⊥ opt. axis, $\alpha^{40} = 1.0025$, $\Delta(2°–80°) = 4.57$ $\alpha^{40} = -1.06$ ∥; $= 1.37$ ⊥ (15, 16, 21, 22, 33)
$MgAl_2(SiO_4)_3$: Pyrope	$\alpha^{40} = 8.27$, $\Delta(20°–70°) = 21.0$ (33)

$3CaO.Fe_2O_3.3SiO_2$ (Andradite):

Melanite	α^{40}	7.34	7.36		2 specimens	(33)
	$\Delta(20°–70°)$	14.3	17.4			
Aplome	α^{40}	7.43	7.45		2 specimens	(33)
	$\Delta(20°–70°)$	7.0	17.8			
$3CaO.Al_2O_3.3SiO_2$: Grossularite	α^{40}	6.93	6.93	6.84	3 specimens	(33)
	$\Delta(20°–70°)$	18.7	16.0	16.0		
$Ca_6(AlOHF)Al_2(SiO_4)_5$: Vesuvianite	α^{40}	7.40 ∥	8.39 ⊥			(9, 33)
	$\Delta(20°–70°)$	17.4 ∥	16.7 ⊥			

$HCa_2(Al, Fe)_3Si_3O_{13}$: Epidote	α_1^{40} ∥ b-axis $= 9.13$, $\Delta(20°–70°) = 25.5$ (21, 22, 33)* $\alpha_2^{40} = 3.34$; $\alpha_3^{40} = 10.86$
$KAlSi_3O_8$: Adularia	$\alpha_1^{40} = -2.01$, $\Delta(20°–70°) = 13$ (21, 22, 33) $\alpha_2^{40} = 19.06$; $\alpha_3^{40} = -1.50$

IX. OTHER COMPOUNDS

$CoAs_2$: Smaltite	$\alpha^{40} = 9.19$, $\Delta(20°–70°) = 16.4$ (9, 33)
CoS_2CoAs_2: Cobaltite	$\alpha^{40} = 9.19$, $\Delta(20°–70°) = 17.0$ (9, 33)
$(NH_4)_2Cr_2O_7$	$d_4^{25} = 2.1600$ (38)
$6MgO.MgCl_2.8B_2O_3$: Boracite	$\alpha^{40} = 3.91$, $\Delta(20°–70°) = 16.9$ (14, 33)
K_2CrO_4	$d_4^{18.6} = 2.7320$, $d_4^{56.6} = 2.7216$ (1)
SiC: Carborundum	$l_t = l_0(1 + 2.118 \times 10^{-6}t + 2.741 \times 10^{-9}t^2)$ ([illegible]) (57)

* α_1 along b-axis, α_2, α_3 along other two axes of the thermal ellipsoid.

† α_1 along bisector of acute <; α_2 along bisector of obtuse <; α_3 along normal to plane containing optic axes.

LITERATURE

(For a key to the periodicals see end of volume)

(1) Andreae, *7*, **76**: 491; 11. (2) Andreae, *7*, **82**: 109; 13. (3) Bäckström, *388*, **51**: 545; 94. (3.5) Barnes, *69*, **3 III**: 3; 09. (4) Baxter and Brink, *1*, **30**: 46; 08. (5) Baxter and Hawkins, *1*, **38**: 266; 16. (6) Baxter and Wallace, *1*, **38**: 259; 16. (7) Bedson and Williams, *25*, **14**: 2556; 81. (8) Bellati and Finazzi, *24*, **69 II**: 1151; 10. (9) Benoît, *238*, **6**; 88.

(10) Berkeley, *4*, **91**: 56; 07. (11) Böeseken and Rutgers, *70*, **42**: 1017; 23. (12) DeFoe and Compton, *2*, **25**: 618; 25. (13) Ditte, *34*, **85**: 1069; 77. (14) Fizeau, *Annuaire pour l'an 1888* (Paris, Bureau des longitudes). (15) Fizeau, *8*, **126**: 611; 65. (16) Fizeau, *34*, **60**: 1161; 65. (17) Fizeau, *8*, **128**: 564; 66. (18) Fizeau, *34*, **62**: 1101, 1133; 66. (19) Fizeau, *8*, **132**: 292; 67.

(20) Fizeau, *34*, **64**: 314; 771; 67. (21) Fizeau, *8*, **135**: 372; 68. (22) Fizeau, *34*, **66**: 1005, 1072; 68. (23) Geiss, *8*, **76**: 403; 25. (24) Goodwin and Mailey, *78*, **9**: 89; 06. (25) Guinchant, *34*, **149**: 569; 09. (26) Haigh, *1*, **34**: 1137; 12. (27) Henglein, *7*, **115**: 91; 25. (28) van't Hoff, Kenrick and Dawson, *7*, **39**: 27; 01. (29) Johnston and Adams, *1*, **34**: 563; 12.

(30) Johnston and Adams, *93*, **76**: 274; 12. (31) Jones, *1*, **31**: 191; 09. (32) Körber, *8*, **37**: 1014; 12. (33) Liebisch, *Physikalische Kristallographie*, p. 92 (Leipzig, Veit) 1891. (34) Lindemann, *63*, **13**: 737; 12. (35) Lindman, *426*, **46**: No. 6; 16. *427*, **2**: 709; 21. (35.5) Maass and Barnes, *5*, **111**: 224; 26. (36) Maass and Hatcher, *1*, **42**: 2548; 20. (36.5) Merritt, *78*, **50**: Preprint; 26. (37) Metzl, *93*, **48**: 140; 06. (38) Moles and González, *132*, **21**: 204; 23. (39) Palmaer, *9*, **29**: 415; 23.

(40) Pulfrich, *8*, **45**: 609; 92. (41) Richards and Hönigschmid, *1*, **32**: 1577; 10. (42) Richards and Willard, *1*, **32**: 4; 10. (43) Röntgen, *213*, **1912**: 381. (44) Schrauf, *94*, **9**: 433; 84. (45) Spangenberg, *94*, **57**: 494; 23. (46) Spring, *93*, **7**: 371; 94. (47) Timofejew, *7*, **78**: 299; 11. (48) Tutton, *62*, **192**: 455; 99. (49) Tutton, *94*, **31**: 426; 99.

(50) Tutton, *94*, **38**: 602; 04. (51) Tutton, *94*, **41**: 321; 05. (52) Tutton, *94*, **41**: 381; 05. (53) Valasek, *2*, **20**: 639; 22. (54) Valentiner and Wallot, *88*, **16**: 757; 14. (55) Valentiner and Wallot, *8*, **46**: 837; 15. (56) Weidmann, *8*, **38**: 453; 89. (57) Weigel, *188*, **1915**: 309.

DENSITY AND THERMAL EXPANSION OF ORGANIC COMPOUNDS IN THE CRYSTALLINE STATE

J. S. Clark

This section includes only substances for which density values reliable to four decimals or values over a temperature range are available. For less accurate values at individual temperatures *v.* Vol. I, p. 176.

ℭ-TABLE

Formula	Name	M. P., °C	d_4^t	t, °C	Lit.
CHI_3	Iodoform		4.4459	−188	(1)
			4.1955	+ 17	(1)
CH_4N_2O	Urea		1.3617	−188	(1)
			1.3190	+ 17	(1)
CH_4O	Methyl alcohol	− 94.9	0.9673	− 94.9	(3)
$C_2H_3Cl_3O_2$	Chloral hydrate		1.9744	−188	(1)
			1.9151	+ 17	(1)
C_2H_5Br	Ethyl bromide	−125.5	1.8832	−125.5	(3)
C_2H_5I	Ethyl iodide	−118	2.4046	−118	(3)
$C_2H_6O_6$	Oxalic acid dihydrate		1.7024	−188	(1)
			1.6145	+ 17	(1)
C_3H_6O	Acetone	− 99	0.9686	− 99	(3)
$C_4H_6O_4$	Dimethyl oxalate		1.5278	−188	(1)
			1.4260	+ 17	(1)
$C_4H_{10}O$	Ethyl ether	−117.6	0.9212	−117.6	(3)
$C_6H_5NO_2$	Nitrobenzene	8.7	1.2229	0.0	(8)
$C_6H_{12}O_5$	Quercitol	225	1.5845	13	(7)
$C_6H_{12}O_6$	Glucose		1.5620	18	(9)
$C_8H_6O_2$	Phthalide (stable form)		1.4084	17.5	(5)
			1.4051	30.0	(5)
			1.3990	44.1	(5)
$C_8H_{16}O_2$	Octoic acid	16.2	1.0326	10	(2)
			1.0274	15	(2)
$C_9H_{18}O_2$	Nonoic acid	12.3	0.9952	5	(2)
			0.9916	10	(2)
$C_{10}H_8$	Naphthalene		1.2355	−188	(1)
			1.1589	+ 17	(1)
$C_{10}H_{14}O$	Thymol	51.5	0.9689	24.4	(6)
$C_{10}H_{20}O_2$	*n*-Capric acid	31.2	1.0266	15	(2)
			1.0176	25	(2)
$C_{11}H_{22}O_2$	Undecylic acid	28.25	1.0431	0.12	(2)
			1.0373	10	(2)
			0.9948	20	(2)
			0.9905	25	(2)
$C_{12}H_{22}O_{11}$	Sucrose		1.5877	18	(9)
$C_{12}H_{24}O_2$	Lauric acid	43.75	1.0099	35	(2)
			1.0055	40	(2)
$C_{12}H_{28}ClN$	Tetrapropylammonium chloride		1.0334	3	(4)
			1.0296	13	(4)

The values from (2) are densities in air. Information on this point is lacking for the other values in the table.

LITERATURE

(For a key to the periodicals see end of volume)

(1) Dewar, *135*, **91**: 216; 05. (2) Garner and Ryder, *4*, **127**: 720; 25. (3) Körber, *8*, **37**: 1014; 12. (4) M'David, *68*, **30**: 515; 10. (5) Müller, *7*, **86**: 177; 13. (6) Nasini and Bernheimer, *36*, **15**: 59; 85. (7) Prunier, *34*, **85**: 808; 77. (8) Timmermans, *64V*, **13**: 508; 10. (9) Varga, *Diss.*, Budapest, 1911.

COMPRESSIBILITY OF CRYSTALS

P. W. Bridgman

1. NON-METALLIC ELEMENTARY SUBSTANCES

$$\beta = \frac{10^6}{V_1} \times \frac{V_1 - V_2}{P_2 - P_1} \text{ per atm.}$$

C, diamond. $\beta = 0.16$, room temp., 4000–10 000 atm. (1).

H, hydrogen. Density of solid at −259.9° and 14 500 atm. > 0.1301. 0.1301 × 0.58 = density of liquid at −259.9° and 1 atm. Whence, for solid hydrogen, $\beta > 29$ (2).

I, iodine. $\beta = 13.2$, 20°C, 100–500 atm. (3).

P, red phosphorus. $\beta = 9.3$, 20°C, 100–500 atm. (3).

P, white phosphorus. $\beta = 20.8$, 20°C, 100–500 atm. (3).

S, sulfur. $\beta = 13.1$, 20°C, 100–500 atm. (3).

LITERATURE

(For a key to the periodicals see end of volume)

(1) Adams, *128*, **11**: 45; 21. (2) Bridgman, *65*, **59**: 173; 24. (3) Richards, *1*, **37**: 1643; 15.

COMPRESSIBILITY OF PURE METALS

W. Rosenhain, Special Editor

C. Benedicks (CB); C. H. Desch (CHD); D. Hanson (DH); C. H. M. Jenkins (CHMJ); P. D. Merica (PDM); T. K. Rose (TKR); P. W. Bridgman (PWB)*

Linear compressibility, $\varphi = -\frac{1}{l_0}\frac{\partial l}{\partial P}$.

Cubic compressibility, $\beta = -\frac{1}{V_0}\frac{\partial V}{\partial P}$.

$$A_P = \frac{1}{\beta_0}\left[\frac{\partial \beta}{\partial P}\right]_{P=0} \qquad A_t = \frac{1}{\beta_0}\left[\frac{\partial \beta}{\partial t}\right]_{P=0,\ t=t0}$$

$$\beta' = 3\varphi \text{ (for any substance)}$$

$$A'_P = \frac{1}{\beta'_0}\left[\frac{\partial \beta'}{\partial P}\right]_{P=0} \qquad A'_t = \frac{1}{\beta'_0}\left[\frac{\partial \beta'}{\partial t}\right]_{P=0,\ t=t_0}$$

l = length, V = volume, P = pressure in normal atmospheres. Where a range of P is given, values are a mean over this range.

CUBIC COMPRESSIBILITY OF PURE METALS

Metal	t, °C	P, or ΔP, atm.	$10^6\beta$	Remarks	Lit.	Coop. Exp.
Ag	30	0	1.020	3φ*	(3)	TKR
	30	11 600	0.911			
	20	99–493	1.02	Hg standard†	(9)	
	20	0–9870	0.98	Fe standard‡	(1)	
	ca. 20	Stresses within elastic limit	.93	From E and λ§	(6)	
	−191		.732	Mallock's method‖	(7)	
	16		.789			
	134		.863			
	166		.891			
Al	30	0	1.384	3φ*	(3)	Ed.
	30	11 600	1.298			
	20	99–493	1.49	Hg standard†	(9)	
	20	0–9870	1.34	Fe standard‡	(1)	
	ca. 20	Stresses within elastic limit	1.36	From E and λ§	(6)	
	−191		1.36	Mallock's method‖	(7)	
	15		1.51			
	125		1.76			
As	20	99–493	4.55	Hg standard†	(9)	CHD
Au	30	0	0.603	3φ*	(3)	TKR
	30	11 600	.552			
	20	99–493	.65	Hg standard†	(9)	
	20	0–9870	.58	Fe standard‡	(1)	
	ca. 20	Stress < EL¶	.61	From E and λ§	(6)	
B	20	99–493	0.3	Hg standard†	(9)	CHD
Bi	20	99–493	3.0	Hg standard†	(9)	Ed.
	20	0	3.04	Fe standard‡	(1)	
	20	9870	2.60			
	ca. 20	Stress < EL¶	3.2	From E and λ§	(6)	
C**	20	99–493	3.0	Hg standard†	(9)	Ed.
Ca	30	0	5.885	3φ*	(3)	Ed.
	30	11 600	5.300			
	20	99–493	5.8	Hg standard†	(9)	CHD
Cd	20	0	2.27	Fe standard‡	(1)	CHMJ
	20	9870	1.72			
	20	99–493	2.1	Hg standard†	(9)	
	ca. 20	Stress < EL¶	2.4	From E and λ§	(6)	

* Data marked "Ed." have been added by the editorial office.

Metal	t, °C	P, or ΔP, atm.	$10^6\beta$	Remarks	Lit.	Coop. Exp.
Ce	30	0	3.692	3φ*	(3)	Ed.
	30	11 600	3.223			
Co	30	0	0.557	3φ*	(3)	Ed.
	30	11 600	.506			
Cr	20	99–493	0.9	Hg standard†	(9)	CHD
Cs	20	99–493	62	Hg standard†	(9)	CHD

v. also Fig. 1 (5)

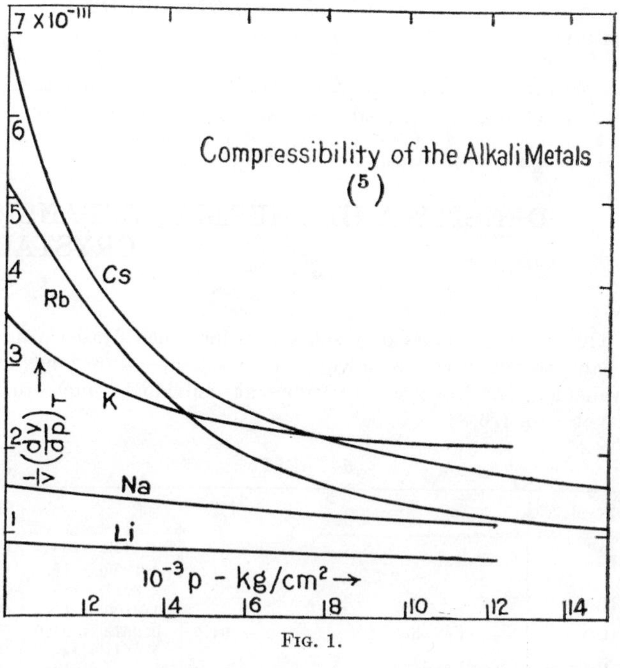

Fig. 1.

Metal	t, °C	P, or ΔP, atm.	$10^6\beta$	Remarks	Lit.	Coop. Exp.
Cu	30	0	0.756	3φ*	(3)	DH
	30	11 600	.689			
	20	99–493	.76	Hg standard†	(9)	
	20	0–9870	.76	Fe standard‡	(1)	
	ca. 20	Stresses within elastic limit	.75	From E and λ§	(6)	
	−191		.742	Mallock's method‖	(7)	
	17.5		.799			
	113		.843			
	165		.856			

Metal	t, °C	P, or ΔP, atm.	$10^6\beta$	Remarks	Lit.	Coop. Exp.
Fe	30	0	0.606	3φ*	(3)	DH
	30	11 600	.555			
	20	99–493	.61	Hg standard†	(9)	Ed.
	20	0–9870	.61	C, 0.2 %‡	(1)	
	ca. 20	Stresses within elastic limit	.63	From E and λ§	(6)	
	−190		.626	Mallock's method‖	(7)	
	18		.654			
	128		.686			
	165		.698			
Ga	20	99–493	1.6–2.4	Solid	(10)	CHD
	M. P.	99–493	4	Liquid		
Ge	30	0	1.423	3φ*	(3)	Ed.
	30	11 600	1.255			
Hg	20	99–493	4.00	Hg standard†	(9)	Ed.
		v. infra.				
In	20	99–493	2.7	Hg standard†	(1)	CHD
Ir	30	0	0.277	3φ*	(3)	TKR
	30	11 600	.244			
K	20	99–493	32.1	Hg standard†	(9)	CHD
		v. also Fig. 1 (5)				
Li	30	0	8.979	3φ*	(3)	CHD
	30	11 600	6.566			
	20	99–493	9.1	Hg standard†	(9)	
		v. also Fig. 1 (5)				
Mg	20	99–493	2.9	Hg standard†	(9)	Ed.
Mn	20	99–493	0.85	Hg standard†	(9)	CHD
Mo	30	0	0.358	3φ*	(3)	Ed.
	30	11 600	.328			
	20	99–493	.465	Hg standard†	(9)	CHD
Na	20	99–493	15.8	Hg standard†	(9)	CHD
		v. also Fig. 1 (5)				
Ni	30	0	0.542	3φ*	(3)	PDM
	30	11 600	.491			
	20	99–493	.435	Hg standard†	(9)	Ed.
	ca. 20	Stress < EL¶	.58	From E and λ§	(6)	Ed.
Pb	30	0	2.381	3φ*	(3)	Ed.
	30	11 600	2.077			
	20	0	2.24	Fe standard‡	(1)	
	20	9870	2.19			
	20	99–493	2.36	Hg standard†	(9)	
	ca. 20	Stress < EL¶	2.0	From E and λ§	(6)	
Pd	30	0	0.536	3φ*	(3)	TKR
	30	11 600	.485			
	20	99–493	.55	Hg standard†	(9)	
	ca. 20	Stress < EL¶	.58	From E and λ§	(6)	
Pt	30	0	0.372	3φ*	(3)	TKR
	30	11 600	.328			
	20	99–493	.385	Hg standard†	(9)	
	ca. 20	Stresses within elastic limit	.405	From E and λ§	(6)	
	−189		.385	Mallock's method‖	(7)	
	16.8		.405			
	133		.415			
	164		.417			
Rb	20	99–493	40.5	Hg standard†	(9)	CHD
		v. also Fig. 1 (5)				
Rh	30	0	0.384	3φ*	(3)	TKR
	30	11 600	.318			
Sb	20	99–493	2.43	Hg standard†	(9)	Ed.
Se	20	99–493	12.2	Hg standard†	(8)	Ed.
Si	20	99–493	0.325	Hg standard†	(9)	CHD
Sn	30	0	2.017	3φ*	(3)	Ed.
	30	11 600	1.780			
	20	0	1.91	Fe standard‡	(1)	
	20	9870	1.66			
	20	99–493	1.9	Hg standard†	(9)	
	ca. 20	Stresses < EL¶	1.9	From E and λ§	(6)	
	−190		2.2	Mallock's method‖	(7)	
Ta	30	0	0.495	3φ*	(3)	CHD
	30	11 600	.489			
	20	99–493	.54	Hg standard†	(9)	
Tl	20	99–493	2.3	Hg standard†	(9)	Ed.
W	30	0	0.303	3φ*	(3)	Ed.
	30	11 600	.266			
	20	99–493	.275	Hg standard†	(9)	CHD
Zn	20	0	1.76	Fe standard‡	(1)	CB
	20	9870	1.45			
	20	99–493	1.7	Hg standard†	(9)	

* Metal crystallizes in cubic system, test pieces assumed isotropic.
† Based on $\beta_{Hg} = 4.00 \times 10^{-6}$ at 20°C.
‡ Based on $\beta_{Fe} = 0.606 \times 10^{-6}$ at 20°C.
§ β computed from elastic constants E and λ. E from tensile test, λ from tensile test and torsional vibration test.
‖ Mallock's method (8) gives β directly from deformation of tube under internal pressure.
¶ Stresses within elastic limit.
** Graphite.

Hg, MERCURY

P. W. Bridgman

Relative volumes (2)

P, atm.	−20°	−10°	0°	+10°	20°
1	0.99638	0.99819	1.00000	1.00181	1.00362
1 000	.99268	.99441	0.99614	0.99786	0.99959
2 000	.98904	.99071	.99237	.99403	.99569
3 000	.98549	.98710	.98871	.99032	.99194
4 000	.98204	.98361	.98517	.98675	.98833
5 000		.98024	.98177	.98332	.98486
6 000		.97701	.97851	.98003	.98154
7 000			.97539	.97688	.97836
8 000				.97387	.97534
9 000	Freezes			.97101	.97246
10 000				.96831	.96974
11 000					.96718
12 000					.96476

P, atm.	−30°
1	0.99457
1 000	.99095
2 000	.98738

Solid Mercury

Along the melting curve the compressibility of the solid is about 10% less than that of the liquid with which it is in equilibrium.

LINEAR COMPRESSIBILITY OF PURE METALS (Ed.) (3, 4)

$$\frac{V'_0 - V'}{V'_0} = 3\,\frac{(l_0 - l)}{l_0} = aP - bP^2$$

between 0 and 11 600 atm., except for alkali metals where higher powers of P are needed to express results.

$$\beta' = -\frac{1}{V'_0}\frac{\partial V'}{\partial P} = a - 2bP$$

$$A'_P = \frac{1}{\beta'_0}\left[\frac{\partial \beta'}{\partial P}\right]_{P=0} = \frac{2b}{a}$$

$$A'_t = \frac{1}{\beta'}\left[\frac{\partial \beta'}{\partial t}\right]_{P=0} = \frac{1}{a}\frac{\partial a}{\partial t}$$

(*Tables on p. 48–49*)

LINEAR COMPRESSIBILITY OF PURE METALS.—(*Continued*)

Metal	Crystal system*	Axial ratio	Treatment	t, °C	10^6a	$10^{12}b$	$10^6A'_P$	$10^4A'_t$
Ag	C		Drawn rod, annealed at bright red heat	30	1.020	4.7	9.2	3.7
				75	1.037	4.8	9.2_5	
Al	C		Hard drawn	30	1.384	3.7	5.3_5	
			Hard drawn and annealed	30	1.378	3.7	5.3_5	9.5
				75	1.437	3.7	5.1_5	
			As cast	30	1.387	5.3	$76._5$	5.5
				75	1.421	5.4_5	7.6_5	
Au	C		Drawn rod, annealed at bright red heat, long rod	30	0.596	3.3	11.1	−2.6
				75	.589	2.2	$7._5$	
			Drawn rod, annealed at bright red heat, short rod	30	.603	2.2	7.3	
Bi	H		Extruded cylinder (*v. infra.*)	30	3.652	29.9	16.4	3.7
				75	3.713	30.6	16.5	
			Cast in graphite mold, chilled at bottom	30	2.275	9.6	8.4_5	0.8_8
				75	2.284	9.6	8.4	
Ca	C			30	5.885	50.4	18.4	6.0
				75	6.043	56.3	18.6	
Cd	H	1.89	Cast in graphite mold, chilled at bottom	30	2.018	11.4	11.1	7.5
				75	2.086	11.7	11.2	
			Extruded	30	1.464	8.0	10.9	5.6
				75	1.501	8.5	11.3	
			Unicrystalline casting	30	0.885	4.0_5	9.1_5	
Ce	C		Extruded (probably impure)	30	3.692	20.2	10.9	0.3_6
				75	3.698	21.0	11.4	
Co	C		Swaged, drawn at bright red heat, annealed at red heat	30	0.551	2.2	7.9	3.2
				75	.565	2.2	7.8	
Cu	C		Commercial drawn rod	30	.756	2.9	7.7	2.1
				75	.763	2.9	7.6	
			Same, annealed	30	.753	2.9	7.7	2.4
				75	.761	2.9	7.6	
			Pure ("Best Select")	30	.743	2.8	7.5_5	4.5
				75	.758	2.9	7.6_5	
Fe	C		"Armco" iron, annealed at red heat	30	.606	2.2	7.2_5	2.6
				75	.613	2.2	7.2	
Ge	C		Cast	30	1.423	7.2_5	10.2	−2.2
				75	1.409	7.2_5	10.3	
Ir	C		Swaged at red heat	30	0.277	1.4	10.1	9.6
				75	.290	2.3_5	16.2	
Li	C		Extruded cold	30	8.979	104.0	23.2	7.1
				75	9.266	114.6	24.7	
Mg	H	1.624	Extruded at 500°C, annealed at 300°C	30	3.058	21.6	14.1	2.8
				75	3.096	19.2	12.4	
Mo	C		Swaged	30	0.358	1.3	7.3	0.6
				75	.359	1.3	7.2_5	
			Drawn wire	30	.373	1.1	5.9	0.[illegible]
				75	.374	1.1	5.9	
Ni	C		99% Ni; drawn, annealed at bright red heat	30	.542	2.2	8.1	1.2
				75	.545	2.2	8.1	
			Chill cast, forged, drawn, and annealed at bright red heat	30	.546	2.2	8.0_5	2.8_5
				75	.553	2.2	7.9_5	
Pb	C		Cast in graphite mold, bottom chilled	30	2.451	18.4	15.0	5.6
				75	2.513	18.9	15.0	
			Same, extruded 1.5–0.75 cm diam., annealed at 230°C	30	2.381	13.1	11.0	[illegible]
				75	2.441	13.1	10.7	
Pd	C		Massive, annealed 2 hours at 800°C, cooled slowly	30	0.536	2.2	8.2	−3.3
				75	.528	2.1	7.9_5	
			Drawn wire, annealed at bright red heat	30	.545	2.2	8.1	1.6
				75	.549	2.2	8.0	
Pt	C		Drawn rod, annealed at 800°C	30	.372	1.9	10.2	2.4
				75	.376	1.9	10.1	

Metal	Crystal system*	Axial ratio	Treatment	t, °C	10^6a	$10^{12}b$	$10^6A'_P$	$10^4A'_t$
Pt	C		Drawn wire, annealed	30	0.315	0.0	0.0	0.0
				75	.319	0.0	0.0	
Rh	C		Swaged at red heat	30	.384	2.85	14.8	5.2
				75	.393	2.85	14.5	
Sb	H	2.647	Cast in graphite mold, chilled at bottom	30	1.517	6.6	8.7	1.8
				75	1.529	6.7	8.8	
			Chill cast (*v. infra.*)	30	2.108	13.8	13.1	1.05
				75	2.118	13.8	13.0	
Sn	C		Cast in graphite mold, annealed at 150°C	30	1.757	5.52	6.3	3.4
				75	1.794	6.14	6.85	
			Extruded at 125°, aged at 150°C (*v. infra.*)	30	2.017	10.2	10.1	6.6
				75	2.077	10.6	10.2	
Sr			Extruded at 270°C	30	8.454	77.4	18.3	2.2
				75	8.538	76.5	17.9	
Ta	C		Drawn wire	30	0.495	0.27	1.09	5.85
				75	.508	.27	1.06	
Tl‡	H?							
U	†		Rolled strip	30	0.998	2.7	5.4	−2.5
				75	.987	2.35	4.8	
W	C		Swaged (*v. infra.*)	30	0.303	1.6	10.6	1.5
				75	.305	1.6	10.5	
			Drawn wire	30	.325	1.7	10.5	0.7
				75	.326	1.6	10.1	
Zn	H	1.860	*v. infra*§					

* For data on crystal structure, *v.* Vol. I, p. 340. C = cubic, H = hexagonal.
† Said to be not cubic.
‡ For Tl remelted and extruded from 1.2–0.6 cm:

P, atm. \ t, °C	$100\frac{V - V}{V'_0}$ 30	75
3 000	−0.978	−1.011
6 000	+1.872	+1.908
9 000	2.700	2.724
12 000	3.505	3.554

§ For cast Zn: $10^6\beta'$ = 0.9–2.4. For cast and extruded Zn: $10^6\beta'$ = 0.86–1.28. For unicrystalline casting of Zn, measurements in mutually perpendicular directions gave: $10^6\beta'_1$ = 0.498; $10^6\beta'_2$ = 1.59; $10^6\beta'_3$ = 2.14. Mean = $10^6\beta$ = 1.41.

Values for Single Crystals (Ed.) (12)

$$\frac{-\Delta l}{l_0} = aP - bP^2 \qquad \frac{-\Delta V}{V_0} = AP - BP^2$$

P in kg/cm²; range, 0 to 12 000 kg/cm²

Metal	Axis of ref.	Direction	30°C 10^6a	$10^{12}b$	10^6A	$10^{12}B$	75°C 10^6a	$10^{12}b$	10^6A	$10^{12}B$
Bi	Hex.	∥	1.592	11.1	2.917	22.43	1.580	11.6	2.989	31.13
		⊥	0.6624	4.39			0.7044	8.40		
Sb	Trig.	∥	1.648	20.5	2.699	31.6	1.637	18.0	2.655	25.3
		⊥	0.5256	4.56			0.5091	3.04		
Sn	Tet.	∥	0.6719	4.07	1.876	13.6	0.6956	3.91	1.924	13.7
		⊥	0.6022	4.20			0.6144	4.26		
Te	Trig.	∥	−0.4137	−9.6	5.082	101.1	−0.5132	−13.2	5.041	85.6
		⊥	2.748	52.7			2.777	53.6		
W	Cubic				0.318	1.4			0.318	1.5
Zn	Hex.	∥	1.298	5.32	1.687	8.08	1.355	7.82	1.760	11.35
		⊥	0.1946	1.11			0.2025	1.47		

LITERATURE

(For a key to the periodicals see end of volume)

(1) Adams, Williamson and Johnston, *1*, **41**: 12; 19. (2) Bridgman, *65*, **47**: 345; 11. (3) Bridgman, *65*, **58**: 166; 23. (4) Bridgman, *65*, **59**: 109; 23. (5) Bridgman, *2*, **27**: 68; 26. (6) Grüneisen, *8*, **25**: 825; 08. (7) Grüneisen, *8*, **33**: 1239; 10. (8) Mallock, *5*, **74**: 50; 04. (9) Richards, *1*, **37**: 1643; 15. (10) Richards and Boyer, *1*, **43**: 274; 21. (11) Richards and Sameshima, *1*, **42**: 49; 20. (12) Bridgman, *65*, **60**: 305; 25.

COMPRESSIBILITY OF CRYSTALLINE COMPOUNDS, MINERALS AND ROCKS

L. H. Adams

The compressibility β is here defined by the equation:

$$\beta = -\frac{1}{V_0}\left(\frac{\partial V}{\partial P}\right)_t$$

in which (for a given temperature t) V is the volume at the pressure P, and V_0 is the volume at P = 1 and (unless otherwise specified) at the temperature t, as given in the third column. The compressibility depends upon the temperature and also on the pressure; its variation with temperature is given by the expression, $A_p = \frac{1}{\beta_0}\left(\frac{\partial\beta}{\partial t}\right)_P$, and with pressure by the expression, $A_t = \frac{1}{\beta_0}\left(\frac{\partial\beta}{\partial P}\right)_t$, in which β_0 is the value of β at a specified temperature—usually the same as given in the third column—and at a specified pressure, P = 1. The unit of pressure is here the megabarye, Vol. I, p. 34, and hence the values of β are expressed in reciprocal megabaryes. It may be noted that $10^4\frac{1}{\beta_0}\left(\frac{\partial\beta}{\partial t}\right)_P$ is the relative change of β, in %, for 100° change in temperature. Similarly, $10^4\frac{1}{\beta_0}\left(\frac{\partial\beta}{\partial P}\right)_t$ is the relative change of β, in %, for 100 megabaryes change in pressure.

The change of α, the thermal expansibility, with pressure is readily calculated from the values for $\frac{1}{\beta_0}\frac{\partial\beta}{\partial t}$, for if

$$\alpha = \frac{1}{V_0}\left(\frac{\partial V}{\partial t}\right)_P,$$

we have the mathematical identity

$$\left(\frac{\partial \alpha}{\partial P}\right)_t = -\left(\frac{\partial \beta}{\partial t}\right)_P.$$

For most solids $\frac{1}{\beta_0}\left(\frac{\partial \beta}{\partial P}\right)_t$ is independent of temperature within the error of experiment. Hence it follows that $\frac{1}{\beta_0}\left(\frac{\partial \beta}{\partial t}\right)_P$ is independent of pressure. It also happens that for most solids the variation of $\frac{1}{\beta_0}\left(\frac{\partial \beta}{\partial P}\right)_t$ with pressure is too small to be measurable.

Usually β is measured by determining the difference between the compressibility of the given substance and that of a reference substance of known compressibility, commonly iron or mercury. *The values of β given here have, when necessary, been recalculated to the basis* $\beta_{Hg} = 4.0 \times 10^{-6}$, and $\beta_{Fe} = 0.598 \times 10^{-6}$, at $t = 20$ and $P = 1$ (5, 8, 13). For Hg, $10^4 \frac{1}{\beta_0}\frac{\partial \beta}{\partial P} = -0.32$ and $10^4 \frac{1}{\beta_0}\frac{\partial \beta}{\partial t} = 18$. Thus at $t = 20°$, $P = 300$, $10^6\beta = 3.97$, and at $t = 0°$, $P = 125$, $10^6\beta = 3.85$. For Fe, $10^4 \frac{1}{\beta_0}\frac{\partial \beta}{\partial P} = -0.072$ and $10^4 \frac{1}{\beta_0}\frac{\partial \beta}{\partial t} = 2.2$. Thus at $t = 27$, $P = 7000$, $10^6\beta = 0.569$.

Where possible the value of β is given at $t = 25$, $P = 1$, but in certain cases when the values of the temperature and pressure coefficients of β are unknown and the temperature and pressure at which β has been determined vary too widely from $t = 25$, $P = 1$, it has been necessary to give β at the particular pressure and temperature at which it was measured.

B-TABLE, STANDARD ARRANGEMENT

In addition to the values recorded below, the compressibility of the solid along the P, T, melting curve may be obtained from the compressibility of the liquid and the observed compressibility difference, for which *see* Vol. IV, p. 9.

	Formula	Name	t	P	$10^6\beta$	-10^4A_t	10^4A_P	Lit.
	H_2O	Ice I	−7	300	12			(6, 7, 18)
	H_2O	Ice VI	10	7500	4.7			(6, 7)
14	Sb_2S_3	Stibnite	0	125	1.50			(12)
	Bi_2S_3	Bismuthinite	0	125	3.32			(12)
	C_6H_6	Benzene	0	1	32.9	2.6	70	(11, 15)
	$C_{10}H_8$	Naphthalene	25	1	18.5	1.5	17	(11)
	SiO_2	Quartz	25	1	2.75	0.20	2	(3, 10, 12, 21)
	TiO_2	Rutile	0	125	0.59			(12)
	$ZrO_2.SiO_2$	Zircon	0	125	0.86			(12)
	SnO_2	Cassiterite	0	125	0.49			(12)
	$PbCl_2$		20	300	3.4			(19)
	PbS	Galena	25	1	1.91	0.07	6.7	(10, 12)
	$PbSO_4$	Anglesite	0	125	1.94			(12)
	$PbCO_3$	Cerussite	0	125	1.91			(12)
	TlCl		20	300	4.9			(16)
	TlBr		20	300	5.3			(16)
	TlI		20	300	6.9			(16)
	ZnO	Zincite	0	125	0.78			(12)
	ZnS	Sphalerite	25	1	1.30	0.03	−4.1	(10, 12)
	ZnS	Wurtzite	25	1	1.36			(12)
	$CdCl_2$		20	300	5.95			(19)
32	AgCl		20	300	2.40			(16)
	AgBr		20	300	2.74			(14, 16)
	AgI		20	300	4.11			(16)
	Ag_2S	Argentite	25	1	2.7	0.03		(10, 12)
	$AgNO_3$		0	125	3.67			(12)
	$MnCO_3$	Rhodochrosite	0	125	1.3			(12)
	Fe_2O_3	Hematite	0	125	0.60			(12)
	Fe_3O_4	Magnetite	0	1	0.55	0.07	−1	(10, 12)
	FeS_2	Pyrite	25	1	0.70	0.06	1	(3, 10, 12)
	FeS_2	Marcasite	25	1	0.82			(12)
	FeAsS	Arsenopyrite	0	125	0.99			(12)
	$FeCO_3$	Siderite	0	125	1.00			(12)
	$FeTiO_3$	Ilmenite	0	125	0.56			(12)
31	$CuFeS_2$	Chalcopyrite	0	125	1.29			(12)
	CoAsS	Cobaltite	25	1	0.77	0.08	4	(10, 12)
	Al_2O_3	Corundum	0	125	0.40			(12)
	$3BeO.Al_2O_3.6SiO_2$	Beryl	0	1	0.60			(12, 21)
76	MgO		0	125	0.72			(12)
	CaF_2	Fluorite	25	1	1.23	0.11	6	(10, 12, 21)
	$CaCl_2$		20	300	4.36			(19)
	$CaBr_2$		20	300	4.84			(19)
	$CaSO_4$	Anhydrite	0	125	1.84			(12)
	$CaSO_4.2H_2O$	Gypsum	0	125	2.50			(12)
	$CaCO_3$	Calcite	25	1	1.36	0.06	4	(4, 10, 12, 21)
	$CaCO_3$	Aragonite	25	1	1.55			(12)
	$CaCO_3.MgCO_3$	Dolomite	0	125	1.22			(12)
	$CaSiO_3.MgSiO_3$	Diopside	25	7000	1.06			(3)
	$SrCl_2$		20	300	3.32			(19)
	$SrBr_2$		20	300	4.11			(19)
	$SrSO_4$	Celestite	25	1	1.59	0.10	3	(10, 12)
	$SrCO_3$	Strontianite	0	125	1.75			(12)
	$BaCl_2$		20	300	2.77			(19)
	$BaBr_2$		20	300	3.66			(19)
	$BaSO_4$	Barite	0	125	1.80			(12, 21)
	$BaCO_3$	Witherite	0	125	2.03			(12)
81	LiF		25	1	1.53	0.12	2	(20)
	LiCl		25	1	3.50	0.20	7	(17, 19, 20)
	LiBr		25	1	4.30	0.25	8	(17, 19, 20)
	LiI		25	1	7.2			(17, 19)
	$LiAl(SiO_3)_2$	Spodumene	25	1	0.68			(10)
	NaCl		25	1	4.18	0.20	7	(4, 11, 12, 16, 20, 21)
	NaBr		25	1	5.09	0.26	8	(16, 20)
	NaI		25	1	7.1			(16)
	$NaNO_3$		0	125	3.84			(12)
	KF		25	1	3.30	0.20	1	(20)
	KCl		25	1	5.65	0.27	5	(12, 16, 20)
	KBr		25	1	6.68	0.32	6	(16, 20)
	KI		25	1	8.56	0.39	6	(16, 20)
	$K_2O.Al_2O_3.6SiO_2$	Orthoclase	25	1	1.85	0.15		(3, 12)
	RbCl		25	1	7.40			(17, 19)
	RbBr	(Low-pressure form)	25	1	7.97	0.35		(17, 19, 20)
	RbI	(Low-pressure form)	25	1	9.54	0.43	7	(17, 19, 20)
	CsCl		25	1	5.9			(17, 19)
	CsBr	(Low-pressure form)	25	1	7.0			(17, 19)
	CsI		25	1	9.3			(17, 19)

Crystalline Materials (More Than One Component)

Composition	Name	t	P	$10^6\beta$	-10^4A_t	Lit.
$(MgSiO_3)_{88}(FeSiO_3)_{12}$.......	Enstatite	25	7000	1.00		(3)
$(MgSiO_3)_{70}(FeSiO_3)_{30}$.......	Hypersthene	25	7000	0.98		(3)
$(Mg_2SiO_4)_{90}(Fe_2SiO_4)_{10}$......	Olivine	25	7000	0.81		(2)
$Ab_{18}An_{22}$*................	Oligoclase	25	1	1.74	0.12	(3)
$Ab_{48}An_{52}$*................	Labradorite	25	1	1.55	0.17	(3)
$Or_{91}Ab_9$*..................	Microcline	25	1	1.9	0.15	(3)
	Phlogopite mica†	25	1	2.34	0.17	(3)
	Actinolite‡	25	7000	1.29		(3)
	Augite§	25	7000	1.01		(3)
	Cast iron‖	25	2000	0.88	0.2	(3)
	Cast iron	25	300	1.45		(1)
	Tourmaline¶	0	125	0.82		(12)
	Topaz**	25	1	0.61		(21)
	Opal (Mexican)	0	125	6.1		(12)

* An is written for $CaO.Al_2O_3.2SiO_2$. Ab is written for $Na_2O.Al_2O_3.6SiO_2$. Or is written for $K_2O.Al_2O_3.6SiO_2$.

† Essentially $R_3Mg_3Al(SiO_4)_3$ where R = H, K, Mg, F.

‡ Essentially $CaO.3(Mg, Fe)O.4SiO_2$.

§ Essentially $CaSiO_3.(Mg, Fe)SiO_3$ (diopside), with Al_2O_3 and Fe_2O_3.

‖ Soft gray cast iron. Density at 23°, 7.193.

¶ Essentially $H_9Al_3(BOH)_2Si_4O_{19}$ with Fe, Mg, Ca, F, Na, K.

** Essentially $Al(F, OH)_2SiO_4$.

Rocks

At high pressures the compressibilities of most rocks depend mainly on the composition; on the other hand, at pressures below 2000 megabaryes the compressibility may be abnormally high and depends on the degree of compactness of the particular sample. In most instances $\frac{1}{\beta_0}\frac{\partial\beta}{\partial P}$ at pressures above 2000 megabaryes is independent of pressure (within the error of experiment), but at pressures below 2000 it may change rapidly with pressure. In the table here given $\frac{1}{\beta_0}\frac{\partial\beta}{\partial P}$ refers to pressures higher than the pressures for which β is given. In all cases the temperature is approximately 25°.

Rock	P	$10^6\beta$	-10^4A_t	10^4A_P	Lit.
Westerly granite	2000	2.00	0.10		(3)
Westerly granite	300	3.2			(1)
Washington granite	2000	2.28	0.29		(3)
Stone Mt. granite	2000	1.97	0.12		(3)
Baveno granite	300	3.2			(1)
Peterhead granite	300	3.0			(1)
Lily Lake granite	300	3.2			(1)
Quincy granite	300	3.4			(1)
Stanstead granite	300	3.7			(1)
Montreal nepheline syenite	300	2.3			(1)
Sudbury diabase	7000	1.23			(3)
Sudbury diabase	300	1.36			(1)
Palisade diabase	2000	1.8	0.3		(3)
New Jersey basalt	2000	2.4	0.4		(3)
Basalt	1	1.59	0.17	0.0	(9)
New Glasgow gabbro	2000	1.34	0.2		(3)
New Glasgow gabbro	300	1.5			(1)
New Glasgow anorthosite	500	1.7			(1)
Mt. Johnson essexite	300	2.1			(1)
Balsam Gap dunite	7000	0.81			(2)
Colorado marble	7000	1.36			(3)
Black Belgian marble	300	1.7			(1)
Carrara marble	300	2.4			(1)
Vermont marble	300	2.7			(1)
Tennessee marble	300	2.4			(1)
Montreal limestone	300	2.3			(1)
Solenhofen limestone	6000	1.36		9	(9)
Ohio sandstone	140	8			(1)
Serpentine (talc schist)	2000	1.79	0.3		(1)
Talc	1	1.86	0.3		(9)

Compressibilities of a Series of Typical Plutonic Rocks (3)
Average composition (by volume)

Rock	Quartz	Orthoclase	Andesine, Ab_2An_1		Biotite	Amphibole	P, megabaryes	$10^6\beta$
Granite	30	65			5		2 000	2.11
							10 000	1.85
Granodiorite	11	20	52		10	7	2 000	1.82
							10 000	1.62
Syenite		90			5	5	2 000	1.86
							10 000	1.64
Diorite			80		5	15	2 000	1.61
							10 000	1.45
		Labradorite, Ab_1An_2	Augite	Hypersthene	Olivine	Metallic iron		
Gabbro		50	40	10			2 000	1.20
							10 000	1.12
Pyroxenite			50	50			2 000	1.03
							10 000	0.96
Peridotite				50	50		2 000	0.93
							10 000	0.87
Dunite					100		2 000	0.84
							10 000	0.79
Pallasite					50	50	2 000	0.72
							10 000	0.68
Siderite						100	2 000	0.59
							10 000	0.56

LITERATURE

(For a key to the periodicals see end of volume)

(1) Adams and Coker, *152*, No. **46;** 06. (2) Adams and Gibson, *197*, **12:** 275; 26. (3) Adams and Williamson, *143*, **195:** 475; 23. (4) Adams, Williamson and Johnston, *1*, **41:** 12; 19. (5) Bridgman, *65*, **47:** 345; 11. (6) Bridgman, *65*, **47:** 439; 12. (7) Bridgman, *65*, **48:** 310; 12. (8) Bridgman, *65*, **58:** 166; 23. (9) Bridgman, *12*, **7:** 81; 24.
(10) Bridgman, *12*, **10:** 483; 25. (11) Essex, *93*, **88:** 189; 14. (12) Madelung and Fuchs, *8*, **65:** 289; 21. (13) de Metz, *8*, **47:** 706; 92. (14) Richards and Bartlett, *1*, **37:** 470; 15. (15) Richards, Bartlett and Hodges, *1*, **43:** 1538; 21. (16) Richards and Jones, *1*, **31:** 158; 09. (17) Richards and Saerens, *1*, **46:** 934; 24. (18) Richards and Speyers, *1*, **36:** 491; 14. (19) Saerens, *28*, **33:** 17; 24.
(20) Slater, *2*, **23:** 488; 24. *65*, **61:** 135; 26. (21) Voigt, *8*, **31:** 474, 701; 87. **34:** 981; 88. **35:** 642; 88. **39:** 412; 90.

DENSITY (SPECIFIC GRAVITY) AND THERMAL EXPANSION (UNDER ATMOSPHERIC PRESSURE) OF AQUEOUS SOLUTIONS OF INORGANIC SUBSTANCES AND OF STRONG ELECTROLYTES

L. J. Gillespie, Special Editor

J. A. Beattie [JAB], B. T. Brooks [BTB], L. J. Gillespie [LJG], George Scatchard [GS], Walter C. Schumb [WCS] and Ralph F. Tefft [RFT]*

Contents	Matières	Inhaltsverzeichnis	Indice	Page
Introduction.	Introduction.	Einleitung.	Introduzione	52
Systems containing one solute.	Systèmes ne contenant qu'un corps dissout.	Systeme mit einem gelöste Stoffe.	Sistemi contenenti un solo soluto	54
Systems containing more than one solute.	Systèmes contenant plus qu'un corps dissout.	Systeme mit mehr als einem gelöste Stoffe.	Sistemi contenenti più di uno soluto	95
Density of saturated solutions.	Densité des solutions saturées.	Gesättigte Lösungen.	Soluzioni sature	104
Temperature of maximum density.	Température de la densité maximum.	Temperatur des Dichtemaximums.	Temperatura del massimo di densità	107

* The tables for which the respective Cooperating Experts are responsible are marked with the initials indicated above, following the formula of the compound, thus, **$BaCl_2$** [GS]. When a different Cooperating Expert has been responsible for collecting the pertinent literature references, this is indicated in a similar manner by his initials following the list of reference numbers.

* Les tables pour lesquelles les experts coopérants respectifs sont responsables sont marquées avec les initiales indiquées ci-dessus suivant la formule du composé, ainsi, **$BaCl_2$** [GS]. Lorsqu'un expert coopérant autre que celui mentionné ci-dessus a été chargé de recueillir les références bibliographiques convenables, cela est indiqué d'une manière similaire par ses initiales suivant la liste des nombres de références.

INTRODUCTION

Sources of Data.—Each table is the result of a critical examination of all pertinent data. The reference numbers are in some cases marked according to the weight assigned to the authors' values, thus, * some weight, ** greater weight. When such distinction is made, references not specially marked have not been utilized, or contain data of less reliability.

Literature reference numbers which follow the symbol α contain thermal expansion data.

Abbreviations and Units.—The quantities recorded in the tables are temperature in °C, Wt. % of the solute, and density of the solution in g/ml (=specific gravity, $t°/4°$). The Wt. % refers to the formula given except when water of hydration is shown, in which case it refers to the anhydrous substance. Densities and per cents are throughout based on weights *in vacuo*, unless otherwise indicated.

Interpolation.—In general, at least up to 20 or 30 %, linear interpolation may safely be employed throughout the tables for a given temperature. By forming the first and second tabular differences, the error introduced by linear interpolation can easily be estimated: It may reach about ⅛ of the second tabular difference. No general statement can be made as to whether the accuracy of the original data warrants a refinement over linear interpolation. If desired, the interpolation formula may be used, or the convenient and accurate method (*a*).

(*a*) To find the density of a solution containing W_1 Wt. % of solute at θ°C when θ is given in the table. Form the function

$$F = \frac{d_S - 1}{W},$$

where d_S is the density of a solution of W Wt. % solute at $\theta°$. Construct the graph, F against W, and interpolate F for W_1.

(*b*) To find the Wt. % of solute, W_1, from the density, when θ is given in the table. Construct the graph, F against $d_S - 1$. Divide $d_S - 1$ by the interpolated value of F.

(*c*) To find the density of a solution of θ°C, when θ is not given in the table. It is better to define the function

$$F' = \frac{d_S - d_W}{W},$$

where d_W is the density of water (*v.* p. 24) at $t°$. Construct the graphs, F' against W, for the two given temperatures which enclose the temperature θ, and by interpolation construct the graph for the temperature θ. Check by constructing the graphs of F' against t for the two given values of W which enclose W_1, and interpolate the graph for W_1.

(*d*) To find the density of a solution containing C grams (resp. moles, formula wts., equiv. wts.) of solute per liter of solution at t°C. Construct for $t°$ a graph of $W \times d_S$ against d_S, and obtain by interpolation the value of d_S for which $W \times d_S = \frac{1}{10}\, C$ (resp. $\frac{1}{10}\, C \times M$, where M is the mol. wt., formula wt., equiv. wt., as the case may be). This is the value sought.

INTRODUCTION

Sources des données.—Chaque table est le résultat d'un examen critique de toutes les données convenables. Les nombres de références sont dans certains cas marqués selon le poids assigné aux valeurs des auteurs, ainsi, * un peu de poids, ** poids plus grand. Lorsqu'une telle distinction est faite, les références qui ne sont pas spécialement marquées n'ont pas été utilisées, ou elles contiennent des données moins dignes de confiance.

Les nombres de références bibliographiques qui suivent le symbole α contiennent des données de dilatation thermique.

Abréviations et unités.—Les quantités mentionnées dans les tables sont: la température en °C, le % poids du corps dissout, et la densité de la solution en g/ml (= poids spécifique, $t°/4°$). Le % poids se rapporte à la formule donnée excepté lorsque l'eau d'hydratation est mise en évidence, auquel cas le % poids se rapporte à la substance anhydre. Les densités et les pour cent sont partout basés sur les poids dans le vide, à moins d'une autre indication.

Interpolation.—En général, on peut employer sans danger dans les tables et pour une température donnée, l'interpolation linéaire au moins jusqu'à 20 ou 30%. On peut trouver de suite les cas où l'interpolation linéaire introduit des erreurs, en formant la première et la deuxième différence tabulaire: l'erreur due à l'interpolation linéaire peut atteindre ⅛ de la deuxième différence tabulaire. On ne peut établir d'une façon générale si la précision des données originales justifie une correction après avoir fait l'interpolation linéaire. On peut utiliser si l'on veut ou la formule d'interpolation ou la méthode précise et convenable (*a*).

(*a*) Pour trouver la densité d'une solution contenant W_1 % poids de corps dissout à θ°C lorsque θ est donné dans la table, il faut former la fonction

$$F = \frac{d_S - 1}{W},$$

où d_S est la densité d'une solution contenant W % poids de corps dissout à $\theta°$, construire le graphique, F par rapport à W et interpoler F pour W_1.

(*b*) Pour trouver le % poids de corps dissout, W_1, à partir de la densité, lorsque θ est donné dans la table, il faut construire le graphique, F par rapport à $d_S - 1$ et diviser $d_S - 1$ par la valeur interpolée de F.

(*c*) Pour trouver la densité d'une solution à θ°C, lorsque θ n'est pas donné dans la table, il est préférable de définir la fonction

$$F' = \frac{d_S - d_W}{W},$$

où d_W est la densité de l'eau (*v.* p. 24) à $t°$. Construire les graphiques, F' par rapport à W, pour les deux températures données entre lesquelles se trouve la température θ, et par interpolation construire le graphique pour la température θ. Vérifier, en construisant les graphiques de F' par rapport à t pour les deux valeurs données de W entre lesquelles se trouve W_1, et interpoler le graphique pour W_1.

(*d*) Pour trouver la densité d'une solution contenant C grammes (resp. mol. gr., formule poids, équiv. poids) de corps dissout par litre de solution à t°C, construire pour $t°$ un graphique de $W \times d_S$ par rapport à d_S et obtenir par interpolation la valeur de d_S pour laquelle $W \times d_S = \frac{1}{10}\, C$ (resp. $\frac{1}{10}\, C \times M$, où M est le poids mol., la formule poids, l'équiv. poids, suivant le cas). On obtient ainsi la valeur cherchée.

EINLEITUNG

Quellen.—Jede Tafel ist das Ergebnis einer kritischen Prüfung aller zweckdienlicher Daten. Die Literaturzahlen sind in einigen Fällen mit Zeichen versehen, welche das Gewicht bezeichnen das den Angaben der Autoren beigelegt worden ist, z. B.* einiges Gewicht,** grösseres Gewicht. Ist eine solche Auswahl getroffen, so sind Angaben, die nicht besonders bezeichnet sind, nicht verwendet, oder enthalten Werte von geringerer Verlässlichkeit.

Literaturzahlen die dem Zeichen α folgen, enthalten Daten für die thermische Ausdehnung.

Abkürzungen und Einheiten.—Die Zahlenangaben der Tafeln beziehen sich auf Temperaturen in °C, auf Gewichtsprozente (Wt. %) des gelösten Stoffes, die Dichte der Lösung in g/ml (= Spezifisches Gewicht, $t°/4°$). Die Gewichtsprozente (Wt. %) beziehen sich auf die angegebene Formel, ausgenommen, wenn Hydratationswasser angegeben ist, in diesem Fall beziehen sie sich auf den wasserfreien Stoff. Dichte und Prozente beziehen sich durchwegs auf das Gewicht im Vakuum, ausser es ist anders angegeben.

Interpolation.—Bis mindestens zu 20 und 30 % hinauf kann man in allen Tafeln bei bestimmter Temperatur sicher linear interpolieren. Ob dies einen Fehler verursacht, kann leicht durch Bildung der ersten und zweiten Tafeldifferenz gefunden werden. Der durch die lineare Interpolation sich ergebende Fehler wird kaum ⅛ der zweiten Tafeldifferenz ausmachen. Es kann keine allgemeine Aussage darüber gemacht werden, ob die Genauigkeit der Originalwerte eine Verfeinerung über diejenige der linearen Interpolation zulässt. Wenn nötig, so kann man die Interpolationsformel verwenden oder die bequeme und genaue Methode (*a*).

(*a*) Es ist die Dichte einer Lösung zu finden, die W_1 Gewichtsprozente (Wt. %) des gelösten Stoffes bei θ°C enthält, wenn θ in der Tafel sich vorfindet. Ist d_S die Dichte einer Lösung die W Gewichtsprozente (Wt. %) des gelösten Stoffes enthält, so berechne man F nach der Gleichung

$$F = \frac{d_S - 1}{W}$$

und trage F und W im Koordinatenpapier auf, woraus sich F für das gegebene W_1 ergibt.

(*b*) Es sind die Gewichtsprozente W_1 (Wt. %) einer Lösung aus der Dichte d_S zu finden, wenn θ in der Tafel sich vorfindet. Man trage F und $d_S - 1$ im Koordinatenpapier auf und dividiere $d_S - 1$ durch den interpolierten Wert von F.

(*c*) Es ist die Dichte einer Lösung bei θ°C zu finden, wenn θ sich nicht in der Tafel vorfindet. Es ist am besten die Gleichung

$$F' = \frac{d_S - d_W}{W}$$

zu verwenden, in welcher d_W die Dichte des Wassers (*siehe* p. 24) bei t° bedeutet. Man trägt zuerst im Koordinatenpapier F' und W für zwei θ einschliessende Temperaturen auf, durch Interpolation kann man dann die Kurve für θ konstruieren. Trägt man in gleicher Weise F' als Funktion von t für zwei Werte von W auf, welche W_1 einschliessen, so erhält man durch Interpolation W_1.

(*d*) Es ist die Dichte d_S einer Lösung zu finden, welche C Gramme (bezw. Mole, Grammformelgewicht, Äquivalentgewicht) in 1 Liter bei t°C gelöst enthält. Man entwerfe wie oben eine Kurve mit $W \times d_S$ und d_S wodurch man durch Interpolation einen Wert für d_S erhält. Es ist dann $W \times d_S = \frac{1}{10}\, C$ (bezw. $\frac{1}{10}\, C \times M$ wo M gleich ist dem Molgewicht, Grammformelgewicht oder Äquivalentgewicht). Dies ist der gesuchte Wert.

INTRODUZIONE

Origine di dati.—Ogni tabella è il risultato dell'esame critico di tutti i dati relativi. In alcuni casi, per ricordare il valore attribuito ai singoli dati, si son fatti seguire i numeri di riferimento da annotazioni come queste: * alcuno valore, ** più di valore. Quando è fatta una distinzione tra le varie citazioni, quelle senza contrassegno speciale non sono state utilizzate, oppure contengono dati di minore attendibilità.

I numeri di riferimento della letteratura, quando sono preceduti dal simbolo α, contengono dati di dilatazione termica.

Abbreviazioni e unità.—Le quantità riportate nelle tabelle sono temperature in °C, percentuali in peso di soluto, e densità delle soluzioni in g/ml (= peso specifico, $t°/4°$). La percentuale in peso si riferisce alla formula data tranne che non sia inclusa in questa l'acqua di idratazione, nel qual caso si riferisce alla sostanza anidra. Le densità e le percentuali sono sempre riferite a pesate nel vuoto salvo che non sia indicato diversamente.

Interpolazione.—In genere, almeno fino al 20 o 30%, si può adoperare con sicurezza la interpolazione lineare in tutte le tabelle per una data temperatura. Si può vedere se la interpolazione lineare introduce errori formando le differenze prime e seconde: l'errore dovuto alla interpolazione lineare appena potrebbe eccedere ⅛ delle differenze seconde. Non si può stabilire in maniera generica se l'accuratezza dei dati originali consente una precisione superiore a quella che dà la interpolazione lineare. Se si desidera, si può adoperare la formula di interpolazione oppure si può ricorrere al metodo preciso (*a*).

(*a*) Si desideri la densità di una soluzione contenente W_1 percento in peso di soluto a θ°C, quando θ è dato nella tabella. Si ricava allora

$$F = \frac{d_S - 1}{W},$$

dove d_S è la densità della soluzione con W percento in peso di soluto a θ°; si riporta in un diagramma la variazione di F rispetto a W, e si interpola F per W_1.

(*b*) Si desideri ricavare il percento in peso di soluto, W_1, dalla densità, quando θ è dato nella tabella. Si riporta in un diagramma F rispetto a $d_S - 1$, e si divide $d_S - 1$ per il valore interpolato di F.

(*c*) Si desideri la densità di una soluzione a θ°C, quando θ non è dato nella tabella. Si calcola il valore di

$$F' = \frac{d_S - d_W}{W},$$

dove d_W è la densità dell'acqua (*v.* p. 24) a t°, si traccia la curva che rappresenta il variare di F' rispetto a W per le due temperature che comprendono la temperatura θ, e per interpolazione si costruisce il diagramma per la temperatura θ. Si fa la riprova costruendo i diagrammi che danno i valori di F' rispetto a t per i due valori di W che comprendono W_1, e si interpola il grafico per W_1.

(*d*) Si desideri stabilire la densità di una soluzione contenente C g (oppure moli, pesi corrispondenti alle formule, pesi equivalenti) di soluto per litro di soluzione a t°C. Si traccia per t° un diagramma che rappresenta come varia $W \times d_S$ con d_S, e si ricava per interpolazione il valore di d_S per il quale $W \times d_S = \frac{1}{10}\, C$ (oppure $\frac{1}{10}\, C \times M$, dove M è il peso molecolare, il peso corrispondente alla formula, o il peso equivalente a seconda dei casi). Questo è il valore cercato.

SYSTEMS CONTAINING ONE SOLUTE

Standard arrangement

H_2O_2 [JAB] (399)**; (77, 90) [LJG]

%	d_4^0	d_4^{18}	%	d_4^0	d_4^{18}	%	d_4^0	d_4^{18}
1	1.0038	1.0022	20	1.0797	1.0725	55	1.2322	1.2188
2	1.0078	1.0058	22	1.0879	1.0802	60	1.2559	1.2416
4	1.0157	1.0131	24	1.0962	1.0880	65	1.2804	1.2652
6	1.0236	1.0204	26	1.1046	1.0959	70	1.3056	1.2897
8	1.0316	1.0277	28	1.1131	1.1040	75	1.3314	1.3149
10	1.0395	1.0351	30	1.1216	1.1122	80	1.3576	1.3406
12	1.0475	1.0425	35	1.1431	1.1327	85	1.3842	1.3667
14	1.0555	1.0499	40	1.1648	1.1536	90	1.4112	1.3931
16	1.0635	1.0574	45	1.1868	1.1749	95	1.4385	1.4197
18	1.0716	1.0649	50	1.2092	1.1966	100	1.4660	1.4465

HF [JAB] (148, 296, 648)**; (165, 267, 660)

%	d_4^0	d_4^{20}	%	d_4^0
5	1.020	1.017	70	1.258
10	1.040	1.035	72	1.261
15	1.060	1.053	74	1.262
20	1.080	1.070	76	1.262
25	1.099	1.086	78	1.261
30	1.119	1.101	80	1.259
35	1.139	1.116	82	1.255
40	1.159	1.130	84	1.246
45	1.178	1.143	86	1.233
50	1.198	1.155	88	1.213
55	1.217		90	1.178
60	1.235		95	1.089
65	1.248		100	1.0005

$HClO_3$ [JAB] (288, 514)**; (529)*; (327) [LJG]

%	d_4^{18}	d_4^{25}
1	1.0044	1.0030
2	1.0103	1.0089
4	1.0222	1.0208
6	1.0344	1.0328
8	1.0468	1.0449
10	1.0594	
12	1.0723	
14	1.0856	
16	1.0991	
18	1.1130	
20	1.1273	
22	1.1419	
24	1.1568	

$HClO_4$ [LJG] (171, 514, 658)**; (521, 529)

%	d_4^{15}	d_4^{25}	d_4^{50}	%	d_4^{15}	d_4^{20}	d_4^{50}
1	1.0050	1.0020	0.9933	26	1.1738	1.1697	1.1490
2	1.0109	1.0070	0.9986	28	1.1900	1.1851	1.1645
4	1.0228	1.0169	0.9906	30	1.2067	1.2013	1.1800
6	1.0348	1.0270	1.0205	32	1.2239	1.2183	1.1960
8	1.0471	1.0372	1.0320	34	1.2418	1.2359	1.2130
10	1.0597	1.0475	1.0440	36	1.2603	1.2542	1.2310
12	1.0726		1.0560	38	1.2794	1.2732	1.2490
14	1.0859		1.0680	40	1.2991	1.2927	1.2680
16	1.0995		1.0810	45	1.3521	1.3450	1.3180
18	1.1135		1.0940	50	1.4103	1.4018	1.3730
20	1.1279		1.1070	55	1.4733	1.4636	1.4320
22	1.1428		1.1205	60	1.5389	1.5298	1.4950
24	1.1581		1.1345	65	1.6059	1.5986	1.5620
				70	1.6736	1.6680	1.6290

%.....	75	80	82	84	86	88
d_4^{50}.....	1.6970	1.7540	1.7670	1.7740	1.7765	1.7755

%.....	90	92	94	96	98	100
d_4^{20}.....			1.8086	1.7995	1.7868	1.7676
d_4^{50}.....	1.7720	1.7655	1.7570	1.7460	1.7310	1.7098

Br [JAB] (325, 565)** [LJG]

%.....	0.5	1.0	1.5	2.0	2.5	3.0
$d_4^{15.56}$..	1.0033	1.0074	1.0113	1.0150	1.0185	1.0218
$d_4^{32.5}$..	0.9982	1.0016	1.0051	1.0088	1.0125	

HCl [JAB] (348, 349), α (368)**; (20, 391, 556, 557, 653)*; (18, 43, 44, 98, 106, 125, 144, 167, 170, 197, 200, 204, 214, 221, 224, 239, 247, 273, 306, 312, 313, 318, 319, 321, 323, 327, 333, 340, 344, 354, 378, 385, 387, 409, 418, 451, 463, 483, 491, 514, 519, 528, 529, 551, 589, 592, 593, 596, 628, 645, 654, 660), α (151, 211, 466, 555, 609, 610)

%	−5°C	0°C	+10°C	20°C	25°C	30°C	40°C	50°C	60°C	80°C	100°C
1	1.0048	1.0052	1.0048	1.0032	1.0020	1.0006	0.9970	0.9929	0.9881	0.9768	0.9636
2	1.0104	1.0106	1.0100	1.0082	1.0069	1.0055	1.0019	0.9977	0.9930	0.9819	0.9688
4	1.0213	1.0213	1.0202	1.0181	1.0167	1.0152	1.0116	1.0073	1.0026	0.9919	0.9791
6	1.0321	1.0319	1.0303	1.0279	1.0264	1.0248	1.0211	1.0168	1.0121	1.0016	0.9892
8	1.0428	1.0423	1.0403	1.0376	1.0360	1.0343	1.0305	1.0262	1.0215	1.0111	0.9992
10	1.0536	1.0528	1.0504	1.0474	1.0457	1.0439	1.0400	1.0357	1.0310	1.0206	1.0090
12	1.0645	1.0634	1.0607	1.0574	1.0556	1.0537	1.0497	1.0453	1.0406	1.0302	1.0188
14	1.0754	1.0741	1.0711	1.0675	1.0656	1.0636	1.0594	1.0549	1.0502	1.0398	1.0286
16	1.0864	1.0849	1.0815	1.0776	1.0756	1.0735	1.0692	1.0646	1.0598	1.0494	1.0383
18	1.0975	1.0958	1.0920	1.0878	1.0856	1.0834	1.0790	1.0743	1.0694	1.0590	1.0479
20	1.1087	1.1067	1.1025	1.0980	1.0957	1.0934	1.0888	1.0840	1.0790	1.0685	1.0574
22	1.1200	1.1177	1.1131	1.1083	1.1059	1.1034	1.0986	1.0937	1.0886	1.0780	1.0668
24	1.1314	1.1287	1.1238	1.1187	1.1162	1.1135	1.1085	1.1033	1.0982	1.0874	1.0761
26	1.1426	1.1396	1.1344	1.1290	1.1264	1.1236	1.1183	1.1129	1.1076	1.0967	1.0853
28	1.1537	1.1505	1.1449	1.1392	1.1365	1.1336	1.1280	1.1224	1.1169	1.1058	1.0942
30	1.1648	1.1613	1.1553	1.1493	1.1465	1.1435	1.1376	1.1318	1.1260	1.1149	1.1030
32				1.1593							
34				1.1691							
36				1.1789							
38				1.1885							
40				1.1980							

(348, 349, 586)**

%	$d_4^{17.15}$	%	$d_4^{17.15}$
0.2	0.999 802	1.2	1.004 845
0.4	1.000 819	1.4	1.005 846
0.6	1.001 830	1.6	1.006 845
0.8	1.002 837	1.8	1.007 842
1.0	1.003 842	2.0	1.008 837

3.38% (588)

d_4^t	t
0.9669	110
0.9606	120
0.9537	130
0.9456	140

HBr [JAB] (288, 483, 557)**; (514)*; (12, 29, 43, 44, 244, 319, 321, 327, 340, 463, 490, 519, 520, 547, 589, 600)

%	d_4^4	d_4^{10}	d_4^{20}	d_4^{25}
1	1.0073	1.0068	1.0053	1.0041
2	1.0146	1.0139	1.0124	1.0111
4	1.0295	1.0285	1.0269	1.0255
6	1.0448	1.0435	1.0417	1.0402
8	1.0604	1.0589	1.0568	1.0552
10	1.0764	1.0747	1.0723	1.0707
12	1.0928	1.0910	1.0883	1.0867
14	1.1097	1.1078	1.1048	1.1032
16	1.1272	1.1251	1.1219	1.1202
18	1.1453	1.1430	1.1396	1.1377
20	1.1640	1.1615	1.1579	1.1557
22	1.1832	1.1806	1.1767	1.1743
24	1.2030	1.2003	1.1961	1.1935
26	1.2235	1.2206	1.2161	1.2134
28	1.2446	1.2415	1.2367	1.2340
30	1.2663	1.2630	1.2580	1.2552
35	1.3243	1.3208	1.3150	1.3118
40	1.3877	1.3838	1.3772	1.3736
45	1.4564	1.4521	1.4446	1.4405
50	1.5305	1.5257	1.5173	1.5127
55	1.6100	1.6047	1.5953	1.5902
60	1.6950	1.6892	1.6787	1.6731
65	1.7854	1.7792	1.7675	1.7613

HI [JAB] (288, 483)**; (557)*; (12, 43, 44, 224, 327, 340, 463, 600)

%	d_4^4	d_4^{10}	d_4^{20}	d_4^{25}
1	1.0075	1.0070	1.0054	1.0042
2	1.0150	1.0144	1.0127	1.0114
4	1.0305	1.0296	1.0277	1.0262
6	1.0465	1.0452	1.0431	1.0415
8	1.0629	1.0612	1.0589	1.0573
10	1.0797	1.0777	1.0751	1.0735
12	1.0970	1.0947	1.0918	1.0902
14	1.1148	1.1122	1.1091	1.1074
16	1.1331	1.1303	1.1270	1.1252
18	1.1521	1.1491	1.1456	1.1437
20	1.1719	1.1687	1.1649	1.1629
22	1.1925	1.1891	1.1850	1.1829
24	1.2139	1.2103	1.2059	1.2037
26	1.2361	1.2323	1.2277	1.2254
28	1.2591	1.2551	1.2503	1.2479
30	1.2829	1.2788	1.2737	1.2712
35	1.3460	1.3416	1.3357	1.3329
40	1.4143	1.4096	1.4029	1.3998
45	1.4880	1.4829	1.4755	1.4720

HIO_3 [JAB] (245, 288, 358)**; (594)*; (327, 517, 529) [LJG]

%	d_4^0	d_4^{18}	d_4^{25}	%	d_4^0	d_4^{18}
1	1.0085	1.0071	1.0055	18	1.1796	1.1740
2	1.0172	1.0157	1.0139	20	1.2026	1.1969
4	1.0352	1.0334	1.0314	22	1.2263	1.2206
6	1.0539	1.0517	1.0495	24	1.2507	1.2450
8	1.0733	1.0706	1.0682	26	1.2759	1.2700
10	1.0934	1.0900	1.0875	28		1.2956
12	1.1141	1.1100	1.1073	30		1.3218
14	1.1354	1.1306	1.1277	35		1.3900
16	1.1572	1.1519		40		1.4640

HIO_4 [LJG] (594)

%	d_4^{17}	%	d_4^{17}	%	d_4^{17}	%	d_4^{17}
1	1.0076	10	1.0944	20	1.2116	30	1.3545
2	1.0165	12	1.1161	22	1.2376	32	1.3875
4	1.0349	14	1.1388	24	1.2647		
6	1.0539	16	1.1623	26	1.2931		
8	1.0737	18	1.1865	28	1.3230		

SO_2 [JAB] (231)**; (591)*; (9, 253, 254, 549, 602) [LJG]

%...........	1	2	4	6	8	10
$d_4^{15.5}$.........	1.0040	1.0091	1.0191	1.0292	1.0393	1.0493

H_2SO_4, *see* p. 56–57

$H_2S_2O_6$ [LJG]; with 4.05 %, d_4^{25} = 1.0234 (529)

$H_2S_2O_8$ [JAB] (169) [LJG]

%	d_4^{14}	%	d_4^{14}	%	d_4^{14}	%	d_4^{14}
1	1.005	10	1.059	18	1.113	26	1.173
2	1.011	12	1.072	20	1.127	28	1.189
4	1.022	14	1.085	22	1.142	30	1.205
6	1.034	16	1.099	24	1.157	35	1.245
8	1.046						

SeO_2 [JAB] (602)**; (123, 463, 663) [LJG]

%	d_4^{15}	%	d_4^{15}	%	d_4^{15}	%	d_4^{15}
1	1.0072	6	1.0495	10	1.0858	14	1.1242
2	1.0153	8	1.0674	12	1.1047	16	1.1443
4	1.0321						

H_2SeO_4 [JAB] (149)**; (91, 663) [LJG]

%	d_4^{20}	%	d_4^{20}	%	d_4^{20}	%	d_4^{20}
1	1.0059	26	1.2229	52	1.549	78	2.073
2	1.0136	28	1.2438	54	1.581	80	2.122
4	1.0291	30	1.2653	56	1.614	82	2.174
6	1.0447	32	1.2874	58	1.649	84	2.226
8	1.0605	34	1.3101	60	1.685	86	2.278
10	1.0766	36	1.3334	62	1.722	88	2.332
12	1.0931	38	1.3573	64	1.761	90	2.386
14	1.1101	40	1.3819	66	1.802	92	2.436
16	1.1276	42	1.4073	68	1.844	94	2.483
18	1.1455	44	1.4336	70	1.887	96	2.527
20	1.1639	46	1.4609	72	1.932	98	2.570
22	1.1829	48	1.4892	74	1.978	100	2.611
24	1.2026	50	1.5186	76	2.025		

H_2TeO_3 [JAB] (602) [LJG]

%...........	1	2	4	6	8	10
d_4^{15}..........	1.008	1.017	1.034	1.050	1.066	1.083

N_2H_4, Hydrazine [JAB] (152)**; (78)

%	d_4^{15}	%	d_4^{15}	%	d_4^{15}	%	d_4^{15}
1	1.0002	16	1.0164	35	1.035	75	1.043
2	1.0013	18	1.0186	40	1.038	80	1.040
4	1.0034	20	1.0207	45	1.042	85	1.036
6	1.0056	22	1.0228	50	1.044	90	1.030
8	1.0077	24	1.0248	55	1.046	95	1.022
10	1.0099	26	1.0267	60	1.047	100	1.011
12	1.0121	28	1.0286	65	1.047		
14	1.0143	30	1.0305	70	1.046		

H_2SO_4 [JAB] (156), α (370, 371)**; (20, 247, 248, 335, 340, 341, 344, 348, 349, 390, 392, 393)*; (47, 60, 86, 98, 104, 106, 144, 197, 204, 214, 221, 224, 261, 279, 286, 311, 318, 319, 320, 323, 350, 351, 353, 387, 418, 419, 451, 463, 482, 485, 489, 494, 519, 529, 547, 551, 557, 592, 593, 596), α (151, 203, 355, 359, 409, 466, 489, 547, 555)

%	0°C	10°C	15°C	20°C	25°C	30°C	40°C	50°C	60°C	80°C	100°C
1	1.0074	1.0068	1.0060	1.0051	1.0038	1.0022	0.9986	0.9944	0.9895	0.9779	0.9645
2	1.0147	1.0138	1.0129	1.0118	1.0104	1.0087	1.0050	1.0006	0.9956	0.9839	0.9705
3	1.0219	1.0206	1.0197	1.0184	1.0169	1.0152	1.0113	1.0067	1.0017	0.9900	0.9766
4	1.0291	1.0275	1.0264	1.0250	1.0234	1.0216	1.0176	1.0129	1.0078	0.9961	0.9827
5	1.0364	1.0344	1.0332	1.0317	1.0300	1.0281	1.0240	1.0192	1.0140	1.0022	0.9888
6	1.0437	1.0414	1.0400	1.0385	1.0367	1.0347	1.0305	1.0256	1.0203	1.0084	0.9950
7	1.0511	1.0485	1.0469	1.0453	1.0434	1.0414	1.0371	1.0321	1.0266	1.0146	1.0013
8	1.0585	1.0556	1.0539	1.0522	1.0502	1.0481	1.0437	1.0386	1.0330	1.0209	1.0076
9	1.0660	1.0628	1.0610	1.0591	1.0571	1.0549	1.0503	1.0451	1.0395	1.0273	1.0140
10	1.0735	1.0700	1.0681	1.0661	1.0640	1.0617	1.0570	1.0517	1.0460	1.0338	1.0204
11	1.0810	1.0773	1.0753	1.0731	1.0710	1.0686	1.0637	1.0584	1.0526	1.0403	1.0269
12	1.0886	1.0846	1.0825	1.0802	1.0780	1.0756	1.0705	1.0651	1.0593	1.0469	1.0335
13	1.0962	1.0920	1.0898	1.0874	1.0851	1.0826	1.0774	1.0719	1.0661	1.0536	1.0402
14	1.1039	1.0994	1.0971	1.0947	1.0922	1.0897	1.0844	1.0788	1.0729	1.0603	1.0469
15	1.1116	1.1069	1.1045	1.1020	1.0994	1.0968	1.0914	1.0857	1.0798	1.0671	1.0537
16	1.1194	1.1145	1.1120	1.1094	1.1067	1.1040	1.0985	1.0927	1.0868	1.0740	1.0605
17	1.1272	1.1221	1.1195	1.1168	1.1141	1.1113	1.1057	1.0998	1.0938	1.0809	1.0674
18	1.1351	1.1298	1.1271	1.1243	1.1215	1.1187	1.1129	1.1070	1.1009	1.0879	1.0744
19	1.1430	1.1375	1.1347	1.1318	1.1290	1.1261	1.1202	1.1142	1.1081	1.0950	1.0814
20	1.1510	1.1453	1.1424	1.1394	1.1365	1.1335	1.1275	1.1215	1.1153	1.1021	1.0885
21	1.1590	1.1531	1.1501	1.1471	1.1441	1.1410	1.1349	1.1288	1.1226	1.1093	1.0957
22	1.1670	1.1609	1.1579	1.1548	1.1517	1.1486	1.1424	1.1362	1.1299	1.1166	1.1029
23	1.1751	1.1688	1.1657	1.1626	1.1594	1.1563	1.1500	1.1437	1.1373	1.1239	1.1102
24	1.1832	1.1768	1.1736	1.1704	1.1672	1.1640	1.1576	1.1512	1.1448	1.1313	1.1176
25	1.1914	1.1848	1.1816	1.1783	1.1750	1.1718	1.1653	1.1588	1.1523	1.1388	1.1250
26	1.1996	1.1929	1.1896	1.1862	1.1829	1.1796	1.1730	1.1665	1.1599	1.1463	1.1325
27	1.2078	1.2010	1.1976	1.1942	1.1909	1.1875	1.1808	1.1742	1.1676	1.1539	1.1400
28	1.2160	1.2091	1.2057	1.2023	1.1989	1.1955	1.1887	1.1820	1.1753	1.1616	1.1476
29	1.2243	1.2173	1.2138	1.2104	1.2069	1.2035	1.1966	1.1898	1.1831	1.1693	1.1553
30	1.2326	1.2255	1.2220	1.2185	1.2150	1.2115	1.2046	1.1977	1.1909	1.1771	1.1630
31	1.2409	1.2338	1.2302	1.2267	1.2232	1.2196	1.2126	1.2057	1.1988	1.1849	1.1708
32	1.2493	1.2421	1.2385	1.2349	1.2314	1.2278	1.2207	1.2137	1.2068	1.1928	1.1787
33	1.2577	1.2504	1.2468	1.2432	1.2396	1.2360	1.2289	1.2218	1.2148	1.2008	1.1866
34	1.2661	1.2588	1.2552	1.2515	1.2479	1.2443	1.2371	1.2300	1.2229	1.2088	1.1946
35	1.2746	1.2672	1.2636	1.2599	1.2563	1.2526	1.2454	1.2383	1.2311	1.2169	1.2027
36	1.2831	1.2757	1.2720	1.2684	1.2647	1.2610	1.2538	1.2466	1.2394	1.2251	1.2109
37	1.2917	1.2843	1.2805	1.2769	1.2732	1.2695	1.2622	1.2550	1.2477	1.2334	1.2192
38	1.3004	1.2929	1.2891	1.2855	1.2818	1.2780	1.2707	1.2635	1.2561	1.2418	1.2276
39	1.3091	1.3016	1.2978	1.2941	1.2904	1.2866	1.2793	1.2720	1.2646	1.2503	1.2361
40	1.3179	1.3103	1.3065	1.3028	1.2991	1.2953	1.2880	1.2806	1.2732	1.2589	1.2446
41	1.3268	1.3191	1.3153	1.3116	1.3079	1.3041	1.2967	1.2893	1.2819	1.2675	1.2532
42	1.3357	1.3280	1.3242	1.3205	1.3167	1.3129	1.3055	1.2981	1.2907	1.2762	1.2619
43	1.3447	1.3370	1.3332	1.3294	1.3256	1.3218	1.3144	1.3070	1.2996	1.2850	1.2707
44	1.3538	1.3461	1.3423	1.3384	1.3346	1.3308	1.3234	1.3160	1.3086	1.2939	1.2796
45	1.3630	1.3553	1.3515	1.3476	1.3437	1.3399	1.3325	1.3251	1.3177	1.3029	1.2886
46	1.3724	1.3646	1.3608	1.3569	1.3530	1.3492	1.3417	1.3343	1.3269	1.3120	1.2976
47	1.3819	1.3740	1.3702	1.3663	1.3624	1.3586	1.3510	1.3435	1.3362	1.3212	1.3067
48	1.3915	1.3835	1.3797	1.3758	1.3719	1.3680	1.3604	1.3528	1.3455	1.3305	1.3159
49	1.4012	1.3931	1.3893	1.3854	1.3814	1.3775	1.3699	1.3623	1.3549	1.3399	1.3253
50	1.4110	1.4029	1.3990	1.3951	1.3911	1.3872	1.3795	1.3719	1.3644	1.3494	1.3348
51	1.4209	1.4128	1.4088	1.4049	1.4009	1.3970	1.3893	1.3816	1.3740	1.3590	1.3444
52	1.4310	1.4228	1.4188	1.4148	1.4109	1.4069	1.3991	1.3914	1.3837	1.3687	1.3540
53	1.4412	1.4329	1.4289	1.4248	1.4209	1.4169	1.4091	1.4013	1.3936	1.3785	1.3637
54	1.4515	1.4431	1.4391	1.4350	1.4310	1.4270	1.4191	1.4113	1.4036	1.3884	1.3735
55	1.4619	1.4535	1.4494	1.4453	1.4412	1.4372	1.4293	1.4214	1.4137	1.3984	1.3834
56	1.4724	1.4640	1.4598	1.4557	1.4516	1.4475	1.4396	1.4317	1.4239	1.4085	1.3934
57	1.4830	1.4746	1.4703	1.4662	1.4621	1.4580	1.4500	1.4420	1.4342	1.4187	1.4035
58	1.4937	1.4852	1.4809	1.4768	1.4726	1.4685	1.4604	1.4524	1.4446	1.4290	1.4137
59	1.5045	1.4959	1.4916	1.4875	1.4832	1.4791	1.4709	1.4629	1.4551	1.4393	1.4240
60	1.5154	1.5067	1.5024	1.4983	1.4940	1.4898	1.4816	1.4735	1.4656	1.4497	1.4344
61	1.5264	1.5177	1.5133	1.5091	1.5048	1.5006	1.4923	1.4842	1.4762	1.4602	1.4449

H_2SO_4.—(*Continued*)

%	0°C	10°C	15°C	20°C	25°C	30°C	40°C	50°C	60°C	80°C	100°C
62	1.5375	1.5287	1.5243	1.5200	1.5157	1.5115	1.5031	1.4950	1.4869	1.4708	1.4554
63	1.5487	1.5398	1.5354	1.5310	1.5267	1.5225	1.5140	1.5058	1.4977	1.4815	1.4660
64	1.5600	1.5510	1.5465	1.5421	1.5378	1.5335	1.5250	1.5167	1.5086	1.4923	1.4766
65	1.5714	1.5623	1.5578	1.5533	1.5490	1.5446	1.5361	1.5277	1.5195	1.5031	1.4873
66	1.5828	1.5736	1.5691	1.5646	1.5602	1.5558	1.5472	1.5388	1.5305	1.5140	1.4981
67	1.5943	1.5850	1.5805	1.5760	1.5715	1.5671	1.5584	1.5499	1.5416	1.5249	1.5089
68	1.6059	1.5965	1.5920	1.5874	1.5829	1.5785	1.5697	1.5611	1.5528	1.5359	1.5198
69	1.6176	1.6081	1.6035	1.5989	1.5944	1.5899	1.5811	1.5724	1.5640	1.5470	1.5307
70	1.6293	1.6198	1.6151	1.6105	1.6059	1.6014	1.5925	1.5838	1.5753	1.5582	1.5417
71	1.6411	1.6315	1.6268	1.6221	1.6175	1.6130	1.6040	1.5952	1.5867	1.5694	1.5527
72	1.6529	1.6433	1.6385	1.6338	1.6292	1.6246	1.6155	1.6067	1.5981	1.5806	1.5637
73	1.6648	1.6551	1.6503	1.6456	1.6409	1.6363	1.6271	1.6182	1.6095	1.5919	1.5747
74	1.6768	1.6670	1.6622	1.6574	1.6526	1.6480	1.6387	1.6297	1.6209	1.6031	1.5857
75	1.6888	1.6789	1.6740	1.6692	1.6644	1.6597	1.6503	1.6412	1.6322	1.6142	1.5966
76	1.7008	1.6908	1.6858	1.6810	1.6761	1.6713	1.6619	1.6526	1.6435	1.6252	1.6074
77	1.7128	1.7026	1.6976	1.6927	1.6878	1.6829	1.6734	1.6640	1.6547	1.6361	1.6181
78	1.7247	1.7144	1.7093	1.7043	1.6994	1.6944	1.6847	1.6751	1.6657	1.6469	1.6286
79	1.7365	1.7261	1.7209	1.7158	1.7108	1.7058	1.6959	1.6862	1.6766	1.6575	1.6390
80	1.7482	1.7376	1.7323	1.7272	1.7221	1.7170	1.7069	1.6971	1.6873	1.6680	1.6493
81	1.7597	1.7489	1.7435	1.7383	1.7331	1.7279	1.7177	1.7077	1.6978	1.6782	1.6594
82	1.7709	1.7599	1.7544	1.7491	1.7437	1.7385	1.7281	1.7180	1.7080	1.6882	1.6692
83	1.7815	1.7704	1.7649	1.7594	1.7540	1.7487	1.7382	1.7279	1.7179	1.6979	1.6787
84	1.7916	1.7804	1.7748	1.7693	1.7639	1.7585	1.7479	1.7375	1.7274	1.7072	1.6878
85	1.8009	1.7897	1.7841	1.7786	1.7732	1.7678	1.7571	1.7466	1.7364	1.7161	1.6966
86	1.8095	1.7983	1.7927	1.7872	1.7818	1.7763	1.7657	1.7552	1.7449	1.7245	1.7050
87	1.8173	1.8061	1.8006	1.7951	1.7897	1.7842	1.7736	1.7632	1.7529	1.7324	1.7129
88	1.8243	1.8132	1.8077	1.8022	1.7968	1.7914	1.7809	1.7705	1.7602	1.7397	1.7202
89	1.8306	1.8195	1.8141	1.8087	1.8033	1.7979	1.7874	1.7770	1.7669	1.7464	1.7269
90	1.8361	1.8252	1.8198	1.8144	1.8091	1.8038	1.7933	1.7829	1.7729	1.7525	1.7331
91	1.8410	1.8302	1.8248	1.8195	1.8142	1.8090	1.7986	1.7883	1.7783	1.7581	1.7388
92	1.8453	1.8346	1.8293	1.8240	1.8188	1.8136	1.8033	1.7932	1.7832	1.7633	1.7439
93	1.8490	1.8384	1.8331	1.8279	1.8227	1.8176	1.8074	1.7974	1.7876	1.7681	1.7485
94	1.8520	1.8415	1.8363	1.8312	1.8260	1.8210	1.8109	1.8011	1.7914		
95	1.8544	1.8439	1.8388	1.8337	1.8286	1.8236	1.8137	1.8040	1.7944		
96	1.8560	1.8457	1.8406	1.8355	1.8305	1.8255	1.8157	1.8060	1.7965		
97	1.8569	1.8466	1.8414	1.8364	1.8314	1.8264	1.8166	1.8071	1.7977		
98	1.8567	1.8463	1.8411	1.8361	1.8310	1.8261	1.8163	1.8068	1.7976		
99	1.8551	1.8445	1.8393	1.8342	1.8292	1.8242	1.8145	1.8050	1.7958		
100	1.8517	1.8409	1.8357	1.8305	1.8255	1.8205	1.8107	1.8013	1.7922		

H_2SO_4.—(*Continued*)

(346)		(348, 349, 586)**		
%	$d_4^{5.96}$	%	$d_4^{13.00}$	$d_4^{18.00}$
0.005	1.000 0140	0.05	0.999 810	0.999 028
0.01	1.000 0576	0.1	1.000 185	0.999 400
0.02	1.000 1434	0.2	1.000 912	1.000 119
0.03	1.000 2276	0.3	1.001 623	1.000 820
0.04	1.000 3104	0.4	1.002 326	1.001 512
0.05	1.000 3920	0.5	1.003 023	1.002 197
0.06	1.000 4726	0.6	1.003 716	1.002 877
0.07	1.000 5523	0.8	1.005 090	1.004 227
0.08	1.000 6313	1.0	1.006 452	1.005 570
0.09	1.000 7098	1.2	1.007 807	1.006 909
0.10	1.000 7880	1.4	1.009 159	1.008 247
0.15	1.001 1732	1.6	1.010 510	1.009 583
0.20	1.001 5514	1.8	1.011 860	1.010 918
0.25	1.001 9254	2.0	1.013 209	1.012 252
0.30	1.002 2961	2.2	1.014 557	1.013 586
0.35	1.002 6639	2.4	1.015 904	1.014 919
0.40	1.003 0292			
0.45	1.003 3923			
0.50	1.003 7534			

H_2SO_4.—(*Continued*)

% (588)	1	2	3	4	5
d_4^{110}	0.9562	0.9616	0.9672	0.9730	0.9790
d_4^{120}	0.9488	0.9544	0.9602	0.9662	0.9724
d_4^{130}	0.9408	0.9466	0.9526	0.9588	0.9653
d_4^{140}	0.9322	0.9382	0.9443	0.9506	0.9571

HNO_3, *see* p. 58–59
NH_3, *see* p. 59

NH_2OH, Hydroxylamine [JAB] (15)**; (79)

%	d_4^{20}	%	d_4^{20}	%	d_4^{20}	%	d_4^{20}
1	1.0002	12	1.0235	24	1.0499	45	1.0997
2	1.0023	14	1.0278	26	1.0545	50	1.1122
4	1.0065	16	1.0322	28	1.0591	55	1.1249
6	1.0107	18	1.0366	30	1.0637		
8	1.0149	20	1.0410	35	1.0755		
10	1.0192	22	1.0454	40	1.0875		

HNO_3 [JAB] (**60, 98, 621, 623, 624**), α (**203, 370, 463, 555, 622**)**; (**110, 394, 557**)*; (**44, 78, 106, 144, 197, 214, 221, 224, 247, 313, 318, 319, 321, 323, 344, 347, 352, 378, 386, 463, 483, 485, 504, 514, 519, 529, 551, 574, 592, 596, 628, 649, 660**), α (**151, 211, 372, 545, 605**)

%	0°C	5°C	10°C	15°C	20°C	25°C	30°C	40°C	50°C	60°C	80°C	100°C
1	1.0058	1.00572	1.00534	1.00464	1.00364	1.00241	1.0009	0.9973	0.9931	0.9882	0.9767	0.9632
2	1.0117	1.01149	1.01099	1.01018	1.00909	1.00778	1.0061	1.0025	0.9982	0.9932	0.9816	0.9681
3	1.0176	1.01730	1.01668	1.01576	1.01457	1.01318	1.0114	1.0077	1.0033	1.9982	0.9865	0.9730
4	1.0236	1.02315	1.02240	1.02137	1.02008	1.01861	1.0168	1.0129	1.0084	1.0033	0.9915	0.9779
5	1.0296	1.02904	1.02816	1.02702	1.02563	1.02408	1.0222	1.0182	1.0136	1.0084	0.9965	0.9829
6	1.0357	1.03497	1.03397	1.03272	1.03122	1.02958	1.0277	1.0235	1.0188	1.0136	1.0015	0.9879
7	1.0418	1.0410	1.0399	1.0385	1.0369	1.0352	1.0333	1.0289	1.0241	1.0188	1.0066	0.9929
8	1.0480	1.0471	1.0458	1.0443	1.0427	1.0409	1.0389	1.0344	1.0295	1.0241	1.0117	0.9980
9	1.0543	1.0532	1.0518	1.0502	1.0485	1.0466	1.0446	1.0399	1.0349	1.0294	1.0169	1.0032
10	1.0606	1.0594	1.0578	1.0561	1.0543	1.0523	1.0503	1.0455	1.0403	1.0347	1.0221	1.0083
11	1.0669	1.0656	1.0639	1.0621	1.0602	1.0581	1.0560	1.0511	1.0458	1.0401	1.0273	1.0134
12	1.0733	1.0718	1.0700	1.0681	1.0661	1.0640	1.0618	1.0567	1.0513	1.0455	1.0326	1.0186
13	1.0797	1.0781	1.0762	1.0742	1.0721	1.0699	1.0676	1.0624	1.0568	1.0509	1.0379	1.0238
14	1.0862	1.0845	1.0824	1.0803	1.0781	1.0758	1.0735	1.0681	1.0624	1.0564	1.0432	1.0289
15	1.0927	1.0909	1.0887	1.0865	1.0842	1.0818	1.0794	1.0739	1.0680	1.0619	1.0485	1.0341
16	1.0992	1.0973	1.0950	1.0927	1.0903	1.0879	1.0854	1.0797	1.0737	1.0675	1.0538	1.0393
17	1.1057	1.1038	1.1014	1.0989	1.0964	1.0940	1.0914	1.0855	1.0794	1.0731	1.0592	1.0444
18	1.1123	1.1103	1.1078	1.1052	1.1026	1.1001	1.0974	1.0913	1.0851	1.0787	1.0646	1.0496
19	1.1189	1.1168	1.1142	1.1115	1.1088	1.1062	1.1034	1.0972	1.0908	1.0843	1.0700	1.0547
20	1.1255	1.1234	1.1206	1.1178	1.1150	1.1123	1.1094	1.1031	1.0966	1.0899	1.0754	1.0598
21	1.1322	1.1300	1.1271	1.1242	1.1213	1.1185	1.1155	1.1090	1.1024	1.0956	1.0808	1.0650
22	1.1389	1.1366	1.1336	1.1306	1.1276	1.1247	1.1217	1.1150	1.1083	1.1013	1.0862	1.0701
23	1.1457	1.1433	1.1402	1.1371	1.1340	1.1310	1.1280	1.1210	1.1142	1.1070	1.0917	1.0753
24	1.1525	1.1501	1.1469	1.1437	1.1404	1.1374	1.1343	1.1271	1.1201	1.1127	1.0972	1.0805
25	1.1594	1.1569	1.1536	1.1503	1.1469	1.1438	1.1406	1.1332	1.1260	1.1185	1.1027	1.0857
26	1.1663	1.1638	1.1603	1.1569	1.1534	1.1502	1.1469	1.1394	1.1320	1.1244	1.1083	1.0910
27	1.1733	1.1707	1.1670	1.1635	1.1600	1.1566	1.1533	1.1456	1.1381	1.1303	1.1139	1.0963
28	1.1803	1.1777	1.1738	1.1702	1.1666	1.1631	1.1597	1.1519	1.1442	1.1362	1.1195	1.1016
29	1.1874	1.1847	1.1807	1.1770	1.1733	1.1697	1.1662	1.1582	1.1503	1.1422	1.1251	1.1069
30	1.1945	1.1917	1.1876	1.1838	1.1800	1.1763	1.1727	1.1645	1.1564	1.1482	1.1307	1.1122
31	1.2016	1.1988	1.1945	1.1906	1.1867	1.1829	1.1792	1.1708	1.1625	1.1542	1.1363	1.1175
32	1.2088	1.2059	1.2014	1.1974	1.1934	1.1896	1.1857	1.1772	1.1687	1.1602	1.1419	1.1228
33	1.2160	1.2131	1.2084	1.2043	1.2002	1.1963	1.1922	1.1836	1.1749	1.1662	1.1476	1.1281
34	1.2233	1.2203	1.2155	1.2113	1.2071	1.2030	1.1988	1.1901	1.1812	1.1723	1.1533	1.1335
35	1.2306	1.2275	1.2227	1.2183	1.2140	1.2098	1.2055	1.1966	1.1876	1.1784	1.1591	1.1390
36	1.2375	1.2344	1.2294	1.2249	1.2205	1.2163	1.2119	1.2028	1.1936	1.1842	1.1645	1.1440
37	1.2444	1.2412	1.2361	1.2315	1.2270	1.2227	1.2182	1.2089	1.1995	1.1899	1.1699	1.1490
38	1.2513	1.2479	1.2428	1.2381	1.2335	1.2291	1.2245	1.2150	1.2054	1.1956	1.1752	1.1540
39	1.2581	1.2546	1.2494	1.2446	1.2399	1.2354	1.2308	1.2210	1.2112	1.2013	1.1805	1.1589
40	1.2649	1.2613	1.2560	1.2511	1.2463	1.2417	1.2370	1.2270	1.2170	1.2069	1.1858	1.1638
41	1.2717	1.2680	1.2626	1.2576	1.2527	1.2480	1.2432	1.2330	1.2229	1.2126	1.1911	1.1687
42	1.2786	1.2747	1.2692	1.2641	1.2591	1.2543	1.2494	1.2390	1.2287	1.2182	1.1963	1.1735
43	1.2854	1.2814	1.2758	1.2706	1.2655	1.2606	1.2556	1.2450	1.2345	1.2238	1.2015	1.1783
44	1.2922	1.2880	1.2824	1.2771	1.2719	1.2669	1.2618	1.2510	1.2403	1.2294	1.2067	1.1831
45	1.2990	1.2947	1.2890	1.2836	1.2783	1.2732	1.2680	1.2570	1.2461	1.2350	1.2119	1.1879
46	1.3058	1.3014	1.2955	1.2901	1.2847	1.2795	1.2742	1.2630	1.2519	1.2406	1.2171	1.1927
47	1.3126	1.3080	1.3021	1.2966	1.2911	1.2858	1.2804	1.2690	1.2577	1.2462	1.2223	1.1976
48	1.3194	1.3147	1.3087	1.3031	1.2975	1.2921	1.2867	1.2750	1.2635	1.2518	1.2275	1.2024
49	1.3263	1.3214	1.3153	1.3096	1.3040	1.2984	1.2929	1.2811	1.2693	1.2575	1.2328	1.2073
50	1.3327	1.3277	1.3215	1.3157	1.3100	1.3043	1.2987	1.2867	1.2748	1.2628	1.2377	1.2118
51	1.3391	1.3339	1.3277	1.3218	1.3160	1.3102	1.3045	1.2923	1.2802	1.2680	1.2425	1.2163
52	1.3454	1.3401	1.3338	1.3278	1.3219	1.3160	1.3102	1.2978	1.2856	1.2731	1.2473	1.2208
53	1.3517	1.3462	1.3399	1.3338	1.3278	1.3218	1.3159	1.3033	1.2909	1.2782	1.2521	1.2252
54	1.3579	1.3523	1.3459	1.3397	1.3336	1.3275	1.3215	1.3087	1.2961	1.2833	1.2568	1.2296
55	1.3640	1.3583	1.3518	1.3455	1.3393	1.3331	1.3270	1.3141	1.3013	1.2883	1.2615	1.2339
56	1.3700	1.3642	1.3576	1.3512	1.3449	1.3386	1.3324	1.3194	1.3064	1.2932	1.2661	1.2382
57	1.3759	1.3700	1.3634	1.3569	1.3505	1.3441	1.3377	1.3246	1.3114	1.2981	1.2706	1.2424
58	1.3818	1.3757	1.3691	1.3625	1.3560	1.3495	1.3430	1.3298	1.3164	1.3029	1.2751	1.2466
59	1.3875	1.3813	1.3747	1.3680	1.3614	1.3548	1.3482	1.3348	1.3213	1.3077	1.2795	1.2507
60	1.3931	1.3868	1.3801	1.3734	1.3667	1.3600	1.3533	1.3398	1.3261	1.3124	1.2839	1.2547
61	1.3986	1.3922	1.3855	1.3787	1.3719	1.3651	1.3583	1.3447	1.3308	1.3169	1.2881	1.2587
62	1.4039	1.3975	1.3907	1.3838	1.3769	1.3700	1.3632	1.3494	1.3354	1.3213	1.2922	1.2625
63	1.4091	1.4027	1.3958	1.3888	1.3818	1.3748	1.3679	1.3540	1.3398	1.3255	1.2962	1.2661

HNO_3.—(*Continued*)

%	5°C	10°C	15°C	20°C	25°C	30°C
64	1.4078	1.4007	1.3936	1.3866	1.3795	1.3725
65	1.4128	1.4055	1.3984	1.3913	1.3841	1.3770
66	1.4177	1.4103	1.4031	1.3959	1.3887	1.3814
67	1.4224	1.4150	1.4077	1.4004	1.3932	1.3857
68	1.4271	1.4196	1.4122	1.4048	1.3976	1.3900
69	1.4317	1.4241	1.4166	1.4091	1.4019	1.3942
70	1.4362	1.4285	1.4210	1.4134	1.4061	1.3983
71	1.4406	1.4328	1.4252	1.4176	1.4102	1.4023
72	1.4449	1.4371	1.4294	1.4218	1.4142	1.4063
73	1.4491	1.4413	1.4335	1.4258	1.4182	1.4103
74	1.4532	1.4454	1.4376	1.4298	1.4221	1.4142
75	1.4573	1.4494	1.4415	1.4337	1.4259	1.4180
76	1.4613	1.4533	1.4454	1.4375	1.4296	1.4217
77	1.4652	1.4572	1.4492	1.4413	1.4333	1.4253
78	1.4690	1.4610	1.4529	1.4450	1.4369	1.4288
79	1.4727	1.4647	1.4565	1.4486	1.4404	1.4323
80	1.4764	1.4683	1.4601	1.4521	1.4439	1.4357
81	1.4800	1.4718	1.4636	1.4555	1.4473	1.4391
82	1.4835	1.4753	1.4670	1.4589	1.4507	1.4424

%	5°C	10°C	15°C	20°C	25°C	30°C
83	1.4869	1.4787	1.4704	1.4622	1.4540	1.4456
84	1.4903	1.4820	1.4737	1.4655	1.4572	1.4487
85	1.4936	1.4852	1.4769	1.4686	1.4603	1.4518
86	1.4968	1.4883	1.4799	1.4716	1.4633	1.4548
87	1.4999	1.4913	1.4829	1.4745	1.4662	1.4577
88	1.5029	1.4942	1.4858	1.4773	1.4690	1.4605
89	1.5058	1.4970	1.4885	1.4800	1.4716	1.4631
90	1.5085	1.4997	1.4911	1.4826	1.4741	1.4656
91	1.5111	1.5023	1.4936	1.4850	1.4766	1.4681
92	1.5136	1.5048	1.4960	1.4873	1.4789	1.4704
93	1.5156	1.5068	1.4979	1.4892	1.4807	1.4722
94	1.5177	1.5088	1.4999	1.4912	1.4826	1.4741
95	1.5198	1.5109	1.5019	1.4932	1.4846	1.4761
96	1.5220	1.5130	1.5040	1.4952	1.4867	1.4781
97	1.5244	1.5152	1.5062	1.4974	1.4889	1.4802
98	1.5278	1.5187	1.5096	1.5008	1.4922	1.4835
99	1.5327	1.5235	1.5144	1.5056	1.4969	1.4881
100	1.5402	1.5310	1.5217	1.5129	1.5040	1.4952

NH_3 [LJG] (**197, 503**), α(**670**)**; (**665**)*; (**44, 98, 106, 167, 253, 328, 378, 395, 463, 483, 519, 529, 664, 667, 669, 670, 671**), α (**211, 336, 664**)

%	−15°C	−10°C	−5°C	0°C	+5°C	10°C
1		0.9943	0.9954	0.9959	0.9958	0.9955
2		0.9906	0.9915	0.9919	0.9917	0.9913
4		0.9834	0.9840	0.9842	0.9837	0.9832
6	0.977	0.9766	0.9769	0.9767	0.9760	0.9753
8	0.970	0.9701	0.9701	0.9695	0.9686	0.9677
10	0.964	0.9638	0.9635	0.9627	0.9616	0.9604
12	0.958	0.9576	0.9571	0.9561	0.9548	0.9534
14	0.952	0.9517	0.9510	0.9497	0.9483	0.9467
16	0.947	0.9461	0.9450	0.9435	0.9420	0.9402
18		0.9406	0.9392	0.9375	0.9357	0.9338
20		0.9353	0.9335	0.9316	0.9296	0.9275
22		0.9300	0.9280	0.9258	0.9237	0.9214
24		0.9249	0.9226	0.9202	0.9179	0.9155
26		0.9199	0.9174	0.9148	0.9123	0.9097
28		0.9150	0.9122	0.9094	0.9067	0.9040
30		0.9101	0.9070	0.9040	0.9012	0.8983

%	15°C	20°C	25°C
1	0.9948	0.9939	0.993
2	0.9905	0.9895	0.988
4	0.9822	0.9811	0.980
6	0.9742	0.9730	0.972
8	0.9665	0.9651	0.964
10	0.9591	0.9575	0.956
12	0.9519	0.9501	0.948
14	0.9450	0.9430	0.941
16	0.9383	0.9362	0.934
18	0.9317	0.9295	
20	0.9253	0.9229	
22	0.9190	0.9164	
24	0.9129	0.9101	
26	0.9069	0.9040	
28	0.9010	0.8980	
30	0.8951	0.8920	
32	0.8892		
34	0.8832		
36	0.8772		
38	0.8712		
40	0.8651		

Determined in a sealed tube (**665**)

%	d_4^{15}
45	0.849
50	0.832
55	0.815
60	0.796
65	0.776
70	0.755
75	0.733
80	0.711
85	0.688
90	0.665
95	0.642
100	0.618

NH_4NO_3 [JAB] (**36, 106, 449, 483, 660**), α (**203, 375**)**; (**222, 223, 224, 225**), α (**570, 608**)*; (**1, 190, 195, 218, 229, 307, 328, 342, 385, 508, 519, 529, 530, 543, 570, 573, 592**), α (**271**)

%	0°C	10°C	20°C	25°C	30°C	40°C
1	1.0043	1.0039	1.0023	1.0011	0.9996	0.9961
2	1.0088	1.0082	1.0064	1.0051	1.0036	1.0000
4	1.0178	1.0168	1.0147	1.0132	1.0116	1.0079
6	1.0268	1.0254	1.0230	1.0214	1.0197	1.0158
8	1.0358	1.0340	1.0313	1.0297	1.0278	1.0238
10	1.0448	1.0427	1.0397	1.0380	1.0360	1.0319
12	1.0539	1.0515	1.0482	1.0464	1.0443	1.0400
14	1.0630	1.0603	1.0567	1.0548	1.0527	1.0482
16	1.0721	1.0691	1.0653	1.0633	1.0612	1.0565
18	1.0813	1.0780	1.0740	1.0719	1.0697	1.0649
20	1.0905	1.0870	1.0828	1.0806	1.0783	1.0734
22	1.0997	1.0960	1.0916	1.0894	1.0870	1.0820
24	1.1090	1.1051	1.1005	1.0982	1.0958	1.0907
26	1.1183	1.1142	1.1095	1.1071	1.1047	1.0994
28	1.1277	1.1234	1.1186	1.1161	1.1136	1.1082
30	1.1371	1.1327	1.1277	1.1252	1.1226	1.1171
35	1.1613	1.1565	1.1512	1.1486	1.1458	1.1402
40	1.1862	1.1810	1.1754	1.1727	1.1697	1.1640
45	1.2118	1.2062	1.2003	1.1975	1.1943	1.1885
50	1.2380	1.2320	1.2258	1.2229	1.2195	1.2136

%	50°C	60°C	80°C	%	50°C	60°C	80°C
1	0.9919	0.9870	0.9755	20	1.0682	1.0627	1.0506
2	0.9958	0.9908	0.9793	22	1.0767	1.0711	1.0589
4	1.0036	0.9985	0.9869	24	1.0852	1.0796	1.0673
6	1.0114	1.0063	0.9946	26	1.0938	1.0882	1.0758
8	1.0193	1.0142	1.0024	28	1.1025	1.0968	1.0844
10	1.0272	1.0221	1.0102	30	1.1113	1.1055	1.0931
12	1.0352	1.0301	1.0181	35	1.1342	1.1281	1.1154
14	1.0433	1.0381	1.0261	40	1.1579	1.1515	1.1385
16	1.0515	1.0462	1.0342	45	1.1822	1.1757	1.1623
18	1.0598	1.0544	1.0424	50	1.2072	1.2006	1.1868

% (**150**)...	1	2	3	4	5
d_4^{16}	1.00314	1.00730	1.01145	1.01560	1.01975

7.769 %† (**256**)

°C	0	10	20	30	40	50
d^t	1.03490	1.03314	1.03044	1.02695	1.02308	1.01816

† For 3.945 % NH_4NO_3, d_4^{20} = 1.01451 (**256**).

NH_4F [JAB] (288)**; (36, 190)

%	d_4^{18}	%	d_4^{18}	%	d_4^{18}	%	d_4^{18}
1	1.0034	4	1.0178	8	1.0346	12	1.0487
2	1.0085	6	1.0265	10	1.0420	14	1.0547

NH_4Cl [JAB] (548), α (219)**; (551)*; (1, 36, 38, 45, 86, 87, 101, 105, 106, 144, 190, 199, 215, 218, 219, 221, 223, 224, 225, 229, 247, 261, 278, 328, 344, 347, 378, 385, 425, 447, 449, 477, 483, 519, 529, 533, 543, 573, 592, 596, 618, 644), α (38, 151, 211, 271, 609)

%	0°C	10°C	20°C	25°C	30°C
1	1.0033	1.0029	1.0013	1.0002	0.9987
2	1.0067	1.0062	1.0045	1.0033	1.0018
4	1.0135	1.0126	1.0107	1.0093	1.0077
6	1.0201	1.0189	1.0168	1.0153	1.0136
8	1.0266	1.0251	1.0227	1.0212	1.0195
10	1.0329	1.0311	1.0286	1.0270	1.0253
12	1.0391	1.0370	1.0344	1.0327	1.0310
14	1.0451	1.0428	1.0401	1.0383	1.0366
16	1.0510	1.0485	1.0457	1.0439	1.0422
18	1.0568	1.0541	1.0512	1.0494	1.0477
20	1.0625	1.0596	1.0567	1.0549	1.0532
22	1.0681	1.0651	1.0621	1.0603	1.0587
24	1.0736	1.0705	1.0674	1.0657	1.0641

%	40°C	50°C	60°C	80°C	100°C
1	0.9952	0.9910	0.9861	0.9749	0.9617
2	0.9982	0.9940	0.9891	0.9780	0.9651
4	1.0041	0.9999	0.9950	0.9842	0.9718
6	1.0100	1.0058	1.0009	0.9903	0.9784
8	1.0158	1.0116	1.0067	0.9963	0.9849
10	1.0216	1.0174	1.0125	1.0022	0.9912
12	1.0273	1.0231	1.0182	1.0081	0.9975
14	1.0329	1.0287	1.0239	1.0140	1.0036
16	1.0385	1.0343	1.0296	1.0198	1.0096
18	1.0441	1.0399	1.0353	1.0255	1.0155
20	1.0496	1.0454	1.0409	1.0312	1.0213
22	1.0551	1.0509	1.0465	1.0369	1.0271
24	1.0605	1.0564	1.0520	1.0426	1.0327

Values of $d_4^{20.004}$ (373)

0.01 %	0.02 %	0.03 %	0.04 %	0.05 %
0.998 26593	0.998 29988	0.998 33343	0.998 36668	0.998 39973

5.2733 % (27)

d_4^{0}	d_4^{10}	d_4^{20}	d_4^{25}	d_4^{30}	d_4^{40}	d_4^{50}
1.01769	1.01654	1.01454	1.01322	1.01171	1.00821	1.00397

% (150).....	0.5	1	2	3
d_4^{16}..........	1.00063	1.00225	1.00544	1.00859

N_2H_5Cl, Hydrazine hydrochloride [JAB]; 7.60 %, d_4^{20} = 1.0295 (15)

NH_4OCl, Hydroxylamine hydrochloride [JAB] (15)

%	d_4^{20}	%	d_4^{20}	%	d_4^{20}	%	d_4^{20}
1	1.0026	6	1.0246	12	1.0509	18	1.0770
2	1.0070	8	1.0334	14	1.0596		
4	1.0158	10	1.0422	16	1.0683		

$N_2H_6Cl_2$, Hydrazine dihydrochloride [JAB] (15)

%.....	1	2	4	6	8	10
d_4^{20}.....	1.0026	1.0070	1.0158	1.0247	1.0338	1.0431

NH_4ClO_3 [LJG]; with 2.54 %, d_4^{25} = 1.00831 (529)

NH_4ClO_4 [LJG] (291, 414)**; (529)*

%	d_4^{15}	d_4^{20}	d_4^{25}	%	d_4^{15}	d_4^{20}	d_4^{25}
1	1.0039	1.0029	1.0018	8	1.0386	1.0370	1.0355
2	1.0088	1.0077	1.0065	10	1.0489	1.0470	1.0455
4	1.0186	1.0173	1.0160	12	1.0594	1.0572	1.0557
6	1.0285	1.0271	1.0257	14	1.0701	1.0676	1.0660

NH_4Br [JAB] (229, 287, 483)**; (36, 166, 190, 519, 543, 573, 596)

%	d_4^{18}	d_4^{25}	%	d_4^{18}	d_4^{25}	%	d_4^{18}	d_4^{25}
1	1.0043	1.0027	14	1.0822	1.0799	28	1.1782	1.1753
2	1.0100	1.0084	16	1.0950	1.0927	30	1.1933	1.1901
4	1.0215	1.0198	18	1.1081	1.1058	32	1.2088	1.2053
6	1.0332	1.0314	20	1.1215	1.1191	34	1.2247	1.2209
8	1.0451	1.0432	22	1.1352	1.1327	36		1.2369
10	1.0572	1.0552	24	1.1492	1.1466	38		1.2533
12	1.0696	1.0674	26	1.1635	1.1608	40		1.2702

NH_4I [JAB] (287)**; (36, 190, 225, 229, 342, 378, 483, 511, 519, 543, 618)

%	d_4^{18}	%	d_4^{18}	%	d_4^{18}	%	d_4^{18}
1	1.0050	10	1.0652	20	1.1407	30	1.2265
2	1.0114	12	1.0795	22	1.1570	35	1.2745
4	1.0244	14	1.0942	24	1.1737	40	1.3264
6	1.0377	16	1.1093	26	1.1908	45	1.3823
8	1.0513	18	1.1248	28	1.2084		

NH_4HSO_4 [JAB]; 66.67 %, d_4^{15} = 1.4429 %; d_4^{25} = 1.4387 % (483)

$(NH_4)_2SO_4$ [JAB] (204, 505), α (375, 587)**; (106, 155)*; (1, 36, 101, 190, 221, 223, 224, 225, 328, 342, 405, 425, 477, 483, 517, 519, 529, 533, 573, 592, 615, 618, 642)

%	0°C	10°C	20°C	25°C	30°C
1	1.0061	1.0058	1.0041	1.0030	1.0015
2	1.0124	1.0119	1.0101	1.0089	1.0074
4	1.0248	1.0240	1.0220	1.0207	1.0191
6	1.0372	1.0360	1.0338	1.0324	1.0308
8	1.0495	1.0480	1.0456	1.0441	1.0425
10	1.0618	1.0600	1.0574	1.0558	1.0542
12	1.0740	1.0719	1.0691	1.0675	1.0658
14	1.0861	1.0837	1.0808	1.0791	1.0774
16	1.0980	1.0954	1.0924	1.0907	1.0889
18	1.1098	1.1070	1.1039	1.1022	1.1003
20	1.1215	1.1186	1.1154	1.1136	1.1117
22	1.1332	1.1302	1.1269	1.1250	1.1231
24	1.1448	1.1417	1.1383	1.1364	1.1345
26	1.1563	1.1531	1.1496	1.1477	1.1458
28	1.1677	1.1645	1.1609	1.1589	1.1570
30	1.1791	1.1757	1.1721	1.1701	1.1681
35	1.2072	1.2037	1.2000	1.1980	1.1960
40	1.2350	1.2314	1.2277	1.2257	1.2237
45	1.2626	1.2589	1.2552	1.2532	1.2512
50	1.2899	1.2862	1.2825	1.2805	1.2785

%	40°C	50°C	60°C	80°C	100°C
1	0.9980	0.9939	0.9890	0.9777	0.9644
2	1.0039	0.9997	0.9948	0.9836	0.9705
4	1.0155	1.0113	1.0064	0.9953	0.9826
6	1.0271	1.0228	1.0180	1.0070	0.9946
8	1.0387	1.0344	1.0296	1.0187	1.0066
10	1.0503	1.0460	1.0412	1.0304	1.0185
12	1.0619	1.0576	1.0527	1.0421	1.0303
14	1.0734	1.0691	1.0642	1.0537	1.0421
16	1.0849	1.0805	1.0757	1.0653	1.0539
18	1.0963	1.0919	1.0872	1.0768	1.0656
20	1.1077	1.1033	1.0986	1.0883	1.0772
22	1.1191	1.1147	1.1100	1.0997	1.0888
24	1.1304	1.1260	1.1214	1.1111	1.1003
26	1.1417	1.1373	1.1327	1.1225	1.1118
28	1.1529	1.1485	1.1439	1.1338	1.1232
30	1.1640	1.1597	1.1550	1.1451	1.1346
35	1.1919	1.1876	1.1829	1.1731	1.1629
40	1.2196	1.2153	1.2107	1.2011	1.1910
45	1.2471	1.2429	1.2384	1.2290	1.2189
50	1.2745	1.2704	1.2660	1.2568	1.2466

$(NH_4)_2SO_4$.—(*Continued*)

% (150)...	1	2	3	4	5
d_4^{16}........	1.00500	1.01097	1.01689	1.02277	1.02861

$(NH_4)_2S_2O_6$ [LJG]; with 2.45 %, d_4^{25} = 1.00968 (529)
$(NH_4)_2S_2O_8$ [JAB]; (602) [LJG]

%......	1	2	3	4
d_4^{15}......	1.0042	1.0093	1.0144	1.0195

NH_4HSeO_3 [LJG]; with 4.87 %, d_4^{20} = 1.0305 (463)
$(NH_4)_2SeO_3$ [LJG]; with 4.08 %, d_4^{20} = 1.0255 (463)
HPO_3 [LJG]; d_4^{15} = 1.0141 with 1.954 %; = 1.1083 with 16.23 % (17, 602)

H_3PO_3 [LJG] (463, 660)

%	d_4^{20}	%	d_4^{10}	%	$d_4^{26.8}$	%	$d_4^{25.6}$
4.10	1.0179	26.77	1.1336	30.66	1.1609	73.69	1.4665

H_3PO_4 [LJG] (338, 525), α (203)**; (349, 514), α (247)*; (98, 144, 253, 254, 340, 463, 517, 526, 536, 551, 634, 635, 660)

°C	1 %	2 %	4 %	6 %	8 %	10 %	12 %	14 %	16 %	18 %	20 %
0	1.0057	1.0113	1.0226	1.0339	1.0454	1.0571	1.0690	1.0811	1.0934	1.1061	1.1192
10	1.0054	1.0109	1.0219	1.0330	1.0442	1.0557	1.0673	1.0792	1.0914	1.1039	1.1167
20	1.0038	1.0092	1.0200	1.0309	1.0420	1.0532	1.0647	1.0764	1.0884	1.1008	1.1134
25	1.0026	1.0079	1.0187	1.0295	1.0405	1.0517	1.0631	1.0747	1.0866	1.0990	1.1115
30	1.0012	1.0065	1.0172	1.0279	1.0388	1.0499	1.0612	1.0728	1.0847	1.0969	1.1094
40	0.9976	1.0029	1.0135	1.0241	1.0349	1.0459	1.0571	1.0685	1.0803	1.0925	1.1048

°C	22 %	24 %	26 %	28 %	30 %	35 %	40 %	45 %	50 %	55 %	60 %
10	1.1298	1.1431	1.1567	1.1705	1.1846	1.221	1.259	1.299	1.341	1.385	1.432
20	1.1263	1.1395	1.1529	1.1665	1.1805	1.216	1.254	1.293	1.335	1.379	1.426
25	1.1243	1.1374	1.1507	1.1643	1.1782	1.214	1.251	1.291	1.332	1.376	1.423
30	1.1222	1.1352	1.1484	1.1620	1.1758	1.211	1.249	1.288	1.329	1.373	1.420

°C	65 %	70 %	75 %	80 %	85 %	90 %	92 %	94 %	96 %	98 %	100 %
10	1.481	1.533									
20	1.475	1.526	1.579	1.633	1.689	1.746	1.770	1.794	1.819	1.844	1.870
25	1.471	1.522	1.575	1.629	1.685	1.743	1.766	1.790	1.815	1.840	1.866
30	1.468	1.519	1.572	1.626	1.682	1.738	1.762	1.786	1.811	1.836	1.862
40						1.730	1.754	1.778	1.803	1.828	1.854
50						1.723	1.747	1.771	1.796	1.821	1.846
60						1.715	1.740	1.764	1.789	1.815	1.841

%†	d_4^{18} (349)	%†	d_4^{18} (349)	%†	d_4^{18} (349)
0.1	0.999 221	0.8	1.003 095	2.5	1.012 33
0.2	0.999 793	1.0	1.004 19	3.0	1.015 05
0.4	1.000 900	1.5	1.006 91	4.0	1.020 52
0.6	1.002 000	2.0	1.009 61		

† A correction of 1 % was applied to the concentrations of this table.

$NH_4H_2PO_3$ [LJG]; with 3.30 %, d_4^{20} = 1.0131 (463)
$(NH_4)_2HPO_3$ [LJG]; with 2.90 %, d_4^{20} = 1.0141 (463)
$NH_4H_2PO_4$ [LJG]; with 2.88 %, d_4^{20} = 1.0174 (463)
$(NH_4)_2HPO_4$ [LJG]; with 6.36 %, d_4^{15} = 1.038 (144); with 6.90 %, d_4^{20} = 1.0360 (561)
$(NH_4)_3PO_4$ [LJG]; with 2.49 %, d_4^{20} = 1.00971 (463)
As_2O_3 [JAB] (112) [LJG]; d_4^{15} = 1.0032 with 0.5 %; = 1.0073 with 1.0 %

H_3AsO_4 [JAB] (514)**; (76, 356, 453, 463, 496, 517, 536) [LJG]

%	d_4^{15}	d_4^{25}	%	d_4^{15}	%	d_4^{15}
1	1.0057	1.0037	16	1.1128	35	1.2829
2	1.0124	1.0103	18	1.1285	40	1.3370
4	1.0260	1.0237	20	1.1447	45	1.3959
6	1.0398	1.0373	22	1.1614	50	1.4602
8	1.0538	1.0512	24	1.1785	55	1.5304
10	1.0681	1.0655	26	1.1961	60	1.6070
12	1.0826	1.0803	28	1.2143	65	1.6904
14	1.0975	1.0956	30	1.2331	70	1.7811

AsI_3 [LJG]; with 1.90 %, d_4^{19} = 1.0192 (76)
$NH_4H_2AsO_4$ [LJG]; with 4.00 %, d_4^{20} = 1.0235 (463)
$(NH_4)_3AsO_4$ [LJG]; with 3.22 %, d_4^{20} = 1.0170 (463)
$C_{12}H_{10}ClI$, Diphenyliodonium chloride [JAB] (583)

%......................	1	2	3
d_4^{20}......................	1.0025	1.0067	1.0110

$C_5H_{12}SO_2$, Trimethylsulfonium acetate, [JAB]; with 3.41 %, d_4^{25} = 1.0018 (529)
C_3H_9ClS, Trimethylsulfonium chloride, [JAB]; with 2.82 %, d_4^{25} = 1.0014 (529)
C_3H_9BrS, Trimethylsulfonium bromide, [JAB]; with 1.00 %, d_4^{25} = 0.9993 (35)
C_3H_9IS, Trimethylsulfonium iodide, [JAB]; with 1.00 %, d_4^{25} = 0.9975 (35)
$C_{24}H_{20}I_2SO_4$, Diphenyliodonium sulfate, [JAB]; with 6.43 %, d_4^{20} = 1.0291 (583)

HCN [JAB] (238, 617)**; (88) [LJG]; *cf.* (672)

%	d_4^{5}	d_4^{10}	d_4^{15}	d_4^{20}	%	d_4^{15}
80				0.759	1	0.998
82			0.758	0.752	2	0.996
84		0.757	0.751	0.745	4	0.993
86	0.757	0.751	0.744	0.738	6	0.989
88	0.751	0.744	0.738	0.731	8	0.984
90	0.744	0.737	0.731	0.724	10	0.978
92	0.738	0.731	0.724	0.717	12	0.971
94	0.731	0.724	0.717	0.711	14	0.964
96	0.725	0.717	0.711	0.704	16	0.956
98	0.718	0.711	0.704	0.697		
100	0.712	0.704	0.697	0.691		

NH_4CHO_2, Formate [JAB] (484)**; (211, 463)

%	d_4^{15}	d_4^{25}	%	d_4^{15}	d_4^{25}	%	d_4^{15}	d_4^{25}
1	1.0019	0.9998	14	1.0366	1.0339	28	1.0713	1.0678
2	1.0046	1.0025	16	1.0418	1.0389	30	1.0760	1.0724
4	1.0101	1.0078	18	1.0469	1.0439	35	1.0874	1.0836
6	1.0155	1.0131	20	1.0519	1.0488	40	1.0984	1.0944
8	1.0209	1.0184	22	1.0568	1.0536	45	1.1089	1.1048
10	1.0262	1.0236	24	1.0617	1.0584	50	1.1189	1.1148
12	1.0314	1.0288	26	1.0665	1.0631	55	1.1285	1.1245

"$(NH_4)_2CO_3$" ($NH_4HCO_3.NH_4CO_2NH_2$) [JAB] (215)**; (241, 242, 395, 509, 510) [LJG]

%	d_4^{15}	%	d_4^{15}	%	d_4^{15}	%	d_4^{15}
1	1.0026	10	1.0335	20	1.0675	30	1.1006
2	1.0061	12	1.0403	22	1.0742	35	1.1157
4	1.0130	14	1.0471	24	1.0808	40	1.1294
6	1.0199	16	1.0539	26	1.0874	45	1.1417
8	1.0267	18	1.0607	28	1.0940		

$NH_4C_2HO_4$, Acid oxalate [JAB]; with 3.57 %, d_4^{20} = 1.0140 (463)

$NH_4C_2H_3O_2$, Acetate [JAB] (288, 484)**; (211, 224, 463, 529)

%	d_4^{15}	d_4^{18}	d_4^{25}	%	d_4^{15}	d_4^{18}	d_4^{25}
1	1.0013	1.0008	0.9992	20	1.0397	1.0393	1.0368
2	1.0034	1.0030	1.0013	22	1.0434	1.0429	1.0404
4	1.0077	1.0074	1.0055	24	1.0470	1.0465	1.0439
6	1.0119	1.0117	1.0096	26	1.0505	1.0500	1.0473
8	1.0161	1.0159	1.0136	28	1.0540	1.0535	1.0507
10	1.0202	1.0200	1.0176	30	1.0573	1.0569	1.0540
12	1.0242	1.0240	1.0216	35	1.0654		1.0618
14	1.0282	1.0279	1.0255	40	1.0729		1.0691
16	1.0321	1.0318	1.0294	45	1.0800		1.0760
18	1.0359	1.0356	1.0331				

$NH_4C_2H_3O_3$, Glycolate [JAB]; with 4.65 %, d_4^{20} = 1.0263 (463)

$(NH_4)_2C_2O_4$, Oxalate [JAB]; (463)

%	1	2	3	4
d_4^{20}	1.0031	1.0080	1.0128	1.0176

$NH_4C_3H_5O_2$, Propionate [JAB] (484)**; (463)

%	d_4^{15}	d_4^{25}	%	d_4^{15}	d_4^{25}	%	d_4^{15}	d_4^{25}
1	1.0011	0.9989	16	1.0285	1.0254	35	1.0549	1.0506
2	1.0030	1.0008	18	1.0318	1.0285	40	1.0599	1.0554
4	1.0069	1.0045	20	1.0350	1.0316	45	1.0642	1.0595
6	1.0107	1.0081	22	1.0381	1.0345	50	1.0678	1.0629
8	1.0145	1.0117	24	1.0410	1.0373	55	1.0707	1.0657
10	1.0182	1.0153	26	1.0438	1.0400	60	1.0729	1.0679
12	1.0218	1.0188	28	1.0465	1.0425			
14	1.0252	1.0222	30	1.0491	1.0450			

$NH_4C_3H_5O_3$, Lactate [JAB]; with 5.36 %, d_4^{20} = 1.0169 (463)

$NH_4C_4H_5O_4$, Acid succinate [JAB]; with 4.50 %, d_4^{20} = 1.0140 (463)

$NH_4C_4H_5O_5$, Acid malate, [JAB] (463, 546)**

%	d_4^{20}	%	d_4^{20}	%	d_4^{20}	%	d_4^{20}
1	1.002	8	1.030	16	1.063	24	1.098
2	1.006	10	1.038	18	1.072	26	1.107
4	1.014	12	1.047	20	1.081		
6	1.022	14	1.055	22	1.089		

$NH_4C_4H_7O_2$, *n*-Butyrate, [JAB]; with 5.26 %, d_4^{20} = 1.0062 (463)

$NH_4C_4H_7O_2$, Isobutyrate, [JAB]; with 5.26 %, d_4^{20} = 1.0064 (463)

$C_4H_{12}N_2O_3$, Tetramethylammonium nitrate, [JAB]; with 3.40 %, d_4^{25} = 1.0014 (529)

$(NH_4)_2C_4H_4O_4$, Succinate, [JAB]; with 3.80 %, d_4^{20} = 1.0126 (463)

$(NH_4)_2C_4H_4O_5$, Malate (JAB] (463, 546)**

%	d_4^{20}	%	d_4^{20}	%	d_4^{20}	%	d_4^{20}
1	1.002	12	1.046	24	1.095	45	1.185
2	1.006	14	1.054	26	1.104	50	1.207
4	1.014	16	1.062	28	1.112	55	1.230
6	1.022	18	1.070	30	1.120	60	1.253
8	1.030	20	1.079	35	1.142		
10	1.038	22	1.087	40	1.163		

$(NH_4)_2C_4H_4O_6$, Tartrate [JAB]; 4.60 %, d_4^{20} = 1.0200 (463)**; (571)

$NH_4C_6H_7O_7$, Dihydrogen citrate [JAB]; 5.23 %, d_4^{20} = 1.0207 (463)

$C_6H_{15}NO_2$, Tetramethylammonium acetate [JAB]; with 3.33 %, d_4^{25} = 0.9981 (529)

$(NH_4)_3C_6H_5O_7$, Citrate [JAB]; with 4.05 %, d_4^{20} = 1.0172 (463)

CH_6ClN, Methylamine hydrochloride [JAB]; with 19.67 %, d_4^{20} = 1.0343 (15)

C_2H_8ClN, Dimethylamine hydrochloride [JAB] (15)

%	d_4^{20}	%	d_4^{20}	%	d_4^{20}	%	d_4^{20}
1	0.9992	4	1.0024	8	1.0065	12	1.0104
2	1.0003	6	1.0045	10	1.0085	14	1.0123

C_2H_8ClN, Ethylamine hydrochloride [LJG] (542)**; (483)*; (15, 328, 329) [JAB]

%	d_4^{21}	%	d_4^{21}	%	d_4^{21}	%	d_4^{21}
1	0.9992	10	1.0096	20	1.0204	45	1.0413
2	1.0003	12	1.0118	25	1.0254	50	1.0441
4	1.0027	14	1.0140	30	1.0300	55	1.0464
6	1.0050	16	1.0162	35	1.0342	60	1.0482
8	1.0073	18	1.0183	40	1.0380	65	1.0495

$C_4H_{12}ClN$, Diethylamine hydrochloride [LJG] (542)**; (483)*; (15) [JAB]

%	d_4^{21}	%	d_4^{21}	%	d_4^{21}	%	d_4^{21}
1	0.99835	12	1.00209	24	1.00675	45	1.0136
2	0.99869	14	1.00280	26	1.00758	50	1.0144
4	0.99936	16	1.00354	28	1.00839	55	1.0147
6	1.00004	18	1.00431	30	1.00918	60	1.0145
8	1.00072	20	1.00510	35	1.0110		
10	1.00140	22	1.00592	40	1.0125		

$C_4H_{12}ClN$, Tetramethylammonium chloride, [JAB] (15, 529)

%	d_4^{20}	%	d_4^{20}	%	d_4^{20}	%	d_4^{20}
1	0.9984	4	0.9991	8	1.0003	12	1.0015
2	0.9987	6	0.9997	10	1.0009	14	1.0021

C_6H_8ClN, Aniline hydrochloride [JAB] (18)

%	d_4^{12}?	%	d_4^{12}?	%	d_4^{12}?	%	d_4^{12}?
1	1.0020	10	1.0205	20	1.0409	30	1.0613
2	1.0041	12	1.0246	22	1.0450	35	1.0715
4	1.0082	14	1.0287	24	1.0491		
6	1.0123	16	1.0327	26	1.0531		
8	1.0164	18	1.0368	28	1.0572		

$C_6H_{16}ClN$, Triethylamine hydrochloride [JAB] (542)

%	d_4^{21}	%	d_4^{21}	%	d_4^{21}	%	d_4^{21}
1	0.9980	12	0.9991	24	1.0025	45	1.0118
2	0.9981	14	0.9995	26	1.0033	50	1.0142
4	0.9982	16	1.0000	28	1.0041	55	1.0166
6	0.9984	18	1.0006	30	1.0049		
8	0.9986	20	1.0012	35	1.0071		
10	0.9988	22	1.0018	40	1.0094		

$C_8H_{20}ClN$, Tetraethylammonium chloride [JAB] (542)

%	d_4^{21}	%	d_4^{21}	%	d_4^{21}	%	d_4^{21}
1	0.9983	12	1.0011	24	1.0060	45	1.0199
2	0.9986	14	1.0017	26	1.0072	50	1.0241
4	0.9990	16	1.0024	28	1.0084	55	1.0287
6	0.9995	18	1.0032	30	1.0097	60	1.0337
8	1.0000	20	1.0041	35	1.0127		
10	1.0006	22	1.0050	40	1.0161		

$C_{12}H_{28}ClN$, Tetrapropylammonium chloride [JAB] (416)

%	0°C	10°C	20°C	25°C	30°C	40°C	50°C
1	0.9997	0.9995	0.9980	0.9968	0.9954	0.9916	0.9872
2	.9995	.9993	.9977	.9965	.9950	.9911	.9864
4	.9992	.9989	.9972	.9960	.9944	.9901	.9849
6	.9990	.9986	.9968	.9955	.9938	.9892	.9836
8	.9989	.9984	.9965	.9951	.9933	.9884	.9825
10	.9990	.9983	.9963	.9948	.9929	.9877	.9816
12	.9991	.9984	.9962	.9945	.9925	.9871	.9808
14	.9993	.9985	.9961	.9943	.9922	.9866	.9801
16	.9997	.9987	.9960	.9942	.9920	.9862	.9795

$C_{12}H_{28}ClN$.—(*Continued*)

%	0°C	10°C	20°C	25°C	30°C	40°C	50°C
18	1.0003	0.9989	0.9961	0.9941	0.9918	0.9859	0.9791
20	1.0011	.9993	.9962	.9941	.9917	.9857	.9788
22	1.0020	.9999	.9965	.9943	.9919	.9856	.9786
24	1.0031	1.0007	.9970	.9947	.9922	.9858	.9787
26	1.0044	1.0017	.9977	.9953	.9926	.9862	.9789
28	1.0058	1.0029	.9986	.9961	.9931	.9868	.9793

$NH_4C_2H_2ClO_2$, Chloroacetate [JAB]; 5.58 %, d_4^{20} = 1.0191 (**463**)
$NH_4C_2HCl_2O_2$, Dichloroacetate [JAB]; 7.30 %, d_4^{20} = 1.0282 (**463**)
$NH_4C_2Cl_3O_2$, Trichloroacetate [JAB]; 9.02 %, d_4^{20} = 1.0391(**463**)

$C_3H_6ClNO_2$, Methyl chloroaminoacetic acid [JAB] (**15**)

%	d_4^{20}	%	d_4^{20}	%	d_4^{20}	%	d_4^{20}
1	1.0004	4	1.0069	8	1.0156	12	1.0242
2	1.0026	6	1.0113	10	1.0199	14	1.0284

$C_{12}H_{10}INO_3$, Diphenyliodonium nitrate [JAB] (**583**)

%	1	2	3
d_4^{20}.	1.0024	1.0068	1.0114

NH_4CNS [JAB] (**236, 288**)**; (**155, 555**) [LJG]

%	d_4^{18}	%	d_4^{18}	%	d_4^{25}	%	d_4^{25}
1	1.0009	16	1.0356	30	1.0645	46	1.1007
2	1.0032	18	1.0402	32	1.0687	48	1.1057
4	1.0078	20	1.0448	34	1.0730	50	1.1108
6	1.0124	22	1.0495	36	1.0774	52	1.1161
8	1.0170	24	1.0542	38	1.0818	54	1.1214
10	1.0216	26	1.0589	40	1.0863	56	1.1268
12	1.0263	28	1.0636	42	1.0910	58	1.1322
14	1.0309			44	1.0958		

$(NH_4)_2CH_2(SO_3)_2$, Methanedisulfonate [JAB]; with 5.28 %, d_4^{20} = 1.0108 (**529**)

$NH_4C_2H_5SO_4$, Hydroxyethylsulfonate [JAB]; with 3.58 %, d_4^{20} = 1.0115 (**529**)

$C_3H_9NO_3S$, Trimethylsulfonium nitrate [JAB]; with 3.48 %, d_4^{20} = 1.0056 (**529**)

$NH_4C_6H_5SO_3$, Benzenesulfonate [JAB]; with 4.38 %, d_4^{20} = 1.0110 (**529**)

$C_6H_{15}O_2P$, Tetramethylphosphonium acetate [JAB]; with 2.76 %, d_4^{25} = 0.9972 (**529**)

$C_4H_{12}ClP$, Tetramethylphosphonium chloride [JAB]; with 3.17 %, d_4^{25} = 0.9968 (**529**)

$C_4H_{12}O_3NP$, Tetramethylphosphonium nitrate [JAB]; with 3.83 %, d_4^{25} = 1.0005 (**529**)

$PbCl_2$ [LJG] (**602**) ‖ **$Pb(ClO_3)_2$** [JAB] (**602**) [LJG]

%	d_4^{15}	%	d_4^{15}	%	d_4^{15}	%	d_4^{15}
0.1	1.00006	0.6	1.00472	1	1.0075	10	1.0911
0.2	1.00099	0.8	1.00658	2	1.0161	12	1.1115
0.4	1.00285	1.0	1.00844	4	1.0338	14	1.1326
				6	1.0523	16	1.1544
				8	1.0714		

$Pb(NO_3)_2$ [LJG] (**250, 291**)**; (**46, 84, 106, 144, 205, 206, 224, 278, 360, 361, 375, 378, 384, 509, 510, 533, 534, 561, 592, 629**), α (**375**)

°C	1 %	2 %	4 %	6 %	8 %
0	1.0089	1.0180	1.0364	1.0554	1.0749
10	1.0086	1.0175	1.0357	1.0544	1.0737
18†	1.0074	1.0163	1.0344	1.0529	1.0720
20	1.0070	1.0159	1.0339	1.0524	1.0715
25	1.0058	1.0146	1.0325	1.0509	1.0699
30	1.0044	1.0132	1.0310	1.0493	1.0682
40	1.0009	1.0096	1.0273	1.0454	1.0642
50	0.9967	1.0053	1.0228	1.0409	1.0595
60	0.9917	1.0003	1.0178	1.0357	1.0542
70	0.9863	0.9948	1.0122	1.0300	1.0483

$Pb(NO_3)_2$.—(*Continued*)

°C	10 %	12 %	14 %	16 %	18 %
0	1.0951	1.1160	1.1377	1.1602	1.1838
10	1.0936	1.1143	1.1357	1.1580	1.1814
18†	1.0918	1.1123	1.1336	1.1557	1.1789
20	1.0912	1.1117	1.1329	1.1550	1.1782
25	1.0896	1.1100	1.1311	1.1531	1.1762
30	1.0878	1.1081	1.1291	1.1511	1.1741
40	1.0836	1.1038	1.1247	1.1465	1.1692
50	1.0788	1.0988	1.1196	1.1412	
60	1.0733	1.0932	1.1138	1.1353	
70	1.0673	1.0870	1.1074	1.1287	

°C	20 %	22 %	24 %	26 %	28 %	30 %
0	1.2083	1.2334	1.2590	1.2848	1.3107	1.3363
10	1.2057	1.2306	1.2559	1.2815	1.3072	1.3326
18†	1.2030	1.2277	1.2529	1.2783	1.3037	1.3289
20	1.2022	1.2269	1.2520	1.2774	1.3028	1.3279
25	1.2002	1.2248	1.2498	1.2750	1.3002	1.3254
30	1.1979	1.2224	1.2473	1.2725	1.2977	1.3226
40	1.1928	1.2171	1.2418	1.2667	1.2917	1.3164

† Density data are discordant except at 18°C.

$Pb(C_2H_3O_2)_2$, Acetate [JAB]; (**288**)**; (**144, 221, 223, 426, 469, 509**)

%	d_4^{18}	%	d_4^{18}	%	d_4^{18}	%	d_4^{18}
1	1.0061	10	1.0768	20	1.1663	30	1.2711
2	1.0137	12	1.0936	22	1.1860	35	1.3304
4	1.0290	14	1.1109	24	1.2063	40	1.3994
6	1.0446	16	1.1283	26	1.2273		
8	1.0605	18	1.1473	28	1.2489		

$SnCl_2$ [JAB] (**221**)**; (**106**) [LJG]

%	d_4^{15}	%	d_4^{15}	%	d_4^{15}	%	d_4^{15}
1	1.0068	12	1.0986	24	1.2159	45	1.4897
2	1.0146	14	1.1167	26	1.2377	50	1.5729
4	1.0306	16	1.1353	28	1.2603	55	1.6656
6	1.0470	18	1.1545	30	1.2837	60	1.7695
8	1.0638	20	1.1743	35	1.3461	65	1.8865
10	1.0810	22	1.1948	40	1.4145		

$SnCl_4$ [JAB] (**221, 291**)**; (**106, 272**) [LJG]

%	d_4^{15}	d_4^{18}	%	d_4^{15}	d_4^{18}	%	d_4^{15}	%	d_4^{15}
1	1.007	1.0065	12	1.099	1.0974	24	1.212	45	1.475
2	1.015	1.0145	14	1.117	1.1150	26	1.233	50	1.555
4	1.031	1.0306	16	1.135	1.1331	28	1.255	55	1.644
6	1.047	1.0469	18	1.154	1.1516	30	1.278	60	1.742
8	1.064	1.0634	20	1.173	1.1706	35	1.337	65	1.851
10	1.081	1.0802	22	1.192	1.1901	40	1.403	70	1.971

$ThCl_4$ [JAB] (**291**) [LJG]

%	d_4^{18}	%	d_4^{18}	%	d_4^{18}	%	d_4^{18}
1	1.0080	8	1.0786	16	1.1707	24	1.2769
2	1.0175	10	1.1005	18	1.1958	26	1.3063
4	1.0371	12	1.1231	20	1.2218	28	1.3371
6	1.0575	14	1.1465	22	1.2488		

$Th(NO_3)_4$ [JAB] (**357**) [LJG]

%	d_4^{15}	%	d_4^{15}	%	d_4^{15}	%	d_4^{15}
1	1.0079	6	1.0546	12	1.1176	18	1.1885
2	1.0169	8	1.0747	14	1.1404		
4	1.0354	10	1.0957	16	1.1640		

$InBr_3$ [JAB] (**289**) [LJG]

%	d_4^{18}	%	d_4^{18}	%	d_4^{18}	%	d_4^{18}
1	1.0070	10	1.0888	20	1.1956	30	1.3230
2	1.0155	12	1.1088	22	1.2191	32	1.3523
4	1.0329	14	1.1295	24	1.2434		
6	1.0509	16	1.1508	26	1.2687		
8	1.0695	18	1.1728	28	1.2952		

TlOH [JAB] (16)**; (529) [LJG]

%	d_4^{15}	%	d_4^{15}	%	d_4^{15}	%	d_4^{15}
20	1.220	24	1.284	28	1.347	32	1.411
22	1.252	26†	1.315	30	1.379	34	1.443

† Supersaturated above 26 %.

TlF [JAB] (291)**; (602) [LJG]

%	d_4^{18}	%	d_4^{18}	%	d_4^{18}	%	d_4^{18}
1	1.0082	8	1.0804	16	1.1765	24	1.2868
2	1.0179	10	1.1031	18	1.2026	26	1.3174
4	1.0379	12	1.1267	20	1.2296	28	1.3495
6	1.0587	14	1.1512	22	1.2576	30	1.3833

$TlClO_3$ [LJG]; with 2.210 %, d_4^{15} = 1.01791 (602)

Tl_2SO_4 [JAB] (291, 309, 602)**; (106, 206, 529) [LJG]

%	15°C	20°C	25°C	30°C
1	1.0084	1.0076	1.0064	1.0049
2	1.0178	1.0170	1.0158	1.0142
3	1.0274	1.0265	1.0253	1.0237
4	1.0370	1.0360	1.0348	1.0333
5		1.0456		

$TlNO_3$ [JAB] (317, 602, 629)**; (529) [LJG]

%	0°C	10°C	15°C	20°C	25°C
1	1.0088	1.0086	1.0077	1.0067	1.0056
2	1.0179	1.0172	1.0164	1.0154	1.0142
3	1.0271	1.0263	1.0253	1.0242	1.0230
4			1.0344		1.0319
5			1.0436		1.0409
6					1.0501
7					1.0594

$TlC_2H_3O_2$, Acetate [JAB]; with 2.19 %, d_4^{25} = 1.0154 (529)

$ZnCl_2$ [GS] (288, 366)**; (507, 657)*; (23, 86, 106, 150, 203, 261, 384, 417.5, 462, 464, 466, 599, 618, 628, 629)

%	0°C	10°C	20°C	25°C	30°C	40°C
2	1.0192	1.0186	1.0167	1.0154	1.0138	1.0099
4	1.0384	1.0373	1.0350	1.0335	1.0317	1.0274
6	1.0576	1.0559	1.0532	1.0515	1.0495	1.0448
8	1.0769	1.0746	1.0715	1.0696	1.0673	1.0624
10	1.0963	1.0934	1.0819	1.0878	1.0853	1.0801
12	1.1159	1.1124	1.1085	1.1063	1.1036	1.0980
14	1.1357	1.1318	1.1275	1.1251	1.1223	1.1163
16	1.1558	1.1515	1.1468	1.1442	1.1413	1.1350
18	1.1762	1.1715	1.1665	1.1638	1.1607	1.1541
20	1.1970	1.1919	1.1866	1.1836	1.1804	1.1736
25	1.2500	1.2441	1.2380	1.2348	1.2313	1.2240
30	1.3062	1.2996	1.2928	1.2894	1.2856	1.2778
35	1.3668	1.3595	1.3522	1.3485	1.3445	1.3362
40	1.4329	1.4250	1.4173	1.4133	1.4090	1.4003
45	1.5050	1.4972	1.4890	1.4847	1.4802	1.4711
50	1.5860	1.5771	1.5681	1.5636	1.5590	1.5495
55			1.655	1.651	1.646	
60			1.749	1.745	1.740	
65			1.851	1.847	1.842	
70			1.962	1.957	1.952	
75				2.076		

%	50°C	60°C	70°C	80°C	90°C	100°C
2	1.0055	1.0003	0.9945	0.9882	0.9812	0.9739
4	1.0227	1.0172	1.0110	1.0044	0.9971	0.9894
6	1.0398	1.0340	1.0274	1.0206	1.0130	1.0051
8	1.0570	1.0508	1.0439	1.0369	1.0291	1.0211
10	1.0744	1.0679	1.0606	1.0535	1.0456	1.0374
12	1.0921	1.0853	1.0779	1.0704	1.0625	1.0541
14	1.1101	1.1030	1.0955	1.0877	1.0798	1.0712
16	1.1284	1 1212	1.1135	1.1055	1.0975	1.0888

$ZnCl_2$.—(*Continued*)

%	50°C	60°C	70°C	80°C	90°C	100°C
18	1.1472	1.1399	1.1320	1.1238	1.1137	1.1069
20	1.1665	1.1590	1.1510	1.1428	1.1345	1.1255
25	1.2163	1.2084	1.1999	1.1914	1.1827	1.1734
30	1.2696	1.2614	1.2526	1.2438	1.2347	1.2252
35	1.3276	1.3190	1.3101	1.3009	1.2915	1.2818
40	1.3913	1.3824	1.3732	1.3637	1.3542	1.3441
45	1.4617	1.4525	1.4428	1.4331	1.4238	1.4130
50	1.5399	1.5300	1.5199	1.5097	1.5009	1.4892

$Zn(ClO_3)_2$ [GS] (287)**; (602)*

%	d_4^{18}	%	d_4^{18}	%	d_4^{18}	%	d_4^{18}
2	1.0146	10	1.0823	18	1.1579	35	1.3535
4	1.0309	12	1.1004	20	1.1783		
6	1.0476	14	1.1190	25	1.2322		
8	1.0647	16	1.1381	30	1.2908		

$ZnBr_2$ [GS] (366, 368, 507)

%	0°C	10°C	20°C	25°C	30°C	40°C
2	1.0188	1.0184	1.0167	1.0154	1.0139	1.0102
4	1.0381	1.0374	1.0354	1.0340	1.0324	1.0285
6	1.0578	1.0567	1.0544	1.0529	1.0512	1.0471
8	1.0777	1.0763	1.0738	1.0721	1.0704	1.0660
10	1.0980	1.0962	1.0935	1.0917	1.0899	1.0852
12	1.1186	1.1165	1.1135	1.1116	1.1096	1.1046
14	1.1396	1.1371	1.1338	1.1318	1.1296	1.1244
16	1.1609	1.1580	1.1544	1.1523	1.1500	1.1445
18	1.1825	1.1792	1.1753	1.1730	1.1706	1.1649
20	1.2043	1.2007	1.1965	1.1941	1.1915	1.1855
25	1.2641	1.2594	1.2543	1.2516	1.2485	1.2418
30	1.3288	1.3229	1.3170	1.3139	1.3104	1.3030
35	1.3995	1.3926	1.3859	1.3823	1.3785	1.3703
40	1.477	1.470	1.462	1.458	1.454	1.445
45	1.564	1.556	1.547	1.543	1.538	1.529
50	1.661	1.652	1.643	1.638	1.633	1.623
55	1.770	1.760	1.750	1.745	1.739	1.728
60	1.891	1.880	1.869	1.864	1.858	1.845
65	2.026	2.013	2.002	1.995	1.989	1.976

%	50°C	60°C	70°C	80°C	90°C	100°C
2	1.0059	1.0008	0.9952	0.9890	0.9823	0.9751
4	1.0240	1.0187	1.0129	1.0065	0.9995	0.9921
6	1.0424	1.0369	1.0308	1.0242	1.0171	1.0094
8	1.0611	1.0554	1.0490	1.0422	1.0348	1.0270
10	1.0800	1.0742	1.0676	1.0604	1.0528	1.0448
12	1.0992	1.0932	1.0864	1.0789	1.0712	1.0629
14	1.1187	1.1124	1.1055	1.0978	1.0899	1.0813
16	1.1385	1.1320	1.1248	1.1169	1.1088	1.1000
18	1.1586	1.1519	1.1445	1.1363	1.1279	1.1190
20	1.1790	1.1720	1.1643	1.1560	1.1474	1.1382
25	1.2347	1.2270	1.2188	1.2101	1.2009	1.1911
30	1.2952	1.2868	1.2780	1.2688	1.2591	1.2489
35	1.3618	1.3529	1.3435	1.3337	1.3236	1.3131
40	1.436	1.427	1.417	1.406	1.396	1.385
45	1.519	1.510	1.499	1.488	1.477	1.465
50	1.612	1.602	1.590	1.579	1.568	1.555
55	1.717	1.706	1.694	1.682	1.670	1.657
60	1.834	1.822	1.810	1.797	1.784	1.771
65	1.964	1.951	1.938	1.924	1.911	1.898

$Zn(BrO_3)_2$ [GS] (291)

%	d_4^{18}	%	d_4^{18}	%	d_4^{18}	%	d_4^{18}
2	1.0166	10	1.0913	18	1.1774	35	1.4070
4	1.0346	12	1.1116	20	1.2007		
6	1.0528	14	1.1327	25	1.2629		
8	1.0716	16	1.1547	30	1.3312		

ZnI_2 [GS] (366, 369, 507)

%	0°C	20°C	40°C	60°C	80°C	100°C
2	1.018	1.016	1.010	1.000	0.989	0.975
4	1.036	1.034	1.028	1.018	1.006	0.992
6	1.055	1.053	1.046	1.036	1.023	1.009
8	1.075	1.072	1.064	1.054	1.041	1.027
10	1.095	1.091	1.084	1.073	1.059	1.045
12	1.115	1.111	1.103	1.092	1.078	1.063
14	1.136	1.131	1.122	1.111	1.097	1.081
16	1.158	1.152	1.142	1.131	1.117	1.100
18	1.180	1.174	1.164	1.152	1.138	1.121
20	1.204	1.197	1.187	1.174	1.159	1.142
25	1.266	1.258	1.247	1.233	1.216	1.198
30	1.335	1.325	1.312	1.297	1.279	1.260
35	1.410	1.398	1.383	1.367	1.348	1.327
40	1.491	1.478	1.461	1.443	1.423	1.401
45	1.581	1.566	1.547	1.527	1.506	1.483
50	1.680	1.663	1.643	1.621	1.598	1.574
55	1.791	1.770	1.749	1.725	1.701	1.675
60	1.916	1.893	1.870	1.844	1.818	1.790
65	2.061	2.036	2.010	1.982	1.954	1.925
70	2.230	2.202	2.173	2.143	2.113	2.082
75	2.424	2.393	2.361	2.328	2.296	2.263

$ZnSO_4$ [GS] (200, 203, 247, 342, 348, 375, 655)**; (18, 20, 89, 105, 116, 184, 192, 220, 221, 278, 322, 329, 344, 349, 401, 402, 425, 449, 462, 464, 466, 506, 533, 535, 618, 628, 629)

%	0°C	10°C	20°C	30°C	40°C	50°C
2	1.0212	1.0208	1.0190	1.0163	1.0126	1.0084
4	1.0431	1.0423	1.0403	1.0373	1.0335	1.0291
6	1.0654	1.0642	1.0620	1.0588	1.0549	1.0503
8	1.0882	1.0867	1.0842	1.0808	1.0769	1.0721
10	1.1117	1.1098	1.1071	1.1035	1.0996	1.0946
12	1.1360	1.1338	1.1308	1.1270	1.1230	1.1179
14	1.1610	1.1585	1.1553	1.1513	1.1471	1.1421
16	1.1867	1.1840	1.1806	1.1764	1.1721	1.1670

%	d_4^{60}	d_4^{70}	d_4^{80}	%	d_4^{18}	d_4^{25}†
2	1.0034	0.9978	0.9918	2	1.0194	1.0178
4	1.0240	1.0183	1.0122	4	1.0407	1.0389
6	1.0451	1.0394	1.0330	6	1.0624	1.0605
8	1.0668	1.0610	1.0545	8	1.0847	1.0825
10	1.0892	1.0833	1.0767	10	1.1077	1.1054
12	1.1124	1.1063	1.0996	12	1.1315	1.1290
14	1.1364	1.1301	1.1232	14	1.1560	1.1534
16	1.1612	1.1547	1.1477	16	1.1813	1.1786

%......	18	20	25	30	35
d_4^{18}......	1.2074	1.2343	1.3058	1.3834	1.4672

† With 36.28 %, d_4^{25} = 1.4858; with 36.69 %, d_4^{25} = 1.4924.

% (373)	$d_4^{20.004}$	% (373)	$d_4^{20.004}$
0.00	0.998 23150‡	0.05	0.998 76084
0.01	0.998 33798	0.06	0.998 86596
0.02	0.998 44412	0.07	0.998 97091
0.03	0.998 54995	0.08	0.999 07571
0.04	0.998 65551		

‡ The small figures are significant only for ratios within the table.

$Zn(NO_3)_2$ [GS] (288)**; (20, 469)*; (150, 208, 322, 628, 629)

%	d_4^{18}	%	d_4^{18}	%	d_4^{18}	%	d_4^{18}
2	1.0154	10	1.0859	18	1.1652	35	1.3678
4	1.0322	12	1.1048	20	1.1865	40	1.4378
6	1.0496	14	1.1244	25	1.2427	45	1.5134
8	1.0675	16	1.1445	30	1.3029	50	1.5944

$Zn(C_2H_3O_2)_2$, Acetate [JAB] (192)**; (329)

%	$d_4^{23.5}$	%	$d_4^{23.5}$	%	$d_4^{23.5}$	%	$d_4^{23.5}$
1	1.004	6	1.040	12	1.082	18	1.124
2	1.011	8	1.054	14	1.096	20	1.137
4	1.026	10	1.068	16	1.110	22	1.151

$CdCl_2$ [GS] (48, 291, 367)**; (249, 440, 507)*; (261, 312, 313, 366, 378, 417.5, 451, 459, 618, 628, 629, 641)

%	0°C	10°C	20°C	25°C	30°C	40°C
2	1.0179	1.0175	1.0159	1.0146	1.0131	1.0094
4	1.0364	1.0358	1.0339	1.0325	1.0309	1.0271
6	1.0554	1.0545	1.0524	1.0509	1.0492	1.0453
8	1.0750	1.0737	1.0715	1.0699	1.0681	1.0640
10	1.0952	1.0936	1.0912	1.0895	1.0877	1.0834
12	1.1161	1.1141	1.1115	1.1098	1.1078	1.1034
14	1.1377	1.1353	1.1324	1.1307	1.1286	1.1239
16	1.1598	1.1571	1.1540	1.1522	1.1500	1.1451
18	1.1825	1.1796	1.1762	1.1743	1.1719	1.1668
20	1.2059	1.2029	1.1992	1.1970	1.1945	1.1892
25	1.2687	1.2648	1.2604	1.2580	1.2551	1.2492
30	1.3370	1.3324	1.3273	1.3246	1.3213	1.3147
35	1.4122	1.4068	1.4010	1.3979	1.3943	1.3870
40	1.4961	1.4899	1.4833	1.4797	1.4759	1.4679
45	1.5893	1.5823	1.5748	1.5706	1.5668	1.5582
50	1.6921	1.6845	1.6762	1.6719	1.6676	1.6582

%	50°C	60°C	70°C	80°C	90°C	100°C
2	1.0051	1.0002	0.9946	0.9885	0.9819	0.9748
4	1.0227	1.0176	1.0119	1.0056	0.9989	0.9916
6	1.0407	1.0354	1.0296	1.0231	1.0163	1.0089
8	1.0592	1.0538	1.0478	1.0412	1.0342	1.0266
10	1.0783	1.0728	1.0666	1.0599	1.0527	1.0449
12	1.0981	1.0924	1.0860	1.0792	1.0719	1.0639
14	1.1185	1.1126	1.1060	1.0991	1.0916	1.0835
16	1.1394	1.1334	1.1266	1.1195	1.1118	1.1036
18	1.1610	1.1548	1.1478	1.1405	1.1326	1.1243
20	1.1832	1.1768	1.1697	1.1621	1.1540	1.1456
25	1.2427	1.2357	1.2280	1.2199	1.2114	1.2026
30	1.3076	1.3000	1.2918	1.2832	1.2741	1.2650
35	1.3793	1.3710	1.3622	1.3530	1.3434	1.3338
40	1.4594	1.4506	1.4411	1.4314	1.4212	1.4111
45	1.5490	1.5394	1.5293	1.5190	1.5082	1.4976
50	1.6484	1.6381	1.6273	1.6164	1.6050	1.5939

$Cd(ClO_3)_2$ [GS] (288)**; (602)*

%	d_4^{18}	%	d_4^{18}	%	d_4^{18}	%	d_4^{18}
2	1.0147	10	1.0839	18	1.1620	35	1.368
4	1.0313	12	1.1025	20	1.1831	40	1.441
6	1.0483	14	1.1217	25	1.2394		
8	1.0659	16	1.1415	30	1.301		

$CdBr_2$ [GS] (291, 368)**; (249, 313, 440)*; (204, 259, 312, 366, 378, 507, 618, 641)

%	0°C	10°C	20°C	25°C	30°C	40°C
2	1.0179	1.0175	1.0158	1.0146	1.0131	1.0094
4	1.0364	1.0358	1.0339	1.0326	1.0310	1.0272
6	1.0554	1.0546	1.0524	1.0510	1.0494	1.0455
8	1.0749	1.0739	1.0714	1.0700	1.0683	1.0643
10	1.0950	1.0937	1.0910	1.0895	1.0877	1.0836
12	1.1158	1.1141	1.1112	1.1097	1.1077	1.1034
14	1.1372	1.1353	1.1322	1.1306	1.1285	1.1239
16	1.1594	1.1573	1.1540	1.1523	1.1501	1.1453
18	1.1825	1.1801	1.1766	1.1747	1.1725	1.1675
20	1.2064	1.2037	1.2000	1.1979	1.1955	1.1904
25	1.2683	1.2648	1.2605	1.2583	1.2555	1.2498
30	1.3377	1.3334	1.3286	1.3259	1.3229	1.3165
35	1.4155	1.4105	1.4049	1.4017	1.3984	1.3913
40			1.4902	1.4866	1.4829	1.4752

$CdBr_2$.—(*Continued*)

%	50°C	60°C	70°C	80°C	90°C	100°C
2	1.0052	1.0002	0.9947	0.9886	0.9820	0.9749
4	1.0228	1.0176	1.0120	1.0058	0.9991	0.9918
6	1.0409	1.0355	1.0279	1.0234	1.0165	1.0092
8	1.0595	1.0540	1.0479	1.0414	1.0344	1.0271
10	1.0786	1.0730	1.0667	1.0600	1.0529	1.0455
12	1.0983	1.0925	1.0861	1.0793	1.0720	1.0645
14	1.1187	1.1127	1.1062	1.0993	1.0918	1.0841
16	1.1399	1.1337	1.1271	1.1200	1.1124	1.1045
18	1.1618	1.1656	1.1488	1.1414	1.1337	1.1256
20	1.1846	1.1782	1.1712	1.1637	1.1558	1.1476
25	1.2435	1.2365	1.2291	1.2212	1.2129	1.2043
30	1.3096	1.3021	1.2942	1.2858	1.2771	1.2681
35	1.3838	1.3758	1.3673	1.3583	1.3491	1.3396
40	1.4670	1.4583	1.4491	1.4396	1.4297	1.4197

CdI_2 [GS] (**151, 249, 312, 313, 369**)**; (**2, 204, 366, 440**)*; (**18, 378, 507, 618, 641**)

%	0°C	10°C	20°C	25°C	30°C	40°C
2	1.0173	1.0169	1.0153	1.0141	1.0127	1.0090
4	1.0351	1.0345	1.0328	1.0314	1.0300	1.0263
6	1.0533	1.0525	1.0507	1.0492	1.0478	1.0439
8	1.0719	1.0710	1.0690	1.0675	1.0660	1.0620
10	1.0911	1.0900	1.0879	1.0863	1.0847	1.0805
12	1.1110	1.1098	1.1075	1.1058	1.1042	1.0997
14	1.1317	1.1303	1.1278	1.1261	1.1244	1.1198
16	1.1532	1.1516	1.1489	1.1471	1.1454	1.1406
18	1.1755	1.1737	1.1709	1.1690	1.1672	1.1622
20	1.1987	1.1967	1.1937	1.1917	1.1898	1.1846
25	1.2608	1.2583	1.2546	1.2524	1.2501	1.2446
30			1.3219	1.3194	1.3167	1.3107
35			1.3967	1.3938	1.3908	1.3841
40			1.4801	1.4767	1.4734	1.4660
45			1.5726	1.5689	1.5651	1.5571

%	50°C	60°C	70°C	80°C	90°C	100°C
2	1.0048	0.9998	0.9943	0.9882	0.9815	0.9746
4	1.0219	1.0167	1.0112	1.0049	0.9981	0.9911
6	1.0393	1.0340	1.0285	1.0220	1.0150	1.0079
8	1.0572	1.0517	1.0461	1.0394	1.0323	1.0251
10	1.0756	1.0700	1.0642	1.0574	1.0502	1.0429
12	1.0947	1.0890	1.0830	1.0761	1.0687	1.0613
14	1.1146	1.1087	1.1026	1.0955	1.0879	1.0805
16	1.1352	1.1292	1.1229	1.1157	1.1079	1.1004
18	1.1567	1.1504	1.1440	1.1366	1.1287	1.1210
20	1.1789	1.1725	1.1658	1.1584	1.1502	1.1424
25	1.2384	1.2315	1.2243	1.2165	1.2080	1.1997
30	1.3040	1.2967	1.2888	1.2805	1.2716	1.2628
35	1.3769	1.3691	1.3606	1.3518	1.3425	1.3331
40	1.4582	1.4498	1.4408	1.4313	1.4214	1.4114
45	1.5485	1.5393	1.5298	1.5196	1.5090	1.4983

$CdSO_4$ [GS] (**249, 313, 655**)**; (**115, 440**)*; (**20, 116, 312, 322, 329, 378, 451, 550, 618, 629**)

%	d_4^{18}	d_4^{30}	%	d_4^{18}	d_4^{30}	(**477**)**; (**641**)*	
						%	d_4^{18}
2	1.0182	1.0149	18	1.1982	1.1941		
4	1.0383	1.0348	20	1.2243	1.2201	0.2	1.00068
6	1.0590	1.0552	25	1.2940	1.2897	0.4	1.00259
8	1.0803	1.0766	30	1.3714	1.3662	0.6	1.00454
10	1.1023	1.0986	35	1.4551	1.4511	0.8	1.00654
12	1.1250	1.1213	40	1.5470	1.5445	1.0	1.00859
14	1.1485	1.1447	45		1.6477		
16	1.1729	1.1689					

$Cd(NO_3)_2$ [GS] (**249**)**; (**440**)*; (**208, 318, 322, 378, 618, 628, 629, 641**)

%	d_4^{18}	%	d_4^{18}	%	d_4^{18}	%	d_4^{18}
2	1.0154	10	1.0869	18	1.1682	35	1.3822
4	1.0326	12	1.1061	20	1.1904	40	1.4590
6	1.0502	14	1.1261	25	1.2488	45	1.5438
8	1.0683	16	1.1468	30	1.3124	50	1.6356

$Cd(CHO_2)_2$, Formate [JAB]; with 9.42 %, $d_4^{21.6}$ = 1.0761 (**329**)

$HgCl_2$ [GS] (**552, 602**)**; (**106**)*; (**49, 224, 249, 378, 417.5, 511, 517, 550, 628, 629**)

%	0°C	10°C	20°C	25°C	30°C
1	1.00821	1.00806	1.00653	1.00534	1.00391
2	1.01676	1.01657	1.01499	1.01378	1.01232
3	1.02547	1.02524	1.02359	1.02234	1.02085
4	1.03429	1.03400	1.03229	1.03100	1.02947
5	1.04319	1.04282	1.04105	1.03973	1.03815

$Hg(ClO_3)_2$ [GS] (**602**)		$HgBr_2$ [GS] (**249**)		Hg_2SO_4 [GS] (**602**)	
%	d_4^{15}	%	d_4^{18}	%	d_4^{15}
1	1.0080	0.223	1.0007	0.070	0.99985
2	1.0170	0.422	1.0025		
3	1.0260				

$Hg(CN)_2$ [GS] (**76, 378, 511, 550**)		$Hg(C_2H_3O_2)_2$, Acetate [JAB] (**329**)	
%	d_4^{20}	%	d_4^{22}
2	1.0138	21.03	1.1656
4	1.0298		
6	1.0461		
8	1.0629		

$CuCl_2$ [WCS] (**110, 288**)**; (**105, 192, 225**)*; (**27, 45, 106, 162, 178, 182, 206, 208, 261, 270, 278, 298, 308, 319, 323, 451, 462, 462.5, 548, 604, 629**)

%	0°C	10°C	20°C	25°C	30°C	40°C
1	1.0095	1.0087	1.0072	1.0062	1.005	1.002
2	1.0191	1.019	1.0171	1.0159	1.0143	1.0101
4	1.0387	1.038	1.036	1.0346	1.0331	1.0305
6	1.0586	1.0579	1.0555	1.054	1.0522	1.048
8	1.0788	1.078	1.0754	1.0736	1.0718	1.0682
10	1.0996	1.0985	1.0956	1.0938	1.0918	1.0875
12	1.1208	1.1196	1.1165	1.1145	1.1124	1.107
14	1.1427	1.1415	1.1377	1.1357	1.1335	1.1285
16	1.1653	1.164	1.1595	1.1575	1.1552	1.151
18	1.1884	1.1866	1.182	1.1797	1.1776	1.173
20	1.2121	1.2102	1.2052	1.203	1.2004	1.1953

%	0°C	%	50°C	60°C
25	1.2737	1	0.998	0.9945
30	1.3396	2	1.0064	1.001
35	1.4114	4	1.0275	1.0245

$Cu(ClO_3)_2$ [WCS] (**288**)**; (**602**)

%	d_4^{18}	%	d_4^{18}	%	d_4^{18}	%	d_4^{18}
1	1.0068	8	1.0667	16	1.1424	30	1.2993
2	1.0150	10	1.0847	18	1.1629		
4	1.0318	12	1.1033	20	1.1840		
6	1.0489	14	1.1224	25	1.2393		

$CuBr_2$ [WCS] (**45**)

%	d_4^0	%	d_4^0	%	d_4^0	%	d_4^0
0.2	1.004	0.6	1.011	1.0	1.018	4.0	1.072
0.4	1.007	0.8	1.014	2.0	1.036	6.0	1.113

$CuSO_4$ [WCS] (**299, 313, 342, 344, 619**)**; (**11, 105, 184, 220, 221, 224, 264, 308**)*; (**106, 144, 162, 175, 189, 192, 203, 206, 225, 246, 270, 275, 278, 329, 377, 400, 403, 404, 406, 425, 449, 451, 462, 462.5, 506, 533, 534, 535, 572, 580, 595, 604, 629**)

%	0°C	10°C	20°C	25°C	30°C	40°C
1	1.0104	1.010	1.0086	1.0073	1.0058	1.0024
2	1.0211	1.0206	1.019	1.0176	1.0161	1.0126
4	1.0429	1.042	1.0401	1.0387	1.037	1.0332
6	1.0654	1.0638	1.0616	1.0602	1.0585	1.0545
8	1.0887	1.0866	1.084	1.0825	1.0807	1.0764
10	1.1128	1.1101	1.1071	1.1054	1.1035	1.0990
12	1.1379	1.1345	1.1308	1.1289	1.1267	1.1222
14		1.1590	1.1544			
16		1.183	1.180			
18		1.208	1.206			

$Cu(NO_3)_2$ [WCS] (**288**)**; (**323, 384, 488, 629**)*; (**106, 162, 164, 194, 208, 217, 270, 308, 319, 329, 462, 462.5**)

%	d_4^{15}	d_4^{20}	d_4^{25}	%	d_4^{15}	d_4^{20}
1	1.0078	1.0065	1.0050	14	1.1283	1.1260
2	1.0159	1.015	1.0128	16	1.1485	1.1468
4	1.0334	1.0320	1.0297	18	1.170	1.1678
6	1.0520	1.0500	1.0475	20	1.192	1.1893
8	1.0700	1.0685	1.0655	25	1.248	1.2475
10	1.0885	1.0875		30	1.310	
12	1.1085	1.1065		35	1.377	

$(NH_4)_2Cu(SO_4)_2$ [WCS]; 7.73 %, $d_4^{19\pm1} = 1.0243$ (**506**); *cf.* (**534**)

$Cu(CHO_2)_2$, Formate [WCS] (**434, 563**)

%	d_4^{18}	%	d_4^{18}	%	d_4^{18}	%	d_4^{30}
0.2	1.0002	0.8	1.0048	4.0	1.0297	3.7	1.0166
0.4	1.0017	1.0	1.0064				
0.6	1.0033	2.0	1.0142				

$Cu(C_2H_3O_2)_2$, Acetate [WCS] (**291**)**; (**563**)*; (**288**)

%	d_4^{18}	%	d_4^{18}	%	d_4^{18}	%	d_4^{18}
0.2	0.9997	0.6	1.0020	1.0	1.0046	4.0	1.0223
0.4	1.0008	0.8	1.0032	2.0	1.0106	6.0	1.0340

$Cu(C_3H_5O_2)_2$, Propionate [WCS] (**563**)

%	d_4^{18}	%	d_4^{18}	%	d_4^{18}	%	d_4^{18}
0.2	0.9997	0.6	1.0017	1.0	1.0038	4.0	1.0192
0.4	1.0007	0.8	1.0027	2.0	1.0089		

AgF [WCS] (**288**)**; (**251**)*

%	d_4^{18}	%	d_4^{18}	%	d_4^{18}	%	d_4^{18}
1	1.0088	10	1.1071	20	1.2394	45	1.70
2	1.0191	12	1.1316	25	1.3146	50	1.85
4	1.0399	14	1.1572	30	1.40	55	2.03
6	1.0613	16	1.1837	35	1.48	60	2.26
8	1.0838	18	1.2110	40	1.58	65	2.55

$AgClO_3$ [WCS] (**602**)

%	1	2	4	6	8
d_4^{15}	1.0074	1.0158	1.0327	1.0503	1.0683

Ag_2SO_4 [WCS] (**262, 295**)*; (**602**) ‖ **Ag_2SeO_4** [WCS] (**602**)

%	d_4^{15}	d_4^{25}	%	d_4^{15}
0.59	1.0048		0.18	1.00085
0.83		1.0053		
0.88	1.0076			

$AgNO_3$ [WCS] (**64, 262**)**; (**291, 530, 531**)*; (**18, 106, 189, 224, 225, 313, 329, 342, 411, 508, 517, 555, 605, 606, 608, 609, 610, 629**)

%	10°C	30°C	40°C	60°C	80°C
2.0	1.0170	1.0127	1.0091	0.9999	0.9885
10.0	1.0908	1.0848	1.0807	1.0706	1.0585
70.0		2.2234	2.2131	2.1924	2.1709

$AgNO_3$.—(*Continued*)

%	d_4^{20}	d_4^{25}	d_4^{100}†	%	d_4^{20}	d_4^{25}	d_4^{100}†
0.2		0.9988		20.0	1.1942	1.1918	1.143
0.4		1.0006		25.0	1.2545	1.2525	1.201
0.6		1.0023		30.0	1.3205	1.3185	1.263
0.8		1.0040		35.0	1.3931	1.3905	1.333
1.0	1.0070	1.0057	0.966	40.0	1.4743	1.469	1.410
2.0	1.0154	1.0141	0.974	45.0	1.565	1.557	1.508
4.0	1.0327	1.0315	0.990	50.0	1.668	1.659	1.611
6.0	1.0506	1.0491	1.007	55.0	1.786	1.779	1.724
8.0	1.0690	1.0674	1.025	60.0	1.916	1.912	1.852
10.0	1.0882	1.0866	1.043	65.0		2.06	1.992
12.0	1.1080	1.105	1.062	70.0	2.2333	2.2283	2.151
14.0	1.1284	1.125	1.08	75.0			2.345
16.0	1.1495	1.146	1.10	80.0			2.570
18.0	1.1715	1.168	1.12	85.0			2.838

† With 0.423 %, $d_4^{155.6} = 0.9160$, $d_4^{217.6} = 0.8481$; with 0.843 %, $d_4^{306} = 0.7068$; with 1.675 %, $d_4^{155.8} = 0.9264$, $d_4^{218.1} = 0.8581$ (**455**).

$AgC_2H_3O_2$, Acetate [WCS]; with 1 %, $d_4^{15} = 1.0059$; $d_4^{25} = 1.0020$ (**295, 602**)

$AgC_2H_2ClO_2$, Chloroacetate [WCS]; with 1.51 %, $d_4^{25} = 1.0066$ (**295**)

$AgTl(NO_3)_2$ [WCS] (**508**)

%	d_4^{100}	%	d_4^{100}	%	d_4^{100}	%	d_4^{100}
1	0.966	14	1.080	40	1.436	75	2.435
2	0.974	16	1.100	45	1.533	80	2.686
4	0.990	18	1.122	50	1.637	85	3.008
6	1.006	20	1.144	55	1.748	90	3.425
8	1.024	25	1.204	60	1.867	95	3.964
10	1.042	30	1.272	65	2.036	100	4.658
12	1.060	35	1.349	70	2.224		

$AuCl_3$ [WCS]

%	d_4^{15} (**602**)†	d_4^{17} (**158**)	%	d_4^{15} (**602**)†	d_4^{17} (**158**)
1	1.0060	1.0072	6	1.0434	1.0460
2	1.0132	1.0156	8	1.0591	
4	1.0281	1.0312	10	1.0750	

† Solutions contained 1 mole HCl per mole $AuCl_3$.

$Au(CN)_3$ [WCS]; with 2.643 %, $d_4^{19.5} = 1.0181$ (**76**)

OsO_4 [WCS]; with 1.316 %, $d_4^{19} = 1.0061$ (**76**)

$PtCl_4$ [WCS] (**397, 433, 497**)

%	d_4^{room}	%	d_4^{room}	%	d_4^{room}	%	d_4^{room}
1	1.008	10	1.095	20	1.212	45	1.663
2	1.017	12	1.117	25	1.283	50	1.782
4	1.035	14	1.139	30	1.360		
6	1.054	16	1.163	35	1.448		
8	1.074	18	1.186	40	1.543		

$PdCl_2$ [WCS]; $d_4^{19} = 1.0022$ with 0.37 %; $d_4^{20} = 1.0157$ with 2.193 %; $= 1.0224$ with 3.00 % (**76, 602**)

$HMnO_4$ [LJG]; with 6.00 %, $d_4^{25} = 1.0354$ (**529**)

$MnCl_2$ [JAB] (**291, 629**)**; (**225, 278, 312, 384, 561**) [LJG]

%	d_4^{18}	d_4^{25}	%	d_4^{18}	%	d_4^{18}
1	1.0069	1.0055	12	1.1046	24	1.2283
2	1.0153	1.0139	14	1.1238	26	1.2511
4	1.0324	1.0309	16	1.1435	28	1.2746
6	1.0498	1.0482	18	1.1638	30	1.2988
8	1.0676		20	1.1846		
10	1.0859		22	1.2061		

$MnBr_2$ [JAB] (**291**) [LJG]

%	d_4^{18}	%	d_4^{18}	%	d_4^{18}	%	d_4^{18}
1	1.0071	10	1.0886	20	1.1942	30	1.3206
2	1.0157	12	1.1083	22	1.2176	32	1.3489
4	1.0332	14	1.1287	24	1.2419		
6	1.0511	16	1.1498	26	1.2672		
8	1.0695	18	1.1716	28	1.2934		

$MnSO_4$ [JAB] (**105, 225, 278**)**; (**629**)*; (**144, 192, 206, 221, 312, 477, 550, 561**) [LJG]

%	0°C	10°C	15°C	20°C	25°C
1	1.0100	1.0098	1.0089	1.0080	1.0068
2	1.0202	1.0197	1.0188	1.0178	1.0165
4	1.0409	1.0399	1.0389	1.0378	1.0364
6	1.0620	1.0606	1.0595	1.0583	1.0569
8	1.0836	1.0819	1.0807	1.0794	1.0780
10	1.1057	1.1036	1.1025	1.1012	1.0998
12	1.1282	1.1259	1.1248	1.1236	1.1224
14	1.1511	1.1488	1.1478	1.1467	1.1458
16	1.1744	1.1723	1.1714	1.1705	1.1699
18	1.1982	1.1965	1.1956	1.1950	1.1948

%	20	22	24	26	28	30
15°C	1.2205	1.2461	1.2725	1.2997	1.3277	1.3565
25°C†	1.2203	1.2464	1.2731	1.3004	1.3283	1.3568

† d_4^{25} = 1.3860 with 32 %.

$Mn(NO_3)_2$ [JAB] (**291**)**; (**225, 278, 469, 629**) [LJG]

%	d_4^{18}	%	d_4^{18}	%	d_4^{18}	%	d_4^{18}
1	1.0063	12	1.0969	24	1.2125	45	1.4662
2	1.0140	14	1.1149	26	1.2338	50	1.5378
4	1.0298	16	1.1333	28	1.2557	55	1.6146
6	1.0459	18	1.1522	30	1.2781		
8	1.0624	20	1.1717	35	1.3367		
10	1.0794	22	1.1918	40	1.3993		

NH_4MnO_4 [LJG]; with 3.43 %, d_4^{25} = 1.0154 (**529**)

$Mn(C_2H_3O_2)_2$, Acetate [JAB] (**509**)

%	d_4^{20}	%	d_4^{20}	%	d_4^{20}	%	d_4^{20}
1	1.0033	8	1.0398	16	1.0827	24	1.1288
2	1.0085	10	1.0503	18	1.0939	26	1.1410
4	1.0189	12	1.0609	20	1.1053	28	1.1536
6	1.0293	14	1.0717	22	1.1169	30	1.1666

$Fe(OH)_3$, Dialyzed [WCS] (**198, 377**)

%	d_4^{20}	d_4^{25}	%	d_4^{20}	d_4^{25}	%	d_4^{20}
1	1.0050	1.0040	2	1.0121	1.0105	3	1.0194

$FeCl_2$ [WCS] (**27, 45, 163, 225, 291, 506**)

%	$d_4^{15.5}$	d_4^{18}	%	$d_4^{15.5}$	d_4^{18}	%	$d_4^{15.5}$	d_4^{18}
1	1.0080	1.0075	10	1.0940	1.0923	20	1.2020	1.1996
2	1.0172	1.0165	12	1.1145	1.1126	25	1.2610	1.2596
4	1.0356	1.0348	14	1.1355	1.1336	30	1.3275	
6	1.0545	1.0535	16	1.1575	1.1551	35	1.4020	
8	1.0738	1.0726	18	1.1795	1.1771			

$FeCl_3$ [WCS] (**291**)**; (**27, 208, 254, 279, 319, 328, 430, 506, 554**)

%	0°C	10°C	15°C	20°C	25°C	30°C
1	1.0086	1.0084	1.0078	1.0068	1.0053	1.0040
2	1.0174	1.0168	1.0162	1.0152	1.0137	1.0122
4	1.0347	1.0341	1.0335	1.0324	1.0309	1.0292
6	1.0520	1.0511	1.0502	1.0492	1.0478	1.0460
8	1.0703	1.0692	1.0681	1.0669	1.0653	1.0636
10	1.0898	1.0883	1.0867	1.0851	1.0835	1.0817
12	1.1088	1.1071	1.1056	1.1040	1.1024	1.1006
14	1.1280	1.1257	1.1242	1.1227	1.1212	1.1196
16	1.1475	1.1449	1.1434	1.1418	1.1402	1.1386
18	1.1670	1.1644	1.1631	1.1617	1.1602	1.1586
20	1.1870	1.1847	1.1834	1.1820	1.1805	1.1786
25	1.2400	1.2380	1.2360	1.2340	1.2320	1.2290
30	1.2970	1.2950	1.2935	1.2910	1.2885	1.2850
35	1.3605	1.3580	1.3555	1.3530	1.3505	1.3475
40	1.4280	1.4235	1.4205	1.4175	1.4145	1.4115
45		1.4920	1.4885	1.4850		
50		1.5610	1.5560	1.5510		

$FeCl_3$.—(*Continued*)

%	d_4^{35}	%	d_4^{35}	%	d_4^{35}	%	d_4^{35}
1	1.0025	8	1.0617	16	1.1370	30	1.2820
2	1.0107	10	1.0799	18	1.1569	35	1.3450
4	1.0272	12	1.0990	20	1.1767	40	1.4085
6	1.0441	14	1.1180	25	1.2260		

$FeBr_2$ [WCS] (**291**)

%	d_4^{18}	%	d_4^{18}	%	d_4^{18}	%	d_4^{18}
1	1.0076	8	1.0728	16	1.1576	30	1.3393
2	1.0166	10	1.0929	18	1.1807	35	1.4186
4	1.0347	12	1.1138	20	1.2047		
6	1.0534	14	1.1353	25	1.2685		

$FeBr_3$ [WCS]; with 1.56 %, d_4^{19} = 1.0107; 8.016 %, d_4^{20} = 1.0640 (**76**)

$FeSO_4$ [WCS] (**220, 221, 334, 477**)*; (**18, 270, 404, 406, 449, 506, 533, 535, 595, 604**)

%	18°C	20°C	%	15°C	18°C	%	15°C	18°C
0.2	1.0006s	1.0002	2	1.0185	1.0180	12	1.1235	1.1220
0.4	1.00275	1.0022	4	1.0380	1.0375	14	1.1460	1.1445
0.6	1.00463	1.0042	6	1.0580	1.0575	16	1.1690	1.1675
0.8	1.00645	1.0062	8	1.0790	1.0785	18	1.1920	1.1905
1†	1.0085	1.0082	10	1.1010	1.1000	20	1.2150	1.2135

† For 1 %, d_4^{15} = 1.0090.

$Fe_2(SO_4)_3$† [WCS] (**208**)*; (**225, 254, 377**)

%	d_4^{15} (**225**)	$d_4^{17.5}$ (**208**)*	d_4^{18} (**254**)	%	d_4^{15} (**225**)	$d_4^{17.5}$ (**208**)*	d_4^{18} (**254**)
1	1.008	1.0072	1.0066	20	1.204	1.1811	1.2061
2	1.018	1.0157	1.0156	25	1.264	1.2410	1.2689
4	1.037	1.0327	1.0346	30	1.330	1.3073	1.3347
6	1.056	1.0498	1.0554	35	1.400	1.3764	1.4085
8	1.076	1.0670	1.0754	40	1.476	1.4487	1.4873
10	1.095	1.0840	1.0954	45	1.560	1.5278	
12	1.116	1.1028	1.1164	50	1.647	1.6127	
14	1.137	1.1215	1.1382	55		1.7028	
16	1.158	1.1409	1.1602	60		1.7983	
18	1.181	1.1609	1.1822				

† Discordant data. For data at 20°C, *v.* (**377**).

$Fe(NO_3)_2$ [WCS] (**217, 602**)

%.............	1	2	4	6
d_4^{20}.............	1.0063	1.0144	1.0309	1.0480

$Fe(NO_3)_3$ [WCS] (**291**)**; (**208, 319, 602**)

%	d_4^{18}	%	d_4^{18}	%	d_4^{18}	%	d_4^{18}
1	1.0065	6	1.0468	12	1.0989	18	1.1551
2	1.0144	8	1.0636	14	1.1172	20	1.1748
4	1.0304	10	1.0810	16	1.1359	25	1.2281

$FeSO_4.(NH_4)_2SO_4$ [WCS] (**199, 533, 534**)*; (**221, 506**)

%.............	1	2	4	6	8
$d_4^{16.5}$............	1.0078	1.0159	1.0323	1.0485	1.0654
d_4^{25}.............	1.005	1.013	1.029	1.045	1.062
%.............	10	12	14	16	18
$d_4^{16.5}$............	1.0827	1.1002	1.1182	1.1362	1.1547
d_4^{25}.............	1.080	1.098	1.116		

$Fe_2(SO_4)_3.(NH_4)_2SO_4$ [WCS] (**225**)*; (**188**)

%	d_4^{15}	%	d_4^{15}	%	d_4^{15}	%	d_4^{15}
1	1.0072	6	1.0498	12	1.1038	18	1.1609
2	1.0157	8	1.0675	14	1.1224	20	1.1809
4	1.0324	10	1.0856	16	1.1412	40	1.3799

$Fe_2(C_2O_4)_3$, Oxalate [WCS]; with 3.04 %, $d_4^{30.1}$ = 1.0126; with 23.85 %, $d_4^{30.0}$ = 1.1480 (**434**)

$CoCl_2$† [WCS] (**291**)**; (**66, 629**)*; (**45, 76, 162, 178, 192, 208, 225, 319, 323, 397, 433, 451, 506, 604, 640**)

%....	1	2	4	6	8	10
d_4^{18}....	1.0076	1.0168	1.0356	1.0549	1.0747	1.0949
d_4^{20}....	1.0073	1.0165	1.0350	1.0538	1.0735	1.0940
d_4^{25}....	1.0060	1.0150	1.0335	1.0525		

%............	12	14	16	18	20
d_4^{18}............	1.1157	1.1370	1.1590	1.1817	1.2051
d_4^{20}............	1.1150	1.1365	1.1585	1.1815	1.2050

† Data on this salt, especially at higher concentrations, are rather discordant.

$Co(ClO_3)_2$ [WCS] (**291**)**; (**421**)

%	d_4^{18}	%	d_4^{18}	%	d_4^{18}	%	d_4^{18}
1	1.0064	8	1.0642	16	1.1373	30	1.2880
2	1.0144	10	1.0817	18	1.1569	35	1.3503
4	1.0305	12	1.0996	20	1.1772	40	1.4182
6	1.0472	14	1.1182	25	1.2305		

$CoBr_2$ [WCS] (**291**)**

%	d_4^{18}	%	d_4^{18}	%	d_4^{18}	%	d_4^{18}
1	1.0075	8	1.0735	16	1.1592	30	1.3437
2	1.0165	10	1.0938	18	1.1826		
4	1.0350	12	1.1148	20	1.2069		
6	1.0539	14	1.1367	25	1.2718		

$CoSO_4$ [WCS] (**105, 162, 435, 449, 506, 629**)

%............	1	2	4†	6	8
d_4^{0}............	1.0107	1.0215	1.0436	1.0662	1.0890
d_4^{25}............	1.0072	1.0174	1.0380	1.0588	1.0800

† With 4 %, d_4^{20} = 1.0411.

$Co(NO_3)_2$ [WCS] (**291**)**; (**602, 629**)*; (**162, 206, 208, 217, 319, 323**)

%	d_4^{18}	d_4^{20}	d_4^{25}	%	d_4^{18}	d_4^{20}
1	1.0068	1.0064	1.0054	14	1.1229	1.1220
2	1.0150	1.0145	1.0135	16	1.1427	1.1420
4	1.0317	1.0315	1.0304	18	1.1632	1.1630
6	1.0488	1.0485	1.0475	20	1.1841	1.1840
8	1.0666	1.0660	1.0648	25	1.2396	1.2390
10	1.0848	1.0840		30	1.2998	1.2990
12	1.1036	1.1030				

$CoSO_4.(NH_4)_2SO_4$ [WCS]; with 12.64 %, $d_4^{19\pm1}$ = 1.104 (**506**)

$Co(C_2H_3O_2)_2$, Acetate [JAB] (**509**)

%	d_4^{20}	%	d_4^{20}	%	d_4^{20}	%	d_4^{20}
1	1.006	3	1.020	5	1.031	7	1.040
2	1.013	4	1.026	6	1.036		

$Co(CNS)_2$ [WCS] (**640**)

%	$d_4^{0.2}$	d_4^{95}	%	$d_4^{0.2}$	d_4^{95}	%	$d_4^{0.2}$	d_4^{95}
1	1.0062	0.9695	8†	1.0575	1.0180	16	1.1255	1.0810
2	1.0128	0.9763	10	1.0735	1.0325	18	1.1440	1.0990
4	1.0270	0.9903	12	1.0900	1.0480	20	1.1635	1.1175
6	1.0420	1.0040	14	1.1075	1.0640	25	1.2155	1.1665

† With 8.07 %, d_4^{25} = 1.0552.

$NiCl_2$ [WCS] (**291**)**; (**66, 629**)*; (**27, 45, 162, 192, 208, 225, 319, 397, 431, 433, 451, 506**)

%	d_4^{18}	d_4^{20}	d_4^{25}	%	d_4^{18}	d_4^{20}
1	1.0082	1.0078	1.0060	14	1.1442	1.1434
2	1.0179	1.0175	1.0152	16	1.1674	1.1665
4	1.0375	1.0370	1.0345	18	1.1915	1.1905
6	1.0577	1.0571	1.0545	20	1.2163	1.2150
8	1.0785	1.0777		25		1.2800
10	1.0998	1.0990		30		1.3525
12	1.1217	1.1209				

$Ni(ClO_3)_2$ [WCS] (**291**)**

%	d_4^{18}	%	d_4^{18}	%	d_4^{18}	%	d_4^{18}
1	1.0068	8	1.0664	16	1.1426	30	1.2999
2	1.0150	10	1.0846	18	1.1631		
4	1.0317	12	1.1033	20	1.1842		
6	1.0488	14	1.1227	25	1.2399		

$NiBr_2$ [WCS] (**291**)**

%	d_4^{18}	%	d_4^{18}	%	d_4^{18}	%	d_4^{18}
1	1.0078	8	1.0758	16	1.1648	30	1.3565
2	1.0170	10	1.0969	18	1.1889		
4	1.0359	12	1.1188	20	1.2140		
6	1.0555	14	1.1414	25	1.2815		

$NiSO_4$ [WCS] (**105, 334, 406.5, 629**)*; (**76, 162, 192, 206, 225, 431, 449, 506**)

%	d_4^{0}	d_4^{18}	d_4^{20}	d_4^{25}	%	d_4^{18}
1	1.0107	1.0091	1.0089	1.0073	10	1.1085
2	1.0215	1.0198	1.0196	1.0177	12	1.1325
4	1.0435	1.0415	1.0413	1.0389	14	1.1575
6		1.0630	1.0625	1.0610	16	1.1825
8		1.0852			18	1.2090

$Ni(NO_3)_2$† [WCS] (**291**)**; (**76, 162, 192, 208, 225, 319, 323, 602, 629**)

%	d_4^{18}	d_4^{20}	d_4^{25}	%	d_4^{18}	d_4^{20}	d_4^{25}
1	1.0070	1.0065	1.0055	14	1.1277	1.1270	1.1230
2	1.0155	1.0150	1.0141	16	1.1484	1.1480	1.1430
4	1.0330	1.0325	1.0316	18	1.1696	1.1690	1.1640
6	1.0508	1.0503	1.0494	20	1.1914	1.1910	1.1860
8	1.0693	1.0688	1.0675	25	1.2493	1.2490	1.2430
10	1.0882	1.0877	1.0850	30	1.3114	1.3110	1.3040
12	1.1076	1.1070	1.1040	35	1.3777	1.3770	1.3700

† The 18°C values are considered more reliable than the 20°C values, which are in the main derived from the former.

$NiSO_4.(NH_4)_2SO_4$ [WCS]; with 4.89 %, $d_4^{19\pm1}$ = 1.041 (**506**)

CrO_3 [JAB] (**661**)**; (**138, 224, 463, 517**) [LJG]

%	d_4^{15}	%	d_4^{15}	%	d_4^{15}	%	d_4^{15}
1	1.006	12	1.093	24	1.200	45	1.435
2	1.014	14	1.110	26	1.220	50	1.505
4	1.030	16	1.127	28	1.240	55	1.581
6	1.045	18	1.145	30	1.260	60	1.663
8	1.060	20	1.163	35	1.313		
10	1.076	22	1.181	40	1.371		

$CrCl_3$ [JAB] (**291**) [LJG]

%	d_4^{18} "Violet"	d_4^{18} "Green"	d_4^{18} Equilibrium mixture "violet" and "green"
1	1.0076	1.0071	1.0075
2	1.0166	1.0157	1.0165
4	1.0349	1.0332	1.0347
6	1.0535	1.0510	1.0533
8	1.0724	1.0691	1.0722
10	1.0917	1.0876	1.0915
12	1.1114	1.1065	1.1111
14	1.1316		

$CrBr_3$ [JAB] (**291**) [LJG]

%	d_4^{18}	%	d_4^{18}	%	d_4^{18}	%	d_4^{18}
1	1.0074	8	1.0726	16	1.1565	24	1.2532
2	1.0162	10	1.0926	18	1.1794	26	1.2797
4	1.0344	12	1.1132	20	1.2031	28	1.3071
6	1.0532	14	1.1345	22	1.2277	30	1.3355

$Cr_2(SO_4)_3$ [JAB] (225)**; (76, 189, 237) [LJG]

%	d_4^{15} "Green"	d_4^{15} "Violet"	%	d_4^{15} "Green"	d_4^{15} "Violet"
1	1.0081	1.0091	18	1.1851	1.1966
2	1.0172	1.0191	20	1.2091	1.2218
4	1.0358	1.0395	22	1.2339	1.2479
6	1.0551	1.0604	24	1.2594	1.2750
8	1.0751	1.0817	26	1.2856	1.3032
10	1.0958	1.1034	28	1.3125	1.3325
12	1.1172	1.1257	30	1.3401	
14	1.1392	1.1486	35	1.4123	
16	1.1618	1.1722	40	1.4893	

$(NH_4)_2CrO_4$ [LJG] (463, 566)

%	°C	d_4^t	%	°C	d_4^t
3.80	20	1.0219	19.75	13.7	1.1189
10.52	13	1.0627	28.04	19.6	1.1707

$(NH_4)_2Cr_2O_7$ [JAB] (566)**; (463) [LJG]

%	d_4^{12}	%	d_4^{12}	%	d_4^{12}	%	d_4^{12}
1	1.0051	6	1.0342	12	1.0715	18	1.1120
2	1.0108	8	1.0463	14	1.0846	20	1.1263
4	1.0223	10	1.0588	16	1.0981		

$Cr(NO_3)_3$ [JAB] (291, 602)** [LJG]

%	d_4^{15} "Violet"	d_4^{18} Color not stated	%	d_4^{15} "Violet"	d_4^{18} Color not stated
1	1.0073	1.0065	16	1.1407	1.1391
2	1.0155	1.0145	18	1.1606	1.1588
4	1.0322	1.0309	20	1.1810	1.1790
6	1.0492	1.0477	22	1.2020	1.1998
8	1.0666	1.0650	24	1.2236	1.2213
10	1.0844	1.0828	26	1.2459	1.2435
12	1.1027	1.1011	28	1.2690	1.2665
14	1.1214	1.1198	30	1.2929	1.2904

$(NH_4)_2SO_4.Cr_2(SO_4)_3.24H_2O$ [JAB] (225)**; (187, 188) [LJG]

% Anhyd.	d_4^{15} "Violet"	d_4^{15} "Green"	% Anhyd.	d_4^{15} "Green"
1	1.0081	1.007	10	1.082
2	1.0172	1.015	12	1.100
4	1.0357	1.031	14	1.118
6	1.0545	1.048	16	1.137
8		1.065	18	1.156

% Anhyd.	d_4^{15} "Green"	% Anhyd.	d_4^{15} "Green"
20	1.176	30	1.283
22	1.196	35	1.341
24	1.217	40	1.403
26	1.238	45	1.470
28	1.260	50	1.542

MoO_3 [JAB]; with 1%, d_4^{20} = 1.0062 (517) [LJG]

$(NH_4)_6Mo_7O_{24}$ [JAB] (509, 510)**; (135, 517) [LJG]

%†	1	2	4	6	8	10
d_4^{20}	1.0055	1.0129	1.0282	1.0440	1.0603	1.0772

† With 23.51 %, d_4^{20} = 1.2019.

WO_3 [LJG] (532)

%	$d_4^{17.5}$	%	$d_4^{17.5}$	%	$d_4^{17.5}$	%	$d_4^{17.5}$
1	1.0078	12	1.118	24	1.272	36	1.466
2	1.0170	14	1.141	26	1.301	38	1.505
4	1.0357	16	1.166	28	1.331	40	1.546
6	1.0550	18	1.191	30	1.363	42	1.590
8	1.075	20	1.217	32	1.396	44	1.638
10	1.096	22	1.244	34	1.430		

$SiO_2.12MoO_3$ [LJG] (13)

%	10°C	20°C	30°C	40°C
2	1.0169	1.0153	1.0126	1.0090
4	1.0345	1.0327	1.0299	1.0262
6	1.0524	1.0505	1.0476	1.0437
8	1.0707	1.0687	1.0657	1.0616
10	1.0894	1.0873	1.0841	1.0799
12	1.1085	1.1063	1.1029	1.0986
14	1.1281	1.1258	1.1223	1.1178
16	1.1482	1.1457	1.1421	1.1375

UO_2Cl_2 [LJG] (122)

$UONO_3$ [LJG] (117, 124)

$UO_2(NO_3)_2$ [LJG] (226, 233, 620)**; (27, 76)

%	d_4^{17}	d_4^{25}	%	d_4^{17}	d_4^{25}	%	d_4^{17}	d_4^{25}
1	1.008	1.0037	20	1.194	1.177	40	1.466	1.455
2	1.017	1.0104	22	1.218	1.201	42	1.498	1.489
4	1.036	1.0242	24	1.243	1.226	44	1.531	1.524
6	1.054	1.039	26	1.269	1.251	46	1.567	1.559
8	1.072	1.055	28	1.295	1.277	48	1.606	1.595
10	1.091	1.072	30	1.322	1.304	50	1.649	1.630
12	1.110	1.091	32	1.349	1.331	52	1.696	
14	1.129	1.111	34	1.377	1.360	54	1.748	
16	1.149	1.132	36	1.406	1.390			
18	1.171	1.154	38	1.436	1.422			

USO_4 [LJG] (119, 121)

$(UO)_2SO_4$ [LJG] (121)

$UO_2(C_2H_3O_2)_2$ Acetate [JAB] (509)

%	1	2	3	4
d_4^{20}	1.0055	1.0129	1.0203	1.0278

NH_4VO_3 [LJG] (602)

%	d_4^{15}	%	d_4^{15}	%	d_4^{15}	%	d_4^{15}
0.1	0.99973	0.4	1.00154	0.8	1.00401	1.2	1.00653
0.2	1.00033	0.6	1.00277	1.0	1.00526		

H_3BO_3 [JAB] (225)**; (28, 52, 101, 243) [LJG]

%	1	2	3
d_4^{15}	1.0045	1.0103	1.0165

$AlCl_3$ [JAB] (291)**; (106, 144, 219, 323) [LJG]

%	d_4^{18}	%	d_4^{18}	%	d_4^{18}
1	1.0075	6	1.0526	12	1.1093
2	1.0164	8	1.0711	14	1.1290
4	1.0344	10	1.0900	16	1.1491

$AlBr_3$ [JAB] (602)**; (76) [LJG]

%	d_4^{20}	%	d_4^{20}	%	d_4^{20}	%	d_4^{20}
1	1.0057	6	1.0451	12	1.0969	18	1.1528
2	1.0133	8	1.0619	14	1.1150	20	1.1725
4	1.0289	10	1.0792	16	1.1336	22	1.1928

$Al_2(SO_4)_3$ [JAB] (225, 629)**; (76, 106, 187, 188, 189, 206, 404, 406, 513, 517, 561) [LJG]

%	d_4^{15}	d_4^{25}	%	d_4^{15}	%	d_4^{15}
1	1.0093	1.0069	10	1.1062	20	1.2272
2	1.0195	1.0167	12	1.1293	22	1.2534
4	1.0404	1.0370	14	1.1529	24	1.2803
6	1.0618	1.0580	16	1.1770	26	1.3079
8	1.0837		18	1.2017		

$Al(NO_3)_3$ [JAB] (291)**; (602) [LJG]

%	d_4^{18}	%	d_4^{18}	%	d_4^{18}	%	d_4^{18}
1	1.0065	10	1.0811	20	1.1745	30	1.2805
2	1.0144	12	1.0989	22	1.1946	32	1.3036
4	1.0305	14	1.1171	24	1.2153		
6	1.0469	16	1.1357	26	1.2365		
8	1.0638	18	1.1549	28	1.2582		

$(NH_4)_2SO_4.Al_2(SO_4)_3$ [JAB] (46)**; (225)* [LJG]

%	d_4^{15}	%	d_4^{15}	%	d_4^{15}	%	d_4^{15}
1	1.0079	8	1.0723	16	1.1541	24	1.2420
2	1.0167	10	1.0919	18	1.1757	26	1.2644
4	1.0348	12	1.1121	20	1.1976	28	1.2870
6†	1.0533	14	1.1329	22	1.2197	30	1.3098

† Solutions above *ca.* 6 % are supersaturated.

$Al(CNS)_3$ [LJG]; with 23.30 %; d_4^{18} = 1.1582 (155)

$Tl_2SO_4.Al_2(SO_4)_3$ [JAB]; with 5.39 %, d_4^{20} = 1.0510 (378) [LJG]

$La_2(SO_4)_3$ [LJG]; with 1.38 %, d_4^{0} = 1.0131; $d_4^{5.1}$ = 1.0128; d_4^{69} = 0.9923; d_4^{99} = 0.9734 (206)

$La(NO_3)_3$ [JAB] (291) [LJG]

%	d_4^{18}	%	d_4^{18}	%	d_4^{18}	%	d_4^{18}
1	1.0076	10	1.0945	20	1.2052	30	1.3360
2	1.0167	12	1.1153	22	1.2295	32	1.3653
4	1.0353	14	1.1368	24	1.2547		
6	1.0545	16	1.1589	26	1.2809		
8	1.0742	18	1.1817	28	1.3080		

$Ce_2(SO_4)_3$ [JAB] (67) [LJG]

%	d_4^{15}	%	d_4^{15}	%	d_4^{15}	%	d_4^{15}
1	1.0090	8	1.0823	16	1.1770	24	1.2876
2	1.0190	10	1.1047	18	1.2030		
4	1.0395	12	1.1279	20	1.2300		
6	1.0606	14	1.1520	22	1.2582		

$Sa(NO_3)_3$ [JAB] (291) [LJG]

%	d_4^{18}	%	d_4^{18}	%	d_4^{18}	%	d_4^{18}
1	1.0061	8	1.0604	16	1.1271	24	1.2005
2	1.0136	10	1.0766	18	1.1447	26	1.2201
4	1.0289	12	1.0931	20	1.1628	28	1.2403
6	1.0445	14	1.1099	22	1.1814		

$BeCl_2$ [GS] (291)**; (84)*

%†	2	4	6	8	10	12
d_4^{18}	1.0118	1.0251	1.0386	1.0523	1.0663	1.0806

† With 14 %, d_4^{18} = 1.0952.

$Be(ClO_3)_2$ [GS] (602)

%	1	2	3
d_4^{15}	1.00527	1.01141	1.01754

$BeSO_4$ [GS] (629)

%	1	2	3	4	5†
d_4^{25}	1.0058	1.0147	1.0237	1.0327	1.0417

† d_4^{20} = 1.0870 with 10 %; = 1.1769 with 20 % (312).

$Be(NO_3)_2$ [GS] (291)

%	d_4^{18}	%	d_4^{18}	%	d_4^{18}	%	d_4^{18}
2	1.0108	10	1.0624	18	1.1193	26	1.1819
4	1.0233	12	1.0761	20	1.1344	28	1.1985
6	1.0361	14	1.0902	22	1.1499		
8	1.0491	16	1.1046	24	1.1657		

$MgCl_2$ [GS] (20, 70, 366)**; (221, 342, 608, 611)*; (18, 49, 105, 106, 150, 173, 177, 219, 250, 261, 278, 322, 347, 417.5, 462, 464, 466, 469, 505, 533, 539, 618, 629)

%	0°C	10°C	20°C	25°C	30°C	40°C
2	1.0168	1.0163	1.0146	1.0134	1.0119	1.0084
4	1.0338	1.0330	1.0311	1.0298	1.0282	1.0248
6	1.0510	1.0499	1.0478	1.0463	1.0447	1.0413
8	1.0683	1.0669	1.0646	1.0631	1.0615	1.0580
10	1.0858	1.0840	1.0816	1.0801	1.0785	1.0749
12	1.1035	1.1014	1.0989	1.0974	1.0957	1.0921
14	1.1214	1.1190	1.1164	1.1149	1.1132	1.1095
16	1.1395	1.1369	1.1342	1.1326	1.1309	1.1272
18	1.1578	1.1551	1.1523	1.1506	1.1489	1.1452
20	1.1764	1.1735	1.1706	1.1689	1.1672	1.1635
25	1.2246	1.2216	1.2184	1.2167	1.2149	1.2111
30	1.2754	1.2722	1.2688	1.2671	1.2652	1.2614

$MgCl_2$.—(*Continued*)

%	50°C	60°C	70°C	80°C	90°C	100°C
2	1.0043	0.9995	0.9942	0.9883	0.9820	0.9753
4	1.0207	1.0159	1.0107	1.0050	0.9988	0.9923
6	1.0372	1.0325	1.0274	1.0218	1.0158	1.0095
8	1.0539	1.0493	1.0442	1.0388	1.0330	1.0269
10	1.0708	1.0663	1.0613	1.0560	1.0504	1.0444
12	1.0880	1.0836	1.0787	1.0735	1.0680	1.0622
14	1.1055	1.1011	1.0963	1.0912	1.0859	1.0803
16	1.1232	1.1188	1.1141	1.1092	1.1041	1.0984
18	1.1412	1.1368	1.1322	1.1275	1.1225	1.1170
20	1.1595	1.1552	1.1506	1.1460	1.1412	1.1359
25	1.2072	1.2031	1.1987	1.1942	1.1896	1.1847
30	1.2575	1.2535	1.2493	1.2451	1.2406	1.2360

%	10	12	14	16	%	35
d_4^{-5}	1.0865	1.1044	1.1225	1.1408	d_4^{20}	1.3220

$Mg(ClO_3)_2$ [GS] (288, 602)**

%	d_4^{18}	%	d_4^{18}	%	d_4^{18}	%	d_4^{18}
2	1.0135	10	1.0758	18	1.1442	26	1.2196
4	1.0287	12	1.0922	20	1.1624	28	1.2395
6	1.0441	14	1.1091	22	1.1810	30	1.2598
8	1.0597	16	1.1264	24	1.2001		

$MgBr_2$ [GS] (287, 367)**; (76, 318, 322, 366, 442)

%	0°C	10°C	20°C	25°C	30°C	40°C
2	1.0171	1.0167	1.0151	1.0139	1.0124	1.0089
4	1.0347	1.0341	1.0324	1.0311	1.0296	1.0260
6	1.0527	1.0519	1.0501	1.0487	1.0472	1.0435
8	1.0713	1.0702	1.0683	1.0668	1.0653	1.0615
10	1.0904	1.0891	1.0871	1.0855	1.0839	1.0800
12	1.1101	1.1087	1.1065	1.1049	1.1032	1.0992
14	1.1305	1.1289	1.1265	1.1248	1.1231	1.1191
16	1.1516	1.1497	1.1471	1.1455	1.1437	1.1395
18	1.1733	1.1711	1.1683	1.1666	1.1648	1.1605
20	1.1957	1.1933	1.1903	1.1885	1.1866	1.1823
25	1.2547	1.2517	1.2482	1.2462	1.2441	1.2396
30	1.3186	1.3150	1.3110	1.3089	1.3067	1.3020
35	1.388	1.383	1.379	1.377	1.374	1.370
40	1.462	1.457	1.452	1.450	1.448	1.443
45	1.541	1.537	1.532	1.529	1.527	1.522

%	50°C	60°C	70°C	80°C	90°C	100°C
2	1.0047	0.9998	0.9944	0.9884	0.9819	0.9750
4	1.0218	1.0168	1.0114	1.0053	0.9988	0.9920
6	1.0393	1.0342	1.0288	1.0227	1.0161	1.0094
8	1.0572	1.0521	1.0466	1.0405	1.0340	1.0274
10	1.0756	1.0706	1.0650	1.0590	1.0525	1.0459
12	1.0946	1.0897	1.0841	1.0780	1.0716	1.0650
14	1.1143	1.1094	1.1038	1.0977	1.0913	1.0848
16	1.1347	1.1297	1.1242	1.1181	1.1117	1.1052
18	1.1557	1.1507	1.1452	1.1391	1.1327	1.1263
20	1.1775	1.1724	1.1669	1.1608	1.1544	1.1481
25	1.2347	1.2296	1.2241	1.2182	1.2119	1.2057
30	1.2970	1.2918	1.2863	1.2805	1.2743	1.2682
35	1.364	1.359	1.354	1.348	1.342	1.336
40	1.438	1.432	1.427	1.421	1.415	1.409
45	1.516	1.511	1.505	1.500	1.494	1.488

$Mg(BrO_3)_2$ [GS] (**291**)

%	d_4^{18}	%	d_4^{18}	%	d_4^{18}	%	d_4^{18}
2	1.0157	10	1.0871	18	1.1690	26	1.2617
4	1.0328	12	1.1066	20	1.1911	28	1.2869
6	1.0502	14	1.1268	22	1.2140	30	1.3134
8	1.0683	16	1.1476	24	1.2375		

MgI_2 [GS] (**287, 368**)**; (**365**)*; (**442**)

%	0°C	10°C	20°C	25°C	30°C	40°C
2	1.0169	1.0165	1.0149	1.0137	1.0122	1.0086
4	1.0345	1.0339	1.0321	1.0307	1.0292	1.0255
6	1.0526	1.0518	1.0498	1.0483	1.0467	1.0429
8	1.0713	1.0702	1.0680	1.0665	1.0648	1.0609
10	1.0907	1.0893	1.0869	1.0854	1.0836	1.0796
12	1.1107	1.1091	1.1065	1.1049	1.1030	1.0989
14	1.1314	1.1295	1.1268	1.1251	1.1231	1.1189
16	1.1529	1.1507	1.1478	1.1460	1.1440	1.1395
18	1.1751	1.1727	1.1695	1.1676	1.1656	1.1609
20	1.1981	1.1953	1.1920	1.1900	1.1879	1.1830
25	1.2591	1.2557	1.2519	1.2497	1.2473	1.2421
30	1.3265	1.3223	1.3180	1.3156	1.3131	1.3074
35	1.4012	1.3962	1.3914	1.3887	1.3861	1.3799
40	1.4839	1.4784	1.4730	1.4702	1.4672	1.4607

%	50°C	60°C	70°C	80°C	90°C	100°C
2	1.0043	0.9994	0.9940	0.9879	0.9814	0.9745
4	1.0212	1.0161	1.0107	1.0045	0.9980	0.9910
6	1.0385	1.0333	1.0279	1.0217	1.0151	1.0080
8	1.0564	1.0511	1.0456	1.0394	1.0328	1.0257
10	1.0749	1.0696	1.0640	1.0578	1.0511	1.0441
12	1.0941	1.0888	1.0830	1.0768	1.0701	1.0631
14	1.1140	1.1086	1.1027	1.0965	1.0897	1.0827
16	1.1346	1.1291	1.1231	1.1169	1.1100	1.1029
18	1.1559	1.1503	1.1442	1.1379	1.1311	1.1239
20	1.1779	1.1722	1.1661	1.1597	1.1529	1.1457
25	1.2367	1.2307	1.2244	1.2178	1.2108	1.2037
30	1.3017	1.2954	1.2889	1.2821	1.2750	1.2679
35	1.3738	1.3673	1.3606	1.3536	1.3464	1.3392
40	1.4542	1.4475	1.4406	1.4334	1.4260	1.4186

$MgSO_4$ [GS] (**219, 221, 342, 346, 374, 375**)**; (**505**)*; (**7, 8, 18, 20, 46, 49, 105, 106, 150, 192, 204, 250, 278, 298, 318, 329, 336, 344, 348, 349, 401, 402, 403, 404, 425, 449, 469, 506, 533, 534, 550, 573, 618, 629**)

%	0°C	10°C	20°C	25°C	30°C	40°C
2	1.0210	1.0204	1.0186	1.0173	1.0158	1.0123
4	1.0423	1.0413	1.0392	1.0378	1.0362	1.0326
6	1.0639	1.0625	1.0602	1.0587	1.0570	1.0532
8	1.0858	1.0841	1.0816	1.0800	1.0782	1.0743
10	1.1081	1.1061	1.1034	1.1017	1.0999	1.0958
12	1.1309	1.1286	1.1256	1.1239	1.1220	1.1179
14	1.1541	1.1516	1.1484	1.1466	1.1447	1.1405
16	1.1777	1.1750	1.1717	1.1698	1.1679	1.1637
18	1.2018	1.1989	1.1955	1.1936	1.1916	1.1874
20	1.2264	1.2233	1.2198	1.2179	1.2159	1.2117
22	1.2515	1.2483	1.2447	1.2428	1.2408	1.2365
24	1.2771	1.2738	1.2701	1.2682	1.2662	1.2619
26	1.3032	1.2998	1.2961	1.2942	1.2922	1.2879

%	50°C	60°C	70°C	80°C	%	50°C
2	1.0081	1.0032	0.9978	0.9916	16	1.1592
4	1.0283	1.0234	1.0180	1.0118	18	1.1829
6	1.0489	1.0440	1.0386	1.0324	20	1.2072
8	1.0700	1.0650	1.0596	1.0534	22	1.2321
10	1.0915	1.0864	1.0810	1.0748	24	1.2576
12	1.1135	1.1083	1.1029	1.0968	26	1.2836
14	1.1361	1.1308	1.1253	1.1193		

$MgSO_4$.—(*Continued*)

%	$d_4^{6.29}$ (**346**)	$d_4^{20.004}$ (**373**)	%	$d_4^{6.29}$ (**346**)
0.00	0.999 9585	0.998 23150†	0.07	1.000 7042
0.01	1.000 0659	0.998 33872	0.08	1.000 8100
0.02	1.000 1728	0.998 44553	0.09	1.000 9157
0.03	1.000 2794	0.998 55198	0.1	1.001 0213
0.04	1.000 3858	0.998 65812	0.2	1.002 0733
0.05	1.000 4921	0.998 76403	0.3	1.003 1199
0.06	1.000 5982	0.998 86973	0.4	1.004 1645

† The small figures are significant only for ratios within the table.

$Mg(NO_3)_2$ [GS] (**110, 287, 342**)**; (**606, 609**)*; (**20, 106, 150, 278, 322, 462, 464, 466, 469, 533, 535, 618, 628, 629**)

%	0°C	10°C	20°C	25°C	30°C	40°C
2	1.0157	1.0151	1.0132	1.0119	1.0104	1.0068
4	1.0318	1.0307	1.0285	1.0271	1.0254	1.0216
6	1.0482	1.0466	1.0441	1.0426	1.0408	1.0367
8	1.0649	1.0629	1.0600	1.0584	1.0565	1.0522
10	1.0819	1.0795	1.0762	1.0745	1.0725	1.0681
12	1.0992	1.0964	1.0928	1.0910	1.0889	1.0843
14	1.1168	1.1137	1.1098	1.1079	1.1057	1.1009
16		1.1314	1.1272	1.1251	1.1229	
18		1.1494	1.1449	1.1427	1.1404	
20		1.1677	1.1630	1.1607	1.1582	
22		1.1864	1.1815	1.1790	1.1764	
24		1.2055	1.2004	1.1977	1.1949	

$Mg(CHO_2)_2$, Formate [JAB] (**291**)**; (**329**)

%..............	1	2	3	4	5
d_4^{18}..............	1.0060	1.0134	1.0209	1.0284	1.0360

$Mg(C_2H_3O_2)_2$, Acetate [JAB] (**288**)**; (**561**)

%................	1	2	4	6	8	10
d_4^{18}................	1.0043	1.0101	1.0216	1.0331	1.0447	1.0564
%................	12	14	16	18	20	22
d_4^{18}................	1.0682	1.0802	1.0923	1.1045	1.1169	1.1295

$MgCrO_4$ [GS] (**288**)**; (**566**)

%	d_4^{18}	%	d_4^{18}	%	d_4^{18}	%	d_4^{18}
2	1.0185	10	1.1018	18	1.1946	26	1.2965
4	1.0387	12	1.1240	20	1.2194		
6	1.0592	14	1.1469	22	1.2446		
8	1.0802	16	1.1704	24	1.2703		

$Ca(OH)_2$ [GS] (**98, 102, 529, 631**)

%	d_4^{15}	d_4^{25}	%	d_4^{15}	d_4^{25}
0.05	0.99979	0.99773	0.15	1.00110	0.99904
0.10	1.00044	0.99838			

$CaCl_2$ [GS] (**219, 221, 342, 367, 588**)**; (**68, 69, 84, 312, 363, 493, 606, 608, 609, 611**)*; (**18, 49, 50, 98, 105, 106, 139, 159, 173, 177, 189, 190, 192, 261, 318, 320, 321, 322, 347, 355, 401, 402, 407, 417.5, 506, 529, 533, 535, 550, 564, 573, 613, 618, 640**)

%	−5°C	0°C	+10°C	20°C	25°C	30°C
2		1.0171	1.0166	1.0148	1.0135	1.0120
4		1.0346	1.0337	1.0316	1.0302	1.0286
6		1.0523	1.0509	1.0486	1.0471	1.0455
8	1.0708	1.0703	1.0684	1.0659	1.0643	1.0626
10	1.0894	1.0886	1.0863	1.0835	1.0818	1.0800
12	1.1083	1.1072	1.1045	1.1015	1.0997	1.0978
14	1.1275	1.1261	1.1231	1.1198	1.1180	1.1160
16	1.1471	1.1454	1.1421	1.1386	1.1366	1.1345
18	1.1670	1.1651	1.1616	1.1578	1.1557	1.1535
20	1.1874	1.1853	1.1815	1.1775	1.1753	1.1730
25		1.2376	1.2330	1.2284	1.2260	1.2236
30		1.2922	1.2869	1.2816	1.2790	1.2764
35				1.3373	1.3345	1.3316
40				1.3957	1.3927	1.3895

$CaCl_2$.—(*Continued*)

%	40°C	50°C	60°C	70°C	80°C	90°C
2	1.0084	1.0043	0.9994	0.9940	0.9881	0.9816
4	1.0249	1.0207	1.0158	1.0104	1.0046	0.9981
6	1.0416	1.0373	1.0324	1.0270	1.0213	1.0148
8	1.0586	1.0542	1.0492	1.0439	1.0382	1.0317
10	1.0760	1.0715	1.0664	1.0611	1.0554	1.0490
12	1.0937	1.0891	1.0840	1.0787	1.0730	1.0667
14	1.1117	1.1070	1.1019	1.0966	1.0909	1.0847
16	1.1301	1.1254	1.1202	1.1148	1.1092	1.1031
18	1.1490	1.1442	1.1389	1.1335	1.1279	1.1219
20	1.1684	1.1635	1.1581	1.1528	1.1471	1.1412
25	1.2186	1.2134	1.2079	1.2024	1.1965	1.1906
30	1.2709	1.2654	1.2597	1.2539	1.2478	1.2419
35	1.3255	1.3196	1.3137	1.3075	1.3013	1.2953
40	1.3826	1.3762	1.3700	1.3635	1.3571	1.3510

%	100°C†	110°C	120°C	130°C	140°C
2	0.9748	0.9674	0.9596	0.9514	0.9428
4	0.9915	0.9842	0.9765	0.9685	0.9601
6	1.0085	1.0012	0.9937	0.9859	0.9776
8	1.0257	1.0185	1.0111	1.0035	0.9954
10	1.0432	1.0361	1.0287	1.0213	1.0134
12	1.0610	1.0539	1.0466	1.0394	1.0317
14	1.0790	1.0720	1.0649	1.0577	1.0503
16	1.0973	1.0905	1.0835	1.0763	1.0691
18	1.1160	1.1094	1.1025	1.0954	1.0883
20	1.1352	1.1287	1.1219	1.1150	1.1080
25	1.1846				
30	1.2359				
35	1.2893				
40	1.3450				

† Values over 100°C corrected to one atmosphere pressure.

$CaOCl_2$, Bleaching powder [GS] (389)

[$CaOCl_2$, 89.51%; $CaCl_2$, 7.31%; $Ca(ClO_3)_2$, 0.26%; $Ca(OH)_2$, 2.92%]

% total salt..	2	4	6	8	10	12
d_4^{15}..........	1.0169	1.0345	1.0520	1.0697	1.0876	1.1060

$Ca(ClO_3)_2$ [GS] (288)**; (602)

%	d_4^{18}	%	d_4^{18}	%	d_4^{18}	%	d_4^{18}
2	1.0135	10	1.0768	18	1.1469	26	1.2247
4	1.0288	12	1.0936	20	1.1656	28	1.2454
6	1.0444	14	1.1109	22	1.1848	30	1.2665
8	1.0604	16	1.1286	24	1.2045		

$CaBr_2$ [GS] (287, 368)**; (312, 363)*; (139, 318, 322, 618)

%	0°C	10°C	20°C	25°C	30°C	40°C
2	1.0173	1.0169	1.0152	1.0139	1.0125	1.0089
4	1.0352	1.0345	1.0326	1.0312	1.0296	1.0260
6	1.0535	1.0525	1.0504	1.0489	1.0473	1.0435
8	1.0724	1.0711	1.0688	1.0672	1.0655	1.0616
10	1.0919	1.0903	1.0877	1.0860	1.0843	1.0802
12	1.1119	1.1099	1.1071	1.1054	1.1035	1.0994
14	1.1325	1.1302	1.1272	1.1254	1.1234	1.1192
16	1.1538	1.1512	1.1480	1.1461	1.1441	1.1396
18	1.1759	1.1730	1.1696	1.1676	1.1655	1.1608
20	1.1988	1.1955	1.1919	1.1897	1.1876	1.1827
25	1.2584	1.2542	1.2499	1.2475	1.2451	1.2397
30	1.3226	1.3175	1.3125	1.3099	1.3072	1.3014
35	1.393	1.387	1.381	1.378	1.375	1.369
40	1.469	1.463	1.457	1.453	1.450	1.443
45	1.555	1.548	1.541	1.537	1.534	1.526
50	1.650	1.642	1.635	1.631	1.627	1.619

$CaBr_2$.—(*Continued*)

%	50°C	60°C	70°C	80°C	90°C	100°C
2	1.0047	0.9988	0.9943	0.9883	0.9817	0.9748
4	1.0217	1.0168	1.0112	1.0052	0.9985	0.9917
6	1.0391	1.0342	1.0285	1.0225	1.0158	1.0090
8	1.0570	1.0521	1.0464	1.0403	1.0337	1.0269
10	1.0756	1.0705	1.0648	1.0587	1.0520	1.0452
12	1.0947	1.0894	1.0837	1.0775	1.0708	1.0641
14	1.1143	1.1090	1.1032	1.0970	1.0903	1.0836
16	1.1346	1.1293	1.1234	1.1172	1.1105	1.1038
18	1.1557	1.1503	1.1443	1.1381	1.1314	1.1247
20	1.1775	1.1720	1.1660	1.1598	1.1530	1.1463
25	1.2343	1.2285	1.2224	1.2160	1.2092	1.2024
30	1.2957	1.2896	1.2833	1.2768	1.2698	1.2630
35	1.363	1.356	1.350	1.343	1.336	1.329
40	1.437	1.430	1.423	1.416	1.409	1.402
45	1.519	1.512	1.505	1.498	1.490	1.483
50	1.612	1.604	1.597	1.589	1.582	1.574

CaI_2 [GS] (287, 369)**; (322, 365, 618)

%	0°C	10°C	20°C	25°C	30°C	40°C
2	1.0171	1.0166	1.0150	1.0138	1.0123	1.0087
4	1.0348	1.0341	1.0323	1.0309	1.0293	1.0256
6	1.0530	1.0521	1.0500	1.0485	1.0468	1.0430
8	1.0718	1.0706	1.0683	1.0668	1.0650	1.0610
10	1.0913	1.0897	1.0873	1.0857	1.0838	1.0796
12	1.1115	1.1096	1.1069	1.1053	1.1033	1.0989
14	1.1325	1.1303	1.1273	1.1256	1.1236	1.1190
16	1.1542	1.1517	1.1485	1.1466	1.1446	1.1398
18	1.1765	1.1737	1.1703	1.1683	1.1662	1.1613
20	1.1996	1.1965	1.1928	1.1906	1.1884	1.1834
25	1.2612	1.2573	1.2530	1.2506	1.2482	1.2427
30	1.3292	1.3244	1.3195	1.3168	1.3141	1.3081
35	1.4040	1.3984	1.3928	1.3897	1.3867	1.3802
40	1.4862	1.4798	1.4734	1.4700	1.4666	1.4596

%	50°C	60°C	70°C	80°C	90°C	100°C
2	1.0045	0.9995	0.9940	0.9879	0.9814	0.9745
4	1.0213	1.0162	1.0107	1.0045	0.9879	0.9910
6	1.0385	1.0333	1.0278	1.0216	1.0148	1.0079
8	1.0563	1.0510	1.0454	1.0392	1.0323	1.0253
10	1.0748	1.0695	1.0637	1.0574	1.0505	1.0434
12	1.0940	1.0886	1.0827	1.0763	1.0694	1.0622
14	1.1140	1.1085	1.1025	1.0960	1.0889	1.0818
16	1.1347	1.1290	1.1229	1.1163	1.1091	1.1020
18	1.1560	1.1502	1.1440	1.1373	1.1300	1.2228
20	1.1778	1.1719	1.1656	1.1589	1.1516	1.1443
25	1.2367	1.2304	1.2238	1.2168	1.2093	1.2018
30	1.3016	1.2950	1.2880	1.2808	1.2730	1.2653
35	1.3732	1.3662	1.3588	1.3513	1.3431	1.3352
40	1.4521	1.4445	1.4368	1.4288	1.4204	1.4123

$CaSO_4$ [GS]; d_4^{25} = 0.99756 with 0.05%; = 0.99805 with 0.10% (98)

$Ca(HS)_2$ [GS] (154)

%	d_4^{23}	%	$d_4^{23.5}$
32	1.255	37.5	1.310

$Ca(NO_3)_2$ [GS] (110)**; (137, 342, 606, 628)*; (189, 190, 192, 208, 222, 223, 261, 322, 329, 378, 407, 529, 618, 629)

%	6°C	18°C	25°C	30°C	%	18°C
2	1.0157	1.0137	1.0120	1.0105	30	1.260
4	1.0316	1.0291	1.0272	1.0256	35	1.311
6	1.0477	1.0448	1.0427	1.0409	40	1.365
8	1.0641	1.0608	1.0585	1.0565	45	1.422
10	1.0808	1.0771	1.0746	1.0724		
12	1.0979	1.0937	1.0911	1.0887		

$Ca(NO_3)_2$.—*(Continued)*

%	6°C	18°C	25°C	30°C	%	18°C
14	1.1153	1.1106	1.1079	1.1055		
16	1.1330	1.1279	1.1250	1.1224		
18	1.1510	1.1455	1.1424	1.1397		
20	1.1694	1.1636	1.1602	1.1575		
25	1.2168	1.2106	1.2065	1.2032		
68†		1.747	1.741	1.736		

† Supercooled tetrahydrate (M.P., 41.4°C).

$CaH_4(PO_4)_2$ [GS]; with 2.506 %, d_4^{19} = 1.0171 (76)

$Ca(CHO_2)_2$, Formate [JAB] (291)**; (329)

%	d_4^{18}	%	d_4^{18}	%	d_4^{18}	%	d_4^{18}
1	1.0056	4	1.0268	8	1.0560	12	1.0858
2	1.0126	6	1.0413	10	1.0708		

$Ca(C_2H_3O_2)_2$, Acetate [JAB] (288)**; (208, 224, 529)

%	d_4^{18}	%	d_4^{18}	%	d_4^{18}	%	d_4^{18}
1	1.0043	6	1.0331	12	1.0679	18	1.1029
2	1.0100	8	1.0447	14	1.0795	20	1.1146
4	1.0215	10	1.0563	16	1.0912	22	1.1263

$Ca(C_3H_5O_2)_2$, Propionate [JAB] (291)

%	d_4^{18}	%	d_4^{18}	%	d_4^{18}	%	d_4^{18}
1	1.0035	8	1.0376	16	1.0766	24	1.1157
2	1.0084	10	1.0474	18	1.0864	26	1.1254
4	1.0181	12	1.0571	20	1.0962		
6	1.0279	14	1.0669	22	1.1059		

$Ca(CNS)_2$ [GS]; with 33.79 %, d_4^{17} = 1.2182 (155)

$Ca_2Fe(CN)_6$ [GS] (41, 42)

%	d_4^{0}	%	d_4^{0}	%	d_4^{0}	%	d_4^{0}
2	1.01687	10	1.08781	18	1.16374	26	1.24459
4	1.03416	12	1.10630	20	1.18353	28	1.26546
6	1.05175	14	1.12513	22	1.20362	30	1.28659
8	1.06963	16	1.14428	24	1.22398	32	1.30798

$CaCrO_4$ [GS] (250)

%	d_4^{18}	%	d_4^{18}	%	d_4^{18}	%	d_4^{18}
1	1.0083	3	1.0278	5	1.0477	7	1.0680
2	1.0180	4	1.0377	6	1.0578		

$Sr(OH)_2$ [GS] (100)**; (529)

%	15°C	20°C	25°C	30°C
0.1	1.00043	0.99948	0.99827	0.99681
0.2	1.00179	1.00081	0.99957	0.99811
0.3	1.00321	1.00225	1.00100	0.99954

$SrCl_2$ [GS] (221, 342, 347, 367, 548)**; (18, 105, 106, 189, 190, 192, 261, 278, 312, 363, 378, 407, 417.5, 451, 529, 573, 618, 627, 629)

%	0°C	10°C	20°C	25°C	30°C	40°C
2	1.0183	1.0178	1.0161	1.0149	1.0134	1.0097
4	1.0372	1.0364	1.0344	1.0331	1.0315	1.0277
6	1.0567	1.0554	1.0532	1.0518	1.0501	1.0462
8	1.0767	1.0750	1.0726	1.0711	1.0693	1.0653
10	1.0973	1.0952	1.0925	1.0909	1.0891	1.0849
12	1.1185	1.1160	1.1130	1.1113	1.1094	1.1051
14	1.1402	1.1374	1.1341	1.1323	1.1303	1.1259
16	1.1625	1.1593	1.1558	1.1539	1.1518	1.1472
18	1.1853	1.1819	1.1781	1.1761	1.1739	1.1691
20	1.2088	1.2051	1.2010	1.1990	1.1966	1.1917
25	1.269	1.265	1.260	1.258	1.255	1.250
30			1.325	1.322	1.319	1.314
35			1.396	1.393	1.390	1.384

$SrCl_2$.—*(Continued)*

%	50°C	60°C	70°C	80°C	90°C	100°C
2	1.0055	1.0005	0.9951	0.9891	0.9826	0.9758
4	1.0233	1.0183	1.0129	1.0069	1.0004	0.9936
6	1.0417	1.0366	1.0312	1.0252	1.0187	1.0119
8	1.0607	1.0555	1.0500	1.0440	1.0375	1.0307
10	1.0802	1.0750	1.0694	1.0634	1.0569	1.0502
12	1.1003	1.0950	1.0894	1.0834	1.0768	1.0702
14	1.1209	1.1156	1.1100	1.1039	1.0973	1.0907
16	1.1422	1.1368	1.1311	1.1250	1.1184	1.1118
18	1.1641	1.1586	1.1528	1.1467	1.1401	1.1335
20	1.1866	1.1810	1.1752	1.1690	1.1625	1.1559
25	1.245	1.239	1.233	1.227	1.220	1.213
30	1.308	1.302	1.296	1.289	1.282	1.276
35	1.378	1.372	1.365	1.358	1.351	1.345

$Sr(ClO_3)_2$ [GS] (288)**; (602)*

%	d_4^{18}	%	d_4^{18}	%	d_4^{18}	%	d_4^{18}
2	1.0147	10	1.0825	18	1.1593	35	1.3563
4	1.0310	12	1.1010	20	1.1800		
6	1.0476	14	1.1203	25	1.2348		
8	1.0647	16	1.1394	30	1.2935		

$SrBr_2$ [GS] (287, 367)**; (363)*; (18, 189, 190, 312, 318, 320, 322)

%	0°C	10°C	20°C	25°C	30°C	40°C
2	1.0178	1.0174	1.0157	1.0145	1.0130	1.0093
4	1.0363	1.0356	1.0337	1.0324	1.0308	1.0270
6	1.0553	1.0543	1.0522	1.0508	1.0492	1.0452
8	1.0748	1.0735	1.0712	1.0697	1.0680	1.0639
10	1.0949	1.0932	1.0907	1.0891	1.0873	1.0831
12	1.1156	1.1136	1.1109	1.1092	1.1072	1.1029
14	1.1369	1.1346	1.1317	1.1299	1.1279	1.1234
16	1.1591	1.1564	1.1532	1.1513	1.1493	1.1447
18	1.1821	1.1791	1.1757	1.1738	1.1716	1.1668
20	1.2060	1.2029	1.1992	1.1971	1.1949	1.1899
25	1.270	1.266	1.262	1.259	1.257	1.251
30	1.339	1.335	1.330	1.327	1.324	1.318
35	1.416	1.411	1.405	1.402	1.398	1.392
40	1.501	1.495	1.489	1.486	1.482	1.475
45	1.597	1.590	1.583	1.579	1.575	1.568
50			1.686			

%	50°C	60°C	70°C	80°C	90°C	100°C
2	1.0051	1.0002	0.9947	0.9887	0.9821	0.9752
4	1.0227	1.0177	1.0121	1.0060	0.9994	0.9925
6	1.0408	1.0357	1.0301	1.0238	1.0172	1.0103
8	1.0594	1.0541	1.0485	1.0422	1.0357	1.0286
10	1.0785	1.0731	1.0675	1.0611	1.0545	1.0473
12	1.0982	1.0927	1.0870	1.0805	1.0738	1.0667
14	1.1186	1.1130	1.1071	1.1006	1.0938	1.0868
16	1.1397	1.1340	1.1281	1.1215	1.1147	1.1077
18	1.1616	1.1559	1.1499	1.1433	1.1364	1.1293
20	1.1846	1.1788	1.1727	1.1661	1.1591	1.1519
25	1.246	1.240	1.233	1.227	1.219	1.212
30	1.312	1.306	1.299	1.293	1.285	1.278
35	1.386	1.379	1.372	1.365	1.358	1.350
40	1.468	1.461	1.454	1.446	1.439	1.431
45	1.561	1.553	1.545	1.538	1.530	1.522

$Sr(BrO_3)_2$ [GS] (291)

%	d_4^{18}	%	d_4^{18}	%	d_4^{18}	%	d_4^{18}
2	1.0157	8	1.0700	14	1.1297	20	1.1948
4	1.0332	10	1.0893	16	1.1508	22	1.2177
6	1.0513	12	1.1092	18	1.1725		

SrI_2 [GS] (287, 369)**; (365)*; (322)

%	0°C	10°C	20°C	25°C	30°C	40°C
2	1.0175	1.0171	1.0154	1.0142	1.0127	1.0090
4	1.0357	1.0350	1.0331	1.0318	1.0302	1.0265
6	1.0544	1.0535	1.0513	1.0499	1.0482	1.0444
8	1.0738	1.0726	1.0701	1.0686	1.0669	1.0629
10	1.0938	1.0923	1.0896	1.0880	1.0862	1.0821
12	1.1146	1.1128	1.1099	1.1082	1.1062	1.1020
14	1.1361	1.1339	1.1308	1.1290	1.1270	1.1225
16	1.1584	1.1559	1.1526	1.1506	1.1486	1.1439
18	1.1817	1.1789	1.1753	1.1732	1.1711	1.1662
20	1.2060	1.2028	1.1990	1.1967	1.1944	1.1894
25	1.2693	1.2654	1.2608	1.2583	1.2558	1.2502
30	1.3395	1.3347	1.3295	1.3267	1.3238	1.3176
35	1.4173	1.4116	1.4058	1.4026	1.3994	1.3924
40	1.5036	1.4970	1.4904	1.4869	1.4834	1.4757
45	1.5991	1.5917	1.5844	1.5804	1.5766	1.5684

%	50°C	60°C	70°C	80°C	90°C	100°C
2	1.0048	0.9999	0.9944	0.9882	0.9817	0.9748
4	1.0220	1.0170	1.0114	1.0052	0.9986	0.9916
6	1.0398	1.0346	1.0289	1.0227	1.0160	1.0090
8	1.0582	1.0529	1.0471	1.0408	1.0340	1.0269
10	1.0773	1.0718	1.0659	1.0595	1.0526	1.0455
12	1.0970	1.0914	1.0853	1.0789	1.0719	1.0648
14	1.1174	1.1117	1.1055	1.0990	1.0918	1.0847
16	1.1386	1.1328	1.1265	1.1198	1.1126	1.1054
18	1.1607	1.1547	1.1483	1.1415	1.1342	1.1270
20	1.1837	1.1775	1.1711	1.1642	1.1568	1.1495
25	1.2440	1.2376	1.2309	1.2235	1.2161	1.2084
30	1.3110	1.3042	1.2970	1.2893	1.2815	1.2737
35	1.3855	1.3781	1.3705	1.3625	1.3544	1.3463
40	1.4683	1.4605	1.4521	1.4441	1.4356	1.4272
45	1.5603	1.5523	1.5436	1.5348	1.5259	1.5172

$Sr(NO_3)_2$ [GS] (375)**; (192, 224, 361, 384, 629)*; (84, 189, 190, 261, 318, 329, 360, 378, 407, 451, 529, 605, 618, 628)

%	0°C	10°C	20°C†	30°C	40°C	50°C
2	1.017	1.016	1.015	1.012	1.008	1.004
4	1.034	1.033	1.031	1.028	1.024	1.020
6	1.052	1.050	1.048	1.045	1.041	1.036
8	1.070	1.068	1.065	1.062	1.058	1.052
10	1.088	1.086	1.083	1.079	1.074	1.069
12	1.107	1.104	1.101	1.097	1.092	1.086
14	1.126	1.123	1.119	1.115	1.110	1.104
16	1.146	1.142	1.138	1.134	1.129	1.123
18	1.166	1.163	1.158	1.154	1.148	1.142
20	1.187	1.184	1.179	1.174	1.168	1.162
25	1.245	1.239	1.233	1.227	1.221	1.215

%	60°C	70°C	80°C	%	60°C	70°C	80°C
2	0.999	0.993	0.987	14	1.098	1.092	1.086
4	1.015	1.009	1.003	16	1.117	1.111	1.104
6	1.031	1.025	1.019	18	1.136	1.129	1.123
8	1.047	1.041	1.035	20	1.156	1.149	1.142
10	1.064	1.057	1.051	25	1.208	1.201	1.194
12	1.081	1.074	1.068				

† d_4^{20} = 1.290 with 30 %; = 1.352 with 35 %; = 1.419 with 40 %.

$Sr(CHO_2)_2$, Formate [JAB] (288)**; (329)

%	d_4^{18}	%	d_4^{18}	%	d_4^{18}	%	d_4^{18}
1	1.0067	4	1.0312	8	1.0647	12	1.0998
2	1.0148	6	1.0478	10	1.0820		

$Sr(C_2H_3O_2)_2$, Acetate [JAB] (288)**; (529, 561)

%	d_4^{18}	%	d_4^{18}	%	d_4^{18}	%	d_4^{18}
1	1.0054	8	1.0543	16	1.1138	24	1.1770
2	1.0122	10	1.0688	18	1.1293		
4	1.0260	12	1.0836	20	1.1450		
6	1.0400	14	1.0986	22	1.1609		

$Sr_2Fe(CN)_6$ [GS] (42)

%	d_4^0	%	d_4^0	%	d_4^0	%	d_4^0
2	1.0175	8	1.0738	14	1.1342	20	1.1996
4	1.0357	10	1.0935	16	1.1554		
6	1.0546	12	1.1136	18	1.1772		

$Ba(OH)_2$ [GS] (342, 472)**; (529)*; (100, 252); d_4^{20} = 1.0193 with 2 %; = 1.0420 with 4 %

$BaCl_2$ [GS] (364)**; (36, 38, 106, 110, 219, 221, 312, 342, 347, 608, 611)*; (49, 105, 128, 139, 189, 199, 261, 278, 313, 344, 363, 378, 411, 417.5, 425, 451, 529, 533, 534, 535, 573, 618, 629)

%	0°C	10°C	20°C	25°C	30°C	40°C
2	1.0181	1.0176	1.0159	1.0147	1.0132	1.0096
4	1.0368	1.0360	1.0341	1.0328	1.0312	1.0275
6	1.0561	1.0550	1.0528	1.0514	1.0497	1.0459
8	1.0760	1.0746	1.0721	1.0706	1.0688	1.0648
10	1.0965	1.0948	1.0921	1.0905	1.0885	1.0844
12	1.1178	1.1157	1.1128	1.1111	1.1090	1.1047
14	1.1399	1.1374	1.1342	1.1325	1.1303	1.1259
16	1.1627	1.1599	1.1564	1.1546	1.1524	1.1478
18	1.1862	1.1831	1.1793	1.1774	1.1752	1.1704
20	1.2105	1.2071	1.2031	1.2010	1.1987	1.1938
22		1.2319	1.2277	1.2255	1.2230	1.2180
24		1.2575	1.2531	1.2508	1.2482	1.2430
26		1.2839	1.2793	1.2769	1.2742	1.2688

%	50°C	60°C	70°C	80°C	90°C	100°C
2	1.0054	1.0004	0.9950	0.9890	0.9824	0.9755
4	1.0232	1.0181	1.0126	1.0066	1.0000	0.9931
6	1.0415	1.0363	1.0307	1.0247	1.0181	1.0112
8	1.0603	1.0551	1.0495	1.0434	1.0368	1.0299
10	1.0798	1.0746	1.0689	1.0627	1.0561	1.0492
12	1.1001	1.0948	1.0890	1.0827	1.0761	1.0692
14	1.1211	1.1157	1.1098	1.1034	1.0968	1.0899
16	1.1428	1.1373	1.1313	1.1249	1.1182	1.1113
18	1.1653	1.1596	1.1536	1.1472	1.1404	1.1334
20	1.1885	1.1828	1.1767	1.1702	1.1634	1.1563
22	1.2125	1.2068	1.2006	1.1940	1.1872	1.1800
24	1.2374	1.2316	1.2253	1.2186	1.2117	1.2045
26	1.2631	1.2571	1.2507	1.2440	1.2370	1.2298

$Ba(ClO_3)_2$ [GS] (110, 288)**

%	d_4^6	d_4^{18}	d_4^{30}	%	d_4^6	d_4^{18}	d_4^{30}
2	1.0166	1.0148	1.0117	14	1.1263	1.1224	1.1177
4	1.0335	1.0314	1.0280	16	1.1466	1.1424	1.1374
6	1.0509	1.0485	1.0449	18	1.1675	1.1631	1.1577
8	1.0688	1.0661	1.0622	20	1.1891	1.1843	1.1787
10	1.0874	1.0843	1.0801	22	1.2114	1.2062	1.2004
12	1.1065	1.1031	1.0986	24	1.2343	1.2287	1.2227

$BaBr_2$ [GS] (287, 367)**; (18, 190, 307, 312, 318, 322, 361, 378)

%	0°C	10°C	20°C	25°C	30°C	40°C
2	1.0176	1.0172	1.0156	1.0143	1.0129	1.0093
4	1.0360	1.0353	1.0335	1.0321	1.0306	1.0269
6	1.0549	1.0540	1.0519	1.0505	1.0489	1.0450
8	1.0745	1.0733	1.0710	1.0695	1.0678	1.0638
10	1.0948	1.0933	1.0907	1.0892	1.0874	1.0833
12	1.1158	1.1139	1.1111	1.1096	1.1076	1.1034
14	1.1375	1.1353	1.1323	1.1306	1.1286	1.1242
16	1.1599	1.1575	1.1543	1.1524	1.1504	1.1458

$BaBr_2$.—(*Continued*)

%	0°C	10°C	20°C	25°C	30°C	40°C
18	1.1831	1.1805	1.1770	1.1750	1.1729	1.1681
20	1.2072	1.2043	1.2006	1.1985	1.1963	1.1913
25	1.2714	1.2677	1.2634	1.2610	1.2585	1.2531
30	1.3421	1.3375	1.3325	1.3299	1.3270	1.3212
35	1.4197	1.4143	1.4087	1.4057	1.4025	1.3961
40	1.5052	1.4989	1.4926	1.4893	1.4858	1.4789

%	50°C	60°C	70°C	80°C	90°C	100°C
2	1.0050	1.0001	0.9946	0.9885	0.9820	0.9750
4	1.0224	1.0175	1.0119	1.0059	0.9992	0.9921
6	1.0404	1.0354	1.0297	1.0236	1.0169	1.0098
8	1.0591	1.0540	1.0482	1.0420	1.0353	1.0282
10	1.0785	1.0733	1.0674	1.0611	1.0543	1.0472
12	1.0985	1.0931	1.0872	1.0809	1.0739	1.0668
14	1.1192	1.1137	1.1077	1.1013	1.0942	1.0871
16	1.1407	1.1351	1.1290	1.1225	1.1153	1.1082
18	1.1629	1.1572	1.1510	1.1444	1.1372	1.1300
20	1.1860	1.1801	1.1739	1.1672	1.1599	1.1526
25	1.2474	1.2413	1.2347	1.2278	1.2203	1.2129
30	1.3150	1.3086	1.3016	1.2945	1.2869	1.2792
35	1.3895	1.3826	1.3754	1.3679	1.3601	1.3522
40	1.4717	1.4643	1.4568	1.4489	1.4407	1.4327

BaI_2 [GS] (287, 369)**; (365)*; (76, 322)

%	0°C	10°C	20°C	25°C	30°C	40°C
2	1.0174	1.0171	1.0154	1.0142	1.0127	1.0091
4	1.0356	1.0350	1.0331	1.0318	1.0302	1.0265
6	1.0543	1.0534	1.0513	1.0499	1.0482	1.0443
8	1.0735	1.0724	1.0701	1.0686	1.0668	1.0628
10	1.0934	1.0921	1.0896	1.0880	1.0861	1.0819
12	1.1141	1.1126	1.1099	1.1081	1.1062	1.1018
14	1.1356	1.1338	1.1308	1.1290	1.1271	1.1225
16	1.1580	1.1558	1.1525	1.1506	1.1486	1.1439
18	1.1811	1.1786	1.1750	1.1730	1.1709	1.1660
20	1.2050	1.2021	1.1984	1.1963	1.1939	1.1889
25	1.2692	1.2655	1.2610	1.2587	1.2560	1.2504
30	1.3386	1.3340	1.3289	1.3263	1.3232	1.3171
35	1.416	1.410	1.404	1.401	1.398	1.391
40	1.503	1.496	1.490	1.486	1.483	1.475
45	1.602	1.594	1.587	1.583	1.579	1.571
50	1.715	1.706	1.698	1.694	1.689	1.680
55	1.844	1.834	1.825	1.820	1.815	1.805
60			1.970	1.965	1.959	1.949

%	50°C	60°C	70°C	80°C	90°C	100°C
2	1.0048	0.9998	0.9943	0.9883	0.9817	0.9747
4	1.0220	1.0169	1.0114	1.0053	0.9986	0.9915
6	1.0398	1.0345	1.0289	1.0227	1.0159	1.0087
8	1.0581	1.0528	1.0470	1.0406	1.0338	1.0266
10	1.0771	1.0717	1.0658	1.0593	1.0524	1.0452
12	1.0968	1.0914	1.0853	1.0788	1.0717	1.0644
14	1.1173	1.1117	1.1055	1.0989	1.0918	1.0844
16	1.1385	1.1327	1.1264	1.1197	1.1125	1.1050
18	1.1605	1.1545	1.1481	1.1414	1.1340	1.1264
20	1.1832	1.1771	1.1706	1.1637	1.1563	1.1485
25	1.2444	1.2378	1.2309	1.2237	1.2161	1.2081
30	1.3105	1.3036	1.2964	1.2887	1.2808	1.2727
35	1.384	1.377	1.369	1.361	1.353	1.345
40	1.468	1.460	1.451	1.443	1.434	1.426
45	1.562	1.554	1.545	1.536	1.527	1.518
50	1.671	1.662	1.653	1.643	1.634	1.624
55	1.796	1.786	1.776	1.766	1.756	1.746
60	1.938	1.928	1.917	1.907	1.896	1.886

BaS_2O_3 [GS]; d_4^{19} = 1.0157 for 1.15%; = 1.1050 for 12.024% (76)

$Ba(NO_3)_2$ [GS] (287)**; (342)*; (190, 224, 261, 329, 360, 361, 378, 411, 425, 451, 472, 529, 618, 628, 629)

%............	2	4	6	8
d_4^{18}............	1.0151	1.0320	1.0494	1.0674

%(84)	d_4^{15}	$d_4^{19.5}$	%(84)	$d_4^{19.5}$
0.2	1.00078	0.99999	1.0	1.00658
0.4	1.00244	1.00164	1.2	1.00823
0.6	1.00410	1.00329	1.4	1.00988
0.8	1.00575	1.00493	1.6	1.01153

$Ba(CHO_2)_2$, Formate [LJG] (291)**; (329) [JAB]

%	d_4^{18}	%	d_4^{18}	%	d_4^{18}	%	d_4^{18}
1	1.0069	6	1.0492	12	1.1039	18	1.1634
2	1.0152	8	1.0669	14	1.1233	20	1.1840
4	1.0320	10	1.0851	16	1.1431		

$Ba(C_2H_3O_2)_2$, Acetate [LJG] (288)**; (208, 224, 329, 529) [JAB]

%	d_4^{18}	%	d_4^{18}	%	d_4^{18}	%	d_4^{18}
1	1.0059	10	1.0745	20	1.1599	30	1.2554
2	1.0133	12	1.0908	22	1.1782	35	1.3069
4	1.0282	14	1.1075	24	1.1970	40	1.3608
6	1.0433	16	1.1246	26	1.2161		
8	1.0587	18	1.1421	28	1.2356		

$Ba(C_3H_5O_2)_2$, Propionate [LJG] (291) [JAB]

%	d_4^{18}	%	d_4^{18}	%	d_4^{18}	%	d_4^{18}
1	1.0053	8	1.0538	16	1.1136	24	1.1791
2	1.0120	10	1.0683	18	1.1294		
4	1.0257	12	1.0831	20	1.1456		
6	1.0396	14	1.0982	22	1.1622		

$BaC_4H_4O_5$, Malate [LJG] (546) [JAB]

%....	1	2	4	6	8	10
d_4^{20}....	1.0064	1.0146	1.0311	1.0475	1.0640	1.0804

$Ba(CNS)_2$ [GS]; with 11.26%, d_4^{25} = 1.0918; $d_4^{75.2}$ = 1.0659 (629)

$Ba(CN)_2.2CuCN$ [WCS]; d_4^{20} = 1.039_5 with 6%; = 1.056_5 with 8% (602)

LiOH [JAB] (73, 290)**; (225, 342, 519, 529)

%	0°C	10°C	20°C	25°C	30°C
1	1.0122	1.0115	1.0102	1.0090	1.0075
2	1.0240	1.0230	1.0217	1.0203	1.0188
4	1.0468	1.0456	1.0437	1.0422	1.0407
6	1.0690	1.0674	1.0650	1.0636	1.0621
8	1.0908	1.0888	1.0862	1.0847	1.0830
10	1.1125	1.1102	1.1074	1.1057	1.1038

%	40°C	50°C	60°C	80°C
1	1.0041	1.0000	0.9958	0.9860
2	1.0155	1.0114	1.0072	0.9973
4	1.0371	1.0331	1.0286	1.0189
6	1.0582	1.0541	1.0496	1.0397
8	1.0790	1.0747	1.0701	1.0600
10	1.0996	1.0952	1.0906	1.0803

LiCl, Main Table, p. 77

% (373)	0.01	0.02	0.03	0.04
$d_4^{20.004}$	$0.998\ 2908_5$	$0.998\ 3498_4$	$0.998\ 4087_5$	$0.998\ 4676_0$

$LiClO_3$ [JAB] (288)**; (442) [LJG]

%	d_4^{18}	%	d_4^{18}	%	d_4^{18}	%	d_4^{18}
1	1.0048	6	1.0365	12	1.0764	18	1.1190
2	1.0111	8	1.0495	14	1.0903		
4	1.0237	10	1.0628	16	1.1045		

LiCl [JAB] (26), α (364, 367, 370)**; (25, 150, 250, 256)*; (1, 36, 38, 45, 64, 73, 106, 125, 204, 206, 219, 221, 223, 224, 225, 239, 274, 304, 312, 313, 342, 344, 347, 363, 374, 379, 386, 486, 487, 519, 529, 530, 573, 618, 629, 633), α (38, 151, 219, 256, 448, 606, 609)

%	0°C	10°C	20°C	25°C	30°C	40°C	50°C	60°C	80°C	100°C
1	1.00604	1.00574	1.00411	1.00292	1.00150	0.99806	0.99391	0.9891	0.9779	0.9646
2	1.01213	1.01168	1.00993	1.00870	1.00726	1.00381	0.99969	0.9950	0.9838	0.9708
4	1.02417	1.02344	1.02148	1.02019	1.01872	1.01527	1.01121	1.0066	0.9958	0.9831
6	1.03606	1.03509	1.03296	1.03161	1.03012	1.02668	1.02269	1.0182	1.0077	0.9953
8	1.04787	1.04670	1.04443	1.04303	1.04152	1.03809	1.03418	1.0298	1.0196	1.0076
10	1.05966	1.05833	1.05594	1.05449	1.05296	1.04954	1.04571	1.0414	1.0315	1.0199
12	1.07148	1.07002	1.06752	1.06602	1.06447	1.06107	1.05731	1.0532	1.0435	1.0322
14	1.08337	1.08180	1.07919	1.07765	1.07608	1.07271	1.06901	1.0650	1.0556	1.0447
16	1.09536	1.09369	1.09098	1.08941	1.08782	1.08449	1.08084	1.0769	1.0679	1.0572
18	1.10749	1.10571	1.10292	1.10132	1.09972	1.09643	1.09283	1.0890	1.0802	1.0700
20	1.11979	1.11789	1.11504	1.11342	1.11181	1.10855	1.10500	1.1013	1.0927	1.0829
22	1.13228	1.13027	1.12736	1.12574	1.12412	1.12088	1.11738	1.1137	1.1053	1.0960
24	1.14499	1.14287	1.13991	1.13831	1.13667	1.13344	1.12999	1.1264	1.1181	1.1093
26	1.15794	1.15571	1.15271	1.15115	1.14949	1.14625	1.14285	1.1393	1.1310	1.1228
28	1.17115	1.16881	1.16578	1.16428	1.16260	1.15933	1.15598	1.1525	1.1442	1.1367
30	1.18464	1.18219	1.17914	1.17771	1.17602	1.17269	1.16940	1.1659	1.1576	1.1507
35				1.21274	1.21092	1.20738	1.20402			
40				1.25002	1.24806	1.24427	1.24081			
45				1.28980	1.28768	1.28361	1.28003			

LiBr [JAB] (26), α (367)**; (25, 287)*; (45, 221, 319, 322, 366, 519, 618), α (151)

%	0°C	10°C	20°C	25°C	30°C	40°C	50°C	60°C	80°C	100°C
1	1.00731	1.00705	1.00547	1.00428	1.00285	0.99939	0.99519	0.9904	0.9790	0.9656
2	1.01484	1.01447	1.01280	1.01158	1.01013	1.00663	1.00241	0.9976	0.9862	0.9729
4	1.03012	1.02953	1.02769	1.02642	1.02492	1.02135	1.01708	1.0123	1.0009	0.9877
6	1.04574	1.04494	1.04293	1.04161	1.04006	1.03642	1.03211	1.0273	1.0159	1.0029
8	1.06173	1.06072	1.05854	1.05717	1.05557	1.05186	1.04752	1.0427	1.0313	1.0184
10	1.07812	1.07690	1.07455	1.07313	1.07148	1.06770	1.06334	1.0585	1.0471	1.0344
12	1.09493	1.09351	1.09099	1.08952	1.08782	1.08397	1.07959	1.0747	1.0634	1.0508
14	1.11219	1.11057	1.10789	1.10636	1.10461	1.10069	1.09629	1.0914	1.0801	1.0676
16	1.12993	1.12811	1.12528	1.12368	1.12188	1.11789	1.11347	1.1086	1.0972	1.0849
18	1.14817	1.14616	1.14318	1.14151	1.13965	1.13560	1.13115	1.1262	1.1149	1.1027
20	1.16695	1.16476	1.16162	1.15988	1.15795	1.15384	1.14936	1.1444	1.1331	1.1210
22	1.18631	1.18394	1.18063	1.17882	1.17682	1.17264	1.16813	1.1632	1.1519	1.1399
24	1.20628	1.20372	1.20024	1.19835	1.19629	1.19204	1.18750	1.1826	1.1713	1.1593
26	1.22689	1.22413	1.22047	1.21850	1.21639	1.21207	1.20750	1.2026	1.1913	1.1794
28	1.24817	1.24520	1.24135	1.23931	1.23716	1.23277	1.22815	1.2232	1.2119	1.2001
30	1.27017	1.26697	1.26292	1.26081	1.25862	1.25417	1.24949	1.2445	1.2333	1.2215
35	1.32850	1.32477	1.32040	1.31813	1.31582	1.31115	1.30629	1.3012	1.2899	1.2782
40	1.39233	1.38827	1.38360	1.38117	1.37871	1.37376	1.36869	1.3635	1.3520	1.3404
45	1.46259	1.45851	1.45354	1.45095	1.44829	1.44299	1.43767	1.4323	1.4207	1.4092
50				1.52878	1.52584	1.52010	1.51448	1.5089	1.4971	
55				1.61637	1.61302	1.60673	1.60074	1.5948	1.5829	
60				1.71595	1.71198	1.70499	1.69853	1.6923	1.6800	
65				1.83037	1.82547	1.81756	1.81049	1.8038	1.7913	

LiI [JAB] (26), α (369)**; (25, 287)*; (45, 221, 225, 261, 319, 320, 322, 342, 519, 618), α (151)

%	0°C	10°C	20°C	25°C	30°C	40°C	50°C	60°C	80°C	100°C
1	1.00746	1.00721	1.00563	1.00443	1.00300	0.99952	0.99530	0.9905	0.9790	0.9655
2	1.01514	1.01479	1.01312	1.01189	1.01043	1.00690	1.00264	0.9978	0.9863	0.9728
4	1.03083	1.03027	1.02843	1.02712	1.02560	1.02198	1.01763	1.0127	1.0011	0.9876
6	1.04697	1.04620	1.04418	1.04279	1.04120	1.03749	1.03305	1.0281	1.0163	1.0028
8	1.06358	1.06260	1.06039	1.05892	1.05726	1.05345	1.04892	1.0439	1.0320	1.0184
10	1.08069	1.07949	1.07708	1.07553	1.07380	1.06988	1.06527	1.0601	1.0481	1.0345
12	1.09832	1.09689	1.09428	1.09265	1.09085	1.08681	1.08212	1.0769	1.0648	1.0512
14	1.11649	1.11483	1.11202	1.11031	1.10844	1.10427	1.09950	1.0942	1.0819	1.0683
16	1.13523	1.13334	1.13033	1.12854	1.12660	1.12229	1.11744	1.1121	1.0996	1.0860
18	1.15457	1.15245	1.14924	1.14736	1.14535	1.14091	1.13597	1.1305	1.1179	1.1042
20	1.17455	1.17220	1.16878	1.16680	1.16472	1.16016	1.15512	1.1496	1.1368	1.1231
22	1.19520	1.19263	1.18898	1.18690	1.18475	1.18007	1.17491	1.1693	1.1564	1.1427
24	1.21656	1.21377	1.20988	1.20770	1.20547	1.20067	1.19538	1.1896	1.1766	1.1629
26	1.23867	1.23566	1.23152	1.22924	1.22692	1.22199	1.21657	1.2107	1.1976	1.1838
28	1.26156	1.25833	1.25395	1.25157	1.24915	1.24407	1.23853	1.2326	1.2193	1.2054

LiI.—(*Continued*)

%	0°C	10°C	20°C	25°C	30°C	40°C	50°C	60°C	80°C	100°C
30	1.28527	1.28181	1.27720	1.27472	1.27219	1.26695	1.26130	1.2553	1.2418	1.2279
35	1.34859	1.34444	1.33928	1.33656	1.33382	1.32816	1.32218	1.3159	1.3020	1.2879
40	1.41839	1.41355	1.40783	1.40485	1.40188	1.39580	1.38948	1.3829	1.3686	1.3542
45	1.49582	1.49029	1.48399	1.48073	1.47751	1.47099	1.46433	1.4575	1.4426	1.4280
50	1.58235	1.57613	1.56922	1.56565	1.56215	1.55517	1.54816	1.5410	1.5255	1.5105
55	1.67986	1.67295	1.66538	1.66145	1.65764	1.65018	1.64279	1.6352	1.6192	1.6038
60	1.79074	1.78314	1.77481	1.77046	1.76631	1.75835	1.75052	1.7425	1.7260	1.7100
65				1.89559	1.89107	1.88259	1.87421	1.8658	1.8489	

$LiIO_3$ [JAB] (288)**; (250)* [LJG]

%	d_4^{18}	%	d_4^{18}	%	d_4^{18}	%	d_4^{18}
1	1.0072	10	1.0915	20	1.2023	30	1.3328
2	1.0160	12	1.1120	22	1.2268	32	1.3619
4	1.0339	14	1.1333	24	1.2520	34	1.3925
6	1.0525	16	1.1555	26	1.2780	36	1.4248
8	1.0717	18	1.1785	28	1.3049	38	1.4590

Li_2SO_4 [JAB] (250, 291), α (370)**; (616), α (203)*; (1, 76, 106, 150, 204, 225, 312, 342, 344, 405, 477, 519, 529, 618, 629), α (151)

%	1	2	4	6	8	10
0°C	1.0089	1.0179	1.0360	1.0543	1.0726	1.0910
10°C	1.0084	1.0173	1.0350	1.0528	1.0709	1.0890
20°C	1.0068	1.0155	1.0329	1.0505	1.0684	1.0863
25°C	1.0056	1.0142	1.0316	1.0491	1.0669	1.0848
30°C	1.0042	1.0128	1.0301	1.0476	1.0653	1.0831
40°C	1.0007	1.0092	1.0264	1.0439	1.0615	1.0792
50°C	0.9964	1.0049	1.0221	1.0396	1.0572	1.0749
60°C	0.9917	1.0001	1.0174	1.0349	1.0526	1.0703
80°C	0.9801	0.9886	1.0061	1.0238	1.0416	1.0595
100°C	0.9669	0.9756	0.9932	1.0111	1.0292	1.0474

%	12	14	16	18	20	22	24
0°C	1.1095	1.1280	1.1465	1.1656			
10°C	1.1073	1.1256	1.1441	1.1629			
20°C	1.1044	1.1228	1.1411	1.1599	1.1789	1.1984	1.2182
25°C	1.1029	1.1212	1.1394	1.1582			
30°C	1.1012	1.1193	1.1376	1.1565			
40°C	1.0972	1.1153	1.1335	1.1526			
50°C	1.0929	1.1109	1.1291	1.1483			
60°C	1.0882	1.1063	1.1246	1.1437			
80°C	1.0776	1.0959	1.1143	1.1335			
100°C	1.0658	1.0844	1.1028	1.1220			

$LiNO_3$ [JAB] (10, 84, 287), α (256, 370)**, α (203)*; (45, 106, 150, 250, 256, 342, 485, 517, 519, 529), α (151, 605)

%	1	2	4	6	8	10
0°C	1.00616	1.01253	1.02533	1.03826	1.05135	1.06461
10°C	1.00578	1.01188	1.02418	1.03667	1.04935	1.06222
20°C	1.00409	1.01002	1.02198	1.03413	1.04647	1.05903
25°C	1.00287	1.00872	1.02054	1.03255	1.04477	1.05721
30°C	1.00142	1.00721	1.01892	1.03081	1.04291	1.05524
40°C	0.99788	1.00358	1.01509	1.02681	1.03875	1.05091
50°C	0.99365	0.99929	1.01068	1.02227	1.03406	1.04607
60°C	0.9888	0.9944	1.0057	1.0172	1.0289	1.0409
80°C	0.9774	0.9829	0.9942	1.0056	1.0173	1.0291
100°C	0.9639	0.9695	0.9808	0.9922	1.0039	1.0157

%	12	14	16	18	20	22
0°C	1.07804	1.09168	1.10554	1.11965	1.13401	1.14862
10°C	1.07529	1.08857	1.10208	1.11585	1.12989	1.14422
20°C	1.07181	1.08482	1.09807	1.11159	1.12539	1.13948
25°C	1.06987	1.08276	1.09590	1.10931	1.12300	1.13699
30°C	1.06780	1.08059	1.09363	1.10694	1.12053	1.13442

$LiNO_3$.—(*Continued*)

%	12	14	16	18	20	22
40°C	1.06330	1.07591	1.08877	1.10190	1.11532	1.12904
50°C	1.05830	1.07077	1.08349	1.09650	1.10980	1.12341
60°C	1.0530	1.0653	1.0780	1.0908	1.1040	1.1176
80°C	1.0411	1.0534	1.0659	1.0787	1.0918	1.1052
100°C	1.0278	1.0401	1.0527	1.0655	1.0786	1.0919

%	24	26	28	30	35	40
0°C	1.16351	1.17866	1.19406	1.20971	1.2510	
10°C	1.15883	1.17373	1.18893	1.20435	1.2451	
20°C	1.15387	1.16857	1.18355	1.19879	1.2392	1.2837
25°C	1.15128	1.16588	1.18076	1.19592	1.2361	1.2804
30°C	1.14861	1.16311	1.17790	1.19298	1.2330	1.2771
40°C	1.14308	1.15744	1.17209	1.18703	1.2267	1.2706
50°C	1.13734	1.15159	1.16613	1.18097	1.2204	1.2640
60°C	1.1314	1.1456	1.1601	1.1748	1.2139	1.2572
80°C	1.1189	1.1330	1.1473	1.1619	1.2007	1.2436
100°C	1.1056	1.1196	1.1338	1.1484	1.1870	1.2296

$Li_2C_2O_4$, Oxalate [JAB]; with 3.31 %, $d_4^{21.6}$ = 1.0232 (329)

$LiCHO_2$, Formate [JAB] (291)**; (329)

%	d_4^{18}	%	d_4^{18}	%	d_4^{18}	%	d_4^{18}
1	1.0035	6	1.0285	12	1.0588	18	1.0896
2	1.0085	8	1.0385	14	1.0690	20	1.1000
4	1.0185	10	1.0486	16	1.0793		

$LiC_2H_3O_2$, Acetate [JAB] (288)**; (529)

%	d_4^{18}	%	d_4^{18}	%	d_4^{18}	%	d_4^{18}
1	1.0024	8	1.0297	16	1.0616	24	1.0947
2	1.0063	10	1.0376	18	1.0698		
4	1.0141	12	1.0455	20	1.0780		
6	1.0219	14	1.0535	22	1.0863		

$LiC_4H_5O_5$, Acid malate [JAB] (546)

%	d_4^{20}	%	d_4^{20}	%	d_4^{20}	%	d_4^{20}
1	1.0033	10	1.0496	20	1.1031	30	1.1594
2	1.0084	12	1.0601	22	1.1141	35	1.1887
4	1.0186	14	1.0707	24	1.1253	40	1.2189
6	1.0288	16	1.0814	26	1.1366	45	1.2502
8	1.0391	18	1.0922	28	1.1480	50	1.2829

$Li_2C_4H_4O_4$, Succinate [JAB]; with 8.58 %, $d_4^{23.0}$ = 1.0468 (329)

$Li_2C_4H_4O_5$, Malate [JAB] (546)

%	d_4^{20}	%	d_4^{20}	%	d_4^{20}	%	d_4^{20}
1	1.0043	10	1.0600	20	1.1231	30	1.1880
2	1.0105	12	1.0725	22	1.1360	35	1.2210
4	1.0228	14	1.0851	24	1.1489	40	1.2545
6	1.0352	16	1.0977	26	1.1619		
8	1.0476	18	1.1103	28	1.1749		

$Li_2C_4H_4O_6$, Tartrate [JAB]; with 8.56 %, $d_4^{23.0}$ = 1.0530 (329)

LiCNS [JAB] (291) [LJG]

%	d_4^{18}	%	d_4^{18}	%	d_4^{18}	%	d_4^{18}
1	1.0025	6	1.0220	12	1.0458	18	1.0700
2	1.0064	8	1.0299	14	1.0538		
4	1.0142	10	1.0378	16	1.0619		

Li_2CrO_4 [JAB] (288) [LJG]

%	d_4^{18}	%	d_4^{18}	%	d_4^{18}	%	d_4^{18}
1	1.0072	6	1.0508	12	1.1052	18	1.1627
2	1.0158	8	1.0686	14	1.1240	20	1.1826
4	1.0332	10	1.0867	16	1.1432	22	1.2028

$Li_2Cr_2O_7$ [JAB] (291) [LJG]

%	d_4^{18}	%	d_4^{18}	%	d_4^{18}	%	d_4^{18}
1	1.0055	6	1.0412	12	1.0868	18	1.1355
2	1.0125	8	1.0561	14	1.1026	20	1.1528
4	1.0267	10	1.0713	16	1.1188		

NaOH [BTB] (63)**; (12, 98, 106, 248, 279, 290, 328, 342, 378, 387, 432, 449, 451, 463, 492, 519, 529, 555, 586, 639, 646, 666), α(211)

%	0°C	10°C	15°C	18°C	20°C	30°C	40°C	50°C	60°C	70°C	80°C	90°C	100°C
1	1.0124	1.0115	1.01065	1.01003	1.0095	1.0069	1.0033	0.9990	0.9941	0.9884	0.9824	0.9760	0.9693
2	1.0244	1.0230	1.02198	1.02127	1.0207	1.0177	1.0139	1.0095	1.0045	0.9989	0.9929	0.9865	0.9797
3	1.0364	1.0345	1.03322	1.03241	1.0318	1.0285	1.0246	1.0201	1.0150	1.0094	1.0035	0.9970	0.9903
4	1.0482	1.0459	1.04441	1.04349	1.0428	1.0393	1.0352	1.0305	1.0254	1.0198	1.0139	1.0075	1.0009
5	1.0598	1.0571	1.05554	1.05454	1.0538	1.0501	1.0458	1.0412	1.0359	1.0302	1.0243	1.0179	1.0115
6	1.0713	1.0683	1.06666	1.06559	1.0648	1.0609	1.0564	1.0517	1.0463	1.0407	1.0347	1.0284	1.0220
7	1.0828	1.0795	1.07777	1.07664	1.0758	1.0717	1.0672	1.0623	1.0569	1.0513	1.0453	1.0390	1.0326
8	1.0943	1.0908	1.08887	1.08769	1.0869	1.0826	1.0780	1.0730	1.0676	1.0619	1.0560	1.0497	1.0432
9	1.1057	1.1020	1.09997	1.09872	1.0979	1.0934	1.0887	1.0836	1.0782	1.0725	1.0665	1.0602	1.0537
10	1.1171	1.1132	1.11107	1.10977	1.1089	1.1043	1.0995	1.0942	1.0889	1.0831	1.0771	1.0708	1.0643
12	1.1399	1.1355	1.13327	1.13188	1.1309	1.1261	1.1210	1.1157	1.1101	1.1043	1.0983	1.0920	1.0855
14	1.1624	1.1578	1.15545	1.15400	1.1530	1.1480	1.1428	1.1373	1.1316	1.1257	1.1195	1.1132	1.1066
16	1.1849	1.1801	1.17761	1.17610	1.1751	1.1699	1.1645	1.1588	1.1531	1.1471	1.1408	1.1343	1.1277
18	1.2073	1.2023	1.19973	1.19817	1.1972	1.1918	1.1963	1.1805	1.1746	1.1685	1.1621	1.1556	1.1489
20	1.2296	1.2244	1.22183	1.22022	1.2191	1.2136	1.2079	1.2020	1.1960	1.1898	1.1833	1.1768	1.1700
22	1.2519	1.2465	1.24386	1.24220	1.2411	1.2354	1.2296	1.2236	1.2174	1.2111	1.2046	1.1980	1.1912
24	1.2741	1.2686	1.26582	1.26412	1.2629	1.2571	1.2512	1.2451	1.2388	1.2324	1.2259	1.2192	1.2124
26	1.2963	1.2906	1.2877	1.2860	1.2848	1.2789	1.2728	1.2666	1.2603	1.2538	1.2472	1.2405	1.2336
28	1.3182	1.3124	1.3094	1.3076	1.3064	1.3002	1.2942	1.2878	1.2814	1.2750	1.2682	1.2615	1.2546
30	1.3400†	1.3340	1.3309	1.3290	1.3279	1.3217	1.3154	1.3090	1.3025	1.2959	1.2892	1.2824	1.2755
32	1.3614	1.3552	1.3520	1.3502	1.3490	1.3427	1.3362	1.3298	1.3232	1.3165	1.3097	1.3029	1.2960
34	1.3823	1.3760	1.3728	1.3708	1.3696	1.3632	1.3566	1.3501	1.3434	1.3367	1.3299	1.3230	1.3161
36	1.4030	1.3965	1.3933	1.3913	1.3900	1.3835	1.3768	1.3702	1.3634	1.3567	1.3498	1.3429	1.3360
38	1.4234	1.4168	1.4135	1.4115	1.4101	1.4035	1.3967	1.3900	1.3832	1.3763	1.3695	1.3626	1.3556
40	1.4435	1.4367	1.4334	1.4314	1.4300	1.4232	1.4164	1.4095	1.4027	1.3958	1.3889	1.3820	1.3750
42	1.4632	1.4561	1.4529	1.4508	1.4494	1.4425	1.4356	1.4287	1.4217	1.4148	1.4079	1.4009	1.3940
44	1.4825	1.4755	1.4720	1.4699	1.4685	1.4615	1.4545	1.4475	1.4405	1.4335	1.4266	1.4196	1.4127
46	1.5018	1.4947†	1.4911	1.4890	1.4873	1.4805	1.4734	1.4663	1.4593	1.4523	1.4454	1.4384	1.4315
48	1.5210	1.5138	1.5102	1.5080	1.5065	1.4994	1.4922	1.4851	1.4781	1.4711	1.4641	1.4572	1.4503
50	1.5400	1.5326	1.5290	1.5268	1.5253	1.5181	1.5109	1.5038	1.4967	1.4897	1.4827	1.4759	1.4690

† Supersaturated.

NaCl [JAB] (24, 258)**; (20, 25, 59, 62, 84, 110, 250, 256), α (256, 364, 367, 370)*; (1, 2, 18, 26, 27, 36, 37, 38, 45, 57, 86, 101, 105, 106, 125, 136, 144, 145, 151, 190, 200, 206, 215, 219, 221, 223, 224, 225, 228, 246, 255, 261, 273, 274, 278, 297, 312, 313, 331, 342, 344, 347, 360, 361, 378, 409, 418, 425, 429, 447, 448, 449, 450, 451, 452, 459, 486, 505, 514, 517, 519, 526, 529, 533, 536, 545, 547, 553, 573, 592, 618, 630, 632, 644), α (37, 38, 151, 211, 219, 271, 448, 466, 545, 555, 606, 609)

%	0°C	10°C	20°C	25°C	30°C	40°C	50°C	60°C	80°C	100°C
1	1.00747	1.00707	1.00534	1.00409	1.00261	0.99908	0.99482	0.9900	0.9785	0.9651
2	1.01509	1.01442	1.01246	1.01112	1.00957	1.00593	1.00161	0.9967	0.9852	0.9719
4	1.03038	1.02920	1.02680	1.02530	1.02361	1.01977	1.01531	1.0103	0.9988	0.9855
6	1.04575	1.04408	1.04127	1.03963	1.03781	1.03378	1.02919	1.0241	1.0125	0.9994
8	1.06121	1.05907	1.05589	1.05412	1.05219	1.04798	1.04326	1.0381	1.0264	1.0134
10	1.07677	1.07419	1.07068	1.06879	1.06676	1.06238	1.05753	1.0523	1.0405	1.0276
12	1.09244	1.08946	1.08566	1.08365	1.08153	1.07699	1.07202	1.0667	1.0549	1.0420
14	1.10824	1.10491	1.10085	1.09872	1.09651	1.09182	1.08674	1.0813	1.0694	1.0565
16	1.12419	1.12056	1.11621	1.11401	1.11171	1.10688	1.10170	1.0962	1.0842	1.0713
18	1.14031	1.13643	1.13190	1.12954	1.12715	1.12218	1.11691	1.1113	1.0993	1.0864
20	1.15663	1.15254	1.14779	1.14533	1.14285	1.13774	1.13238	1.1268	1.1146	1.1017
22	1.17318	1.16891	1.16395	1.16140	1.15883	1.15358	1.14812	1.1425	1.1303	1.1172
24	1.18999	1.18557	1.18040	1.17776	1.17511	1.16971	1.16414	1.1584	1.1463	1.1331
26	1.20709	1.20254	1.19717	1.19443	1.19170	1.18614	1.18045	1.1747	1.1626	1.1492

NaF [JAB] (288)**; (190, 224)

%............	1	2	3	4	5
d_4^{18}............	1.0092	1.0198	1.0304	1.0409	1.0515

NaCl (348, 349, 586)**

%	$d_4^{14.07}$	$d_4^{18.55}$	%	$d_4^{18.55}$
0.5	1.002 886	1.002 112	2.0	1.012 856
1.0	1.006 506	1.005 694	2.5	1.016 440
1.5	1.010 120	1.009 274	3.0	1.020 024

NaCl.—(*Continued*)

% (588)	d_4^{110}	d_4^{120}	d_4^{130}
2.71	0.9697	0.9618	0.9537
5.32	0.9868	0.9791	0.9709
10.88	1.0269	1.0189	1.0115

NaCl.—(*Continued*)

% (373)	$d_4^{20.004}$	% (373)	$d_4^{20.004}$
0.01	0.998 3041$_5$	0.04	0.998 5202$_7$
0.02	0.998 3762$_9$	0.05	0.998 5924$_6$
0.03	0.998 4480$_8$	0.06	0.998 6646$_6$

$NaClO_3$ [JAB] (288)**; (360, 361, 378, 449, 514, 529, 561) [LJG]

%	d_4^{18}	%	d_4^{18}	%	d_4^{18}	%	d_4^{18}
1	1.0053	10	1.0681	20	1.1449	30	1.2307
2	1.0121	12	1.0827	22	1.1614	32	1.2491
4	1.0258	14	1.0977	24	1.1782	34	1.2680
6	1.0397	16	1.1131	26	1.1953		
8	1.0538	18	1.1288	28	1.2128		

$NaClO_4$ [LJG] (291)**; (514, 529)

%	d_4^{18}	%	d_4^{18}	%	d_4^{18}	%	d_4^{18}
1	1.0051	10	1.0656	20	1.1396	30	1.2227
2	1.0116	12	1.0798	22	1.1554	32	1.2407
4	1.0247	14	1.0943	24	1.1717	34	1.2591
6	1.0381	16	1.1090	26	1.1883	36	1.2779
8	1.0517	18	1.1241	28	1.2053	38	1.2969

NaBr [JAB] (26), α (367)**, (25, 287)*; (1, 12, 36, 106, 144, 189, 190, 221, 228, 246, 261, 307, 312, 313, 319, 320, 322, 323, 360, 361, 378, 447, 451, 459, 514, 519, 547, 573, 596, 618), α (151, 607)

%	0°C	10°C	20°C	25°C	30°C	40°C	50°C	60°C	80°C	100°C
1	1.00798	1.00765	1.00599	1.00476	1.00331	0.99979	0.99555	0.9907	0.9792	0.9657
2	1.01618	1.01566	1.01385	1.01255	1.01104	1.00743	1.00312	0.9982	0.9867	0.9731
4	1.03285	1.03196	1.02984	1.02840	1.02678	1.02299	1.01854	1.0135	1.0018	0.9882
6	1.04991	1.04866	1.04623	1.04465	1.04292	1.03895	1.03436	1.0293	1.0174	1.0037
8	1.06739	1.06579	1.06305	1.06133	1.05949	1.05534	1.05061	1.0454	1.0334	1.0196
10	1.08532	1.08338	1.08033	1.07847	1.07652	1.07219	1.06732	1.0620	1.0498	1.0359
12	1.10373	1.10146	1.09810	1.09610	1.09404	1.08953	1.08452	1.0791	1.0667	1.0526
14	1.12265	1.12005	1.11638	1.11424	1.11207	1.10738	1.10223	1.0967	1.0842	1.0699
16	1.14210	1.13917	1.13519	1.13292	1.13063	1.12576	1.12047	1.1148	1.1021	1.0876
18	1.16210	1.15885	1.15455	1.15217	1.14975	1.14470	1.13927	1.1335	1.1206	1.1059
20	1.18268	1.17911	1.17449	1.17207	1.16946	1.16423	1.15866	1.1527	1.1396	1.1247
22	1.20387	1.19997	1.19505	1.19249	1.18980	1.18439	1.17867	1.1726	1.1592	1.1442
24	1.22569	1.22147	1.21627	1.21360	1.21079	1.20520	1.19932	1.1931	1.1795	1.1642
26	1.24817	1.24364	1.23817	1.23538	1.23246	1.22669	1.22064	1.2143	1.2004	1.1849
28	1.27135	1.26652	1.26078	1.25786	1.25484	1.24889	1.24267	1.2362	1.2221	1.2063
30	1.29526	1.29014	1.28413	1.28107	1.27795	1.27182	1.26544	1.2588	1.2444	1.2284
35	1.35860	1.35284	1.34615	1.34277	1.33934	1.33271	1.32594	1.3190	1.3039	1.2873
40	1.42734	1.42124	1.41384	1.41017	1.40643	1.39928	1.39219	1.3849	1.3691	1.3520

$NaBrO_3$, *see* p. 81

NaI [JAB] (26), α (368)**, (25, 287)*; (2, 12, 36, 106, 144, 189, 190, 221, 225, 246, 261, 312, 319, 322, 342, 365, 447, 487, 507, 519, 547, 596, 618), α (151)

%	0°C	10°C	20°C	25°C	30°C	40°C	50°C	60°C	80°C	100°C
1	1.00789	1.00759	1.00596	1.00474	1.00329	0.99977	0.99553	0.9906	0.9791	0.9656
2	1.01603	1.01557	1.01380	1.01253	1.01103	1.00742	1.00310	0.9981	0.9865	0.9730
4	1.03264	1.03186	1.02981	1.02843	1.02683	1.02304	1.01857	1.0135	1.0016	0.9879
6	1.04972	1.04862	1.04629	1.04479	1.04309	1.03912	1.03450	1.0293	1.0172	1.0033
8	1.06729	1.06587	1.06326	1.06164	1.05983	1.05568	1.05091	1.0455	1.0332	1.0191
10	1.08538	1.08364	1.08075	1.07900	1.07708	1.07275	1.06782	1.0623	1.0496	1.0354
12	1.10402	1.10196	1.09878	1.09690	1.09487	1.09035	1.08525	1.0795	1.0666	1.0522
14	1.12324	1.12086	1.11738	1.11537	1.11322	1.10851	1.10323	1.0974	1.0842	1.0696
16	1.14307	1.14037	1.13658	1.13444	1.13217	1.12726	1.12179	1.1158	1.1023	1.0875
18	1.16354	1.16052	1.15641	1.15414	1.15175	1.14663	1.14097	1.1348	1.1211	1.1060
20	1.18469	1.18134	1.17691	1.17450	1.17199	1.16665	1.16080	1.1545	1.1405	1.1251
22	1.20655	1.20287	1.19812	1.19556	1.19293	1.18736	1.18132	1.1748	1.1605	1.1450
24	1.22915	1.22514	1.22007	1.21736	1.21460	1.20880	1.20257	1.1959	1.1813	1.1655
26	1.25252	1.24819	1.24279	1.23993	1.23704	1.23101	1.22459	1.2177	1.2029	1.1869
28	1.27669	1.27205	1.26631	1.26331	1.26029	1.25403	1.24741	1.2403	1.2252	1.2090
30	1.30171	1.29674	1.29067	1.28754	1.28437	1.27789	1.27107	1.2638	1.2484	1.2320
35	1.36842	1.36248	1.35562	1.35217	1.34869	1.34164	1.33429	1.3265	1.3103	1.2933
40	1.44158	1.43476	1.42711	1.42334	1.41954	1.41189	1.40399	1.3957	1.3785	1.3608
45	1.52224	1.51463	1.50620	1.50211	1.49799	1.48970	1.48122	1.4723	1.4541	1.4357
50	1.61168	1.60336	1.59418	1.58977	1.58534	1.57636	1.57626	1.5577	1.5385	1.5193
55	1.71152	1.70256	1.69268	1.68795	1.68323	1.67350	1.66373	1.6536	1.6331	1.6144
60	1.82382	1.81428	1.80377	1.79872	1.79373	1.78319	1.77269	1.7619	1.7405	1.7220

$NaBrO_3$ [JAB] (291)**; (360, 361, 378) [LJG]

%	d_4^{18}	%	d_4^{18}	%	d_4^{18}	%	d_4^{18}
1	1.0064	8	1.0641	16	1.1373	24	1.2193
2	1.0143	10	1.0816	18	1.1569		
4	1.0305	12	1.0996	20	1.1771		
6	1.0471	14	1.1182	22	1.1979		

$NaIO_3$ [LJG] (250, 363, 529)

%	d_4^{18}	%	d_4^{25}	%	$d_4^{19.5}$
3.83	1.0333	4.95	1.0415	7.52	1.068

$NaPO_3$ [LJG] (28, 206)**; (451)

%...	1	2	4	6	8
d_4^{20}...	1.0064	1.0145	1.0304	1.0461	1.0614

Na_3PO_4 [LJG] (536)**; (206, 463, 537)

%.....	1	2	4	6	8	10
d_4^{15}.....	1.0092	1.0194	1.0405	1.0624	1.0850	1.1083

$Na_4P_2O_7$ [LJG] (206, 451)

%......	1	2	3	4
d_4^{20}......	1.0090	1.0190	1.0283	1.0369

NaH_2PO_3 [LJG]; with 3.47 %, d_4^{20} = 1.0218 (463)
Na_2HPO_3 [LJG]; with 3.15 %, d_4^{20} = 1.0277 (463)
NaH_2PO_4 [LJG] (514)**; (432, 451, 463)

%.....	1	2	4	6	8	10
d_4^{25}.....	1.0045	1.0120	1.0270	1.0422	1.0575	1.0730

Na_2HPO_4 [LJG] (432)**; (533)*; (98, 241, 242, 451, 534, 561)

%......	1	2	4	6
d_4^{18}......	1.009	1.020	1.043	1.067

Na_2S [JAB] (52) [LJG]

%	d_4^{18}	%	d_4^{18}
1	1.0098	10	1.1146
2	1.0211	12	1.1388
4	1.0440	14	1.1634
6	1.0672	16	1.1885
8	1.0907	18	1.2140

Na_2SO_3 [JAB] (106) [LJG]

%	d_4^{19}	%	d_4^{19}
1	1.0078	10	1.0948
2	1.0172	12	1.1146
4	1.0363	14	1.1346
6	1.0556	16	1.1549
8	1.0751	18	1.1755

Na_2SO_4 [JAB] (20, 229.5, 409, 603), α (370)**; (1, 2, 14, 36, 85, 86, 101, 106, 144, 146, 147, 151, 155, 187, 190, 192, 204, 206, 215, 219, 221, 223, 224, 225, 246, 261, 297, 312, 342, 344, 360, 361, 378, 385, 405, 422, 425, 449, 451, 477, 485, 519, 529, 533, 540, 544, 550, 585, 598, 618, 629, 646), α (151, 219, 271, 466)

%	0°C	10°C	20°C	25°C	30°C
1	1.0094	1.0089	1.0073	1.0061	1.0046
2	1.0189	1.0182	1.0164	1.0151	1.0135
4	1.0381	1.0370	1.0348	1.0332	1.0315
6	1.0576	1.0560	1.0535	1.0515	1.0497
8	1.0773	1.0753	1.0724	1.0701	1.0682
10	1.0972	1.0948	1.0915	1.0890	1.0870
12	1.1174	1.1145	1.1109	1.1083	1.1062
14	1.1378	1.1345	1.1306	1.1279	1.1257
16	1.1585	1.1548	1.1506	1.1479	1.1456
18	1.1795	1.1754	1.1709	1.1683	1.1659
20	1.2008	1.1963	1.1915	1.1890	1.1865
22	1.2224	1.2175	1.2124	1.2102	1.2076
24	1.2443	1.2390	1.2336	1.2318	1.2292

Na_2SO_4.—(*Continued*)

%	40°C	50°C	60°C	80°C	100°C
1	1.0010	0.9969	0.9919	0.9805	0.9671
2	1.0098	1.0057	1.0007	0.9892	0.9758
4	1.0276	1.0235	1.0184	1.0068	0.9934
6	1.0456	1.0415	1.0363	1.0246	1.0112
8	1.0639	1.0598	1.0544	1.0426	1.0292
10	1.0825	1.0783	1.0728	1.0609	1.0475
12	1.1015	1.0971	1.0915	1.0795	1.0661
14	1.1209	1.1162	1.1105	1.0984	1.0850
16	1.1406	1.1356	1.1299	1.1176	1.1042
18	1.1608	1.1553	1.1496	1.1371	
20	1.1813	1.1753	1.1696	1.1569	
22	1.2023				
24	1.2237				

% (586)	$d_4^{18.080}$	% (586)	$d_4^{18.080}$
0.1	0.999 533	0.5	1.003 207
0.2	1.000 455	0.6	1.004 121
0.3	1.001 375	0.7	1.005 033
0.4	1.002 292	0.8	1.005 943

% (588)	d_4^{110}	d_4^{120}	d_4^{130}	d_4^{140}
1.69	0.9654	0.9573	0.9494	0.9404
3.35	0.9797	0.9719	0.9638	0.9555

% (229.5)	d_4^{25}	d_4^{30}	d_4^{40}	% (229.5)	d_4^{25}	d_4^{30}	d_4^{40}
1	1.00610_2	1.00462_0	1.00104_8	16	1.14791_8	1.14558_3	1.14062_4
2	1.01509_4	1.01353_9	1.00984_9	17	1.15805_0	1.15567_3	1.15064_3
3	1.02411_7	1.02249_1	1.01868_8	18	1.16827_8	1.16585_9	1.16075_9
4	1.03319_5	1.03150_0	1.02758_3	19	1.17860_6	1.17614_7	1.17097_9
5	1.04233_0	1.04057_2	1.03655_2	20	1.18903_6	1.18653_9	1.18130_3
6	1.05153_0	1.04971_1	1.04559_4	21	1.19957_0	1.19703_5	1.19173_4
7	1.06079_8	1.05891_9	1.05470_8	22	1.21020_7	1.20763_5	1.20227_1
8	1.07013_4	1.06820_0	1.06389_9	23	1.22094_8	1.21834_0	1.21292_0
9	1.07954_7	1.07755_7	1.07316_6	24	1.23179_6	1.22915_2	1.22367_3
10	1.08904_3	1.08700_0	1.08252_4	25	1.24275_4	1.24007_8	1.23453_7
11	1.09862_7	1.09653_2	1.09197_2	26	1.25382_4	1.25111_5	1.24551_9
12	1.10830_3	1.10615_6	1.10151_0	27	1.26500_0	1.26226_0	1.25660_7
13	1.11807_1	1.11587_2	1.11114_3	28	1.27627_6	1.27350_6	1.26780_0
14	1.12792_9	1.12568_2	1.12087_3	(29)	(1.28766_4)		
15	1.13787_8	1.13558_6	1.13070_0				

$Na_2S_2O_3$ [JAB] (509, 510, 536)**; (137)*; (106, 537) [LJG]

%	d_4^{20}	%	d_4^{20}	%	d_4^{20}	%	d_4^{20}
1	1.0065	10	1.0827	20	1.1740	30	1.2739
2	1.0148	12	1.1003	22	1.1932	35	1.3273
4	1.0315	14	1.1182	24	1.2128	40	1.3827
6	1.0483	16	1.1365	26	1.2328		
8	1.0654	18	1.1551	28	1.2532		

$Na_2S_2O_6$ [LJG]; with 2.58 %, d_4^{25} = 1.0162 (529)

$NaHSO_4$ [JAB] (409)**; (451, 458)*; (432)

%	0°C	10°C	20°C	25°C	30°C
1	1.0083	1.0077	1.0059	1.0047	1.0032
2	1.0166	1.0157	1.0137	1.0124	1.0108
4	1.0335	1.0319	1.0293	1.0279	1.0261
6	1.0505	1.0482	1.0451	1.0435	1.0415
8	1.0676	1.0647	1.0611	1.0593	1.0571
10	1.0849	1.0814	1.0773	1.0753	1.0728
12	1.1023	1.0982	1.0937	1.0915	1.0887
14	1.1199	1.1152	1.1103	1.1079	1.1049
16	1.1376	1.1324	1.1271	1.1245	1.1214
18	1.1555	1.1499	1.1441	1.1413	1.1381
20	1.1736	1.1676	1.1614	1.1583	1.1551
22	1.1919	1.1856	1.1789	1.1755	1.1724

$NaHSeO_3$ [LJG]; with 5.03 %, d_4^{20} = 1.0395 (463)
Na_2SeO_3 [LJG]; with 4.32 %, d_4^{20} = 1.0402 (463)

Na_2SeO_4 [JAB] (602) [LJG]

%	d_4^{15}	%	d_4^{15}	%	d_4^{15}	%	d_4^{15}
1	1.0081	4	1.0355	8	1.0735	12	1.1129
2	1.0171	6	1.0543	10	1.0930	14	1.1333

NaN_3 [LJG] (74)

%	0°C	10°C	20°C	25°C	30°C	40°C
1	1.0065	1.0060	1.0040	1.0030	1.0015	0.9975
2	1.013	1.012	1.010	1.009	1.007	1.003
4	1.026	1.024	1.022	1.021	1.019	1.015
6	1.039	1.037	1.034	1.033	1.031	1.027
8	1.052	1.050	1.047	1.045	1.043	1.039
10	1.065	1.063	1.059	1.057	1.055	1.051
12	1.079	1.076	1.072	1.070	1.068	1.063
14	1.093	1.089	1.085	1.083	1.081	1.076
16	1.107	1.103	1.099	1.096	1.094	1.089
18	1.121	1.117	1.112	1.109	1.107	1.102
20	1.136	1.131	1.126	1.123	1.121	1.115
22	1.151	1.146	1.140	1.137	1.135	1.129
24	1.166	1.161	1.155	1.152	1.149	1.143
26	1.182	1.176	1.170	1.167	1.164	1.157
28	1.199	1.192	1.186	1.182	1.179	1.172
30	1.216	1.209	1.202	1.198	1.195	1.188

%	50°C	60°C	70°C	80°C	90°C	100°C
1	0.9935	0.9885	0.9835	0.9775	0.9705	0.9635
2	0.999	0.994	0.988	0.983	0.976	0.969
4	1.010	1.005	1.000	0.994	0.987	0.980
6	1.022	1.016	1.011	1.005	0.998	0.991
8	1.034	1.028	1.022	1.016	1.009	1.002
10	1.046	1.040	1.034	1.028	1.021	1.014
12	1.058	1.052	1.046	1.040	1.033	1.026
14	1.070	1.064	1.058	1.052	1.045	1.038
16	1.083	1.076	1.070	1.064	1.057	1.050
18	1.096	1.089	1.083	1.076	1.070	1.063
20	1.109	1.102	1.096	1.089	1.083	1.076
22	1.122	1.115	1.109	1.102	1.096	1.089
24	1.136	1.129	1.123	1.116	1.110	1.103
26	1.150	1.143	1.137	1.130	1.124	1.107
28	1.165	1.158	1.152	1.145	1.138	1.131
30	1.181	1.174	1.167	1.160	1.153	1.146

$NaNO_2$ [JAB] (602) [LJG]

%	d_4^{15}	%	d_4^{15}	%	d_4^{15}	%	d_4^{15}
1	1.0058	6	1.0397	12	1.0816	18	1.1248
2	1.0125	8	1.0535	14	1.0959	20	1.1394
4	1.0260	10	1.0675	16	1.1103		

$NaNO_3$ [JAB] (84, 110, 250, 256), α (256, 370)**; (20, 448, 449, 451, 452, 646), α (203, 211, 375, 466)*; (1, 36, 86, 106, 144, 190, 195, 206, 214, 215, 221, 223, 224, 225, 228, 246, 261, 312, 344, 360, 361, 378, 385, 422, 514, 519, 529, 533, 592, 593), α (151, 446, 605)

%	0°C	10°C	20°C	25°C	30°C
1	1.0071	1.0066	1.0049	1.0037	1.0022
2	1.0144	1.0136	1.0117	1.0104	1.0088
4	1.0290	1.0277	1.0254	1.0239	1.0221
6	1.0438	1.0420	1.0392	1.0376	1.0356
8	1.0587	1.0565	1.0532	1.0515	1.0493
10	1.0738	1.0712	1.0674	1.0656	1.0632
12	1.0891	1.0861	1.0819	1.0799	1.0774
14	1.1046	1.1012	1.0967	1.0945	1.0919
16	1.1203	1.1166	1.1118	1.1094	1.1067
18	1.1363	1.1323	1.1272	1.1246	1.1219
20	1.1526	1.1483	1.1429	1.1402	1.1374
22	1.1692	1.1645	1.1589	1.1561	1.1532
24	1.1860	1.1810	1.1752	1.1723	1.1693

$NaNO_3$.—(*Continued*)

%	0°C	10°C	20°C	25°C	30°C
26	1.2031	1.1977	1.1917	1.1888	1.1856
28	1.2204	1.2147	1.2085	1.2055	1.2022
30	1.2380	1.2320	1.2256	1.2225	1.2191
35	1.2834	1.2770	1.2701	1.2668	1.2632
40	1.3316	1.3248	1.3175	1.3140	1.3102
45		1.3760	1.3683	1.3646	1.3607

%	40°C	50°C	60°C	80°C	100°C
1	0.9986	0.9944	0.9894	0.9779	0.9644
2	1.0050	1.0007	0.9956	0.9840	0.9704
4	1.0180	1.0135	1.0082	0.9964	0.9826
6	1.0312	1.0265	1.0210	1.0090	0.9951
8	1.0447	1.0397	1.0340	1.0218	1.0078
10	1.0584	1.0532	1.0473	1.0348	1.0208
12	1.0724	1.0669	1.0609	1.0481	1.0340
14	1.0867	1.0809	1.0749	1.0617	1.0475
16	1.1013	1.0953	1.0892	1.0757	1.0614
18	1.1162	1.1100	1.1038	1.0901	1.0756
20	1.1314	1.1250	1.1187	1.1048	1.0901
22	1.1470	1.1404	1.1340	1.1198	1.1049
24	1.1629	1.1561	1.1496	1.1351	1.1200
26	1.1791	1.1721	1.1655	1.1507	1.1355
28	1.1955	1.1884	1.1816	1.1667	1.1513
30	1.2122	1.2051	1.1980	1.1830	1.1674
35	1.2560	1.2486	1.2413	1.2258	1.2100
40	1.3027	1.2950	1.2875	1.2715	1.2555
45	1.3528	1.3448	1.3371	1.3206	1.3044

8.066 % (256)

°C	d_4^t	°C	d_4^t	°C	d_4^t
0	1.04834	25	1.05580	50	1.06777
10	1.05059	30	1.05791		
20	1.05386	40	1.06260		

4.141 % (256)

°C	d_4^t
20	1.02646

NaH_2AsO_4 [JAB] (514)**; (463) [LJG]		Na_2HAsO_4 [JAB] (536)**; (241, 242, 537) [LJG]		Na_3AsO_4 [JAB] (536)**; (206, 463) [LJG]	
%	d_4^{25}	%	d_4^{14}	%	d_4^{17}
1	1.0050	1	1.0083	1	1.0097
2	1.0129	2	1.0175	2	1.0207
4	1.0291	4	1.0365	4	1.0431
6	1.0457	6	1.0563	6	1.0659
8	1.0626	8	1.0768	8	1.0892
10	1.0798	10	1.0980	10	1.1130
12	1.0974	12	1.1197	12	1.1373
14	1.1153	14	1.1419		
		16	1.1645		

Na_2CO_3 [JAB] (219), α (219)**; (668)*; (68, 69, 71, 98, 190, 192, 206, 261, 271, 279, 312, 328, 342, 344, 348, 349, 432, 451, 519, 632, 637, 639)

%	0°C	10°C	15°C	20°C	25°C	30°C
1	1.0109	1.0103	1.0096	1.0086	1.0073	1.0058
2	1.0219	1.0210	1.0201	1.0190	1.0176	1.0159
4	1.0439	1.0423	1.0411	1.0398	1.0381	1.0363
6	1.0659	1.0636	1.0622	1.0606	1.0588	1.0568
8	1.0878	1.0850	1.0834	1.0816	1.0797	1.0775
10	1.1097	1.1065	1.1048	1.1029	1.1008	1.0986
12	1.1319	1.1284	1.1265	1.1244	1.1223	1.1200
14	1.1543	1.1506	1.1485	1.1463	1.1442	1.1417

%	30°C	%	40°C	50°C	60°C	70°C
16	1.1636	1	1.0022	0.9979	0.9929	0.9874
18	1.1859	2	1.0122	1.0078	1.0027	0.9970
20	1.2086	4	1.0323	1.0278	1.0223	1.0165

Na_2CO_3.—(*Continued*)

%	30°C	%	40°C	50°C	60°C	70°C
22	1.2317	6	1.0527	1.0478	1.0422	1.0364
24	1.2552	8	1.0732	1.0681	1.0625	1.0565
26	1.2790	10	1.0939	1.0888	1.0830	1.0770
28	1.3031	12	1.1150	1.1097	1.1039	1.0978
30	1.3274	14	1.1365	1.1310	1.1251	1.1189

%	80°C	90°C	100°C	% (373)	$d_4^{20.004}$
1	0.9814	0.9750	0.9683	0.005	0.998 2840
2	0.9910	0.9847	0.9782	0.01	0.998 3370
4	1.0105	1.0042	0.9980	0.02	0.998 4432
6	1.0302	1.0241	1.0180	0.03	0.998 5496
8	1.0503	1.0441	1.0380	0.04	0.998 6560
10	1.0707	1.0644	1.0582	0.05	0.998 7625
12	1.0914	1.0850	1.0787		
14	1.1125	1.1059	1.0996		

$Na_2C_2O_4$, Oxalate [JAB] (**376, 377, 451, 463, 632**)**; (**329**)

%	d_4^{20}	d_4^{25}	%	d_4^{20}	d_4^{25}
1	1.0064	1.0054	3	1.0229	1.0221
2	1.0147	1.0137	4	1.0312	

$Na_2C_4O_4$, Acetylenedicarboxylate [JAB]; d_4^{25} = 1.0055 with 1 %; = 1.0143 with 2 % (**376**)

$NaCHO_2$, Formate [JAB] (**291, 484**)**; (**144, 329, 377, 378, 449, 463, 514, 632**)

%	d_4^{15}	d_4^{18}	d_4^{25}	%	d_4^{15}	d_4^{18}	d_4^{25}
1	1.005	1.0049	1.003	18	1.118	1.1164	1.114
2	1.012	1.0112	1.009	20	1.132	1.1300	1.127
4	1.025	1.0139	1.022	22	1.146	1.1439	1.141
6	1.038	1.0368	1.035	24	1.160	1.1580	1.155
8	1.051	1.0498	1.048	26	1.175		1.170
10	1.064	1.0630	1.061	28	1.189		1.184
12	1.077	1.0762	1.074	30	1.204		1.199
14	1.091	1.0895	1.087	35	1.242		1.236
16	1.104	1.1029	1.100	40	1.281		1.274

$NaHCO_3$ [JAB] (**432**)**; (**144, 193, 241, 242, 509, 510**) [LJG]

%	d_4^{18}	%	d_4^{18}	%	d_4^{18}	%	d_4^{18}
1	1.0059	3	1.0206	5	1.0354	7	1.0505
2	1.0132	4	1.0280	6	1.0429	8	1.0581

$NaC_2H_3O_2$, Acetate [JAB] (**288**), α (**271, 374**)**; (**515, 632**)*; (**18, 46, 134, 192, 208, 222, 223, 224, 342, 343, 362, 376, 377, 378, 388, 449, 451, 463, 484, 509, 514, 529, 586, 592, 602**)

%	10°C	18°C	20°C	25°C	30°C
1	1.0049	1.0037	1.0033	1.0021	1.0007
2	1.0101	1.0088	1.0084	1.0072	1.0057
4	1.0205	1.0191	1.0186	1.0173	1.0157
6	1.0310	1.0294	1.0289	1.0275	1.0258
8	1.0415	1.0397	1.0392	1.0377	1.0359
10	1.0520	1.0500	1.0495	1.0479	1.0461
12	1.0626	1.0604	1.0598	1.0582	1.0563
14	1.0733	1.0709	1.0702	1.0686	1.0666
16	1.0841	1.0815	1.0807	1.0790	1.0769
18	1.0950	1.0922	1.0913	1.0895	1.0873
20	1.1060	1.1030	1.1021	1.1001	1.0978
22	1.1171	1.1139	1.1130	1.1109	1.1085
24	1.1282	1.1249	1.1240	1.1218	1.1193
26	1.1394	1.1360	1.1351	1.1327	1.1302
28	1.1508	1.1472	1.1462	1.1437	1.1412

%	40°C	50°C	60°C	70°C	80°C
1	0.9971	0.9930	0.9881	0.9826	0.9766
2	1.0021	0.9979	0.9930	0.9875	0.9815
4	1.0120	1.0077	1.0028	0.9972	0.9912
6	1.0220	1.0176	1.0126	1.0070	1.0009

$NaC_2H_3O_2$.—(*Continued*)

%	40°C	50°C	60°C	70°C	80°C
8	1.0320	1.0275	1.0224	1.0168	1.0107
10	1.0420	1.0375	1.0322	1.0266	1.0205
12	1.0521	1.0475	1.0421	1.0364	1.0303
14	1.0623	1.0575	1.0521	1.0463	1.0402
16	1.0725	1.0676	1.0621	1.0562	
18	1.0828	1.0778	1.0722	1.0662	
20	1.0931	1.0880	1.0824	1.0763	
22	1.1035	1.0983	1.0926	1.0865	
24	1.1141	1.1087	1.1029	1.0968	
26	1.1248	1.1192	1.1133	1.1072	
28	1.1355	1.1298	1.1238	1.1176	

$NaC_2H_3O_3$, Glycolate [JAB] (**376**)**; (**378, 463**)

%	d_4^{25}	%	d_4^{25}	%	d_4^{25}
1	1.0029	4	1.0206	7	1.0387
2	1.0087	5	1.0266	8	1.0448
3	1.0146	6	1.0326	9	1.0509

$NaC_3H_5O_2$, Propionate [JAB] (**291**)**; (**377, 378, 463, 484, 514**)

%	d_4^{18}	%	d_4^{18}	%	d_4^{18}	%	d_4^{18}
1	1.0030	8	1.0342	16	1.0705	24	1.1071
2	1.0075	10	1.0432	18	1.0796	26	1.1164
4	1.0164	12	1.0523	20	1.0887		
6	1.0253	14	1.0614	22	1.0979		

$NaC_3H_5O_3$, Lactate [JAB] (**514**)**; (**378, 463**)

%	d_4^{25}	%	d_4^{25}	%	d_4^{25}
1	1.0022	4	1.0173	8	1.0377
2	1.0072	6	1.0275	10	1.0478

$NaC_3H_5O_4$, Glycerate [JAB] (**378**)

%.....	1	2	3	4	5	6
d_4^{20}.....	1.0041	1.0102	1.0165	1.0229	1.0295	1.0363

$NaC_4H_5O_5$, Acid malate [JAB] (**376**)**; (**463**)

%	d_4^{20}	%	d_4^{20}	%	d_4^{20}	%	d_4^{20}
1	1.0038	12	1.0670	24	1.1414	45	1.2854
2	1.0094	14	1.0790	26	1.1544	50	1.3224
4	1.0207	16	1.0911	28	1.1676	55	1.3605
6	1.0321	18	1.1034	30	1.1809	60	1.3996
8	1.0436	20	1.1159	35	1.2147		
10	1.0552	22	1.1286	40	1.2495		

$NaC_4H_5O_6$, Acid tartrate [JAB] (**515**)**; (**432**)*; (**451, 463, 571**)

%	d_4^{18}	%	d_4^{18}	%	d_4^{18}	%	d_4^{18}
1	1.0061	3	1.0170	5	1.0280	7	1.0391
2	1.0115	4	1.0225	6	1.0335		

$NaC_4H_7O_2$, *n*-Butyrate [JAB] (**378, 449, 463**)**; (**484, 514**)

%.....	1	2	4	6	8	10
d_4^{20}.....	1.0018	1.0055	1.0130	1.0207	1.0286	1.0367

$NaC_4H_7O_2$, Isobutyrate [JAB] (**514**)**; (**463**)

%.....	1	2	4	6	8	10
d_4^{25}.....	1.0009	1.0046	1.0121	1.0195	1.0268	1.0341

$NaC_5H_9O_2$, Isovalerate [JAB] (**514**)

%	d_4^{25}	%	d_4^{25}	%	d_4^{25}	%	d_4^{25}
1	1.0003	4	1.0100	8	1.0229	12	1.0358
2	1.0035	6	1.0164	10	1.0293		

$NaC_6H_7O_7$, Dihydrogen citrate [JAB] with 19.20 %, d_4^{18} = 1.1063; with 5.35 %, d_4^{20} = 1.0205 (**463, 515**)**

$NaC_6H_{11}O_2$, Isocaproate [JAB] (**514**)

%	d_4^{25}	%	d_4^{25}	%	d_4^{25}	%	d_4^{25}
1	0.9999	4	1.0081	8	1.0191	12	1.0299
2	1.0026	6	1.0136	10	1.0245	14	1.0352

$NaC_7H_5O_2$, Benzoate [JAB] (376, 514)**

%	d_4^{25}	%	d_4^{25}	%	d_4^{25}	%	d_4^{25}
1	1.0012	4	1.0135	8	1.0301	12	1.0469
2	1.0053	6	1.0218	10	1.0385	14	1.0554

$NaC_7H_5O_3$, Hydroxybenzoates [JAB] (376, 514)**

%	d_4^{25}			%	d_4^{25}		
	o-(514)	m-	p-		o-(514)	m-	p-
1	1.0013	1.0015	1.0015	10	1.0396	1.0432	1.0432
2	1.0055	1.0060	1.0060	12	1.0483	1.0528	1.0528
4	1.0139	1.0151	1.0151	14	1.0570	1.0626	1.0626
6	1.0224	1.0243	1.0243	16	1.0658	1.0724	1.0724
8	1.0310	1.0337	1.0337				

$NaC_8H_7O_2$, Toluates [JAB] (376)

%	d_4^{25}			%	d_4^{25}	
	o-	m-	p-		m-	p-
1	1.0007	1.0007	1.0006	10	1.0342	1.0334
2	1.0043	1.0043	1.0041	12	1.0418	1.0408
4	1.0116	1.0116	1.0113	14	1.0495	1.0483
6		1.0190	1.0186	16	1.0573	1.0558
8		1.0266	1.0260			

$NaC_8H_7O_2$, Phenylacetate [JAB] (376)

%	d_4^{25}	%	d_4^{25}	%	d_4^{25}	%	d_4^{25}
1	1.0007	6	1.0188	10	1.0338	14	1.0490
2	1.0043	8	1.0262	12	1.0414	16	1.0566
4	1.0115						

$NaC_8H_7O_3$, Phenylglycolate [JAB] (376)

%	d_4^{25}	%	d_4^{25}	%	d_4^{25}	%	d_4^{25}
1	1.0011	6	1.0216	10	1.0382	14	1.0550
2	1.0052	8	1.0299	12	1.0466	16	1.0635
4	1.0134						

$NaC_8H_7O_3$, Anisate [JAB] (376)

%	d_4^{25}	%	d_4^{25}	%	d_4^{25}	%	d_4^{25}
1	1.0008	3	1.0084	5	1.0162	7	1.0242
2	1.0046	4	1.0123	6	1.0202	8	1.0282

$NaC_8H_7O_3$, Phenoxyacetate [JAB] (376)

%	d_4^{25}	%	d_4^{25}	%	d_4^{25}	%	d_4^{25}
1	1.0009	6	1.0202	10	1.0359	14	1.0518
2	1.0047	8	1.0280	12	1.0438	16	1.0600
4	1.0124						

$NaC_9H_7O_2$, Cinnamate [JAB] (376)

%	d_4^{25}	%	d_4^{25}	%	d_4^{25}	%	d_4^{25}
1	1.0006	3	1.0076	5	1.0147	7	1.0219
2	1.0041	4	1.0112	6	1.0183	8	1.0256

$NaC_9H_9O_2$, Hydrocinnamate [JAB] (376)

%	d_4^{25}	%	d_4^{25}	%	d_4^{25}	%	d_4^{25}
1	1.0002	6	1.0161	10	1.0290	14	1.0422
2	1.0034	8	1.0225	12	1.0356	16	1.0488
4	1.0097						

$NaC_{16}H_{31}O_2$, Palmitate [JAB] (134)

%	d_4^{90}	%	d_4^{90}	%	d_4^{90}	%	d_4^{90}
1	0.9652	8	0.9644	16	0.9637	24	0.9629
2	0.9651	10	0.9642	18	0.9635	26	0.9627
4	0.9649	12	0.9640	20	0.9633	28	0.9626
6	0.9647	14	0.9638	22	0.9631	30	0.9624

$NaC_{18}H_{35}O_2$, Stearate [JAB] (134)

%	d_4^{90}	%	d_4^{90}	%	d_4^{90}	%	d_4^{90}
1	0.965	6	0.963	10	0.962	14	0.961
2	0.964	8	0.962	12	0.961	16	0.960
4	0.964						

$Na_2C_3H_2O_4$, Malonate [JAB] (376)

%	d_4^{25}	%	d_4^{25}	%	d_4^{25}	%	d_4^{25}
1	1.0044	3	1.0191	5	1.0341	7	1.0495
2	1.0117	4	1.0266	6	1.0417		

$Na_2C_4H_2O_4$, Fumarate [JAB] (376)**; (329)

%	d_4^{25}	%	d_4^{25}	%	d_4^{25}	%	d_4^{25}
1	1.0035	3	1.0166	5	1.0299	7	1.0434
2	1.0100	4	1.0232	6	1.0366		

$Na_2C_4H_2O_4$, Maleate [JAB] (376)

%	d_4^{25}	%	d_4^{25}	%	d_4^{25}	%	d_4^{25}
1	1.0038	3	1.0174	5	1.0312	7	1.0453
2	1.0106	4	1.0243	6	1.0382	8	1.0524

$Na_2C_4H_4O_4$, Succinate [JAB] (376, 377, 463)**; (329)

%	d_4^{20}	d_4^{25}	%	d_4^{20}
1	1.0048	1.0036	12	1.0805
2	1.0114	1.0102	14	1.0951
4	1.0247	1.0235	16	1.1100
6	1.0382	1.0368	18	1.1252
8	1.0520	1.0503	20	1.1406
10	1.0661			

$Na_2C_4H_4O_4$, Isosuccinate [JAB] (376)

%	d_4^{25}	%	d_4^{25}	%	d_4^{25}	%	d_4^{25}
1	1.0039	3	1.0176	5	1.0313	7	1.0451
2	1.0107	4	1.0245	6	1.0382	8	1.0521

$Na_2C_4H_4O_5$, Malate [JAB] (376)**; (444, 463, 546)

%	d_4^{25}	%	d_4^{25}	%	d_4^{25}	%	d_4^{25}
1	1.0038	3	1.0176	5	1.0317	7	1.0462
2	1.0106	4	1.0246	6	1.0389	8	1.0536

$Na_2C_4H_4O_6$, Tartrate [JAB] (376, 499, 500)**; (451)*; (210, 221, 223, 329, 330, 432, 463, 571)

%	d_4^{20}	d_4^{25}	%	d_4^{20}
1	1.0052	1.0040	16	1.1156
2	1.0123	1.0110	18	1.1313
4	1.0266	1.0251	20	1.1471
6	1.0410	1.0393	22	1.1633
8	1.0555	1.0537	24	1.1797
10	1.0702	1.0683	26	1.1963
12	1.0851		28	1.2132
14	1.1002			

$Na_2C_5H_4O_4$, Citraconate [JAB] (376)

%	d_4^{25}	%	d_4^{25}	%	d_4^{25}	%	d_4^{25}
1	1.0033	3	1.0159	5	1.0286	7	1.0414
2	1.0096	4	1.0223	6	1.0350	8	1.0479

$Na_2C_5H_4O_4$, Itaconate [JAB] (376)

%	d_4^{25}	%	d_4^{25}	%	d_4^{25}	%	d_4^{25}
1	1.0032	3	1.0159	5	1.0288	7	1.0419
2	1.0095	4	1.0223	6	1.0353	8	1.0485

$Na_2C_5H_4O_4$, Mesaconate [JAB] (376)

%	d_4^{25}	%	d_4^{25}	%	d_4^{25}	%	d_4^{25}
1	1.0031	3	1.0152	5	1.0274	7	1.0397
2	1.0091	4	1.0213	6	1.0335	8	1.0460

$Na_2C_5H_6O_4$, Pyrotartrate [JAB] (376)

%	d_4^{25}	%	d_4^{25}	%	d_4^{25}	%	d_4^{25}
1	1.0029	3	1.0147	5	1.0266	7	1.0387
2	1.0088	4	1.0206	6	1.0326	8	1.0448

$Na_2C_6H_6O_7$, Hydrogen citrate [JAB]; 20.77 %, d_4^{18} = 1.1372 (515)

$Na_2C_8H_4O_4$, Phthalates [JAB] (376)

%	d_4^{25} o-	d_4^{25} m-	d_4^{25} p-	%	d_4^{25} o-	d_4^{25} m-	d_4^{25} p-
1	1.0031	1.0027	1.0024	6	1.0334	1.0313	1.0299
2	1.0092	1.0083	1.0078	8	1.0456	1.0431	
4	1.0213	1.0197	1.0187	10	1.0579	1.0551	

$Na_2C_6H_8O_4$, Adipate [JAB] (376)

%	d_4^{25}	%	d_4^{25}	%	d_4^{25}	%	d_4^{25}
1	1.0024	4	1.0185	6	1.0293	8	1.0403
2	1.0078	5	1.0239	7	1.0348	9	1.0458
3	1.0131						

$Na_2C_8H_{12}O_4$, Suberate [JAB] (376)

%...	1	2	3	4	5
d_4^{25}...	1.0017	1.0064	1.0112	1.0160	1.0208

$Na_2C_9H_{14}O_4$, Azelate [JAB] (376)

%	d_4^{25}	%	d_4^{25}	%	d_4^{25}	%	d_4^{25}
1	1.0013	4	1.0138	8	1.0306	12	1.0473
2	1.0055	6	1.0222	10	1.0389		

$Na_3C_6H_5O_7$, Citrate [JAB] (376)**; (463, 515)

%	d_4^{25}	%	d_4^{25}	%	d_4^{25}	%	d_4^{25}
1	1.0047	3	1.0201	5	1.0355	7	1.0510
2	1.0124	4	1.0278	6	1.0432	8	1.0589

$Na_4C_{11}H_2O_{10}$, Benzenepentacarboxylate [JAB] (457)

	1%	2%		1%	2%		1%	2%
d_4^{0}....	1.0078	1.0158	d_4^{25}...	1.0046	1.0121	d_4^{50}...	0.9953	1.0024
d_4^{10}...	1.0074	1.0152	d_4^{30}...	1.0031	1.0106			
d_4^{20}...	1.0058	1.0134	d_4^{40}...	0.9995	1.0068			

$Na_5C_{11}HO_{10}$, Benzenepentacarboxylate [JAB] (457)

	1%	2%		1%	2%		1%	2%
d_4^{0}....	1.0083	1.0169	d_4^{25}...	1.0051	1.0133	d_4^{50}...	0.9958	1.0038
d_4^{10}...	1.0079	1.0163	d_4^{30}...	1.0036	1.0118			
d_4^{20}...	1.0063	1.0145	d_4^{40}...	1.0000	1.0081			

$NaC_2Cl_3O_2$, Trichloroacetate [JAB] (377, 378, 463)**

%	d_4^{20}	%	d_4^{20}	%	d_4^{20}	%	d_4^{20}
1	1.0039	6	1.0331	10	1.0578	14	1.0837
2	1.0096	8	1.0453	12	1.0706	16	1.0971
4	1.0212						

$NaC_2H_2ClO_2$, Chloroacetate [JAB] (377, 378, 463, 586)**

%	0.1	0.2	0.4	0.6	0.8	1.0
d_4^{18}	0.999 206	0.999 790	1.000 958	1.002 126	1.003 296	1.004 466

%..........	1.0	2	4	6	8	10	12
d_4^{20}..........	1.0040	1.0099	1.0217	1.0335	1.0454	1.0573	1.0693

$NaC_2HCl_2O_2$, Dichloroacetate [JAB] (377, 378, 463)**

%	d_4^{20}	%	d_4^{20}	%	d_4^{20}	%	d_4^{20}
1	1.004	4	1.022	8	1.046	12	1.070
2	1.010	6	1.034	10	1.058	14	1.083

$NaC_4H_4Cl_3O_2$, Trichlorobutyrate [JAB] (378)

%	d_4^{20}	%	d_4^{20}	%	d_4^{20}	%	d_4^{20}
1	1.0033	3	1.0135	5	1.0238	7	1.0342
2	1.0084	4	1.0186	6	1.0290	8	1.0395

$NaC_7H_4ClO_2$, *m*-Chlorobenzoate [JAB] (376)

%	d_4^{25}	%	d_4^{25}	%	d_4^{25}	%	d_4^{25}
1	1.0015	6	1.0240	10	1.0426	14	1.0619
2	1.0059	8	1.0332	12	1.0522	16	1.0718
4	1.0149						

$NaC_7H_4BrO_2$, Bromobenzoates [JAB] (376)

%	d_4^{25} m-	d_4^{25} p-	%	d_4^{25} m-	d_4^{25} p-
1	1.0025	1.0023	6	1.0301	1.0298
2	1.0079	1.0077	8	1.0415	1.0413
4	1.0189	1.0186	10	1.0531	1.0530

$NaC_2H_5SO_4$, Ethyl sulfate [JAB] (155)

%	$d_4^{12.4}$	%	$d_4^{13.5}$	%	d_4^{14}
32.97	1.1699	39.89	1.2380	32.09	1.1689

$NaC_2H_5SO_4$, Hydroxyethylsulfonate [JAB]; with 3.70%, d_4^{25} = 1.0171 (529)

$NaC_6H_5SO_3$, Benzenesulfonate [JAB]; 4.50%, d_4^{25} = 1.0164 (529)

$Na_2CH_2S_2O_6$, Methanedisulfonate [JAB]; 2.75%, d_4^{25} = 1.0161 (529)

$NaC_7H_4NO_4$, Nitrobenzoates [JAB] (376, 514)**

%	d_4^{25} o-	d_4^{25} m-(514)	d_4^{25} p-	%	d_4^{25} o-	d_4^{25} m-(514)	d_4^{25} p-
1	1.0017	1.0015	1.0018	10	1.0450	1.0427	1.0441
2	1.0063	1.0060	1.0065	12	1.0550	1.0522	
4	1.0157	1.0151	1.0159	14	1.0651	1.0617	
6	1.0253	1.0242	1.0253	16	1.0754	1.0713	
8	1.0351	1.0334	1.0347	18	1.0858	1.0810	

$NaC_8H_4NO_2$, *m*-Cyanobenzoate [JAB] (376)

%	d_4^{25}	%	d_4^{25}	%	d_4^{25}	%	d_4^{25}
1	1.0011	3	1.0092	5	1.0176	7	1.0260
2	1.0051	4	1.0134	6	1.0218	8	1.0302

NaCNS [JAB] (291)**; (155)* [LJG]

%	d_4^{18}	%	d_4^{18}	%	d_4^{18}	%	d_4^{18}
1	1.0038	10	1.0520	20	1.1081	30	1.1677
2	1.0090	12	1.0630	22	1.1197	35	1.196_0
4	1.0196	14	1.0741	24	1.1314	40	1.228_0
6	1.0303	16	1.0853	26	1.1433	45	1.265_0
8	1.0411	18	1.0966	28	1.1554		

Na_2SiO_3 [JAB] (288)**; (345, 577, 602) [LJG]

%	d_4^{18}	%	d_4^{18}	%	d_4^{18}	%	d_4^{18}
1	1.0094	8	1.0884	16	1.1866	24	1.2926
2	1.0203	10	1.1122	18	1.2123	26	1.3204
4	1.0425	12	1.1365	20	1.2385		
6	1.0652	14	1.1613	22	1.2653		

$Na_2O.xSiO_2$ [JAB] (578) [LJG]; values of d_4^{20}

x	1%	2%	4%	6%	8%	10%
3.90	1.006	1.014	1.030	1.046	1.063	1.080
3.36	1.006	1.014	1.030	1.047	1.065	1.083
2.40	1.007	1.016	1.034	1.052	1.071	1.090
2.06	1.007	1.016	1.035	1.054	1.073	1.093
1.69	1.007	1.017	1.036	1.056	1.077	1.098

x	12%	14%	16%	18%	20%	22%
3.90	1.098	1.116	1.134	1.153	1.172	1.191
3.36	1.101	1.120	1.139	1.159	1.179	1.200
2.40	1.110	1.130	1.151			
2.06	1.113	1.134	1.156	1.178	1.200	1.223
1.69	1.119	1.141	1.163	1.186	1.210	1.234

x	24%	26%	28%	30%	32%	34%
3.90	1.211	1.232	1.253	1.275	1.298	
3.36	1.222	1.244	1.267	1.290	1.314	1.339
2.44			1.285	1.309	1.334	1.360
2.06	1.247	1.271	1.296	1.321	1.346	1.371
1.69	1.259	1.284	1.310	1.337	1.365	1.394

$Na_2O.xSiO_2$.—(*Continued*)

x	36 %	38 %	40 %	45 %	50 %	55 %
3.36	1.365	1.393				
2.44	1.387	1.415	1.445			
2.06	1.397	1.423	1.450	1.520	1.594	1.673
1.69	1.424	1.456				

Na_2SnO_3 [JAB] (602)**; (460) [LJG]

%	d_4^{20}	%	d_4^{20}	%	d_4^{20}	%	d_4^{20}
1	1.006	6	1.051	12	1.107	18	1.166
2	1.015	8	1.069	14	1.126	20	1.187
4	1.033	10	1.088	16	1.146		

$NaHgCl_3$ [GS]; d_4^{16} = 1.09514 with 11.0736 %; = 1.13296 with 14.9370 % (550)

$Na_2Cd(SO_4)_2$ [GS]; d_4^{18} = 1.0911 with 9.56 %; = 1.1145 with 11.80 % (550)

$NaCu(CN)_2$ [WCS]; d_4^{20} = 1.0040 with 1 %; = 1.0098 with 2 %; = 1.0212 with 4 % (602)

$NaMnO_4$ [LJG]; with 3.55 %, d_4^{25} = 1.0221 (529)

Na_2MoO_4 [JAB] (602) [LJG]

%	d_4^{15}	%	d_4^{15}	%	d_4^{15}	%	d_4^{15}
1	1.0078	6	1.0526	12	1.1102	18	1.1724
2	1.0165	8	1.0713	14	1.1304	20	1.1943
4	1.0343	10	1.0905	16	1.1511	22	1.2168

Na_2CrO_4 [JAB] (288)**; (463, 566) [LJG]

%	d_4^{18}	%	d_4^{18}	%	d_4^{18}	%	d_4^{18}
1	1.0074	8	1.0718	16	1.1518	24	1.2383
2	1.0163	10	1.0912	18	1.1728	26	1.2611
4	1.0344	12	1.1110	20	1.1942		
6	1.0529	14	1.1312	22	1.2160		

$Na_2Cr_2O_7$ [JAB] (575)**; (463) [LJG]

%	d_4^{15}	%	d_4^{15}	%	d_4^{15}	%	d_4^{15}
1	1.006	10	1.070	20	1.140	30	1.207
2	1.013	12	1.084	22	1.153	35	1.244
4	1.027	14	1.098	24	1.166	40	1.279
6	1.041	16	1.112	26	1.179	45	1.312
8	1.056	18	1.126	28	1.193	50	1.342

Na_2WO_4† [LJG] (207)

%	d_4^{15} (602)*	d_4^{20} (481)*	%	d_4^{15} (602)*	d_4^{20} (481)*	%	d_4^{15} (602)*	d_4^{20} (481)*
1	1.0082	1.0074	14	1.1376	1.1372	28	1.3182	1.3146
2	1.0174	1.0166	16	1.1606	1.1598	30	1.3473	1.3444
4	1.0359	1.0354	18	1.1846	1.1833	32	1.3769	1.3756
6	1.0548	1.0546	20	1.2096	1.2076	34	1.4069	1.4084
8	1.0743	1.0742	22	1.2355	1.2328	36	1.4372	1.4428
10	1.0945	1.0944	24	1.2622	1.2590	38		1.4786
12	1.1156	1.1154	26	1.2898	1.2862	40		1.5156

† Isotherms are inconsistent. Six-point figures indicate only that uncertainty which is due to interpolation.

$2Na_2O.P_2O_5.24WO_3$ [LJG] (65)

%	d_4^{20}	%	d_4^{20}	%	d_4^{20}	%	d_4^{20}	%	d_4^{20}
1	1.007	10	1.091	20	1.198	30	1.336	55	1.871
2	1.016	12	1.110	22	1.223	35	1.418	60	2.033
4	1.034	14	1.130	24	1.249	40	1.510		
6	1.053	16	1.152	26	1.277	45	1.614		
8	1.072	18	1.175	28	1.306	50	1.733		

$NaVO_3$ [LJG] (602)

%	d_4^{20}	%	d_4^{20}	%	d_4^{20}	%	d_4^{20}
1	1.0060	4	1.0302	8	1.0640	12	1.0991
2	1.0140	6	1.0469	10	1.0814		

$NaBO_2$ [JAB] (602) [LJG]

%	d_4^{20}	%	d_4^{20}	%	d_4^{20}	%	d_4^{20}
1	1.0089	4	1.0417	8	1.0866	12	1.1327
2	1.0198	6	1.0640	10	1.1095		

$Na_2B_4O_7$ [JAB] (225)**; (28, 205, 206, 241, 242) [LJG]; d_4^{15} = 1.0084 with 1 %; = 1.0179 with 2 %; = 1.0274 with 3 %

$Na_2Mg(SO_4)_2$ [GS]; d_4^{16} = 1.0665 with 7 %; = 1.0766 with 8 %; = 1.0867 with 9 % (550)

KOH [BTB] (492)**; (12, 98, 106, 248, 279, 290, 328, 342, 344, 378, 387, 432, 449, 451, 463, 519, 529, 555, 666), α(211)

%	d_4^{15}	%	d_4^{15}	%	d_4^{15}	%	d_4^{15}	%	d_4^{15}
1	1.0083	10	1.0918	20	1.1884	30	1.2905	40	1.3991
2	1.0175	11	1.1013	21	1.1984	31	1.3010	41	1.4103
3	1.0267	12	1.1108	22	1.2083	32	1.3117	42	1.4215
4	1.0359	13	1.1203	23	1.2184	33	1.3224	43	1.4329
5	1.0452	14	1.1299	24	1.2285	34	1.3331	44	1.4443
6	1.0544	15	1.1396	25	1.2387	35	1.3440	45	1.4558
7	1.0637	16	1.1493	26	1.2489	36	1.3549	46	1.4673
8	1.0730	17	1.1590	27	1.2592	37	1.3659	47	1.4790
9	1.0824	18	1.1688	28	1.2695	38	1.3769	48	1.4907
		19	1.1786	29	1.2800	39	1.3879	49	1.5025

%	50	51	51.7†	52
d_4^{15}	1.5143	1.5262	1.5355	1.5382

† Satd. soln. (196).

KF [JAB] (287, 548)**; (36, 45, 101, 190, 225, 246, 342)

%	d_4^{18}	%	d_4^{18}	%	d_4^{18}	%	d_4^{18}
1	1.0072	8	1.0693	16	1.1448	24	1.2260
2	1.0159	10	1.0877	18	1.1646	26	1.2471
4	1.0334	12	1.1064	20	1.1847		
6	1.0512	14	1.1254	22	1.2052		

KCl, *see* p. 87

$KClO_3$ [JAB] (268, 548), α (206)**; (287, 511)*; (84, 106, 342, 343, 344, 360, 361, 449, 509, 510, 529, 561, 583), α (271) [LJG]

°C	1 %	2 %	3 %	4 %	5 %	6 %
0	1.0061	1.0124	1.0189	1.0256		
10	1.0059	1.0122	1.0187	1.0254		
18	1.0049	1.0113	1.0178	1.0245	1.0312	1.0380
20	1.0045	1.0109	1.0174	1.0241		
25	1.0034	1.0099	1.0165	1.0233		
30	1.0020	1.0085	1.0151	1.0218		
40	0.9986	1.0051	1.0116	1.0183		
50	0.9944	1.0008	1.0073	1.0140		
60	0.9895	0.9959	1.0024	1.0091		
70	0.9841	0.9905	0.9970	1.0036		
80	0.9781	0.9845	0.9910	0.9977		
90	0.9716	0.9780	0.9845	0.9912		
100	0.9646	0.9709	0.9774	0.9840		

%	d_4^{15} (46)	%	d_4^{15} (46)	%	d_4^{15} (46)	%	d_4^{15} (46)
1	1.0056	8	1.0518	16	1.1063	24	1.1657
2	1.0122	10	1.0651	18	1.1206		
4	1.0253	12	1.0786	20	1.1352		
6†	1.0385	14	1.0923	22	1.1502		

† Solutions above *ca.* 6 % are supersaturated.

$KClO_4$ [LJG] (602)**; (99)

%	d_4^{15}	%	d_4^{15}	%	d_4^{15}	%	d_4^{15}
0.1	0.9997	0.6	1.0029	1.2	1.0067	1.8	1.0105
0.2	1.0004	0.8	1.0041	1.4	1.0079		
0.4	1.0016	1.0	1.0054	1.6	1.0092		

KCl [JAB] (24, 26, 150), α (364, 367, 370)**; (20, 21, 25, 58, 83, 84, 110, 250, 256), α (219, 256)*; (1, 2, 18, 22, 27, 36, 37, 38, 45, 101, 105, 106, 125, 144, 151, 190, 199, 201, 206, 215, 219, 221, 223, 224, 225, 228, 246, 261, 269, 277, 278, 297, 312, 313, 314, 344, 347, 360, 361, 378, 385, 418, 425, 447, 448, 449, 451, 452, 459, 487, 505, 511, 517, 519, 520, 529, 533, 547, 573, 583, 589, 592, 618, 629, 632, 633, 660), α (37, 38, 151, 159, 211, 271, 448, 606, 609)

%	0°C	10°C	20°C	25°C	30°C	40°C	50°C	60°C	80°C	100°C
1	1.00661	1.00627	1.00463	1.00342	1.00198	0.99847	0.99426	0.9894	0.9780	0.9646
2	1.01335	1.01280	1.01103	1.00977	1.00829	1.00471	1.00046	0.9956	0.9842	0.9708
4	1.02690	1.02595	1.02391	1.02255	1.02099	1.01727	1.01294	1.0080	0.9966	0.9834
6	1.04055	1.03920	1.03690	1.03544	1.03380	1.02995	1.02554	1.0206	1.0092	0.9960
8	1.05431	1.05257	1.05003	1.04847	1.04675	1.04278	1.03829	1.0333	1.0219	1.0088
10	1.06820	1.06609	1.06332	1.06167	1.05987	1.05578	1.05122	1.0461	1.0347	1.0218
12	1.08222	1.07978	1.07679	1.07506	1.07318	1.06897	1.06435	1.0592	1.0478	1.0350
14	1.09638	1.09366	1.09046	1.08865	1.08669	1.08237	1.07770	1.0725	1.0611	1.0483
16	1.11068	1.10775	1.10434	1.10245	1.10041	1.09600	1.09128	1.0861	1.0746	1.0619
18	1.12513	1.12207	1.11845	1.11647	1.11435	1.10987	1.10510	1.0998	1.0884	1.0757
20	1.13973	1.13663	1.13280	1.13072	1.12852	1.12399	1.11917	1.1138	1.1024	1.0897
22	1.15449	1.15144	1.14740	1.14521	1.14294	1.13836	1.13349	1.1281	1.1166	1.1040
24			1.16226	1.15995	1.15762	1.15299	1.14807	1.1425	1.1311	1.1185
26				1.17495	1.17254	1.16788	1.16291	1.1573	1.1458	1.1333
28						1.18304	1.17802	1.1723	1.1609	1.1483

% (373)	$d_4^{20.004}$	% (373)	$d_4^{20.004}$	°C (588)	3.79 %	7.45 %	13.62 %
0.01	0.99829644	0.05	0.99855557	110	0.9733	0.9978	1.0388
0.02	0.99836135	0.06	0.99862004	120	0.9663	0.9899	1.0313
0.03	0.99842620	0.07	0.99868435	130	0.9583	0.9827	1.0238
0.04	0.99849095			140	0.9502	0.9745	1.0159

KBr [JAB] (25, 26), α (367)**; (83, 84, 110, 287, 548), α (203, 375, 609)*; (1, 12, 36, 45, 106, 144, 190, 201, 206, 221, 225, 228, 246, 261, 277, 307, 312, 313, 319, 322, 344, 360, 361, 378, 447, 451, 459, 519, 530, 547, 573, 589, 596, 618), α (151)

°C	1 %	2 %	4 %	6 %	8 %	10 %
0	1.00732	1.01484	1.03016	1.04584	1.06189	1.07833
10	1.00704	1.01442	1.02945	1.04483	1.06058	1.07672
20	1.00542	1.01268	1.02747	1.04261	1.05811	1.07399
25	1.00421	1.01143	1.02612	1.04116	1.05656	1.07235
30	1.00277	1.00995	1.02456	1.03952	1.05484	1.07055
40	0.99928	1.00639	1.02087	1.03570	1.05090	1.06649
50	0.99505	1.00211	1.01648	1.03120	1.04629	1.06176
60	0.9902	0.9972	1.0115	1.0261	1.0411	1.0565
80	0.9787	0.9857	0.9999	1.0145	1.0294	1.0446
100	0.9653	0.9722	0.9863	1.0009	1.0157	1.0309

°C	12 %	14 %	16 %	18 %	20 %	22 %
0	1.09517	1.11243	1.13012	1.14826	1.16687	1.18597
10	1.09327	1.11025	1.12768	1.14558	1.16396	1.18285
20	1.09028	1.10701	1.12420	1.14187	1.16005	1.17876
25	1.08855	1.10518	1.12227	1.13985	1.15794	1.17655
30	1.08667	1.10323	1.12025	1.13775	1.15575	1.17427
40	1.08249	1.09892	1.11580	1.13314	1.15097	1.16931
50	1.07763	1.09392	1.11065	1.12785	1.14554	1.16374
60	1.0724	1.0886	1.1053	1.1224	1.1401	1.1582
80	1.0603	1.0765	1.0930	1.1100	1.1276	1.1456
100	1.0466	1.0627	1.0792	1.0962	1.1136	1.1316

0°C	24 %	26 %	28 %	30 %	35 %	40 %
0	1.20559	1.22576				
10	1.20227	1.22225				
20	1.19802	1.21784	1.23825	1.25927	1.31467	1.37457
25	1.19570	1.21541	1.23570	1.25660	1.31173	1.37149
30	1.19333	1.21294	1.23313	1.25392	1.30887	1.36851
40	1.18819	1.20764	1.22769	1.24838	1.30306	1.36247
50	1.18248	1.20180	1.22173	1.24230	1.29674	1.35593
60	1.1769	1.1961	1.2160	1.2365	1.2907	1.3496
80	1.1641	1.1832	1.2030	1.2233	1.2771	1.3356
100	1.1501	1.1691	1.1888	1.2090	1.2627	1.3211

$KBrO_3$ [JAB] (84, 509, 510), α (206)**; (360, 361) [LJG]

%	0°C	10°C	20°C	25°C	30°C	40°C
1	1.0074	1.0072	1.00562	1.0044	1.0030	0.9996
2	1.0150	1.0148	1.01308	1.0119	1.0104	1.0070
3	1.0227	1.0224	1.02061	1.0194	1.0179	1.0145
4	1.0304	1.0301	1.02821	1.0270	1.0255	1.0221
5	1.0383	1.0379	1.03587	1.0346	1.0332	1.0297

%	50°C	60°C	70°C	80°C	90°C	100°C
1	0.9954	0.9905	0.9851	0.9792	0.9728	0.9658
2	1.0028	0.9979	0.9925	0.9866	0.9803	0.9733
3	1.0103	1.0054	1.0000	0.9941	0.9878	0.9808
4	1.0178	1.0129	1.0075	1.0017	0.9954	0.9885
5	1.0254	1.0205	1.0151	1.0094	1.0031	0.9962

KI, *see* p. 88

KIO_3 [JAB] (548), α (206)**; (84, 287)*; (250, 360, 361, 529, 583) [LJG]

°C	1 %	2 %	3 %	°C	1 %	2 %	3 %
0	1.0082	1.0167	1.0254	50	0.9969	1.0058	1.0148
10	1.0081	1.0166	1.0253	60	0.9921	1.0011	1.0102
18†	1.00711	1.01572	1.02446	70	0.9868	0.9958	1.0050
20	1.0068	1.0155	1.0243	80	0.9808	0.9899	0.9992
25	1.0057	1.0144	1.0232	90	0.9744	0.9835	0.9928
30	1.0043	1.0131	1.0220	100	0.9674	0.9764	0.9856
40	1.0010	1.0098	1.0188				

† d_4^{18} = 1.03334 with 4 %; = 1.04236 with 5%; = 1.05153 with 6 %.

K_2SO_3 [JAB] (602)**; (519) [LJG]

%	d_4^{15}	%	d_4^{15}	%	d_4^{15}	%	d_4^{15}
1	1.0073	8	1.0667	16	1.1402	24	1.2197
2	1.0155	10	1.0844	18	1.1596	26	1.2404
4	1.0322	12	1.1026	20	1.1793		
6	1.0493	14	1.1212	22	1.1993		

K_2SO_4, *see* p. 88

$K_2S_2O_6$ [JAB] (276)**; (529) [LJG]

%..........	1	2	3	4	5	6
d_4^{20}..........	1.00499	1.01179	1.01863	1.02551	1.03244	1.03943

$K_2S_2O_7$ [JAB] (602) [LJG]

%	d_4^{15}	%	d_4^{15}	%	d_4^{15}	%	d_4^{15}
1	1.0067	6	1.0450	12	1.0926	18	1.1421
2	1.0143	8	1.0606	14	1.1089	20	1.1589
4	1.0296	10	1.0765	16	1.1254	22	1.1759

KI [JAB] (26), α (368)**; (25, 83, 84, 110, 250, 287), α (203)*; (1, 2, 12, 27, 36, 45, 57, 101, 106, 190, 201, 206, 221, 223, 224, 225, 228, 246, 261, 269, 277, 307, 312, 315, 319, 322, 342, 344, 360, 361, 378, 447, 517, 519, 530, 533, 547, 550, 573, 583, 589, 596, 618, 660), α (151, 587)

%	0°C	10°C	20°C	25°C	30°C	40°C	50°C	60°C	80°C	100°C
1	1.00742	1.00715	1.00554	1.00434	1.00290	0.99940	0.98522	0.9903	0.9788	0.9653
2	1.01508	1.01468	1.01297	1.01172	1.01024	1.00667	1.00236	0.9975	0.9859	0.9723
4	1.03070	1.03004	1.02811	1.02677	1.02521	1.02151	1.01705	1.0121	1.0003	0.9867
6	1.04675	1.04582	1.04367	1.04223	1.04059	1.03674	1.03216	1.0271	1.0152	1.0014
8	1.06324	1.06204	1.05966	1.05812	1.05640	1.05241	1.04771	1.0425	1.0305	1.0166
10	1.08019	1.07872	1.07610	1.07446	1.07266	1.06853	1.06371	1.0584	1.0462	1.0321
12	1.09762	1.09588	1.09302	1.09128	1.08939	1.08512	1.08018	1.0748	1.0623	1.0482
14	1.11555	1.11354	1.11044	1.10860	1.10662	1.10220	1.09714	1.0916	1.0790	1.0647
16	1.13401	1.13173	1.12839	1.12645	1.12438	1.11980	1.11461	1.1089	1.0961	1.0818
18	1.15303	1.15048	1.14689	1.14485	1.14269	1.13795	1.13262	1.1268	1.1138	1.0993
20	1.17263	1.16981	1.16597	1.16383	1.16158	1.15668	1.15120	1.1453	1.1321	1.1174
22	1.19284	1.18975	1.18566	1.18342	1.18108	1.17601	1.17038	1.1643	1.1509	1.1361
24	1.21369	1.21033	1.20599	1.20365	1.20121	1.19597	1.19019	1.1840	1.1704	1.1554
26	1.23521	1.23158	1.22700	1.22455	1.22201	1.21660	1.21066	1.2044	1.1905	1.1753
28	1.25743	1.25353	1.24872	1.24615	1.24352	1.23794	1.23183	1.2254	1.2113	1.1959
30	1.28037	1.27622	1.27118	1.26849	1.26577	1.26002	1.25373	1.2472	1.2329	1.2173
35	1.34120	1.33641	1.33082	1.32787	1.32490	1.31867	1.31191	1.3050	1.2901	1.2740
40	1.40745	1.40203	1.39590	1.39269	1.38945	1.38272	1.37548	1.3682	1.3527	1.3361
45	1.47992	1.47387	1.46721	1.46374	1.46022	1.45297	1.44524	1.4377	1.4215	1.4044
50	1.55961	1.55294	1.54575	1.54203	1.53822	1.53042	1.52222	1.5143	1.4975	1.4799
55	1.64772	1.64044	1.63272	1.62875	1.62464	1.61627	1.60756	1.5993	1.5818	1.5637

K_2SO_4 [JAB] (250, 603), α (203, 370)**; (20, 21), α (219)*; (1, 11, 22, 36, 101, 106, 144, 147, 151, 155, 184, 190, 206, 219, 221, 223, 224, 225, 246, 261, 297, 312, 342, 344, 360, 361, 374, 378, 385, 405, 415, 422, 425, 432, 449, 451, 505, 517, 519, 529, 573, 585, 598, 615, 618, 629), α (151)

°C	1%	2%	4%	6%	8%	10%
0	1.0084	1.0170	1.0342	1.0516		
10	1.0080	1.0163	1.0331	1.0501	1.0673	
20	1.0063	1.0145	1.0310	1.0477	1.0646	1.0817
25	1.0051	1.0132	1.0296	1.0462	1.0630	1.0800
30	1.0037	1.0117	1.0280	1.0445	1.0612	1.0781
40	1.0001	1.0081	1.0242	1.0406	1.0572	1.0740
50	0.9959	1.0038	1.0198	1.0361	1.0526	1.0693
60	0.9911	0.9989	1.0148	1.0310	1.0475	1.0642
80	0.9796	0.9874	1.0033	1.0195	1.0360	1.0527
100	0.9662	0.9741	0.9901	1.0063	1.0227	1.0393

$K_2S_2O_8$ [JAB] (602) [LJG]; d_4^{15} = 1.0057 with 1%; = 1.0123 with 2%

$K_2S_3O_6$ [JAB] (276) [LJG]

%	d_4^{20}	%	d_4^{20}	%	d_4^{20}	%	d_4^{20}
1	1.00471	4	1.02443	8	1.05144	12	1.07950
2	1.01124	6	1.03782	10	1.06532		

$K_2S_4O_6$ [JAB] (276) [LJG]

%	d_4^{20}	%	d_4^{20}	%	d_4^{20}	%	d_4^{20}
1	1.00445	4	1.02340	8	1.04942	12	1.07648
2	1.01072	6	1.03629	10	1.06281		

$K_2S_5O_6$ [JAB] (276) [LJG]

%	d_4^{20}	%	d_4^{20}	%	d_4^{20}	%	d_4^{20}
1	1.00420	4	1.02236	8	1.04730	12	1.07337
2	1.01021	6	1.03471	10	1.06017	14	1.08694

KHS [JAB] (52) [LJG]

%	d_4^{18}	%	d_4^{18}	%	d_4^{18}	%	d_4^{18}
1	1.0045	10	1.0583	20	1.1196	30	1.1829
2	1.0105	12	1.0704	22	1.1321	35	1.2152
4	1.0224	14	1.0826	24	1.1447	40	1.2479
6	1.0343	16	1.0949	26	1.1574	45	1.2810
8	1.0463	18	1.1072	28	1.1701	50	1.3144

$KHSO_4$ [JAB] (225, 248, 451), α (203)**; (342, 405)*; (432)

°C	1%	2%	4%	6%	8%	10%
0	1.0073	1.0148	1.0299	1.0452	1.0607	1.0764
10	1.0068	1.0139	1.0284	1.0431	1.0581	1.0734
15	1.0061	1.0131	1.0273	1.0418	1.0566	1.0717
20	1.0051	1.0120	1.0260	1.0403	1.0549	1.0698
25	1.0039	1.0107	1.0245	1.0386	1.0530	1.0677
30	1.0024	1.0091	1.0228	1.0367	1.0509	1.0655
40	0.9987	1.0052	1.0185	1.0321	1.0461	1.0605

°C	12%	14%	16%	18%	20%	22%
0	1.0924	1.1086	1.1250			
10	1.0890	1.1048	1.1208			
15†	1.0871	1.1027	1.1185	1.1345	1.1508	1.1673
20	1.0850	1.1004	1.1161			
25	1.0827	1.0980	1.1136			
30	1.0804	1.0956	1.1110			
40	1.0752	1.0902	1.1055			

† d_4^{15} = 1.1841 with 24%; = 1.2012 with 26%.

KOH.KHS [JAB] (52) [LJG]

%	d_4^{18}	%	d_4^{18}	%	d_4^{18}	%	d_4^{18}
1	1.0057	12	1.0863	24	1.1801	45	1.3630
2	1.0129	14	1.1014	26	1.1964	50	1.4106
4	1.0274	16	1.1167	28	1.2130	55	1.4598
6	1.0420	18	1.1323	30	1.2297		
8	1.0564	20	1.1481	35	1.2726		
10	1.0714	22	1.1640	40	1.3170		

KOH.3KHS [JAB] (52) [LJG]

%	d_4^{18}	%	d_4^{18}	%	d_4^{18}	%	d_4^{18}
1	1.0047	10	1.0599	20	1.1224	30	1.1869
2	1.0108	12	1.0723	22	1.1351	35	1.2202
4	1.0230	14	1.0847	24	1.1479	40	1.2544
6	1.0353	16	1.0972	26	1.1608	45	1.2894
8	1.0476	18	1.1098	28	1.1738	50	1.3252

3KOH.KHS [JAB] (52) [LJG]

%	d_4^{18}	%	d_4^{18}	%	d_4^{18}	%	d_4^{18}
1	1.0061	12	1.0894	24	1.1839	45	1.3635
2	1.0136	14	1.1049	26	1.2001	50	1.4107
4	1.0286	16	1.1205	28	1.2165	55	1.4603
6	1.0437	18	1.1362	30	1.2330		
8	1.0588	20	1.1520	35	1.2750		
10	1.0740	22	1.1679	40	1.3184		

K_2SeO_3 [JAB] (602)**; (463) [LJG]

%	d_4^{15}	%	d_4^{15}	%	d_4^{15}	%	d_4^{15}
1	1.007	6	1.051	12	1.106	18	1.166
2	1.016	8	1.069	14	1.125	20	1.187
4	1.034	10	1.088	16	1.145		

K_2SeO_4 [JAB] (602, 614)** [LJG]

%	d_4^{15}	%	d_4^{15}	%	d_4^{15}	%	d_4^{15}
1	1.0073	4	1.0324	8	1.0668	12	1.1026
2	1.0156	6	1.0494	10	1.0845	14	1.1212

%	d_4^{20}	%	d_4^{20}	%	d_4^{20}	%	d_4^{20}
36	1.3620	40	1.4140	44	1.4695	48	1.5283
38	1.3876	42	1.4413	46	1.4985	50	1.5590

$KHSeO_3$ [LJG]; with 5.57 %, d_4^{20} = 1.0415 (463)

K_2TeO_3 [JAB] (602) [LJG]

%	d_4^{15}	%	d_4^{15}	%	d_4^{15}	%	d_4^{15}
1	1.0075	6	1.0514	12	1.1085	18	1.1711
2	1.0160	8	1.0699	14	1.1287	20	1.1932
4	1.0334	10	1.0889	16	1.1496	22	1.2160

KN_3 [LJG] (74)

%	0°C	10°C	20°C	25°C	30°C	40°C
1	1.0059	1.0054	1.0037	1.0026	1.0012	0.9976
2	1.0118	1.0111	1.0093	1.0081	1.0067	1.0031
4	1.0237	1.0226	1.0206	1.0192	1.0177	1.0140
6	1.0358	1.0342	1.0319	1.0304	1.0289	1.0250
8	1.0480	1.0459	1.0434	1.0418	1.0402	1.0361
10	1.0603	1.0578	1.0550	1.0534	1.0516	1.0473
12	1.0727	1.0700	1.0669	1.0651	1.0632	1.0587
14	1.0853	1.0824	1.0790	1.0770	1.0750	1.0702
16	1.0982	1.0949	1.0913	1.0891	1.0869	1.0819
18	1.1113	1.1076	1.1036	1.1014	1.0990	1.0938
20	1.1245	1.1204	1.1161	1.1138	1.1113	1.1059
22	1.1378	1.1334	1.1288	1.1264	1.1238	1.1183
24	1.1512	1.1465	1.1417	1.1391	1.1365	1.1308
26	1.1647	1.1597	1.1547	1.1520	1.1493	1.1435
28	1.1783	1.1731	1.1678	1.1650	1.1622	1.1563
30	1.1919	1.1865	1.1809	1.1781	1.1752	1.1692
32	1.2055	1.1999	1.1941	1.1912	1.1883	1.1822
34	1.2191	1.2133	1.2074	1.2045	1.2015	1.1952

KN_3.—(*Continued*)

%	50°C	60°C	70°C	80°C	90°C	100°C
1	0.9934	0.9885	0.9831	0.9772	0.9708	0.9639
2	0.9987	0.9938	0.9884	0.9826	0.9762	0.9695
4	1.0094	1.0044	0.9991	0.9934	0.9872	0.9806
6	1.0203	1.0152	1.0099	1.0043	0.9982	0.9918
8	1.0313	1.0261	1.0209	1.0153	1.0093	1.0030
10	1.0424	1.0372	1.0319	1.0264	1.0205	1.0143
12	1.0536	1.0484	1.0430	1.0376	1.0318	1.0257
14	1.0651	1.0598	1.0543	1.0489	1.0433	1.0372
16	1.0767	1.0713	1.0658	1.0604	1.0548	1.0488
18	1.0885	1.0831	1.0775	1.0720	1.0664	1.0605
20	1.1006	1.0950	1.0893	1.0838	1.0782	1.0723
22	1.1128	1.1070	1.1012	1.0957	1.0901	1.0842
24	1.1251	1.1192	1.1133	1.1077	1.1020	1.0961
26	1.1376	1.1316	1.1256	1.1198	1.1141	1.1081
28	1.1503	1.1441	1.1379	1.1320	1.1262	1.1203
30	1.1630	1.1566	1.1503	1.1443	1.1384	1.1325
32	1.1758	1.1693	1.1629	1.1567	1.1507	1.1448
34	1.1886	1.1820	1.1755	1.1692	1.1630	1.1572

KNO_2 [JAB] (106, 468)** [LJG]

%	$d_4^{17.5}$	%	$d_4^{17.5}$	%	$d_4^{17.5}$	%	$d_4^{17.5}$
1	1.005	14	1.088	28	1.187	60	1.484
2	1.011	16	1.102	30	1.203	65	1.540
4	1.024	18	1.116	35	1.242	70	1.598
6	1.037	20	1.130	40	1.284	75	1.658
8	1.049	22	1.144	45	1.329		
10	1.062	24	1.158	50	1.378		
12	1.075	26	1.172	55	1.430		

KNO_3, *v. infra*

K_3PO_4 [LJG] (203,† 463)

%	d_4^{20} (463)	%	d_4^{18} (203)
3.54	1.0345	17.98	1.1805

† For α, 0–30°C, 9.7 and 18 %, *v.* (203).

K_2HPO_3 [LJG]; with 3.96 %, d_4^{20} = 1.0308 (463)

KH_2PO_3 [LJG]; with 4.00 %, d_4^{20} = 1.0238 (463)

K_2HPO_4 [LJG]; with 8.23 %, d_4^{15} = 1.0569 (144); with 27.58 %, d_4^{18} = 1.2633 (203). For α at 0–40°C, 8, 15 and 28 %, *v.* (203)

KH_2PO_4, *see* p. 90

K_3AsO_4 [LJG]; with 4.27 %, d_4^{20} = 1.0390 (463)

KH_2AsO_4 [LJG]; with 4.50 %, d_4^{20} = 1.0316 (463)

$KSbO_3$ [JAB]; d_4^{20} = 1.0067 with 1 %; = 1.0152 with 2 % (602) [LJG]

$K_4Sb_2O_7$ [JAB]; d_4^{20} = 1.0068 with 1 %; = 1.0155 with 2 % (602) [LJG]

KNO_3 [JAB] (84, 250, 256, 448, 449, 451, 452), α (256, 370)**; (20), α (203, 211)*; (1, 36, 87, 101, 106, 144, 190, 206, 215, 219, 221, 223, 224, 225, 228, 246, 269, 271, 312, 342, 344, 360, 361, 385, 422, 519, 529, 533, 536, 573, 583, 592, 629, 660), α (151, 605)

%	0°C	10°C	20°C	25°C	30°C	40°C	50°C	60°C	80°C	100°C
1	1.00654	1.00615	1.00447	1.00324	1.00178	0.99825	0.99401	0.9890	0.9776	0.9641
2	1.01326	1.01262	1.01075	1.00946	1.00794	1.00430	0.99999	0.9949	0.9834	0.9699
4	1.02677	1.02566	1.02344	1.02203	1.02038	1.01652	1.01207	1.0068	0.9951	0.9816
6	1.04041	1.03887	1.03632	1.03479	1.03301	1.02892	1.02432	1.0189	1.0070	0.9935
8	1.05419	1.05226	1.04940	1.04775	1.04584	1.04152	1.03676	1.0313	1.0192	1.0056
10	1.06812	1.06584	1.06269	1.06093	1.05889	1.05434	1.04941	1.0439	1.0316	1.0179
12	1.08221	1.07963	1.07620	1.07433	1.07217	1.06740	1.06229	1.0567	1.0442	1.0304
14			1.08994	1.08796	1.08569	1.08072	1.07542	1.0698	1.0571	1.0432
16			1.10392	1.10183	1.09947	1.09432	1.08882	1.0831	1.0703	1.0562
18			1.11814	1.11595	1.11351	1.10821	1.10251	1.0967	1.0837	1.0695
20			1.13261	1.13033	1.12782	1.12240	1.11650	1.1106	1.0974	1.0831
22			1.14734	1.14497	1.14240	1.13691	1.13080	1.1247	1.1113	1.0969
24			1.16233	1.15988	1.15726	1.15175	1.14543	1.1391	1.1256	1.1110

KH_2PO_4 [LJG] (342, 343)**; (203, 451)*; (463), α (203)

%	0°C	10°C	20°C	25°C	30°C	40°C
1	1.0074	1.0070	1.0054	1.0042	1.0027	0.9992
2	1.0148	1.0142	1.0125	1.0112	1.0097	1.0061
4	1.0293	1.0284	1.0264	1.0251	1.0235	1.0198
6	1.0437	1.0425	1.0403	1.0388	1.0372	1.0334
8	1.0581	1.0567	1.0542	1.0527	1.0510	1.0471
10	1.0729	1.0711	1.0685	1.0669	1.0651	1.0611
12	1.0883	1.0863	1.0835	1.0818	1.0799	1.0758
14	1.1051	1.1028	1.0998	1.0981	1.0962	1.0919

K_2CO_3 [JAB] (342, 343), α (219)**; (219)*; (144, 261, 312, 328, 344, 509, 510, 548, 585, 632), α (206, 253, 254) [LJG]

%	0°C	10°C	20°C	25°C	30°C	40°C
1	1.0094	1.0089	1.0072	1.0060	1.0045	1.0010
2	1.0189	1.0182	1.0163	1.0149	1.0134	1.0098
4	1.0381	1.0369	1.0345	1.0330	1.0314	1.0276
6	1.0574	1.0557	1.0529	1.0513	1.0496	1.0457
8	1.0768	1.0746	1.0715	1.0699	1.0681	1.0640
10	1.0963	1.0937	1.0904	1.0887	1.0868	1.0825
12	1.1160	1.1131	1.1096	1.1078	1.1058	1.1013
14	1.1359	1.1329	1.1291	1.1272	1.1251	1.1204
16	1.1562	1.1530	1.1490	1.1470	1.1448	1.1399
18	1.1768	1.1734	1.1692	1.1672	1.1649	1.1598
20	1.1977	1.1941	1.1898	1.1877	1.1853	1.1801
22	1.2189	1.2152	1.2107	1.2085	1.2061	1.2008
24	1.2405	1.2366	1.2320	1.2297	1.2272	1.2219
26	1.2624	1.2583	1.2536	1.2512	1.2487	1.2434
28	1.2846	1.2804	1.2756	1.2731	1.2705	1.2652
30	1.3071	1.3028	1.2979	1.2953	1.2926	1.2873
35	1.3646	1.3600	1.3548	1.3522	1.3494	1.3440
40	1.4244	1.4195	1.4141	1.4114	1.4086	1.4029
45	1.4867	1.4815	1.4759	1.4731	1.4703	1.4644
50	1.5517	1.5462	1.5404	1.5374	1.5347	1.5285

%	50°C	60°C	70°C	80°C	90°C	100°C
1	0.9968	0.9919	0.9864	0.9803	0.9739	0.9670
2	1.0055	1.0005	0.9950	0.9889	0.9825	0.9756
4	1.0231	1.0180	1.0124	1.0063	0.9999	0.9931
6	1.0410	1.0358	1.0301	1.0239	1.0176	1.0110
8	1.0592	1.0538	1.0480	1.0418	1.0355	1.0291
10	1.0776	1.0720	1.0662	1.0600	1.0538	1.0475
12	1.0963	1.0906	1.0847	1.0786	1.0725	1.0663
14	1.1154	1.1096	1.1036	1.0976	1.0916	1.0854
16	1.1349	1.1290	1.1230	1.1170	1.1111	1.1049
18	1.1547	1.1488	1.1428	1.1368	1.1309	1.1248
20	1.1749	1.1690	1.1630	1.1570	1.1512	1.1451
22	1.1955	1.1896	1.1836	1.1776	1.1719	1.1658
24	1.2165	1.2106	1.2046	1.1986	1.1930	1.1869
26	1.2379	1.2320	1.2260	1.2200	1.2144	1.2083
28	1.2596	1.2538	1.2478	1.2418	1.2361	1.2301
30	1.2816	1.2759	1.2700	1.2640	1.2582	1.2522
35	1.3383	1.3324	1.3266	1.3206	1.3148	1.3089
40	1.3972	1.3913	1.3855	1.3795	1.3737	1.3678
45	1.4587	1.4528	1.4468	1.4408	1.4349	1.4290
50	1.5228	1.5169	1.5109	1.5048	1.4988	1.4928

$K_2C_2O_4$, Oxalate [JAB] (632)**; (250)*; (144, 155, 208, 224, 329, 342, 343, 432, 451, 463)

%	d_4^{18}	d_4^{25}	%	d_4^{18}	d_4^{25}	%	d_4^{18}	d_4^{25}
1	1.0061	1.0045	6	1.0441	1.0421	12	1.0912	1.0887
2	1.0136	1.0119	8	1.0596	1.0574	14	1.1072	1.1047
4	1.0288	1.0269	10	1.0753	1.0729			

$KHCO_2$, Formate [JAB]; with 4.21 %, d_4^{20} = 1.0232; with 13.67 %, d_4^{21} = 1.0786 (329, 463)

$KHCO_3$ [JAB] (342, 343), α (206)**; (432)* [LJG]

°C	1 %	2 %	4 %	°C	1 %	2 %	4 %
0	1.0066	1.0134	1.0270	50	0.9949	1.0017	1.0154
10	1.0064	1.0132	1.0268	60	0.9901	0.9969	1.0106
15†	1.0058	1.0125	1.0260	70	0.9847	0.9915	1.0053
20	1.0049	1.0117	1.0252	80	0.9786	0.9855	0.9993
25	1.0038	1.0106	1.0241	90	0.9722	0.9791	0.9929
30	1.0024	1.0092	1.0228	100	0.9653	0.9722	0.9860
40	0.9990	1.0058	1.0195				

† d_4^{15} = 1.0396 with 6 %; = 1.0534 with 8 %; = 1.0674 with 10 %.

KHC_2O_4, Acid oxalate [JAB] (208)

%............	1	2	3	4
$d_4^{17.5}$............	1.0050	1.0112	1.0174	1.0235

$KC_2H_3O_2$, Acetate [LJG] (287, 548, 632)**; (529)*; (18, 144, 211, 222, 223, 224, 342, 343, 344, 362, 451, 463, 561, 660) [JAB]

%	d_4^{18}	d_4^{25}	%	d_4^{18}	d_4^{25}
1	1.0038	1.0022	22	1.1131	1.1104
2	1.0089	1.0072	24	1.1241	1.1213
4	1.0191	1.0173	26	1.1353	1.1324
6	1.0293	1.0274	28	1.1466	1.1436
8	1.0395	1.0375	30	1.1579	1.1549
10	1.0497	1.0476	35	1.1868	1.1835
12	1.0599	1.0577	40	1.2162	1.2127
14	1.0703	1.0680	45	1.2460	1.2423
16	1.0808	1.0784	50	1.2761	1.2723
18	1.0914	1.0889	55	1.3065	1.3026
20	1.1022	1.0996	60	1.3372	1.3330

$KC_2H_3O_3$, Glycolate [JAB]; with 5.71 %, d_4^{20} = 1.0428 (463)

$KC_3H_5O_2$, Propionate [JAB] (291)**; (463)

%	d_4^{18}	%	d_4^{18}	%	d_4^{18}	%	d_4^{18}
1	1.0029	10	1.0425	20	1.0880	30	1.1349
2	1.0073	12	1.0514	22	1.0973	32	1.1443
4	1.0160	14	1.0604	24	1.1067	34	1.1537
6	1.0248	16	1.0695	26	1.1161	36	1.1632
8	1.0336	18	1.0787	28	1.1255	38	1.1727

$KC_3H_5O_3$, Lactate [JAB]; with 6.41 %, d_4^{20} = 1.0331 (463)

$KC_4H_3O_8$, Tetroxalate [JAB]; $d_4^{17.5}$ = 1.0041 with 1 %; =1.0096 with 2 % (208)

$KC_4H_5O_4$, Acid succinate [JAB]; with 5.21 %, d_4^{20} = 1.0246 (463)

$KC_4H_5O_5$, Acid malate [JAB] (463, 546)**

%	d_4^{20}	%	d_4^{20}	%	d_4^{20}	%	d_4^{20}
1	1.0034	8	1.0410	16	1.0865	24	1.1347
2	1.0087	10	1.0521	18	1.0983	26	1.1471
4	1.0193	12	1.0634	20	1.1103		
6	1.0301	14	1.0748	22	1.1224		

$KC_4H_7O_2$, *n*-Butyrate [JAB]; with 6.31 %, d_4^{20} = 1.0223 (463)

$KC_4H_7O_2$, Isobutyrate [JAB]; with 6.31 %, d_4^{20} = 1.0225 (463)

$KC_6H_7O_7$, Dihydrogen citrate [JAB]; with 5.75 %, d_4^{20} = 1.0287 (463)

$K_2C_4H_4O_4$, Succinate [JAB]; with 4.86 %, d_4^{20} = 1.0288 (463)

$K_2C_4H_4O_5$, Malate [JAB] (546)**; (463)

%	d_4^{20}	%	d_4^{20}	%	d_4^{20}	%	d_4^{20}
1	1.0047	12	1.0785	24	1.1662	45	1.338_0
2	1.0112	14	1.0926	26	1.1816	50	1.382_0
4	1.0244	16	1.1069	28	1.1972	55	1.427_0
6	1.0377	18	1.1214	30	1.2130	60	1.473_0
8	1.0511	20	1.1361	35	1.253_0		
10	1.0647	22	1.1510	40	1.295_0		

$K_2C_4H_4O_6$, Tartrate [JAB] (**451, 463, 499, 500**)**; (**221, 222, 223, 329, 330, 432, 571, 632**)

%	d_4^{20}	%	d_4^{20}	%	d_4^{20}	%	d_4^{20}
1	1.0048	10	1.0657	20	1.1387	30	1.2181
2	1.0114	12	1.0798	22	1.1540	35	1.2606
4	1.0248	14	1.0941	24	1.1696	40	1.3051
6	1.0383	16	1.1087	26	1.1855	45	1.3516
8	1.0519	18	1.1236	28	1.2017	50	1.4001

$K_3C_6H_5O_7$, Citrate [JAB] (**632**)**; (**463**)

%	d_4^{18}	d_4^{25}	%	d_4^{18}	d_4^{25}
1	1.0054	1.0037	18	1.1272	1.1247
2	1.0122	1.0104	20	1.1427	1.1400
4	1.0259	1.0239	22	1.1584	1.1556
6	1.0398	1.0377	24	1.1743	1.1714
8	1.0538	1.0517	26	1.1905	1.1875
10	1.0680	1.0659	28	1.2070	1.2039
12	1.0824	1.0803	30	1.2237	1.2206
14	1.0971	1.0949	32	1.2406	1.2375
16	1.1120	1.1097	34	1.2578	1.2547

$KC_2Cl_3O_2$, Trichloroacetate [JAB]; 10.07 %, d_4^{20} = 1.0559 (**463**)
$KC_2H_2ClO_2$, Chloroacetate [JAB]; with 6.63 %, d_4^{20} = 1.0354 (**463**)
$KC_2HCl_2O_2$, Dichloroacetate [JAB]; with 8.35 %, d_4^{20} = 1.0447 (**463**)

$K_2CS_3(K_2SCS_2)$ [JAB] (**143**) [LJG]

%	d_4^{15}	%	d_4^{15}	%	d_4^{15}	%	d_4^{15}
1	1.006	12	1.085	24	1.176	45	1.347
2	1.013	14	1.100	26	1.191	50	1.393
4	1.028	16	1.115	28	1.206	55	1.441
6	1.042	18	1.130	30	1.221	60	1.491
8	1.056	20	1.146	35	1.261	65	1.544
10	1.070	22	1.161	40	1.303	70	1.600

KCH_3SO_4, Methyl sulfate [JAB]; with 45.79 %, $d_4^{13.5}$ = 1.2914 (**155**); with 14.67 %, d_4^{22} = 1.0794 (**329**)
$KC_2H_5SO_4$, Hydroxyethyl sulfonate [JAB]; with 4.11 %, d_4^{25} = 1.0188 (**529**)
$KC_2H_5SO_4$, Ethyl sulfate [JAB]; with 38.60 %, d_4^{12} = 1.2033 (**155**); with 42.82 %, d_4^{13} = 1.2315 (**155**); 15.47 %, d_4^{22} = 1.0737 (**329**)
$KC_6H_5SO_3$, Benzene sulfonate [JAB]; 4.91 %, d_4^{25} = 1.0181 (**529**)
$K_2CH_2S_2O_6$, Methane disulfonate [JAB]; 3.15 %, d_4^{25} = 1.0178 (**529**)

KCN† [JAB] (**378**)** (20°C); (**342, 343, 602**)** (15°C); (**561**) (15°C); **517**** (25°C) [LJG]

%.....	1	2	4	6	8	10
d_4^{15}.....	1.0041	1.0092	1.0194	1.0297	1.0401	1.0506
d_4^{20}.....	1.0035	1.0088	1.0195	1.0301	1.0408	1.0514
d_4^{25}.....	1.0024	1.0078	1.0187	1.0298		

%.....	12	14	16	18		
d_4^{15}.....	1.0612	1.0718	1.0825	1.0931		
d_4^{20}.....	1.0620	1.0727				

† Isotherms are discordant.

KCNO [JAB] (**602**) [LJG]

%	d_4^{15}	%	d_4^{15}	%	d_4^{15}	%	d_4^{15}
1	1.0051	10	1.0603	20	1.1242	30	1.1908
2	1.0111	12	1.0728	22	1.1373	32	1.2046
4	1.0232	14	1.0855	24	1.1505	34	1.2185
6	1.0355	16	1.0983	26	1.1638		
8	1.0479	18	1.1112	28	1.1772		

KCNSe [LJG]; with 32.77 %, d_4^{25} = 1.1514; with 43.55 %, $d_4^{22.1}$ = 1.2455 (**663**)

$KSbOC_4H_4O_6$, Antimonyl tartrate [JAB] (**224**)

%.....	1	2	3	4	5	6
$d_4^{17.5}$...	1.005	1.012	1.019	1.026	1.034	1.042

KCNS [JAB] (**236, 287, 548**)**; (**602, 640**) [LJG]

%	d_4^{18}	%	d_4^{18}	%	d_4^{25}
1	1.0035	16	1.0817	35	1.1899
2	1.0085	18	1.0927	40	1.2200
4	1.0186	20	1.1039	45	1.2517
6	1.0288	22	1.1152	50	1.2849
8	1.0391	24	1.1266	55	1.3195
10	1.0495	26	1.1382	60	1.3554
12	1.0601	28	1.1500	65	1.3925
14	1.0708	30	1.1618	70	1.4307

K_2SiO_3 [JAB] (**602**) [LJG]

%	d_4^{20}	%	d_4^{20}	%	d_4^{20}	%	d_4^{20}
1	1.0072	8	1.0727	16	1.1533	24	1.2411
2	1.0163	10	1.0923	18	1.1745	26	1.2644
4	1.0347	12	1.1123	20	1.1962	28	1.2884
6	1.0535	14	1.1326	22	1.2184		

K_2SnO_3 [LJG]; d_4^{20} = 1.212 with 22.73 %; = 1.379 with 36.53 % (**602**)

$K_2SO_4.PbSO_4$ [JAB] (**75**) [LJG]

%......	0.2	0.4	0.6	0.8
d_4^{22}......	0.99935	1.00092	1.00252	1.00415

$K_2Zn(SO_4)_2$ [GS]; with 10 %, d_4^{15} = 1.0938 (**534**)

K_2CdI_4 [GS] (**249**)**; (**641**)

%	d_4^{18}	%	d_4^{18}	%	d_4^{18}	%	d_4^{18}
2	1.0143	10	1.0808	18	1.1564	35	1.3556
4	1.0303	12	1.0988	20	1.1766	40	1.4280
6	1.0467	14	1.1174	25	1.2310	45	1.5066
8	1.0635	16	1.1366	30	1.2903		

K_2HgI_4 [GS] (**550**)

%............	8	10	12
d_4^{16}............	1.0650	1.0824	1.1003

$2KCl.CuCl_2$ [WCS] (**319, 321**)

%	d_4^{25}?	%	d_4^{25}?	%	d_4^{25}?	%	d_4^{25}?
1	1.0075	6	1.0468	12	1.0968	18	1.1502
2	1.0151	8	1.0633	14	1.1142	20	1.1688
4	1.0306	10	1.0800	16	1.1320		

$K_2SO_4.CuSO_4$ [WCS] (**189, 191, 604**)

%	d_4^{18}	%	d_4^{18}	%	$d_4^{20.2}$
0.755	1.0039	6.874	1.0606	14.31	1.0692

$KAg(CN)_2$[WCS] (**602**) | **$KAu(CN)_2$** [WCS] (**602**)

%	d_4^{15}	%	d_4^{15}	%	d_4^{15}
1	1.0055	6	1.0387	1	1.0068
2	1.0120	8	1.0526	2	1.0145
4	1.0252			4	1.0300

K_2IrCl_6 [WCS]; with 1 % d_4^{20} = 1.005 (**602**)

K_2PtCl_4 [WCS] (**602**)

%...	1	2	4	6	8
d_4^{20}...	1.0057	1.0134	1.0295	1.0460	1.0628

K_2PtCl_6 [WCS]; with 1 %, d_4^{20} = 1.005 (**602**)

K_2PdCl_4 [WCS] (**602**)

%	d_4^{20}	%	d_4^{20}	%	d_4^{20}	%	d_4^{20}
1	1.0050	2	1.0120	4	1.0265	6	1.0415

$KMnO_4$ [JAB] (**509, 510, 602, 603**)**; (**144, 241, 242, 529, 561**) [LJG]

%.....	1	2	3	4	5	6
d_4^{15}.....	1.0060	1.0130	1.0200	1.0271	1.0342	1.0414
d_4^{20}.....	1.0049	1.0117	1.0185	1.0254	1.0324	
d_4^{25}†....	1.0037	1.0104	1.0172	1.0240	1.0309	1.0379

† d_4^{25} = 1.0450 with 7 %; = 1.0457 with 7.1 % (satd. soln.).

$K_2SO_4.Fe_2(SO_4)_3$† [WCS] (188, 208, 225)

%	d_4^{15} (225)	$d_4^{17.5}$	%	d_4^{15} (225)	$d_4^{17.5}$
1	1.0079	1.0082	12	1.1100	1.0930
2	1.0167	1.0179	14	1.1303	1.1100
4	1.0341	1.0336	16	1.1511	1.1293
6	1.0525	1.0473	18	1.1731	
8	1.0711	1.0617	20	1.1960	
10	1.0904	1.0768			

† Discordant data.

$K_3Fe(CN)_6$ [WCS] (291)**; (511)*; (1, 158, 221, 375, 506, 536, 629)

%	d_4^{15}	d_4^{20}	d_4^{25}
1	1.0047	1.0034	1.0024
2	1.0101	1.0090	1.0078
4	1.0212	1.0201	1.0188
6	1.0325	1.0314	1.0300
8	1.0438	1.0427	1.0413
10	1.0556	1.0542	1.0526
12	1.0671	1.0656	1.0641
14	1.0789	1.0774	1.0756
16	1.0910	1.0890	1.0870
18	1.1030	1.1010	1.0990
20	1.1150	1.1130	1.1110

$K_4Fe(CN)_6$ [WCS] (291)**; (511, 536)*; (158, 221, 266, 506, 629)

%	d_4^{15}	d_4^{20}	d_4^{25}
1	1.0058	1.0051	1.0039
2	1.0125	1.0119	1.0106
4	1.0264	1.0256	1.0242
6	1.0404	1.0395	1.0376
8	1.0545	1.0536	1.0514
10	1.0687	1.0678	1.0653
12	1.0835	1.0823	1.0795
14	1.0985	1.0971	1.0942
16	1.1139	1.1120	1.1089

K_2CrO_4 [JAB] (548, 602)**; (287)*; (101, 138, 144, 206, 360, 361, 463, 533, 561, 566, 629) [LJG]

%	d_4^{15}	d_4^{18}	%	d_4^{18}
1	1.0073	1.0066	16	1.1366
2	1.0155	1.0147	18	1.1555
4	1.0321	1.0311	20	1.1748
6	1.0489	1.0477	22	1.1945
8	1.0659	1.0647	24	1.2147
10	1.0832	1.0821	26	1.2354
12	1.1009	1.0999	28	1.2566
14		1.1181	30	1.2784

$K_2Cr_2O_7$ [JAB] (184, 291, 360, 509, 510)**; (361)*; (138, 144, 205, 206, 328, 463, 561, 566) [LJG]

%	1	2	4	6	8	10
d_4^{10}	1.0069	1.0141	1.0287	1.0435	1.0585	1.0738
d_4^{18}	1.0054	1.0124	1.0266	1.0412	1.0561	
d_4^{20}†	1.0052	1.0122	1.0264	1.0408	1.0554	1.0703

† With 12 %, d_4^{20} = 1.0855.

$K_2SO_4.Cr_2(SO_4)_3$ [JAB] (225)**; (187, 188) [LJG]

%	d_4^{15}	%	d_4^{15}	%	d_4^{15}	%	d_4^{15}
"Violet"		"Green"		"Green"		"Green"	
1	1.0086	1	1.007	14	1.129	28	1.289
2	1.0182	2	1.016	16	1.150	30	1.315
4	1.0376	4	1.034	18	1.171	35	1.383
6	1.0573	6	1.052	20	1.193	40	1.456
8	1.0773	8	1.070	22	1.216	45	1.533
		10	1.089	24	1.239	50	1.615
		12	1.109	26	1.263		

K_2MoO_4 [JAB] (602) [LJG]

%	d_4^{15}	%	d_4^{15}	%	d_4^{15}	%	d_4^{15}
1	1.0071	6	1.0484	10	1.0834	14	1.1200
2	1.0152	8	1.0657	12	1.1015	16	1.1389
4	1.0316						

$2K_2O.SiO_2.12MoO_3$ [LJG] (13)

%	d_4^{10}	d_4^{20}	%	d_4^{10}	d_4^{20}
1	1.0074	1.0058	10	1.0845	1.0822
2	1.0152	1.0135	12	1.1034	1.1009
4	1.0315	1.0297	14	1.1228	1.1202
6	1.0486	1.0466	16	1.1429	1.1401
8	1.0663	1.0641			

K_2WO_4 [LJG] (602)

%	d_4^{15}	%	d_4^{15}	%	d_4^{15}	%	d_4^{15}
1	1.0077	6	1.0523	12	1.1105	18	1.1750
2	1.0164	8	1.0711	14	1.1312		
4	1.0341	10	1.0905	16	1.1527		

KVO_3 [LJG] (602)

%	d_4^{20}	%	d_4^{20}	%	d_4^{20}	%	d_4^{20}
0.5	1.00186	2	1.0128	4	1.0277	6	1.0430
1	1.0055	3	1.0202	5	1.0353	7	1.0508

$K_2SO_4.Al_2(SO_4)_3$ [JAB] (225, 342, 343, 404, 406, 509)**; (510)*; (46, 144, 205, 206, 223, 378) [LJG]

%	d_4^{15}	d_4^{20}	%	d_4^{15}	d_4^{20}
1	1.0086	1.0078	5	1.0476	1.0469
2	1.0182	1.0175	6	1.0577	1.0569
3	1.0279	1.0272	7	1.0679	
4	1.0377	1.0370			

$K_2Mg(SO_4)_2$ [GS]; with 15.4 %, d_4^{14} = 1.1457 (536, 537)

$KNaC_4H_4O_6$, Tartrate [LJG] (221, 650)**; (222, 223, 432, 451)*; (509) [JAB]

%	20°C	25°C	30°C	40°C	50°C	60°C
1	1.0049	1.0037	1.0022	0.9987	0.9945	0.9897
2	1.0116	1.0103	1.0088	1.0053	1.0010	0.9961
4	1.0252	1.0238	1.0222	1.0186	1.0142	1.0092
6	1.0390	1.0375	1.0358	1.0322	1.0276	1.0225
8	1.0530	1.0514	1.0496	1.0459	1.0413	1.0360
10	1.0673	1.0656	1.0637	1.0599	1.0552	1.0498
12	1.0818	1.0800	1.0781	1.0741	1.0693	1.0638
14	1.0965	1.0946	1.0926	1.0885	1.0836	1.0780
16	1.1114	1.1094	1.1073	1.1031	1.0981	1.0925
18	1.1265	1.1244	1.1222	1.1180	1.1128	1.1072
20	1.1419	1.1397	1.1374	1.1331	1.1278	1.1221
22	1.1576	1.1552	1.1529	1.1485	1.1431	1.1373
24	1.1735	1.1710	1.1687	1.1641	1.1586	1.1527
26	1.1896	1.1870	1.1847	1.1799	1.1743	1.1683
28	1.2059	1.2033	1.2009	1.1959	1.1902	1.1841
30	1.2225	1.2198	1.2173	1.2121	1.2064	1.2002
32	1.2394	1.2366	1.2340	1.2286	1.2229	1.2166
34	1.2566	1.2537	1.2510	1.2454	1.2397	1.2333
36	1.2742	1.2712	1.2684	1.2626	1.2568	1.2503

RbOH [JAB] (212, 290)**

%	d_4^{18}	d_4^{25}	%	d_4^{18}
1	1.0080	1.0065	16	1.1665
2	1.0174	1.0158	18	1.1905
4	1.0368	1.0346	20	1.2152
6	1.0568	1.0535	22	1.2407
8	1.0774	1.0725	24	1.2670
10	1.0987	1.0916	26	1.2941
12	1.1206		28	1.3220
14	1.1432			

RbF [JAB] (291)

%	d_4^{18}	%	d_4^{18}	%	d_4^{18}	%	d_4^{18}
1	1.0074	10	1.0920	20	1.2000	30	1.3259
2	1.0163	12	1.1123	22	1.2236	32	1.3535
4	1.0345	14	1.1332	24	1.2479		
6	1.0532	16	1.1548	26	1.2731		
8	1.0723	18	1.1771	28	1.2991		

RbCl [JAB] (26)**; (83, 84, 111, 256, 287, 288, 548), α (256)*; (45, 125, 206, 224, 378, 487, 629), α (607, 609)

%	0°C	10°C	20°C	25°C	30°C	40°C	50°C
1	1.00749	1.00722	1.00561	1.00441	1.00298	0.99950	0.99528
2	1.01519	1.01478	1.01307	1.01183	1.01036	1.00683	1.00257
4	1.03085	1.03017	1.02825	1.02693	1.02539	1.02176	1.01741
6	1.04686	1.04592	1.04379	1.04239	1.04078	1.03704	1.03260
8	1.06324	1.06205	1.05971	1.05823	1.05655	1.05269	1.04816
10	1.08002	1.07859	1.07604	1.07448	1.07273	1.06874	1.06412
12	1.09723	1.09556	1.09281	1.09117	1.08935	1.08522	1.08051
14	1.11488	1.11299	1.11004	1.10832	1.10643	1.10216	1.09736
16	1.13299	1.13090	1.12775	1.12595	1.12399	1.11959	1.11469
18	1.15158	1.14931	1.14596	1.14408	1.14205	1.13753	1.13252
20	1.17067	1.16824	1.16469	1.16273	1.16063	1.15600	1.15088
22	1.19030	1.18771	1.18396	1.18192	1.17975	1.17502	1.16979
24	1.21049	1.20774	1.20379	1.20167	1.19943	1.19461	1.18927
26	1.23127	1.22836	1.22421	1.22201	1.21970	1.21479	1.20934
28	1.25268	1.24959	1.24524	1.24296	1.24058	1.23558	1.23002
30	1.27475	1.27145	1.26691	1.26455	1.26210	1.25701	1.25134
35			1.32407	1.32151	1.31891	1.31354	1.30763
40			1.38599	1.38318	1.38041	1.37476	1.36861
45			1.45330	1.45018	1.44721	1.44127	1.43489
50			1.52675	1.52325	1.52005	1.51381	1.50720

$RbClO_3$ [JAB] (84) [LJG]

%	1	2	3	4
$d_4^{19.5}$	1.00530	1.01224	1.01915	1.02602

RbBr [JAB] (26)**; (83, 84, 111, 288)*; (378)

%	0°C	10°C	20°C	25°C	30°C	40°C	50°C
1	1.00776	1.00751	1.00593	1.00473	1.00329	0.99981	0.99559
2	1.01574	1.01539	1.01372	1.01248	1.01101	1.00747	1.00321
4	1.03207	1.03150	1.02965	1.02833	1.02679	1.02314	1.01878
6	1.04887	1.04808	1.04604	1.04464	1.04303	1.03927	1.03480
8	1.06616	1.06515	1.06291	1.06143	1.05975	1.05588	1.05129
10	1.08396	1.08272	1.08028	1.07872	1.07697	1.07298	1.06827
12	1.10229	1.10082	1.09817	1.09653	1.09471	1.09059	1.08576
14	1.12118	1.11947	1.11661	1.11489	1.11300	1.10874	1.10379
16	1.14065	1.13870	1.13563	1.13383	1.13186	1.12746	1.12239
18	1.16073	1.15854	1.15526	1.15338	1.15132	1.14678	1.14159
20	1.18145	1.17902	1.17554	1.17357	1.17142	1.16674	1.16143
22	1.20285	1.20018	1.19650	1.19443	1.19219	1.18737	1.18194
24	1.22497	1.22206	1.21817	1.21600	1.21367	1.20871	1.20315
26	1.24784	1.24470	1.24059	1.23832	1.23590	1.23080	1.22510
28	1.27150	1.26814	1.26380	1.26143	1.25892	1.25367	1.24783
30	1.29599	1.29241	1.28784	1.28536	1.28277	1.27735	1.27138
35	1.36125	1.35705	1.35191	1.34917	1.34634	1.34051	1.33416
40		1.42830	1.42233	1.41924	1.41616	1.40991	1.40319
45		1.50712	1.50010	1.49654	1.49321	1.48653	1.47945
50			1.58639	1.58222	1.57863	1.57151	1.56408
55			1.68254	1.67758	1.67372	1.66615	1.65838

$RbBrO_3$ [JAB] (84) [LJG]

%	0.5	1.0	1.5
$d_4^{19.5}$	1.00220	1.00609	1.01001

RbI [JAB] (26)**; (83, 84, 111, 288, 548)*; (229)

%	0°C	10°C	20°C	25°C	30°C	40°C	50°C
1	1.00776	1.00751	1.00591	1.00471	1.00327	0.99978	0.99555
2	1.01576	1.01540	1.01370	1.01246	1.01099	1.00744	1.00315
4	1.03210	1.03153	1.02963	1.02831	1.02677	1.02309	1.01868
6	1.04892	1.04814	1.04604	1.04464	1.04303	1.03922	1.03469
8	1.06624	1.06525	1.06296	1.06147	1.05979	1.05585	1.05120
10	1.08409	1.08289	1.08041	1.07883	1.07708	1.07300	1.06823
12	1.10250	1.10109	1.09842	1.09675	1.09492	1.09070	1.08580
14	1.12150	1.11988	1.11701	1.11525	1.11333	1.10898	1.10394
16	1.14112	1.13929	1.13621	1.13436	1.13235	1.12787	1.12268
18	1.16140	1.15935	1.15605	1.15411	1.15201	1.14739	1.14204
20	1.18237	1.18010	1.17657	1.17453	1.17234	1.16757	1.16206
22	1.20406	1.20157	1.19781	1.19566	1.19338	1.18844	1.18278
24	1.22651	1.22379	1.21980	1.21754	1.21516	1.21004	1.20424
26	1.24975	1.24680	1.24257	1.24020	1.23772	1.23241	1.22647
28	1.27382	1.27063	1.26616	1.26368	1.26110	1.25559	1.24951
30	1.29876	1.29532	1.29061	1.28801	1.28534	1.27962	1.27340
35	1.36537	1.36131	1.35598	1.35307	1.35014	1.34389	1.33729
40	1.43873	1.43403	1.42806	1.42481	1.42158	1.41480	1.40776
45	1.51993	1.51456	1.50792	1.50428	1.50075	1.49337	1.48582
50	1.61033	1.60426	1.59691	1.59281	1.58898	1.58091	1.57276
55	1.71156	1.70476	1.69667	1.69203	1.68790	1.67904	1.67017
60			1.80924				1.78004
65			1.93722				1.90492

$RbIO_3$ [JAB] (84) [LJG]

%	0.5	1.0	1.5
$d_4^{19.5}$	1.0025	1.0068	1.0111

Rb_2SO_4 [JAB] (111, 288, 616)**; (615)

%	0°C	10°C	20°C	25°C	30°C	40°C	50°C
1	1.0086	1.0082	1.0066	1.0054	1.0039	1.0003	0.9961
2	1.0173	1.0168	1.0150	1.0138	1.0122	1.0085	1.0041
4	1.0350	1.0343	1.0322	1.0309	1.0292	1.0253	1.0208
6	1.0530	1.0521	1.0499	1.0485	1.0467	1.0426	1.0382
8	1.0714	1.0703	1.0680	1.0664	1.0646	1.0603	1.0560
10	1.0903	1.0889	1.0864	1.0848	1.0829	1.0786	1.0743
12	1.1096	1.1080	1.1052	1.1036	1.1016	1.0972	1.0931
14	1.1294	1.1276	1.1246	1.1229	1.1209	1.1165	1.1123
16	1.1498	1.1477	1.1446	1.1428	1.1407	1.1364	1.1321
18	1.1708	1.1685	1.1652	1.1633	1.1611	1.1568	1.1525
20	1.1926	1.1900	1.1864	1.1844	1.1822	1.1779	1.1735
22	1.2151	1.2121	1.2083	1.2062	1.2040	1.1996	1.1951
24		1.2349	1.2309	1.2287	1.2265		
26		1.2583	1.2542	1.2519	1.2498		
28		1.2824	1.2782	1.2759	1.2739		
30		1.3071	1.3028	1.3006	1.2985		
32		1.3325	1.3281	1.3260	1.3238		

Rb_2SeO_4 [LJG]; d_4^{20} = 1.4688 with 40.60%; = 1.5806 with 47.07% (614)

$RbNO_3$ [JAB] (84, 111, 288)**; (45, 76)

%	0°C	10°C	20°C	25°C	30°C
1	1.0073	1.0070	1.0053	1.0042	1.0027
2	1.0147	1.0143	1.0125	1.0113	1.0098
4	1.0298	1.0292	1.0272	1.0258	1.0242
6	1.0452	1.0444	1.0422	1.0407	1.0389
8	1.0610	1.0600	1.0575	1.0559	1.0540
10	1.0772	1.0760	1.0731	1.0715	1.0695
12	1.0938	1.0923	1.0892	1.0875	1.0854
14	1.1109	1.1090	1.1057	1.1040	1.1018
16	1.1284	1.1261	1.1227	1.1209	1.1187
18	1.1464	1.1437	1.1401	1.1382	1.1360
20	1.1649	1.1618	1.1580	1.1560	1.1537
22	1.1839	1.1804	1.1763	1.1742	1.1718

$RbNO_3$.—(*Continued*)

%	0°C	10°C	20°C	25°C	30°C
24	1.2033	1.1995	1.1952	1.1929	1.1903
26			1.2146	1.2121	1.2093
28			1.2346	1.2319	1.2289
30			1.2552	1.2523	1.2490
32			1.2764	1.2732	1.2697

Values for 13.395 % (**256**)

d_4^0	d_4^{10}	d_4^{20}†	d_4^{25}	d_4^{30}	d_4^{40}	d_4^{50}
1.10632	1.10404	1.10084	1.09898	1.09689	1.09222	1.08699

† With 7.023 %, d_4^{20} = 1.04989.

$RbCHO_2$, Formate; [JAB] with 7.60 %, $d_4^{20.0}$ = 1.0494 (**329**)

$Rb_2C_4H_4O_6$, Tartrate [JAB] (**498, 516**)**

%	d_4^{20}	%	d_4^{20}	%	d_4^{20}	%	d_4^{20}
1	1.0056	12	1.0907	24	1.1989	45	1.4380
2	1.0130	14	1.1074	26	1.2188	50	1.5070
4	1.0280	16	1.1247	28	1.2393	55	1.5810
6	1.0432	18	1.1425	30	1.2605	60	1.6610
8	1.0587	20	1.1608	35	1.3150	65	1.7470
10	1.0745	22	1.1796	40	1.3740		

$Rb_2SO_4.Al_2(SO_4)_3$ [JAB]; with 0.32 % d_4^0 = 1.0025 (**206**) [LJG]

CsCl [JAB] (**26**)**; (**83, 84, 110, 256, 287, 548**), α (**256**)*; (**45, 206, 261, 487, 507, 508, 629**)

%	0°C	10°C	20°C	25°C	30°C	40°C
1	1.00774	1.00751	1.00593	1.00473	1.00330	0.99982
2	1.01573	1.01540	1.01374	1.01251	1.01105	1.00752
4	1.03204	1.03151	1.02969	1.02839	1.02687	1.02324
6	1.04881	1.04808	1.04609	1.04472	1.04314	1.03941
8	1.06607	1.06514	1.06297	1.06153	1.05988	1.05605
10	1.08384	1.08271	1.08036	1.07884	1.07712	1.07319
12	1.10214	1.10082	1.09828	1.09668	1.09489	1.09085
14	1.12100	1.11949	1.11676	1.11507	1.11321	1.10906
16	1.14044	1.13874	1.13582	1.13404	1.13211	1.12785
18	1.16049	1.15860	1.15549	1.15362	1.15162	1.14724
20	1.18118	1.17910	1.17580	1.17385	1.17178	1.16727
22	1.20255	1.20028	1.19679	1.19476	1.19262	1.18798
24	1.22463	1.22218	1.21849	1.21638	1.21417	1.20940
26	1.24746	1.24482	1.24093	1.23874	1.23645	1.23156
28	1.27108	1.26824	1.26414	1.26187	1.25950	1.25450
30	1.29553	1.29248	1.28817	1.28581	1.28337	1.27826
35	1.36061	1.35699	1.35218	1.34960	1.34695	1.34149
40	1.43198	1.42777	1.42245	1.41964	1.41677	1.41094
45	1.51059	1.50578	1.49993	1.49688	1.49378	1.48755
50	1.59757	1.59215	1.58575	1.58245	1.57910	1.57244
55	1.69466	1.68842	1.68137	1.67776	1.67413	1.66701
60	1.80353	1.79644	1.78859	1.78460	1.78066	1.77304
65			1.90966	1.90523	1.90097	1.89278

%	50°C	60°C	80°C	%	50°C	60°C	80°C
1	0.99561	0.9908	0.9793	24	1.20416	1.1985	1.1853
2	1.00327	0.9984	0.9869	26	1.22621	1.2205	1.2071
4	1.01891	1.0140	1.0023	28	1.24904	1.2432	1.2297
6	1.03500	1.0300	1.0182	30	1.27269	1.2667	1.2531
8	1.05156	1.0465	1.0346	35	1.33566	1.3295	1.3154
10	1.06861	1.0635	1.0514	40	1.40483	1.3984	1.3838
12	1.08618	1.0810	1.0688	45	1.48113	1.4744	1.4593
14	1.10430	1.0991	1.0867	50	1.56567	1.5586	1.5429
16	1.12300	1.1177	1.1051	55†	1.65984	1.6524	1.6361
18	1.14230	1.1369	1.1242	60	1.76541	1.7576	1.7406
20	1.16224	1.1568	1.1439	65	1.88462	1.8763	1.8585
22	1.18285	1.1773	1.1643				

† d_4^{100} = 1.616 with 55%; = 1.717 with 60 %; = 1.832 with 65%; = 1.968 with 70 %.

$Rb_2SO_4.Fe_2(SO_4)_3$ [WCS] (**378**)

%	1	2	4	6
d_4^{20}	1.0070	1.0155	1.0335	1.0518

$CsClO_3$ [JAB] (**84**) [LJG]

%	1	2	3	4	5
$d_4^{19.5}$	1.00573	1.01322	1.02082	1.02851	1.03629

CsBr [JAB] (**26**)**; (**83, 84, 291**)*

%	0°C	10°C	20°C	25°C	30°C	40°C
1	1.00792	1.00769	1.00612	1.00492	1.00349	1.00001
2	1.01608	1.01577	1.01412	1.01289	1.01143	1.00790
4	1.03277	1.03228	1.03048	1.02918	1.02766	1.02403
6	1.04996	1.04929	1.04734	1.04597	1.04439	1.04065
8	1.06768	1.06683	1.06472	1.06328	1.06164	1.05779
10	1.08596	1.08493	1.08265	1.08114	1.07943	1.07547
12	1.10483	1.10362	1.10116	1.09958	1.09779	1.09372
14	1.12432	1.12293	1.12029	1.11863	1.11676	1.11257
16	1.14447	1.14289	1.14007	1.13832	1.13637	1.13206
18	1.16531	1.16354	1.16053	1.15869	1.15666	1.15222
20	1.18688	1.18491	1.18170	1.17978	1.17767	1.17309
22	1.20922	1.20704	1.20362	1.20162	1.19944	1.19471
24	1.23238	1.22998	1.22634	1.22425	1.22200	1.21712
26	1.25639	1.25377	1.24990	1.24772	1.24539	1.24037
28	1.28129	1.27844	1.27435	1.27208	1.26966	1.26450
30	1.30712	1.30404	1.29973	1.29737	1.29486	1.28954
35	1.37619	1.37251	1.36764	1.36503	1.36230	1.35658
40	1.45248	1.44819	1.44275	1.43986	1.43689	1.43074
45	1.53717	1.53227	1.52626	1.52305	1.51981	1.51317
50			1.61970	1.61610	1.61253	1.60531
55			1.72492	1.72081	1.71679	1.70888

%	50°C	60°C	80°C	%	50°C	60°C	80°C
1	0.99580	0.9909	0.9794	22	1.18940	1.1836	1.1703
2	1.00364	0.9987	0.9872	24	1.21170	1.2058	1.1923
4	1.01968	1.0147	1.0029	26	1.23483	1.2288	1.2151
6	1.03621	1.0311	1.0192	28	1.25883	1.2526	1.2387
8	1.05325	1.0481	1.0360	30	1.28373	1.2774	1.2633
10	1.07083	1.0656	1.0533	35	1.35039	1.3438	1.3290
12	1.08898	1.0836	1.0712	40	1.42414	1.4171	1.4018
14	1.10772	1.1023	1.0897	45	1.50613	1.4987	1.4827
16	1.12709	1.1216	1.1088	50	1.59780	1.5899	1.5731
18	1.14713	1.1416	1.1286	55	1.70088	1.6925	1.6749
20	1.16789	1.1622	1.1491				

$CsBrO_3$ [JAB] (**84**) [LJG]

%	0.5	1.0	1.5
$d_4^{19.5}$	1.00225	1.00621	1.01022

CsI [JAB] (**26**)**; (**83, 84**)*

%	0°C	10°C	20°C	25°C	30°C	40°C
1	1.00787	1.00765	1.00608	1.00487	1.00344	0.99996
2	1.01598	1.01568	1.01402	1.01279	1.01133	1.00779
4	1.03258	1.03212	1.03029	1.02899	1.02747	1.02382
6	1.04970	1.04907	1.04707	1.04570	1.04411	1.04035
8	1.06737	1.06655	1.06438	1.06294	1.06128	1.05740
10	1.08561	1.08459	1.08225	1.08074	1.07901	1.07500
12	1.10445	1.10323	1.10071	1.09912	1.09732	1.09318
14	1.12392	1.12250	1.11979	1.11811	1.11624	1.11196
16	1.14406	1.14244	1.13953	1.13775	1.13580	1.13138
18	1.16490	1.16308	1.15996	1.15808	1.15604	1.15148
20	1.18648	1.18446	1.18112	1.17915	1.17701	1.17230
22	1.20884	1.20661	1.20305	1.20099	1.19875	1.19388
24	1.23203	1.22958	1.22580	1.22364	1.22131	1.21627
26	1.25609	1.25342	1.24942	1.24715	1.24473	1.23952
28	1.28107	1.27817	1.27395	1.27157	1.26906	1.26368
30	1.30701	1.30388	1.29944	1.29694	1.29434	1.28878

CsI.—(*Continued*)

%	0°C	10°C	20°C	25°C	30°C	40°C
35			1.36776	1.36497	1.36203	1.35593
40			1.44354	1.44044	1.43711	1.43037
45			1.52803	1.52460	1.52082	1.51332
50			1.62278	1.61900	1.61470	1.60627

%	50°C	60°C	80°C	%	50°C	60°C	80°C
1	0.99573	0.9909	0.9794	20	1.16702	1.1611	1.1475
2	1.00351	0.9986	0.9870	22	1.18847	1.1825	1.1686
4	1.01943	1.0144	1.0026	24	1.21071	1.2046	1.1904
6	1.03585	1.0307	1.0187	26	1.23379	1.2275	1.2131
8	1.05279	1.0476	1.0353	28	1.25776	1.2513	1.2367
10	1.07028	1.0650	1.0525	30	1.28267	1.2761	1.2612
12	1.08835	1.0829	1.0702	35	1.34938	1.3424	1.3269
14	1.10702	1.1015	1.0885	40	1.42329	1.4159	1.3996
16	1.12633	1.1207	1.1075	45	1.50560	1.4976	1.4806
18	1.14632	1.1406	1.1271	50	1.59778	1.5892	1.5714

$CsIO_3$ [JAB] (**84**) [LJG]

%.....	0.5	1.0	1.5	2.0
$d_4^{19.5}$.....	1.0025	1.0068	1.0112	1.0156

Cs_2SO_4 [JAB] (**616**)**; (**615**)

%	10°C	20°C	25°C	30°C	40°C	50°C
1	1.0080	1.0061	1.0050	1.0038	1.0006	0.9962
2	1.0164	1.0144	1.0132	1.0119	1.0087	1.0046
4	1.0338	1.0316	1.0304	1.0291	1.0259	1.0220
6	1.0517	1.0494	1.0480	1.0464	1.0431	1.0396
8	1.0703	1.0676	1.0661	1.0645	1.0613	1.0576
10	1.0897	1.0870	1.0856	1.0841	1.0807	1.0770
12	1.1099	1.1071	1.1056	1.1041	1.1009	1.0973
14	1.1305	1.1275	1.1260	1.1245	1.1212	1.1177
16	1.1514	1.1484	1.1469	1.1453	1.1419	1.1383
18	1.1728	1.1696	1.1680	1.1663	1.1628	1.1592
20	1.1944	1.1913	1.1897	1.1880	1.1842	1.1800
22	1.2167	1.2137	1.2122	1.2105	1.2065	1.2017
24	1.2408	1.2375	1.2359	1.2341	1.2302	1.2252
26	1.2681	1.2643	1.2623	1.2602	1.2561	1.2513

Cs_2SeO_4 [LJG]; d_4^{20} = 1.5841 with 45.94 %; = 1.7432 with 53.43 % (**614**)

$CsNO_3$ [JAB] (**84, 291, 420**)**; (**45, 76, 633**)

%	0°C	10°C	20°C	25°C	17.076 % °C	(**256**)† d_4^t
1	1.00759	1.00727	1.00566	1.00445		
2	1.01539	1.01492	1.01319	1.01194	20	1.14091
4	1.03128	1.03055	1.02859	1.02725	30	1.13681
6	1.04755	1.04661	1.04443	1.04299	40	1.13191
8	1.06422	1.06313	1.06072	1.05918	50	1.12652
10		1.08013	1.07745	1.07584		
12		1.09761	1.09463	1.09298		
14			1.11227	1.11062		

† d_4^{20} = 1.07001 with 9.104 % (**256**).

$CsCHO_2$, Formate [JAB]; with 2.73 %, $d_4^{21.0}$ = 1.0169 (**329**)

SYSTEMS CONTAINING MORE THAN ONE SOLUTE[1]

Contents

[1] This section was compiled by Ralph F. Tefft under the direction of the Special Editor.

Abbreviations and Symbols

% Wt. %.
g Grams per liter.
Mol % Formula weights per 100 formula wts. of mixture.
Vol. % cm^3 per 100 cm^3.
M g-equivalents/kg of solution.
m g-equivalents/kg of solvent.
N g-equivalents/liter of solution.
satd. Saturated solution.
? Doubtful.

In most cases no concentration is indicated for isolated points.

A-B TABLE, STANDARD ARRANGEMENT (*v.* p. viii)

Two Solutes

H_2O

C	*t*, °C	Concn. range B	Concn. range C	Lit.
		B = **HCl**		
H_2SO_4	15			(**144**)
	17	0–43 %	0–90 %	(**126**)
	40	0–36 %	4–84 %	(**126**)
	70	0–33 %	2–84 %	(**126**)
HNO_3	?	4–10 %	17–40 %	(**257**)
NH_4Cl	0	0–6 *N*	satd.	(**172, 177**)
	20			(**463**)
$(NH_4)_2SO_4$	20			(**462, 466**)
$SbCl_3$	?	?	270–2160 g	(**27**)
$BiCl_3$	?	?	330–1300 g	(**27**)
$BiOCl$	25	0.35–6.1 *m* in Cl	satd.	(**456**)
$SnCl_2$	0	0–7.8 *N*	satd.	(**178**)
$SnCl_4$	28			(**178**)
$PbCl_2$	0	0–11.2 *N*	satd.	(**178**)
$ZnCl_2$	20			(**462, 466**)
$ZnSO_4$	20			(**462, 466**)
$CdCl_2$	25	0.12–1 *N*	0.12–1 *N*	(**328**)
$HgCl_2$	0	0–7.1 *N*	satd.	(**178**)
	20			(**378**)
	25	0.12–1 *N*	0.12–1 *N*	(**328**)
	25			(**659**)
$CuCl_2$	0	0–34 Mol %	23–49 Mol %	(**105**)
	0	0–12.8 *N*	satd.	(**178**)
	18			(**604**)
	20			(**462, 466**)
	25			(**659**)
Cu_2Cl_2	0	0.9–6 *N*	satd.	(**178**)
$CuSO_4$	20			(**462, 466**)
$MnCl_2$	12			(**506**)
$FeCl_3$	25	0.12–1 *N*	0.12–1 *N*	(**328**)
$CoCl_2$	0	0–13.9 *N*	satd.	(**178**)
	20	0–10.6 *N*	constant (not given)	(**305**)
	25			(**659**)
$U(SO_4)_2$	16–18	*d* = 1.046	1–5 %	(**119, 121**)
$PrCl_3$	16			(**413**)
$MgCl_2$	?	?	satd.	(**174**)
	0	0–7.6 *N*	satd.	(**177**)
	20			(**462, 466**)
$MgSO_4$	20			(**462, 466**)
$CaCl_2$	?	?	satd.	(**174**)
	0	0–9.5 *N*	satd.	(**177**)
$SrCl_2$	0	0–2.3 *N*	satd.	(**172**)
	0	0–5.3 *N*	satd.	(**177**)
	25	0–9.2 *m*	satd.	(**263**)

C	t, °C	Concn. range B	Concn. range C	Lit.
B = HCl.—(*Continued*)				
$BaCl_2$	0	0–5 *N*	satd.	(172, 177)
	30	0–10.25 *N*	satd.	(411)
LiCl	0	0–8.1 *N*	satd.	(177)
NaOH	15	series of mixtures		(300)
NaCl	0	0.1–5.6 *N*	satd.	(172)
	0	0–5.6 *N*	satd.	(177)
	20			(463)
	20	series of mixtures		(464)
	30	0–7.2 *N*	satd.	(411)
Na_2SO_4	20			(462, 466)
	20	series of mixtures		(464)
$NaC_2HCl_2O_2$, Dichloroacetate	20			(463)
KCl	0	0–6.5 *N*	satd.	(177)
	20			(463)
K_2SO_4	20			(462, 466)
$KC_2HCl_2O_2$, Dichloroacetate	20			(463)
B = Br_2				
NaBr	25	satd.	92–408 g	(31)
KBr	0			(316)
	32.4	0–5 *m*	satd.	(326)
B = HBr				
NH_4Br	20			(463)
$UO_2(NO_3)_2$	15–17	*d* = 1.21	1–5 %	(118, 124)
$SrCl_2$	25	0–1.2 *m*	satd.	(263)
NaBr	20			(463)
KBr	20			(463)
B = I_2				
$Pb(NO_3)_2$	20	satd.	satd.	(194)
KI	0	satd.	0–0.1 *N*	(315)
	7.9	satd.	2–13 %	(157)
	25	0–satd.	satd.–0	(474)
B = HI				
NH_4I	20			(463)
$SrCl_2$	25	0–0.8 *m*	satd.	(263)
NaI	20			(463)
KI	20			(463)
B = HIO_3				
HNO_3	0–60	satd.	28–41 %	(245)
MoO_3	25			(517)
B = SO_2				
H_2SO_4	15	satd.	0–96 %	(353)
B = SO_3				
H_2SO_4	15, 35, 45	100–0 %	0–100 %	(335)
	18			(351)
CrO_3	25, 45	solid phase present		(230)
B = H_2SO_4				
$H_2S_2O_8$	14	6–33 %	7–35 %	(169)
N_2O_3	15	40–100 %	satd.	(353)
HNO_3	18	?	?	(410)
	20	series of mixtures		(464)
	3–35	0–100 %	0–100 %	(475, 476)
NH_4NO_3	20			(462, 466)
NH_4Cl	20			(466)
$HSNO_5$	18	70–100 %	0.1 %	(410)
$(NH_4)_2SO_4$	15	series of mixtures		(300)
	20			(462, 466)
As_2O_3	18	70–100 %	0.1 %	(410)
$PbSO_4$	18	70–100 %	0.1 %	(410)

C	t, °C	Concn. range B	Concn. range C	Lit.
B = H_2SO_4.—(*Continued*)				
$ZnCl_2$	20			(462, 466)
$ZnSO_4$	15	series of mixtures		(300)
	20			(462, 466)
$Zn(NO_3)_2$	20			(462, 466)
$CdSO_4$	0	?	satd.	(175)
$CuCl_2$	20			(462, 466)
$CuSO_4$	0	?	satd.	(175)
	15	series of mixtures		(300)
	20			(462, 466)
	25	0–3.7 *N*	satd.	(234)
	25	9–75 % SO_3	satd.	(34)
	25, 40	0–25 %	0–25 %	(299)
$Cu(NO_3)_2$	20			(462, 466)
$Fe_2(SO_4)_3$	18	70–100 %	0.1 %	(410)
UO_2SO_4	20–22	*d* = 1.168	1–5 %	(121)
$U(SO_4)_2$	17–19	*d* = 1.14	1–5 %	(119, 121)
$UO_2(NO_3)_2$	11–12	*d* = 1.138	1–5 %	(120, 124)
$Al_2(SO_4)_3$	15	series of mixtures		(300)
	18	70–100 %	0.1 %	(410)
$MgCl_2$	20			(462, 466)
$MgSO_4$	15	series of mixtures		(300)
	18	70–100 %	0.1 %	(410)
	20			(462, 466)
$Mg(NO_3)_2$	20			(462, 466)
$CaSO_4$	18	70–100 %	0.1 %	(410)
NaCl	20			(462, 466)
Na_2SO_4	0	0.9–2.1 Mol %	1–2.2 Mol %	(105)
	15	series of mixtures		(300)
	18	70–100 %	0.1 %	(410)
	20	series of mixtures		(464)
	20			(462, 466)
$NaNO_3$	20			(462, 466)
KCl	20			(462, 466)
K_2SO_4	15	series of mixtures		(300)
	20	several points		(462, 466)
KNO_3	20			(462, 466)
$K_2Cr_2O_7$	25	0.12–1 *N*	0.12–1 *N*	(328)
B = H_2SeO_4				
$(NH_4)_2SeO_4$	20			(463)
Na_2SeO_4	20			(463)
K_2SeO_4	20			(463)
B = NH_3				
NH_4NO_3	25	0.12–1 *N*	0.12–1 *N*	(328)
NH_4Cl	0	0–17 *N*	satd.	(179)
	25	0–4.75 *N*	1.05 *N*	(50)
	25	0.12–1 *N*	0.12–1 *N*	(328)
$CuSO_4$	15			(101)
$Cu(CNS)_2$	25	0.5–18 *m*	satd.	(303)
AgCl	15	0.6–10 *N*	satd.	(55)
AgBr	15.5	1–6 *N*	satd.	(55)
$CaCl_2$	25	0–6 *N*	1.09 *N*	(50)
LiCl	25	0–7.6 *N*	0.5 and 1.5 *N*	(50)
Li_2SO_4	25	0–6.5 *N*	2.2 *N*	(50)
$NaNO_3$	15	5.4–7.5 *N*	satd.	(195)
KCl	15			(101)
B = HNO_3				
NH_4NO_3	0	?	satd.	(176)
	20			(463)
	23			(542, 543)
$(NH_4)_2SO_4$	20			(462, 466)
$Pb(NO_3)_2$	15			(144)

C	t, °C	Concn. range B	Concn. range C	Lit.
		B = HNO_3.—(*Continued*)		
$TlCl$	25	0–22 %	satd.	(294, 295)
$ZnSO_4$	20			(462, 466)
$Zn(NO_3)_2$	20			(462, 466)
$CuSO_4$	20			(462, 466)
$Cu(NO_3)_2$	20			(462, 466)
$AgIO_3$	25	1–40 %	satd.	(294, 295)
Ag_2SO_4	25	0–49 %	satd.	(294, 295)
$AgNO_3$	30	0–12.5 *N*	satd.	(411)
$Ag_2C_2O_4$, Oxalate	25	1.6–31 %	satd.	(294, 295)
$AgC_2H_3O_2$, Acetate	25	0–34 %	satd.	(294, 295)
$AgC_2H_2ClO_2$, Chloro-acetate	25	0–27 %	satd.	(294, 295)
$UO_2(NO_3)_2$	11–12	*d* = 1.153	1–5 %	(120, 124)
$Al(NO_3)_3$	0–60	5–75 %	satd.	(427)
$MgSO_4$	20			(462, 466)
$Mg(NO_3)_2$	20			(462, 466)
$SrCl_2$	25	0–1.3 *m*	satd.	(263)
$Ba(NO_3)_2$	25	0.12–1 *N*	0.12–1 *N*	(328)
	30	0–5 *N*	satd.	(411)
Na_2SO_4	15, 22	?	?	(652)
	20	series of mixtures		(464)
	20			(462, 466)
$NaHSO_4$	15, 22	?	?	(652)
$NaNO_3$	0	?	satd.	(176)
	15, 22	?	?	(652)
	20			(463)
	20	series of mixtures		(464)
$NaC_2HCl_2O_2$, Dichloro-acetate	20			(463)
K_2SO_4	20			(462, 466)
KNO_3	0	?	satd.	(176)
	20			(463)
$KC_2HCl_2O_2$, Dichloro-acetate	20			(463)
		B = NH_4OH		
$NaOH$	15			(144)
		B = NH_4NO_3		
NH_4Cl	23			(542, 543)
	25	0.12–1 *N*	0.12–1 *N*	(328)
$Ba(NO_3)_2$	25	0.12–1 *N*	0.12–1 *N*	(328)
$NaNO_3$	0, 15, 30	0–satd.	0–satd.	(195)
	25	0.12–1 *N*	0.12–1 *N*	(328)
$NaHCO_3$	15			(144)
KNO_3	23			(542, 543)
	25	0.12–1 *N*	0.12–1 *N*	(328)
		B = NH_4Cl		
$MnCl_2$	25	0–29 %	0–44 %	(113)
	60	0–33 %	3–50 %	(113)
$FeCl_3$	25	0.12–1 *N*	0.12–1 *N*	(328)
$BaCl_2$	25	0.12–1 *N*	0.12–1 *N*	(328)
$NaCl$	0–5			(227)
	0	0–satd.	satd.–0	(193)
	15	0–satd.	satd.–0	(193)
		1–5 *N*	2–4 *N*	(38)
	30	satd.	satd.	(193)
KCl	0–5			(227)

C	t, °C	Concn. range B	Concn. range C	Lit.
		B = NH_4Cl.—(*Continued*)		
KCl	25	entire range of satd. solutions		(202)
	25	0.12–1 *N*	0.12–1 *N*	(328)
K_2SO_4	15	series of mixtures		(144)
		B = NH_4Br		
KBr	25	entire range of satd. solutions		(202)
		B = $(NH_4)_2SO_4$		
$CuSO_4$	25	0.12–1 *N*	0.12–1 *N*	(328)
$MnSO_4$	25	0.12–1 *N*	0.12–1 *N*	(328)
$FeSO_4$	15			(144)
$Al_2(SO_4)_3$	25	0.12–1 *N*	0.12–1 *N*	(328)
	25			(517)
$MgSO_4$	15			(101)
$CaSO_4$	25	0–6 *N*	satd.	(262, 584)
	50	0–560 g	satd.	(32)
Na_2CO_3	?	?	?	(191)
$Na_2B_4O_7$	?	?	?	(191)
K_2SO_4	25	0–satd.	satd.–0	(202)
	25	0.12–1 *N*	0.12–1 *N*	(328)
	25			(517)
		B = H_3PO_4		
$(NH_4)_3PO_4$	20			(463)
$FePO_4$	25	1–24 % P_2O_5	satd.	(93)
MoO_3	25			(517)
$MgHPO_4$	25	7.3–835 g P_2O_5	satd.	(93)
Na_2SO_4	15			(144)
Na_3PO_4	20			(463)
KOH	12–12.5	0–6 *N*	2–0 *N*	(133)
K_3PO_4	20			(463)
		B = $(NH_4)_2HPO_4$		
$KMnO_4$	15			(144)
		B = H_3AsO_4		
$(NH_4)_3AsO_4$	20			(463)
MoO_3	25			(517)
CaO	35			(568)
Na_3AsO_4	20			(463)
K_3AsO_4	20			(463)
		B = PbO		
$PbC_4H_6O_4$, Acetate	25	phase rule study		(310)
		B = $PbCl_2$		
$Pb(NO_3)_2$	25	satd.	0.02–0.1*N*	(262)
		B = $PbSO_4$		
K_2SO_4	22	satd.		(75)
		B = PbS_2O_6		
SrS_2O_6	25	0–satd.	satd.–0	(202)
		B = $Pb(NO_3)_2$		
$Cu(NO_3)_2$	20	satd.	0–satd.	(194)
$Sr(NO_3)_2$	25	0–satd.	satd.–0	(202)
$Ba(NO_3)_2$	17			(183)
	25	0–satd.	satd.–0	(202)
$NaNO_3$	25	0.12–1 *N*	0.12–1 *N*	(328)
KNO_3	25	0.12–1 *N*	0.12–1 *N*	(328)
		B = $PbC_2H_2O_4$, Formate		
$BaC_2H_2O_4$, Formate	25	satd.–0	0–satd.	(202)
		B = $PbC_4H_6O_4$, Acetate		
$NaNO_3$	15			(144)
		B = $TlNO_3$		
KNO_3	25	0–satd.	satd.–0	(202)

C	t, °C	Concn. range B	Concn. range C	Lit.
B = $ZnCl_2$				
NaI	15			(144)
B = $ZnSO_4$				
$MnSO_4$	15			(144)
K_2SO_4	18			(604)
B = $CdCl_2$				
KCN	25			(517)
B = $CdSO_4$				
Na_2SO_4	16			(550)
B = $HgCl_2$				
NaCl	16			(550)
KCl	20	several mixtures		(601)
	34, 56, 80, 100	complete range		(601)
KI	25			(517)
KCN	25			(517)
B = HgI_2				
KI	16			(550)
B = CuO				
$CuCl_2$	18			(604)
$CuSO_4$	25	satd.	1.2–8.7 % Cu	(34)
B = $CuCl_2$				
$MgCl_2$	25			(659)
$SrCl_2$	25	0–2.3 *m*	satd.	(263)
LiCl	25	several points		(659)
NaCl	18			(604)
	25			(659)
KCl	18			(604)
	25			(659)
B = $CuSO_4$				
$MnSO_4$	25	0.12–1 *N*	0.12–1 *N*	(328)
$CaSO_4$	25	0–225 g	satd.	(33)
	25	0–13.5 %	satd.	(264)
Na_2SO_4	25	0.12–1 *N*	0.12–1 *N*	(328)
K_2SO_4	18	0.04–0.5 *m*	0.04–0.5 *m*	(11)
	18			(604)
	25	0.12–1 *N*	0.12–1 *N*	(328)
B = Ag_2SO_4				
$AgNO_3$	25	satd.	0.025–0.1 *N*	(262)
$AgC_2H_3O_2$, Acetate	17			(183)
$MgSO_4$	25	satd.	0.02–0.2 *N*	(262)
$Mg(NO_3)_2$	25	satd.	0.025–0.1 *N*	(262)
$CaSO_4$	17, 25			(183)
K_2SO_4	25	satd.	0.025–0.2 *N*	(262)
KNO_3	25	satd.	0.025–0.1 *N*	(262)
B = $AgNO_3$				
$LiNO_3$	25			(517)
KCN	25			(517)
B = $MnSO_4$				
Na_2SO_4	16			(550)
	25	0.12–1 *N*	0.12–1 *N*	(328)
K_2SO_4	25	0.12–1 *N*	0.12–1 *N*	(328)
B = $FeCl_3$				
$MgSO_4$	15			(144)
B = $Fe(NH_4)_2(SO_4)_2$				
$AlCl_3$	15			(144)
B = $CoCl_2$				
$MgCl_2$	25			(659)
LiCl	25	several points		(659)
B = $CoCl_2$.—(*Continued*)				
NaCl	18			(604)
	25	several points		(659)
KCl	18			(604)
	25	several points		(659)
B = $NiSO_4$				
K_2CrO_4	15			(144)
B = H_2CrO_4				
$(NH_4)_2CrO_4$	20			(463)
MoO_3	25			(517)
Na_2CrO_4	20			(463)
K_2CrO_4	20			(463)
B = $Al_2(SO_4)_3$				
Na_2SO_4	25	0.12–1 *N*	0.12–1 *N*	(328)
K_2SO_4	25			(517)
B = $La(IO_3)_3$				
$La(NO_3)_3$	25	satd.	0–0.2 *N*	(265)
$La(NO_3)_3$.-$2NH_4NO_3$	25	satd.	0–1.6 *N*	(265)
$NaIO_3$	25	satd.	0–0.007 *N*	(265)
$NaNO_3$	25	satd.	0–3 *N*	(265)
KIO_3	25	satd.	0–0.002 *N*	(265)
B = $MgCl_2$				
$K_2Cr_2O_7$	15			(144)
B = $MgSO_4$				
$CaSO_4$	25	0–satd.	satd.	(92)
	25	0–0.18 %	satd.	(264)
Na_2SO_4	16			(550)
K_2SO_4	18	0–1 *N*	0–1 *N*	(415)
B = $Mg(NO_3)_2$				
$CaSO_4$	25	0–514 g	satd.	(560)
$Ba(BrO_3)_2$	25			(262)
B = $Ca(OH)_2$				
$Ca(NO_3)_2$	25	satd.	30–920 g	(96)
B = $CaCl_2$				
$Ca(OCl)_2$	15	0–72 g available Cl		(389)
NaCl	25	0–satd.	satd.	(94)
	25	satd.	0–satd.	(94)
B = $CaSO_4$				
$Ca(NO_3)_2$	25	satd.	0–544 g	(560)
	25	satd.	0–0.6 *N*	(262)
Na_2SO_4	25	satd.	20–2570 g	(95)
	25	satd.	0.03–3.6 *N*	(262)
$NaNO_3$	25	satd.	0–655 g	(560)
K_2SO_4	25	satd.	0.06–0.35 *N*	(262)
	25	satd.	50–960 g	(95)
KNO_3	25	satd.	0–1 %	(264)
	25	satd.	0–260 g	(560)
B = $CaCO_3$				
NaCl	25	satd.	20–300 g	(94)
Na_2SO_4	25	satd.	10–240 g	(94)
KCl	25	satd.	0–26 %	(97)
K_2SO_4	25	satd.	0–11 %	(97)
B = $Sr(OH)_2$				
$Sr(NO_3)_2$	25	0–satd.	satd.–0	(473)
B = $SrCl_2$				
$Sr(NO_3)_2$	25	satd.	0–3.3 *m*	(263)
$NaNO_3$	25	satd.	0–6.9 *m*	(263)
KCl	25	satd.	0–1.6 *m*	(263)
KI	25	satd.	0–1.5 *m*	(263)
KNO_3	25	satd.	0–0.5 *m*	(263)
B = $SrBr_2$				
$Sr(NO_3)_2$	25	satd.	0–1.9 *m*	(266)

C	t, °C	Concn. range B	Concn. range C	Lit.
		B = $Sr(NO_3)_2$		
$NaNO_3$	25	0.12–1 *N*	0.12–1 *N*	(328)
KNO_3	25	0.12–1 *N*	0.12–1 *N*	(328)
		B = $Ba(OH)_2$		
$Ba(NO_3)_2$	25	0–satd.	satd.–0	(472)
		B = $BaCl_2$		
$Ba(NO_3)_2$	25	0.12–1 *N*	0.12–1 *N*	(328)
NaCl	15	1–3 *N*	1–3 *N*	(38)
	25	0.12–1 *N*	0.12–1 *N*	(328)
$NaC_2H_3O_2$, Acetate	15			(144)
KCl	15	1–3 *N*	1–3 *N*	(38)
	25	0.12–1 *N*	0.12–1 *N*	(328)
		B = $Ba(BrO_3)_2$		
$Ba(NO_3)_2$	25	satd.	0.025–0.2 *N*	(262)
$KBrO_3$	25	satd.	0.025–0.1 *N*	(262)
KNO_3	25	satd.	0.025–0.1 *N*	(262)
		B = $Ba(NO_3)_2$		
$NaNO_3$	25	0.12–1 *N*	0.12–1 *N*	(328)
KNO_3	17			(183)
	25	0.12–1 *N*	0.12–1 *N*	(328)
	30			(183)
		B = LiCl		
NaCl	15	1–6 *N*	2–4 *N*	(38)
		B = NaOH		
NaCl	0	?	satd.	(180)
	0	0–5 *N*	satd.	(179)
	0–55	30–200 g	75–230 g	(145)
	20	10–320 g	satd.	(647)
	20	0–60%	26.4–0.8%	(302)
	60	0–60%	27–1.5%	(302)
	100	0–60%	28–3%	(302)
$NaNO_3$	0	0–6 *N*	satd.	(179)
Na_2CO_3	11.5, 60, 80	series of mixtures		(639)
$NaC_{16}H_{31}O_2$, Palmitate	90	series of mixtures		(134)
Na_2SiO_3	17.5			(625)
KOH	25	0.12–1 *N*	0.12–1 *N*	(328)
		B = NaCl		
$NaClO_3$	20	5–150 g	satd.	(647)
Na_2SO_4	20	series of mixtures		(464)
	25	0–320 g	0–270 g	(94)
$NaNO_3$	15	0–190 g	satd.	(54)
	15.5	satd.	0–380 g	(54)
	19.5	series of measurements		(362)
	20	satd.	satd.	(450)
	25	0.12–1 *N*	0.12–1 *N*	(328)
$NaHCO_3$	0	0–6 *m*	satd.	(193)
	0	satd.	0–0.09 *m*	(193)
	15	0–6 *m*	satd.	(193)
	15	satd.	0–0.12 *m*	(193)
	30	0–6 *m*	satd.	(193)
	30	satd.	0–0.17 *m*	(193)
	45	0–6 *m*	satd.	(193)
	45	satd.	0–0.23 *m*	(193)
Na_2SiO_3	17.5			(625)
KCl	0	2.9–6.2 Mol %	0.4–3.3 Mol %	(105)
	0–5			(227)
	15	0.25–4 *N*	0.2–3.5 *N*	(37)
	15.6	satd.	satd.	(470)

C	t, °C	Concn. range B	Concn. range C	Lit.
		B = NaCl.—(*Continued*)		
KCl	18	0–1 *N*	1–0 *N*	(59)
	19.5	series of mixtures		(362)
	20	satd.	satd.	(450)
	25	0.12–1 *N*	0.12–1 *N*	(328)
	25			(517, 576)
K_2SO_4	15.6	satd.	satd.	(470)
	18	range of concentrations		(11)
KNO_3	15	0.25–120 g	0.25–120 g	(144)
	15.6	satd.	satd.	(470)
	19.5	series of mixtures		(362)
		B = NaBr		
KBr	25			(576)
$K_2C_2O_4$, Oxalate	15			(144)
		B = NaI		
KI	25			(576)
		B = Na_2SO_3		
Na_2SO_4	0.1	3–12%	1–3%	(107)
	17.5	2.6–19%	2–12%	(107)
	25	2.5–27%	1.7–21%	(107)
	37.5	2.6–28%	2–30%	(107)
		B = Na_2SO_4		
$NaNO_3$	16			(422)
	20	series of mixtures		(464)
Na_2CO_3	20			(585)
KCl	15			(297)
K_2SO_4	18	0.05–0.7 *m*	0.025–0.5 *m*	(11)
	25	0.12–1 *N*	0.12–1 *N*	(328)
KNO_3	16	20–70 g	50–140 g	(422)
$KMnO_4$	25	0–22%	satd.	(603)
		B = $NaNO_2$		
$NaNO_3$	18	satd.	satd.	(467)
		B = $NaNO_3$		
$NaHCO_3$	0, 15	0–satd.	0–satd.	(195)
K_2SO_4	15	30–100 g	30–100 g	(422)
KNO_3	15.6	satd.	satd.	(470)
	16	0–140 g	0–140 g	(422)
	20	satd.	satd.	(450)
	25	0.12–1 *N*	0.12–1 *N*	(328)
		B = Na_2CO_3		
KOH	15			(144)
K_2CO_3	25	0.12–1 *N*	0.12–1 *N*	(328)
		B = Na_4SiO_4		
Na_2WO_4	30	series of mixtures		(383)
		B = $Na_4Fe(CN)_6$		
$K_4Fe(CN)_6$	25	0–1 *m*	satd.	(266)
	25	satd.	0–1 *m*	(266)
		B = KOH		
KCl	0	0–3.5 *N*	satd.	(179)
	20	10–430 g	satd.	(647)
	0–80	25–200 g	70–210 g	(314)
K_2S	8–18	4–55% solutes	Mol ratio 1:1	(52)
		B = KCl		
$KClO_3$	20	0–120 g	satd.	(647)
KBr	25	0–satd.	satd.–0	(202)
KI	19.5			(84)
K_2SO_4	18	0.48–0.025 *N*	0.05–0.3 *N*	(22)
KNO_3	17.5	satd.	0–153 g	(54)
	20	satd.	satd.	(450)
	20.5	0–250 g	satd.	(54)
	25	0.12–1 *N*	0.12–1 *N*	(328)

C	t, °C	Concn. range B	Concn. range C	Lit.
		B = **KCl**.—(*Continued*)		
$K_2Al_2(SO_4)_4$	15			(144)
		B = **KBr**		
$CuC_4H_6O_4$, Acetate	15			(144)
		B = **KI**		
KCN	25			(517)
		B = **K_2S**		
KHS	8–18	3–52% solutes	Mol ratio 1:1	(52)

C	t, °C	Concn. range B	Concn. range C	Lit.
		B = **K_2SO_4**		
$KHSO_4$	15	series of mixtures		(300)
KNO_3	15			(183)
	18	66–73 g	42–29 g	(422)
	25			(183)
K_2CO_3	20			(585)
$KMnO_4$	25	0–11%	satd.	(603)
K_2CrO_4	15			(101)
	25	0–satd.	satd.–0	(202)
$K_2Cr_2O_7$	25	0.12–1 *N*	0.12–1 *N*	(328)
		B = **K_2HPO_4**		
K_2CO_3	15			(144)

Three or More Solutes

H_2O

Three Solutes

B	C	D	t, °C	Concn. range B	Concn. range C	Concn. range D	Lit.
HCl	H_2SO_4	Na_2SO_4	20		series of mixtures		(464)
	NaCl	KCl	25	0–4 *m*	0–4 *m*	0–1.5 *m*	(527)
I_2	PbI_2	$Pb(NO_3)_2$	20		all satd.		(194)
H_2SO_4	HNO_3	Na_2SO_4	20		series of mixtures		(464)
	$La_2(SO_4)_3$	$La_2C_6O_{12}$, Oxalate	25	4–4.6 *M*	satd.	satd.	(651)
NH_3	NH_4NO_3	$NaNO_3$	15				(195)
HNO_3	Na_2SO_4	$NaNO_3$	20		series of mixtures		(464)
NH_4NO_3	NH_4HCO_3	$NaHCO_3$	0, 15		all satd.		(195)
	$NaNO_3$	$NaHCO_3$	0, 15		all satd.		(195)
			15	satd.	1.9–3.4 *N*	satd.	(195)
NH_4Cl	$CuSO_4$	K_2SO_4	15		series of mixtures		(144)
	NaCl	KCl	0–5				(227)
$(NH_4)_2SO_4$	$NaNO_3$	KCl	?	?	?	?	(191)
Tl_2SO_4	$Al_2(SO_4)_3$	K_2SO_4	25	0–satd.	0–satd.	0–satd.	(202)
$CaSO_4$	NaCl	Na_2SO_4	25	0.3–6 g	0–310 g	0–260 g	(94)
$CaCO_3$	NaCl	Na_2SO_4	25	satd.	0–320 g	0–270 g	(94)
$BaSO_4$	K_2SO_4	K_2CO_3	25		equilibrium mixtures		(424)
NaCl	$NaNO_3$	KNO_3	15.6	satd.	satd.	satd.	(470)
	KCl	K_2SO_4	15.6	satd.	satd.	satd.	(470)
	KCl	KNO_3	15.6	satd.	satd.	satd.	(470)
	KI	KNO_3	15		series of mixtures		(144)

Four Solutes

B	C	D	E	t, °C	Concn. range B	Concn. range C	Concn. range D	Concn. range E	Lit.
I_2	PbI_2	$Pb(NO_3)_2$	$Cu(NO_3)_2$	20	satd.	satd.	0.14–0.8 *N*	1–3.4 *N*	(194)

Sea Water [JAB] (339)**; α (81)*; (292, 408.5), α (153, 168, 380, 408, 445, 597)

% Cl	% total salts	0°C	5°C	10°C	15°C	20°C	25°C	30°C	35°C
0.1	0.184	1.00140	1.00149	1.00120	1.00058	0.99966	0.99849	0.99708	0.99545
0.2	0.364	1.00287	1.00293	1.00261	1.00197	1.00104	0.99985	0.99842	0.99678
0.3	0.545	1.00433	1.00436	1.00402	1.00335	1.00241	1.00120	0.99976	0.99811
0.4	0.725	1.00579	1.00579	1.00542	1.00474	1.00377	1.00256	1.00110	0.99944
0.5	0.906	1.00725	1.00722	1.00683	1.00612	1.00514	1.00391	1.00245	1.00077
0.6	1.086	1.00871	1.00865	1.00823	1.00751	1.00651	1.00526	1.00379	1.00210
0.7	1.267	1.01016	1.01007	1.00963	1.00889	1.00787	1.00661	1.00513	1.00343
0.8	1.447	1.01162	1.01150	1.01103	1.01027	1.00924	1.00796	1.00647	1.00476
0.9	1.628	1.01307	1.01292	1.01243	1.01165	1.01060	1.00931	1.00780	1.00608
1.0	1.808	1.01452	1.01434	1.01383	1.01303	1.01196	1.01066	1.00914	1.00741
1.1	1.989	1.01597	1.01577	1.01523	1.01441	1.01333	1.01201	1.01048	1.00874
1.2	2.169	1.01742	1.01719	1.01663	1.01579	1.01469	1.01336	1.01182	1.01007
1.3	2.350	1.01887	1.01861	1.01803	1.01717	1.01605	1.01472	1.01316	1.01140
1.4	2.530	1.02032	1.02003	1.01943	1.01855	1.01742	1.01607	1.01450	1.01274
1.5	2.711	1.02177	1.02146	1.02083	1.01993	1.01879	1.01742	1.01585	1.01407

SEA WATER.—(*Continued*)

% Cl	% total salts	0°C	5°C	10°C	15°C	20°C	25°C	30°C	35°C
1.6	2.891	1.02322	1.02288	1.02223	1.02131	1.02016	1.01878	1.01720	1.01541
1.7	3.072	1.02468	1.02431	1.02364	1.02270	1.02153	1.02014	1.01855	1.01675
1.8	3.252	1.02613	1.02574	1.02504	1.02408	1.02290	1.02150	1.01989	1.01809
1.9	3.433	1.02758	1.02716	1.02644	1.02547	1.02427	1.02286	1.02124	1.01944
2.0	3.613	1.02904	1.02859	1.02785	1.02686	1.02564	1.02422	1.02260	1.02079
2.1	3.794	1.03049	1.03002	1.02926	1.02825	1.02701	1.02558	1.02395	1.02214
2.2	3.974	1.03195	1.03145	1.03067	1.02964	1.02839	1.02695	1.02531	1.02349
2.3	4.155	1.03341	1.03289	1.03208	1.03104	1.02978	1.02831	1.02667	1.02484

ℭ-TABLE, THE ℭ-ARRANGEMENT

Two Solutes in H_2O

t = 20° (463)

Formula	Name
B = CH_2O_2, Formic acid	
CH_5NO_2	NH_4 Formate
$C_2H_7NO_3$	NH_4 Glycolate
$C_3H_9NO_2$	NH_4 Propionate
$C_3H_9NO_3$	NH_4 Lactate
$C_4H_{11}NO_2$	NH_4 Butyrate
$C_4H_{11}NO_2$	NH_4 Isobutyrate
$C_4H_{12}N_2O_4$	NH_4 Succinate
$C_4H_{12}N_2O_5$	NH_4 Malate
B = CH_5NO_2, Ammonium formate	
$C_2HCl_3O_2$	Trichloroacetic acid
$C_2H_4O_2$	Acetic acid
$C_3H_6O_3$	Lactic acid
$C_4H_8O_2$	Butyric acid
$C_4H_8O_2$	Isobutyric acid
B = $C_2HCl_3O_2$, Trichloroacetic acid	
$C_2H_4Cl_3NO_2$	NH_4 Trichloroacetate
$C_2H_5Cl_2NO_2$	NH_4 Dichloroacetate
$C_2H_6ClNO_2$	NH_4 Chloroacetate
B = $C_2H_2Cl_2O_2$, Dichloroacetic acid	
$C_2H_5Cl_2NO_2$	NH_4 Dichloroacetate
$C_3H_9NO_3$	NH_4 Lactate
B = $C_2H_3ClO_2$, Chloroacetic acid	
$C_2H_4Cl_3NO_2$	NH_4 Trichloroacetate
$C_2H_6ClNO_2$	NH_4 Chloroacetate
B = $C_2H_4O_2$, Acetic acid	
$C_2H_7NO_2$	NH_4 Acetate
$C_4H_{11}NO_2$	NH_4 Butyrate
$C_4H_{11}NO_2$	NH_4 Isobutyrate
B = $C_2H_5Cl_2NO_2$, NH_4 Dichloroacetate	
$C_3H_6O_3$	Lactic acid
B = C_2H_6O, Ethyl alcohol	
$C_7H_9NO_2$*	NH_4 Benzoate
$C_7H_9NO_3$†	NH_4 Salicylate
B = $C_2H_7NO_2$, NH_4 Acetate	
$C_4H_8O_2$	Butyric acid
$C_4H_8O_2$	Isobutyric acid
B = $C_3H_6O_2$, Propionic acid	
$C_3H_9NO_2$	NH_4 Propionate
B = $C_3H_6O_3$, Lactic acid	
$C_3H_9NO_3$	NH_4 Lactate
B = $C_4H_6O_4$ Succinic acid	
$C_4H_{12}N_2O_4$	NH_4 Succinate
B = $C_4H_6O_5$, Malic acid	
$C_4H_{12}N_2O_5$	NH_4 Malate
B = $C_4H_8O_2$, Butyric acid	
$C_4H_{11}NO_2$	NH_4 Butyrate
B = $C_4H_8O_2$, Isobutyric acid	
$C_4H_{11}NO_2$	NH_4 Isobutyrate
B = $C_6H_8O_7$, Citric acid	
$C_6H_{17}N_3O_7$	NH_4 Citrate

* At 25° C, B concn. = 0–100 %, C concn. = satd. (559).

† At 25° C, B concn. = entire range, C concn. = satd. (559).

THE KEY FORMULA OF AT LEAST ONE SOLUTE (THE B-SOLUTE) DOES NOT BEGIN WITH 16

Two Solutes in H_2O

The B-solute in Standard Arrangement, the C-solute in the ℭ-arrangement

C Formula	C Name	t, °C	Concn. range B	Concn. range C	Lit.
		B = HCl			
$C_2H_2Cl_2O_2$	Dichloroacetic acid	25	0.12–1*N*	0.12–1*N*	(328)
$C_2H_2O_4$	Oxalic acid	30	0–9.7 *N*	satd.	(412)
$C_2H_4O_2$	Acetic acid	25	0.12–1 *N*	0.12–1 *N*	(328)
$C_2H_5Cl_2NO_2$	NH_4 Dichloro-acetate	20			(463)
C_2H_6O	Ethyl alcohol	25	0.3–3.2 *N*	100 %–?	(324)
C_6H_7N	Aniline	25	range of concn.		(562)
$C_6H_{12}O_6$	Invert sugar	25			(56)
$C_8H_6O_4$	Phthalic acid	25	0.2–1.9 *m*	satd.	(518)
$C_{10}H_8O_3S$	β-Naphthalene-sulfonic acid	30	0–9.9 *N*	satd.	(412)
$C_{12}H_{22}O_{11}$	Sucrose	0, 25			(56)
		B = I_2			
$C_3H_8O_3$	Glycerol	25	satd.	0–100 %	(283)
		B = S			
C_3H_6O	Acetone	25	satd.	85–100 %	(283)
		B = H_2SO_4			
$C_2H_2O_4$	Oxalic acid	25	0–8.4 *N*	satd.	(651)
$C_4H_6O_5$	Malic acid	20	2.5–11 %	6–7 %	(546)
$C_4H_{10}O$	Ethyl ether	30	50–100 %	entire range	(495)
		B = HNO_3			
$C_2H_2O_4$	Oxalic acid	30	0–21.6 *N*	satd.	(412)
$C_2H_4O_2$	Acetic acid	25	0.12–1 *N*	0.12–1 *N*	(328)
$C_2H_5Cl_2NO_2$	NH_4 Dichloro-acetate	20			(463)
$C_{18}H_{32}O_{16}$	Raffinose	25			(232)
		B = NH_4NO_3			
NH_4HCO_3		15	0–satd.	0–satd.	(195)
$C_8H_{14}O_6$	Ethyl tartrate	26			(479)
		B = NH_4Cl			
NH_4HCO_3		0	0–5.4 *m*	satd.	(193)
			satd.	0–0.46 *m*	(193)
		15	0–6.4 *m*	satd.	(193)
			satd.	0–0.81 *m*	(193)
C_3H_6O	Acetone	25	satd.	0–90 Vol. %	(283)
$C_3H_8O_3$	Glycerol	25	satd.	0–100 %	(283)
$C_8H_6O_4$	Phthalic acid	25	0.06–1.9 *m*	satd.	(518)
$C_7H_{14}O_6$	Ethyl tartrate	26			(479)
		B = $(NH_4)_2SO_4$			
C_2H_6O	Ethyl alcohol	9	satd.	0–142 g	(53)
		15	satd.	entire system	(53)
$C_8H_{14}O_6$	Ethyl tartrate	26			(479)
		B = $PbC_4H_6O_4$, Acetate			
C_2H_6O	Ethyl alcohol	25	satd.	0–100 %	(559)

C Formula	C Name	t, °C	Concn. range B	Concn. range C	Lit.
			B = $ZnC_4H_6O_4$, Acetate		
C_2H_6O	Ethyl alcohol	25	satd.	0–100 %	(559)
			B = $ZnC_{10}H_{18}O_4$, Valerate		
C_2H_6O	Ethyl alcohol	25	satd.	entire range	(559)
			B = $ZnC_{12}H_{10}O_8S_2$, *p*-Phenolsulfonate		
C_2H_6O	Ethyl alcohol	25	satd.	entire range	(559)
			B = $HgCl_2$		
CH_4O	Methyl alcohol	25	satd.	0–100 %	(280)
C_2H_6O	Ethyl alcohol	20	satd.	0–100 %	(280)
$C_4H_8O_2$	Ethyl acetate	25	satd.	0–100 %	(280)
			B = $HgBr_2$		
CH_4O	Methyl alcohol	25	satd.	0–100 %	(280)
C_2H_6O	Ethyl alcohol	25	satd.	0–100 %	(280)
$C_4H_8O_2$	Ethyl acetate	25	satd.	0–100 %	(280)
			B = HgI_2		
CH_4O	Methyl alcohol	25	satd.	47–100 %	(280)
C_2H_6O	Ethyl alcohol	25	satd.	67–100 %	(283)
			satd.	70–100 %	(280)
$C_4H_8O_2$	Ethyl acetate	25	satd.	0–100 %	(280)
			B = $Hg(CN)_2$		
CH_4O	Methyl alcohol	25	satd.	0–100 %	(280)
C_2H_6O	Ethyl alcohol	25	satd.	0–100 %	(280)
$C_4H_8O_2$	Ethyl acetate	25	satd.	0–100 %	(280)
$C_8H_6O_4$	Phthalic acid	25	0.06–0.8 *m*	satd.	(518)
			B = $CuC_2H_2O_4$, Formate		
CH_2O_2	Formic acid	?			(563)
			B = $CuC_4H_6O_4$, Acetate		
$C_2H_4O_2$	Acetic acid	?			(563)
			B = $CuC_6H_{10}O_4$, Propionate		
$C_3H_6O_2$	Propionic acid	?			(563)
			B = $AgClO_4$		
C_6H_6	Benzene			complete study	(293)
			B = MoO_3		
$C_2H_2O_4$	Oxalic acid				(517)
$C_2H_4O_2$	Acetic acid	25			(517)
$C_2H_4O_3$	Glycolic acid	25			(517)
$C_3H_6O_2$	Propionic acid	25			(517)
$C_3H_6O_3$	Lactic acid	25			(517)
$C_4H_6O_4$	Succinic acid	25			(517)
$C_4H_6O_5$	Malic acid	25			(517)
$C_4H_6O_6$	Tartaric acid	25			(517)
$C_6H_8O_7$	Citric acid	25			(517)
$C_7H_{12}O_6$	Quinic acid	25			(517)
$C_8H_8O_2$	Phenylacetic acid	25			(517)
$C_8H_8O_3$	Mandelic acid	25			(517)
			B = $(NH_4)_6Mo_7O_{24}$		
$C_4H_6O_6$	Tartaric acid	25			(135, 517)
			B = $UO_2(NO_3)_2$		
$C_2H_4O_2$	Acetic acid	10–17	1–7 %	d = 1.055	(124)
			B = H_3BO_3		
CH_4O	Methyl alcohol	25	satd.	12–100 Mol %	(437)
C_2H_6O	Ethyl alcohol	25	satd.	9–100 Mol %	(437)
$C_3H_6O_3$	Lactic acid	25	satd.	2–36 Mol %	(437)
C_3H_8O	*n*-Propyl alcohol	25	satd.	24–100 Mol %	(437)
$C_3H_8O_3$	Glycerol	25	satd.	25–91 Mol %	(437)
				0–100 %	(283)
$C_4H_{10}O$	Isobutyl alcohol	25	satd.	0.7–100 Mol %	(437)
$C_5H_{12}O$	Amyl alcohol	25	satd.	?	(437)
$C_5H_{12}O$	Isoamyl alcohol	25	satd.	0.5–100 Mol %	(437)
$C_6H_{14}O_6$	Mannitol	25	satd.	0.8–1.6 Mol %	(437)
$C_6H_{14}O_6$	Dulcitol	25	satd.	0.07–0.3 Mol %	(437)
			B = $MgCl_2$		
$C_8H_6O_4$	Phthalic acid	25	0.12–2.6 *m*	satd.	(518)
			B = $CaCl_2$		
$C_8H_6O_4$	Phthalic acid	25	0.08–0.6 *m*	satd.	(518)
			B = $Ca(NO_3)_2$		
C_2H_6O	Ethyl alcohol	25	0–5 *N*	0–100 %	(436)
			B = $SrC_{14}H_{10}O_6$, Salicylate		
C_2H_6O	Ethyl alcohol	25	satd.	entire range	(559)
			B = $Ba(OH)_2$		
C_3H_6O	Acetone	25	satd.	0–70 %	(282)
			B = $BaCl_2$		
$C_8H_6O_4$	Phthalic acid	25	0.1–1.4 *m*	satd.	(518)
$C_8H_{14}O_6$	Ethyl tartrate	26			(479)

C Formula	C Name	t, °C	Concn. range B	Concn. range C	Lit.
			B = $LiCl$		
$C_8H_6O_4$	Phthalic acid	25	0.1–1.7 *m*	satd.	(518)
$C_{12}H_{22}O_{11}$	Sucrose	25			(240)
			B = $LiC_7H_5O_2$, Benzoate		
C_2H_6O	Ethyl alcohol	25	satd.	0–100 %	(559)
			B = $LiC_7H_5O_3$, Salicylate		
C_2H_6O	Ethyl alcohol	25	satd.	entire range	(559)
			B = $Li_3C_6H_5O_7$, Citrate		
C_2H_6O	Ethyl alcohol	25	satd.	0–100 %	(559)
			B = $NaCl$		
C_2H_6O	Ethyl alcohol	11.5–13	satd.	0–720 g	(53)
$C_3H_8O_3$	Glycerol	25	satd.	0–100 %	(283)
$C_5H_{12}O$	Amyl alcohol	25	equil. with	0–5 *N* B in A	(437)
$C_8H_6O_4$	Phthalic acid	25	0.1–3 *m*	satd.	(518)
$C_8H_{14}O_6$	Ethyl tartrate	26			(479)
$C_{12}H_{22}O_{11}$	Sucrose	20	?	?	(51)
			B = $NaClO_3$		
$C_8H_{14}O_6$	Ethyl tartrate	26			(479)
			B = NaI		
$C_8H_{14}O_6$	Ethyl tartrate	26			(479)
			B = Na_2SO_4		
$C_8H_6O_4$	Phthalic acid	25	0.1–3.0 *m*	satd.	(518)
			B = $NaNO_3$		
C_2H_6O	Ethyl alcohol	13–16.5	satd.	0–630 g	(53)
$C_8H_6O_4$	Phthalic acid	25, 35	0.2–3.0 *m*	satd.	(518)
$C_8H_{14}O_6$	Ethyl tartrate	26			(479)
			B = $NaCHO_2$, Formate		
CH_2O_2	Formic acid	20			(463)
$C_2HCl_3O_2$	Trichloroacetic acid	20			(463)
$C_2H_4O_2$	Acetic acid	20			(463)
$C_3H_6O_3$	Lactic acid	20			(463)
$C_4H_8O_2$	Butyric acid	20			(463)
$C_4H_8O_2$	Isobutyric acid	20			(463)
			B = $NaHCO_3$		
NH_4HCO_3		0	satd.–0	0–satd.	(193)
		15	satd.–0	0–satd.	(193)
			0–satd.	0–satd.	(195)
			B = $NaC_2H_3O_2$, Acetate		
$C_2H_4O_2$	Acetic acid	20			(463)
		25	0.12–1 *N*	0.12–1 *N*	(328)
C_2H_6O	Ethyl alcohol	25	satd.	0–100 %	(559)
$C_4H_8O_2$	Butyric acid	20			(463)
$C_4H_8O_2$	Isobutyric acid	20			(463)
$C_8H_{14}O_6$	Ethyl tartrate	26			(479)
			B = $NaC_2H_3O_3$, Glycolate		
CH_2O_2	Formic acid	20			(463)
			B = $NaC_3H_5O_2$, Propionate		
CH_2O_2	Formic acid	20			(463)
$C_3H_6O_2$	Propionic acid	20			(463)
			B = $NaC_3H_5O_3$, Lactate		
CH_2O_2	Formic acid	20			(463)
$C_2H_2Cl_2O_2$	Dichloroacetic acid	20			(463)
$C_3H_6O_3$	Lactic acid	20			(463)
			B = $NaC_4H_7O_2$, Butyrate		
CH_2O_2	Formic acid	20			(463)
$C_2H_4O_2$	Acetic acid	20			(463)
$C_4H_8O_2$	Butyric acid	20			(463)
			B = $NaC_4H_7O_2$, Isobutyrate		
CH_2O_2	Formic acid	20			(463)
$C_2H_4O_2$	Acetic acid	20			(463)
$C_4H_8O_2$	Isobutyric acid	20			(463)
			B = $NaC_7H_5O_2$, Benzoate		
C_2H_6O	Ethyl alcohol	25	satd.	0–100 %	(559)
			B = $Na_2C_4H_4O_4$, Succinate		
CH_2O_2	Formic acid	20			(463)
$C_4H_6O_4$	Succinic acid	20			(463)
			B = $Na_2C_4H_4O_5$, Malate		
CH_2O_2	Formic acid	20			(463)
$C_4H_6O_5$	Malic acid	20			(463)
			B = $Na_2C_4H_4O_6$, Tartrate		
CH_2O_2	Formic acid	20			(463)
$C_4H_6O_6$	Tartaric acid	20			(463)
$C_{12}H_{22}O_{11}$	Sucrose	15	30–40 g	180–290 g	(210)
			B = $Na_3C_6H_5O_7$, Citrate		
C_2H_6O	Ethyl alcohol	25	satd.	0–100 %	(559)
$C_6H_8O_7$	Citric acid	20			(463)

C Formula	C Name	t, °C	Concn. range B	Concn. range C	Lit.
B = $NaC_2Cl_3O_2$, Trichloroacetate					
$C_2HCl_3O_2$	Trichloroacetic acid	20			(463)
$C_2H_3ClO_2$	Chloroacetic acid	20			(463)
B = $NaC_2H_2ClO_2$, Chloroacetate					
$C_2HCl_3O_2$	Trichloroacetic acid	20			(463)
$C_2H_3ClO_2$	Chloroacetic acid	20			(463)
B = $NaC_2HCl_2O_2$, Dichloroacetate					
$C_2HCl_3O_2$	Trichloroacetic acid	20			(463)
$C_2H_2Cl_2O_2$	Dichloroacetic acid	20			(463)
$C_3H_6O_3$	Lactic acid	20			(463)
B = $NaC_6H_5O_4S$, *p*-Phenolsulfonate					
C_2H_6O	Ethyl alcohol	25	satd.	entire range	(559)
B = $Na_2Cr_2O_7.2H_2O$					
C_2H_6O	Ethyl alcohol	19.4	51 g		(512)
B = KF					
$C_8H_6O_4$	Phthalic acid	25	0.1–0.6 *m*	satd.	(518)
B = KCl					
C_2H_6O	Ethyl alcohol	14.5	satd.	0–90 %	(53)
		25	0.04–0.5 *N*	50 Vol. %	(201)
C_3H_6O	Acetone	25	satd.	0–100 %	(281)
$C_3H_8O_3$	Glycerol	25	satd.	0–100 %	(283)
$C_8H_6O_4$	Phthalic acid	25, 35	0.1–2.7 *m*	satd.	(518)
$C_8H_{14}O_6$	Ethyl tartrate	26			(479)
B = $KClO_3$					
$C_8H_6O_4$	Phthalic acid	25	0.03–0.6 *m*	satd.	(518)
$C_8H_{14}O_6$	Ethyl tartrate	26			(479)
B = KBr					
C_2H_6O	Ethyl alcohol	18	0.01–0.07 *N*	25 % and 50 %	(313)
		25	0.04–1 *N*	50 Vol. %	(201)
C_3H_6O	Acetone	25	satd.	0–100 %	(281)
		25	satd.	0–90 Vol. %	(283)
$C_3H_8O_3$	Glycerol	25	satd.	0–100 %	(283)
$C_8H_6O_4$	Phthalic acid	25	0.1–1.8 *m*	satd.	(518)
B = $KBrO_3$					
$C_8H_6O_4$	Phthalic acid	25	0.02–0.4 *m*	satd.	(518)
B = KI					
C_2H_6O	Ethyl alcohol	20			(137)
		20	10–100 g	45 %	(509)
		25	0.1–2 *N*	50 Vol. %	(201)
C_3H_6O	Acetone	25	satd.	0–100 %	(281)
$C_8H_6O_4$	Phthalic acid	25	0.1–2.0 *m*	satd.	(518)
$C_8H_{14}O_6$	Ethyl tartrate	26			(479)
B = KIO_3					
$C_8H_6O_4$	Phthalic acid	25	0.02–0.4 *m*	satd.	(518)
B = K_2SO_4					
$C_8H_6O_4$	Phthalic acid	25	0.06–1.2 *m*	satd.	(518)
B = KNO_3					
C_2H_6O	Ethyl alcohol	17.7–18	satd.	0–90 %	(53)
$C_8H_6O_4$	Phthalic acid	25	0.1–2.2 *m*	satd.	(518)
$C_8H_{14}O_6$	Ethyl tartrate	26			(479)
B = KH_2PO_4					
$C_{12}H_{22}O_{11}$	Sucrose	18	50–170 g	?	(210)
B = $KCHO_2$, Formate					
CH_2O_2	Formic acid	20			(463)
$C_2HCl_3O_2$	Trichloroacetic acid	20			(463)
$C_2H_4O_2$	Acetic acid	20			(463)
$C_3H_6O_3$	Lactic acid	20			(463)
$C_4H_8O_2$	Butyric acid	20			(463)
$C_4H_8O_2$	Isobutyric acid	20			(463)
B = $KC_2H_3O_2$, Acetate					
$C_2H_4O_2$	Acetic acid	20			(463)
C_2H_6O	Ethyl alcohol	25	satd.	0–100 %	(559)
$C_4H_8O_2$	Butyric acid	20			(463)
$C_4H_8O_2$	Isobutyric acid	20			(463)
$C_8H_6O_4$	Phthalic acid	25	0.1–0.6 *m*	satd	(518)
B = $KC_2H_3O_3$, Glycolate					
CH_2O_2	Formic acid	20			(463)
B = $KC_3H_5O_2$, Propionate					
CH_2O_2	Formic acid	20			(463
$C_3H_6O_2$	Propionic acid	20			(463
B = $KC_3H_5O_3$, Lactate					
CH_2O_2	Formic acid	20			(463)
$C_2H_2Cl_2O_2$	Dichloroacetic acid	20			(463)
$C_3H_6O_3$	Lactic acid	20			(463)
B = $KC_4H_5O_6$, Acid tartrate					
C_2H_6O	Ethyl alcohol	25	satd.	entire range	(559)
B = $KC_4H_7O_2$, Butyrate					
CH_2O_2	Formic acid	20			(463)
$C_2H_4O_2$	Acetic acid	20			(463)
$C_4H_8O_2$	Butyric acid	20			(463)
B = $KC_4H_7O_2$, Isobutyrate					
CH_2O_2	Formic acid	20			(463)
$C_2H_4O_2$	Acetic acid	20			(463)
$C_4H_8O_2$	Isobutyric acid	20			(463)
B = $K_2C_4H_4O_4$, Succinate					
CH_2O_2	Formic acid	20			(463)
$C_4H_6O_4$	Succinic acid	20			(463)
B = $K_2C_4H_4O_5$, Malate					
CH_2O_2	Formic acid	20			(463)
$C_4H_6O_5$	Malic acid	20			(463)
B = $K_3C_6H_5O_7$, Citrate					
C_2H_6O	Ethyl alcohol	25	satd.	0–100 %	(559)
$C_6H_8O_7$	Citric acid	20			(463)
B = $KC_2Cl_3O_2$, Trichloroacetate					
$C_2HCl_3O_2$	Trichloroacetic acid	20			(463)
$C_2H_3ClO_2$	Chloroacetic acid	20			(463)
B = $KC_2H_2ClO_2$, Chloroacetate					
$C_2HCl_3O_2$	Trichloroacetic acid	20			(463)
$C_2H_3ClO_2$	Chloroacetic acid	20			(463)
B = $KC_2HCl_2O_2$, Dichloroacetate					
$C_2HCl_3O_2$	Trichloroacetic acid	20			(463)
$C_2H_2Cl_2O_2$	Dichloroacetic acid	20			(463)
$C_3H_6O_3$	Lactic acid	20			(463)
B = KCNS					
$C_8H_{14}O_6$	Ethyl tartrate	26			(479)
B = $KSbC_4H_4O_7$, Antimonyl tartrate					
C_2H_6O	Ethyl alcohol	25	satd.	entire range	(559)
B = $KNaC_4H_4O_6$, Tartrate					
C_2H_6O	Ethyl alcohol	15	60–90 g	210–300 g	(210)
		25	satd.	entire range	(559)
B = RbCl					
$C_8H_6O_4$	Phthalic acid	25	0.1–2.1 *m*	satd.	(518)
B = CsCl					
$C_8H_6O_4$	Phthalic acid	25	0.07–1.5 *m*	satd.	(518)

Three or More Solutes in H_2O

I_2 (0–satd.) + C_2H_6O, Ethyl alcohol (40 and 60%) + KI (satd.-0); at 25°C (471).

H_2SO_4 (5–6.4 *M*) + $C_2H_2O_4$, Oxalic acid (satd.) + $La_2(SO_4)_3$ (satd.); at 25°C (651).

H_2SO_4 + $C_2H_2O_4$, Oxalic acid + $La_2(SO_4)_3$ + $La_2C_6O_{12}$, Lanthanum oxalate; at 25°C (651).

H_2SO_4 (1.2–4.8 *M*) + $C_2H_2O_4$, Oxalic acid (satd.) + $La_2C_6O_{12}$, Lanthanum oxalate (satd.); at 25°C (651).

CO_2 (satd. 1 atm.) + $CaSO_4$ (satd.) + $CaCO_3$ (satd.) + NaCl (0–310 g) + Na_2SO_4 (0–260 g); at 25°C (94).

CO_2 (satd. 1 atm.) + $CaCO_3$ (satd.) + NaCl (10–360 g); at 25°C (94).

$C_4H_6O_6$, Tartaric acid + $C_{12}H_{22}O_{11}$, Sucrose + $Na_2C_4H_4O_6$, Sodium tartrate; at 15°C (209).

$C_5H_{12}O$, Amyl alcohol + H_3BO_3 (satd.) + NaCl (0–4 *N*) at 25°C (437).

NH_4HCO_3 (satd.) + $NaNO_3$ (0.4–1.25 *N*) + $NaHCO_3$ (satd.); at 15°C (195).

DENSITY OF SATURATED SOLUTIONS

When H_2O is written in the formula, the per cent refers to the anhydrous substance except when otherwise noted.

HCl [JAB] p_{HCl} = 1 atm. (528)

t	%	d_4^t
−20	67.7	1.276
−10	66.7	1.261
0	65.8	1.249
+10	64.9	1.239
20	64.0	1.231
25	63.6	1.228
30	63.2	1.225
40	62.4	1.221
50	61.7	1.219

HIO_3 [JAB] (245) [LJG]

13.5	74.10	2.4256
18	74.55	2.4711

NH_4NO_3 [JAB] (438)**; (114, 580)

0	54.33	1.264
10	58.85	1.2909
15	62.51	1.3003
20	65.63	1.3103
25	68.29	1.3200
30	70.74	1.3303
32	71.72	1.3345
32.3	71.87	1.3351
34	72.35	1.3380
36	73.05	1.3411
38	73.85	1.3438
40	74.79	1.3464

NH_4Cl [JAB] (537, 580)**

15	26.3	1.0750

NH_4Br [JAB] (567)

15	41.72	1.29
113	61.5	1.66
137	65.4	1.71
158	67.9	1.76

NH_4ClO_4 [LJG] (99)

0	11.0	1.061
10	15.1	1.080
20	19.1	1.098
30	23.0	1.115
40	26.8	1.131
50	30.4	1.146
60	33.8	1.160
70	37.1	1.174
80	40.3	1.188
90	43.5	1.202
100	46.6	1.215

NH_4IO_4 [LJG] (19)

16	2.63	1.0178

$(NH_4)_2SO_4$ (JAB] (642)

20	42.55	1.248

$(NH_4)_2HPO_4$ [LJG] (241, 242)

14.5	56.24	1.3427

$NH_4C_7H_5O_2$, Benzoate [JAB] (559)

25	18.6	1.040

$NH_4C_7H_5O_3$, Salicylate [JAB] (559)

25	50.8	1.145

Ammonium bismuth citrate (47.5 % Bi_2O_3) [JAB] (559)

25	22.25	1.25

$(NH_4)_2SiF_6$ [LJG] (581)

t	%	d_4^t
17.5	15.67	1.0946

$PbCl_2$ [LJG] (382)**; (262)*

0	0.67	1.0065
10	0.815	1.0075
20	0.98	1.0072
25	1.073	1.0069
30	1.18	1.0064
40	1.41	1.0050
50	1.665	1.0030
60	1.94	1.0006
70	2.235	0.9978
80	2.55	0.9946
90	2.885	0.9911
100	3.24	0.9873

$Pb(ClO_3)_2$ [JAB] (442)

18	60.2	1.944

$PbBr_2$ [LJG] (382)

0	0.45	1.0042
10	0.61	1.0050
20	0.83	1.0057
25	0.97	1.0059
30	1.12	1.0060
40	1.47	1.0060
50	1.86	1.0053
60	2.29	1.0037
70	2.75	1.0016
80	3.26	1.0001
90	3.83	0.9995
100	4.47	0.9991

PbI_2 [LJG] (382)

0	0.044	1.00043
10	0.054	1.00010
20	0.069	0.99893
25	0.079	0.9979
30	0.091	0.9966
40	0.121	0.9934
50	0.157	0.9894
60	0.199	0.9849
70	0.247	0.9798
80	0.301	0.9745
90	0.361	0.9694
100	0.428	0.9645

$Pb(NO_3)_2$ [LJG]

17.5 (534)	34.8	1.380
20 (194)	35.5	1.4185
25 (185)	37.075	1.44450
25 (185)	37.035†	1.44359

† From radioactive lead.

$Pb(C_2H_3O_2)_2$, Acetate [JAB] (241, 242, 559)

15.56	26.44	1.2330
25	36.54	1.340

TlCl [JAB] (39) [LJG]

0	0.17	1.0012
10	0.24	1.0018
20	0.34	1.0013
25	0.40	1.0005
30	0.47	0.9996
40	0.62	0.9976
50	0.80	0.9951

TlCl.—(*Continued*)

t	%	d_4^t
60	1.02	0.9921
70	1.29	0.9889
80	1.59	0.9855
90	1.93	0.9820
100	2.38	0.9785

$TlClO_4$ [LJG] (99)

0	5.8	1.060
10	7.4	1.077
20	11.1	1.104
25	13.5	1.122
30	16.2	1.143
40	22.1	1.194
50	28.3	1.257
60	34.4	1.332
70	40.1	1.420
80	45.2	1.521

Tl_2SO_4 [JAB] (39) [LJG]

0	2.72	1.0247
10	3.70	1.0335
20	4.85	1.0424
25	5.48	1.0469
30	6.16	1.0514
40	7.62	1.0606
50	9.21	1.0698
60	10.91	1.0791
70	12.70	1.0884
80	14.58	1.0978
90	16.53	1.1072
100	18.53	1.1167

$TlNO_3$ [JAB] (39) [LJG]

0	3.8	1.034
10	6.0	1.055
20	8.7	1.076
25	10.4	1.093
30	12.4	1.114
40	17.3	1.161
50	23.6	1.227
60	31.6	1.330
70	41.2	1.483
80	52.9	1.722
90	66.4	2.135
100	79.6	2.787
104.5 (B. P.)	85.6	3.191

$Zn(ClO_3)_2$ [GS] (442)

18	65	1.914

$Zn(C_2H_3O_2)_2$, Acetate [JAB] (559)

25	25.73	1.165

$Zn(C_5H_9O_2)_2$, Valerate [JAB] (559)

25	1.27	1.001

$Zn(C_6H_5SO_3)_2$, *p*-Benzenesulfonate [JAB] (559)

25	29.49	1.182

$HgCl_2$ [GS] (260)

0	4.2	1.039
10	4.9	1.042
20	5.9	1.049
30	7.3	1.059
40	9.3	1.073

$HgCl_2$.—(*Continued*)

t	%	d_4^t
50	11.9	1.091
60	15.2	1.114
70	19.5	1.142
80	25.2	1.180
90	33.3	1.233
100	55.7	1.354

$Cu(ClO_3)_2$ [WCS] (421)*

18	62.17	1.692

$CuSO_4.(NH_4)_2SO_4$ [WCS] (534)

19.0	15.3	1.1316

$MnCl_2$ [JAB] (140) [LJG]

α-$MnCl_2.4H_2O$

25	43.56	1.4491
30	44.66	1.5049
40	46.97	1.5348
50	49.53	1.5744

$MnCl_2.2H_2O$

57.65	51.31	1.6097
60	52.06	1.6108
70	52.52	1.6134

MnC_2O_4 [LJG] (103) [JAB]

$MnC_2O_4.2H_2O$

0	0.0198	1.0001

$MnC_2O_4.3H_2O$

0	0.0326	1.0002

$MnSiF_6$ [LJG] (582)

17.5	37.68	1.4458

$FeCl_3$ [WCS] (430)

25	73.1	1.793
35	73.4	1.785

$Fe(NO_3)_2$ [WCS] (461)

15	44.35	1.485
20	45.65	1.495
25	46.86	1.505

$FeSO_4.(NH_4)_2SO_4$ [WCS] (221, 533, 534)

16.5	19.13	1.1651

$Co(ClO_3)_2$ [WCS] (421)

18	64.2	1.857

$Co(ClO_4)_2$ [WCS] (590)

0	64.03	1.5639
7.5	65.09	1.5658
18	66.24	1.5670
26	71.76	1.5811
45	72.49	1.5878

$Co(NO_3)_2$ [WCS] (217)

18	49.73	1.572

$Ni(ClO_3)_2$ [WCS] (99, 421)

16	60.9	1.75
18	56.74	1.658

$Ni(ClO_4)_2$ [WCS] (590)

0	66.48	1.5726
7.5	67.76	1.5755
18	69.83	1.5760
26	70.80	1.5841
45	74.42	1.5936

CrO_3 [JAB] (243, 443) [LJG]

16.4	62.8	1.708
18	62.45	1.703

$(WO_3)_4.H_2O$, Metatungstic acid [LJG] (569)

t	%	d_4^t
0	24.6†	1.6025
22	39.3	2.5240
43.5	44.2	3.6500

† Per cent WO_3.

$H_3PO_4.12WO_3.21H_2O$ [LJG] (569)

t	%	d_4^t
0	12.3	1.189
22	29.4	1.691
43	30.9	1.826
92	41.1	2.581

UO_2Cl_2 [LJG] (441)

t	%	d_4^t
18	76.2	2.736

$3(NH_4)_2O.SiO_2.V_2O_5.xMoO_3.yH_2O$ [LJG] (213)

x	y	%†	d_4^t
9	20	26.4	1.2132
10	21	28.0	1.2527
11	27	29.5	1.2927
15	24	34.1	1.4376

† Per cent refers to the hydrate. Density may be 18/18 or 18/4.

$Al_2(SO_4)_3.Tl_2SO_4.24H_2O$ [JAB] (39) [LJG]

t	%	d_4^t
0	3.08	1.0294
10	4.40	1.0412
20	6.03	1.0572
25	7.14	1.0678
30	8.61	1.0812
40	12.80	1.1207
50	18.64	1.1848
60	26.10	1.2807

$La(IO_3)_3$ [LJG] (265, 266)

t	%	d_4^t
25	0.06853	0.998251

$PrCl_3$ [LJG] (413)

t	%	d_4^t
14	51.0	1.685

$Mg(ClO_3)_2$ [GS] (442)

t	%	d_4^t
18	56.3	1.594

$Mg(IO_3)_2.4H_2O$ [GS] (442)

t	%	d_4^t
18	6.44	1.078

$MgCrO_4.7H_2O$ [GS] (442)

t	%	d_4^t
18	42	1.422

$Ca(ClO_3)_2.2H_2O$ [GS] (442)

t	%	d_4^t
18	64	1.729

$Ca(NO_2)_2$ [GS] (468)

t	%	d_4^t
16	42.3	1.4198

$Ca_2Fe(CN)_6$ [LJG] (186) [GS]

t	%	d_4^t
25	36.50	1.3565
30	39.72	1.3670
40	40.27	1.3844
50	42.14	1.3972
60	43.75	1.4052
65	44.48	1.4076

$Sr(ClO_3)_2$ [GS] (442)

t	%	d_4^t
18	63.6	1.839

$Sr(NO_2)_2$ [GS] (468)

t	%	d_4^t
19	39.3	1.4454

$Sr(NO_3)_2$ [GS] (40)

t	%	d_4^t
0	28.247	1.28124
5	31.567	1.31889
10	34.826	1.35709
15	38.016	1.39600
20	41.139	1.43585
25	44.229	1.47699
29.3†	46.902	1.51420
35	47.170	1.51352
40	47.404	1.51272
45	47.638	1.51192
50	47.872	1.51119
55	48.106	1.51074
60	48.343	1.51052
65	48.623	1.51046
70	48.931	1.51053
75	49.227	1.51071
80	49.519	1.51100
85	49.808	1.51139
90	50.095	1.51186

† Transition point.

$Sr(C_7H_5O_3)_2$ Salicylate [JAB] (559)

t	%	d_4^t
25	4.58	1.019

$Ba(ClO_3)_2$ [GS] (99)

t	%	d_4^t
0	19.2	1.195
10	23.0	1.234
20	26.6	1.274
30	30.3	1.315
40	33.9	1.355
50	37.2	1.395
60	40.2	1.433
70	42.8	1.470
80	45.3	1.508
90	47.8	1.545
100	50.1	1.580
105.6	51.5	1.600

$Ba(ClO_4)_2$ [GS] (99)

t	%	d_4^t
0	67.3	1.782
20	74.3	1.912
40	78.2	2.009
60	81.2	2.070
80	83.2	2.114
100	84.9	2.155
120	86.6	2.195
140	88.3	2.230

$Ba(NO_2)_2$ [GS] (468)

t	%	d_4^t
17	40	1.4895

$Ba(NO_3)_2$ [GS] (611)

t	%	d_4^t
0	4.9	1.043
10	6.5	1.056
20	8.4	1.073
30	10.4	1.087
40	12.4	1.104
50	14.6	1.121
60	16.9	1.137
70	19.1	1.146

LiF [LJG] (442)

t	%	d_4^t
18	0.27	1.002

$LiBrO_3$ [LJG] (442)

t	%	d_4^t
18	60.4	1.830

$LiIO_3$ [JAB] (442) [LJG]

t	%	d_4^t
18	44.6	1.566

$LiNO_2$ [LJG] (468)

t	%	d_4^t
19	48.9	1.3184

$LiCHO_2$, Formate [JAB] (244)

t	%	d_4^t
18	27.85	1.140

$LiC_7H_5O_2$, Benzoate [JAB] (529)

t	%	d_4^t
25	27.64	1.100

$LiC_7H_5O_3$, Salicylate [JAB] (529)

t	%	d_4^t
25	52.70	1.206

$Li_3C_6H_5O_7$, Citrate [JAB] (559)

t	%	d_4^t
25	31.78	1.2124

NaF [LJG] (442)

t	%	d_4^t
18	4.3	1.043

$NaCl$ [JAB] (39)**; (4, 5)*; (450, 470, 537, 580, 611)

t	%	d_4^t
−10		1.200
0	26.34	1.2093
+10	26.35	1.2044
20	26.43	1.1999
25	26.48	1.1978
30	26.56	1.1957
40	26.71	1.1914
50	26.89	1.1872
60	27.09	1.1830
70	27.30	1.1787
80	27.53	1.1745
90	27.80	1.1703
100	28.12	1.1660
107.0 (B. P.)	28.39	1.1631

$NaClO_3$ [JAB] (99) [LJG]

t	%	d_4^t
−15	41.9	1.380
0	44.1	1.389
+10	47.4	1.409
20	50.2	1.430
25	51.7	1.440
30	53.1	1.451
40	55.8	1.472
50	58.2	1.493
60	60.8	1.514
70	63.1	1.536
80	65.4	1.559
90	67.6	1.581
100	69.7	1.604
110	72.0	1.625
120	73.8	1.649
122 (B. P.)	74.1	1.654

$NaClO_4$ [LJG] (99)

t	%	d_4^t
15	64.6	1.666
50	71.3	1.731
143	79.1	1.789

Na_2SO_4 [JAB] (39)**; (141)*; (612)

t	%	d_4^t
0	4.47	1.0409
5	5.32	1.0577
10	8.26	1.0787
15	11.84	1.1100
20	16.04	1.1513
25	21.81	1.2081
30	29.14	1.2860
32.35†	33.15	1.3323
35	32.93	1.3283
40	32.52	1.3206

Na_2SO_4.—(*Continued*)

t	%	d_4^t
50	31.80	1.3058
60	31.15	1.2919
70	30.60	1.2789
80	30.19	1.2674
90	29.90	1.2569
100	29.69	1.2469
101.9 (B. P.)	29.67	1.2450

† Transition point.

Na_2SeO_4 [JAB] (216) [LJG]

t	%	d_4^t
18	29.00	1.313

$NaNO_2$ [JAB] (241, 242, 468)

t	%	d_4^t
15.6	42.8	1.3464
20	45.8	1.3584

$NaNO_3$ [JAB] (39)**; (450, 470, 611)

t	%	d_4^t
0	42.23	1.3532
10	44.54	1.3683
20	46.80	1.3834
25	47.92	1.3910
30	49.02	1.3986
40	51.20	1.4139
50	53.35	1.4293
60	55.48	1.4447
70	57.59	1.4603
80	59.67	1.4759
90	61.73	1.4916
100	63.77	1.5074
110	65.80	1.5231
119.0 (B. P.)	67.62	1.5374

$NaNH_4SO_4$ [LJG] (538)

t	%	d_4^t
15	25.2	1.174

NaH_2PO_2 [LJG] (241, 242)

t	%	d_4^t
16	52.1	1.386

Na_2HPO_4 [LJG] (534)

t	%	d_4^t
17	4.2	1.043

Na_3PO_4 [LJG] (537)

t	%	d_4^t
14	9.5	1.103

$Na_3PO_4.NaF$ [LJG] (72)

t	%	d_4^t
25	52.4	1.030

$Na_3AsO_4.NaF$ [LJG] (72)

t	%	d_4^t
25	50.9	1.031

$NaCHO_2$, Formate [JAB] (244)

t	%	d_4^t
18	44.73	1.316

$NaC_2H_3O_2$, Acetate [JAB] (559)

t	%	d_4^t
25	33.61	1.205

$NaC_6H_5SO_3$, Benzenesulfonate [JAB] (559)

t	%	d_4^t
25	16.37	1.076

$NaC_7H_5O_2$, Benzoate [JAB] (559)

t	%	d_4^t
25	35.99	1.152

$NaC_7H_5O_3$, Salicylate [JAB] (559)

t	%	d_4^t
25	53.56	1.248

$Na_3C_6H_5O_7.5H_2O$, Citrate [JAB] (559)

t	%	d_4^t
25	48.10	1.2723

$Na_4Fe(CN)_6$ [LJG] (186)**; (265, 266) [WCS]

t	%	d_4^t
25	17.1	1.131_0
30	18.8	1.144_5
40	22.4	1.172_0

$Na_4Fe(CN)_6$.—(*Continued*)

t	%	d_4^t
50	26.1	1.200
60	29.7	1.228
70	33.4	1.256
80†	37.2	1.283
85	38.1	1.292
90	38.2	1.294
95	38.0	1.291
100	37.6	1.284

† Transition point at 81.7°C.

Na_2CrO_4 [JAB] (443)**; (442) [LJG]

18	40.10	1.430

$Na_2Cr_2O_7$ [JAB] (443) [LJG]

18	63.9	1.743

$Na_2Cr_3O_{10}.H_2O$ [LJG] (443)

18	80.60	2.056

$Na_2Cr_4O_{13}.4H_2O$ [LJG] (443)

18	74.60	1.923

$Na_4CrO_5.13H_2O$ [LJG] (443)

18	37.50	1.444

Na_2MoO_4 [JAB] (216) [LJG]

18	39.40	1.435

$Na_2O.4WO_3.10H_2O$ [LJG] (532)

room	77.7	3.017

$(Na_2O)_3(WO_3)_7.16H_2O$ [LJG] (532)

0	26.7	1.316

$2Na_2O.P_2O_5.24WO_3.27H_2O$ [LJG] (65)

20	59.13	2.001

$KF.2H_2O$ [LJG] (442)

18	48	1.500

KCl [JAB] (39)**; (82)*; (450, 470, 543, 580, 611)

0	21.90	1.1531
10	23.86	1.1647
20	25.65	1.1742
25	26.48	1.1783
30	27.28	1.1820
40	28.77	1.1884
50	30.14	1.1937
60	31.41	1.1981
70	32.60	1.2017
80	33.73	1.2047
90	34.82	1.2073
100	35.89	1.2097
108 (B. P.)	36.75	1.2118

$KClO_3$ [JAB] (99)**; (6, 84) [LJG]

0	3.21	1.021
10	5.01	1.033
20	6.96	1.045
25	8.0	1.051
30	9.3	1.058
40	12.1	1.073
50	15.6	1.092
60	19.4	1.115
70	23.4	1.139
80	27.4	1.165
90	31.6	1.192
100	35.9	1.219
104 (B. P.)	37.6	1.230

$KClO_4$ [LJG] (99)**; (439)

t	%	d_4^t
0	0.80	1.007
10	1.35	1.009
20	2.15	1.012
30	3.20	1.016
40	4.45	1.021
50	6.00	1.026
60	7.85	1.032
70	9.95	1.040
80	12.3	1.050
90	14.9	1.060
100	17.7	1.069

KBr [JAB] (82, 277)**

23.4	40.54	1.3711
25.0	40.63	1.3797

$KBrO_3$ [JAB] (84) [LJG]

19.2	6.25	1.0458

KI [JAB] (82)

24.3	59.74	1.7175

KIO_3 [JAB] (84) [LJG]

18.6	7.93	1.0692

KIO_4 [LJG] (19)

13	0.655	1.0051

K_2SO_4 [JAB] (39)**; (470, 580, 611)

0	6.87	1.0584
10	8.51	1.0706
20	10.08	1.0814
25	10.83	1.0863
30	11.57	1.0908
40	12.97	1.0987
50	14.28	1.1052
60	15.49	1.1104
70	16.61	1.1144
80	17.64	1.1174
90	18.59	1.1195
100	19.44	1.1206
101.1 (B. P.)	19.54	1.1207

KNO_3 [JAB] (39)**; (450, 470, 580, 611)

0	9.46	1.0528
10	16.88	1.1090
20	24.29	1.1652
25	28.00	1.1933
30	31.70	1.2214
40	39.11	1.2776
50	46.39	1.3338
60	52.62	1.3899
70	58.07	1.4413
80	62.79	1.4886
90	67.10	1.5325
100	71.00	1.5732
110	74.41	1.6119
114 (B. P.)	75.71	1.6269

$KCHO_2$, Formate [JAB] (244)

18	76.8	1.571

$KHCO_3$ [JAB] (241, 242) [LJG]

16	23.8	1.1674

$KC_2H_3O_2$, Acetate [LJG] (559) [JAB]

25	68.73	1.413

$KC_4H_5O_6$, Acid tartrate [JAB] (481, 559)

t	%	d_4^t
18	0.55	1.0018
25	0.65	0.999_0

$K_3C_6H_5O_7$, Citrate [JAB] (559)

25	60.91	1.5136

$KSbO_3$ [JAB] (337) [LJG]

18	2.73	1.0249

$KSbOC_4H_4O_6$ [JAB] (559)

25	7.64	1.049

K_2SnO_3 [LJG] (460)

15.5	42.7	1.620

$K_4Fe(CN)_6$ [LJG] (186)**; (265, 266) [WCS]

25	24.0	1.173_0
30	26.1	1.188_0
40	29.8	1.214_0
50	33.1	1.236_0
60	35.9	1.255_0
70	38.4	1.272_0
80	40.5	1.286_5
90	42.3	1.299_5
100	43.8	1.312_0

K_2CrO_4 [JAB] (534) [LJG]

19.5	38.4	1.3764

$K_2Cr_2O_7$ [JAB] (184, 241, 242) [LJG]

10	7.69	1.0561
15.8	9.19	1.0659

$2K_2O.(NH_4)_2O.SiO_2.V_2O_5.$-$xMoO_3.yH_2O$ [LJG] (213)

x	*y*	%†	d_4^{18}
9	20	20.5	1.1703
10	21	21.7	1.1918
11	12	23.0	1.2138

† Per cent refers to the hydrate. Density may be 18/18 or 18/4.

$K_2SO_4.Al_2(SO_4)_3.24H_2O$ [JAB] (39) [LJG]

t	%	d_4^t
0	2.90	1.0289
10	3.80	1.0396
20	5.44	1.0525
25	6.51	1.0604
30	7.74	1.0699
40	10.66	1.0948
50	14.39	1.1289
60	19.71	1.1805

$KNaCO_3$ [LJG] (579)

15	33.8	1.364

$KNaC_4H_4O_6.4H_2O$, Tartrate [LJG] (559) [JAB]

25	39.71	1.308

RbCl [JAB] (39)**; (82)*

0	43.47	1.4393
10	45.70	1.4656
20	47.70	1.4893
25	48.57	1.4998
30	49.41	1.5094
40	50.90	1.5270
50	52.28	1.5421
60	53.60	1.5554
70	54.84	1.5684
80	56.01	1.5803

RbCl.—(*Continued*)

t	%	d_4
90	57.09	1.5912
100	58.11	1.6014
110	59.08	1.6110
114 (B. P.)	59.46	1.6148

$RbClO_3$ [JAB] (84) [LJG]

16.2	4.73	1.0328

$RbClO_4$ [LJG] (99)

0	1.09	1.0070
10	1.22	1.0085
20	1.55	1.0100
30	2.21	1.0130
40	3.16	1.0170
50	4.40	1.0220
60	5.94	1.0285
70	7.73	1.0370
80	9.72	1.0480
90	11.81	1.0600
100	13.94	1.0730

RbBr [JAB] (82)

23	52.67	1.6252

$RbBrO_3$ [JAB] (84) [LJG]

16	2.15	1.0159

RbI [JAB] (82)

24.3	63.62	1.8497

$RbIO_3$ [JAB] (84) [LJG]

15.6	2.72	1.0223

$RbIO_4$ [LJG] (19)

16†	0.645	1.0052

† Satd. at 13°C.

Rb_2SO_4 [JAB] (39)

0	26.65	1.2720
10	29.80	1.3097
20	32.55	1.3403
25	33.77	1.3543
30	34.90	1.3673
40	36.98	1.3908
50	38.75	1.4102
60	40.28	1.4264
70	41.66	1.4415
80	42.89	1.4545
90	44.05	1.4654
100	45.01	1.4736
102.4 (B. P.)	45.23	1.4753

$RbNO_3$ [JAB] (39)

0	16.34	1.0766
10	26.01	1.1964
20	35.43	1.3157
25	40.05	1.3751
30	44.46	1.4348
40	53.13	1.5531
50	61.08	1.6679
60	66.80	1.7691
70	71.54	1.8589
80	75.68	1.9397
90	78.98	2.0114
100	81.72	2.0779
110	84.14	2.1394
118.3 (B. P.)	86.06	2.1867

$Rb_2SO_4.Al_2(SO_4)_3.24H_2O$ [JAB] (39) [LJG]

0	0.71	1.0071
10	1.05	1.0091
20	1.48	1.0123
25	1.77	1.0137

$Rb_2SO_4.Al_2(SO_4)_3.24H_2O$.—(*Continued*)

t	%	d_4^t
30	2.13	1.0154
40	3.17	1.0215
50	4.66	1.0314
60	6.88	1.0474
70	11.07	1.0815

CsCl [JAB] (39)**; (82)*

t	%	d_4^t
0	61.84	1.8431
10	63.63	1.8786
20	65.08	1.9095
25	65.74	1.9233
30	66.36	1.9362
40	67.52	1.9598
50	68.59	1.9813
60	69.59	2.0008
70	70.53	2.0185
80	71.41	2.0351
90	72.23	2.0507
100	72.99	2.0644
110	73.70	2.0761
119.4 (B. P.)	74.36	2.0863

$CsClO_3$ [JAB] (84) [LJG]

t	%	d_4^t
16	5.32	1.0391

$CsClO_4$ [LJG] (99)

5	0.96	1.0070
25	2.01	1.0100
80	14.6	1.0840

CsBr [JAB] (82)

21.4	53.05	1.6933

$CsBrO_3$ [JAB] (84) [LJG]

16	2.55	1.0192

CsI [JAB] (82)**; (30)

22.8	47.96	1.5451

$CsIO_3$ [JAB] (84) [LJG]

15.4	2.17	1.0178

$CsIO_4$ [LJG] (19)

15	2.10	1.0166

Cs_2SO_4 [JAB] (39)

0	62.57	1.9754
10	63.36	1.9918
20	64.11	2.0063

Cs_2SO_4.—(*Continued*)

t	%	d_4^t
25	64.48	2.0130
30	64.82	2.0193
40	65.48	2.0309
50	66.10	2.0417
60	66.67	2.0517
70	67.21	2.0611
80	67.74	2.0699
90	68.26	2.0782
100	68.76	2.0863
108.6 (B. P.)	69.18	2.0923

$CsNO_3$ [JAB] (39)

0	8.57	1.0695
10	13.09	1.1038
20	18.71	1.1582
25	21.94	1.1874
30	25.34	1.2191
40	32.28	1.2898
50	39.08	1.3710
60	45.56	1.4574
70	51.80	1.5493

$CsNO_3$.—(*Continued*)

t	%	d_4^t
80	57.34	1.6388
90	62.03	1.7259
100	66.31	1.8122
106.2 (B. P.)	68.78	1.8657

$Cs_2SO_4.Al_2(SO_4)_3.24H_2O$ [JAB] (39) [LJG]

0	0.21	1.0017
10	0.29	1.0022
20	0.41	1.0019
25	0.50	1.0015
30	0.60	1.0009
40	0.87	0.9998
50	1.27	0.9991
60	1.96	1.0002
70	3.14	1.0056
80	5.4	1.018
90	9.6	1.051
100	18.1	1.124
100.4 (B. P.)	18.6	1.129

TEMPERATURE OF MAXIMUM DENSITY

ONE SOLUTE

Standard Arrangement

HCl [JAB] (610)**; (656)

%	t_m, °C
1	1.96
2	+ 0.38
3	− 1.49
4	− 4.00
5	− 7.29
6	−11.12
7	−15.18
8	−19.23
9	−23.15
10	−26.87

HBr [JAB] (656)

1	3.1
2	2.2
4	0.3

HI [JAB] (656)

1	3.2
2	2.5
3	1.7
4	1.0

H_2SO_4 [JAB] (127, 147)**; (522, 523, 524)*; (656)

1	+ 1.5
2	− 1.0
3	− 3.5
4	− 6.0
5	− 8.6
6	−11.3
7	−14.0

HNO_3 [JAB] (656)

1	2.0
2	0.1

NH_3 [JAB] (670)

%	t_m, °C
1	2.2
2	+ 0.3
4	− 3.3
6	− 7.0
8	−10.6

NH_4NO_3 [JAB] (161)**; (375, 656)

0.5	3.13
1.0	2.29
1.5	1.44
2.0	+ 0.59
12	− 47
20	− 82
44	−225

NH_4Cl [JAB] (108, 130, 131)**; (227, 656)

1	2.65
2	+1.26
3	−0.21

NH_4Br [JAB] (131)**; (656)

2.10	1.62

NH_4I [JAB] (131)**; (656)

5.56	−0.54

$(NH_4)_2SO_4$ [JAB] (160, 375)**

1	2.33
2	+ 0.70
4	− 5.1
12	− 30.3
20	− 70.4
50	−178

NH_4CHO_2, Formate [JAB] (656)

%	t_m, °C
1	2.9
2	1.7
3	+0.5
4	−0.7
5	−2.0
6	−3.2

$NH_4C_2H_3O_2$, Acetate [JAB] (656)

1	3.2
2	2.3
3	1.5
4	+0.6
5	−0.3
6	−1.1
7	−2.0

$NH_4C_3H_5O_2$, Propionate [JAB] (656)

1	3.2
2	2.5
3	1.7
4	0.9
5	+0.1
6	−0.7
7	−1.6
8	−2.5

$Pb(NO_3)_2$ [LJG] (375)**; (397, 398)

5	− 3.5
10	−12.5
15	−23
20	−35

Tl_2SO_4 [JAB] (160) [LJG]

%	t_m, °C
1	3.39
2	2.82
3	2.25

$ZnCl_2$ [GS] (161)

1	2.81
2	1.50

$ZnSO_4$ [GS] (160, 375)

%		t_m, °C
1	(160)	2.56
2	(160)	+1.17
2.24	(375)	−0.56
5.60	(375)	−10.0
11.19	(375)	−22.2
16.78	(375)	−44.8

$Zn(NO_3)_2$ [GS] (161)

1	2.48
2	1.01

$CdCl_2$ [GS] (161)

1	3.06
2	2.15
3	1.22
4	0.10

$CdBr_2$ [GS] (397, 398)

1	3.24

$CdSO_4$ [GS] (160)

1	2.96
2	1.95

$Cd(NO_3)_2$ [GS] (161)

1	2.88
2	1.74

$CuCl_2$ [LJG] (162)

%	t_m, °C
1	2.67
2	1.27

$CuSO_4$ [LJG] (162)**; (147)*

0.5	3.20
1.0	2.44
1.5	1.70
2.0	1.00
2.5	+0.37
3.0	−0.17
3.5	−0.58

$Cu(NO_3)_2$ [LJG] (162)

0.5	3.20
1.0	2.42
1.5	1.64
2.0	0.86
2.5	0.08

$PtCl_4$ [LJG] (398)

1.27	3.4

$MnCl_2$ [JAB] (161) [LJG]

1	2.82
2	1.92
3	1.20

$MnSO_4$ [JAB] (160) [LJG]

1	2.59
2	1.29

$Mn(NO_3)_2$ [JAB] (161) [LJG]

1	2.46
2	0.91

$CoCl_2$ [LJG] (162)**; (398)

%	t_m, °C
0.5	3.33
1.0	2.69
2.0	1.39
3.0	0.10

$CoSO_4$ [LJG] (162)

0.5	3.26
1.0	2.56
1.5	1.88
2.0	1.22

$Co(NO_3)_2$ [LJG] (162)

0.5	3.21
1.0	2.44
1.5	1.67
2.0	0.89

$NiCl_2$ [LJG] (162)**; (398)

0.5	3.34
1.0	2.69
2.0	1.40

$NiSO_4$ [LJG] (162)

0.5	3.27
1.0	2.55
1.5	1.83

$Ni(NO_3)_2$ [LJG] (162)

0.5	3.19
1.0	2.40
1.5	1.62

$Al_2(SO_4)_3$ [JAB] (160) [LJG]

1	2.42
2	0.87

$Al(NO_3)_3$ [JAB] (161) [LJG]

%	t_m, °C
1	2.34
2	0.63

$BeSO_4$ [GS] (161)

%	t_m, °C
1	2.65

$Be(NO_3)_2$ [GS] (161)

%	t_m, °C
1	2.69
2	1.35

$MgCl_2$ [GS] (161)

%	t_m, °C
1	2.54
2	1.16

$MgSO_4$ [GS] (160, 375)

%	t_m, °C
1	2.35
2	0.75
1.85	+ 0.13
4.84	− 8.2
9.61	−20.7
14.37	−46.3

$Mg(NO_3)_2$ [GS] (161)

%	t_m, °C
1	2.23
2	0.40

$CaCl_2$ [GS] (132)**; (146)

%	t_m, °C
1	0.58

$CaBr_2$ [GS] (132)

%	t_m, °C
1	1.83

CaI_2 [GS] (132)

%	t_m, °C
1	2.03

$CaSO_4$ [GS] (160)

%	t_m, °C
0.2	3.56

$Ca(NO_3)_2$ [GS] (161)

%	t_m, °C
1	2.16
2	0.32

$SrCl_2$ [GS] (161)

%	t_m, °C
1	2.62
2	1.19

SrI_2 [GS] (397, 398)

%	t_m, °C
1	3.31

$Sr(NO_3)_2$ [GS] (161, 375)

%	t_m, °C
1	2.44
2	+ 1.34
4	− 6.1
8	− 15.3
15	− 49.6
25	−106

$BaCl_2$ [GS] (128)

%	t_m, °C
1	2.82
2	1.62
3	+0.42
4	−0.85

$BaBr_2$ [GS] (132)

%	t_m, °C
1	2.17
2	0.42

BaI_2 [GS] (132)

%	t_m, °C
1	2.42

$Ba(NO_3)_2$ [GS] (161)**; (397, 398)

%	t_m, °C
1	2.67
2	1.49

LiCl [JAB] (129, 131)**; (656)

%	t_m, °C
1	2.58
2	+1.10
3	−0.46
4	−2.07
5	−3.71

LiBr [JAB] (130, 131)**; (656)

%	t_m, °C
1	3.17
2	2.34
3	1.48
4	0.58

LiI [JAB] (130, 131)**; (656)

%	t_m, °C
1	3.38
2	2.75
3	2.09
4	1.40
5	+0.68
6	−0.05

Li_2SO_4 [JAB] (160)

%	t_m, °C
1	2.20
2	0.44

$LiNO_3$ [JAB] (161)**; (656)

%	t_m, °C
1	2.09
2	+0.23
4	−3.5
6	−7.2

NaCl [JAB] (127, 129, 131, 396, 397)**; (142, 146, 147, 219, 227, 522, 523, 524, 656)

%	t_m, °C
1	+ 1.77
2	− 0.57
3	− 3.04
4	− 5.61
5	− 8.26
6	−10.98
7	−13.76
8	−16.60

NaBr [JAB] (131)**; (656)

%	t_m, °C
1	2.54
2	+1.12
3	−0.30

NaI [JAB] (131)**; (656)

%	t_m, °C
1	2.84
2	1.68
3	0.47

Na_2SO_4 [JAB] (127, 160);** (147, 219, 397, 522, 523, 524, 585, 656)

%	t_m, °C
1	+ 1.67
2	− 0.64

Na_2SO_4.—(*Cont'd.*)

%	t_m, °C
3	− 2.97
4	− 5.31
5	− 7.67
6	−10.04
7	−12.43

$NaHSO_4$ [JAB] (656)

%	t_m, °C
1	+ 1
2	− 1
4	− 7
6	−13
8	−19
10	−25
12	−31

$NaNO_3$ [JAB] (161)**; (375, 397, 398, 656)

%	t_m, °C
1	+1.69
2	−0.58

Na_2CO_3 [JAB] (147)

%	t_m, °C
1	+ 0.9
2	− 2.2
4	− 8.3
6	−14.5

$Na_2C_2O_4$, Oxalate [JAB] (656)

%	t_m, °C
1	+1.6
2	−0.8
3	−3.2
4	−5.6

$NaCHO_2$, Formate [JAB] (656)

%	t_m, °C
1	+2.0
2	0.0
3	−2.0
4	−4.0
5	−6.1
6	−8.1

$NaHC_2O_4$, Acid oxalate [JAB] (656)

%	t_m, °C
1	2.3
2	+0.5
3	−1.3

$NaC_2H_3O_2$, Acetate [JAB] (656)

%	t_m, °C
1	2.6
2	+1.1
3	−0.3
4	−1.8
5	−3.4
6	−5.1
7	−6.9

$NaC_3H_5O_2$, Propionate [JAB] (656)

%	t_m, °C
1	2.7
2	+1.4
4	−1.3
6	−4.1
8	−6.9

$NaC_4H_5O_4$, Acid succinate [JAB] (656)

%	t_m, °C
1	2.5
2	+1.1
3	−0.4
4	−1.8

$Na_2C_4H_4O_4$, Succinate [JAB] (656)

%	t_m, °C
1	2.5
2	+1.0
3	−0.6

KOH [JAB] (147)

%	t_m, °C
1	+ 1.4
2	− 1.2
4	− 6.8
6	−13.0

KCl [JAB] (127, 129, 131)**; (227, 656)

%	t_m, °C
1	2.39
2	+0.82
3	−0.75

KBr [JAB] (131)**; (375, 656)

%	t_m, °C
1	2.91
2	1.81
3	+0.66
4	−0.54

KI [JAB] (127, 131)**; (656)

%	t_m, °C
1	3.04
2	2.09

KI.—(*Cont'd.*)

%	t_m, °C
3	1.11
4	+0.10
5	−0.95

K_2SO_4 [JAB] (127, 160)**; (397)*; (147, 219, 522, 523, 524, 585)

%	t_m, °C
1	2.26
2	+0.53
3	−1.23
4	−3.02
5	−4.84
6	−6.68

KNO_3 [JAB] (161)**; (396, 398)*; (397, 656)

%	t_m, °C
1	2.23
2	0.52

K_2CO_3 [JAB] (147, 585) [LJG]

%	t_m, °C
1	+ 1.8
2	− 0.4
3	− 2.6
4	− 4.9
5	− 7.3
6	− 9.9
7	−12.7

$K_3Fe(CN)_6$ [LJG] (375)

%	t_m, °C
5	− 8
10	−21
15	−36
20	−52

RbCl [JAB] (129, 131)**

%	t_m, °C
1	3.01
2	2.03
3	+1.03
4	−0.02
5	−1.11
6	−2.24

RbBr [JAB] (131)

%	t_m, °C
2	2.35

RbI [JAB] (131)

%	t_m, °C
3	1.71

Rb_2SO_4 [JAB] (160)

%	t_m, °C
1	2.87
2	1.77
3	0.65

$RbNO_3$ [JAB] (161)

%	t_m, °C
1	2.77
2	1.55
3	0.28

CsCl [JAB] (161)

%	t_m, °C
1	3.26
2	2.54
3	1.79
4	1.01

Cs_2SO_4 [JAB] (160)

%	t_m, °C
1	3.10
2	2.23

$CsNO_3$ [JAB] (161)

%	t_m, °C
1	3.06
2	2.12
3	1.17

Two or More Solutes

Sea Water [JAB] (380, 408, 445, 522, 523, 524, 636)

Wt. % Cl	0.5	1.0	1.5	2.0
Wt. % total solids	0.91	1.81	2.71	3.61
t_m, °C	2.4	0.5	−1.3	−3.2

For other solutions, *v.* (108, 227, 398).

LITERATURE

(For a key to the periodicals see end of volume)

(1) Abegg, *7*, **11**: 248; 93. (2) Agerer, *75*, **114 IIa**: 803; 05. (3) Almén, *388*, **55**: 735; 98. (4) Andreae, *52*, **30**: 305; 84. (5) Andreae, *52*, **30**: 312; 84. (6) Andreae, *7*, **82**: 109; 13. (7) Anthon, *52*, **7**: 70; 36. (8) Anthon, *52*, **9**: 1; 37. (9) Anthon, *185*, **1860**: 744.

(10) Applebey, *4*, **97**: 2000; 10. (11) Archibald, *292*, **9**: 335; 97. (12) Armstrong and Wheeler, *135*, **103**: 133; 11. (13) Asch, *93*, **28**: 273; 01. (14) Atwell and Fuwa, *45*, **15**: 617; 23. (15) Bach, *7*, **9**: 241; 92. (16) Bahr, *93*, **71**: 79; 11. (17) Balareff, *93*, **71**: 70; 11. (18) Barbier and Roux, *27*, **3**: 424; 90. (19) Barker, *4*, **93**: 15; 08.

(20) Barnes and Scott, *50*, **2**: 536; 98. (21) Barnes and Johnson, *69*, **9 III**: 31; 03. (22) Barnes, *292*, **10**: 49; 99. *35*, **7**: 75; 00. (23) Bateman, *Wood Preserving*, **3**: 54; 16. (24) Baxter, Harvard University, *0*. (25) Baxter, Boylston, Mueller, Black and Goode, *1*, **33**: 901; 11. (26) Baxter and Wallace, *1*, **38**: 70; 16. (27) Becquerel, *6*, **12**: 5; 77. (28) Bedson and Williams, *25*, **14**: 2549; 81. (29) Beil, *498*, **21**: 6; 82. *185*, **1882**: 147.

(30) Beketov, *134*, **34**: 197; 92. (31) Bell and Buckley, *1*, **34**: 14; 12. (32) Bell and Taber, *50*, **10**: 119; 06. (33) Bell and Taber, *50*, **11**: 637; 07. (34) Bell and Taber, *50*, **12**: 171; 08. (35) Bencowitz and Renshaw, *1*, **47**: 1904; 25. (36) Bender, *8*, **20**: 560; 83. (37) Bender, *8*, **22**: 179; 84. (38) Bender, *8*, **31**: 872; 87. (39) Berkeley, *62*, **203**: 189; 04.

(40) Berkeley and Appleby, *5*, **85**: 489; 11. (41) Berkeley, Hartley and Burton, *62*, **209**: 177; 09. (42) Berkeley, Hartley and Stephenson, *62*, **209**: 319; 09. (43) Berthelot, *34*, **76**: 679; 73. *27*, **19**: 351; 73. (44) Berthelot, *6*, **4**: 445; 75. (45) Biltz, *7*, **40**: 185; 02. (46) Bindel, *8*, **40**: 370; 90. (47)

Biron, *53*, **31**: 171; 99. (48) Biron, *53*, **39**: 1502; 07. (49) Bischof, *499*, **23**: 619; 50.

(50) Blanchard and Pushee, *1*, **34**: 28; 12. (51) Blaszkowska, *27*, **33**: 562; 23. (52) Bock, *8*, **30**: 631; 87. (53) Bodländer, *7*, **7**: 308; 91. (54) Bodländer, *7*, **7**: 358; 91. (55) Bodländer, *7*, **9**: 730; 92. (56) de Boer, *Diss.*, Utrecht, 1913. *10*, **4**: 57; 16. (57) Bolenbaugh, *284*, **5**: 38; 16. (58) Bousfield, *7*, **53**: 257; 05. (59) Bousfield, *62*, **206**: 101; 06.

(60) Bousfield, *4*, **107**: 1405; 15. (61) Bousfield, *4*, **115**: 45; 19. (62) Bousfield and Bousfield, *5*, **103**: 429; 23. (63) Bousfield and Lowry, *62*, **204**: 253; 05. (64) Bousfield and Lowry, *83*, **6**: 85; 10. (65) Brandhorst and Kraut, *13*, **249**: 373; 88. (66) Brant, *2*, **17**: 678; 21. (67) Brauner, *4*, **53**: 357; 88. (68) Bremer, *70*, **7**: 269; 88. (69) Bremer, *7*, **3**: 423; 89.

(70) Bremer, *18*, **6**: 455; 01. (71) Bremer, *70*, **21**: 59; 02. (72) Briegleb, *13*, **97**: 95; 56. (73) Briner, Tykociner and Alfimoff, *42*, **18**: 3; 20. (74) Briner and Winkler, *42*, **20**: 201; 23. (75) Brönsted, *7*, **77**: 315; 11. (76) Bromer, *75*, **110 IIa**: 929; 01. (77) Brühl, *25*, **28**: 2847; 95. (78) Brühl, *7*, **22**: 373; 97. (79) de Brüyn, *70*, **11**: 18; 92.

(80) de Brüyn, *70*, **15**: 174; 96. (81) Buchanan, *5*, **23**: 301; 75. (82) Buchanan, *12*, **21**: 25; 06. (83) Buchanan, *68*, **31**: 635; 11. (84) Buchanan, *174*, **49**: 1; 12. (85) Buchholz, *500*, **3**: 275; 56. (86) Buchkremer, *7*, **6**: 161; 90. (87) Buliginsky, *8*, **134**: 440; 68. (88) Bussy and Buignet, *6*, **3**: 231; 64. (89) Callendar and Barnes, *5*, **62**: 117; 98.

(90) Calvert, *8*, **1**: 483; 00. (91) Cameron and Macallan, *5*, **46**: 13; 89. (92) Cameron and Bell, *50*, **10**: 210; 06. (93) Cameron and Bell, *50*, **11**: 364; 07. (94) Cameron, Bell and Robinson, *50*, **11**: 396; 07. (95) Cameron and Breazeale, *50*, **8**: 335; 04. (96) Cameron and Robinson, *50*, **11**: 273; 07. (97) Cameron and Robinson, *50*, **11**: 578; 07. (98) Cameron and Robinson, *50*, **14**: 569; 10. (99) Carlson, *Klason Festskrift*, **1911**: 247.

(100) Carse, *68*, **25**: 281; 04. (101) Cavazzi, *36*, **44 I**: 448; 14. (102) Cavazzi, *36*, **45 I**: 529; 15. (103) Chamberlain, Hume and Topley, *4*, **1926**: 2620. (104) Chapman and Messel, *54*, **4**: 520; 85. (105) Charpy, *6*, **29**: 5; 93. (106) Chéneveau, *6*, **12**: 145; 07. *250*, **1908**: 177. (107) Cherbury, Rivett and Lewis, *70*, **42**: 954; 23. (108) Cinelli, *59*, **3**: 141; 96. (109) Clark, *302*, **60**: No. 13; 12.

(110) Clausen, *8*, **37**: 51; 12. (111) Clausen, *8*, **44**: 1067; 14. (112) Clayton, *135*, **64**: 27; 91. (113) Clendinnen and Rivett, *4*, **119**: 1329; 21. (114) Cohen and Kooij, *64P*, **27**: 65; 24. *7*, **109**: 81; 24. (115) Cohen and Moesveld, *7*, **95**: 305; 20. (116) Cohen and Sinnige, *7*, **67**: 513; 09. (117) de Coninck, *34*, **131**: 1219; 00. (118) de Coninck, *186*, **1901**: 222. (119) de Coninck, *186*, **1901**: 483.

(120) de Coninck, *34*, **132**: 90; 01. (121) de Coninck, *6*, **28**: 5; 03. (122) de Coninck, *6*, **3**: 500; 04. (123) de Coninck, *34*, **142**: 571; 06. (124) de Coninck, *27*, **17**: 422; 15. (125) Conroy, *5*, **64**: 308; 99. (126) Coppadoro, *36*, **39 II**: 616; 09. (127) de Coppet, *Bull. Soc. Vaudoise Sci. Nat.*, **29**: 1; 93. (128) de Coppet, *34*, **125**: 533; 97. (129) de Coppet, *34*, **128**: 1559; 99.

(130) de Coppet, *34*, **131**: 178; 00. (131) de Coppet, *34*, **132**: 1218; 01. (132) de Coppet and Muller, *34*, **134**: 1208; 02. (133) Cornec, *6*, **29**: 490; 13. (134) Cornish, *7*, **76**: 210; 11. (135) Counson, *149*, **5**: 361; 23. (136) Dahlmann, *Württemb. Naturw. Jahreshefte*, **10**: 275; 54. *167*, **1854**: 323. (137) Damien, *Ann. Sci. l'École Norm. Supér.*, **10**: 233; 81. (138) Datta and Dhar, *1*, **38**: 1303; 16. (139) Davidts, *7*, **79**: 303; 12.

(140) Dawson and Williams, *7*, **31**: 59; 99. (141) Dawson and Williams, *50*, **4**: 370; 00. (142) Dekhuijzen, *Neder. Tidsch. Geneeskunde*, **66 I**: 2304; 22. (143) Delachanal, *6*, **12**: 141; 77. (144) Delaite, *501*, **51**: 18; 95. (145) Demolis, *42*, **4**: 528; 06. (146) Despretz, *34*, **4**: 435; 37. *8*, **41**: 58; 37. (147) Despretz, *6*, **70**: 49; 39. (148) Deussen, *93*, **49**: 297; 06. (149) Diemer and Lenher, *50*, **13**: 505; 09.

(150) Dijken, *7*, **24**: 81; 97. (151) Dinkhauser, *75*, **114 IIa**: 1001; 05. (152) Dito, *64P*, **4**: 756; 02. (153) Dittman, *B81*, **I**: 1889. (154) Divers and Shimidzu, *4*, **45**: 270; 84. (155) Dixon and Taylor, *4*, **97**: 927; 10. (156) Domke and Bein, *93*, **43**: 125; 05. *90*, **5**: 5; 04. (157) Dossios and Weith, *467*, **5**: 379; 69. (158) Doumer, **Thesis**, Paris, 1892. *B3*, **I**: 402; 23. (159) Drecker, *8*, **34**: 952; 88.

(160) Dreyer, *169*, **12**: 32; 09. (161) Dreyer, *169*, **14**: 193; 10. (162) Dreyer, *169*, **11**: 662; 09. *10*, **1**: 30; 10. (163) Dunn, *54*, **21**: 390; 02. (164) Ebeling, *8*, **30**: 530; 87. (165) Eckelt, *92*, **1898**: 298. *136*, **22**: 225; 98. (166) Eder, *75*, **82 II**: 1284; 80. (167) Edwards, *11*, **16**: 625; 94. (168) Ekman, *468*, **9**: No. 4; 70. (169) Elbs and Schönherr, *9*, **2**: 245; 95.

(170) Ellis, *1*, **38**: 737; 16. (171) van Emster, *93*, **52**: 270; 07. (172) Engel, *27*, **45**: 653; 86. (173) Engel, *27*, **47**: 318; 87. (174) Engel, *34*, **104**: 433; 87. (175) Engel, *34*, **104**: 506; 87. (176) Engel, *34*, **104**: 911; 87. (177) Engel, *6*, **13**: 370; 88. (178) Engel, *6*, **17**: 338; 89. (179) Engel, *27*, **6**: 15; 91.

(180) Engel, *34*, **112**: 1130; 91. (181) Erman, *8*, **101**: 577; 57. (182) Étard, *6*, **2**: 503; 94. (183) Euler, *7*, **49**: 303; 04. (184) Ewing and MacGregor, *174*, **27**: 51; 72. (185) Fajans and Lembert, *93*, **95**: 297; 16. (186) Farrow, *4*, **1926**: 49. (187) Favre and Valson, *34*, **75**: 330; 72. (188) Favre and Valson, *34*, **75**: 798; 72. (189) Favre and Valson, *34*, **77**: 577; 73.

(190) Favre and Valson, *34*, **77**: 802; 73. (191) Favre and Valson, *34*, **77**: 907; 73. (192) Favre and Valson, *34*, **79**: 968; 74. (193) Fedotiev, *7*, **49**: 162; 04. (194) Fedotiev, *93*, **73**: 173; 11. (195) Fedotiev and Koltunov, *169*, **20**: 410; 13. *93*, **85**: 247; 14. (196) Ferchland, *93*, **30**: 130; 02. (197) Ferguson, *54*, **24**: 781; 05. *92*, **19**: 342; 06. (198) Findlay and Creighton, *4*, **97**: 536; 10. (199) Findlay and Shen, *4*, **101**: 1459; 12.

(200) Fink, *8*, **26**: 481; 85. (201) Flatt, *Diss.*, Zürich, 1923. (202) Fock, *94*, **28**: 337; 97. (203) Forch, *8*, **55**: 100; 95. (204) Forchheimer, *7*, **34**: 20; 00. (205) Forster, *Mitt. d. Naturf. Ges. Bern*, **1878**: 3. (206) Fouqué, *Ann. Observ. Paris*, **9**: 172; 68. (207) Franz, *52*, **4**: 238; 71. (208) Franz, *52*, **5**: 274; 72. (209) Fresenius and Grünhut, *91*, **51**: 23; 12.

(210) Fresenius and Grünhut, *91*, **51**: 104; 12. (211) Freund, *7*, **66**: 555; 09. (212) Fricke, *93*, **139**: 419; 24. (213) Friedheim and Castendyck, *25*, **33**: 1611; 00. (214) Fuchs, *92*, **1898**: 745. (215) Fuchs, *92*, **1898**: 909. (216) Funk, *25*, **33**: 3696; 00. (217) Funk, Wrochem, Mylius and Dietz, *89*, **3**: 427; 00. (218) Geritsch, *53*, **23 I**: 343; 91. (219) Gerlach, *Salzlösungen*, Freiberg, 1859.

(220) Gerlach, *112*, **181**: 129; 66. (221) Gerlach, *91*, **8**: 245; 69. (222) Gerlach, *317*, **9**: 241; 86. (223) Gerlach, *91*, **26**: 413; 87. (224) Gerlach, *91*, **27**: 271; 88. (225) Gerlach, *91*, **28**: 466; 89. (226) Germann, *1*, **44**: 1466; 22. (227) Gerosa and Mai, *22*, **4**: 134; 87. (228) Getman, *42*, **5**: 344; 07. (229) Getman, *1*, **30**: 721; 08. (229.5) Gibson, Geophysical Laboratory, Washington, D. C., *0*.

(230) Gilbert, Buckley and Masson, *4*, **121**: 1934; 22. (231) Giles and Shearer, *54*, **4**: 303; 85. (232) Glover, *4*, **99**: 371; 11. (233) Gomez, *132*, **17**: 21; 19. *10*, **5**: 34; 22. (234) Goodwin and Horsch, *33*, **21**: 181; 19. (235) Gore, *62*, **159**: 173; 68. *4*, **22**: 368; 69. (236) Gorke, *Diss.*, Leipzig, 1905. (237) Graham, *11*, **48**: 145; 12. (238) Gray and Hulbirt, *Bull. Univer. Calif.*, **308**: 421; 19. (239) Green, *4*, **93**: 2023; 08.

(240) Green, *4*, **93**: 2049; 08. (241) Greenish and Smith, *347*, **66**: 774; 01. (242) Greenish and Smith, *347*, **66**: 806; 01. (243) Greenish and Smith, *347*, **68**: 510; 02. (244) Groschuff, *25*, **36**: 1783; 03. (245) Groschuff, *93*, **47**: 331; 05. (246) Groshans, *3*, **18**: 405; 84. (247) Grotrian, *8*, **160**: 238; 77. (248) Grotrian, *8*, **8**: 529; 79. (249) Grotrian, *8*, **18**: 177; 83.

(250) Grüneisen, *89*, **4**: 237; 05. (251) Guntz and Guntz, *6*, **2**: 101; 14. (252) Haff, *135*, **86**: 283; 02. (253) Hager, *Adjumenta varia chemica et pharmaceutica*, Leipzig, Günther, 1876. Quoted in (224). (254) Hager, *Commentar z. Pharm. Germanica*. Berlin, 1883. (255) Hahn, *1*, **20**: 621; 98. (256) Haigh, *1*, **34**: 1137; 12. (257) Hall, Jaques and Leslie, *54*, **41**: 285; 22. (258) Hall, *128*, **14**: 167; 24. (259) Hallwachs, *8*, **68**: 1; 99.

(260) Hannay, *4*, **26**: 565; 73. (261) Happart, *Mém. Soc. Roy. Sci. Liège*, **4**: No. 10; 02. (262) Harkins, *1*, **33**: 1807; 11. (263) Harkins and Paine, *1*, **38**: 2709; 16. (264) Harkins and Paine, *1*, **41**: 1155; 19. (265) Harkins and Pearce, *1*, **38**: 2679; 16. (266) Harkins and Pearce, *1*, **38**: 2714; 16. (267) Hart, *320*, **3**: 372; 90. *91*, **29**: 444; 90. (268) Hartley and Barrett, *4*, **99**: 1072; 11. (269) Hartley and Barrett, *4*, **123**: 398; 23.

(270) Hassenfratz, *6*, **28**: 282; 1799. (271) de Heen, *501*, **31**: 38; 81. *Physique Comparée*. Paris, 1888. (272) Heermann, *136*, **31**: 680; 07. (273) Heimbrodt, *8*, **13**: 1028; 04. (274) Henderson and Kellogg, *1*, **35**: 396, 13. (275) Hensgen, *52*, **72**: 345; 05. (276) Hertlein, *7*, **19**: 287; 96. (277) Herz, *93*, **86**: 338; 14. (278) Herz, *93*, **89**: 393; 14. (279) Herz, *93*, **102**: 173; 18.

(280) Herz and Anders, *93*, **52**: 165; 07. (281) Herz and Anders, *93*, **55**: 271; 07. (282) Herz and Knoch, *93*, **41**: 315; 04. (283) Herz and Knoch, *93*, **45**: 262; 05. (284) Herz and Kuhn, *93*, **58**: 159; 08. (285) Herz and Martin, *93*, **132**: 41; 23. (286) Hess, *75*, **114 IIa**: 1231; 05. (287) Heydweiller, *8*, **30**: 873; 09. (288) Heydweiller, *8*, **37**: 739; 12. (289) Heydweiller, *93*, **88**: 103; 14.

(290) Heydweiller, *8*, **48**: 681; 15. (291) Heydweiller, *93*, **116**: 42; 21. (292) Hill, *68*, **27**: 233; 07. (293) Hill, *1*, **44**: 1163; 22. (294) Hill and Simmons, *1*, **31**: 821; 09. (295) Hill and Simmons, *7*, **67**: 594; 09. (296) Hill and Sirkar, *5*, **83**: 130; 09. (297) Hofmann, *8*, **133**: 575; 68. (298) Holland, *8*, **50**: 349; 93. (299) Holler and Peffer, *1*, **38**: 1021; 16. *31A*, **13**: 273; 16.

(300) Holmes and Sageman, *4*, **91**: 1606; 07. (301) Holt and Myers, *4*, **103**: 533; 13. (302) Hooker, *33*, **23**: 961; 20. (303) Horn, *11*, **37**: 467; 07. (304) Hosking, *3*, **7**: 469; 04. (305) Howell, *4*, **1927**: 158. (306) Hulett and Bonner, *1*, **31**: 390; 09. (307) Humberg, *7*, **12**: 401; 93. (308) Irueste, *132*, **13**: 462; 15. (309) Ishikawa, *41*, **43**: 560; 22.

(310) Jackson, *4*, **36**: 2346; 14. (311) Jacquelain, *6*, **30**: 343; 50. (312) Jahn, *8*, **43**: 280; 91. (313) Jahn *et al.*, *7*, **37**: 673; 01. (314) Jaquerod, *42*, **7**: 129; 09. (315) Jones and Hartmann, *1*, **37**: 241; 15. (316) Jones and Hartmann, *78*, **30**: 295; 16. (317) Jones and Schumb, *65*, **56**: 199; 21. (318) Jones, *7*, **55**: 385; 06. (319) Jones, *152*, No. **60**: 07.

(320) Jones and Bassett, *11*, **33**: 534; 05. (321) Jones and Bassett, *11*, **34**: 290; 05. (322) Jones and Getman, *7*, **49**: 385; 04. (323) Jones and Pearce, *11*, **38**: 683; 07. (324) Jones, Lapworth and Lingford, *4*, **103**: 252; 13. (325) Joseph, *4*, **107**: 1; 15. (326) Joseph, *4*, **117**: 377; 20. (327) Kaemmerer, *8*, **138**: 390; 69. (328) Kanitz, *7*, **22**: 336; 97. (329) Kanonnikoff, *52*, **31**: 321; 85.

(330) Kantele, *138*, **1**: No. 6; 22. (331) Karsten, *499*, **20**: 3; 46. *Verhalten d. Auflös. d. Kochsalzes*. Berlin, Reimer, 1846. (332) Katayama and Yemada, *41*, **41**: 207; 20. (333) King, *50*, **25**: 115; 21. (334) Klein, *8*, **27**: 151; 86. (335) Knietsch, *25*, **34**: 4069; 01. (336) Knöfler, *8*, **38**: 136; 89. (337) Knorre and Olschewsky, *25*, **20**: 3043; 87. (338) Knowlton and Mounce, *45*, **13**: 1157; 21. (339) Knudsen, *Hydrographische Tabellen*. Copenhagen, 1901.

(340) Kohlrausch, *8*, **159**: 233; 76. (341) Kohlrausch, *8 Ergzbd.*, **8**: 675; 78. (342) Kohlrausch, *8*, **6**: 1; 79. (343) Kohlrausch, *8*, **6**: 145; 79. (344) Kohlrausch, *8*, **26**: 161; 85. (345) Kohlrausch, *7*, **12**: 773; 93. (346) Kohlrausch, *8*, **56**: 185; 95. (347) Kohlrausch and Grotrian, *8*, **154**: 215; 75. (348) Kohlrausch and Hallwachs, *8*, **50**: 118; 93. *188*, **1893**: 350. (349) Kohlrausch and Hallwachs, *8*, **53**: 14; 94.

(350) Kohlrausch and Nippoldt, *8*, **138**: 370; 69. (351) Kohlrausch, *8*, **17**: 69; 82. (352) Kolb, *34*, **63**: 314; 66. *6*, **10**: 136; 67. (353) Kolb, *Bull. Soc. Ind. Mulhouse*, **42**: 209; 72. *112*, **209**: 268; 73. (354) Kolb, *34*, **74**: 737; 72. *112*, **204**: 322; 72. (355) Kopp, *13*, **93**: 129; 55. (356) Kopp, quoted in (224). (357) Koppel and Holtkamp, *93*, **67**: 266; 10. (358) Kraus and Parker, *1*, **44**: 2429; 22. (359) Kremann and Ehrlich, *75*, **116 IIb**: 733; 07.

(360) Kremers, *8*, **95**: 110; 55. (361) Kremers, *8*, **96**: 39; 55. (362) Kremers, *8*, **98**: 58; 56. (363) Kremers, *8*, **99**: 435; 56. (364) Kremers, *8*, **100**: 394; 57. (365) Kremers, *8*, **103**: 57; 58. (366) Kremers, *8*, **104**: 133; 58. (367) Kremers, *8*, **105**: 360; 58. (368) Kremers, *8*, **108**: 115; 59. (369) Kremers, *8*, **111**: 60; 60.

(370) Kremers, *8*, **114**: 41; 61. (371) Kremers, *8*, **120**: 493; 63. (372) Küster and Kremann, *93*, **41**: 1; 04. (373) Lamb and Lee, *1*, **35**: 1666; 13. (374) Landesen, *322*, No. **14**; 04. (375) de Lannoy, *7*, **18**: 443; 95. (376) Lauenstein, *7*, **9**: 417; 92. (377) Le Blanc, *7*, **4**: 553; 89. (378) Le Blanc and Rohland, *7*, **19**: 261; 96. (379) Lemoine, *34*, **125**: 603; 97.

(380) Lenz, *504*, **29**: No. 4; 81. (381) Lewis, *Diss.*, Breslau, 1908. (382) Lichty, *1*, **25**: 469; 03. (383) van Liempt, *93*, **122**: 175; 22. (384) Long, *8*, **11**: 37; 80. (385) Loomis, *8*, **57**: 495; 96. (386) Loomis, *8*, **60**: 523; 97. (387) Loomis, *8*, **60**: 547; 97. (388) Lorenz and Osswald, *93*, **114**: 209; 20. (389) Lunge and Bachofen, *92*, **6**: 326; 93.

(390) Lunge and Isler, *92*, **11**: 129; 90. *54*, **9**: 501; 90. (391) Lunge and Marchlewski, *92*, **11**: 133; 91. (392) Lunge and Naef, *317*, **6**: 37; 83. (393) Lunge and Naef, *317*, **6**: 128; 83. (394) Lunge and Rey, *92*, **11**: 165; 91. (395) Lunge and Smith, *317*, **6**: 2; 83. (396) Lussana, *59*, **2**: 233; 95. (397) Lussana and Bozzola, *24*, **4**: 785; 92. (398) Lussana and Bozzola, *59*, **35**: 31; 93. (399) Maas and Hatcher, *1*, **42**: 2548; 20.

(400) MacGregor, *69*, **2 III**: 70; 84. (401) MacGregor, *69*, **3 III**: 15; 85. (402) MacGregor, *135*, **55**: 3; 87. (403) MacGregor, *292*, **7**: 368; 89. (404) MacGregor, *69*, **7 III**: 23; 89. (405) MacGregor, *69*, **8 III**: 19; 90. (406) MacGregor, *135*, **62**: 223; 90. (406.5) MacGregor, *69*, **9 III**: 16; 91. (407) MacGregory, *8*, **51**: 126; 94. (408) Makaroff, *53*, **23 II**: 31; 91. (408.5) Manley, *68*, **27**: 210; 07. (409) Marignac, *149*, **39**: 217; 70. *6*, **22**: 385; 71.

(410) Marshall, *54*, **21**: 1508; 02. (411) Masson, *4*, **99**: 1132; 11. (412) Masson, *4*, **101**: 103; 12. (413) Matignon, *6*, **8**: 386; 06. (414) Mazzucchelli and Anselmi, *36*, **52**: 147; 22. (415) McKay, *35*, **6**: 111; 99. (416) M'David, *68*, **30**: 515; 10. (417) Mendelĕev, *53*, **16**: 184; 84. (417.5) Mendelĕev, *53*, **16 I**: 184; 84. (418) Mendelĕev, *53*, **16 I**: 455; 84. *25*, **17**: 2536; 84. (419) Mendelĕev, *7*, **1**: 273; 87. *25*, **19**: 379, 400; 86.

(420) Merton, *4*, **97**: 2454; 10. (421) Meusser, *25*, **35**: 1414; 02. (422) Meyer, *8*, **113**: 383; 61. (423) Meyer, *Diss.*, Erlangen, 1921. (424) Meyerhoffer, *7*, **53**: 513; 05. (425) Michel and Krafft, *6*, **41**: 471; 54. (426) Michel and Krafft, *167*, **1854**: 295. (427) Milligan, *1*, **44**: 567; 22. (428) Moeller, *7*, **12**: 555; 93. (429) Möller, *8*, **7**: 256; 02.

(430) Moles, Marquina and Santos, *132*, **11**: 192; 13. (431) Mond and Nasini, *7*, **8**: 150; 91. (432) Moore, *2*, **3**: 321; 96. (433) Moretto, *59*, **6**: 198; 97. (434) Morgan and McKirahan, *1*, **35**: 1759; 13. (435) Morrison, *292*, **7**: 481; 89. (436) Muchin and Tarle, *181*, **43**: 54; 16. *10*, **4**: 57; 21. (437) Mueller and Abegg, *7*, **57**: 513; 07. (438) Müller and Kaufmann, *7*, **42**: 497; 03. (439) Muir, *135*, **33**: 15; 76.

(440) de Muynck, *8*, **53**: 559; 94. (441) Mylius and Dietz, *25*, **34**: 2774; 01. (442) Mylius and Funk, *25*, **30**: 1716; 97. (443) Mylius and Funk, *25*, **33**: 3686; 00. (444) Nasini and Gennari, *7*, **19**: 113; 96. (445) von Neumann, *8*, **113**: 382; 61. (446) Nicol, *25*, **15**: 1931; 82. (447) Nicol, *68*, **11**: 819; 82. (448) Nicol, *3*, **15**: 91; 83. (449) Nicol, *3*, **16**: 121; 83.

(450) Nicol, *3*, **17**: 537; 84. (451) Nicol, *3*, **18**: 179; 84. (452) Nicol, *3*, **23**: 385; 87. (453) Nietzki, in *B82*, **III**: 808; 00. (454) Nietzki, in *B82*, **IV**: 691; 11. (455) Noyes, *152*, No. **63**: 81; 07. (456) Noyes, Hall and Beattie, *1*, **39**: 2526; 17. (457) Noyes and Lombard, *1*, **33**: 1423; 11. (458) Noyes and Stewart, *1*, **32**: 1151; 10. (459) Oppenheimer, *7*, **27**: 447; 98.

(460) Ordway, *12*, **40**: 173; 65. (461) Ordway, *12*, **40**: 316; 65. (462) Ostwald, *8*, **2**: 429; 77. (462.5) Ostwald, *52*, **16**: 385; 77. (463) Ostwald, *52*, **18**: 328; 78. (464) Oswald, *8 Ergzbd.*, **8**: 154; 78. (465) Ostwald, *52*, **22**: 305; 80. (466) Ostwald, *52*, **16**: 385; 87. (467) Oswald, *34*, **155**: 1504; 12. (468) Oswald, *6*, **1**: 32; 14. (469) Oudemans, *91*, **7**: 419; 68.

(470) Page and Keightley, *4*, **25**: 566; 72. (471) Parsons and Corliss, *1*, **32**: 1367; 10. (472) Parsons and Corson, *1*, **32**: 1383; 10. (473) Parsons and Perkins, *1*, **32**: 1387; 10. (474) Parsons and Whittemore, *1*, **33**: 1933; 11. (475) Pascal, *315*, **20**: 17; 23. (476) Pascal and Garnier, *27*, **25**: 142; 19. (477) Pasea, *69*, **6**: 27; 00. (478) Patterson, *1*, **28**: 1734; 06. (479) Patterson and Anderson, *4*, **101**: 1833; 12.

(480) Paul, *9*, **23**: 65; 17. (481) Pawlewski, *25*, **33**: 1223; 00. (482) Perkin, *4*, **49**: 777; 86. (483) Perkin, *4*, **55**: 680; 89. (484) Perkin, *4*, **59**: 981; 91. (485) Perkin, *4*, **63**: 57; 93. (486) Perkin, *4*, **65**: 20; 94. (487) Perlezveich, *Thesis*, Zürich, 1915. (488) Piccard and Cherbuliez, *149*, **42**: 324; 16. (489) Pickering, *4*, **57**: 64; 90.

(490) Pickering, *3*, **36**: 111; 93. (491) Pickering, *25*, **26**: 277; 93. (492) Pickering, *3*, **37**: 359; 94. (493) Pickering, *25*, **27**: 1379; 94. (494) Pictet, *34*, **119**: 642; 94. (495) Pound, *4*, **121**: 941; 22. (496) Pratolongo, *Ric. R. Sc. Agr. Milan*, **4**: 3; 13. (497) Precht, *91*, **18**: 509; 79. (498) Přibram and Glücksmann, *75*, **106 IIb**: 466; 97. (499) Přibram and Glücksmann, *75*, **107 IIb**: 189; 98.

(500) Přibram and Glücksmann, *75*, **107 IIb**: 198; 98. (501) Přibram and Glücksmann, *57*, **19**: 161; 98. (502) Přibram and Glücksmann, *57*, **19**: 171; 98. (503) Price and Hawkins, *54*, **43**: 113T; 24. (504) Pützer, *136*, **29**: 1221; 05. (505) Pulvermacher, *93*, **113**: 141; 20. (506) Quincke, *8*, **24**: 347; 85. (507) Rabinovich, *7*, **99**: 338; 21. (508) Rabinovich, *7*, **99**: 417; 21. (509) Rakshit, *9*, **31**: 97; 25.

(510) Rakshit, *9*, **31**: 320; 25. (511) Ranken and Taylor, *174*, **45**: 397; 06. (512) Reinitzer, *92*, **26**: 456; 13. (513) Reuss, *25*, **17**: 2888; 84. (514) Reyher, *7*, **2**: 744; 88. (515) Richards and Gucker, *1*, **47**: 1876; 25. (516) Rimbach, *7*, **16**: 671; 95. (517) Rimbach and Wintgen, *7*, **74**: 233; 10. (518) Rivett and Rosenblum, *83*, **9**: 297; 13. (519) Röntgen and Schneider, *8*, **29**: 165; 86.

(520) Röntgen and Schneider, *8*, **34**: 531; 88. (521) Roscoe, *4*, **16**: 82; 63. (522) Rosetti, *24*, **13**: 1419; 68. (523) Rosetti, *6*, **17**: 370; 69. (524) Rosetti, *8 Ergzbd.*, **5**: 258; 71. (525) Ross and Jones, *45*, **17**: 1170; 25. (526) Roth, *7*, **24**: 114; 97. (527) Ruby and Kawai, *1*, **48**: 1119; 26. (528) Rupert, *1*, **31**: 851; 09. (529) Ruppin, *7*, **14**: 467; 94.

(530) Sachanov, *9*, **19**: 588; 13. (531) Sachanov and Rabinovich, *53*, **47**: 859; 15. (532) Scheibler, *52*, **83**: 273; 61. (533) Schiff, *13*, **108**: 326; 58. (534) Schiff, *13*, **109**: 325; 59. (535) Schiff, *13*, **110**: 67; 59. (536) Schiff, *13*, **113**: 183; 60. (537) Schiff, *13*, **113**: 349; 60. (538) Schiff, *13*, **114**: 68; 60. (539) Schiff, *13*, **118**: 90; 61.

(540) Schiff, *8*, **129**: 292; 66. (541) Schiff and Monsacchi, *7*, **21**: 277; 96. (542) Schiff and Monsacchi, *7*, **24**: 513; 97. (543) Schiff and Monsacchi, *36*, **27 I**: 117; 97. (544) Schmidt, *8*, **102**: 122; 57. (545) Schmidt, *8*, **107**: 244; 59. (546) Schneider, *13*, **207**: 257; 81. (547) Schneider, *57*, **11**: 166; 90. (548) Schneider, *Diss.*, Rostock, 1910. *10*, **2**: 8; 11. (549) Schoenfeld, *13*, **95**: 1; 55.

(550) Schönrock, *7*, **11**: 753; 93. (551) Schöttner, *75*, **77 II**: 682; 78. (552) Schröder, *53*, **18 I**: 18; 86. (553) Schütt, *7*, **5**: 349; 90. (554) Schult, *Forhandl. Skand. Naturf., Christiana*, **10**: 450; 68. Quoted in (224). (555) Schulze, *91*, **21**: 167; 82. (556) Schuncke, *7*, **14**: 331; 94. (557) Schwers, *42*, **9**: 325; 11. (558) Scott and Frazier, *50*, **31**: 459; 27. (559) Seidell, *464*, No. **67**; 11.

(560) Seidell and Smith, *50*, **8**: 493; 04. (561) Sentis, *Ann. l'Univ. Grenoble*, **9**: 1; 97. (562) Sidgwick, Pickford and Wilsdon, *4*, **99**: 1122; 11. (563) Sidgwick and Tizard, *4*, **97**: 957; 10. (564) Simeon, *3*, **27**: 95; 14. (565) Slessor, *410*, **7**: 287; 58. (566) Slotte, *8*, **14**: 13; 81. (567) Smith and Eastlack, *1*, **38**: 1261; 16. (568) Smith, *1*, **42**: 259; 20. (569) Sobolew, *93*, **12**: 16; 96.

(570) Somersalo, *60*, **56 A**: No. 10; 14. (571) Sonnenthal, *7*, **9**: 656; 92. (572) Souminen, *138*, **1**: No. 8; 22. (573) Sprung, *8*, **159**: 1; 76. (574) Squires, *91*, **30**: 609; 91. *320*, **5**: 52; 91. (575) Stanley, *135*, **54**: 194; 86. (576) Stearn, *1*, **44**: 670; 22. (577) Steele and Mellor, *82*, **14**: 164; 15. (578) Stericker, *Diss.*, Pittsburgh, 1922. (579) Stolba, *52*, **94**: 406; 65.

(580) Stolba, *52*, **97**: 503; 66. (581) Stolba, *185*, **1877**: 418. (582) Stolba, *185*, **1883**: 292. (583) Sullivan, *7*, **28**: 523; 99. (584) Sullivan, *1*, **27**: 529; 05. (585) Tammann, *7*, **14**: 163; 94. (586) Tammann, *7*, **16**: 91; 95. (587) Tammann, *7*, **17**: 620; 95. (588) Tammann and Zepernick, *7*, **16**: 659; 95. (589) Taylor and Ranken, *68*, **25 I**: 231; 04.

(590) Terlikowski, *Thesis*, Geneva, 1911. *10*, **2**: 443; 11. (591) Thing and Taylor, The Brown Co., Berlin, New Hampshire, U. S. A., *0*. (592) Thomsen, *8*, **142**: 337; 71. (593) Thomsen, *8 Ergzb. Jubelbd.*, **1874**: 135. (594) Thomsen, *25*, **7**: 71; 74. (595) Thomsen, *Thermochemische Untersuchungen*. Leipzig, 1882. (596) Thomsen, *497*, **26**: 322; 19. (597) Thorpe and Rücker, *62*, **166**: 405; 77. (598) Tigerstedt, *138*, **1**: No. 5; 22. (599) Timofeev, *7*, **86**: 113; 13.

(600) Topsöe, *25*, **3**: 402; 70. (601) Tourneux, *6*, **11**: 225; 19. (602) Traube, *93*, **8**: 12; 95. (603) Trimble, *1*, **44**: 451; 22. (604) Trötsch, *8*, **41**: 259; 90. (605) Tschernaj, *53*, **20 I**: 430; 88. (606) Tschernaj, *53*, **20 I**: 486; 88. (607) Tschernaj, *53*, **20 I**: 494; 88. (608) Tschernaj, *53*, **21 I**: 73; 89. (609) Tschernaj, *53*, **21 I**: 176; 89.

(610) Tschernaj, *53*, **40**: 518; 08. (611) Tschernaj, *53*, **44**: 1565; 12. (612) Tschernaj, *53*, **46**: 8; 14. (613) Tucker, *67*, **25**: 111; 13. (614) Tutton, *4*, **71**: 846; 97. (615) Tutton, *4*, **83**: 1049; 03. (616) Tuuha, *60*, **57 A**: No. 18; 15. (617) Ure, *503*, **13**: 312; 1822. (618) Valson, *34*, **74**: 103; 72. (619) Varga, *Diss.*, Budapest, 1911. *10*, **2**: 8; 11.

(620) Vassiliev, *53*, **43**: 1183; 11. *185*, **1912 I**: 1430. (621) Veley and Manley, *5*, **69**: 86; 01. (622) Veley and Manley, *3*, **3**: 118; 02. (623) Veley and Manley, *4*, **83**: 1015; 03. (624) Veley and Manley, *54*, **22**: 1227; 03. (625) Vesterberg, *172*, **8 II**: 235; 12. *185*, **1913**: 777. (626) Vorländer and Schilling, *13*, **310**: 369; 00. (627) Wade, *4*, **75**: 254; 99. (628) Wagner, *8*, **18**: 259; 83. (629) Wagner, *7*, **5**: 31; 90.

(630) Walker, *3*, **27**: 288; 14. (631) Wanklyn, *135*, **55**: 217; 87. (632) Wasastjerna, *426*, **50**: No. 2; 20. (633) Washburn and MacInnes, *1*, **33**: 1686; 11.

(634) Watts, *135*, **12**: 160; 65. (635) Watts, *4*, **19**: 499; 66. (636) Weber, *Ber. Untersch. deut. Meer*, **3**: 1; 78. *427*, **2**: 696; 78. (637) Wegscheider, *57*, **27**: 13; 06. (638) Wegscheider and Amann, *57*, **36**: 633; 15. (639) Wegscheider and Walter, *57*, **26**: 685; 05.
(640) Wernicke, *Diss.*, Buenos Aires, 1912. *10*, **3**: 20; 12. (641) Wershoven, *7*, **5**: 481; 90. (642) Wiener, *202*, **71**: 120; 11. (643) Willigen, *502*, **1**: 74; 68. *18*, **3**: 122; 68. (644) Willigen, *502*, **2**: 222; 69. (645) Willigen, *502*, **2**: 238; 69. (646) Willigen, *502*, **3**: 15; 74. (647) Winteler, *9*, **7**: 360; 00. (648) Winteler, *92*, **15**: 33; 02. (649) Winteler, *136*, **29**: 689; 05.
(650) Winther, *7*, **41**: 161; 02. (651) Wirth, *93*, **58**: 213; 08. (652) Withrow, *45*, **9**: 771; 17. (653) Worden and Motion, *54*, **24**: 178; 05. (654) Wright, *135*, **23**: 253; 71. (655) Wright and Thompson, *3*, **17**: 377; 84. (656) Wright, *4*, **115**: 119; 19. (657) Wüllner, *8*, **133**: 1; 68. (658) van Wyk, *93*, **48**: 1; 05. (659) Yajnik and Uberoy, *1*, **46**: 802; 24.
(660) Zecchini, *36*, **35 II**: 65; 05. (661) Zettnow, *8*, **143**: 474; 71. (662) Zöppritz, *8 Ergzbd.*, **5**: 497; 71. (663) Zoppellari, *36*, **24 II**: 396; 94. (664) Andréef, *13*, **110**: 1; 59. (665) Baud and Gay, *6*, **17**: 398; 09. (666) Berthelot, *34*, **76**: 1041; 73. *6*, **4**: 513, 526; 75. (667) Gerlach, *317*, **12**: 97; 89. (668) Lunge, *317*, **5**: 320; 82. (669) Lunge and Wiernik, *92*, **2**: 181; 89.
(670) Nichols and Wheeler, *3*, **11**: 113; 81. (671) Wachsmuth, *293*, **208**: 510; 76. (672) Bredig and Shirado, *9*, **33**: 209; 27.

DENSITIES (SPECIFIC GRAVITIES) AND THERMAL EXPANSION OF AQUEOUS SOLUTIONS OF ORGANIC COMPOUNDS*

J. L. CRENSHAW

EXPLANATORY

The reader should consult only Table 1, Sec. A, and Table 2. These together constitute a complete index to the subject.

REMARQUE

Le lecteur ne devra consulter que la Table 1, Sec. A, et la Table 2, dont l'ensemble constitue un index complet sur ce sujet.

BEMERKUNG

Man benütze nur die Tabelle 1, Abtlg. A und Tabelle 2. Diese beiden zusammen bilden das vollständige Verzeichnis über diesen Abschnitt.

AVVERTENZA

Si consultino solo la Tabella 1, Sezione A, e la Tabella 2. Le due tabelle costituiscono l'indice completo di questo capitolo.

TABLE 1

d (resp. d_w, d_s) = density of the solution [resp. water (*v.* p. 24), resp. the pure liquid solute] in g/ml. p_s (resp. p_w) = weight % of solute (resp. water) in the solution. "Range" = range of applicability of the equation. ± indicates the maximum error which will probably occur in the range given. Under "Literature" are given the sources (used) of the data upon which the equation is based and (conf.) of confirmatory determinations.

TABLE 1

d (resp. d_w, d_s) = densité de la solution [resp. eau (*v.* p. 24) ou le liquide pur dissout] en g/ml. p_s (resp. p_w) = % poids du corps dissout (resp. de l'eau) dans la solution. "Range" = intervalle d'application de l'équation. ± indique l'erreur maximum qui peut résulter dans l'intervalle donné. Sous "Literature" on a indiqué les sources (used) des valeurs au moyen desquelles on a établi l'équation et celles (conf.) des déterminations de confirmation.

TAFEL 1

d (beziehungsweise d_w, d_s) = Dichte der Lösung [bzw. Wasser (p. 24); reines Lösungsmittel] in g/ml. p_s(bzw. p_w) = Gewichtsprozente des gelösten Stoffes (bzw. Wasser) in der Lösung. "Range" = Gültigkeitsbereich der Gleichung. ± zeigt den maximalen Fehler an, der sich im Gültigkeitsbereich der Gleichung möglicherweise ergibt. Unter "Literature" stehen die Literaturquellen aus denen sich die Daten, die der Gleichung zugrunde liegen, ergeben haben, (used). Unter (conf.) sind diese Gleichung noch bestätigende Angaben verzeichnet.

TABELLA 1

d (oppure d_w, d_s) = densità della soluzione [rispettiv. dell' acqua (p. 24) o del solvente puro] in g/ml. p_s (oppure p_w) = percentuale in peso della sostanza disciolta (o dell'acqua) nella soluzione. "Range" = intervallo di applicabilità dell' equazione. Il segno ± esprime l'errore massimo che può aversi nell'intervallo di applicabilità dell'equazione. Sotto la dicitura "Literature" si trovano i richiami bibliografici dei lavori dai quali sono stati estratti i dati che figurano nelle equazioni (used) e quelli dei lavori che contengono determinazioni di conferma (conf.).

Section A. $d = d_w + Ap_s + Bp_s^2 + Cp_s^3$

Formula	Name	t, °C	Range, p_s	A	B	C	±	Lit. Used	Lit. Conf.
CH_2O	Formaldehyde	15	0– 40	$+0.0_{2}2518$	$-0.0_{5}658$	$+0.0_{6}542$	0.001	(14)	(75)
CH_2O_2	Formic acid	*v.* p. 122							
CH_3NO	Formamide	25	22– 96	$+ .0_{2}1217$	$+ .0_{5}3199$	$- .0_{7}2529$	.001	(77)	
CH_4N_2O	Urea	14.8	0– 12	$+ .0_{2}3213$	$- .0_{4}4802$	$+ .0_{5}1216$	.0001	(45)	(108)
		18	0– 51	$+ .0_{2}2718$	$+ .0_{5}1552$	$+ .0_{7}2573$	.0004	(128)	(142)
		20	0– 35	$+ .0_{2}2702$	$+ .0_{5}3712$	$- .0_{7}2285$	.0002	(142)	(103, 128)
		25	0– 10	$+ .0_{2}2728$	$- .0_{4}1817$	$+ .0_{5}1379$	.0002	(103)	(8)
CH_4N_2S	Thiourea	15	0– 7	$+ .0_{2}2995$	$- .0_{5}374$		.0003	(122)	(126)
CH_4O	Methyl alcohol	*v.* p. 115							
$C_2HCl_3O_2$	Trichloroacetic acid	12.5	0– 61	$+ .0_{2}499$	$+ .0_{4}153$		.0003	(42)	(82)
		20	10– 30	$+ .0_{2}5032$	$+ .0_{4}1387$		.001	(63, 64)	(82)
		25	0– 94	$+ .0_{2}5051$	$+ .0_{5}6119$	$+ .0_{6}1038$	.002	(71)	(42, 63, 64)
$C_2H_2Cl_2O_2$	Dichloroacetic acid	20	0– 30	$+ .0_{2}4427$	$+ .0_{5}537$	$+ .0_{7}7534$	.0002	(71)	(51, 63, 64)
		25	0– 97	$+ .0_{2}4427$	$+ .0_{5}537$	$+ .0_{7}7534$	.003	(71)	
$C_2H_2O_4$	Oxalic acid	0	0– 4	$+ .0_{2}5898$	$- .0_{3}3185$	$+ .0_{4}41$	.0002	(103)	
		15	0– 4	$+ .0_{2}494$	$- .0_{5}8$		.0003	(37)	(103, 136)

* *Id est:* The solute is an organic compound whose key-formula begins with 16. Exceptions: for sugars, *v.* Vol. II, p. 334; for salts, *v.* p. 51.

* Le corps dissout est un composé organique dont la formule clé commence par 16. Exceptions: pour les sucres, *v.* Vol. II, p. 334; pour les sels, *v.* p. 51.

* Der gelöste Stoff ist eine organische Verbindung, deren Schlüsselformel mit 16 beginnt. Ausnahmen: Zuckerarten, Bd. II, p. 334; Salze, p. 51.

* La sostanza disciolta è un composto organico, la cui formula chiave comincia con 16. Eccettuati: gli zuccheri, Vol. II, p. 334 ed i sali, p. 51.

Section A. $d = d_w + Ap_s + Bp_s^2 + Cp_s^3$.—(*Continued*)

Formula	Name	t, °C	Range, p_s	A	B	C	±	Lit. Used	Lit. Conf.
$C_2H_2O_4$	Oxalic acid, *Continued*	17.5	0– 9	$+0.0_{2}494$	$-0.0_{5}8$		0.0005	(37)	(94, 136)
		20	0– 4	$+.0_{2}5264$	$-.0_{3}1996$	$+0.0_{4}254$	.0001	(103)	(82, 94)
		25	0– 4	$+.0_{2}5108$	$-.0_{3}1607$	$+.0_{4}208$	.00005	(103)	(100)
$C_2H_3ClO_2$	Chloroacetic acid	20	0– 32	$+.0_{2}3648$	$+.0_{5}302$		.0005	(63, 64)	(59, 82, 88)
		25	0– 86	$+.0_{2}3602$	$+.0_{5}552$	$+.0_{7}22$	.002	(71)	(63, 82)
$C_2H_3Cl_3O_2$	Chloral hydrate†	0	0– 70	$+.0_{2}4489$	$+.0_{4}2802$	$-.0_{7}1291$	.0004	(125)	(7)
		15	0– 78	$+.0_{2}4455$	$+.0_{4}2198$	$+.0_{7}4366$	.0005	(125)	(7)
		30	0– 90	$+.0_{2}4401$	$+.0_{4}1887$	$+.0_{7}6549$	.0005	(125)	(7, 32)
C_2H_3N	Acetonitrile	15	0– 16	$-.0_{2}1175$	$-.0_{4}2024$		.001	(122)	
C_2H_4O	Acetaldehyde	18	0– 30	$+.0_{3}255$	$-.0_{5}16$		.001	(49, 127, 129)	
$C_2H_4O_2$	Acetic acid	*v.* p. 123							
C_2H_5NO	Acetamide	15	0– 6	$+.0_{3}639$	$+.0_{4}171$		.0002	(121)	(126)
C_2H_6O	Ethyl alcohol	*v.* p. 116							
$C_2H_6O_2$	Ethylene glycol	0	0–100	$+.0_{2}1483$	$+.0_{5}2992$	$-.0_{7}5248$	.001	(111)	‡
		15	0– 6	$+.0_{2}133$	$-.0_{5}108$		.0005	(121)	
C_2H_8ClN	Ethylamine hydrochloride	21	0– 65	$+.0_{2}1193$	$-.0_{5}307$	$-.0_{7}47$	.0005	(107)	
$C_3H_4O_4$	Malonic acid	20	0– 40	$+.0_{2}389$	$+.0_{4}1066$		.001	(118)	(121)
C_3H_6O	Acetone	0	0–100	$-.0_{3}856$	$-.0_{5}449$	$-.0_{7}588$	.001	(113)	‡
		4	0–100	$-.0_{3}7648$	$-.0_{4}1193$	$+.0_{8}272$	.001	(117)	‡
		15	0–100	$-.0_{2}1009$	$-.0_{5}9682$	$-.0_{8}624$	.0005	(117)	‡(121)
		20	0–100	$-.0_{2}1233$	$-.0_{5}3529$	$-.0_{7}5327$	.001	(96)	(59.1, 68)‡
		25	0–100	$-.0_{2}1171$	$-.0_{5}904$	$-.0_{8}56$	.0005	(117)	(113)‡
C_3H_6O	Allyl alcohol†	0	0– 89	$-.0_{3}3729$	$-.0_{4}1232$	$+.0_{7}2984$	.001	(131)	(74)
$C_3H_6O_2$	Methyl acetate	20	0– 20	$+.0_{3}40$	$-.0_{5}74$		.0001	(98)	(121)
$C_3H_6O_2$	Propionic acid	18	0– 10	$+.0_{3}95$	$-.0_{4}172$		.0005	(133)	(52)
		25	0– 40	$+.0_{3}9245$	$-.0_{5}99$	$+.0_{7}361$	.0005	(19, 67, 100)	(97, 133)
$C_3H_6O_3$	Lactic acid	25	0– 9	$+.0_{2}231$	$+.0_{5}186$		.0003	(97, 100)	(35)
$C_3H_7NO_2$	Urethane	20	0– 56	$+.0_{2}1278$	$-.0_{5}245$	~ $.0_{7}3437$	.0002	(99)	(126)
C_3H_8O	Propyl alcohol	*v.* p. 119							
$C_3H_8O_3$	Glycerol	*v.* p. 121							
$C_4H_4O_4$	Maleic acid	25	0– 40	$+.0_{2}34$	$+.0_{5}75$		.0005	(132)	(121)
$C_4H_6O_4$	Succinic acid	25	0–5.5	$+.0_{2}304$			.0002	(102)	(63, 100, 121)
$C_4H_6O_5$	Malic acid	20	0– 40	$+.0_{2}3933$	$+.0_{5}957$		.001	(118)	(79, 134, 137)
		25	0– 40	$+.0_{2}3736$	$+.0_{4}175$		.001	(132)	(25)
$C_4H_6O_6$	Tartaric acid (*d*-, *l*-, or *dl*-)	15	0– 15	$+.0_{2}4482$	$+.0_{4}185$		.0005	(72)	(121)
		17.5	0– 50	$+.0_{2}4455$	$+.0_{4}185$		.0001	(59)	(134)
		20	0– 50	$+.0_{2}4432$	$+.0_{4}1837$		.0005	(134)	(38, 82, 90, 92)
		30	0– 50	$+.0_{2}4335$	$+.0_{4}185$			(134)	
		40	0– 50	$+.0_{2}4265$	$+.0_{4}185$			(134)	
		50	0– 50	$+.0_{2}4205$	$+.0_{4}185$			(134)	
		60	0– 50	$+.0_{2}4155$	$+.0_{4}185$			(134)	
$C_4H_8O_2$	*n*-Butyric acid*	18	0– 10	$+.0_{3}414$	$+.0_{4}131$		.0003	(52, 120)	(121)
		25	0– 62	$+.0_{3}5135$	$-.0_{4}166$	$+.0_{6}11$	.0005	(19, 67)	(97)
$C_4H_8O_2$	Isobutyric acid*	15	0– 9	$+.0_{3}52$			.0001	(121)	(52)
		18	0– 9	$+.0_{3}45$			.0001	(52)	(121)
		25	0– 12	$+.0_{3}37$			.0001	(19, 97)	
$C_4H_{10}O$	Ethyl ether*	20	0– 5	$-.0_{2}221$	$+.0_{4}48$		.0001	(98)	(50)
		25	0–4.5	$-.0_{2}221$	$+.0_{4}35$		.0001	(50)	(98, 113)
$C_4H_{10}O$	*n*-Butyl alcohol*†	20	0–7.9	$-.0_{2}1651$	$+.0_{4}285$		.0002	(96)	(120)
$C_4H_{10}O$	Isobutyl alcohol*	15	0– 8	$-.0_{2}146$	$+.0_{5}6$		.0003	(17, 121)	
		20	0– 8	$-.0_{2}169$	$+.0_{4}38$		.0002	(120)	(130)
$C_4H_{10}O$	Trimethyl carbinol*	20	0–100	$-.0_{2}117$	$-.0_{4}1908$	$+.0_{7}957$	.001	(18)	(139)
		25	0–100	$-.0_{2}1286$	$-.0_{4}176$	$+.0_{7}887$	.001	(18)	(139)
$C_4H_{12}ClN$	Diethylamine hydrochloride	21	0– 36	$+.0_{3}34$	$+.0_{6}76$		.0004	(107)	(64)
$C_5H_4O_2$	Furfural†	20	0– 8	$+.0_{2}1827$	$+.0_{5}366$		.0002	(70)	(112)
		25	0– 8	$+.0_{2}1664$	$+.0_{4}21$		.0004	(70)	(112)
C_5H_5N	Pyridine*†	25	0– 60	$+.0_{3}229$	$-.0_{5}204$	$-.0_{8}28$	.0003	(54)	(24, 30, 43, 113)
$C_5H_{10}O_2$	*n*-Valeric acid	25	0– 3	$+.0_{3}34$	$-.0_{4}27$		.0002	(19)	
$C_5H_{10}O_2$	Isovaleric acid	25	0– 5	$+.0_{3}253$	$-.0_{4}282$		.0002	(19)	(97)
$C_5H_{12}O$	Isoamyl alcohol	20	0–2.5	$+.0_{2}155$	$-.0_{4}3$		.0003	(120)	(113)
$C_6H_5NO_3$	*p*-Nitrophenol	15	0–1.5	$+.0_{2}3216$	$-.0_{4}55$		.0001	(122)	
C_6H_6O	Phenol	15	0– 5	$+.0_{2}111$	$-.0_{4}283$		.0002	(122)	
		80	0– 65	$+.0_{3}462$	$-.0_{6}86$		.001§	(36)	
$C_6H_6O_2$	Resorcinol	18	0– 52	$+.0_{2}201$	$+.0_{5}519$	$-.0_{8}19$	.0005	(128)	(126)
C_6H_7N	α-Picoline*	25	0– 70	$-.0_{4}386$	$+.0_{5}1405$	$-.0_{7}4167$	.0006	(54)	
C_6H_7N	β-Picoline*	25	0– 60	$-.0_{4}683$	$-.0_{5}13$		.0004	(54)	
$C_6H_8O_7 + H_2O$	Citric acid (hydrate)	18	0– 50	$+.0_{2}3824$	$+.0_{4}1141$	$+.0_{7}17$	.0005	(128)	(89)
$C_6H_{16}ClN$	Triethylamine hydrochloride	21	0– 54	$+.0_{4}6$	$+.0_{5}558$	$-.0_{8}69$	.001	(107)	
$C_7H_{14}O_6$	α-Methyl glucoside	0	26– 51	$+.0_{2}3336$	$+.0_{5}996$	$+.0_{7}1544$	.0002	(6)	
		30	26– 51	$+.0_{2}3151$	$+.0_{5}975$	$+.0_{8}978$	.0002	(6)	
$C_8H_8O_3$	Phenylglycolic acid	25	0– 11	$+.0_{2}207$	$+.0_{4}23$		.001	(26)	(100)
$C_8H_{14}O_6$	Ethyl tartrate†	15	0– 95	$+.0_{2}2367$	$+.0_{5}358$	$-.0_{7}6005$	.0005	(48)	(84, 143, 144)
$C_8H_{20}ClN$	Tetraethylammonium chloride	21	0– 63	$+.0_{3}1884$	$+.0_{5}6$	$+.0_{7}122$	.0005	(107)	
$C_{10}H_{14}N_2$	Nicotine*	20	0– 60	$+.0_{3}642$	$+.0_{5}454$	$-.0_{7}687$	.0003	(53)	(91, 135)
$C_{11}H_6O_{10}$	Benzenepentacarboxylic acid	25	0–0.6	$+.0_{2}5616$	$-.0_{2}117$		.00005	(81)	

Section B. $d = d_s + Ap_w + Bp_w^2 + Cp_w^3$

Formula	Name	d_s	t, °C	Range, p_w	A	B	C	±	Lit. Used	Lit. Conf.
$C_4H_8O_2$	*n*-Butyric acid	0.9534	25	0–38	$+0.0_21854$	-0.0_42314		0.001	(19, 67)	‡
$C_4H_8O_2$	Isobutyric acid	0.9425	26	0–80	$+ .0_21808$	$- .0_42358$	$+0.0_61253$	.001	(36, 123)	(20)‡
$C_4H_{10}O$	Ethyl ether	0.7077	25	0–1.1	$+ .0_234$	$+ .0_336$		.0001	(50)	(113)‡
$C_4H_{10}O$	*n*-Butyl alcohol	0.8097	20	0–20	$+ .0_22103$	$- .0_4113$		.0005	(96)	(1)‡
$C_4H_{10}O$	Isobutyl alcohol	0.8170	0	0–14	$+ .0_22437$	$- .0_4285$		.0002	(139)	‡
		0.8055	15	0–16	$+ .0_2224$	$- .0_4129$		.0002	(17)	‡
$C_4H_{10}O$	Trimethyl carbinol	0.7856	20	0–20	$+ .0_22287$	$+ .0_5275$		.0002	(18, 139)	
C_5H_5N	Pyridine	0.9776	25	0–40	$+ .0_21157$	$- .0_5536$	$- .0_62$	.001	(43)	(54, 30)
C_6H_7N	α-Picoline	0.9404	25	0–30	$+ .0_22715$	$- .0_4393$		.0005	(54)	
C_6H_7N	β-Picoline	0.9515	25	0–40	$+ .0_21925$	$- .0_4352$	$+ .0_625$	.0005	(54)	
$C_{10}H_{14}N_2$	Nicotine	1.0093	20	0–40	$+ .0_2199$	$- .0_4331$	$+ .0_7315$	.0002	(91)	(53)‡

Section C. $d_t = d_0 + A_t + B_t^2$

Formula	Name	p_s	d_0‖	Range, °C	A	B	±	Lit. Used	Lit. Conf.
$C_2H_3Cl_3O_2$	Chloral hydrate	2.00	(1.0094)	7–80	-0.0_42597	-0.0_54313	0.0004	(7)	(104, 125)
		10.00	(1.0476)	7–80	$- .0_47955$	$- .0_54253$	.0004	(7)	(104, 125)
C_3H_6O	Allyl alcohol	76.60	0.9122	0–45	$- .0_38$	$- .0_527$	.0003	(74)	(131)
$C_4H_{10}O$	*n*-Butyl alcohol	80.95	0.8614	0–43	$- .0_37292$	$- .0_675$	.001	(1)	(96)
$C_5H_4O_2$	Furfural	4.62	(1.0125)	22–74	$- .0_3232$	$- .0_5254$	.0005	(112)	(70)
		5.69	(1.0140)	22–74	$- .0_3221$	$- .0_5268$	.0005	(112)	(70)
		6.56	(1.0155)	22–74	$- .0_3211$	$- .0_5290$	.0005	(112)	(70)
C_5H_5N	Pyridine	9.34	(1.0055)	11–73	$- .0_3171$	$- .0_53615$	.0005	(113)	(54)
		21.20	(1.0115)	14–73	$- .0_3378$	$- .0_5248$	.0005	(113)	(54)
		29.50	(1.0145)	12–72	$- .0_3463$	$- .0_5235$	.0005	(113)	(54)
		40.40	(1.0182)	9–74	$- .0_3605$	$- .0_5167$	.001	(113)	(54)
$C_8H_{14}O_6$	Ethyl tartrate	5.00	(1.0150)	15–80	$- .0_32103$	$- .0_52544$	.0005	(144)	(48)
		10.00	(1.0270)	15–80	$- .0_32116$	$- .0_52929$	.0005	(144)	(48)
		25.00	(1.0665)	15–80	$- .0_3401$	$- .0_523$	.0005	(144)	(48)

* For data on more concentrated solutions, *v.* Section B.
† For data regarding thermal expansion, *v.* Section C.
‡ The value for 100 % agrees with that given by Brunel and Van Bibber (p. 27) within the limit of error indicated.
§ Above 40 % the limit of error is possibly 0.002.
‖ The values for d_0, which are enclosed in parentheses, have been obtained by extrapolation and are to be used for the purpose of calculation only.

TABLE 2.—MISCELLANEOUS AND FRAGMENTARY DATA (THE ℭ-ARRANGEMENT)

Formula	Name	Range, °C	Range, p_s	Lit.
$CHCl_3$	Chloroform	0–55	Satd. sol.	(10)
CH_2O	Formaldehyde	18	0–37	(2)
CH_3NO	Formamide	25	1.7–100	(23)
CH_4N_2O	Urea	0–84	Satd. sol.	(116)
		5	3–10	(103)
		10	3–10	(103)
		15	3–10	(103)
		15, 30	1.5–5.9	(95)
		15	0–20	(122)
		20	3	(126)
		25	5.9	(31)
		25	1–46	(23)
		30–80	0–11	(61)
CH_5N	Methylamine	25	0–3	(55)
CH_6ClN	Methylamine hydrochloride	25	0–6.7	(55)
C_2HBr_3O	Bromal	40–100	45–100	(29)
$C_2HBr_3O_2$	Tribromoacetic acid	16	20, 30	(51)
C_2HCl_3O	Chloral	50–90	2–100	(60)
$C_2HCl_3O_2$	Trichloroacetic acid	0	21–86	(11)
		0, 15, 30	11–90	(125)
		16	10–20	(51)
		20	10–58	(141)
$C_2H_2Cl_2O_2$	Dichloroacetic acid	16	7.5	(51)
		20	13	(82)
		25	0–12	(55)
		15	2.2	(121)
$C_2H_2O_4$	Oxalic acid	16–30	9	(110)
		17–20	3.5–7	(58)
		17.5	3.5–7	(34)
		18	4.5	(66)
		20	2.4	(80)
		20	7.8	(63)
		21	7.4	(56)
		30	4.3	(78)
		30	12.6	(73)
$C_2H_3BrO_2$	Bromoacetic acid	16	20, 30	(51)
$C_2H_3Cl_3O_2$	Chloral hydrate	0–47	Satd. sol.	(116)
		4–45	75.4	(86)
		11	9–47	(3)
		20	4–33	(56)
		20, 44	0–80	(104)
C_2H_3N	Acetonitrile	29	50 % vol.	(105)
C_2H_4O	Acetaldehyde	17, 18	30–100	(49, 127)
$C_2H_4O_3$	Glycolic acid	20	4, 17	(64)
		20	7.6	(82)
		25	4	(100)
C_2H_5I	Ethyl iodide	15–72	0.3	(113)
C_2H_5NO	Acetamide	0–68	Satd. sol.	(116)
		25	0–69	(23)
		25	5.9	(31)
		25	34	(56)
$C_2H_5NO_2$	Glycocoll	20	3.7	(126)
C_2H_6NO	Methylurea	25	7.4	(31)
$C_2H_6O_2S$	Dimethyl sulfone	26	2.5	(56)
C_2H_7N	Dimethylamine	25	0–3	(55)
C_2H_8ClN	Ethylamine hydrochloride	24	11	(56)
		25	1–8	(55)
C_2H_8ClN	Dimethylamine hydrochloride	25	1–8	(55)
$C_3H_4O_4$	Malonic acid	15–25	59	(87)
C_3H_6O	Allyl alcohol	15	0–6	(121)
C_3H_6O	Acetone	0–60	0–100	(113)
		15	15–100	(39)
		15	1–10	(93)
		20, 25	10–100	(59.1)
		25	10–100	(46)
$C_3H_6O_2$	Propionic acid	0	17–100	(11)
		4, 15, 25	80	(85)
		15	0–7	(121)
		16	10, 33	(51)
		17	50–100	(21)
		20	8–97	(141)

Table 2.—Miscellaneous and Fragmentary Data (the ℭ-Arrangement).—(*Continued*)

Formula	Name	Range, °C	Range, p_s	Lit.
$C_3H_6O_2$	Propionic acid, *Continued*	20	10, 30, 50	(120)
		20	67–89	(62)
		20	13, 15	(64)
		20	7.4	(82)
		25	40–100	(67)
		25	50–100	(19)
$C_3H_6O_2$	Methyl acetate	17–63	5–10, 85–95	(113)
$C_3H_6O_2$	Ethyl formate	10–40	6, 95	(113)
$C_3H_6O_3$	Lactic acid	20	9	(82)
$C_3H_6O_3$	*dl*-Lactic acid	20	15, 34	(64)
$C_3H_6O_4$	Glyceric acid	20	8.5, 11	(64)
C_3H_7N	Allylamine	15	0–5.7	(121)
C_3H_7NO	Propionamide	25	0–70	(23)
		25	7.3	(31)
$C_3H_8N_2O$	Dimethylurea	25	8.8	(31)
$C_3H_8O_2$	Methylal	12–33	10, 20, 30	(113)
C_3H_9N	Propylamine	15	0–6	(121)
C_3H_9N	Trimethylamine	15	15–100	(123)
		25	0–6	(55)
$C_3H_{10}ClN$	Trimethylamine hydrochloride	25	1–9	(55)
$C_4H_4O_4$	Fumaric acid	15	0.3	(121)
$C_4H_4O_4$	Maleic acid	15, 20, 25	44.6	(87)
$C_4H_5Cl_3O_2$	Trichlorobutyric acid	20	15, 18	(64)
$C_4H_6O_2$	Crotonic acid	25	4	(56)
$C_4H_6O_3$	Acetic anhydride	0, 18	50–100	(30)
$C_4H_6O_4$	Methyl oxalate	15	0–1.5	(121)
$C_4H_6O_4$	Succinic acid	20	5.9	(82)
$C_4H_6O_5$	Malic acid	15	2, 4.7	(35)
		15	1.7, 3.3	(121)
		20	8–70	(109)
		20	1.7–24	(41)
		20	6.7	(82)
		25	16	(100)
		9–45	17	(11.5)
$C_4H_6O_5$	Diglycolic acid	20	14	(56)
$C_4H_6O_6$	Tartaric acid	15–20	5–50	(58)
		15	3.7–33	(106)
		15	4–15	(35)
		18	4–45	(119)
		20	1–60	(94)
		20	1–15	(64)
		20	4	(80)
		25	7, 18	(100)
		15	0.4	(121)
$C_4H_7NO_4$	Aspartic acid	20–90	0.5, 1.9	(13)
		20	1.2–2.8	(5)
$C_4H_8O_2$	Methyl propionate	15	1–4.4	(121)
$C_4H_8O_2$	Propyl formate	15	1, 2.2	(121)
$C_4H_8O_2$	*n*-Butyric acid	0	11–71	(11)
		0	98–100	(140)
		15	83–100	(39, 40)
		16	12–35	(51)
		18	10, 19, 36	(44)
		20	30–100	(124)
		20	8.8	(82)
		20	76–90	(62)
$C_4H_8O_2$	Isobutyric acid	15	72–87	(48)
		20	5–20	(120)
		20	8.8	(82)
		20	13, 17	(64)
$C_4H_8O_2$	Ethyl acetate	0–40	6.6–10, Satd. sol.	(76)
		15	0–4.4	(121)
		17–63	4, 7.6, 96	(113)
$C_4H_8NO_2$	Succinamide	0–84	Satd. sol.	(116)
$C_4H_8O_3$	Hydroxyisobutyric acid	15	1.3–5	(121)
$C_4H_8N_2O_3$	Asparagine	20	0–1.4	(5)
C_4H_9NO	Butyramide	25	1–18	(23)
		25	8.7	(31)
$C_4H_{10}O$	Ethyl ether	0	12, 99	(16)
$C_4H_{10}O$	Isobutyl alcohol	15–75	1.5–10 % vol.	(138)
		20	2–8	(22)
		20	82–95	(130)
		25	2–5, 82–95	(130)
$C_4H_{10}O$	*sec.*-Butyl alcohol	20	0–17.8, 64–100	(12)
$C_4H_{10}O$	Trimethyl carbinol	0–70	63–100	(83)
$C_4H_{10}O$	Erythritol	19.5	14.3	(56)
$C_4H_{11}N$	Butylamine	20	8, 15, 29	(64)
$C_4H_{11}N$	Diethylamine	20	11, 15.8	(64)
$C_4H_{12}ClN$	Diethylamine hydrochloride	25	1–7.4	(55)
$C_4H_{12}ClN$	Butylamine hydrochloride	20	5, 7, 9	(64)
$C_4H_{12}ClN$	Tetramethylammonium chloride	25	1–9	(55)
$C_4H_{13}NO$	Tetramethylammonium hydroxide	25	0–4.5	(55)
$C_5H_4O_2$	Furfural	22–97	96	(112)
$C_5H_4O_3$	Pyromucic acid	25.8	2.2	(56)
C_5H_5N	Pyridine	0	9–100	(4)
		0–70	67	(74)
		0–100	33–100	(30)
		9–74	66, 78, 90	(113)
		15	1–36	(122)
		15–87	12–87	(47)
		25	30–60	(27)
$C_5H_6O_4$	Citraconic acid	15–25	47.4	(87)
		27.7	7	(56)
$C_5H_6O_4$	Itaconic acid	24, 25	2.6, 4.2	(56)
		25	1–2	(102)
$C_5H_6O_4$	Mesaconic acid	28	3.7	(56)
$C_5H_8O_2$	Allyl acetate	15	1.2	(121)
$C_5H_8O_4$	Glutaric acid	4, 15, 25	42.3	(87)
$C_5H_8O_4$	Methylsuccinic acid	25	1.1–3.2	(102)
$C_5H_{10}O$	Diethyl ketone	10–71	2.2, 4.8	(113)
$C_5H_{10}O_2$	*n*-Valeric acid	18	0–2.5	(52)
		25	87, 98	(19)
$C_5H_{10}O_2$	Isovaleric acid	15	84–100	(39, 40)
		15	1.3, 2.5	(121)
		20	2, 4, 100	(120)
		25	89, 99	(19)
$C_5H_{10}O_2$	Ethyl propionate	15	0.6, 1.3	(121)
$C_5H_{10}O_2$	Propyl acetate	15	1.3	(121)
$C_5H_{12}O$	*sec.*-Amyl alcohol	20	89.8–100	(12)
$C_5H_{12}O$	Isoamyl alcohol	8–74	3, 94	(113)
		15	1–2	(120)
		15.5	90–96	(33)
		20	0–3.3	(22)
$C_5H_{12}O$	Dimethyl ethyl carbinol	15	1–4.4	(121)
$C_5H_{13}N$	Amylamine	20	5.8, 6.6	(64)
$C_5H_{14}ClN$	Amylamine hydrochloride	20	3.8, 6.6	(64)
C_6H_6O	Phenol	15–90	0–6	(138)
		38–80	9.5–65	(36)
$C_6H_6O_2$	Catechol	20	5.5	(126)
$C_6H_6O_2$	Hydroquinol	20	5.5	(126)
$C_6H_6O_2$	Resorcinol	0–85	Satd. sol.	(116)
$C_6H_6O_3$	Pyrogallol	20	6.3	(126)
C_6H_7N	Aniline	13–97	3, 95	(113)
		15–80	0–3.3 vol. %	(138)
C_6H_8ClN	Aniline hydrochloride	25	22	(114)
$C_6H_8O_7$	Citric acid	12	4–36	(106)
		15	1.9	(35)
		20	1–26	(94)
		20	7	(82)
		25	8.7	(100)
$C_6H_{10}O_3$	Ethyl acetoacetate	14–72	3–10	(113)
$C_6H_{10}O_4$	Ethylene glycol diacetate	16–74	5–81	(113)
$C_6H_{10}O_4$	Ethyl oxalate	17–74	1.8, 4.6	(113)
$C_6H_{10}O_6$	Methyl tartrate	16–79	5–75	(113)
$C_6H_{12}O_2$	Propyl propionate	15	0.4	(121)
$C_6H_{12}O_3$	Paraldehyde	15	1.6–6.6	(121)
		16–70	1.3, 6.4, 7.7	(113)
$C_6H_{12}O_5$	Quercitol	19, 22	5.7, 7.7	(56)
$C_6H_{14}O_6$	Mannitol	20	9	(126)
$C_6H_{16}ClN$	Triethylamine hydrochloride	25	1.7–13.7	(55)
C_7H_8O	*m*-Cresol	11–95	2, 95	(113)
$C_7H_{12}O_6$	Quinic acid	20	10, 18	(56)
		25	5.3	(100)
$C_8H_6O_4$	*o*-Phthalic acid	25	0.7	(101)
$C_8H_8O_2$	Phenylacetic acid	25	0.6	(100)
$C_8H_{10}O_8$	Diacetyltartaric acid	25	0–19	(15)
$C_8H_{14}O_6$	Ethyl tartrate	13–99	50–75	(143, 144)
$C_8H_{20}ClN$	Tetraethylammonium chloride	25	2–16	(55)

Formula	Name	Range, °C	Range, p_s	Lit.
C_9H_7N	Quinoline	8–95	82, 89, 95	(113)
$C_9H_{13}NO_3S$	Trimethylsulfanilic acid	25	0–2	(57)
$C_{10}H_8O_3S$	β-Naphthalenesulfonic acid	30	57	(73)
$C_{10}H_{14}N_2$	Nicotine	0–40	7–51	(135)
		20	9–100	(65)
		20	33–86	(123)
		74	69.2	(48)
$C_{10}H_{16}O_4$	Camphoric acid	21	1	(56)
$C_{11}H_{12}N_2O$	Antipyrine	20	9.3	(126)

LITERATURE

(For a key to the periodicals see end of volume)

(1) Atkins and Wallace, *4*, **103**: 1461; 13. (2) Auerbach and Barschall, *291*, **22**: 584; 05. (3) Barbier and Roux, *27*, **3**: 419; 90. (4) Baud, *27*, **5**: 1022; 09. *34*, **148**: 96; 09. (5) Becker, *25*, **14**: 1028; 81. (6) Berkeley, Hartley and Burton, *62*, **218**: 295; 19. (7) Bousfield and Lowry, *83*, **6**: 85; 10. (8) Burke, *1*, **42**: 2500; 20. (9) Burrows, *316*, **53**: 74; 19.

(10) Chancel and Parmentier, *34*, **100**: 773; 85. (11) Charpy, *6*, **29**: 5; 93. (11.5) Clough, *4*, **107**: 96; 15. (12) Clough and Johns, *45*, **15**: 1030; 23. (13) Cook, *25*, **30**: 294; 97. (14) Davis, *54*, **16**: 502; 97. (15) Deakin and Rivett, *4*, **101**: 127; 12. (16) Desmaroux, *315*, **19**: 322; 22. (17) Doroschevskii, *53*, **41**: 958; 09. (18) Doroschevskii, *53*, **43**: 66; 11. (19) Drucker, *7*, **52**: 641; 05.

(20) Drucker and Moles, *7*, **75**: 405; 11. (21) Drude, *7*, **23**: 267; 97. (22) Duclaux, *6*, **13**: 76; 78. (23) Dunstan and Mussell, *4*, **97**: 1935; 10. (24) Dunstan and Thole, *4*, **93**: 561; 08. (25) Dunstan and Thole, *4*, **93**: 1815; 08. (26) Dunstan and Thole, *4*, **97**: 1249; 10. (27) Dunstan, Thole and Hunt, *4*, **91**: 1728; 07. (29) Efremov, *53*, **50**: 347; 18. *10*, **5**: 39; 25.

(30) Faust, *7*, **79**: 97; 12. (31) Fawsitt, *68*, **25**: 51; 04. (32) Findlay and Shen, *4*, **101**: 1459; 12. (33) Fontein, *7*, **73**: 212; 10. (34) Franz, *52*, **5**: 274; 72. (35) Fresenius and Grünhut, *91*, **51**: 23; 12. (36) Friedlander, *7*, **38**: 385; 01. (37) Gerlach, *317*, **9**: 241; 86. (38) Golse, *Thesis*, Bordeaux, 1911. *10*, **2**: 195; 13. (39) Graham, *13*, **123**: 90; 62.

(40) Graham, *62*, **151**: 373; 61. (41) Grossman and Wieneke, *7*, **54**: 385; 06. (42) Hallwachs, *8*, **68**: 1; 99. (43) Hartley, Thomas and Applebey, *4*, **93**: 538; 08. (44) Hartwig, *8*, **33**: 58; 88. (45) Heimbrodt, *8*, **13**: 1028; 04. (46) Herz and Knoch, *93*, **45**: 262; 05. (47) Holmes, *4*, **89**: 1774; 06. (48) Holmes, *4*, **103**: 2147; 13. (49) Homfray, *4*, **87**: 1430; 05.

(50) Horiba, *41*, **31**: 922; 10. (51) Humburg, *7*, **12**: 401; 93. (52) Jahn, *7*, **16**: 72; 95. (53) Jephcott, *4*, **115**: 104; 19. (54) Jones and Speakman, *1*, **43**: 1867; 21. (55) Kanitz, *7*, **22**: 336; 97. (56) Kanonnikoff, *52*, **31**: 321; 85. (57) Katayama and Yamada, *41*, **41**: 193; 20. (58) Kohlrausch, *8*, **159**: 233; 76. (59) Kohlrausch and Hallwachs, *8*, **50**: 118; 95. (59.1) Krug and MacElroy, *320*, **6**: 184; 92.

(60) Kurnakov and Efremov, *7*, **85**: 401; 13. (61) Landesen, *322*, **14**; 04. *B3*, 462; 23. (62) Landolt, *8*, **117**: 352; 62. (63) LeBlanc, *7*, **4**: 553; 89. (64) LeBlanc and Rohland, *7*, **19**: 261; 96. (65) Levi, *24*, **75 II**: 465; 15. (66) Loomis, *8*, **60**: 547; 97. (67) Lüdeking, *8*, **27**: 72; 86. (68) MacElroy, *1*, **16**: 618; 94.

(70) Mains, *33*, **26**: 779; 22. (71) Mameli, *36*, **41 I**: 291; 11. (72) Marchlevskii, *25*, **25**: 1556; 92. (73) Masson, *4*, **101**: 103; 12. (74) Matthews and Cooke, *50*, **18**: 566; 95. (75) Maue, *319*, **63**: 197; 18. (76) Merriman, *4*, **103**: 1774; 13. (77) Merry and Turner, *4*, **105**: 748; 14. (78) Morgan and McKirahan, *1*, **35**: 1759; 13. (79) Nasini and Gennari, *7*, **19**: 113; 96.

(80) Nicol, *3*, **18**: 179; 84. (81) Noyes and Lombard, *1*, **33**: 1423; 11. (82) Ostwald, *52*, **18**: 328; 78. (83) Paterno and Mieli, *36*, **37 II**: 330; 07. *22*, **16 II**: 153; 07. (84) Patterson and Anderson, *4*, **101**: 1833; 12. (85) Perkin, *4*, **49**: 777; 86. (86) Perkin, *4*, **51**: 808; 87. (87) Perkin, *4*, **53**: 561; 88. (88) Polovzov, *7*, **75**: 513; 11. (89) Pratolongo, *22*, **20 I**: 812; 11. **22 I**: 86; 13.

(90) Pribram, *25*, **20**: 1840; 87. (91) Pribram and Glucksam, *75*, **106**: 296; 97. (92) Pribram and Glucksam, *75*, **107**: 146; 98. (93) Pringsheim, Kuhn and Fritze, *92*, **32**: 287; 19. (94) Rakshit, *9*, **31**: 97; 25. (95) Rankin and Taylor, *174*, **45**: 397; 06. (96) Reilly and Ralph, *117*, **15**: 597; 19. (97) Reyher, *7*, **2**: 744; 88. (98) Richards and Chadwell, *1*, **47**: 2283; 25. (99) Richards and Palitzsch, *1*, **41**: 59; 19.

(100) Rimbach and Wintgen, *7*, **74**: 233; 10. (101) Rivett and Rosenblum, *83*, **9**: 297; 14. (102) Rivett and Sidgwick, *4*, **97**: 1677; 10. (103) Roth, *7*, **24**: 114; 97. (104) Rudolphi, *7*, **37**: 426; 01. (105) Sachonov and Rabinovic, *53*, **47**: 861; 15. *10*, **4**: 36; 21. (106) Schiff, *13*, **113**: 183; 60. (107) Schiff and Monsacchi, *7*, **24**: 513; 97. *36*, **28 I**: 161; 98. (108) Schmidt, *8*, **114**: 337; 61. (109) Schneider, *13*, **207**: 257; 81.

(110) Schultze, *91*, **21**: 167; 82. (111) Schwers, *28*, **1908**: 814. *70*, **28**: 42; 09. (112) Schwers, *28*, **1911**: 641. (113) Schwers, *42*, **9**: 15; 11. (114) Sidgwick, Pickford and Wilsdon, *4*, **99**: 1122; 11. (116) Speyers, *12*, **14**: 293; 02. (117) Squibb, *1*, **17**: 187; 95. (118) Stubbs, *4*, **99**: 2265; 11. (119) Thomsen, *Thermochemistry*, p. 162. N. Y., Longmans, 1908.

(120) Traube, *25*, **19**: 871; 86. (121) Traube, *13*, **265**: 27; 91. (122) Traube, *13*, **290**: 43; 96. (123) Tsakalotos, *7*, **68**: 32; 09. (124) Tsakalotos, *34*, **146**: 1146; 08. (125) Turbaba, *Charkow Gesell. exp. Wiss.*, **18**: 8; 90. **21**: Supp. 19, 56, 69, 111; 93. *Quoted from B3*, 477; 23. (126) Usher, *4*, **97**: 66; 10. (127) Van Aubel, *51*, **4**: 478; 89. (128) Varga, *Diss.*, Budapest, 1911. *10*, **2**: 14; 13. (129) Vaubel, *52*, **59**: 30; 99.

(130) Wad and Gokhale, *318*, **4**: 17; 21. (131) Wallace and Atkins, *4*, **101**: 1179; 12. (132) Weiss and Downs, *1*, **45**: 1003; 23. (133) Wilsdon and Sidgwick, *4*, **103**: 1959; 13. (134) Winther, *7*, **41**: 161; 02. (135) Winther, *7*, **60**: 590; 07. (136) Worden and Motion, *54*, **24**: 178; 05. (137) Woringer, *7*, **36**: 326; 01. (138) Worley, *4*, **105**: 260; 14. (139) Young and Fortey, *4*, **81**: 717; 02.

(140) Zander, *13*, **224**: 56; 84. (141) Zecchini, *36*, **35 II**: 65; 05. (142) Zoppellari, *36*, **35 I**: 355; 05. (143) Patterson, *4*, **79**: 167; 01. (144) Patterson, *4*, **85**: 1116; 04.

DENSITY OF CERTAIN AQUEOUS ORGANIC SOLUTIONS

H. W. Bearce, Grace C. Mulligan and Merriel P. Maslin

A. SOLUTIONS CONTAINING ONE SOLUTE ONLY. AQUEOUS SOLUTIONS OF METHYL, ETHYL, AND PROPYL ALCOHOLS, GLYCEROL AND FORMIC AND ACETIC ACIDS

All compositions are in Wt. % *in vacuo*. All density values are d_4^t = g/ml *in vacuo*.

CH_3OH, Methyl Alcohol

v. also (1, 11, 13, 19, 20, 31, 35, 42, 46, 49, 51, 65, 67, 78, 79, 80, 81, 83, 86, 88)

% \ °C	0 (15)	10 (15)	15.56 (15)	20 (15)	15 (17)
0	0.9999	0.9997	0.9990	0.9982	0.99913
1	.9981	.9980	.9973	.9965	.99727
2	.9963	.9962	.9955	.9948	.99543
3	.9946	.9945	.9938	.9931	.99370
4	.9930	.9929	.9921	.9914	.99198
5	.9914	.9912	.9904	.9896	.99029
6	.9899	.9896	.9889	.9880	.98864
7	.9884	.9881	.9872	9863	.98701
8	.9870	.9865	.9857	.9847	.98547
9	0.9856	0.9849	0.9841	0.9831	0.98394
10	.9842	.9834	.9826	.9815	.98241
11	.9829	.9820	.9811	.9799	.98093
12	.9816	.9805	.9796	.9784	.97945
13	.9804	.9791	.9781	.9768	.97802
14	.9792	.9778	.9766	.9754	.97660
15	.9780	.9764	.9752	.9740	.97518
16	.9769	.9751	.9738	.9725	.97377
17	.9758	.9739	.9723	.9710	.97237
18	.9747	.9726	.9709	.9696	.97096
19	.9736	.9713	.9695	.9681	.96955
20	.9725	.9700	.9680	.9666	.96814
21	.9714	.9687	.9666	.9651	.96673
22	.9702	.9673	.9652	.9636	.96533
23	.9690	.9660	.9638	.9622	.96392
24	.9678	.9646	.9624	.9607	.96251

CH_3OH, Methyl Alcohol.—(*Continued*)

% \ °C	0 (15)	10 (15)	15.56 (15)	20 (15)	15 (17)
25	0.9666	0.9632	0.9609	0.9592	0.96108
26	.9654	.9618	.9595	.9576	.95963
27	.9642	.9604	.9580	.9562	.95817
28	.9629	.9590	.9565	.9546	.95668
29	.9616	.9575	.9550	.9531	.95518
30	.9604	.9560	.9535	.9515	.95366
31	.9590	.9546	.9521	.9499	.95213
32	.9576	.9531	.9505	.9483	.95056
33	.9563	.9516	.9489	.9466	.94896
34	.9549	.9500	.9473	.9450	.94734
35	.9534	.9484	.9456	.9433	.94570
36	.9520	.9469	.9440	.9416	.94404
37	.9505	.9453	.9422	.9398	.94237
38	.9490	.9437	.9405	.9381	.94067
39	.9475	.9420	.9387	.9363	.93894
40	.9459	.9403	.9369	.9345	.93720
41	.9443	.9387	.9351	.9327	.93543
42	.9427	.9370	.9333	.9309	.93365
43	.9411	.9352	.9315	.9290	.93185
44	.9395	.9334	.9297	.9272	.93001
45	.9377	.9316	.9279	.9252	.92815
46	.9360	.9298	.9261	.9234	.92627
47	.9342	.9279	.9242	.9214	.92436
48	.9324	.9260	.9223	.9196	.92242
49	.9306	.9240	.9204	.9176	.92048
50	.9287	.9221	.9185	.9156	.91852
51	.9269	.9202	.9166	.9135	.91653
52	.9250	.9182	.9146	.9114	.91451
53	.9230	.9162	.9126	.9094	.91248
54	.9211	.9142	.9106	.9073	.91044
55	.9191	.9122	.9086	.9052	.90839
56	.9172	.9101	.9065	.9032	.90631
57	.9151	.9080	.9045	.9010	.90421
58	.9131	.9060	.9024	.8988	.90210
59	.9111	.9039	.9002	.8968	.89996
60	.9090	.9018	.8980	.8946	.89781
61	.9068	.8998	.8958	.8924	.89563
62	.9046	.8977	.8936	.8902	.89341
63	.9024	.8955	.8913	.8879	.89117
64	.9002	.8933	.8890	.8856	.88890
65	.8980	.8911	.8867	.8834	.88662
66	.8958	.8888	.8844	.8811	.88433
67	.8935	.8865	.8820	.8787	.88203
68	.8913	.8842	.8797	.8763	.87971
69	.8891	.8818	.8771	.8738	.87739
70	.8869	.8794	.8748	.8715	.87507
71	.8847	.8770	.8726	.8690	.87271
72	.8824	.8747	.8702	.8665	.87033
73	.8801	.8724	.8678	.8641	.86792
74	.8778	.8699	.8653	.8616	.86546
75	.8754	.8676	.8629	.8592	.86300
76	.8729	.8651	.8604	.8567	.86051
77	.8705	.8626	.8579	.8542	.85801
78	0.8680	0.8602	0.8554	0.8518	0.85551
79	.8657	.8577	.8529	.8494	.85300
80	.8634	.8551	.8503	.8469	.85048
81	.8610	.8527	.8478	.8446	.84794
82	.8585	.8501	.8452	.8420	.84536
83	.8560	.8475	.8426	.8394	.84274
84	.8535	.8449	.8400	.8366	.84009
85	.8510	.8422	.8374	.8340	.83742
86	.8483	.8394	.8347	.8314	.83475
87	.8456	.8367	.8320	.8286	.83207
88	.8428	.8340	.8294	.8258	.82937
89	.8400	.8314	.8267	.8230	.82667
90	.8374	.8287	.8239	.8202	.82396
91	.8347	.8261	.8212	.8174	.82124
92	.8320	.8234	.8185	.8146	.81849
93	.8293	.8208	.8157	.8118	.81568
94	.8266	.8180	.8129	.8090	.81285
95	.8240	.8152	.8101	.8062	.80999
96	.8212	.8124	.8073	.8034	.80713
97	.8186	.8096	.8045	.8005	.80428
98	.8158	.8068	.8016	.7976	.80143
99	.8130	.8040	.7987	.7948	.79859
100	.8102	.8009	.7959	.7917	.79577

C_2H_5OH, Ethyl Alcohol (5)

For bibliography, *v.* (56); *v. also* (3, 6, 7, 14, 23, 31, 35, 38, 39, 49, 50, 51, 64, 67, 71, 74, 83, 87)

% \ °C	10	15	20	25	30	35	40
0	0.99973	0.99913	0.99823	0.99708	0.99568	0.99406	0.99225
1	785	725	636	520	379	217	034
2	602	542	453	336	194	031	.98846
3	426	365	275	157	014	.98849	663
4	258	195	103	.98984	.98839	672	485
5	098	032	.98938	817	670	501	311
6	.98946	.98877	780	656	507	335	142
7	801	729	627	500	347	172	.97975
8	660	584	478	346	189	009	808
9	524	442	331	193	031	.97846	641
10	393	304	187	043	.97875	685	475
11	267	171	047	.97897	723	527	312
12	145	041	.97910	753	573	371	150
13	026	.97914	775	611	424	216	.96989
14	.97911	790	643	472	278	063	829
15	800	669	514	334	133	.96911	670
16	692	552	387	199	.96990	760	512
17	583	433	259	062	844	607	352
18	473	313	129	.96923	697	452	189
19	363	191	.96997	782	547	294	023
20	252	068	864	639	395	134	.95856
21	139	.96944	729	495	242	.95973	687
22	024	818	592	348	087	809	516
23	.96907	689	453	199	.95929	643	343
24	787	558	312	048	769	476	168

C_2H_5OH, Ethyl Alcohol (5).—(*Continued*)

% \ °C	10	15	20	25	30	35	40
25	0.96665	0.96424	0.96168	0.95895	0.95607	0.95306	0.94991
26	539	287	020	738	442	133	810
27	406	144	.95867	576	272	.94955	625
28	268	.95996	710	410	098	774	438
29	125	844	548	241	.94922	590	248
30	.95977	686	382	067	741	403	055
31	823	524	212	.94890	557	214	.93860
32	665	357	038	709	370	021	662
33	502	186	.94860	525	180	.93825	461
34	334	011	679	337	.93986	626	257
35	162	.94832	494	146	790	425	051
36	.94986	650	306	.93952	591	221	.92843
37	805	464	114	756	390	016	634
38	620	273	.93919	556	186	.92808	422
39	431	079	720	353	.92979	597	208
40	238	.93882	518	148	770	385	.91992
41	042	682	314	.92940	558	170	774
42	.93842	478	107	729	344	.91952	554
43	639	271	.92897	516	128	733	332
44	433	062	685	301	.91910	513	108
45	226	.92852	472	085	692	291	.90884
46	017	640	257	.91868	472	069	660
47	.92806	426	041	649	250	.90845	434
48	593	211	.91823	429	028	621	207
49	379	.91995	604	208	.90805	396	.89979
50	162	776	384	.90985	580	168	750
51	.91943	555	160	760	353	.89940	519
52	723	333	.90936	534	125	710	288
53	502	110	711	307	.89896	479	056
54	279	.90885	485	079	667	248	.88823
55	055	659	258	.89850	437	016	589
56	.90831	433	031	621	206	.88784	356
57	607	207	.89803	392	.88975	552	122
58	381	.89980	574	162	744	319	.87888
59	154	752	344	.88931	512	085	653
60	.89927	523	113	699	278	.87851	417
61	698	293	.88882	466	044	615	180
62	468	062	650	233	.87809	379	.86943
63	237	.88830	417	.87998	574	142	705
64	006	597	183	763	337	.86905	466
65	.88774	364	.87948	527	100	667	227
66	541	130	713	291	.86863	429	.85987
67	308	.87895	477	054	625	190	747
68	074	660	241	.86817	387	.85950	507
69	.87839	424	004	579	148	710	266
70	602	187	.86766	340	.85908	470	025
71	365	.86949	527	100	667	228	.84783
72	127	710	287	.85859	426	.84986	540
73	.86888	470	047	618	184	743	297
74	648	229	.85806	376	.84941	500	053
75	408	.85988	564	134	698	257	.83809
76	168	747	322	.84891	455	013	564
77	.85927	505	079	647	211	.83768	319
78	0.85685	0.85262	0.84835	0.84403	0.83966	0.83523	0.83074
79	442	018	590	158	720	277	.82827
80	197	.84772	344	.83911	473	029	578
81	.84950	525	096	664	224	.82780	329
82	702	277	.83848	415	.82974	530	079
83	453	028	599	164	724	279	.81828
84	203	.83777	348	.82913	473	027	576
85	.83951	525	095	660	220	.81774	322
86	697	271	.82840	405	.81965	519	067
87	441	014	583	148	708	262	.80811
88	181	.82754	323	.81888	448	003	552
89	.82919	492	062	626	186	.80742	291
90	654	227	.81797	362	.80922	478	028
91	386	.81959	529	094	655	211	.79761
92	114	688	257	.80823	384	.79941	491
93	.81839	413	.80983	549	111	669	220
94	561	134	705	272	.79835	393	.78947
95	278	.80852	424	.79991	555	114	670
96	.80991	566	138	706	271	.78831	388
97	698	274	.79846	415	.78981	542	100
98	399	.79975	547	117	684	247	.77806
99	094	670	243	.78814	382	.77946	507
100	.79784	360	.78934	506	075	641	203

Density (g/ml) of Mixtures of C_2H_5OH and H_2O at 20°C

* indicates change in the first two decimal places

% alcohol by weight	Tenths of %									
	0	1	2	3	4	5	6	7	8	9
0	0.99823	804	785	766	748	729	710	692	673	655
1	636	618	599	581	562	544	525	507	489	471
2	453	435	417	399	381	363	345	327	310	292
3	275	257	240	222	205	188	171	154	137	120
4	103	087	070	053	037	020	003	*987	*971	*954
5	.98938	922	906	890	874	859	843	827	811	796
6	780	765	749	734	718	703	688	673	658	642
7	627	612	597	582	567	553	538	523	508	493
8	478	463	449	434	419	404	389	374	360	345
9	331	316	301	287	273	258	244	229	215	201
10	187	172	158	144	130	117	103	089	075	061
11	047	033	019	006	*992	*978	*964	*951	*937	*923
12	.97910	896	883	869	855	842	828	815	801	788
13	775	761	748	735	722	709	696	683	670	657
14	643	630	617	604	591	578	565	552	539	526
15	514	501	488	475	462	450	438	425	412	400
16	387	374	361	349	336	323	310	297	284	272
17	259	246	233	220	207	194	181	168	155	142
18	129	116	103	089	076	063	050	037	024	010
19	.96997	984	971	957	944	931	917	904	891	877
20	864	850	837	823	810	796	783	769	756	742
21	729	716	702	688	675	661	647	634	620	606
22	592	578	564	551	537	523	509	495	481	467
23	453	439	425	411	396	382	368	354	340	326
24	312	297	283	269	254	240	225	211	196	182

DENSITY (G/ML) OF MIXTURES OF C_2H_5OH AND H_2O AT 20°C. — (*Continued*)

% alcohol by weight	Tenths of % 0	1	2	3	4	5	6	7	8	9
25	0.96168	153	139	124	109	094	080	065	050	035
26	020	005	*990	*975	*959	*944	*929	*914	*898	*883
27	.95867	851	836	820	805	789	773	757	742	726
28	710	694	678	662	646	630	613	597	581	565
29	548	532	516	499	483	466	450	433	416	400
30	382	365	349	332	315	298	281	264	247	230
31	212	195	178	161	143	126	108	091	074	056
32	038	020	003	*985	*967	*950	*932	*914	*896	*878
33	.94860	842	824	806	788	770	752	734	715	697
34	679	660	642	624	605	587	568	550	531	512
35	494	475	456	438	419	400	382	363	344	325
36	306	287	268	249	230	211	192	172	153	134
37	114	095	075	056	036	017	*997	*978	*958	*939
38	.93919	899	879	859	840	820	800	780	760	740
39	720	700	680	660	640	620	599	579	559	539
40	518	498	478	458	437	417	396	376	356	335
41	314	294	273	253	232	212	191	170	149	129
42	107	086	065	044	023	002	*981	*960	*939	*918
43	.92897	876	855	834	812	791	770	749	728	707
44	685	664	642	621	600	579	557	536	515	493
45	472	450	429	408	386	365	343	322	300	279
46	257	236	214	193	171	150	128	106	085	063
47	041	019	*997	*976	*954	*932	*910	*889	*867	*845
48	.91823	801	780	758	736	714	692	670	648	626
49	604	582	560	538	516	494	472	450	428	406
50	384	361	339	317	295	272	250	228	206	183
51	160	138	116	093	071	049	026	004	*981	*959
52	.90936	914	891	869	846	824	801	779	756	734
53	711	689	666	644	621	598	576	553	531	508
54	485	463	440	417	395	372	349	327	304	281
55	258	236	213	190	167	145	122	099	076	054
56	031	008	*985	*962	*939	*917	*894	*871	*848	*825
57	.89803	780	757	734	711	688	665	643	620	597
58	574	551	528	505	482	459	436	413	390	367
59	344	321	298	275	252	229	206	183	160	137
60	113	090	067	044	021	*998	*975	*951	*928	*905
61	.88882	859	836	812	789	766	743	720	696	673
62	650	626	603	580	557	533	510	487	463	440
63	417	393	370	347	323	300	277	253	230	206
64	183	160	136	113	089	066	042	019	*995	*972
65	.87948	925	901	878	854	831	807	784	760	737
66	713	689	666	642	619	595	572	548	524	501
67	477	454	430	406	383	359	336	312	288	265
68	241	218	194	170	147	123	099	075	052	028
69	004	*981	*957	*933	*909	*885	*862	*838	*814	*790
70	.86766	742	718	694	671	647	623	599	575	551
71	527	503	479	455	431	407	383	359	335	311
72	287	263	239	215	191	167	143	119	095	071
73	047	022	*998	*974	*950	*926	*902	*878	*854	*830
74	.85806	781	757	733	709	685	661	636	612	588
75	0.85564	540	515	491	467	443	419	394	370	346
76	322	297	273	249	225	200	176	152	128	103
77	079	055	031	006	*982	*958	*933	*909	*884	*860
78	.84835	811	787	762	738	713	689	664	640	615
79	590	566	541	517	492	467	443	418	393	369
80	344	319	294	270	245	220	196	171	146	121
81	096	072	047	022	*997	*972	*947	*923	*898	*873
82	.83848	823	798	773	748	723	698	674	649	624
83	599	574	549	523	498	473	448	423	398	373
84	348	323	297	272	247	222	196	171	146	120
85	095	070	044	019	*994	*968	*943	*917	*892	*866
86	.82840	815	789	763	738	712	686	660	635	609
87	583	557	531	505	479	453	427	401	375	349
88	323	297	271	245	219	193	167	140	114	088
89	062	035	009	*983	*956	*930	*903	*877	*850	*824
90	.81797	770	744	717	690	664	637	610	583	556
91	529	502	475	448	421	394	366	339	312	285
92	257	230	203	175	148	120	093	066	038	010
93	.80983	955	928	900	872	844	817	789	761	733
94	705	677	649	621	593	565	537	509	480	452
95	424	395	367	338	310	281	253	224	195	166
96	138	109	080	051	022	*993	*963	*934	*905	*875
97	.79846	816	787	757	727	698	668	638	608	578
98	547	517	487	456	426	396	365	335	305	274
99	243	213	182	151	120	089	059	028	*997	*966
100	.78934									

SPECIFIC GRAVITY AT 60/60°F (15.56/15.56°C) OF MIXTURES (BY VOLUME) OF C_2H_5OH AND H_2O

*indicates change in first two decimal places. *See* next line, column 0

% alcohol by volume at 60°F	Tenths of % 0	1	2	3	4	5	6	7	8	9
0	1.00000	*985	*970	*955	*940	*925	*910	*895	*880	*865
1	0.99850	835	820	806	791	776	761	747	732	717
2	703	688	674	659	645	630	616	602	587	573
3	559	545	531	516	502	488	474	460	446	432
4	419	405	391	378	364	350	336	323	309	296
5	282	269	255	242	228	215	202	189	176	163
6	150	137	124	111	098	085	073	060	047	035
7	022	009	*997	*984	*972	*960	*947	*935	*923	*911
8	.98899	887	875	863	851	838	826	814	803	791
9	779	767	755	743	731	720	708	696	684	672
10	661	649	637	625	614	602	590	579	567	556
11	544	532	521	509	498	487	475	464	452	441
12	430	419	408	396	385	374	363	352	341	330
13	319	308	297	286	275	264	254	243	232	221
14	210	200	190	179	168	157	147	136	125	115
15	104	093	083	072	062	051	040	030	019	009
16	.97998	988	977	967	956	946	936	925	915	905
17	895	885	875	864	854	844	834	824	814	804
18	794	784	774	764	754	744	734	724	714	704
19	694	684	674	664	654	645	635	625	615	605

SPECIFIC GRAVITY AT 60/60°F (15.56/15.56°C) OF MIXTURES (BY VOLUME) OF C_2H_5OH AND H_2O.—(*Continued*)

% alcohol by volume at 60°F	Tenths of %									
	0	1	2	3	4	5	6	7	8	9
20	0.97596	586	576	566	556	546	536	526	516	506
21	496	486	476	466	456	446	436	425	415	405
22	395	385	375	365	354	344	334	324	313	303
23	293	283	272	262	252	241	231	221	210	200
24	189	179	168	158	147	137	126	116	105	095
25	084	073	063	052	042	031	020	010	*999	*988
26	.96978	967	957	946	935	924	914	903	892	881
27	870	859	848	837	826	815	804	793	782	771
28	760	749	738	727	715	704	693	682	671	659
29	648	637	625	614	603	591	580	568	557	546
30	534	522	511	499	488	476	464	453	441	429
31	418	406	394	382	370	358	346	334	321	309
32	296	284	271	259	246	234	221	209	196	183
33	170	157	144	132	119	106	093	080	067	054
34	041	028	015	002	*988	*975	*962	*948	*935	*921
35	.95908	894	881	867	854	840	826	812	798	784
36	770	756	742	728	714	700	685	671	657	643
37	628	614	599	585	570	556	541	526	512	497
38	482	467	452	437	423	408	393	378	362	347
39	332	317	302	286	271	256	240	225	209	194
40	178	162	147	131	115	100	084	068	052	036
41	020	004	*988	*972	*956	*940	*923	*907	*891	*875
42	.94858	842	825	809	792	776	759	743	726	710
43	693	676	660	643	626	609	592	575	558	541
44	524	507	490	473	455	438	421	403	386	369
45	351	334	316	298	281	263	245	228	210	192
46	174	156	138	120	102	084	066	048	030	011
47	.93993	975	956	938	920	901	883	864	845	827
48	808	789	771	752	733	714	695	676	657	638
49	619	600	581	562	543	523	504	485	465	446
50	426	407	387	368	348	328	309	289	270	250
51	230	210	190	171	151	131	111	091	071	051
52	031	011	*991	*971	*951	*931	*911	*890	*870	*850
53	.92830	810	789	769	749	728	708	688	667	647
54	626	605	585	564	544	523	502	482	461	440
55	419	398	377	357	336	315	294	273	252	231
56	210	189	168	147	126	105	084	062	041	020
57	.91999	978	956	935	914	892	871	849	827	806
58	784	762	741	719	697	675	653	631	610	588
59	565	543	521	499	477	455	433	410	388	366
60	344	322	299	277	255	232	210	188	165	143
61	120	097	075	052	030	007	*984	*962	*939	*916
62	.90893	870	847	825	802	779	756	733	710	687
63	664	641	618	595	572	549	526	503	480	457
64	434	411	388	365	341	318	295	272	249	225
65	202	179	155	132	108	085	061	038	014	*991
66	.89967	943	920	896	872	848	825	801	777	753
67	729	705	681	657	633	609	585	561	537	513
68	489	465	441	416	392	368	343	319	295	270
69	245	220	196	171	147	122	098	073	048	024
70	.88999	974	950	925	900	875	850	825	801	776
71	751	725	700	675	650	625	600	574	549	524
72	0.88499	474	448	423	397	372	346	321	296	270
73	244	218	193	167	141	116	090	064	039	013
74	.87987	961	935	910	884	858	832	806	780	754
75	728	702	676	650	623	597	571	545	518	492
76	465	439	412	386	359	332	306	279	252	226
77	199	172	145	118	092	065	038	011	*984	*957
78	.86929	902	875	847	820	793	766	738	711	684
79	656	629	601	574	546	518	491	463	435	408
80	380	352	324	296	269	241	213	185	157	129
81	100	072	044	015	*987	*959	*931	*902	*874	*846
82	.85817	789	760	732	703	674	646	617	588	560
83	531	502	473	444	415	386	357	328	299	270
84	240	211	181	152	122	093	063	033	004	*974
85	.84944	914	884	854	824	794	764	734	703	673
86	642	612	581	551	520	490	459	428	398	367
87	336	305	274	243	212	181	150	119	088	056
88	025	*994	*962	*930	*899	*867	*835	*803	*771	*739
89	.83707	675	643	610	578	545	513	480	447	415
90	382	349	315	282	249	216	183	150	116	083
91	049	015	*981	*947	*913	*879	*845	*810	*776	*741
92	.82705	670	635	600	565	529	494	458	423	387
93	351	315	279	243	206	170	133	096	059	022
94	.81984	947	909	871	834	796	757	719	681	642
95	603	564	525	486	446	407	367	327	287	247
96	206	165	125	084	042	001	*960	*918	*876	*834
97	.80792	750	707	664	620	577	533	489	445	401
98	356	311	265	219	173	127	080	033	*985	*937
99	.79889	841	792	743	693	643	593	543	492	441
100	389									

For detailed interpolation tables of temperature corrections to readings of alcoholometers (standard at 60°F) *v.* ([5]).

C_3H_7OH, *n*-PROPYL ALCOHOL ([82])

% \ °C	0	15	30	% \ °C	0	15	30
0	0.9999	0.9991	0.9957	17	0.9817	0.9768	0.9698
1	0.9982	0.9974	0.9940	18	0.9808	0.9752	0.9680
2	0.9967	0.9960	0.9924	19	0.9800	0.9739	0.9661
3	0.9952	0.9944	0.9908				
4	0.9939	0.9929	0.9893	20	0.9789	0.9723	0.9643
				21	0.9776	0.9705	0.9622
5	0.9926	0.9915	0.9877	22	0.9763	0.9688	0.9602
6	0.9914	0.9902	0.9862	23	0.9748	0.9670	0.9583
7	0.9904	0.9890	0.9848	24	0.9733	0.9651	0.9563
8	0.9894	0.9877	0.9834				
9	0.9883	0.9864	0.9819	25	0.9717	0.9633	0.9543
				26	0.9700	0.9614	0.9522
10	0.9874	0.9852	0.9804	27	0.9682	0.9594	0.9501
11	0.9865	0.9840	0.9790	28	0.9664	0.9576	0.9481
12	0.9857	0.9828	0.9775	29	0.9646	0.9556	0.9460
13	0.9849	0.9817	0.9760				
14	0.9841	0.9806	0.9746	30	0.9627	0.9535	0.9439
				31	0.9608	0.9516	0.9418
15	0.9833	0.9793	0.9730	32	0.9589	0.9495	0.9396
16	0.9825	0.9780	0.9714	33	0.9570	0.9474	0.9375

C_3H_7OH, *n*-Propyl Alcohol.—(*Continued*)

% \ °C	0	15	30	% \ °C	0	15	30
34	0.9550	0.9454	0.9354	68	0.8874	0.8759	0.8641
				69	0.8854	0.8739	0.8620
35	0.9530	0.9434	0.9333				
36	0.9511	0.9413	0.9312	70	0.8835	0.8719	0.8600
37	0.9491	0.9392	0.9289	71	0.8815	0.8700	0.8580
38	0.9471	0.9372	0.9269	72	0.8795	0.8680	0.8559
39	0.9450	0.9351	0.9247	73	0.8776	0.8659	0.8539
				74	0.8756	0.8639	0.8518
40	0.9430	0.9331	0.9226				
41	0.9411	0.9310	0.9205	75	0.8736	0.8618	0.8497
42	0.9391	0.9290	0.9184	76	0.8716	0.8598	0.8477
43	0.9371	0.9269	0.9164	77	0.8695	0.8577	0.8456
44	0.9352	0.9248	0.9143	78	0.8675	0.8556	0.8435
				79	0.8655	0.8536	0.8414
45	0.9332	0.9228	0.9122				
46	0.9311	0.9207	0.9100	80	0.8634	0.8516	0.8394
47	0.9291	0.9186	0.9079	81	0.8614	0.8496	0.8373
48	0.9272	0.9165	0.9057	82	0.8594	0.8475	0.8352
49	0.9252	0.9145	0.9036	83	0.8574	0.8454	0.8332
				84	0.8554	0.8434	0.8311
50	0.9232	0.9124	0.9015				
51	0.9213	0.9104	0.8994	85	0.8534	0.8413	0.8290
52	0.9192	0.9084	0.8973	86	0.8513	0.8393	0.8269
53	0.9173	0.9064	0.8952	87	0.8492	0.8372	0.8248
54	0.9153	0.9044	0.8931	88	0.8471	0.8351	0.8227
				89	0.8450	0.8330	0.8206
55	0.9132	0.9023	0.8911				
56	0.9112	0.9003	0.8890	90	0.8429	0.8308	0.8185
57	0.9093	0.8983	0.8869	91	0.8408	0.8287	0.8164
58	0.9073	0.8963	0.8849	92	0.8387	0.8266	0.8142
59	0.9053	0.8942	0.8828	93	0.8364	0.8244	0.8120
				94	0.8342	0.8221	0.8098
60	0.9033	0.8922	0.8807				
61	0.9013	0.8902	0.8786	95	0.8320	0.8199	0.8077
62	0.8994	0.8882	0.8766	96	0.8296	0.8176	0.8054
63	0.8974	0.8861	0.8745	97	0.8272	0.8153	0.8031
64	0.8954	0.8841	0.8724	98	0.8248	0.8128	0.8008
				99	0.8222	0.8104	0.7984
65	0.8934	0.8820	0.8703				
66	0.8913	0.8800	0.8682	100	0.8194	0.8077	0.7958
67	0.8894	0.8779	0.8662				

Doroshevskii and Rozhdestvenskii's Values at 15°C (18); *v. also* (1, 3, 13, 19, 23, 24, 45, 49, 52, 60, 61, 80, 81, 87, 89)

%	d_4^{15}	%	d_4^{15}	%	d_4^{15}	%	d_4^{15}
0	0.99913	15	0.97914	30	0.95318	45	0.92257
1	0.99745	16	0.97788	31	0.95118	46	0.92053
2	0.99580	17	0.97653	32	0.94917	47	0.91848
3	0.99430	18	0.97509	33	0.94715	48	0.91643
4	0.99283	19	0.97358	34	0.94513	49	0.91438
5	0.99141	20	0.97201	35	0.94312	50	0.91234
6	0.99004	21	0.97035	36	0.94109	51	0.91028
7	0.98874	22	0.96863	37	0.93906	52	0.90824
8	0.98748	23	0.96684	38	0.93702	53	0.90619
9	0.98626	24	0.96500	39	0.93497	54	0.90414
10	0.98507	25	0.96310	40	0.93290	55	0.90209
11	0.98390	26	0.96113	41	0.93080	56	0.90003
12	0.98273	27	0.95916	42	0.92876	57	0.89799
13	0.98156	28	0.95717	43	0.92669	58	0.89594
14	0.98037	29	0.95518	44	0.92463	59	0.89389

%	d_4^{15}	%	d_4^{15}	%	d_4^{15}	%	d_4^{15}
60	0.89184	70	0.87158	80	0.85126	90	0.83051
61	0.88980	71	0.86956	81	0.84921	91	0.82836
62	0.88777	72	0.86754	82	0.84716	92	0.82618
63	0.88576	73	0.86552	83	0.84511	93	0.82399
64	0.88373	74	0.86351	84	0.84306	94	0.82179
65	0.88170	75	0.86148	85	0.84101	95	0.81959
66	0.87967	76	0.85944	86	0.83896	96	0.81730
67	0.87764	77	0.85739	87	0.83688	97	0.81490
68	0.87562	78	0.85534	88	0.83478	98	0.81240
69	0.87360	79	0.85330	89	0.83266	99	0.80982
						100	0.80733

C_3H_7OH, Isopropyl Alcohol

v. also (1, 3, 21, 24, 77, 80, 81)

% \ °C	0 (82)	15 (82)	15 (16)	20 (47)	30 (82)
0	0.9999	0.9991	0.99913	0.9982	0.9957
1	0.9980	0.9973	0.9972	0.9962	0.9939
2	0.9962	0.9956	0.9954	0.9944	0.9921
3	0.9946	0.9938	0.9936	0.9926	0.9904
4	0.9930	0.9922	0.9920	0.9909	0.9887
5	0.9916	0.9906	0.9904	0.9893	0.9871
6	0.9902	0.9892	0.9890	0.9877	0.9855
7	0.9890	0.9878	0.9875	0.9862	0.9839
8	0.9878	0.9864	0.9862	0.9847	0.9824
9	0.9866	0.9851	0.9849	0.9833	0.9809
10	0.9856	0.9838	0.9836$_2$	0.9820	0.9794
11	0.9846	0.9826	0.9824	0.9808	0.9778
12	0.9838	0.9813	0.9812	0.9797	0.9764
13	0.9829	0.9802	0.9800	0.9786	0.9750
14	0.9821	0.9790	0.9788	0.9776	0.9735
15	0.9814	0.9779	0.9777	0.9765	0.9720
16	0.9806	0.9768	0.9765	0.9754	0.9705
17	0.9799	0.9756	0.9753	0.9743	0.9690
18	0.9792	0.9745	0.9741	0.9731	0.9675
19	0.9784	0.9730	0.9728	0.9717	0.9658
20	0.9777	0.9719	0.9715$_8$	0.9703	0.9642
21	0.9768	0.9704	0.9703	0.9688	0.9624
22	0.9759	0.9690	0.9689	0.9669	0.9606
23	0.9749	0.9675	0.9674	0.9651	0.9587
24	0.9739	0.9660	0.9659	0.9634	0.9569
25	0.9727	0.9643	0.9642	0.9615	0.9549
26	0.9714	0.9626	0.9624	0.9597	0.9529
27	0.9699	0.9608	0.9605	0.9577	0.9509
28	0.9684	0.9590	0.9586	0.9558	0.9488
29	0.9669	0.9570	0.9568	0.9540	0.9467
30	0.9652	0.9551	0.9549$_3$	0.9520	0.9446
31	0.9634		0.9530	0.9500	0.9426
32	0.9615		0.9510	0.9481	0.9405
33	0.9596		0.9489	0.9460	0.9383
34	0.9577		0.9468	0.9440	0.9361
35	0.9557		0.9446	0.9419	0.9338
36	0.9536		0.9424	0.9399	0.9315
37	0.9514		0.9401	0.9377	0.9292

C_3H_7OH, Isopropyl Alcohol.—(*Continued*)

% \ °C	0 [82]	15 [82]	15 [16]	20 [47]	30 [82]
38	0.9493		0.9379	0.9355	0.9269
39	0.9472		0.9356	0.9333	0.9246
40	0.9450		0.9333$_3$	0.9310	0.9224
41	0.9428		0.9311	0.9287	0.9201
42	0.9406		0.9288	0.9264	0.9177
43	0.9384		0.9266	0.9239	0.9154
44	0.9361		0.9243	0.9215	0.9130
45	0.9338		0.9220	0.9191	0.9106
46	0.9315		0.9197	0.9165	0.9082
47	0.9292		0.9174	0.9141	0.9059
48	0.9270		0.9150	0.9117	0.9036
49	0.9247		0.9127	0.9093	0.9013
50	0.9224		0.9104$_3$	0.9069	0.8990
51	0.9201		0.9081	0 9044	0.8966
52	0.9178		0.9058	0.9020	0.8943
53	0.9155		0.9035	0.8996	0.8919
54	0.9132		0.9011	0.8971	0.8895
55	0.9109		0.8988	0.8946	0.8871
56	0.9086		0.8964	0.8921	0.8847
57	0.9063		0.8940	0.8896	0.8823
58	0.9040		0.8917	0.8874	0.8800
59	0.9017		0.8893	0.8850	0.8777
60	0.8994		0.8869$_0$	0.8825	0.8752
61	0.8970		0.8845	0.8800	0.8728
62	0.8947	0.8829	0.8821	0.8776	0.8704
63	0.8924	0.8805	0.8798	0.8751	0.8680
64	0.8901	0.8781	0.8775	0.8727	0.8656
65	0.8878	0.8757	0.8752	0.8702	0.8631
66	0.8854	0.8733	0.8728	0.8679	0.8607
67	0.8831	0.8710	0.8705	0.8656	0.8583
68	0.8807	0.8686	0.8682	0.8632	0.8559
69	0.8784	0.8662	0.8658	0.8609	0.8535
70	0.8761	0.8639	0.8634$_6$	0.8584	0.8511
71	0.8738	0.8615	0.8611	0.8560	0.8487
72	0.8714	0.8592	0.8588	0.8537	0.8464
73	0.8691	0.8568	0.8564	0.8513	0.8440
74	0.8668	0.8545	0.8541	0.8489	0.8416
75	0.8644	0.8521	0.8517	0.8464	0.8392
76	0.8621	0.8497	0.8493	0.8439	0.8368
77	0.8598	0.8474	0.8470	0.8415	0.8344
78	0.8575	0.8450	0.8446	0.8391	0.8321
79	0.8551	0.8426	0.8422	0.8366	0.8297
80	0.8528	0.8403	0.8397$_9$	0.8342	0.8273
81	0.8503	0.8379	0.8374	0.8317	0.8248
82	0.8479	0.8355	0.8350	0.8292	0.8224
83	0.8456	0.8331	0.8326	0.8268	0.8200
84	0.8432	0.8307	0.8302	0.8243	0.8175
85	0.8408	0.8282	0.8278	0.8219	0.8151
86	0.8384	0.8259	0.8254	0.8194	0.8127
87	0.8360	0.8234	0.8229	0.8169	0.8102
88	0.8336	0.8209	0.8205	0.8145	0.8078
89	0.8311	0.8184	0.8180	0.8120	0.8053
90	0.8287	0.8161	0.8155$_3$	0.8096	0.8029
91	0.8262	0.8136	0.8130	0.8072	0.8004
92	0.8237	0.8110	0.8104	0.8047	0.7979
93	0.8212	0.8085	0.8079	0.8023	0.7954
94	0.8186	0.8060	0.8052	0.7998	0.7929
95	0.8160	0.8034	0.8026	0.7973	0.7904
96	0.8133	0.8008	0.7999	0.7949	0.7878
97	0.8106	0.7981	0.7972	0.7925	0.7852
98	0.8078	0.7954	0.7945	0.7901	0.7826
99	0.8048	0.7926	0.7918	0.7877	0.7799
100	0.8016	0.7896	0.7891$_3$	0.7854	0.7770

$C_3H_8O_3$, Glycerol

% \ °C	15 [27, 29, 32, 34, 48, 76, 90]	15.5 [90]	20 [27, 29, 48, 53, 54, 73, 86, 90]	25 [29, 48, 90]	30 [32, 48]
0	0.9991	0.9990	0.9982	0.9971	0.9957
1	1.0015	1.0014	1.0006	0.9994	0.9978
2	1.0040	1.0039	1.0030	1.0017	0.9999
3	1.0064	1.0063	1.0053	1.0041	1.0020
4	1.0088	1.0087	1.0077	1.0064	1.0042
5	1.0112	1.0111	1.0101	1.0088	1.0064
6	1.0136	1.0135	1.0125	1.0112	1.0086
7	1.0161	1.0159	1.0149	1.0135	1.0109
8	1.0185	1.0183	1.0173	1.0159	1.0133
9	1.0210	1.0208	1.0197	1.0183	1.0158
10	1.0234	1.0232	1.0221	1.0207	1.0183
11	1.0259	1.0257	1.0246	1.0232	1.0208
12	1.0284	1.0282	1.0271	1.0256	1.0232
13	1.0309	1.0307	1.0295	1.0280	1.0256
14	1.0334	1.0332	1.0320	1.0305	1.0281
15	1.0359	1.0357	1.0345	1.0329	1.0306
16	1.0384	1.0382	1.0370	1.0354	1.0331
17	1.0409	1.0407	1.0395	1.0379	1.0356
18	1.0435	1.0432	1.0420	1.0404	1.0380
19	1.0460	1.0458	1.0445	1.0429	1.0405
20	1.0486	1.0483	1.0470	1.0453	1.0430
21	1.0511	1.0509	1.0495	1.0477	1.0454
22	1.0536	1.0535	1.0520	1.0501	1.0479
23	1.0562	1.0561	1.0545	1.0525	1.0504
24	1.0588	1.0587	1.0571	1.0550	1.0529
25	1.0614	1.0613	1.0597	1.0575	1.0554
26	1.0640	1.0639	1.0622	1.0600	1.0579
27	1.0666	1.0665	1.0648	1.0626	1.0605
28	1.0692	1.0691	1.0674	1.0652	1.0631
29	1.0718	1.0717	1.0700	1.0679	1.0657
30	1.0744	1.0744	1.0727	1.0706	1.0683
31	1.0770	1.0770	1.0753	1.0732	1.0709
32	1.0797	1.0797	1.0780	1.0758	1.0735
33	1.0824	1.0824	1.0806	1.0785	1.0762
34	1.0851	1.0851	1.0833	1.0811	1.0788
35	1.0878	1.0878	1.0860	1.0837	1.0814
36	1.0905	1.0905	1.0887	1.0864	1.0840

$C_3H_8O_3$, Glycerol.—(*Continued*)

% \ °C	15	15.5	20	25	30
37	1.0932	1.0932	1.0914	1.0890	1.0867
38	1.0959	1.0959	1.0941	1.0917	1.0894
39	1.0986	1.0986	1.0968	1.0944	1.0920
40	1.1013	1.1013	1.0995	1.0971	1.0947
41	1.1040	1.1040	1.1022	1.0998	1.0974
42	1.1068	1.1067	1.1049	1.1025	1.1001
43	1.1095	1.1094	1.1075	1.1052	1.1028
44	1.1122	1.1122	1.1102	1.1079	1.1054
45	1.1149	1.1149	1.1128	1.1106	1.1081
46	1.1176	1.1176	1.1155	1.1133	1.1108
47	1.1203	1.1203	1.1182	1.1160	1.1135
48	1.1230	1.1230	1.1209	1.1187	1.1161
49	1.1257	1.1257	1.1236	1.1213	1.1188
50	1.1285	1.1285	1.1263	1.1239	1.1215
51	1.1313	1.1312	1.1290	1.1265	1.1242
52	1.1341	1.1340	1.1317	1.1292	1.1269
53	1.1369	1.1368	1.1344	1.1319	1.1296
54	1.1397	1.1396	1.1371	1.1346	1.1323
55	1.1425	1.1423	1.1398	1.1374	1.1350
56	1.1453	1.1451	1.1425	1.1401	1.1378
57	1.1481	1.1478	1.1452	1.1429	1.1406
58	1.1509	1.1506	1.1479	1.1457	1.1433
59	1.1537	1.1534	1.1506	1.1484	1.1460
60	1.1564	1.1562	1.1533	1.1511	1.1487
61	1.1591	1.1589	1.1560	1.1538	1.1515
62	1.1619	1.1617	1.1587	1.1565	1.1543
63	1.1647	1.1644	1.1614	1.1592	1.1571
64	1.1675	1.1672	1.1642	1.1620	1.1598
65	1.1703	1.1700	1.1670	1.1647	1.1625
66	1.1731	1.1728	1.1697	1.1674	1.1652
67	1.1759	1.1755	1.1724	1.1702	1.1680
68	1.1787	1.1783	1.1752	1.1729	1.1707
69	1.1815	1.1811	1.1780	1.1756	1.1734
70	1.1842	1.1838	1.1808	1.1784	1.1761
71	1.1870	1.1866	1.1836	1.1811	1.1788
72	1.1897	1.1893	1.1863	1.1838	1.1814
73	1.1924	1.1920	1.1890	1.1865	1.1840
74	1.1951	1.1948	1.1917	1.1892	1.1867
75	1.1979	1.1975	1.1944	1.1919	1.1894
76	1.2006	1.2003	1.1971	1.1946	1.1921
77	1.2033	1.2030	1.1998	1.1973	1.1948
78	1.2060	1.2057	1.2025	1.2000	1.1974
79	1.2087	1.2084	1.2052	1.2027	1.2000
80	1.2114	1.2111	1.2079	1.2054	1.2025
81	1.2141	1.2138	1.2106	1.2081	
82	1.2168	1.2165	1.2133	1.2108	
83	1.2195	1.2191	1.2160	1.2134	
84	1.2222	1.2218	1.2187	1.2161	
85	1.2249	1.2245	1.2214	1.2187	
86	1.2276	1.2271	1.2241	1.2214	
87	1.2303	1.2298	1.2268	1.2241	
88	1.2330	1.2325	1.2294	1.2268	
89	1.2356	1.2351	1.2320	1.2294	
90	1.2382	1.2378	1.2347	1.2320	
91	1.2408	1.2404	1.2374	1.2346	
92	1.2434	1.2430	1.2401	1.2372	
93	1.2460	1.2457	1.2428	1.2398	
94	1.2486	1.2483	1.2455	1.2424	
95	1.2512	1.2509	1.2482	1.2451	
96	1.2538	1.2535	1.2508	1.2477	
97	1.2564	1.2561	1.2534	1.2503	
98	1.2590	1.2587	1.2559	1.2529	
99	1.2616	1.2612	1.2584	1.2555	
100	1.2641	1.2638	1.2609	1.2580	

CH_2O_2, Formic Acid

v. also (26, 37, 57, 66)

% \ °C	0 (10, 82)	15 (80, 81, 82)	20 (68)	30 (82)
0	0.9999	0.9991	0.9982	0.9957
1	1.0028	1.0019	1.0019	(0.9980)
2	1.0059	1.0045	1.0044	(1.0004)
3	1.0090	1.0072	1.0070	(1.0028)
4	1.0120	1.0100	1.0093	(1.0053)
5	1.0150	1.0124	1.0115	1.0075
6	1.0179	1.0151	1.0141	1.0101
7	1.0207	1.0177	1.0170	1.0125
8	1.0237	1.0204	1.0196	1.0149
9	1.0266	1.0230	1.0221	1.0173
10	1.0295	1.0256	1.0246	1.0197
11	1.0324	1.0281	1.0271	1.0221
12	1.0351	1.0306	1.0296	1.0244
13	1.0379	1.0330	1.0321	1.0267
14	1.0407	1.0355	1.0345	1.0290
15	1.0435	1.0380	1.0370	1.0313
16	1.0463	1.0405	1.0393	1.0336
17	1.0491	1.0430	1.0417	1.0358
18	1.0518	1.0455	1.0441	1.0381
19	1.0545	1.0480	1.0464	1.0404
20	1.0571	1.0505	1.0488	1.0427
21	1.0598	1.0532	1.0512	1.0451
22	1.0625	1.0556	1.0537	1.0473
23	1.0652	1.0580	1.0561	1.0496
24	1.0679	1.0604	1.0585	1.0518
25	1.0706	1.0627	1.0609	1.0540
26	1.0733	1.0652	1.0633	1.0564
27	1.0760	1.0678	1.0656	1.0587
28	1.0787	1.0702	1.0681	1.0609
29	1.0813	1.0726	1.0705	1.0632
30	1.0839	1.0750	1.0729	1.0654
31	1.0866	1.0774	1.0753	1.0676
32	1.0891	1.0798	1.0777	1.0699
33	1.0916	1.0821	1.0800	1.0721
34	1.0941	1.0844	1.0823	1.0743
35	1.0966	1.0867	1.0847	1.0766
36	1.0993	1.0892	1.0871	1.0788

CH_2O_2, Formic Acid.—(*Continued*)

% \ °C	0	15	20	30
37	1.1018	1.0916	1.0895	1.0810
38	1.1043	1.0940	1.0919	1.0832
39	1.1069	1.0964	1.0940	1.0854
40	1.1095	1.0988	1.0963	1.0876
41	1.1122	1.1012	1.0990	1.0898
42	1.1148	1.1036	1.1015	1.0920
43	1.1174	1.1060	1.1038	1.0943
44	1.1199	1.1084	1.1062	1.0965
45	1.1224	1.1109	1.1085	1.0987
46	1.1249	1.1133	1.1108	1.1009
47	1.1274	1.1156	1.1130	1.1031
48	1.1299	1.1179	1.1157	1.1053
49	1.1324	1.1202	1.1185	1.1076
50	1.1349	1.1225	1.1207	1.1098
51	1.1374	1.1248	1.1223	1.1120
52	1.1399	1.1271	1.1244	1.1142
53	1.1424	1.1294	1.1269	1.1164
54	1.1448	1.1318	1.1295	1.1186
55	1.1472	1.1341	1.1320	1.1208
56	1.1497	1.1365	1.1342	1.1230
57	1.1523	1.1388	1.1361	1.1253
58	1.1548	1.1411	1.1381	1.1274
59	1.1573	1.1434	1.1401	1.1295
60	1.1597	1.1458	1.1424	1.1317
61	1.1621	1.1481	1.1448	1.1338
62	1.1645	1.1504	1.1473	1.1360
63	1.1669	1.1526	1.1493	1.1382
64	1.1694	1.1549	1.1517	1.1403
65	1.1718	1.1572	1.1543	1.1425
66	1.1742	1.1595	1.1565	1.1446
67	1.1766	1.1618	1.1584	1.1467
68	1.1790	1.1640	1.1604	1.1489
69	1.1813	1.1663	1.1628	1.1510
70	1.1835	1.1685	1.1655	1.1531
71	1.1858	1.1707	1.1677	1.1552
72	1.1882	1.1729	1.1702	1.1573
73	1.1906	1.1751	1.1728	1.1595
74	1.1929	1.1773	1.1752	1.1615
75	1.1953	1.1794	1.1769	1.1636
76	1.1976	1.1816	1.1785	1.1656
77	1.1999	1.1837	1.1801	1.1676
78	1.2021	1.1859	1.1818	1.1697
79	1 2043	1.1881	1.1837	1.1717
80	1 2065	1.1902	1.1860	1.1737
81	1.2088	1.1924	1.1876	1.1758
82	1.2110	1.1944	1.1896	1.1778
83	1.2132	1.1965	1.1914	1.1798
84	1.2154	1.1985	1.1929	1.1817
85	1.2176	1.2005	1.1953	1.1837
86	1.2196	1.2025	1.1976	1.1856
87	1.2217	1.2045	1.1994	1.1875
88	1.2237	1.2064	1.2012	1.1893
89	1.2258	1.2084	1.2028	1.1910
90	1.2278	1.2102	1.2044	1.1927
91	1.2297	1.2121	1.2059	1.1945
92	1.2316	1.2139	1.2078	1.1961
93	1.2335	1.2157	1.2099	1.1978
94	1.2354	1.2174	1.2117	1.1994
95	1.2372	1.2191	1.2140	1.2008
96	1.2390	1.2208	1.2158	1.2022
97	1.2408	1.2224	1.2170	1.2036
98	1.2425	1.2240	1.2183	1.2048
99	1.2441	1.2257	1.2202	1.2061
100	1.2456	1.2273	1.2212	1.2073

$C_2H_4O_2$, Acetic Acid

% \ °C	0 (10, 49, 58, 59, 82, 88)	10 (58, 59)	15 (41, 58, 59, 61, 62, 80, 81, 82)	20 (2, 4, 19, 33, 43, 46, 55, 57, 58, 59, 61, 62, 80, 81, 84, 85)	25 (19, 25, 49, 51, 58, 59, 61, 62, 66, 69, 70, 72)	30 (19, 58, 59, 82)	40 (58, 59)
0	0.9999	0.9997	0.9991	0.9982	0.9971	0.9957	0.9922
1	1.0016	1.0013	1.0006	.9996	.9987	.9971	.9934
2	.0033	.0029	.0021	1.0012	1.0000	.9984	.9946
3	.0051	.0044	.0036	.0025	.0013	.9997	.9958
4	.0070	.0060	.0051	.0040	.0027	1.0011	.9970
5	0088	.0076	.0066	.0055	.0041	.0024	.9982
6	.0106	.0092	.0081	.0069	.0055	.0037	.9994
7	.0124	.0108	.0096	.0083	.0068	.0050	1.0006
8	.0142	.0124	.0111	.0097	.0081	.0063	.0018
9	.0159	.0140	.0126	.0111	.0094	.0076	.0030
10	.0177	.0156	.0141	.0125	.0107	.0089	.0042
11	.0194	.0171	.0155	.0139	.0120	.0102	.0054
12	.0211	.0187	.0170	.0154	.0133	.0115	.0065
13	.0228	.0202	.0184	.0168	.0146	.0127	.0077
14	.0245	.0217	.0199	.0182	.0159	.0139	.0088
15	.0262	.0232	.0213	.0195	.0172	.0151	.0099
16	.0278	.0247	.0227	.0209	.0185	.0163	.0110
17	.0295	.0262	.0241	.0223	.0198	.0175	.0121
18	.0311	.0276	.0255	.0236	.0210	.0187	.0132
19	.0327	.0291	.0269	.0250	.0223	.0198	.0142
20	.0343	.0305	.0283	.0263	.0235	.0210	.0153
21	.0358	.0319	.0297	.0276	.0248	.0222	.0164
22	.0374	.0333	.0310	.0288	.0260	.0233	.0174
23	.0389	.0347	.0323	.0301	.0272	.0244	.0185
24	.0404	.0361	.0336	.0313	.0283	.0256	.0195
25	.0419	.0375	.0349	.0326	.0295	.0267	.0205
26	.0434	.0388	.0362	.0338	.0307	.0278	.0215
27	.0449	.0401	.0374	.0349	.0318	.0289	.0225

$C_2H_4O_2$, Acetic Acid.—(*Continued*)

% \ °C	0	10	15	20	25	30	40
28	1.0463	1.0414	1.0386	1.0361	1.0329	1.0299	1.0234
29	.0477	.0427	.0399	.0372	.0340	.0310	.0244
30	.0491	.0440	.0411	.0384	.0350	.0320	.0253
31	.0505	.0453	.0423	.0395	.0361	.0330	.0262
32	.0519	.0465	.0435	.0406	.0372	.0341	.0272
33	.0532	.0477	.0446	.0417	.0382	.0351	.0281
34	.0545	.0489	.0458	.0428	.0392	.0361	.0289
35	.0558	.0501	.0469	.0438	.0402	.0371	.0298
36	.0571	.0513	.0480	.0449	.0412	.0380	.0306
37	.0584	.0524	.0491	.0459	.0422	.0390	.0314
38	.0596	.0535	.0501	.0469	.0432	.0399	.0322
39	.0608	.0546	.0512	.0479	.0441	.0408	.0330
40	.0621	.0557	.0522	.0488	.0450	.0416	.0338
41	.0633	.0568	.0532	.0498	.0460	.0425	.0346
42	.0644	.0578	.0542	.0507	.0469	.0433	.0353
43	.0656	.0588	.0551	.0516	.0477	.0441	.0361
44	.0667	.0598	.0561	.0525	.0486	.0449	.0368
45	.0679	.0608	.0570	.0534	.0495	.0456	.0375
46	.0689	.0618	.0579	.0542	.0503	.0464	.0382
47	.0699	.0627	.0588	.0551	.0511	.0471	.0389
48	.0709	.0636	.0597	.0559	.0518	.0479	.0395
49	.0720	.0645	.0605	.0567	.0526	.0486	.0402
50	.0729	.0654	.0613	.0575	.0534	.0492	.0408
51	.0738	.0663	.0622	.0582	.0542	.0499	.0414
52	.0748	.0671	.0629	.0590	.0549	.0506	.0421
53	.0757	.0679	.0637	.0597	.0555	.0512	.0427
54	.0765	.0687	.0644	.0604	.0562	.0518	.0432
55	.0774	.0694	.0651	.0611	.0568	.0525	.0438
56	.0782	.0701	.0658	.0618	.0574	.0531	.0443
57	.0790	.0708	.0665	.0624	.0580	.0536	.0448
58	.0798	.0715	.0672	.0631	.0586	.0542	.0453
59	.0805	.0722	.0678	.0637	.0592	.0547	.0458
60	.0813	.0728	.0684	.0642	.0597	.0552	.0462
61	.0820	.0734	.0690	.0648	.0602	.0557	.0466
62	.0826	.0740	.0696	.0653	.0607	.0562	.0470
63	.0833	.0746	.0701	.0658	.0612	.0566	.0473
64	.0838	.0752	.0706	.0662	.0616	.0571	.0477
65	.0844	.0757	.0711	.0666	.0621	.0575	.0480
66	.0850	.0762	.0716	.0671	.0624	.0578	.0483
67	.0856	.0767	.0720	.0675	.0628	.0582	.0486
68	.0860	.0771	.0725	.0678	.0631	.0585	.0489
69	.0865	.0775	.0729	.0682	.0634	.0588	.0491
70	.0869	.0779	.0732	.0685	.0637	.0590	.0493
71	.0874	.0783	.0736	.0687	.0640	.0592	.0495
72	.0877	.0786	.0738	.0690	.0642	.0594	.0496
73	.0881	.0789	.0741	.0693	.0644	.0595	.0497
74	.0884	.0792	.0743	.0694	.0645	.0596	.0498
75	.0887	.0794	.0745	.0696	.0647	.0597	.0499
76	.0889	.0796	.0746	.0698	.0648	.0598	.0499
77	.0891	.0797	.0747	.0699	.0648	.0598	.0499
78	.0893	.0798	.0747	.0700	.0648	.0598	.0498
79	.0894	.0798	.0747	.0700	.0648	.0597	.0497
80	1.0895	1.0798	1.0747	1.0700	1.0647	1.0596	1.0495
81	.0895	.0797	.0745	.0699	.0646	.0594	.0493
82	.0895	.0796	.0743	.0698	.0644	.0592	.0490
83	.0895	.0795	.0741	.0696	.0642	.0589	.0487
84	.0893	.0793	.0738	.0693	.0638	.0585	.0483
85	.0891	.0790	.0735	.0689	.0635	.0582	.0479
86	.0887	.0787	.0731	.0685	.0630	.0576	.0473
87	.0883	.0783	.0726	.0680	.0626	.0571	.0467
88	.0877	.0778	.0721	.0675	.0620	.0564	.0460
89	.0872	.0773	.0715	.0668	.0613	.0557	.0453
90	.0865	.0766	.0708	.0661	.0605	.0549	.0445
91	.0857	.0758	.0700	.0652	.0597	.0541	.0436
92	.0848	.0749	.0690	.0643	.0587	.0530	.0426
93	.0838	.0739	.0680	.0632	.0577	.0518	.0414
94	.0826	.0727	.0667	.0619	.0564	.0506	.0401
95	.0813	.0714	.0652	.0605	.0551	.0491	.0386
96	.0798		.0632	.0588	.0535	.0473	.0368
97	.0780		.0611	.0570	.0516	.0454	.0348
98	.0759		.0590	.0549	.0495	.0431	.0325
99	.0730		.0567	.0524	.0468	.0407	.0299
100	.0697		.0545	.0498	.0440	.0380	.0271

LITERATURE

(For a key to the periodicals see end of volume)

(1) Atkins and Wallace, *4*, **103**: 1461; 13. (2) Bousfield and Lowry, *4*, **99**: 1432; 11. (3) Brunel, Crenshaw and Tobin, *1*, **43**: 561; 21. *135*, **122**: 256, 269, 281; 21. (4) Buchkremer, *Diss.*, Bonn, 1890. (5) Bureau of Standards, *365*, No. **19**; 16. (6) Burrows, *316*, **53**: 74; 19. (7) Burwinkle, *Diss.*, Münster, 1914. (8) Cameron and Robinson, *50*, **14**: 569; 10. (9) Campbell, *83*, **11**: 91; 15.

(10) Charpy, *6*, **29**: 5; 93. (11) Cheneveau, *Thesis*, Paris, 1907. (12) Comey and Backus, *45*, **2**: 11; 10. (13) Crismer, *28*, **18**: 18; 04. (14) Denison, *83*, **8**: 35; 12. (15) Dittmar and Fawsitt, *174*, **33**: 509; 87. (16) Doroshevskii, *53*, **41**: 958; 09. (17) Doroshevskii and Rozdestvenskii, *53*, **41**: 977; 09. (18) Doroshevskii and Rozdestvenskii, *53*, **41**: 1428; 09. (19) Dunstan and Thole, *4*, **95**: 1556; 09.

(20) Dupré, *5*, **20**: 336; 72. (21) Eisenlohr, *7*, **75**: 585; 10. (22) Fales and Morrell, *1*, **44**: 2071; 22. (23) Frankforter and Frary, *50*, **17**: 402; 13. (24) Frankforter and Temple, *1*, **37**: 2697; 15. (25) Friedländer, *7*, **38**: 385; 01. (26) Garner, Saxton and Parker, *11*, **46**: 236; 11. (27) Gerlach, *317*, **7**: 277; 84. (28) Heimbrodt, *8*, **13**: 1028; 04. (29) Henkel and Roth, *92*, **18**: 1936; 05.

(30) Herz and Knoch, *93*, **45**: 262; 05. (31) Herz and Schuftan, *7*, **101**: 269; 22. (32) Herz and Wegner, *465*, **45**: 53; 25. (33) Holmes, *4*, **89**: 1774; 06. (34) Holmes, *4*, **103**: 2147; 13. (35) Hövelmann, *Diss.*, Münster, 1914. (36) Humburg, *7*, **12**: 401; 93. (37) Jahn, *7*, **16**: 72; 95. (38) Jones, Lapworth and Lingford, *4*, **103**: 252; 13. (39) Joseph and Rae, *54*, **33**: 991; 14.

(40) Kailan, *91*, **51**: 81; 12. (41) Kassel, *Diss.*, Leipzig, 1910. (42) Klason and Norlin, *19*, **2**: No. 27; 06. (43) Kohlrausch, *8*, **159**: 233; 76. (44) Kohlrausch and Hallwachs, *8*, **53**: 14; 94. (45) Landolt and Jahn, *7*, **10**: 289; 92. (46) Le Blanc, *7*, **4**: 553; 89. (47) Lebo, *1*, **43**: 1005; 21. (48) Lewis, *54*, **41**: 97T; 22. (49) Mathews and Cooke, *50*, **18**: 559: 14.

(50) Merriman, *4*, **103**: 1774, 1790; 13. (51) Merry and Turner, *4*, **105**: 748; 14. (52) Mueller and Abegg, *7*, **57**: 513; 07. (53) Nicol, *347*, **18**: 302; 87. (54) Öholm, *147*, **2**: No. 26; 13. (55) Oppenheimer, *7*, **27**: 447; 98. (56) Osborne, McKelvy and Bearce, *31A*, **9**: 327; 13. (57) Otten, *Diss.*, München, 1887. (58) Oudemans, *18*, **1**: 447; 66. (59) Oudemans, *467*, **2**: 750; 66.

(60) Pagliani, *59*, **12**: 229; 82. (61) Perkin, *4*, **45**: 421; 84. (62) Perkin, *4*, **49**: 777; 86. (63) Pisarževskii and Lemcke, *7*, **52**: 479; 05. (64) Price, *4*, **107**: 188; 15. (65) Reid, *11*, **45**: 479; 11. (66) Reyher, *7*, **2**: 744; 88. (67) Richards and Shipley, *1*, **38**: 989; 16. (68) Richardson and Allaire, *11*, **19**: 149; 97. (69) Rimbach and Wintgen, *7*, **74**: 233; 10.

(70) Rivett and Sidgwick, *4*, **97**: 732; 10. (71) Robertson and Acree, *11*, **49**: 474; 13. (72) Rudorf, *7*, **43**: 257; 03. (73) Scheij, *70*, **18**: 169; 99. (74) Schoorl and Regenboden, *64P*, **20**: 831; 18. (75) Schöttner, *75*, **77 II**: 682; 78. (76) Skalweit, *466*, **5**: 17; 85. (77) Thorpe, *4*, **71**: 920; 97. (78) Tijmstra, *7*, **49**: 345; 04. (79) Timmermans, *28*, **24**: 244; 10.

(80) Traube, *25,* **19:** 871; 86. (81) Traube, *13,* **265:** 27; 91. (82) Turbaba, *181,* **Suppl. 5:** 1890–3. (83) Tyrer, *4,* **105:** 2534; 14. (84) Usher, *4,* **97:** 66; 10. (85) Wilsdon and Sidgwick, *4,* **103:** 1959; 13. (86) Winther, *7,* **60:** 563; 07. (87) Wroth and Reid, *1,* **38:** 2316; 16. (88) Young, *117,* **12:** 374; 10. (89) Young and Fortey, *4,* **81:** 717; 02.
(90) Bosart and Snoddy, *45,* **19:** 506; 27.

B. SOLUTIONS CONTAINING MORE THAN ONE SOLUTE. BOTH SOLUTES ARE C-COMPOUNDS‡

The ℭ-arrangement (p. viii)

Unless otherwise indicated all compositions are given in Wt. % in the solution. All density values are d_4^t = g/ml *in vacuo.*

B = **CCl_4,** Carbon tetrachloride

C = **CH_4O,** Methyl alcohol (4)

C = **C_2H_6O,** Ethyl alcohol

t = 19.4°C; R = %B/%C (6); *cf.* (4)

%H_2O \ R	0.05086	0.1096	0.2555	0.4319	0.6313	0.9600
5	0.8251	0.8456	0.8935	0.9423	1.0087	1.0592
10	0.8380	0.8581	0.9031	0.9501	1.0124	1.0601
15	0.8501	0.8693	0.9109	0.9565	1.0150	
20	0.8616	0.8801	0.9185	0.9624		
25	0.8730	0.8903	0.9288			
30	0.8840	0.9000				
35	0.8948	0.9098				
40	0.9052					
100	0.9984					

%H_2O \ R	1.2381
0.0	1.1093
5.3	1.1076

%H_2O \ R	2.3614
0.0	1.2346
4.7	1.2246

C = **C_3H_8O,** *n*-Propyl alcohol (4)

B = **$CHCl_3$,** Chloroform

C = **CH_4O,** Methyl alcohol (4)

C = **C_2H_6O,** Ethyl alcohol (4)

C = **C_3H_6O,** Acetone (4)

C = **C_3H_8O,** *n*-Propyl alcohol (4)

B = **CH_2O_2,** Formic acid

C = **C_2H_6O,** Ethyl alcohol (15)

C = **C_6H_7N,** Aniline, 30°C (24)

%C† \ %B*	44.31	31.33	20.31	%C† \ %B*	44.31	31.33	20.31
0	1.0967	1.0678	1.0432	55	1.0836	1.0664	1.0472
5	1.0993	1.0722	1.0487	60	1.0763	1.0599	1.0437
10	1.1017	1.0763	1.0544	65	1.0687	1.0535	1.0399
15	1.1039	1.0797	1.0592	70	1.0609	1.0476	1.0359
20	1.1057	1.0824	1.0625	75	1.0529	1.0420	1.0320
25	1.1069	1.0841	1.0637	80	1.0448	1.0363	1.0282
30	1.1068	1.0847	1.0631	85	1.0365	1.0303	1.0244
35	1.1053	1.0838	1.0613	90	1.0279	1.0242	1.0205
40	1.1018	1.0813	1.0583	95	1.0200	1.0181	1.0166
45	1.0968	1.0773	1.0546	100	1.0131		
50	1.0906	1.0723	1.0508				

%B* =	%C†	0	5	10	15	96.1
9.64	d_4^{30}	1.0186	1.0254	1.0316	1.0359	1.0146

* Wt. % in solvent, H_2O. † Wt. % in the solution.

B = **CH_4N_2O,** Urea

C = **$C_2H_4O_2$,** Acetic acid (27)

% C	29.6	15.1	7.6	3.8	1.9
% B	0.7	0.7	0.7	0.8	0.8
d_4^{25}	1.037_7	1.019_1	1.008_5	1.004_5	1.002_2

B = **CH_4O,** Methyl alcohol

C = **C_2H_5Br,** Ethyl bromide (4)

C = **C_6H_5Br,** Bromobenzene (4)

‡ Where both solutes are sugars, *see* Vol. II, p. 352.

C = **C_6H_6,** Benzene (1,5)

Aqueous layer			Benzene layer		
% B	% C	d_4^{25}	% B	% C	d_4^{25}
61.5	11.4	0.8675	30.8	65.0	0.8615
61.0	10.2	0.8700	4.2	95.5	0.8698
60.8	9.8	0.8718	4.1	95.6	0.8700
30.8	65.0	0.8615	4.0	95.7	0.8700

C = **C_6H_{14},** Hexane (4)

C = **C_7H_{16},** Heptane (4)

C = **$C_{10}H_{16}O$,** Camphor (22)

% B	99.0	89.1	79.2	69.3	59.4	49.5
% C	0.0	10.0	20.0	30.0	40.0	50.0
d_4^{20}	0.812	0.828	0.842	0.858	0.873	0.888

B = **$C_2H_2Cl_2O_2$,** Dichloroacetic acid

C = **$C_2H_4O_2$,** Acetic acid (19)

B = **$C_2H_4Cl_2$,** 1, 1-Dichloroethane

C = **C_2H_6O,** Ethyl alcohol (4)

B = **$C_2H_4Cl_2$,** Ethylene chloride

C = **C_2H_6O,** Ethyl alcohol (4)

B = **$C_2H_4O_2$,** Acetic acid

C = **$C_4H_7NO_4$,** Aspartic acid (3)

% B	1.13	2.23	3.31	4.37	5.40	7.40	10.25
% C	2.50	2.48	2.45	2.42	2.40	2.34	2.27
$10^4(d_4^{20} - 1)$	104	119	133	147	162	185	223

C = **$C_4H_8N_2O_3$,** Asparagine (3)

% B	1.08	2.12	5.15	7.06	9.80	14.01	17.85
% C	2.36	2.34	2.27	2.22	2.15	2.05	1.96
$10^4(d_4^{20} - 1)$	97	111	151	177	211	264	311

C = **C_6H_6,** Benzene (12)

% B	% C	$d_4^{24.65}$	% B	% C	$d_4^{24.65}$
51.98	40.31	0.9673	50.97	42.01	0.9633
52.48	39.88	0.9681	48.89	45.00	0.9570
54.53	38.15	0.9710	43.03	52.97	0.9412
60.14	33.43	0.9796	32.64	67.30	0.9137
70.51	24.69	0.9955	52.97	39.01	0.9697
99.85	0.0	1.0454	56.43	34.65	0.9788
52.70	40.67	0.9653	64.75	22.99	1.0050
53.97	41.02	0.9632	66.29	12.81	1.0312
55.66	41.81	0.9587	70.08	4.59	1.0520
57.49	42.40	0.9532	55.86	2.60	1.0521

C = **$C_6H_6O_2$,** Hydroquinol (27)

% C = 0.7	% B	29.6	15.0	7.6	3.8
	d_4^{25}	1.036_4	1.020_0	1.009_4	1.004_1

C = **C_6H_7N,** Aniline, 30.4°C (24)

% C† \ % B*	100	93.82	90.36	86.46	75.70	58.46	36.56
0	1.0373	1.0456	1.0500	1.0556	1.0565	1.0534	1.0371
5	.0514	.0578	.0609	.0655	.0650	.0592	.0427
10	.0640	.0682	.0707	.0737	.0716	.0645	.0478
15	.0732	.0754	.0770	.0792	.0756	.0683	.0515
20	.0792	.0797	.0805	.0821	.0776	.0700	.0528
25	.0826	.0816	.0819	.0828	.0777	.0696	.0522
30	.0834	.0814	.0812	.0817	.0763	.0677	.0502
35	.0818	.0796	.0790	.0791	.0735	.0650	.0477
40	.0788	.0763	.0756	.0753	.0699	.0616	.0451
45	.0746	.0720	.0712	.0714	.0656	.0574	.0424
50	.0696	.0670	.0661	.0672	.0608	.0534	.0394

B = $C_2H_4O_2$, Acetic acid.—(*Continued*)
C = C_6H_7N Aniline, 30.4°C (24).—(*Continued*)

% C† \ % B*	100	93.82	90.36	86.46	75.70	58.46	36.56
55	1.0640	1.0615	1.0606	1.0618	1.0557	1.0494	
60	.0578	.0554	.0548	.0554	.0504	.0453	
65	.0514	.0493	.0486	.0487	.0450	.0408	
70	.0449	.0434	.0425	.0425	.0395	.0360	
75	.0382	.0376	.0365	.0365	.0341	.0310	
80	.0325	.0319	.0309	.0305	.0288	.0264	
85	.0274	.0259	.0262		.0238	.0222	
90	.0217				.0196	.0186	
95	.0168					.0154	
100	.0128						

* Wt. % in solvent, H_2O.
† Wt. % in solution.

C = $C_7H_7NO_2$, *m*-Aminobenzoic acid (1)

% B	0.00	0.06	0.60	6.01	14.02	26.84	46.86
% C	0.76	0.79	0.84	1.29	2.66	5.03	7.45
$10^4(d_4^{25} - 1)$	8	72	82	150	300	507	806

C = $C_9H_{13}NO_3S$, Trimethylsulfanilic acid (20)
C = $C_{10}H_{14}N_2$, Nicotine (13)

% B	% C	d_4^{20}	% B	% C	d_4^{20}
22.37	60.44	1.0923	20.64	55.75	1.0996
21.95	59.31	1.0965	20.61	55.69	1.0999
21.30	57.57	1.0976	20.59	55.64	1.1035
21.03	56.81	1.0993	20.56	55.54	1.1295
20.92	56.53	1.0994			

B = C_2H_5Br, Ethyl bromide
C = C_2H_6O, Ethyl alcohol (4)
C = C_3H_8O, *n*-Propyl alcohol (4)
B = C_2H_6O, Ethyl alcohol
C = C_3H_7Br, Propyl bromide (4)
C = $C_3H_7NO_2$, Alanine (17)

Vol. % B*	Wt. % C†	d_4^{25}	Vol. % B*	Wt. % C†	d_4^{25}	Vol. % B*	Wt. % C†	d_4^{25}
0	14.2	1.042	25	6.6	0.989	50	2.3	0.936
5	12.6	1.031	31	5.2	0.976	55	1.8	0.919
10	11.1	1.021	35	4.7	0.967	60	1.6	0.910
15	9.5	1.010	40	3.7	0.958	70	0.84	0.884
20	7.8	0.998	45	3.0	0.945	80	0.37	0.856

* Vol. % in solvent (H_2O) at 15.5°C.
† Wt. % in the solution.

C = $C_3H_8O_3$, Glycerol (11)

% B	12.8	13.4	25.1	39.2	37.9	41.0
% C	5.7	9.4	38.2	3.8	40.7	6.2
d_4^{15}	0.9928	1.0013	1.0442	0.9464	1.0140	0.9469

C = $C_4H_6O_6$, Tartaric acid (29)

% B	% C	d_4^{25}	% B	% C	d_4^{25}
0.0	0.0	0.997	42.2	40.0	1.088
0.0	57.9	1.317	66.0	27.8	0.960
3.8	56.1	1.300	73.1	24.2	0.926
15.5	51.4	1.242	78.3	21.7	0.903
27.1	46.8	1.177	100.0	0.0	0.785

C = $C_4H_8O_2$, Ethyl acetate (31); *cf.* (4)

% C	% B	d_4^{20}	% C	% B	d_4^{20}	% C	% B	d_4^{20}
0	100	0.789	20	40	0.911	50	20	0.920
10	90	0.799	20	30	0.933	60	40	0.852
10	80	0.828	20	20	0.954	60	30	0.880
10	70	0.854	30	70	0.819	60	20	0.907
10	60	0.878	30	60	0.848	70	30	0.863
10	50	0.900	30	50	0.874	70	20	0.892
10	40	0.923	30	40	0.898	80	20	0.874
10	30	0.945	30	30	0.921	80	10	0.904
10	20	0.965	40	60	0.830	90	10	0.887
10	10	0.981	40	50	0.859	100	0	0.900
10	2	0.991	40	40	0.885			
20	80	0.809	40	30	0.909			
20	70	0.838	50	50	0.841			
20	60	0.864	50	40	0.870			
20	50	0.888	50	30	0.896			

% B (29)	0.0	7.9	14.7	18.3	17.7	100.0
% C	7.9	9.6	13.4	31.2	44.6	0.0
d_4^{25}	0.996	0.987	0.966	0.939	0.924	0.785

C = C_4H_9Br, Isobutyl bromide (4)
C = $C_4H_{10}O$, Isobutyl alcohol (4)
C = $C_4H_{10}O$, Ethyl ether (21, 18); *cf.* (4, 28)

% C	% B	d_4^{15}	d_4^{25}	% C	% B	d_4^{15}	d_4^{25}
6	0	0.9878		70	25		0.7488
4	0	0.9913	0.9890	60	25		0.7817
2	0	0.9949	0.9928	10	25		0.9347
0	0	0.9991	0.9971	0	25	0.9642	0.9590
6	5	0.9809	0.9772	70	30	0.7476	
4	5	0.9842	0.9808	60	30	0.7812	0.7700
2	5	0.9872	0.9846	50	30	0.8120	0.8016
0	5	0.9903	0.9882	40	30	0.8421	0.8322
90	10	0.7305	0.7174	30	30	0.8720	0.8616
6	10	0.9744	0.9698	20	30	0.9014	0.8936
4	10	0.9774	0.9736	10	30	0.9319	0.9243
2	10	0.9802	0.9773	0	30	0.9569	0.9507
0	10	0.9830	0.9804	50	35		0.7899
80	15		0.7042	40	35		0.8220
6	15	0.9678	0.9627	30	35		0.8528
4	15	0.9712	0.9663	20	35		0.8830
2	15	0.9742	0.9700	10	35		0.9123
0	15	0.9767	0.9733	0	35	0.9483	0.9415
80	20	0.7396	0.7265	60	40	0.7548	
70	20	0.7730	0.7615	50	40	0.7890	0.7759
10	20	0.9513		40	40	0.8187	0.8084
6	20	0.9606	0.9548	30	40	0.8520	0.8394
4	20	0.9644	0.9588	20	40	0.8821	0.8718
2	20	0.9679	0.9628	10	40	0.9097	0.9022
0	20	0.9707	0.9664	0	40	0.9388	0.9315

% C	% B	d_4^{15}	% C	% B	d_4^{15}	% C	% B	d_4^{15}
50	50	0.7620	30	60	0.8031	0	70	0.8719
40	50	0.7962	20	60	0.8344	20	80	0.7835
30	50	0.8266	10	60	0.8652	10	80	0.8156
20	50	0.8568	0	60	0.8952	0	80	0.8477
10	50	0.8882	30	70	0.7766	10	90	0.7892
0	50	0.9178	20	70	0.8099	0	90	0.8223
40	60	0.7694	10	70	0.8406			

Miscible mixtures (8)

% B	% C	d_4^0	% B	% C	d_4^0	% B	% C	d_4^0
24.4	15.6	0.938	27.2	25.0	0.906	21.5	65.0	0.798
22.0	13.0	.948	27.4	30.0	.889	19.2	70.0	.788
18.9	11.1	.958	27.6	35.0	.874	16.5	75.0	.778
14.5	10.5	.967	27.5	40.0	.859	13.4	80.0	.770
9.5	10.5	.974	27.2	45.0	.845	10.2	85.0	.762
3.8	11.2	.978	26.2	50.0	.832	6.8	90.0	.754
23.9	15.0	.940	25.2	55.0	.820	3.4	95.0	.745
26.0	20.0	.922	23.5	60.0	.808			

Coexistent liquid phases at 0°C (8)

Upper layer			Lower layer		
% B	% C	d_4^0	% B	% C	d_4^0
2.7	96.0	0.743	8.4	10.6	0.975
7.5	89.0	0.755	15.5	10.5	0.965
7.7	88.6	0.755	15.5	10.5	0.965
6.7	90.0	0.754	15.5	10.5	0.965
13.4	80.0	0.770	20.1	11.5	0.955
13.8	79.6	0.771	20.0	11.4	0.956
22.0	64.0	0.800	23.4	16.3	0.934
22.0	63.7	0.801	23.5	16.5	0.934
24.8	56.0	0.818	25.2	20.0	0.922
24.3	56.6	0.816	25.0	19.8	0.923

C = $C_5H_{10}O$, Diethylketone (4)
C = $C_5H_{10}O_2$, Ethyl propionate (4)
C = $C_5H_{11}Br$, Isoamyl bromide (4)
C = $C_5H_{12}O$, Amyl alcohol (9)

Upper layer

% B.........	0.0	6.1	14.2	20.6	25.6	28.1	27.7
% C.........	90.7	82.6	70.7	59.4	47.4	32.4	25.6
$d_4^{15.5}$.........	0.831	0.834	0.840	0.848	0.860	0.888	0.904

Lower layer

% B.........	0.0	5.9	13.0	17.4	21.2	24.8	26.6
% C.........	2.7	2.8	3.0	3.1	4.6	10.8	17.6
$d_4^{15.5}$.........	0.995	0.986	0.976	0.970	0.961	0.942	0.922

C = $C_5H_{12}O$, Isoamyl alcohol (4)
C = $C_6H_3N_3O_6$, 1, 3, 5-Trinitrobenzene (17)

Vol. % B*.....	60	70	75	80	85	90	95	100
% C†.........	0.23	0.38	0.47	0.57	0.78	1.1	1.5	2.3
d_4^{25}............	0.906	0.881	0.871	0.858	0.844	0.829	0.813	0.796

* In the aqueous solvent, 15.5°C. † Wt. % in the solution.

C = C_6H_5Br, Bromobenzene (4)
C = $C_6H_5NO_2$, Nitrobenzene (4)
C = C_6H_7N, Aniline (14)
C = $C_6H_8O_7$, Citric acid (29)

% B	% C	d_4^{25}	% B	% C	d_4^{25}	% B	% C	d_4^{25}
0.0	0.0	0.997	33.8	51.9	1.156	61.6	38.4	1.007
12.6	60.6	1.264	42.6	47.9	1.112	100.0	0.0	0.785
21.8	57.1	1.212	52.1	43.0	1.054			

C = $C_6H_{12}O_2$, Ethyl butyrate (4)
C = C_6H_{14}, Hexane (4)
C = C_7H_6O, Benzaldehyde (4)
C = $C_7H_6O_2$, Benzoic acid (29)

% B	% C	d_4^{25}	% B	% C	d_4^{25}	% B	% C	d_4^{25}
0.0	0.0	0.997	41.9	17.8	0.944	63.1	36.9	0.907
0.0	0.37	0.997	49.1	30.1	0.938	100.0	0.0	0.785
8.7	0.58	0.984	54.1	35.0	0.928			
30.4	4.7	0.955	61.2	36.5	0.910			

C = C_6H_6, Benzene (1,2); *cf.* (4)

% B	% C	d_4^{25}	% B	% C	d_4^{25}
0.00	0.00	0.9971	51.49	32.58	0.8519
0.00	100.00	0.8736	60.00	0.00	0.8870
10.00	0.00	0.9804	60.00	3.90	0.8796
10.00	89.93	0.8631	60.00	7.05	0.8739
10.00	90.00	0.8630	60.00	14.06	0.8618
18.48	81.52	0.8550	60.00	19.16	0.8537
20.00	0.00	0.9664	60.00	23.21	0.8470
20.00	77.69	0.8567	60.00	28.60	0.8380
20.00	80.00	0.8535	60.00	34.47	0.8280
30.00	0.00	0.9507	60.00	40.00	0.8182
30.00	63.81	0.8543	70.00	0.00	0.8634
30.00	65.44	0.8516	70.00	7.46	0.8501
30.00	67.28	0.8490	70.00	10.72	0.8442
30.00	67.58	0.8482	70.00	14.68	0.8372
30.00	70.00	0.8447	70.00	18.09	0.8316
32.42	60.85	0.8529	70.00	22.45	0.8239
38.08	52.46	0.8524	70.00	24.31	0.8201
40.00	0.00	0.9315	70.00	25.64	0.8181
40.00	0.40	0.9306	70.00	30.00	0.8095
40.00	48.61	0.8533	73.46	0.00	0.8551
40.00	54.31	0.8449	80.00	0.00	0.8391
40.00	59.72	0.8360	79.98	3.58	0.8327
40.00	60.00	0.8357	79.98	9.23	0.8227
43.43	44.53	0.8520	79.99	13.75	0.8142
49.85	0.00	0.9102	79.99	15.89	0.8102
49.85	1.22	0.9079	79.99	20.01	0.8010
49.86	4.99	0.9007	89.97	0.00	0.8137
50.00	0.00	0.9098	89.94	2.42	0.8092
50.00	5.87	0.8992	89.92	4.99	0.8042
50.00	8.44	0.8946	89.90	7.53	0.7990
50.00	30.80	0.8779	89.87	10.13	0.7934
50.00	35.76	0.8500	100.00	0.00	0.7851
50.00	39.85	0.8435			
50.00	44.18	0.8361			
50.00	50.00	0.8269			

C = $C_7H_6O_3$, Salicylic acid (29)

% B	% C	d_4^{25}	% B	% C	d_4^{25}	% B	% C	d_4^{25}
0.0	0.0	0.997	44.4	12.8	0.942	66.8	33.2	0.916
0.0	0.22	0.998	53.4	24.0	0.938	100.0	0.0	0.785
8.7	0.34	0.983	60.7	31.0	0.929			
31.1	2.7	0.954	65.2	32.4	0.920			

C = $C_7H_6O_5.H_2O$, Gallic acid (29)

% B	% C	d_4^{25}	% B	% C	d_4^{25}	% B	% C	d_4^{25}
0.0	0.0	0.997	37.1	11.2	0.971	77.9	22.1	0.899
0.0	1.2	0.999	57.6	18.0	0.943	100.0	0.0	0.785
16.4	3.3	0.982	70.7	21.2	0.916			

C = C_7H_7Br, Bromotoluene (4)
C = C_7H_7NO, Benzamide (17)

% B*	% C†	d_4^{25}	% B*	% C†	d_4^{25}	% B*	% C†	d_4^{25}
0.0	1.3	0.999	40	7.9	0.958	75	20.3	0.917
5	1.6	0.992	45	9.9	0.953	80	20.9	0.907
15	2.2	0.982	50	12.1	0.948	83	21.0	0.900
20	2.7	0.976	55	14.1	0.944	85	20.7	0.895
25	3.5	0.972	60	16.0	0.939	90	19.7	0.878
31	5.1	0.966	65	17.8	0.932	95	17.4	0.856
35	5.9	0.963	70	19.3	0.925	100	14.6	0.830

* Vol. % in the aqueous solvent, 15.5°C. † Wt. % in the solution.

C = $C_7H_7NO_2$, *p*-Nitrotoluene (4)

B = C_2H_6O, Ethyl alcohol.—(*Continued*)

C = C_7H_8, Toluene (4)

C = $C_7H_8N_2S$, Phenylthiourea (17)

% B*	% C†	d_4^{25}	% B*	% C†	d_4^{25}	% B*	% C†	d_4^{25}
0	0.24	0.998	50	1.8	0.932	75	4.3	0.881
15	0.38	0.979	55	2.3	0.923	80	4.5	0.868
25	0.56	0.968	60	2.7	0.913	85	4.8	0.854
35	0.83	0.956	65	3.3	0.902	90	4.5	0.839
40	1.1	0.949	70	3.8	0.892	95	4.2	0.820

* Vol. % in the aqueous solvent, 15.5°C.
† Wt. % in the solution.

C = C_7H_8O, Benzyl alcohol (4)

C = C_7H_9N, Methylaniline (4)

C = C_7H_9N, *o*-Toluidine (4)

C = C_7H_{16}, Heptane (4)

C = $C_8H_8O_3$, Methyl salicylate (29)

% B........	0.0	0.0	31.4	47.7	48.1	17.1	100.0
% C........	0.0	0.12	0.61	6.4	31.6	79.1	0.0
d_4^{25}..........	0.997	0.997	0.952	0.921	0.941	1.087	0.785

C = C_8H_9NO, Acetanilide (17)

% B*	% C†	d_4^{25}	% B*	% C†	d_4^{25}	% B*	% C†	d_4^{25}
0	0.54	0.997	45	6.8	0.945	85	26.9	0.900
10	0.93	0.984	50	8.9	0.940	87	27.4	0.896
15	1.0	0.980	55	11.6	0.934	90	27.6	0.890
20	1.3	0.974	60	14.2	0.929	93	27.6	0.881
25	1.7	0.968	65	17.0	0.923	95	26.8	0.874
31	2.5	0.962	70	19.8	0.918	100	24.8	0.851
35	3.5	0.957	75	22.6	0.913			
40	4.8	0.951	80	25.2	0.907			

* Vol. % in the aqueous solvent, 15.5°C.
† Wt. % in the solution.

C = C_8H_{10}, Xylenes (4)

C = $C_8H_{10}O$, Phenetole (4)

C = $C_9H_{10}O_2$, Benzyl acetate (4)

C = $C_9H_{11}NO$, Acettoluide (17)

% B*	% C†	d_4^{25}	% B*	% C†	d_4^{25}	% B*	% C†	d_4^{25}
0	0.12	0.998	45	1.4	0.938	80	7.8	0.868
5	0.13	0.990	50	1.9	0.931	85	8.8	0.858
15	0.16	0.978	55	2.6	0.921	90	9.6	0.844
20	0.23	0.972	60	3.5	0.912	93	9.8	0.834
25	0.31	0.967	65	4.2	0.902	95	9.7	0.828
35	0.66	0.954	70	5.5	0.890	100	9.2	0.807
40	0.95	0.946	75	6.6	0.880			

* Vol. % in the aqueous solvent, 15.5°C.
† Wt. % in the solution.

C = C_9H_{12}, Mesitylene (4)

C = $C_9H_{12}O$, Ethyl benzyl ether (4)

C = $C_{10}H_{16}$, Pinene (4)

C = $C_{10}H_{16}O$, Camphor (22)

% B	% C	d_4^{20}	% B	% C	d_4^{20}	% B	% C	d_4^{20}
90.0	0	0.833	99.0	0	0.793	59.4	40	0.862
81.0	10	0.846	89.1	10	0.811	49.5	50	0.878
72.0	20	0.859	79.2	20	0.826			
63.0	30	0.871	69.3	30	0.844			

C = $C_{10}H_{16}O_4$, Camphoric acid (29)

% B	% C	d_4^{25}	% B	% C	d_4^{25}	% B	% C	d_4^{25}
0.0	0.0	0.997	31.3	38.6	0.997	47.9	50.4	0.967
0.0	0.75	0.997	35.9	48.9	0.997	49.9	50.1	0.957
8.6	1.2	0.997	40.4	51.5	0.982	100.0	0.0	0.785
26.7	16.3	0.997	44.7	51.1	0.977			

C = $C_{10}H_{22}O$, Isoamyl ether (4)

C = $C_{12}H_{11}NO$, Acetnaphthalide (17)

% B*	% C†	d_4^{25}	% B*	% C†	d_4^{25}	% B*	% C†	d_4^{25}
10	0.04	0.984	60	1.4	0.909	90	4.0	0.834
20	0.09	0.972	65	1.8	0.898	93	4.1	0.825
35	0.25	0.954	70	2.3	0.880	95	4.1	0.815
40	0.36	0.946	75	2.7	0.876	100	3.9	0.792
50	0.70	0.929	80	3.1	0.862			
55	1.0	0.920	85	3.6	0.848			

* Vol. % in the aqueous solvent, 15.5°C.
† Wt. % in the solution.

C = $C_{12}H_{22}O_{11}$, Sucrose (11)

% B	% C	$d_4^{17.5}$	% B	% C	$d_4^{17.5}$	% B	% C	$d_4^{17.5}$
0.0	66.0	1.3237	17.0	49.0	1.1831	68.0	7.4	0.8943
3.0	62.7	1.2980	24.8	41.7	1.1289	84.7	1.1	0.8367
6.7	58.8	1.2643	35.4	32.1	1.0568	95.5	0.4	0.8074
11.1	55.1	1.2308	50.4	19.2	0.9744			

C = $C_{13}H_{10}O_3$, Phenyl salicylate (29)

% B	% C	d_4^{25}	% B	% C	d_1^{25}	% B	% C	d_4^{25}
0.0	0.0	0.997	50.5	0.86	0.909	65.3	34.7	0.895
0.0	0.02	0.996	67.2	4.4	0.875	100.0	0.0	0.785
8.7	0.02	0.982	77.5	11.9	0.861			
31.9	0.07	0.947	70.7	26.7	0.876			

C = $C_{13}H_{12}N_2O$, Benzoylphenylhydrazine (17)

% B*	% C†	d_4^{25}	% B*	% C†	d_4^{25}	% B*	% C†	d_4^{25}
40	0.16	0.946	70	1.1	0.884	90	2.2	0.831
50	0.32	0.928	75	1.2	0.872	93	2.9	0.822
55	0.51	0.917	80	1.6	0.859	95	2.4	0.814
65	0.81	0.896	85	1.9	0.846	100	2.3	0.793

* Vol. % in aqueous solvent, 15.5°C.
† Wt. % in the solution.

C = $C_{18}H_{36}O_2$, Stearic acid (29)

% B	% C	d_4^{25}	% B	% C	d_4^{25}	% B	% C	d_4^{25}
0.0	0.0	0.997	41.7	0.12	0.926	90.3	6.4	0.801
0.0	0.03	0.996	69.7	0.81	0.862	91.7	8.3	0.793
16.9	0.03	0.969	86.9	3.2	0.815	100.0	0.0	0.785

C = $C_{19}H_{17}N_3$, Triphenylguanidine (17)

% B*	% C†	d_4^{25}	% B*	% C†	d_4^{25}	% B*	% C†	d_4^{25}
60	0.22	0.905	80	1.0	0.857	95	3.6	0.816
70	0.48	0.883	85	1.6	0.843	100	5.9	0.802
75	0.67	0.870	90	2.3	0.831			

* Vol. % in aqueous solvent, 15.5°C. † Wt. % in the solution.

C = $C_{27}H_{30}N_2O_5.\frac{1}{2}H_2O$, Quinine salicylate (29)

% B	% C	d_4^{25}	% B	% C	d_4^{25}	% B	% C	d_4^{25}
0.0	0.0	0.997	50.7	1.8	0.911	92.7	4.1	0.809
0.0	0.06	0.996	69.1	3.4	0.871	96.7	3.2	0.795
32.2	0.57	0.947	88.3	4.6	0.823	100.0	0.0	0.785

B = C_3H_6O, Acetone

C = $C_4H_{10}O$, *n*-Butyl alcohol (25)

% B	% C	d_4^{20}	% B	% C	d_4^{20}
9.93	0.00	0.9859	40.06	30.26	0.8717
9.44	4.93	0.9790	34.41	40.13	0.8617
8.92	10.13	0.9709	22.92	60.13	0.8431
19.31	0.00	0.9731	71.10	0.00	0.8723
18.33	5.06	0.9667	63.56	10.61	0.8648
17.36	10.10	0.9584	56.80	20.11	0.8600
16.38	15.18	0.9495	49.89	29.89	0.8508
15.40	20.24	0.9398	42.60	40.09	0.8438
29.62	0.00	0.9578	35.50	50.07	0.8376
26.59	10.22	0.9426	79.92	0.00	0.8504
24.01	18.94	0.9277	63.81	20.17	0.8405
21.12	28.70	0.9117	47.51	40.30	0.8313

C = **$C_4H_{10}O$,** *n*-Butyl alcohol.—(*Continued*)

% B	% C	d_4^{20}	% B	% C	d_4^{20}
37.49	0.00	0.9451	31.95	60.03	0.8232
33.69	10.14	0.9309	15.97	80.02	0.8158
29.86	20.34	0.9143	89.58	0.00	0.8224
26.11	30.36	0.8993	80.55	10.08	0.8207
22.37	40.33	0.8851	71.75	19.90	0.8190
50.03	0.00	0.9207	62.72	29.98	0.8173
45.01	10.04	0.9076	54.11	39.59	0.8158
39.84	20.37	0.8945	44.81	49.98	0.8145
35.06	29.93	0.8828	35.85	59.98	0.8134
30.02	40.00	0.8710	18.01	79.90	0.8113
28.23	49.57	0.8603	95.10	0.00	0.8071
57.46	0.00	0.9048	30.86	69.14	0.8038
51.53	10.32	0.8935	50.00	50.00	0.8000
45.85	20.20	0.8822	70.47	29.53	0.7966

Saturated solutions

% B	% C	d_4^{20}	% B	% C	d_4^{20}
0.00	7.90	0.9869	13.42	36.91	0.9072
9.26	12.00	0.9670	13.10	47.02	0.8875
11.62	18.64	0.9485	11.65	53.86	0.8765
12.65	24.68	0.934	8.28	63.68	0.8635
12.95	28.15	0.9261	0.00	79.94	0.8479

C = **C_6H_5Br,** Bromobenzene (4)

C = Cellulose acetate (2)

% C	% B	d_4^{25}	% C	% B	d_4^{25}	% C	% B	d_4^{25}
5.0	95.0	0.807	4.9	92.4	0.814	4.5	86.0	0.834
5.0	94.4	0.808	4.8	91.3	0.818	4.3	81.6	0.850
4.9	94.0	0.810	4.7	90.3	0.823	4.1	77.5	0.862
4.9	92.8	0.811	4.7	88.8	0.826	3.8	72.2	0.878
4.9	92.6	0.815	4.6	87.7	0.846	3.6	67.4	0.890

B = **C_3H_8O,** *n*-Propyl alcohol

C = **C_6H_5Br,** Bromobenzene (4)

C = **C_7H_7Br,** Bromotoluene (4)

B = **$C_3H_8O_3$,** Glycerol

C = **$C_3H_8O_2$,** Trimethyleneglycol, 20°C (5)

% B \ % C	0	2	5	10	15	20	25
100	1.262						
95	1.249						
90	1.235	1.236		100 % C, d_4^{20} = 1.0535			
85	1.222	1.223	1.224				
80	1.208	1.210	1.211	1.213	1.214		
75	1.195	1.196	1.198	1.200	1.202	1.203	
70	1.181	1.183	1.185	1.187	1.190	1.192	1.193
65	1.168	1.169	1.171	1.174	1.177	1.179	1.181
60	1.154	1.156	1.158	1.161	1.164	1.167	1.168
55	1.140	1.142	1.144	1.148	1.151	1.154	1.156
50	1.127	1.128	1.130	1.134	1.138	1.141	1.144
45	1.113	1.114	1.117	1.121	1.125	1.128	1.131
40	1.099	1.100	1.103	1.107	1.111	1.116	1.119
35						1.103	1.106

C = **$C_4H_6O_4$,** Succinic acid (16)

% B*	% C	d_4^{25}	% B*	% C	d_4^{25}	% B*	% C	d_4^{25}
0.0	0.8	1.0213	31.4	0.6	1.0897	68.9	0.4	1.1804
7.1	0.7	1.0407	40.7	0.6	1.1120	99.6	0.4	1.2530
20.3	0.7	1.0644	48.5	0.5	1.1298			

* Impure.

B = **$C_4H_6O_4$,** Succinic acid

C = **$C_4H_{10}O$,** Ethyl ether (10)

B = **$C_4H_8O_2$,** Butyric acid

C = **C_6H_7N,** Aniline, 30°C (24)

% C§ \ %B*	100	96.09	83.46	% C§ \ %B*	100	96.09	83.46
0†	0.9496	0.9652	0.9751	40	0.9994	1.0084	1.0109
5	0.9587	0.9752	0.9837	45	1.0013	1.0093	1.0114
10	0.9673	0.9845	0.9916	50	1.0027	1.0097	1.0114
15	0.9753	0.9923	0.9986	55	1.0038	1.0096	1.0112
20‡	0.9818	0.9981	1.0035	60	1.0048	1.0095	1.0108
25	0.9872	1.0024	1.0066	65	1.0060	1.0096	1.0107
30	0.9925	1.0054	1.0088	70	1.0070	1.0099	1.0108
35	0.9966	1.0073	1.0102	75	1.0080	1.0103	1.0109

* In the water-butyric acid solvent.

† d_4^{30} = 0.9898 for 64.01 % B.

‡ d_4^{30} = 1.0120 for 64.01 % B.

§ In the solution.

B = **C_6H_6O,** Phenol

C = **C_7H_7NO,** Benzamide (23)

B = **C_6H_7N,** Aniline

C = **C_6H_8ClN,** Aniline hydrochloride (30)

The solvent is an aqueous solution containing 1/20 g-mole aniline per liter

% C	d_4^{25}	% C	d_4^{25}	% C	d_4^{25}	% C	d_4^{25}
1.4	1.0008	6.1	1.0102	14.9	1.0278	33.6	1.0653
2.6	1.0036	8.0	1.0138	18.5	1.0352	41.8	1.0794
3.8	1.0058	10.7	1.0198	25.3	1.0490	49.1	1.0937
4.7	1.0077	14.0	1.0267	32.4	1.0624		

C = **C_7H_8,** Toluene (26)

LITERATURE

(For a key to the periodicals see end of volume)

(1) Barbaudy, *27*, **35:** 31; 24. (1.2) Barbaudy, *27*, **39:** 371; 26. (1.5) Barbaudy, *34*, **182:** 1279; 26. (2) Barr and Bircumshaw, *83*, **16:** appendix 72; 21. (3) Becker, *25*, **14:** 1028; 81. (4) Bonner, *50*, **14:** 738; 10. (5) Cocks and Salway, *54*, **41:** 17T; 22. (6) Curtis and Titus, *50*, **19:** 738; 15. (7) Davis and Harvey, *45*, **11:** 443; 19. (8) Desmaroux, *315*, **19:** 322; 22. (9) Fontein, *7*, **73:** 212; 10.

(10) Forbes and Coolidge, *1*, **41:** 150; 19. (11) Fresenius and Grünhut, *91*, **51:** 23, 104; 12. (12) Friedländer, *7*, **38:** 385; 01. (13) Gennari, *7*, **19:** 130; 96. (14) Gladstone and Dale, *62*, **153:** 317; 63. (15) Hartwig, *8*, **33:** 58; 88. (16) Herz and Knoch, *93*, **45:** 262; 05. (17) Holleman and Antusch, *70*, **13:** 277; 94. (18) Horiba, *41*, **31:** 922; 10. (19) Kanitz, *7*, **22:** 336; 97.

(20) Katayama and Yamada, *41*, **41:** 193; 20. (21) Kono, Rep. Gunpowder Res. Dept., Japanese Navy, B. No. 29; 1923. (22) Malosse, *34*, **154:** 1697; 12. (23) Perkin, *4*, **69:** 1216; 96. (24) Pound and Russell, *4*, **125:** 769; 24. (25) Reilly and Ralph, *117*, **15:** 597; 19. (26) Riedel, *7*, **56:** 243; 06. (27) Rudorf, *7*, **43:** 257; 03. (28) Sanfourche and Boutin, *27*, **31:** 546; 22. (29) Seidell, *464*, No. **67**; 10.

(30) Sidgwick and Wilsdon, *4*, **99:** 1118; 11. (31) Steffens and Chenoweth, Brooklyn, N. Y., *O*.

DENSITY AND THERMAL EXPANSION OF HOMOGENEOUS NON-AQUEOUS MIXTURES IN THE LIQUID OR CRYSTALLINE STATE (NON-AQUEOUS LIQUID OR SOLID SOLUTIONS)

MALCOLM M. HARING

INTRODUCTION

Arrangement.—Arrangement is by groups as shown by the table of contents above.

Scope.—For all binary systems the density data are given when the accuracy is 0.1% or better except in the case of fragmentary values and values for saturated solutions (for the latter class of values the reader is referred to Seidell's "Solubilities" (**297**)). Systems under pressures greater than one atmosphere and ternary systems (except a few of considerable importance) are given by literature reference only. References written [1] indicate that the reliable data cover less than three values, and [2] that data for densities of saturated solutions are included.

Units.—All density values and all compositions in mass units are based upon true mass ("weight *in vacuo*").

Temperature Functions.—Variation of density with temperature is sometimes given by recording under "a," (resp. "10^3b") the two terms

$$a, [\text{resp. } 10^3 b(t - t_s)] \text{ of the function:}$$
$$d_4^t = a - b(t - t_s)$$

Example: In Sec. IV, p. 144, the density of a liquid mixture of CCl_4 and $C_6H_4Cl_2$, containing 93.62 Wt. % of CCl_4 is given by

$$d_4^t = [1.5794 - 1.836 \times 10^{-3}(t - 15°)] \pm 0.075\%,$$

for the range 15 − 65°C; and hence, *e.g.*,

$$d_4^{35} = 1.5427 \pm 0.0011 \text{ g/ml.}$$

Conversion Factors.—Conversion of Wt. % to Mol % and *vice versa* is made by means of the relation:

$$\text{Wt. \% A} = \frac{100 \times \text{Mol \% A} \times \text{Molecular Wt. A}}{(\text{Mol \% A} \times \text{Molecular Wt. A}) + (\text{Mol \% B} \times \text{Molecular Wt. B})}.$$

INTRODUCTION

Arrangement.—L'arrangement est fait par groupes ainsi qu'il est indiqué dans la table des matières ci-dessus.

Champ.—Pour tous les systèmes binaires, les valeurs des densités sont données lorsque la précision est de 0,1% ou meilleure, excepté dans les cas de valeurs fragmentaires et de valeurs concernant les solutions saturées (pour cette dernière catégorie de valeurs, le lecteur s'adressera à "Solubilities" de Seidell (297). Les systèmes se trouvant sous des pressions supérieures à une atmosphère et les systèmes ternaires (à l'exception de quelques-uns qui présentent une importance considérable) ne sont donnés que par des références bibliographiques. Les références écrites comme suit [1] indiquent que la donnée digne de confiance se rapporte à moins de trois valeurs, et [2] signifie que les données pour les densités des solutions saturées sont incluses.

Unités.—Toutes les valeurs de densité et toutes les compositions exprimées en unités de masse sont basées sur les masses vraies ("poids dans le vide").

Equations de température.—La variation de la densité avec la température est donnée quelquefois en inscrivant sous "a" (resp. "10^3b") les deux termes

a, [(resp. $10^3b(t - t_s)$] de la fonction:

$$d_4^t = a - b(t - t_s)$$

Exemple: Dans la Section IV, p. 144, la densité d'un mélange liquide de CCl_4 et de $C_6H_4Cl_2$, contenant 93,62% poids de CCl_4 sera donnée par la relation

$$d_4^t = [1{,}5794 - 1{,}836 \times 10^{-3} (t - 15°)] \pm 0{,}075\%,$$

pour l'intervalle 15 – 65°C; de là on tire

$$d_4^{35} = 1{,}5427 \pm 0{,}0011 \text{ g/ml.}$$

Facteurs de conversion.—La conversion des % poids en % molécules et vice-versa se fait par la relation:

$$\% \text{ Poids de A} = \frac{100 \times \% \text{ Mol. de A} \times \text{Poids Mol. de A}}{(\% \text{ Mol. de A} \times \text{Poids Mol. de A}) + (\% \text{ Mol. de B} \times \text{Poids Mol. de B})}$$

EINLEITUNG

Anordnung.—Diese ist nach Gruppen durchgeführt, wie sie oben in dem Inhaltsverzeichnis angegeben ist.

Umfang.—Bei allen binären Systemen ist die Dichte dann angegeben, wenn die Genauigkeit 0,1% oder grösser ist. Ausnahmen sind in Fällen mit unvollständigen Angaben und bei den gesättigten Lösungen gemacht. Für gesättigte Lösungen siehe Seidell ["Solubilities" (297)]. Systeme unter grösserem Druck als 1 Atmosphäre und ternäre Systeme (ausgenommen einiger weniger von grösserer Bedeutung) sind nur durch Literaturnachweise angegeben. Stellen mit der Bezeichnung [1] bedeuten, dass die verwendbaren Daten weniger als drei Werten entsprechen und [2] bedeutet, dass die Dichte der gesättigten Lösungen mit eingeschlossen sind.

Einheiten.—Dichten und Zusammensetzungen beziehen sich immer auf die wirkliche Masse ("Gewicht im Vakuum").

Temperatur-Gleichungen.—Die Änderung der Dichte mit der Temperatur ist zuweilen durch die Angaben unter "a" (bezw. unter "10^3b") gegeben. Es sind dies die zwei Terme

a, [bezw. $10^3b(t - t_s)$] der Gleichung:

$$d_4^t = a - b(t - t_s).$$

Beispiel: In Sec. IV, p. 144, ist die Dichte einer flüssigen Mischung von CCl_4 und $C_6H_4Cl_2$ mit 93,62 Wt. % (Gewichts %) CCl_4 gegeben, durch die Gleichung

$$d_4^t = [1{,}5794 - 1{,}836 \times 10^{-3} (t - 15°)] \pm 0{,}075\%$$

gültig für den Temperatur-Bereich 15 – 65°C. Es ist daher, *z. B.*,

$$d_4^{35} = 1{,}5427 \pm 0{,}0011 \text{ g/ml.}$$

Umrechnungsfaktoren.—Die Umrechnung von Gewichts-Prozenten (Wt. %) auf Mol % und umgekehrt erfolgt nach der Gleichung:

$$\text{Gewichts \% (Wt. \%) A} = \frac{100 \text{ Mol \% A} \times \text{Molekulargewicht A}}{(\text{Mol\%A} \times \text{Molekulargewicht A}) + (\text{Mol\%B} \times \text{Molekulargewicht B})}$$

INTRODUZIONE

Disposizione della materia.—La divisione è fatta per gruppi come risulta dall'indice.

Contenuto.—Per tutti i sistemi binari la densità è riportata solo quando l'esattezza è del 0,1% o maggiore. Sono eccettuati i casi in cui si hanno dati incompleti, e le soluzioni sature. Per le soluzioni sature vedi Seidell "Solubilities" (297). Per i sistemi a pressioni maggiori di una atmosfera e per i sistemi ternari, (eccettuati pochi di considerevole importanza), sono riportate soltanto le indicazioni bibliografiche. Le citazioni contrassegnate con [1] indicano che i dati attendibili comprendono meno di tre valori, e quelle contrassegnate con [2] indicano che vi sono comprese le densità delle soluzioni sature.

Unità.—Densità e composizione si riferiscono sempre alle masse effettive (peso nel vuoto).

Variazioni in funzione della temperatura.—Sotto "a" (oppure "10^3b") sono riportate qualche volta le variazioni di densità con la temperatura, e precisamente sono riprodotti i due termini

a, [oppure $10^3b(t - t_s)$] della equazione:

$$d_4^t = a - b(t - t_s).$$

Esempio: Nella Sezione IV, p. 144, la densità di una miscela liquida di CCl_4 e $C_6H_4Cl_2$ contenente 93,62% (peso %) di CCl_4 è data dall'equazione:

$$d_4^t = 1{,}5794 - 1{,}836 \times 10^{-3} (t - 15°) \pm 0{,}075\%,$$

che é valida per le temperature tra 15 e 65°C. Si avrà perciò per esempio:

$$d_4^{35} = 1{,}5427 \pm 0{,}0011 \text{ g/ml.}$$

Fattori di conversione.—La trasformazione delle percentuali in peso in percentuale in molecole e viceversa, si effettua mediante l'equazione:

$$\text{Peso \% A} = \frac{100 \times \text{Mol. \% di A} \times \text{Peso molecolare di A}}{(\text{Mol. \% di A} \times \text{Peso molec. di A}) + (\text{Mol. \% di B} \times \text{Peso mol. di B})}$$

SEC. I. AT LEAST ONE COMPONENT IS AN ELEMENTARY SUBSTANCE

Arrangement.—The elementary substance is in all cases the A-component and the systems are arranged in order of their A-components, in accordance with the Standard arrangement.

If both components are elementary substances the one with the lower key number is the A-component. Under a given A-component the B-components are arranged in accordance with the Standard (resp. ℭ) arrangement, etc.

1. Two-Component Systems

Cl_2

B = Br_2

Wt. % B	d_4^{25} (±0.1%) (3)
95.577	2.955
92.271	2.853

B = CCl_4 (170.1)

B = $CHCl_3$ (164)

B = ICl_3

(to 29.2 Wt. % B)(244)

d_4^{25} = (3.077 – 0.0049 × Wt. % B) ± 0.25%

B = CCl_4

Wt. % A	d_4^0 (±0.0075%)(143)
0.165	1.7657
0.087	1.7004
0.082	1.6964
0.073	1.6888
0.061	1.6801
0.054	1.6747
0.018	1.6463
0.016	1.6447

Br_2

B = I_2

(to 44.4 Wt. % B)(243)

d_4^{25} = (3.077 + 0.01161 × Wt. % B) ± 0.25%

Br_2.—*(Continued)*

B = CCl_4.—*(Continued)*

(to 3.583 Wt. % A)(147)

$d_4^{32.5} = (1.5676 + 0.0_27535 \times$ Wt. % A) ± 0.01%

a	10^3b
(40° − 75°)	
(±0.075%)(172)	
0.00 Wt. % A	
1.5555	1.895(t − 40)
10.90 Wt. % A	
1.6379	1.978(t − 40)

B = $C_3H_{10}ClN$

Trimethylammonium chloride

Wt. % A	d_4^{18}
(±0.25%)(52)	
100.00	3.131
98.16	3.070
97.12	3.057
93.81	2.953

B = $C_6H_5NO_2$

Nitrobenzene

(to 6.183 Wt. % A)(147)

$d_4^{32.5} = (1.1907 + 0.0_2728 \times$ Wt. % A) ± 0.01%

I_2

B = Se (16)

B = Te (16)

B = CCl_4

Wt. % A	d_4^{18}
(±0.0075%)(54)	
0.000	1.59603
0.722	1.60276
0.728	1.60295
0.820	1.60371
0.824	1.60376

B = CS_2

Wt. % A	d_4^{18}
(±0.0075%)(54)	
0.000	1.26619
1.674	1.28112
3.200	1.29496
6.300	1.32426

B = CH_2I_2

Methylene iodide (260)

B = CH_4O

Methyl alcohol (357)[1]

Wt. % A	d_4^{18}
(±0.0075%)(54)	
0.000	0.79827
3.859	0.82401
3.871	0.82404
7.310	0.84815

B = $C_2H_4Br_2$

Ethylene bromide

(to 2.607 Wt. % A)(54)

$d_4^{18} = (2.18379 + 0.01018 \times$ Wt. % A) ± 0.0075%

B = C_2H_5I

Ethyl iodide

Wt. % A	d_4^{18}
(±0.0075%)(54)	
0.000	1.93936
0.809	1.94843
1.611	1.95762

B = C_2H_6O

Ethyl alcohol (303)

Wt. % A	d_4^{18}
(±0.0075%)(54)	
0.000	0.79152
2.670	0.80909
5.218	0.82656
10.145	0.86278

B = $C_3H_6O_2$

Methyl acetate

Wt. % A	d_4^{18}
(±0.0075%)(54)	
0.000	0.93583
1.701	0.94728
3.319	0.95921
3.329	0.96064

B = $C_3H_8O_3$

Glycerol (116)[1,2]

B = $C_4H_8O_2$

Ethyl acetate

Wt. % A	d_4^{18}
(±0.0075%)(54)	
0.000	0.90166
2.785	0.92142
3.452	0.94128

B = $C_4H_{10}O$

Ethyl ether

Wt. % A	d_4^{18}
(±0.0075%)(54)	
0.000	0.71596
3.311	0.73689
6.420	0.75761

B = C_5H_5N

Pyridine

Wt. % A	d_4^{18}
(±0.0075%)(54)	
0.000	0.97104
3.141	0.99546
6.036	1.01896

B = C_6H_5Cl

Chlorobenzene

Wt. % A	d_4^{18}
(±0.0075%)(54)	
0.000	1.10786
1.122	1.11690
2.239	1.12599
4.326	1.14340

B = $C_6H_5NO_2$

Nitrobenzene

Wt. % A	d_4^{18}
(±0.0075%)(54)	
0.000	1.20544
1.010	1.21380
2.008	1.22220
3.973	1.23890

B = C_6H_6

(8.35 Wt. % A)(25° − 75°)

(±0.075%)(112)

a	10^3b
0.9320	1.108(t − 25)

B = C_7H_8

Toluene

Wt. % A	d_4^{18}
(±0.0075%)(54)	
0.000	0.86767
2.708	0.88660
5.280	0.90536

(±0.075%)(112) (25° − 75°)

a	10^3b
0.00 Wt. % A	
0.8599	0.890(t − 25)
1.16 Wt. % A	
0.8690	0.932(t − 25)
3.92 Wt. % A	
0.8877	0.934(t − 25)

B = C_7H_{16}

Heptane

Wt. % A	d_4^{18}
(±0.0075%)(54)	
0.000	0.73281
1.251	0.74038
1.259	0.74040

B = C_8H_7N

Phenylacetonitrile

Wt. % A	d_4^{18}
(±0.0075%)(54)	
0.000	1.01812
1.066	1.02617
2.127	1.03435

S (Engel)

B = CS_2

(to 7.92 Wt. % A)(7)

$d_4^{25} = (1.256 + 0.002526 \times$ Wt. % A) ± 0.25%

Sλ

B = CS_2

(to 13.12 Wt. % A)(7)

$d_4^{25} = (1.256 + 0.00493 \times$ Wt. % A) ± 0.25%

S

B = CS_2 (174, 297)

Wt. % A	d_4^{15}
(±0.05%)(239)	
0	1.2708
2	1.2802
4	1.2901
6	1.2998
8	1.3096
10	1.3195
12	1.3297
14	1.3399
16	1.3502
18	1.3604
20	1.3709

$$d_4^{15} = d_4^t\left(\frac{1 + at + bt^2}{1 + 15a + 225b}\right)$$

a = 0.0011398

b = 0.0_5137

B = C_3H_6O

Acetone (116)[1,2]

Sπ

B = CS_2 (7)

B = C_7H_8 (7)

Toluene

S$_X$

B = C_7H_8

Toluene (7)

Se

B = CH_2I_2

Methylene iodide (258)

P

B = $C_4H_{10}O$

Ethyl ether (45)[2]

B = C_6H_6 (45)[2]

2. Systems of More than Two Components

I_2

B = CHI_3

Iodoform

C = CH_2I_2

Methylene iodide (260)

B = CH_2I_2

Methylene iodide

C = C_6H_6 (260)

B = CH_2I_2

Methylene iodide

C = C_8H_{10}

Xylene (260)

B = CHI_3

Iodoform

C = CH_2I_2

Methylene iodide

D = C_8H_{10}

Xylene (260)

B = KI

C = CH_4O

Methyl alcohol

±0.1% (357)

Wt. %

A	B	C	$d_4^{25.6}$
14.27	0.00	85.73	0.8899
12.61	2.06	85.33	0.8950
12.40	2.32	85.28	0.8958
12.13	2.65	85.22	0.8975
11.78	3.09	85.13	0.8976
11.31	3.70	84.99	0.8978

B = CHI_3

Iodoform

C = CH_2I_2

Methylene iodide

D = C_6H_6 (260)

SEC. II. ALL COMPONENTS ARE CHEMICAL COMPOUNDS NONE OF WHOSE KEY-FORMULAE BEGINS WITH 16. STANDARD ARRANGEMENT

1. Two-Component Systems

HCl

B = $SbCl_3$ (17)

B = $BiCl_3$ (17)

H_2SO_4

B = HNO_3

(±0.25%)(229)

a	10^3b
(4° – 30°)	
5 Wt. % B	
1.862	1.077(t – 4)
(5° – 28°)	
10 Wt. % B	
1.872	1.000(t – 5)
(3° – 27°)	
15 Wt. % B	
1.883	1.083(t – 3)
(4° – 31°)	
22 Wt. % B	
1.873	1.186(t – 4)
(4° – 36°)	
28 Wt. % B	
1.864	0.969(t – 4)
(5° – 30°)	
44 Wt. % B	
1.814	1.400(t – 5)
(4° – 35°)	
51 Wt. % B	
1.761	1.456(t – 4)
(4° – 25°)	
59 Wt. % B	
1.732	1.857(t – 4)
(5° – 35°)	
65 Wt. % B	
1.715	1.534(t – 5)
(4° – 30°)	
75 Wt. % B	
1.672	1.577(t – 4)

B = ZrO_2

(±1.0%)(42)

Wt. % A	$d_4^{12.4}$
88.89	2.05
80.00	2.20
66.67	2.50
61.55	2.78
57.20	3.02
53.30	3.20
50.00	3.40
47.00	3.45
45.45	3.47
44.40	3.49
43.50	3.52
41.70	3.57
40.00	3.62
36.35	3.65
33.33	3.69
28.57	3.79
25.00	3.87

N_2O_3

B = N_2O_4

(±0.25%)(230)

a	10^3b
(–5° to +5°)	
0 Wt. % A	
1.500	2.0(t + 5)
(–14° to +5°)	
12 Wt. % A	
1.512	1.58(t + 14)
(–5° to +5°)	
20 Wt. % A	
1.488	2.2(t + 5)
(–5° to 0°)	
30 Wt. % A	
1.482	2.0(t + 5)
(–10° to –5°)	
75 Wt. % A	
1.470	2.4(t + 10)
100 Wt. % A	
1.453	2.0(t + 10)

N_2O_4

B = HNO_3 (230)

(±0.05%)(26)

Wt. % B	d_4^4
100.00	1.5375
98.78	1.5417
91.98	1.5687
83.12	1.6026
73.91	1.6329
65.07	1.6536
62.40	1.6577
57.99	1.6629
56.29	1.6636
53.30	1.6634
51.34	1.6627
50.04	1.6618
48.63	1.6602
46.90	1.6564
3.07	1.4852
1.51	1.4837
0.00	1.4823

Wt. % B	d_4^{11}
100.00	1.5228
98.78	1.5291
91.98	1.5567
83.12	1.5911
73.91	1.6212
65.07	1.6417
62.40	1.6456
57.99	1.6502
56.29	1.6509
53.30	1.6504
51.34	1.6494
50.04	1.6484
48.63	1.6463
46.90	1.6421
3.07	1.4693
1.51	1.4679
0.00	1.4663

Wt. % B	d_4^{18}
100.00	1.5120
98.78	1.5164
91.98	1.5446
83.12	1.5793
73.91	1.6093
65.07	1.6294
62.40	1.6332
57.99	1.6375
56.29	1.6379
53.30	1.6371
51.34	1.6357
50.04	1.6343
48.63	1.6320
46.90	1.6270
3.07	1.4532
1.51	1.4517
0.00	1.4500

NH_3

B = NH_4Br

(±0.25%)(83)

Wt. % B	$d_4^{-33.5}$
62.01	1.001
59.30	0.987
37.61	0.852
25.71	0.792
20.09	0.764
15.04	0.742
8.36	0.727
7.53	0.710
4.17	0.697

B = $Cu(NO_3)_2.4NH_3$

(±0.25%)(83)

35.94	0.908
22.17	0.806
11.53	0.741
6.49	0.715
4.28	0.700
2.37	0.692
1.14	0.686
0.62	0.684

B = AgI

(±0.25%)(83)

78.25	2.299
62.60	1.573
42.35	1.113
40.30	1.077
27.94	0.918
26.45	0.899
14.49	0.786
12.08	0.768
8.38	0.738
6.98	0.727
3.49	0.696
1.91	0.694

B = $AgNO_3$

(±0.25%)(83)

15.69	0.798
9.18	0.746
4.60	0.713
2.55	0.698

Wt. % B	$d_4^{-33.5}$
1.91	0.692
1.05	0.687
0.51	0.684
0.28	0.682

B = $NaNO_3$

(±0.25%)(83)

36.88	0.947
20.54	0.813
12.04	0.755
8.73	0.731
5.74	0.713
3.22	0.697
1.56	0.690
0.85	0.686

B = KI

(±0.25%)(83)

56.90	1.290
36.00	0.978
22.70	0.843
21.71	0.838
12.99	0.766
6.59	0.723
3.68	0.704

$(NH_4)_2SO_4$

B = $ZrOSO_4$

(±1.0%)(43)

Mol % A	$d_4^{23..}$
20.00	2.95
33.33	2.74
39.88	2.59
50.00	2.50
60.00	2.35
66.67	2.20
75.00	2.20

B = K_2SO_4

(±0.25%)(259)

Wt. % B	t	d_4
0.00		2.666
5.45	23.0	2.574
8.33	20.5	2.578
15.03	20.0	2.474
18.45	20.0	2.451
20.55	20.5	2.432
26.47	21.0	2.342
29.30	19.0	2.323
42.67	22.5	2.187
65.35	20.5	2.004
83.37	20.0	1.883
100.00		1.774

$SbBr_3$

B = $AlBr_3$

(±0.5%)(137)

Wt. % B	$d_4^{99.5}$
0.00	2.754
9.04	2.736?
14.65	2.806
20.15	2.875
27.76	2.969
100.00	3.845

SiO_2

B = $3NaF.AlF_3$
Cryolite
(±1.0%)(231)

Wt. % B	d_4^{990}
100	2.216
97	2.150

$ZrOSO_4$

B = Na_2SO_4
(±1.0%)(43)

Mol % B	$d_4^{23.12}$
20.00	3.37
33.33	3.22
39.88	3.12
50.00	3.08
60.00	3.02
66.67	2.95
75.00	2.82

$ZrSiO_4$

B = Li_4SiO_4
(±0.5%)(287)

Mol % B	d_4^{20}*
100.0	2.280
90.0	3.145
80.0	3.356
75.0	3.382
70.0	3.401
66.7	3.410
65.0	3.449
60.0	3.479
50.0	3.601
40.0	*sic* { 4.024
35.0	3.905
30.0	4.124
0.0	4.510

* Approx.

PbO

B = Fe_2O_3
(±0.5%)(154)

Wt. % B	d_4^{15}
0.00	9.514
5.00	9.150
19.26	8.531
25.00	8.170
30.00	7.745
39.78	7.296
41.72	7.194
48.52	6.936
50.68	6.712
51.47	6.705
59.88	6.337
63.60	6.119
71.74	5.974
77.66	5.793
81.61	5.661
90.29	5.353
100.00	5.190

$PbCl_2$

B = $ZnCl_2$ (260)

$TlNO_3$

B = $TlC_2H_3O_2$
Acetate (261)

ZnO

B = CoO (109)

$HgCl_2$

B = $HgBr_2$
(±0.5%)(321)

Wt. % B	d_4^{20}
0.00	5.45
26.90	5.61
72.41	5.92
93.11	5.96
100.00	6.06

$HgBr_2$

B = HgI_2 (yellow)
(±0.5%)(321)

Wt. % A	d_4^{20}
100.00	6.06
80.80	6.09
76.34	6.23
66.85	6.17
58.95	6.16
48.30	6.18
30.03	6.28
29.29	6.31
0.00	6.28

HgI_2 (red)

2.88	6.26
0.00	6.29

B = $AlBr_3$
(±0.5%)(137)

Wt. % B	$d_4^{99.5}$
0.00	2.754
9.96	2.827
18.42	3.028
28.14	3.263

HgI_2

B = BaI_2 (260)

B = $KHgI_3$ (260)

Cu_2Cl_2

B = KCl
(to 11.49 Wt. % A)(271)
d_4^{800} = (1.51 + 0.009575 × Wt. % A) ± 1.0%

CuS

B = Cu_2S
(82.68 – 100 Wt. % B)(245)
d_4^t = (4.68 + 0.01101 × Wt. % B) ± 1.0%
d_4^{25} = (4.70 + 0.01105 × Wt. % B) ± 1.0%

AgI

B = $AgNO_3$ (260)

$AgNO_3$

B = $NaNO_3$ (260)

B = KNO_3 (260)

Fe_2O_3

B = CaO
(±1.0%)(155)

Mol % B	d_4^{20}*
0.0	5.19
9.5	5.05
10.0	5.03
15.0	4.96
17.5	4.88
22.0	4.85
27.0	4.79
30.0	4.83
33.3	4.72
37.5	4.74 ?
41.0	4.72
50.0	4.68
51.0	4.67
56.0	4.48
64.0	4.21
100.0	3.32

* Approx.

$FeSO_4.7H_2O$

B = $MgSO_4.7H_2O$
(±0.1%)(259)

Wt. % A	t	d_4^t
	Monoclinic	
100.00	20.0	1.898
94.28	19.0	1.884
86.01	20.0	1.867
83.84	19.5	1.860
78.92	20.5	1.847
78.06	21.0	1.842
68.84	20.5	1.827
66.55	21.0	1.821
58.98	20.5	1.807
56.79	20.0	1.799
45.93	21.0	1.781
0.00	20.0	1.691
	Rhombic	
100.00	20.0	1.875
18.78	20.0	1.711
11.84	21.0	1.697
5.84	21.0	1.687
0.00	20.0	1.677

Nb_2O_5

B = Ta_2O_5 (167, 184)
(±0.75%)(84)

Wt. % A	d_4^{20}
100	4.548
95	4.645
90	4.741
80	4.924
70	5.195
60	5.469
50	5.844
40	6.428
35	6.730
30	7.076
25	7.434
20	7.646
15	7.953
10	8.090
5	8.235
0	8.705

Al_2O_3

B = $3NaF.AlF_3$
Cryolite
(±1.0%)(231)

Wt. % B	t	d_4^t
100	995	2.216
95	970	2.142
90	960	2.115
80	950	2.154
76	935	2.260

$AlBr_3$

B = KBr
(±0.5%)(137)

Wt. % B	$d_4^{99.5}$
0.00	2.754
11.93	2.803
19.01	2.830

$(NH_4)_6Al_2(C_2O_4)_6.6H_2O$

B = $Na_6Al_2(C_2O_4)_6.9H_2O$ (300)

$Al_2(SiO_3)_3$

B = Li_2SiO_3 (11)

$Al_4(SiO_4)_3$

B = Li_4SiO_4 (11)

$Tl_2SO_4.Al_2(SO_4)_3.24H_2O$

B = $K_2SO_4.Al_2(SO_4)_3.24H_2O$
(±0.25%)(259)

Wt. % B	t	d_4^t
0.00		2.318
9.62	19.0	2.246
19.32	21.0	2.190
21.15	20.0	2.110
30.98	20.0	2.109
33.70	19.0	2.070
47.13	25.0	2.015
53.86	25.0	1.985
56.16	24.0	1.966
68.43	26.0	1.898
72.42	23.0	1.877
75.18	25.5	1.864
84.54	21.0	1.821
100.00		1.752

$MgSiO_3$

B = $CaSiO_3$
(±1.0%) (310)

Vol. % B	d_4^{20}
0.00	2.758
4.76	2.777
9.54	2.781
28.92	2.823
38.76	2.835
52.35	2.854
58.75	2.858
62.80	2.872
72.99	2.881
84.60	2.891
94.75	2.899
100.00	2.904

$CaO.Al_2C_3.2SiO_2$

Anorthite
B = $Na_2O.Al_2O_3.6SiO_2$
Albite

(±1.0%)(310)

Wt. % B	d_4^{20}*
100.00	2.382
65.39	2.483
48.50	2.533
32.20	2.591
15.90	2.648
0.00	2.700

CaF_2
Fluorspar
B = **$3NaF.AlF_3$**
Cryolite
(±1.0%)(231)

Wt. % A	t	d_4^t
0.0	995	2.216
12.0	985	2.310
25.4	1000	2.474

Ca_2SiO_4
B = **Li_4SiO_4**
(±0.5%)(287)

Mol % A	d_4^{20}*
0	2.280
10	2.400
20	2.423
25	2.436
30	2.424
35	2.478
40	2.591
45	2.636
50	2.847?
55	2.669
60	2.566?
100	2.970

$CaO.MgO.Al_2O_3.SiO_2$
Gehlenite
B = **$2CaO.MgO.2SiO_2$**
Åkermanite
(±0.1%)(80)
For crystals
$d_4^{25} = 3.038 - 0.0_394 \times$ Wt. % B
For glasses
$d_4^{25} = 2.884 + 0.0_371 \times$ Wt. % B

$NaNO_3$
B = **KNO_3**
(±1.0%)(298)
(35.3 Wt. % A)(230° − 390°)

a	10^3b
1.968	0.75(t − 230)

* Approx.

KCl
B = **KBr**
(±0.5%)(304)

Wt. % B	d_4^{17}*
0.0	1.994
27.3	2.213
43.3	2.236
61.5	2.386
75.6	2.518
90.4	2.649
92.8	2.667
100.0	2.744

B = **$KCl.MgCl_2.6H_2O$**
(±1.0%)(6, 160)

Wt. % A	d_4^{550}
0.5	1.72
4.8	1.71
7.7	1.71
11.5	1.71
13.8	1.69
Wt. % A	**d_4^{650}**
0.0	1.68
0.5	1.68
4.8	1.67
7.7	1.67
11.5	1.66
13.8	1.66
Wt. % A	**d_4^{750}**
0.0	1.64
0.5	1.64
4.8	1.63
7.7	1.63
11.5	1.62
13.8	1.61

KNO_3
B = **$RbNO_3$**
(±1.0%)(301)

Wt. % B	d_4^{20}*
0.0	2.11
6.9	2.14
12.6	2.15
28.8	2.23
30.1	2.25
30.4	2.22
31.4	2.24
32.6	2.25
43.5	2.32
46.5	2.35
47.9	2.34
48.3	2.35
50.6	2.36

* Approx.

2. Three-Component Systems

Al_2O_3; B = **CaF_2**; C = **$3NaF.AlF_3$**, Cryolite (±1.0%)(231)

Wt. % A	Wt. % B	Wt. % C	t	d_4^t
9.09	9.09	81.82	985	2.219
17.75	11.25	71.00	1010	2.228
7.50	25.00	67.50	985	2.275
11.90	25.70	64.30	1010	2.305
17.70	23.00	59.30	1000	2.330
14.30	28.50	57.20	1000	2.385

SEC. III. ALL COMPONENTS CHEMICAL COMPOUNDS

One component (the A-component) has a key-formula which does not begin with 16. All other components have key-formulae beginning with 16. Standard arrangement by A-components. The B (resp. C) components take the ℭ-arrangement.

1. Two-Component Systems

HCl
B = **CH_4O**
Methyl alcohol (358.5)

B = **C_2H_6O**
Ethyl alcohol
(±0.05%)(146) *cf.* (358.5)

Wt. % A	d_4^{25}
0.00	0.7851
1.27	0.7907
5.22	0.8174
13.47	0.8642

B = **$C_4H_{10}O$**
n-Butyl alcohol
(±0.1%)(337)

0	0.8060
1	0.8130
2	0.8195
3	0.8255
4	0.8315
5	0.8370
6	0.8425
7	0.8485
8	0.8540
9	0.8590
10	0.8635
11	0.8685
12	0.8730
13	0.8770
14	0.8810
15	0.8855
16	0.8895
17	0.8935
18	0.8960
19	0.9010
20	0.9050

HBr
B = **C_2H_6O**
Ethyl alcohol (358.5)

SO_2
B = **CCl_4** (170.1)*

B = **CS_2** (170.1)

B = **$CHCl_3$**
Chloroform (170.1)

B = **CH_4O** (170.1)*
Methyl alcohol

B = **C_3H_6O**
Acetone
(±0.25%)(170.1)*

Wt. % A	d_4^{25}
0.00	0.7850
5.34	0.8050
18.02	0.8570
22.22	0.8761
26.52	0.8972
30.62	0.9130
42.44	0.9705

B = **$C_4H_{10}O$**
Ethyl ether
(±0.25%)(170.1)*

0.00	0.7084
5.00	0.7278
8.33	0.7423
11.70	0.7564
14.20	0.7674

B = **C_6H_6**
(±0.25%)(170.1)*

0.00	0.8714
2.72	0.8804
4.52	0.8872
7.38	0.8954

B = **C_7H_8**
Toluene
(±0.25%)(170.1)*

0.00	0.8602
1.29	0.8632
3.21	0.8699
7.48	0.8812
14.00	0.9088

* Data are also given for these systems under pressure of liquid SO_2 at 25°.

B = **C_7H_{16}**
Heptane (170.1)

B = **C_8H_{10}**
Xylene
(± 0.25%)(170.1)

Wt. % A	d_4^{25}
0.00	0.8590
3.52	0.8676
5.00	0.8744
6.72	0.8779
8.78	0.8859
10.92	0.8921
15.43	0.9029

B = **$C_{10}H_{16}O$**
Camphor
(to 79.49 Wt. % B)(277)
$d_4^{20} = (1.092 - 0.0_2381 \times$ (Wt. % B − 64.52) ±0.1%

H_2S
B = **$CHCl_3$**
Chloroform (170.1)

H_2SO_4
B = **$C_2H_4O_2$**
Acetic acid
(±0.075 %)(68, 150)

Wt. % B	d_4^{15}
0.00	1.8405
9.93	1.7582
29.88	1.5920
50.12	1.4222
70.07	1.2708

H_2SO_4.—(*Continued*)

B = $C_2H_4O_2$.—(*Continued*)

Wt. % B	d_4^{15}
90.01	1.1243
100.00	1.0550
Wt. % B	$d_4^{76.5}$
0.00	1.7791
9.93	1.6986
29.88	1.5290
50.12	1.3565
70.07	1.2025
90.01	1.0547
100.00	0.9853

B = $C_2H_6O_4S$

Dimethyl sulfate

(±0.075 %)(**68, 150**)

Wt. % A	d_4^{0}
100.00	1.8546
75.02	1.6955
49.85	1.5732
24.98	1.4483
0.00	1.3516
Wt. % A	$d_4^{76.5}$
100.00	1.7791
75.02	1.6146
49.85	1.4882
24.98	1.3593
0.00	1.2576

B = $C_4H_{10}O$

Ethyl ether (**38**)

(±0.05%)(**246**)

Wt. % A	d_4^{30}
100.00	1.8284
98.68	1.7954
98.00	1.7793
97.39	1.7686
93.18	1.6932
92.97	1.6897
91.55	1.6656
84.86	1.5595
78.09	1.4613
72.04	1.3831
64.90	1.2991
58.34	1.2170
52.14	1.1469
46.21	1.0834
43.04	1.0518
39.16	1.0131
29.62	0.9257
28.54	0.9169
21.80	0.8580
16.79	0.8188
9.84	0.7668
0.00	0.7024

S_2Cl_2

B = $C_{10}H_{16}O$

Camphor

(±0.1%)(**277**)

Wt. % A	d_4^{20}
100.00	1.677
96.56	1.635
90.11	1.562
79.83	1.456

NH_3

B = CH_4O

Methyl alcohol (**56**)

B = CH_4N_2O

Urea

(±0.25%)(**83**)

Wt. % A	$d_4^{-33.5}$
83.21	0.752
84.28	0.751
90.43	0.721
92.09	0.714
94.60	0.700
95.28	0.700
97.41	0.692

B = C_2H_6O

Ethyl alcohol (**56, 299**)[2]

NH_4NO_3

B = CH_3NO

Formamide

(±0.05%) (**360**)

Wt. % A	d_4^{25}
3.500	1.1436
1.760	1.1376
0.707	1.1330
0.000	1.1302

B = CH_4O

Methyl alcohol

(±0.05%)(**135**)

Wt. % A	d_4^{16}
0.00	0.7941
5.68	0.8297
13.25	0.8584

B = C_2H_6O

Ethyl alcohol (**104, 303**)

NH_4Cl

B = CH_4O

Methyl alcohol (**118**)[1,2]

B = C_2H_6O

Ethyl alcohol (**104, 118**)[1,2]

B = C_3H_8O

Propyl alcohol (**118**)[1,2]

B = $C_3H_8O_3$

Glycerol (**116**)[1]

(to 6.75 Wt. % A)(**44**)

d_4^{18} = (1.2646 + 0.0_3918 × Wt. % A) ± 0.05%

NH_4ClO_4

B = CH_4O

Methyl alcohol (**338**)[1,2]

B = C_2H_6O

Ethyl alcohol (**338**)[1,2]

B = C_3H_6O

Acetone (**338**)[1,2]

B = C_3H_8O

n-Propyl alcohol (**338**)[1,2]

B = $C_4H_8O_2$

Ethyl acetate (**338**)[1,2]

B = $C_4H_{10}O$

n-Butyl alcohol (**338**)[1,2]

B = $C_4H_{10}O$

Isobutyl alcohol (**338**)[1,2]

NH_4Br

B = CH_4O

Methyl alcohol (**118**)[1,2]

B = C_2H_6O

Ethyl alcohol (**118**,[1,2] **303**)

B = C_3H_8O

Propyl alcohol (**118**)[1,2]

NH_4I

B = C_2H_6O

Ethyl alcohol (**297**)[2]

B = $C_5H_{12}O$

Isoamyl alcohol

(to 3.23 Wt. % A)(**153**)

d_4^{25} = (0.8110 + 0.00613 × Wt. % A) ± 0.1%

PCl_3

B = CS_2 (**142**)

B = C_6H_6 (**142**)

B = $C_{10}H_{16}O$

Camphor

(±0.1%)(**277**)

Wt. % A	d_4^{-10}
100.00	1.6545
73.87	1.4031
57.92	1.2865
Wt. % A	d_4^{0}
100.00	1.6146
96.93	1.5865
93.27	1.5538
81.70	1.4498
73.87	1.3888
57.92	1.2753
40.89	1.1716
Wt. % A	d_4^{20}
100.00	1.5794
98.95	1.5714
98.81	1.5678
96.93	1.5519
93.27	1.5190
89.97	1.4878
73.87	1.3601
57.92	1.2516
40.89	1.1510
Wt. % A	d_4^{40}
100.00	1.5451
93.27	1.4825
81.70	1.3870
73.87	1.3311
57.92	1.2304
40.89	1.1281

AsI_3

B = CH_2I_2

Methylene iodide (**258**)

$SbCl_3$

B = $C_2H_2Cl_4$

Tetrachloroethane

(to 28.81 Wt. % A)(**58**)

$$\frac{1}{d_4^{25}} = (0.62929 - 0.0_226018 \times (\text{Wt. \% A}) - 0.0_518335(\text{Wt. \% A})^2$$

B = C_3H_6O

Acetone (**163.1, 196, 279**)

(±0.05%)(**164**)

Mol % A	d_4^{25}
0.0	0.7868
25.0	1.4007
33.4	1.5893
50.0	1.9564
62.0	2.2670
66.7	2.3178
Mol % A	d_4^{50}
25.0	1.3619
33.4	1.5709
50.0	1.9084
66.7	2.2155
70.0	2.3081
75.0	2.3624
77.0	2.4007
80.0	2.4585
100.0	2.7302
Mol % A	d_4^{70}
66.7	2.1842
70.0	2.2665
75.0	2.3397
77.0	2.3710
80.0	2.4392

B = $C_4H_8O_2$

Ethyl acetate (**111, 198**)[2]

B = $C_4H_{10}O$

Ethyl ether (**163.1**)

(±0.05%)(**164**)

Mol % A	d_4^{25}
0.0	0.7080
25.0	1.2170
33.4	1.4125
50.0	1.7694
70.0	2.1993
75.0	2.2943
80.0	2.3971
85.0	2.4882
Mol % A	d_4^{32}
0.00	0.6999
25.00	1.2062
33.4	1.4023
50.0	1.7619
70.0	2.1865
75.0	2.2815
80.0	2.3822
85.0	2.4735
Mol % A	d_4^{50}
70.0	2.1498
75.0	2.2502
80.0	2.3402
85.0	2.4344
100.0	2.7302
Mol % A	d_4^{75}
70.0	2.1019
75.0	2.2012
80.0	2.2897
85.0	2.3933
100.0	2.5705

B = C_6H_6 (163.1)

Mol % A	d_4^{75}
(±0.05%)(163)	
0.0	0.8180
25.0	1.2907
33.4	1.4325
50.0	1.8127
66.6	2.0811
75.0	2.2279
85.0	2.4156
100.0	2.6704

B = C_6H_7N
Aniline (163.1)
(±0.05%)(163)

Wt. % A	d_4^{95}
0.00	0.9554
44.76	1.4222
54.87	1.5794
66.55	1.7987
70.86	1.8866
72.88	1.9331
74.82	1.9793
82.94	2.1704
100.00	2.6267
Wt. % A	d_4^{125}
0.00	0.9285
44.76	1.3870
70.86	1.8411
72.88	1.8855
74.82	1.9299
100.00	2.5567

B = $C_{10}H_8$
Naphthalene (163.1)
(±0.05%)(163)

Wt. % A	d_4^{80}
0.00	0.9790
63.87	1.6612
77.95	1.9477
84.13	2.1084
85.89	2.1539
87.61	2.2036
94.09	2.4325
100.00	2.6626
Wt. % A	d_4^{90}
0.00	0.9696
10.00	1.0349
20.00	1.1047
37.08	1.2669
46.26	1.3914
63.87	1.6127
72.62	1.8138
77.95	1.9417
80.94	1.9877
84.13	2.0919
87.61	2.1924
90.92	2.2941
94.09	2.4040
100.00	2.6333
Wt. % A	d_4^{150}
0.00	0.9265
63.87	1.5668
77.95	1.8960
84.13	2.0019
87.61	2.0886
94.09	2.3026
97.11	2.4091
100.00	2.4936

B = $C_{13}H_{12}$
Diphenylmethane (163.1)
(±0.05%)(163)

Wt. % A	d_4^{100}
0.00	0.9444
57.38	1.4928
71.55	1.7581
80.16	1.9565
84.34	2.0702
88.41	2.1893
100.00	2.6156

B = $C_{19}H_{16}$
Triphenylmethane (163.1)
(±0.05%)(163)

0.00	1.0195
31.67	1.2625
38.20	1.3316
43.14	1.3879
48.11	1.4444
64.97	1.6930
100.00	2.6156

$SbBr_3$

B = C_8H_8O
Acetophenone (163.1)
(±0.05%)(163)

Mol % A	d_4^{25}
0	1.0224
25	1.6498
40	2.0599
45	2.1938
48	2.2822
50	2.3498
51	2.3831
60	2.6179
70	2.8375
85	3.1163
Mol. % A	d_4^{50}
0	0.9981
25	1.6248
40	2.0266
45	2.1638
48	2.2445
50	2.2955
51	2.3227
52	2.3668
60	2.5693
70	2.7912
85	3.0874
Mol % A	d_4^{95}
0	0.9891
25	1.5974
40	1.9969
45	2.1339
48	2.2145
50	2.2571
51	2.2899
52	2.3242
54	2.3801
60	2.5065
70	2.7671
85	3.0186
100	3.6894

B = $C_{13}H_{10}O$
Benzophenone (163.1)
(±0.05%)(163)

Wt. % A	d_4^{25}
0.00	1.1063
49.70	1.7215
66.40	2.1172
70.72	2.2509
74.78	2.3906
79.81	2.5910
Wt. % A	d_4^{95}
0.00	1.0496
49.70	1.6342
66.40	2.0076
74.78	2.2678
79.81	2.4525
82.18	2.5553
85.57	2.7142
100.00	3.6894

B = $C_{19}H_{16}$
Triphenylmethane (163)
(±0.05%)(163.1)

Wt. % A	d_4^{75}
32.95	1.3536
59.58	1.8140
68.86	2.0539
74.67	2.2454
77.47	2.3451
81.56	2.5206
Wt. % A	d_4^{95}
0.00	1.0191
32.95	1.3342
59.58	1.7874
68.86	2.0248
74.67	2.2156
77.47	2.3141
81.56	2.4884
100.00	3.6894
Wt. % A	d_4^{100}
0.00	1.0195
49.56	1.5815
54.67	1.6773
59.58	1.7822
68.86	2.0206
74.67	2.2005
81.56	2.4068
100.00	3.6775

SbI_3

B = CH_2I_2
Methylene iodide (258)

$BiCl_3$

B = C_3H_6O
Acetone (196, 279)

B = $C_4H_8O_2$
Ethyl acetate (111, 198)

BiI_3

B = CH_2I_2
Methylene iodide (258)

For systems, all components of which are compounds of C with elements of key numbers 2 to 15, *see* p. 143

$SnCl_2$

B = C_2H_6O
Ethyl alcohol
(±0.05%)(44)

Wt. % A	d_4^{16}
16.10	0.8956
8.53	0.8455
0.00	0.7951

B = C_3H_6O
Acetone (196, 325)[2]

B = $C_4H_8O_2$
Ethyl acetate (111, 198)[2]

$SnCl_4$

B = CS_2
(±0.05%)(290)

Wt. % A	d_4^{25}
0.00	1.2560
13.83	1.3317
27.24	1.4168
38.60	1.4985
44.31	1.5438
66.38	1.7504
80.72	1.9168
100.00	2.2078

B = $CHCl_3$
Chloroform (290)[1]

B = $C_3H_6O_2$
Ethyl formate (163.1)
(±0.05%)(164)

a	10^3b
(30°–50°)	
0.0 Mol % A	
0.9083	1.290(t − 30)
25.0 Mol % A	
1.5216	1.320(t − 30)
30.0 Mol % A	
1.6379	1.470(t − 30)
32.0 Mol % A	
1.6832	1.625(t − 30)
33.5 Mol % A	
1.7046	1.600(t − 30)
36.0 Mol % A	
1.7323	1.635(t − 30)
50.0 Mol % A	
1.8638	1.740(t − 30)
75.0 Mol % A	
2.0540	2.190(t − 30)
100.00 Mol % A	
2.2042	2.620(t − 30)

B = $C_4H_8O_2$
Ethyl acetate (163.1)
(±0.05%)(164)

Mol % A	d_4^{25}
0.0	0.8949
25.0	1.4735
32.6	1.5924
33.4	1.6031
34.6	1.6225
35.9	1.6372
50.0	1.7749
70.0	1.9469
100.0	2.2118

$SnCl_4$.—(*Continued*)

$B = C_4H_8O_2$.—(*Continued*)

Mol % A	d_4^{50}
0.0	0.8641
25.0	1.4393
32.6	1.5500
33.4	1.5613
34.6	1.5831
35.9	1.5986
50.0	1.7353
70.0	1.9177
100.0	2.1506
Mol % A	d_4^{70}
0.0	0.8355
25.0	1.4084
32.6	1.5136
33.4	1.5233
34.6	1.5427
35.9	1.5624
50.0	1.7022
70.0	1.8826
100.0	2.0949

$B = C_4H_8O_2$

Propyl formate (**163.1**)

(±0.05%)(**164**)

Wt. % A	d_4^{50}
0.0	0.8644
25.0	1.3943
32.0	1.5292
33.4	1.5537
35.0	1.5736
50.0	1.7320
75.0	1.9534
100.0	2.1506
Wt. % A	d_4^{70}
0.0	0.8406
25.0	1.3682
32.0	1.4952
33.4	1.5194
35.0	1.5408
50.0	1.6963
75.0	1.9091
100.0	2.0949

$B = C_5H_{10}O_2$

Ethyl propionate (**163.1**)

(±0.05%)(**161**)

Mol % A	d_4^{25}
0.00	0.8831
10.00	1.0662
25.00	1.3545
30.00	1.4494
33.33	1.5054
35.00	1.5326
40.00	1.5875
50.00	1.6960
60.00	1.8026
75.00	1.9625
90.00	2.1159
100.00	2.2118
Mol % A	d_4^{70}
0.00	0.8304
10.00	1.0082
25.00	1.2807
30.00	1.3656
33.33	1.4163
35.00	1.4440
40.00	1.5053
50.00	1.6178
60.00	1.7202
75.00	1.8656
90.00	2.0065
100.00	2.0949

$B = C_5H_{10}O_2$

Methyl butyrate

(±0.05%)(**164**)

Wt. % A	d_4^{25}
35.5	1.5071
100.0	2.2118
Wt. % A	d_4^{50}
35.5	1.4566
100.0	2.1506
Wt. % A	d_4^{70}
35.5	1.4161
100.0	2.0949

$B = C_6H_6$(**163.1**)

(±0.1%)(**284**)

Wt. % A	d_4^{20}
0	0.877
10	0.919
20	0.978
30	1.050
40	1.139
50	1.240
60	1.358
70	1.496
80	1.660
90	1.883
100	2.218

(±0.05%)(**164**)

Mol % A	d_4^{25}
0	0.8730
25	1.2715
50	1.6219
75	1.9027
100	2.2118
Mol % A	d_4^{70}
0	0.8243
25	1.2012
50	1.4826
75	1.8050
100	2.0949

$B = C_6H_{12}O_2$

Ethyl butyrate (**163.1**)

(±0.05%)(**164**)

Mol % A	d_4^{25}
0.0	0.8737
25.0	1.2922
30.8	1.3813
32.5	1.4198
33.3	1.4337
34.0	1.4430
34.5	1.4508
35.0	1.4569
36.0	1.4684
50.0	1.6249
75.0	1.9469
100.0	2.2118
Mol % A	d_4^{50}
0.0	0.8470
25.0	1.2562
30.8	1.3512
32.5	1.3773
33.3	1.3912
34.0	1.3995
34.5	1.4075
35.0	1.4146
36.0	1.4260
50.0	1.5865
75.0	1.9177
100.0	2.1507
Mol % A	d_4^{70}
0.0	0.8261
25.0	1.2245
30.8	1.3140
32.5	1.3392
33.3	1.3561
34.0	1.3629
34.5	1.3690
35.0	1.3771
36.0	1.3880
50.0	1.5549
75.0	1.8826
100.0	2.0949

$B = C_9H_{10}O_2$

Ethyl benzoate (**163.1**)

(±0.05%)(**164**)

Mol % A	d_4^{25}
0.0	1.0422
25.0	1.3567
33.4	1.4686
35.0	1.4852
37.5	1.5169
40.0	1.5455
45.0	1.6051
50.0	1.6606
70.0	1.8759
100.0	2.2118
Mol % A	d_4^{50}
0.0	1.0191
25.0	1.3156
33.4	1.4184
35.0	1.4398
37.5	1.4420
40.0	1.4994
45.0	1.5615
50.0	1.6173
70.0	1.8308
100.0	2.1506
Mol % A	d_4^{70}
0.0	1.0003
25.0	1.2994
33.4	1.3995
35.0	1.4072
37.5	1.4372
40.0	1.4642
45.0	1.5237
50.0	1.5807
70.0	1.7920
100.0	2.0949

SnI_4

$B = CH_2I_2$

Methylene iodide (**258**)

$PbCl_2$

$B = C_5H_5N$

Pyridine

(±0.075%)(**119, 177**)

0.00 Wt. % A

$d_4^t = 1.1213(1 - 0.0_377845 \times (t + 273))$

0.10 Wt. % A

$d_4^t = 1.2724(1 - 0.0_377802 \times (t + 273))$

$PbC_4H_6O_4$, Acetate

$B = C_2H_6O$

Ethyl alcohol (**296**)[1,2]

$PbC_{36}H_{66}O_4$, Oleate

$B = C_4H_{10}O$

Ethyl ether (**308**)

$PbC_{36}H_{70}O_4$, Stearate

$B = C_4H_{10}O$

Ethyl ether (**308**)

$PbC_{48}H_{94}O_4$, Lignocerate

$B = C_4H_{10}O$

Ethyl ether (**308**)

$ZnCl_2$

$B = C_3H_6O$

Acetone (**193, 196**)

$B = C_4H_{10}O$

Ethyl ether

(±0.05%)(**44**)

Wt. % A	d_4^{22}
22.02	0.8964
17.40	0.8475
12.26	0.8045
5.53	0.7521
0.00	0.7132

$ZnC_4H_6O_4$, Acetate

$B = C_2H_6O$

Ethyl alcohol (**296**)[1,2]

$ZnC_{10}H_{18}O_4.2H_2O$

Valerate dihydrate

$B = C_2H_6O$

Ethyl alcohol (**296**)[1,2]

$ZnC_{12}H_{10}S_2O_8.8H_2O$

p-Phenolsulfonate octahydrate

$B = C_2H_6O$

Ethyl alcohol (**296**)[1,2]

$CdCl_2$

$B = C_2H_6O$

Ethyl alcohol (**139**)

$CdBr_2$

$B = C_2H_6O$

Ethyl alcohol

(±0.25%)(**139**)

Wt. % A	d_4^{20}
0.00	0.790
17.07	0.943
25.91	1.045

B = C_3H_6O
Acetone (193, 196)

CdI_2

B = CH_4O
Methyl alcohol
(to 11.555 Wt. % A)(97)
$d_4^{20.5} = (0.7944 + 0.00714 \times \text{Wt. \% A}) \pm 0.05\%$

B = C_2H_3N
Acetonitrile (329)[1]

B = C_2H_6O
Ethyl alcohol (139)
(±0.0075%)(264)

Wt. % A	$d_4^{13.5}$
0.000	0.79596
0.240	0.79764
0.478	0.79929
0.955	0.80259
1.896	0.80924
3.718	0.82235

(to 46.412 Wt. % A)(97)
$d_4^{20.5} = (0.7893 + 0.00684 \times \text{Wt. \% A}) \pm 0.05\%$

B = C_3H_6O
Acetone (193, 196)
(±0.0075%)(264)

Wt. % A	$d_4^{13.2}$
0.000	0.79946
0.237	0.80114
0.477	0.80280
0.942	0.80606
1.890	0.81279
3.696	0.82589

B = $C_4H_8O_2$
Ethyl acetate (111, 198)

$HgCl_2$

B = C_2H_3N
Acetonitrile (329)[1]

B = C_2H_6O
Ethyl alcohol (114,[1] 117,[1] 118,[1] 303)
(±0.0075%)(264)

Wt. % A	$d_4^{14.20}$
0.000	0.79527
0.355	0.79777
0.566	0.80028
1.407	0.80523
2.769	0.81513

(±0.01%)(33)

Wt. % A	d_4^{30}
0.000	0.78090
6.789	0.83023
11.719	0.87011
18.676	0.93307

B = C_3H_6O
Acetone (196, 325)
(±0.05%)(44)

Wt. % A	d_4^{18}
36.46	1.1712
15.31	0.9237
9.91	0.8753
0.00	0.8000

B = $C_3H_6O_2$
Methyl acetate (21, 197[2])

B = C_3H_8O
Propyl alcohol (118)[1,2]

B = $C_4H_8O_2$
Ethyl acetate (1, 114,[1] 195[2])

B = $C_4H_{10}O$
Ethyl ether (303)[2]

B = C_5H_5N
Pyridine
(±0.075%)(119, 177)
0.00 Wt. % A
$d_4^t = 1.1216(1 - 0.0_377845 \times (t + 273))$
13.96 Wt. % A
$d_4^t = 1.4186(1 - 0.0_374305 \times (t + 273))$

$HgBr_2$

B = CH_4O
Methyl alcohol (114,[1] 117,[1] 118[1,2])

B = C_2H_6O
Ethyl alcohol (114,[1] 117,[1] 118[1,2])

B = $C_3H_6O_2$
Methyl acetate (21, 197[2])

B = C_3H_8O
Propyl alcohol (118)[1,2]

B = $C_4H_8O_2$
Ethyl acetate (114)[1,2]

HgI_2

B = CH_2I_2
Methylene iodide (257)

B = CH_4O
Methyl alcohol (114,[1] 117,[1] 118,[1,2] 297)

B = C_2H_3N
Acetonitrile (329)[1]

B = C_2H_6O
Ethyl alcohol (114,[1] 116,[1] 117,[1] 118,[1,2] 297)

B = C_3H_8O
Propyl alcohol (118,[1,2] 297)

B = $C_4H_8O_2$
Ethyl acetate (114)[1,2]

$Hg(CN)_2$

B = CH_4O
Methyl alcohol (114,[1] 117,[1] 118[1,2])

B = C_2H_6O
Ethyl alcohol (114,[1] 117,[1] 118[1,2])

B = C_3H_8O
Propyl alcohol (118)[1,2]

B = $C_4H_8O_2$
Ethyl acetate (114)[1,2]

B = C_5H_5N
Pyridine
(±0.075%)(119, 177)
0.00 Wt. % A
$d_4^t = 1.1216(1 - 0.0_377845 \times (t + 273))$
25.46 Wt. % A
$d_4^t = 1.5351(1 - 0.0_370033 \times (t + 273))$

$CuCl_2$

B = C_2H_6O
Ethyl alcohol
(±0.05%)(44)

Wt. % A	$d_4^{14.5}$
7.84	0.8591
6.00	0.8440
4.06	0.8287
2.07	0.8135
0.00	0.7985

B = C_3H_6O
Acetone (77, 196)

B = $C_3H_6O_2$
Methyl acetate (197, 262)

B = $C_4H_8O_2$
Ethyl acetate (1, 195)

$AgClO_4$

B = C_5H_5N
Pyridine (174.1)[1,2]

B = C_6H_6 (126)[1,2]

B = C_6H_7N
Aniline (127)[1,2]

AgI

B = CH_5N
Methylamine
(±0.25%)(83)

Wt. % A	d_4^0
46.40	1.169
30.69	0.945
27.47	0.926
16.70	0.814
11.86	0.772
10.50	0.766
4.07	0.712
2.39	0.706
1.29	0.698
0.88	0.693

B = C_2H_7N
Dimethylamine (358)

$AgNO_3$

B = CH_5N
Methylamine
(±0.25%)(83)

Wt. % A	d_4^0
48.20	1.260
41.30	1.136
31.08	1.042
25.08	0.934
24.22	0.900
20.45	0.865
16.90	0.853
12.08	0.783
4.81	0.752
4.22	0.750
4.17	0.720
2.85	0.709
2.40	0.706

Wt. % A	d_4^0
1.29	0.698
1.09	0.700
0.87	0.692
0.40	0.693
0.21	0.693
0.08	0.690

B = C_2H_3N
Acetonitrile
(±0.1%)(268)

Wt. % A	d_4^{25}
0.00	0.778
4.80	0.814
14.07	0.893
31.91	1.092
56.93	1.541

B = C_2H_7N
Ethylamine (358)

B = C_3H_6O
Acetone (193, 196[2])

B = C_3H_9N
Propylamine (358)

B = C_5H_5N
Pyridine
(±0.1%)(267)

Wt. % A	d_4^{25}
0.00	0.977
4.04	1.018
9.59	1.055
14.88	1.129
26.07	1.280

B = C_6H_6ClN
m-Chloroaniline
(to 7.89 Wt. % A)(268)
$d_4^{25} = (1.212 + 0.00109 \times \text{Wt. \% A}) \pm 0.1\%$

B = C_6H_7N
Aniline
(±0.1%)(250, 267)

Wt. % A	d_4^{25}
0.00	1.017
1.87	1.032
3.02	1.044
4.93	1.064
6.08	1.074
9.79	1.112
10.21	1.116
16.10	1.158
25.00	1.202
26.00	1.207

B = C_9H_7N
Quinoline
(to 5.92 Wt. % A)(267)
$d_4^{25} = (1.091 + 0.01031 \times \text{Wt. \% A}) \pm 0.1\%$

$FeCl_3$

B = C_2H_6O
Ethyl alcohol (303)

B = C_3H_6O
Acetone (196, 279)

$CoCl_2$

B = C_3H_6O
Acetone (196, 325)

$CoBr_2$

B = $C_3H_6O_2$
Methyl acetate (197, 262)

H_3BO_3

B = CH_4O
Methyl alcohol (190, 191[2])

B = C_2H_6O
Ethyl alcohol (190, 191,[2] 293)

B = C_3H_8O
n-Propyl alcohol (190, 191[2])

B = $C_3H_8O_3$
Glycerol (116)[1,2]

B = $C_4H_{10}O$
Isobutyl alcohol (190, 191[2])

B = $C_5H_{12}O$
Isoamyl alcohol (190, 191[2])

$AlCl_3$

B = CCl_2O
Phosgene
(±0.075%)(94.1)

Wt. % A	d_4^0
0	1.4275
5	1.4530
10	1.4782
15	1.5027
20	1.5270
25	1.5505
30	1.5741
35	1.5972
40	1.6194
45	1.6416
50	1.6632

Wt. % A	d_4^{25}
0	1.3685
5	1.3966
10	1.4225
15	1.4483
20	1.4740
25	1.5000
30	1.5257
35	1.5512
40	1.5765
45	1.6018
50	1.6272
55	1.6526

$MgCl_2$

B = C_2H_6O
Ethyl alcohol
(to 5.24 Wt. % A) (44)
$d_4^{22.5} = (0.7915 + 0.009155 \times \text{Wt. \% A}) \pm 0.05\%$

$Mg(ClO_4)_2$

B = CH_4O
Methyl alcohol (338)[1,2]

B = C_2H_6O
Ethyl alcohol (338)[1,2]

B = C_3H_6O
Acetone (338)[1,2]

B = C_3H_8O
n-Propyl alcohol (338)[1,2]

B = $C_4H_8O_2$
Ethyl acetate (338)[1,2]

B = $C_4H_{10}O$
n-Butyl alcohol (338)[1,2]

B = $C_4H_{10}O$
Isobutyl alcohol (338)[1,2]

B = $C_4H_{10}O$
Ethyl ether (338)[1,2]

$MgBr_2.2(C_2H_5)_2O$

B = $C_4H_{10}O$
Ethyl ether (181)

$CaCl_2$

B = CH_4O
Methyl alcohol
(±0.005%)(319)

Wt. % A	$d_4^{12.87}$
0.000	0.79950
0.996	0.80879
2.070	0.81838
6.434	0.85790
8.549	0.87725

B = C_2H_6O
Ethyl alcohol (303)
(±0.005%)(319)

Wt. % A	$d_4^{12.87}$
0.000	0.79586
1.700	0.81007
3.675	0.82448
4.618	0.83145

(±0.05%)(44)

Wt. % A	d_4^{22}
0.00	0.7903
3.97	0.8190
7.68	0.8474
9.44	0.8604
11.15	0.8730
14.42	0.8984
17.50	0.9264

$Ca(ClO_4)_2$

B = CH_4O
Methyl alcohol (338)[1,2]

B = C_2H_6O
Ethyl alcohol (338)[1,2]

B = C_3H_8O
n-Propyl alcohol (338)[1]

B = $C_4H_8O_2$
Ethyl acetate (338)[1,2]

B = $C_4H_{10}O$
n-Butyl alcohol (338)[1,2]

B = $C_4H_{10}O$
Isobutyl alcohol (338)[1,2]

B = $C_4H_{10}O$
Ethyl ether (338)[1,2]

$CaBr_2$

B = C_2H_6O
Ethyl alcohol
(±0.25%)(139)

Wt. % A	d_4^{20}
0.00	0.790
10.36	0.885
20.81	0.997

$Ca(NO_3)_2$

B = CH_4O
Methyl alcohol (144, 359)[1]

B = C_2H_6O
Ethyl alcohol (144, 359)[1]
(±0.1%)(189)

Wt. % A	d_4^{25}
0.00	0.7850
19.30	0.8500
35.89	0.9140
50.20	0.9800
62.80	1.0437

B = C_3H_6O
Acetone (144, 359)[1]

B = $C_3H_6O_2$
Methyl acetate (21, 197)

$SrCl_2$

B = C_2H_6O
Ethyl alcohol
(to 2.74 Wt. % A)(139)
$d_4^{20} = (0.790 + 0.01533 \times \text{Wt. \% A}) \pm 0.25\%$

$Sr(ClO_4)_2$

B = CH_4O
Methyl alcohol (338)[1,2]

B = C_2H_6O
Ethyl alcohol (338)[1,2]

B = C_3H_6O
Acetone (338)[1,2]

B = C_3H_8O
n-Propyl alcohol (338)[1,2]

B = $C_4H_8O_2$
Ethyl acetate (338)[1,2]

B = $C_4H_{10}O$
n-Butyl alcohol (338)[1,2]

B = $C_4H_{10}O$
Isobutyl alcohol (338)[1,2]

$SrBr_2$

B = C_2H_6O
Ethyl alcohol
(±0.25%)(139)

Wt. % A	d_4^{20}
0.00	0.790
10.08	0.882
17.98	0.964

$Sr(NO_3)_2$

B = CH_3NO
Formamide
(±0.05%)(360)

Wt. % A	d_4^{25}
4.528	1.1676
1.848	1.1457
0.000	1.1310

$SrC_{14}H_{10}O_6.2H_2O$

Salicylate dihydrate
B = C_2H_6O
Ethyl alcohol (294, 296[1,2])

$Ba(ClO_4)_2$

B = CH_4O
Methyl alcohol (338)[1,2]

B = C_2H_6O
Ethyl alcohol (338)[1,2]

B = C_3H_6O
Acetone (338)[1,2]

B = C_3H_8O
n-Propyl alcohol (338)[1,2]

B = $C_4H_8O_2$
Ethyl acetate (338)[1,2]

B = $C_4H_{10}O$
n-Butyl alcohol (338)[1,2]

B = $C_4H_{10}O$
Isobutyl alcohol (338)[1,2]

$BaBr_2$

B = CH_4O
Methyl alcohol
(±0.05%)(135)

Wt. % A	d_4^{16}
0.00	0.7941
12.55	0.9125
17.85	0.9701

$Ba(NO_3)_2$

B = CH_3NO
Formamide
(±0.05%)(360)

Wt. % A	d_4^{25}
5.548	1.1785
2.272	1.1504
0.000	1.1313

LiCl

B = CH_4O
Methyl alcohol
(±0.05%)(44)

Wt. % A	$d_4^{14.5}$
17.49	0.9288
13.11	0.8933
9.41	0.8655
5.12	0.8348
0.00	0.7976

B = CH_5N
Methylamine
(to 10.9 Wt. % A)(83)
$d_4^0 = [0.690 + 0.00841 \times (\text{Wt. \% A} - 0.32)] \pm 0.25\%$

B = C_2H_6O
Ethyl alcohol
(±0.05%)(44)

Wt. % A	$d_4^{14.5}$
10.04	0.8693
7.69	0.8502
5.24	0.8340
2.68	0.8161
0.00	0.7966

B = $C_4H_{10}O$
n-Butyl alcohol (337)[1]

B = $C_5H_{12}O$
Amyl alcohol
(±0.05%)(4)

Wt. % A	d_4^{25}
9.32	0.8466
6.48	0.8432
5.73	0.8392
5.11	0.8298

Wt. % A	d_4^{25}
3.44	0.8244
2.60	0.8156
1.31	0.8115
0.66	0.8095
0.33	0.8081
0.17	0.8077
0.09	0.8073
0.05	0.8070
0.03	0.8070
0.02	0.8071
0.01	0.8070
0.00	0.8070

B = C_8H_8O
Acetophenone
(to 0.25 Wt. % A)(**188**)
d_4^{25} = [(1.0238 + 0.871) × Wt. % A] ± 0.1%

$LiClO_4$*

B = CH_4O
Methyl alcohol (**338**)[1,2]

B = C_2H_6O
Ethyl alcohol (**338**)[1,2]

B = C_3H_6O
Acetone (**338**)[1,2]

B = C_3H_8O
n-Propyl alcohol (**338**)[1,2]

B = $C_4H_8O_2$
Ethyl acetate (**338**)[1,2]

B = $C_4H_{10}O$
n-Butyl alcohol (**338**)[1,2]

B = $C_4H_{10}O$
Isobutyl alcohol (**338**)[1,2]

B = $C_4H_{10}O$
Ethyl ether (**338**)[1,2]

* Data are also given for $LiClO_4.3H_2O$ in the various solvents listed.

LiBr

B = C_8H_8O
Acetophenone
(to 0.5 Wt. % A)(**188**)
d_4^{25} = (1.0238 + 0.00871 × Wt. % A) ± 0.1%

$LiCHO_2$, Formate

B = CH_2O_2
Formic acid
(±0.1%)(**275**)
d_4^{18} = 1.2224 + 0.0222c
d_4^{25} = 1.2142 + 0.0210c
c = Mole A per l soln.

B = CH_3NO
Formamide
(±0.05%) (**360**)

Wt. % A	d_4^{25}
2.279	1.1399
1.143	1.1358
0.458	1.1328
0.000	1.1314

$Li_3C_6H_5O_7.4H_2O$

Citrate tetrahydrate
B = C_2H_6O
Ethyl alcohol (**296**)[1,2]

$LiC_7H_5O_2$, Benzoate

B = C_2H_6O
Ethyl alcohol (**296**)[1,2]

$LiC_7H_5O_3.\frac{1}{2}H_2O$

Salicylate hemihydrate
B = C_2H_6O
Ethyl alcohol (**294, 296**[1,2])

NaCl

B = $C_3H_8O_3$
Glycerol (**116**)[1,2]

B = $C_4H_{10}O$
n-Butyl alcohol (**337**)[1]

$NaClO_4$

B = CH_4O
Methyl alcohol (**338**)[1,2]

B = C_2H_6O
Ethyl alcohol (**338**)[1,2]

B = C_3H_6O
Acetone (**338**)[1,2]

B = C_3H_8O
n-Propyl alcohol (**338**)[1,2]

B = $C_4H_8O_2$
Ethyl acetate (**338**)[1,2]

B = $C_4H_{10}O$
n-Butyl alcohol (**337**,[1,2] **338**[1,2])

B = $C_4H_{10}O$
Isobutyl alcohol (**338**)[1,2]

NaBr

B = CH_4O
Methyl alcohol (**118**,[1] **358.1**)
(±0.05%)(**135**)

Wt. % A	d_4^{16}
0.00	0.7941
7.36	0.8535
9.55	0.8730

B = C_2H_6O
Ethyl alcohol (**40, 118**[1,2])

B = C_3H_8O
Propyl alcohol (**118**)[1,2]

NaI

B = CH_4O
Methyl alcohol (**118**,[1,2] **358.1**)

B = C_2H_6O
Ethyl alcohol (**40, 118**,[1,2] **153.2**,[1,2] **303, 358.5**)

B = C_3H_6O
Acetone (**174.2**)
(±0.025%)(**179**)

Wt. % A	d_4^{9}
0.00	0.8126
6.62	0.8643
Wt. % A	d_4^{25}
0.00	0.7875
6.62	0.8381
11.72	0.8841

Wt. % A	d_4^{25}
17.22	0.9361
22.33	0.9870
Wt. % A	d_4^{40}
0.00	0.7692
6.62	0.8200
11.72	0.8671
17.22	0.9171
22.33	0.9670

B = C_3H_8O
Propyl alcohol (**118**)[1,2]
(±0.1%)(**153**)

Wt. % A	d_4^{25}
0.00	0.8043
1.38	0.8141
1.43	0.8141
8.07	0.8626
9.25	0.8715
15.99	0.9256

B = $C_5H_{12}O$
Isoamyl alcohol
(±0.1%)(**153**)

Wt. % A	d_4^{25}
0.00	0.8110
3.58	0.8346
8.50	0.8712

B = C_8H_8O
Acetophenone
(to 0.9 Wt. % A)(**188**)
d_4^{25} = (1.0238 + 0.00871 × Wt. % A) ±0.1%

$NaNO_3$

B = CH_3NO
Formamide
(±0.05%) (**360**)

Wt. % A	d_4^{25}
3.680	1.1542
1.858	1.1429
0.748	1.1361
0.000	1.1314

B = CH_5N
Methylamine
(±0.25%)(**83**)

Wt. % A	d_4^{0}
11.86	0.770
6.70	0.729
4.62	0.713
2.76	0.695
1.46	0.703
0.99	0.696
0.56	0.693
0.07	0.690
0.04	0.687
0.03	0.686

$NaCHO_2$, Formate

B = CH_2O_2
Formic acid
d_4^{18} = (1.2233 + 0.0335c)(**275**)
d_4^{25} = (1.2142 + 0.0356c)(**276**)
c = Mole A per l soln. (±0.1%)

B = CH_3NO
Formamide
(±0.05%) (**360**)

Wt. % A	d_4^{25}
2.968	1.1469
1.494	1.1393
0.599	1.1345
0.000	1.1314

$NaC_2H_3O_2$, Acetate

B = C_2H_6O
Ethyl alcohol (**296**)[1,2]

$Na_2C_4H_4O_4$, Succinate

B = CH_3NO
Formamide (**360**)[1]

$NaC_6H_5O_3S$

Benzenesulfonate
B = CH_3NO
Formamide (**360**)[1]

$NaC_7H_3N_2O_6$

3, 5-Dinitrobenzoate
B = CH_3NO
Formamide (**360**)[1]

$NaC_7H_5O_2$, Benzoate

B = CH_3NO
Formamide (**360**)[1]

B = C_2H_6O
Ethyl alcohol (**296**)[1,2]

$NaC_7H_5O_3$, Salicylate

B = CH_3NO
Formamide
(±0.05%) (**360**)

Wt. % A	d_4^{25}
3.505	1.1417
1.411	1.1345
0.000	1.1306

B = C_2H_6O
Ethyl alcohol (**294, 296**[1,2])

$NaC_7H_6NO_2$

m-Aminobenzoate
B = CH_3NO
Formamide (**360**)[1]

$NaC_{18}H_{33}O_2$, Oleate

B = C_2H_6O
Ethyl alcohol (**57**)

$NaC_6H_5SO_4.2H_2O$

p-Phenolsulfonate dihydrate
B = C_2H_6O
Ethyl alcohol (**296**)[1,2]

$Na_2CrO_4.2H_2O$

B = C_2H_6O
Ethyl alcohol (**256**)

KCl

B = CH_4O
Methyl alcohol (**115**,[1,2] **358.1**)

B = $C_3H_8O_3$
Glycerol (**116**)[1,2]

$KClO_4$

B = CH_4O
Methyl alcohol (338)[1,2]

B = C_2H_6O
Ethyl alcohol (338)[1,2]

B = C_3H_6O
Acetone (338)[1,2]

B = C_3H_8O
n-Propyl alcohol (338)[1,2]

B = $C_4H_8O_2$
Ethyl acetate (338)[1,2]

B = $C_4H_{10}O$
n-Butyl alcohol (338)[1,2]

B = $C_4H_{10}O$
Isobutyl alcohol (338)[1,2]

KBr

B = CH_4O
Methyl alcohol (115,[1,2] 358.1)

B = $C_3H_8O_3$
Glycerol (116)[1,2]

KI

B = CH_3NO_2
Nitromethane (330)[1]

B = CH_4O
Methyl alcohol (115,[1] 118,[1] 330,[1] 358.1)

(±0.05%)(135)

Wt. % A	d_4^{16}
0.00	0.7941
8.23	0.8560
9.14	0.8633

(±0.05%)(96)

Wt. % A	d_4^{25}
0.00	0.7886
0.87	0.7942
2.98	0.8086
6.58	0.8354
9.01	0.8541
12.17	0.8808

B = CH_5N
Methylamine
(±0.25%)(83)

Wt. % A	d_4^{0}
23.26	0.866
13.70	0.786
9.61	0.753
6.79	0.733
3.44	0.710
1.87	0.699
1.27	0.694
0.99	0.693
0.53	0.693
0.36	0.691
0.12	0.677
0.07	0.688
0.04	0.687

B = C_2H_3N
Acetonitrile (330)[1]

B = C_2H_6O
Ethyl alcohol (118,[1] 303, 330[1])
(±0.0075%)(264)

Wt. % A	$d_4^{14.4}$
0.000	0.79524
0.209	0.79671
0.417	0.79814
0.831	0.80095
1.649	0.80644

(±0.05%)(96)

Wt. % A	d_4^{25}
0.00	0.7870
0.27	0.7890
0.53	0.7906
0.75	0.7929
1.06	0.7937
1.38	0.7960

B = $C_2H_6O_2$
Ethylene glycol (330)[1]
(±0.05%)(96)

Wt. % A	d_4^{25}
0.00	1.1096
4.07	1.1410
8.43	1.1780
12.73	1.2138
15.97	1.2431

B = C_3H_5N
Propionitrile (330)[1]

B = C_3H_6O
Acetone (330)[1]
(±0.0075%)(264)

Wt. % A	$d_4^{14.6}$
0.000	0.79757
0.215	0.79929
0.431	0.80096
0.854	0.80416

(±0.05%)(96)

Wt. % A	d_4^{25}
0.00	0.7878
0.55	0.7924
0.74	0.7942
1.10	0.7965
1.47	0.7988

B = C_3H_8O
Propyl alcohol (118)[1,2]

B = $C_3H_8O_3$
Glycerol
(±0.05%)(96)

Wt. % A	d_4^{25}
0.00	1.2472
4.58	1.2824
7.19	1.3056
8.94	1.3164
13.75	1.3644

B = $C_4H_5NO_2$
Methyl cyanoacetate (330)[1]

B = $C_5H_4O_2$
Furfural (330)[1]
(to 4.173 Wt. % A)(96)
d_4^{25} = (1.1537 + 0.00915 × Wt. % A) ±0.05%

B = C_5H_5N
Pyridine
(±0.05%)(96)

Wt. % A	d_4^{25}
0.00	0.9716
0.06	0.9729
0.12	0.9735

B = $C_5H_7NO_2$
Ethyl cyanoacetate (330)[1]

B = C_7H_5N
Benzonitrile (330)[1]

B = C_7H_6O
Benzaldehyde (330)[1,2]

B = $C_7H_6O_2$
Salicylaldehyde (330)[1]

B = C_8H_8O
Acetophenone
(to 1.0 Wt. % A)(188)
d_4^{25} = (1.02382 + 0.871 × Wt. % A) ±0.1%

B = $C_8H_8O_2$
Anisaldehyde (330)[1]

KNO_3

B = CH_3NO
Formamide
(±0.05%) (360)

Wt. % A	d_4^{25}
2.186	1.1570
0.884	1.1444
0.000	1.1359

$KCHO_2$, Formate

B = CH_2O_2
Formic acid
(±0.1%)(276)
d_4^{25} = 1.2142 + 0.045c
c = Mole A per l soln.

$KC_2H_3O_2$, Acetate

B = C_2H_6O
Ethyl alcohol (40, 296,[1,2] 303)

$KC_4H_5O_6$

Acid tartrate
B = C_2H_6O
Ethyl alcohol (296)[1,2]

$KC_{18}H_{33}O_2$, Oleate

B = C_2H_6O
Ethyl alcohol (57)

$K_3C_6H_5O_7.4H_2O$

Citrate tetrahydrate
B = C_2H_6O
Ethyl alcohol (296)[1,2]

$RbClO_4$

B = CH_4O
Methyl alcohol (338)[1,2]

B = C_2H_6O
Ethyl alcohol (338)[1,2]

B = C_3H_6O
Acetone (338)[1,2]

B = C_3H_8O
n-Propyl alcohol (338)[1,2]

B = $C_4H_8O_2$
Ethyl acetate (338)[1,2]

B = $C_4H_{10}O$
n-Butyl alcohol (338)[1,2]

B = $C_4H_{10}O$
Isobutyl alcohol (338)[1,2]

$RbCHO_2$, Formate

B = CH_2O_2
Formic acid
(±0.25%)(275)
d_4^{18} = 1.2233 + 0.080c
d_4^{25} = 1.2142 + 0.085c
c = Mole A per l soln.

B = CH_3NO
Formamide
(±0.05%) (360)

Wt. % A	d_4^{25}
2.849	1.1462
1.149	1.1370
0.000	1.1313

$CsClO_4$

B = CH_4O
Methyl alcohol (338)[1,2]

B = C_2H_6O
Ethyl alcohol (338)[1,2]

B = C_3H_6O
Acetone (338)[1,2]

B = C_3H_8O
n-Propyl alcohol (338)[1,2]

B = $C_4H_{10}O$
n-Butyl alcohol (338)[1,2]

B = $C_4H_{10}O$
Isobutyl alcohol (338)[1,2]

2. Three-Component Systems

NH_4Cl

B = CH_4O
Methyl alcohol
C = C_2H_6O
Ethyl alcohol (118)[1]

B = C_2H_6O
Ethyl alcohol
C = C_3H_8O
Propyl alcohol (118)[1]

NH_4Br

B = CH_4O
Methyl alcohol
C = C_2H_6O
Ethyl alcohol (118)[1]

B = CH_4O
Methyl alcohol
C = C_3H_8O
Propyl alcohol (118)[1]

B = C_2H_6O
Ethyl alcohol
C = C_3H_8O
Propyl alcohol (118)[1]

$HgCl_2$

B = CH_4O
C = C_2H_6O
Ethyl alcohol (117)[1]

B = CH_4O
C = C_3H_8O
Propyl alcohol (118)[1]

B = C_2H_6O
Ethyl alcohol
C = C_3H_8O
Propyl alcohol (118)[1]

$HgBr_2$

B = CH_4O
Methyl alcohol
C = C_2H_6O
Ethyl alcohol (117)[1]

B = CH_4O
C = C_3H_8O
Propyl alcohol (118)[1]

B = C_2H_6O
Ethyl alcohol
C = C_3H_8O
Propyl alcohol (118)[1]

HgI_2

B = CH_4O
C = C_2H_6O
Ethyl alcohol (117)[1]

B = CH_4O
C = C_3H_8O
Propyl alcohol (118)[1]

B = C_2H_6O
Ethyl alcohol
C = C_3H_8O
Propyl alcohol (118)[1]

$Hg(CN)_2$

B = CH_4O
C = C_2H_6O
Ethyl alcohol (117)[1]

B = CH_4O
C = C_3H_8O
Propyl alcohol (118)[1]

B = C_2H_6O
Ethyl alcohol
C = C_3H_8O
Propyl alcohol (118)[1]

$CuCl_2$

B = C_2H_6O
Ethyl alcohol
C = C_7H_8
Toluene (44)[1]

$AgNO_3$

B = C_2H_3N
Acetonitrile
C = C_5H_5N
Pyridine (268)[1]

B = C_5H_5N
Pyridine
C = C_6H_7N
Aniline (267)[1]

$Ca(NO_3)_2$

B = CH_3NO
Formamide
C = C_2H_6O
Ethyl alcohol (360)[1]

B = CH_4O
C = C_3H_6O
Acetone (144, 359)[1]

B = C_2H_6O
Ethyl alcohol
C = C_3H_6O
Acetone (144, 359)[1]

$LiNO_3$

B = CH_3NO
Formamide
C = C_2H_6O
Ethyl alcohol (360)[1]

NaBr

B = CH_4O
C = C_2H_6O
Ethyl alcohol (118)[1]

B = CH_4O
C = C_3H_8O
Propyl alcohol (118)[1]

B = C_2H_6O
Ethyl alcohol
C = C_3H_8O
Propyl alcohol (118)[1]

NaI

B = CH_4O
C = C_2H_6O
Ethyl alcohol (113)[1]

B = CH_4O
C = C_3H_8O
Propyl alcohol (118)[1]

B = C_2H_6O
Ethyl alcohol
C = C_3H_8O
Propyl alcohol (118)[1]

KI

B = CH_4O
Methyl alcohol
C = C_2H_6O
Ethyl alcohol (118)[1]

B = CH_4O
C = C_3H_8O
Propyl alcohol (118)[1]

B = C_2H_6O
Ethyl alcohol
C = C_3H_8O
Propyl alcohol (118)[1]

RbI_2

B = CH_3NO
Formamide
C = C_2H_6O
Ethyl alcohol (360)[1]

SEC. IV. ALL COMPONENTS ARE CHEMICAL COMPOUNDS HAVING KEY FORMULAE BEGINNING WITH 16

The systems throughout this section are numbered serially and follow the ℭ-arrangement. To find any given substance look for it among the A-components. The data for all systems containing this substance will be found there given or there cross-referenced by serial number.

Two-Component Systems

CCl_4

1. B = CS_2 (61)
(±0.025%)(31)

Mol % B	d_4^{20}
100.000	1.26322
90.158	1.31000
80.523	1.35148
70.320	1.39033
60.021	1.42792
50.019	1.46095
40.834	1.48898
30.217	1.51898
19.766	1.54671
11.527	1.56715
0.000	1.59372

(±0.0075%)(171)

Wt. % B	d_4^{25}
100.000	1.25684
71.725	1.33103
42.845	1.41973
14.285	1.52371
0.000	1.58452

2. B = $CHCl_3$ (14, 61)
(±0.025%)(23)

Wt. % A	d_4^{20}
100.000	1.5937
70.979	1.5642
46.097	1.5382
19.761	1.5093
0.000	1.4867

(±0.0075%)(171)

Wt. % A	d_4^{25}
0.000	1.47577
19.269	1.49373
57.277	1.53260
81.172	1.55963
100.000	1.58300

(±0.05%)(to 55°)(178)
50 Wt. % B

a	10^3b
1.5707	1.059t

3. B = CH_3I (172)[1]

4. B = CH_4O (350)[1]

5. B = C_2Cl_4
(±0.075%)(113, 120)

Wt. % A	d_4^{25}
100.0	1.5829
79.7	1.5868
66.4	1.5894
49.7	1.5940
33.0	1.5981
19.9	1.6003
0.0	1.6074

6. B = $C_2H_2Cl_4$ (113, 120)
(0–100 Wt. % B)
d_4^{25} = (1.5829 + 0.0_446 × Wt. % B) ±0.075%

7. B = $C_2H_4Br_2$
Ethylene bromide (14, 61)
(0–100 Wt. % B)
d_4^{25} = (0.6300 − 0.001704 × Wt. % B) ± 0.025% (285)

8. B = $C_2H_4O_2$
Acetic acid (14)

9. B = C_2H_6O
Ethyl alcohol (35, 81,[1] 128,[1] 153.1)
(±0.025%)(51, 164)

Wt. % A	$d_4^{19.4}$
94.61	1.5114
90.87	1.4591
85.61	1.3919
78.69	1.3118
72.58	1.2485
70.26	1.2324
55.34	1.1073
49.00	1.0576
40.37	1.0043
30.17	0.9328
20.36	0.8816
9.88	0.8327
4.84	0.8110

10. B = C_3H_6O, Acetone
(±0.1%)(270)

Mol % B	d_4^0
0.00	1.632
11.40	1.568
36.44	1.380
51.18	1.273
73.55	1.087
86.53	0.954
96.67	0.852
100.00	0.812

11. B = $C_3H_6O_2$
Methyl acetate (133)

12. B = $C_4H_6O_6$
Tartaric acid (296)[2]

13. B = $C_4H_8O_2$
Ethyl acetate (351)

14. B = $C_4H_{10}O$, Ether (61)

15. B = C_5H_5N
Pyridine (14)

16. B = $C_6H_4Br_2$
p-Dibromobenzene (158)
(±0.005%)(318)

Wt. % A	d_4^{25}
100.000	1.58426
97.452	1.59213
92.842	1.60694

CCl_4.—(*Continued*)

17. B = $C_6H_4Cl_2$
Dichlorobenzene (172)
(±0.075%)(15° – 65°)

a	10^3b
100.00 Wt. % A	
1.6039	1.928(t − 15)
93.62 Wt. % A	
1.5794	1.836(t − 15)

18. B = C_6H_5Br
Bromobenzene (24)
(±0.025%)(to 40°)

a	10^3b
100.00 Wt. % B	
1.5223	1.348t
70.462 Wt. % B	
1.5555	1.500t
47.497 Wt. % B	
1.5810	1.628t
21.826 Wt. % B	
1.6092	1.793t
0.000 Wt. % B	
1.6326	1.940t

(±0.025%)(23)

Wt. % B	d_4^{20}
100.000	1.4960
73.012	1.5232
47.985	1.5481
24.028	1.5713
0.000	1.5937

19. B = C_6H_5Cl
Chlorobenzene (23,[1] 35, 351)
(±0.025%)(to 40°) (24)

a	10^3b
0.000 Wt. % A	
1.1279	1.078t
25.598 Wt. % A	
1.2532	1.268t
56.330 Wt. % A	
1.4074	1.528t
75.761 Wt. % A	
1.5067	1.700t
100.00 Wt. % A	
1.6326	1.940t

20. B = C_6H_6
(23,[1] 31,[1] 59,[1] 66,[1] 81,[1] 99, 122,[1] 133, 158, 171,[1] 178,[1] 251,[1] 280,[1] 309,[1] 351, 352[1])
(± 0.005%)(134)

Wt. % B	d_4^{25}
100.000	0.87372
83.127	0.94523
68.046	1.01993
56.581	1.08485
44.505	1.16321
35.296	1.23075
28.958	1.28261
20.329	1.35940
12.361	1.43947
6.496	1.50491
0.000	1.58456

(±0.005%)(134)

Wt. % B	d_4^{50}
100.000	0.84680
83.127	0.91599
68.046	0.98816
56.581	1.05097
44.505	1.12677
35.296	1.19217
28.958	1.24236
20.329	1.31678
12.361	1.39445
6.496	1.45796
0.000	1.53534

(±0.025%)(to 40°) (24)

a	10^3 b
0.000 Wt. % B	
1.63262	1.941t
27.357 Wt. % B	
1.44442	1.733t
52.362 Wt. % B	
1.26473	1.521t
74.444 Wt. % B	
1.07636	1.287t
100.00 Wt. % B	
0.89993	1.066t

21. B = C_6H_7N
Aniline
(±0.05%)(107)

Wt. % B	d_4^{25}
100.00	1.0175
84.54	1.0786
70.40	1.1409
58.97	1.1964
48.13	1.2540
37.92	1.3127
28.83	1.3696
20.94	1.4228
12.95	1.4806
6.49	1.5307
1.86	1.5685
0.61	1.5794
0.00	1.5847

22. B = $C_7H_6O_2$
Benzoic acid (296)[2]

23. B = $C_7H_6O_3$
Salicylic acid (296)[2]

24. B = C_7H_8 (31,[1] 133, 171,[1] 351)
(±0.025%)(285)

Wt. % A	d_4^{25}
0	1.1593
10	1.1043
20	1.0530
30	1.0000
40	0.9463
50	0.8932
60	0.8420
70	0.7873
80	0.7349
90	0.6820
100	0.6300

25. B = $C_7H_{16}O$
Ethyl amyl ether (61)

26. B = C_8H_{10}
m-Xylene (61)

27. B = $C_8H_{14}O_6$
Ethyl tartrate (228)
(±0.05%)

a	10^3b
(19.35° – 58.2°) 100.00 Wt. % A	
1.5949	1.959(t − 19.35)
(18.91°–29.60°) 91.18 Wt. % A	
1.5499	1.844(t − 18.91)
(18.1°–29.54°) 79.78 Wt. % A	
1.4929	1.687(t − 18.1)
(20.08°–32.76°) 51.07 Wt. % A	
1.3756	1.397(t − 20.08)

28. B = $C_{10}H_8$
Naphthalene
(±0.075%)(172)

Wt. % A	d_4^{15}
100.00	1.6043
96.31	1.5741
92.49	1.5421
92.34	1.5425
86.94	1.5006

(to 1.636 Wt. % B)
d_4^{18} = (1.59605 − 0.008375 × Wt. % B) ±0.0075% (54)

29. B = $C_{10}H_{16}O$
Camphor
(±0.1%)(175)

Wt. % B	d_4^{20}
0	1.5930
10	1.5295
20	1.4664
30	1.4033
40	1.3398
50	1.3082

30. B = $C_{14}H_{10}$
Phenanthrene (158, 318)

a	10^3b
±0.1% (15°–70°) 0.000 Wt. % A	
1.6023	2.130(t − 15)
(±0.01%)(15°–70°) 97.207 Wt. % A	
1.5858	1.880(t − 15)
95.625 Wt. % A	
1.5755	1.008(t − 15)

31. B = $C_{18}H_{36}O_2$
Stearic acid (296)[2]

v. also 1266

CS_2

32. B = $CHCl_3$ (35, 59,[1] 61, 67,[1] 103, 122,[1] 240, 251[1])
(±0.1%)(320)

Wt. % A	d_4^{15}
0	1.491
10	1.461
20	1.434
30	1.410
40	1.387
50	1.364
60	1.344
70	1.324
80	1.306
90	1.289
100	1.271

(±0.0075%)(171)

Wt. % A	d_4^{25}
100.000	1.25559
71.301	1.30461
34.440	1.37471
20.637	1.41663
6.090	1.45698
0.000	1.47579

(±0.05%)(290)

Wt. % A	d_4^{35}
100.00	1.2392
80.85	1.2704
65.19	1.2989
49.38	1.3316
41.06	1.3463
24.24	1.3856
0.00	1.4509

33. B = CH_2I_2
Methylene iodide (353)

34. B = CH_3I
(±0.1%)(309)

Wt. % A	d_4^0
0.00	2.333
21.60	1.984
38.81	1.772
48.11	1.678
68.81	1.498
82.39	1.399
100.00	1.292

35. B = $C_2H_4Br_2$
Ethylene bromide (61)

36. B = $C_2H_4Cl_2$
Ethylene chloride (59)[1]

37. B = $C_2H_4O_2$
Acetic acid
(±0.05%)(291)

a	10^3b
(12.5°–30.4°) 100.0 Wt. % B	
1.0581	1.128(t − 12.5)
(13.0°–30.1°) 80.298 Wt. % B	
1.0780	1.269(t − 13.0)
(14.7°–30.7°) 61.284 Wt. % B	
1.1055	1.375(t − 14.7)
(13.5°–30.8°) 12.076 Wt. % B	
1.2281	1.486(t − 13.5)
(13.45°–33.95°) 0.000 Wt. % B	
1.2731	1.497(t − 13.45)

38. B = $C_2H_4O_2$
Methyl formate (142)

39. B = C_2H_5I
Ethyl iodide (142)

40. B = $C_2H_5NO_3$
Ethyl nitrate (236,[1] 289[1])

41. B = C_2H_6O
Ethyl alcohol (35, 37, 103, 124,[1] 130,[1] 169, 240, 249,[1] 289,[1] 346,[1] 353[1])
(±0.1%)(17.86°–35.96°) (67)

a	10^3b
100.000 Wt. % A	
1.2657	1.497(t − 17.86)
89.97 Wt. % A	
1.1897	1.465(t − 17.86)
79.86 Wt. % A	
1.1238	1.388(t − 17.86)
70.34 Wt. % A	
1.0687	1.304(t − 17.86)
59.40 Wt. % A	
1.0121	1.228(t − 17.86)
50.19 Wt. % A	
0.9693	1.160(t − 17.86)
39.93 Wt. % A	
0.9263	1.089(t − 17.86)
28.91 Wt. % A	
0.8853	1.022(t − 17.86)
20.02 Wt. % A	
0.8552	0.973(t − 17.86)
11.58 Wt. % A	
0.8290	0.917(t − 17.86)
0.00 Wt. % A	
0.7960	0.857(t − 17.86)

42. B = C_3H_6O
Acetone (79, 99, 133, 351)
(±0.005%)(134, 289)

Wt. % B	d_4^{25}
100.000	0.78799
86.755	0.82402
70.674	0.87475
59.671	0.91488
48.239	0.96189
48.201	0.96212
48.098	0.96296
35.267	1.02360
28.863	1.05768
16.717	1.13113
13.108	1.15539
1.000	1.25595
Wt. % B	$d_4^{35.17}$
100.000	0.77626
86.755	0.81166
70.674	0.86177
59.671	0.90132
48.239	0.94785
48.201	0.94806
48.098	0.94887
35.267	1.00902
28.863	1.04311
16.717	1.11601
13.108	1.14011
1.000	1.24054

43. B = C_3H_8O
n-Propyl alcohol
(±0.05%)(130)

Wt. % A	$d_4^{15.5}$
100.00	1.2693
90.93	1.2028
78.32	1.1229
61.43	1.0333
40.81	0.9428
18.76	0.8637
0.00	0.8074

44. B = $C_3H_8O_2$
Methylal (133, 351)
(±0.005%)(134, 289)

Wt. % A	d_4^{25}
0.000	0.85313
12.921	0.88549
28.682	0.93050
38.408	0.96201
43.598	0.98009
45.630	0.98723
53.139	1.01566
60.034	1.04363
62.226	1.05309
62.380	1.05362
65.262	1.06613
75.141	1.11246
86.449	1.17221
100.000	1.25595
Wt. % A	$d_4^{35.17}$
0.000	0.84003
12.921	0.87195
28.682	0.91652
38.408	0.94787
43.598	0.96583
45.630	0.97270
53.139	1.00095
60.034	1.02835
62.226	1.03822
62.380	1.03880
65.262	1.05137
75.141	1.09721
86.449	1.15683
100.000	1.24054

45. B = $C_4H_8O_2$
Isobutyric acid
(±0.05%)(291)

a	10^3b
(13.45°–33.95°)	
100.00 Wt. % A	
1.2731	1.498(t − 13.45)
(13.35°–30.1°)	
79.66 Wt. % A	
1.1833	1.409(t − 13.35)
(12.4°–31.0°)	
54.72 Wt. % A	
1.0961	1.280(t − 12.4)
(13.1°–28.2°)	
31.97 Wt. % A	
1.0314	1.152(t − 13.1)
(11.4°–74.4°)	
0.00 Wt. % A	
0.9621	1.017(t − 11.4)

46. B = $C_4H_8O_2$
Ethyl acetate (142, 158)
(±0.0075%)(171)

Wt. % A	d_4^{25}
100.000	1.25590
88.647	1.16620
60.764	1.06578
33.596	0.97396
0.000	0.88896

47. B = $C_4H_{10}O$
Isobutyl alcohol
(±0.05%)(291)

a	10^3b
(16.25°–74.65°)	
100.00 Wt. % B	
0.8070	0.8300(t − 16.25)
(13.8°–32.4°)	
70.39 Wt. % B	
0.9013	0.9575(t − 13.8)
(15.5°–30.7°)	
50.22 Wt. % B	
0.9792	1.0980(t − 15.5)
(13.9°–34.2°)	
30.01 Wt. % B	
1.0769	1.2070(t − 13.9)
(11.3°–31.7°)	
15.80 Wt. % B	
1.1628	1.3000(t − 11.3)
(13.45°–33.95°)	
0.00 Wt. % B	
1.2731	1.4990(t − 13.45)

48. B = $C_4H_{10}O$
Ethyl ether (59,[1] 61, 103, 158, 290[1])
(±0.0075%)(171)

Wt. % A	d_4^{25}
100.000	1.25559
86.908	1.13931
65.656	0.99091
37.258	0.84461
0.000	0.70769

49. B = C_5H_{10}
Amylene (103)

50. B = $C_5H_{10}O_2$
Isovaleric acid
(±0.05%)(291)

a	10^3b
(13.45°–33.95°)	
100.00 Wt. % A	
1.2731	1.498(t − 13.45)
(12.15°–30.7°)	
71.70 Wt. % A	
1.1471	1.321(t − 12.15)
(14.2°–31.2°)	
54.10 Wt. % A	
1.0809	1.212(t − 14.2)
(10.2°–30.7°)	
37.43 Wt. % A	
1.0328	1.063(t − 10.2)
(17.6°–60.8°)	
0.00 Wt. % A	
0.9333	0.951(t − 17.6)

51. B = $C_6H_4Br_2$
p-Dibromobenzene(158)
(±0.005%)(318)

Wt. % A	d_4^{25}
100.000	1.25568
96.173	1.27299
91.993	1.29256
90.020	1.30149

52. B = C_6H_5Br
Bromobenzene (59,[1] 61)

53. B = C_6H_5Cl
Chlorobenzene (59)[1]

54. B = $C_6H_5NO_2$
Nitrobenzene (142)

55. B = C_6H_6 (59,[1] 99, 103, 133, 142, 158)
(±0.025%)(30)

Wt. % B	$d_4^{19.8}$
100.000	0.8788
87.361	0.9088
75.066	0.9458
60.569	0.9918
59.027	0.9970
49.599	1.0295
38.968	1.0707
34.602	1.0894
27.526	1.1205
20.187	1.1550
17.193	1.1698
5.325	1.2325
0.000	1.2642
(±0.0075%)(171)	
Wt. % B	d_4^{25}
0.000	1.25230
8.868	1.20550
34.847	1.08172
75.878	0.93900
100.000	0.87406

56. B = C_6H_7N
Aniline (142)

57. B = $C_6H_{10}O_3$
Ethyl acetoacetate (142)

58. B = $C_6H_{12}O_2$
d-*β*-Butyl acetate
(±0.1%)(242)

Wt. % A	d_4^{17}
92.44	1.2264
78.60	1.1502
70.13	1.1078
49.85	1.0283
33.55	0.9717

59. B = $C_6H_{12}O_3$
Paraldehyde (142)

60. B = C_7H_5NS
Phenyl thiocyanate (353)

61. B = C_7H_6O
Benzaldehyde (142)

62. B = $C_7H_6O_2$
Benzoic acid (296)[2]

63. B = $C_7H_6O_3$
Salicylic acid (296)[2]

64. B = $C_7H_7NO_2$
o-Nitrotoluene (136)[1]

65. B = $C_7H_7NO_2$
p-Nitrotoluene
(±0.1%)(136)

Wt. % A	d_4^{20}
100.0	1.265
88.6	1.248
79.1	1.236
61.6	1.215
50.7	1.203
47.0	1.198

CS_2.—(*Continued*)

66. B = C_7H_8 (**61, 99, 133, 158**)
(±0.0075%)(**171**)

Wt. % A	d_4^{25}
100.000	1.25559
92.734	1.21400
62.018	1.06441
36.768	0.96939
0.000	0.86053

67. B = $C_7H_8O_6$
Gallic acid monohydrate (**296**)[2]

68. B = C_7H_{16}
Heptane (**61**)

69. B = C_9H_8O
Cinnamic aldehyde (**289, 353**)

70. B = $C_{10}H_7Br$
Bromonaphthalene (**353**)

71. B = $C_{10}H_8$
Naphthalene (**54,[1] 303**)
(±0.005%)(**85**)

Wt. % A	d_4^{18}
100.000	1.26643
95.036	1.25182
90.082	1.23768
86.149	1.22676
80.163	1.21052
74.915	1.19661
70.240	1.18452

72. B = $C_{10}H_{12}O$
Anethole (**289, 353**)

73. B = $C_{10}H_{16}O$
Camphor
(±0.1%)(**277**)

Wt. % B	d_4^{20}
0.00	1.263
3.54	1.249
8.70	1.227
18.46	1.191
24.12	1.170
37.80	1.126
65.20	1.046

74. B = $C_{10}H_{16}O_4$
Camphoric acid (**296**)[2]

75. B = $C_{10}H_{20}O_2$
d-*β*-Octyl acetate
(±0.1%)(**242**)

Wt. % A	d_4^{17}
95.44	1.2144
84.63	1.1766
67.93	1.0965
55.67	1.0393
52.10	1.0255
39.15	0.9810
27.51	0.9411

76. B = $C_{12}H_{10}$
Diphenyl (**158**)
(±0.005%)(**318**)

Wt. % A	d_4^{25}
100.000	1.25568
96.193	1.24510
88.297	1.22320

77. B = $C_{12}H_{10}N_2$
Azobenzene (**158**)
(±0.005%)(**318**)

Wt. % B	d_4^{25}
0.000	1.25568
1.024	1.25371
6.253	1.24262
14.121	1.22641

78. B = $C_{18}H_{36}O_2$
Stearic acid (**296**)[2]

78.5 B = **Turpentine**
(±0.025%)(**123**)

Wt. % A	d_4^{15}
0.000	0.86193
20.332	0.91810
40.485	0.98596
60.116	1.05748
78.750	1.14811
100.000	1.27006

v. also 1

$CHBr_3$

Bromoform

79. B = CHI_3
Iodoform (**20, 254**)

80. B = CH_2I_2
Methylene iodide (**260**)

81. B = CH_4O
Methyl alcohol
(±0.1%)(**200**)

Wt. % B	d_4^{20}
74.72	0.983
85.72	0.886
92.42	0.834
100.00	0.796

82. B = C_2H_6O
Ethyl alcohol
(±0.1%)(**200**)

Wt. % B	d_4^{20}
100.00	0.790
92.43	0.833
85.82	0.891
74.20	0.979

83. B = C_3H_6O
Acetone (**200**)[1]

84. B = C_3H_8O
Propyl alcohol (**200**)[1]

85. B = $C_4H_{10}O$
Ethyl ether (**200**)[1]
(±0.05%)(**64**)

Wt. % B	d_4^{25}
100.000	0.708
78.172	0.852
54.652	1.092
42.728	1.268
31.079	1.504
25.151	1.659
21.640	1.766
19.959	1.820
14.747	2.060
8.494	2.314
3.248	2.635
0.000	2.878

86. B = $C_5H_{12}O$
Isoamyl alcohol (**200**)[1]

87. B = $C_6H_5NO_2$
Nitrobenzene
(±0.075%)(**68, 150**)

Wt. % B	d_4^{10}
0.00	2.8887
9.68	2.4724
25.85	2.0809
50.08	1.6833
65.83	1.4987
88.39	1.2955
100.00	1.2125
Wt. % B	$d_4^{76.5}$
0.00	2.7167
9.68	2.3338
25.85	1.9599
50.08	1.5871
65.83	1.4135
88.39	1.2246
100.00	1.1167

88. B = C_6H_6 (**200**)[1]

89. B = $C_8H_{14}O_6$
Ethyl tartrate
(±0.05%)(**228**)

a	10^3b
(19.07°–25.75°)	
0.00 Wt. % B	
2.8901	$2.601(t - 19.07)$
(19.04°–30.03°)	
7.08 Wt. % B	
2.6181	$2.365(t - 19.04)$
(12.9°–73.0°)	
10.00 Wt. % B	
2.5151	$2.311(t - 12.9)$
(19.25°–32.17°)	
30.92 Wt. % B	
2.0029	$1.803(t - 19.25)$

v. also 1267, 1268

$CHCl_3$

Chloroform

90. B = CH_4O (**44**)[1]
Methyl alcohol

91. B = $C_2H_3Cl_3O_2$
Chloral hydrate (**299**)[1,2]

92. B = $C_2H_4Br_2$
Ethylene bromide (**61**)
(±0.1%)(**251**)
(10.2°–131.3°)
50 Wt. % B

a	10^3b
1.606	$1.551(t - 10.2)$

93. B = $C_2H_4O_2$
Acetic acid (**14**)

94. B = C_2H_6O
Ethyl alcohol (**35, 81,[1] 103, 169, 240, 326[1]**)
(±0.05%)(**67, 290**)
(19.46°–30.96°)

a	10^3b
100.00 Wt. % A	
1.4875	$1.845(t - 19.46)$
89.65 Wt. % A	
1.3636	$1.730(t - 19.46)$
80.06 Wt. % A	
1.2671	$1.548(t - 19.46)$
69.96 Wt. % A	
1.1798	$1.418(t - 19.46)$
59.93 Wt. % A	
1.1048	$1.340(t - 19.46)$
50.03 Wt. % A	
1.0384	$1.218(t - 19.46)$
40.04 Wt. % A	
0.9789	$1.105(t - 19.46)$
30.00 Wt. % A	
0.9255	$1.043(t - 19.46)$
20.03 Wt. % A	
0.8777	$0.973(t - 19.46)$
9.97 Wt. % A	
0.8340	$0.913(t - 19.46)$
0.00 Wt. % A	
0.7947	$0.858(t - 19.46)$

95. B = C_3H_6O
Acetone (**59,[1] 62,[1] 79, 81,[1] 99, 131,[1] 133, 290,[1] 351**)
(±0.005%)(**134**)

Wt. % B	d_4^{25}
0.000	0.78492
16.664	0.85146
33.039	0.92905
45.832	1.00050
56.298	1.06789
64.507	1.12763
72.276	1.19082
79.884	1.25927
88.409	1.34501
94.292	1.41066
100.000	1.47993
Wt. % B	$d_4^{35.17}$
0.000	0.77322
16.664	0.83892
33.039	0.91568
45.832	0.98641
56.298	1.05311
64.507	1.11211
72.276	1.17478
79.884	1.24250
88.409	1.32718
94.292	1.39204
100.000	1.46045

(±0.25%)(0°–40°)(**312**)

a	10^3b
100.00 Mol % B	
0.814	$1.050t$
84.3 Mol % B	
0.932	$1.300t$
63.8 Mol % B	
1.076	$1.375t$
51.7 Mol % B	
1.161	$1.450t$
39.1 Mol % B	
1.253	$1.675t$
17.6 Mol % B	
1.392	$1.350t$
0.0 Mol % B	
1.514	$1.900t$

96. B = C_3H_7NO
Propionamide (**180**)

97. B = $C_3H_7NO_2$
Urethane (**299**)[1,2]

98. B = $C_4H_{10}O$
Ethyl ether (59,[1] 61, 94, 103, 176, 309,[1] 315)
(±0.05%)(63, 280)

Mol % A	d_4^5
100	1.5159
80	1.3150
60	1.1647
40	1.0176
20	0.8548
0	0.7290

Mol % A	d_4^{20}
17.3	0.8219
25.6	0.8801
36.6	0.9585
45.7	1.0268
52.0	1.0746
53.5	1.0863
55.3	1.0994
66.3	1.1869
68.2	1.2012
79.8	1.2968

Mol % A	d_4^{25}
0.00	0.7082
7.46	0.7562
10.06	0.7732
10.46	0.7757
11.95	0.7871
14.37	0.8026
26.49	0.8848
26.90	0.8879
27.92	0.8951
32.02	0.9254
40.21	0.9849
42.57	1.0023
45.04	1.0210
46.96	1.0359
56.23	1.1060
60.92	1.1441
61.14	1.1460
64.60	1.1736
68.40	1.2039
68.76	1.2059
77.08	1.2766
84.23	1.3365
84.95	1.3433
88.41	1.3723
89.63	1.3837
95.52	1.4366
100.00	1.4785

Mol % A	d_4^{30}
5.4	0.7439
12.3	0.7896
15.2	0.8076
20.5	0.8441
25.0	0.8741
29.1	0.9021
33.6	0.9366
39.6	0.9806
44.3	1.0153
49.5	1.0550
59.2	1.1297
68.9	1.2079
72.8	1.2400
89.6	1.3834

99. B = $C_4H_{12}ClN$
Diethylammonium chloride (333)[1]

100. B = $C_4H_{12}N_2O_3$
Diethylammonium nitrate (333)[1]

101. B = C_5H_{10}
Amylene (61, 103)

102. B = C_5H_{12}
Pentane (61)

103. B = $C_5H_{12}O$
n-Amyl alcohol
(±0.01%)(131)

Wt. % B	d_4^{25}
0.000	1.4800
11.090	1.3541
19.471	1.2718
26.778	1.2096
42.037	1.0712
59.865	0.9886
69.308	0.9388
100.000	0.8068

104. B = $C_6H_4Br_2$
p-Dibromobenzene (158)
(to 9.069% B)(318)
d_4^{25} = (1.47737 + 0.003825 × Wt. % B) ±0.005%

105. B = $C_6H_4N_2O_4$
m-Dinitrobenzene (158)
(±0.01%)(318)

Wt. % A	d_4^{15}
100.000	1.4963
97.121	1.4977
93.443	1.4975
Wt. % A	d_4^{20}
100.00	1.4868
97.121	1.4879
93.443	1.4885
Wt. % A	d_4^{30}
100.000	1.4680
97.121	1.4693
93.443	1.4704
Wt. % A	d_4^{40}
100.000	1.4489
97.121	1.4503
93.443	1.4522
Wt. % A	d_4^{50}
100.000	1.4296
97.121	1.4318
93.443	1.4339
Wt. % A	d_4^{60}
100.000	1.4100
97.121	1.4134
93.443	1.4162

106. B = C_6H_5Br
Bromobenzene
(0–100 Mol % B)
d_4^0 = (1.526 − 0.0$_4$4 × Mol % B) ± 0.1% (269)

107. B = $C_6H_5NO_3$
o-Nitrophenol
(±0.075%)(15°–55°)(172)

a	10^3b
100.00 Wt. % A	
1.4898	1.838(t − 15)
91.72 Wt. % A	
1.4774	1.758(t − 15)

108. B = C_6H_6 (35, 61, 99, 103, 158, 171[1])
(±0.05%)(280, 282)

Mol % B	d_4^5
0.0	1.5159
20.0	1.3761
40.0	1.2449
60.0	1.1142
80.0	0.9500
100.0	0.8907
Mol % B	d_4^{20}
0.0	1.4754
20.0	1.3450
40.0	1.2210
60.0	1.0972
80.0	0.9823
100.0	0.8787
Mol % B	d_4^{26}
0.0	1.4671
20.0	1.3350
40.0	1.2103
60.0	1.0834
80.0	0.9716
100.0	0.8750

(±0.025%)(to 70°)(178)
50 Wt. % B

a	10^3b
1.1282	1.347t

109. B = C_6H_6O
Phenol
(±0.005%)(319)

Wt. % A	$d_4^{12.87}$
100.000	1.50180
96.127	1.48012
93.066	1.46362
87.997	1.43697
77.971	1.38685

110. B = $C_6H_{10}O_8$
Citric acid monohydrate (296)[2]

111. B = $C_6H_{16}ClN$
Triethylammonium chloride (333)[1]

112. B = $C_7H_5N_3O_6$
Trinitrotoluene
(±0.005%)(319)

Wt. % A	$d_4^{12.87}$
100.000	1.50180
98.398	1.50340
97.445	1.50448
96.897	1.50480

113. B = $C_7H_6O_2$
Benzoic acid (296)[1]
(±0.005%)(319)

Wt. % A	$d_4^{12.87}$
100.000	1.50180
98.469	1.49564
96.470	1.48750
91.569	1.46832

114. B = $C_7H_6O_3$
Salicylic acid (296)[2]

115. B = C_7H_8 (35, 172[1])

116. B = C_7H_9N
p-Toluidine (299)[1,2]

117. B = C_7H_{16}
Heptane (61)

118. B = $C_7H_{16}O$
Ethyl amyl ether (61)

119. B = C_8H_8O
Acetophenone
(±0.1%)(270)

Mol % A	d_4^{25}
100.00	1.475
66.30	1.285
49.90	1.215
28.75	1.125
11.25	1.062
0.00	1.025

120. B = C_8H_9NO
Acetanilide (299)[1,2]

121. B = $C_8H_{10}O$
Phenetole
(±0.1%)(269)

Mol % A	d_4^0
100.00	1.5261
90.91	1.4472
67.62	1.2858
51.82	1.2113
19.91	1.0531
0.00	0.9841

122. B = $C_8H_{12}O_6$
Dimethyl acetylmalate
(±0.05%)(227)

a	10^3b
(10.44°–29.2°)	
95.96 Wt. % A	
1.4940	1.892(t − 10.44)
(14.3°–28.5°)	
90.45 Wt. % A	
1.4662	1.782(t − 14.3)

123. B = $C_8H_{14}O_6$
Ethyl tartrate (343,[1] 344[1])
(±0.05%)(207, 217)

a	10^3b
(12.8°–51.0°)	
98.00 Wt. % A	
1.4931	1.882(t − 12.8)
(18.0°–54.°0)	
91.01 Wt. % A	
1.4588	1.775(t − 18.0)
(17.3°–60.0°)	
80.88 Wt. % A	
1.4267	1.661(t − 17.3)
(14.5°–59.3°)	
60.09 Wt. % A	
1.3668	1.427(t − 14.5)
(13.5°–57.3°)	
39.96 Wt. % A	
1.3110	1.248(t − 13.5)
(11.3°–52.3°)	
30.05 Wt. % A	
1.2616	1.108(t − 11.3)

$CHCl_3$.—(*Continued*)

124. B = $C_8H_{20}BrN$
Tetraethylammonium bromide
(±0.05%)(334)

Wt. % A	d_4^{25}
100.00	1.4761
93.88	1.4692
92.52	1.4682
Wt. % A	d_4^{50}
100.00	1.4268
93.88	1.4275
92.52	1.4262

125. B = $C_8H_{20}ClN$
Tetraethylammonium chloride
(333)[1]

126. B = $C_9H_{11}NO$
Methylacetanilide (180)

127. B = $C_{10}H_4Cl_4$
Naphthalene tetrachloride
(148)[1]

128. B = $C_{10}H_8$
Naphthalene (299)[1]
(±0.005%)(85)

Wt. % A	d_4^{18}
100.000	1.47921
95.237	1.45038
89.857	1.41826
84.213	1.38632
80.885	1.36810
74.987	1.33716
68.966	1.30650

129. B = $C_{10}H_{14}$
Durene
(±0.005%)(318)

Wt. % A	d_4^{25}
100.000	1.47737
98.055	1.45696
95.351	1.42978
89.859	1.37821
85.759	1.34476

130. B = $C_{10}H_{14}N_2$
Nicotine (343)[1]

131. B = $C_{10}H_{16}O$
Camphor
(±0.05%)(343)

Wt. % B	d_4^{20}
0.00	1.4749
1.15	1.4664
2.19	1.4586
4.03	1.4452
5.31	1.4361
35.27	1.2476

132. B = $C_{10}H_{16}O_4$
Camphoric acid (296)[2]

133. B = $C_{10}H_{24}ClN$
Diamylammonium chloride
(333)[1]

134. B = $C_{12}H_{10}$
Acenaphthene (158, 299[1])
(±0.005%)(318)

Wt. % A	d_4^{25}
100.000	1.47737
98.508	1.46921
96.033	1.45677
92.624	1.43966
86.801	1.41004

135. B = $C_{12}H_{10}$
Diphenyl (158)
(±0.005%)(318)

Wt. % A	d_4^{25}
100.000	1.47737
98.373	1.46776
95.809	1.45224
94.683	1.44500
89.721	1.41573
86.855	1.39880

136. B = $C_{12}H_{10}N_2$
Azobenzene
(±0.005%)(318)

Wt. % B	d_4^{25}
0.000	1.47737
3.116	1.46158
7.482	1.43984
10.829	1.42258

(10 Wt. % B)(±0.25%)(158)

t	d_4^t
20	1.425
30	1.405
50	1.363
60	1.335

137. B = $C_{12}H_{10}O$
Diphenyl ether
(±0.1%)(269)

Mol % A	d_4^{25}
0.00	1.072
31.36	1.150
56.96	1.239
81.70	1.357
100.00	1.526

138. B = $C_{14}H_8O_2$
Anthraquinone (297[1,2] 317[1,2])

139. B = $C_{14}H_{10}O_2$
Benzil (158)
(±0.005%)(318)

Wt. % A	d_4^{25}
100.000	1.47737
97.968	1.47020
96.177	1.46381
90.491	1.44321
84.679	1.42148

140. B = $C_{18}H_{36}O_2$
Stearic acid (296)[2]

141. B = $C_{19}H_{16}$
Triphenylmethane (158)
(±0.005%)(318)

Wt. % A	d_4^{25}
100.000	1.47737
97.325	1.46327
93.168	1.44148
92.979	1.44005
90.795	1.42863

142. B = $C_{27}H_{46}O$
Cholesterol (148)[1]

v. also 2, 32

CHI_3

Iodoform
v. 79, 1267, 1268, 1269, 1270

CH_2Cl_2

Methylene chloride
143. B = C_3H_6O
Acetone
(±0.1%)(270)

Mol % B	d_4^0
0.00	1.378
12.76	1.281
42.35	1.107
60.46	1.009
81.12	0.905
92.27	0.850
100.00	0.812

144. B = $C_8H_{14}O_6$
Ethyl tartrate
(±0.05%)(228)

a	10^3b
(18.05°–26.23°) 0.00 Wt. % B	
1.3393	1.847(t − 18.05)
(19.34°–25.96°) 5.12 Wt. % B	
1.3283	1.784(t − 19.34)
(18.57°–28.13°) 9.75 Wt. % B	
1.3221	1.717(t − 18.57)
(20.37°–27.20°) 17.10 Wt. % B	
1.3079	1.625(t − 20.37)
(19.50°–27.33°) 32.90 Wt. % B	
1.2866	1.481(t − 19.50)
(18.86°–26.45°) 61.88 Wt. % B	
1.2485	1.238(t − 18.86)

CH_2I_2

Methylene iodide
145. B = C_6H_6 (254)

146. B = $C_6H_{10}O_4$
Ethyl oxalate (236)[1]

147. B = C_8H_{10}
Xylene (254)

148. B = $C_8H_{14}O_6$
Ethyl tartrate
(±0.05%) (228)

a	10^3b
(19.41°–29.15°) 0.00 Wt. % B	
3.3233	2.579(t − 19.41)
(21.06°–33.48°) 1.42 Wt. % B	
3.2338	2.625(t − 21.06)

v. also 33, 80, 1269, 1270

CH_2O_2

Formic acid
149. B = CH_3NO
Formamide
(±0.075%)(183)

Mol % A	d_4^{25}
0.00	1.1315
10.00	1.1442
19.99	1.1540
30.00	1.1639
39.99	1.1783
49.98	1.1828
60.00	1.1917
69.85	1.1993
79.95	1.2060
90.00	1.2109
100.00	1.2133
Mol % A	d_4^{40}
10.00	1.1310
19.99	1.1406
30.00	1.1500
39.99	1.1593
49.98	1.1676
60.00	1.1761
69.85	1.1828
79.95	1.1889
90.00	1.1931
100.00	1.1943

150. B = CH_4O
Methyl alcohol
(±0.1%)(108)

Wt. % B	d_4^{18}
0.00	1.2190
33.13	1.0258
61.88	0.9233
75.70	0.8716
80.92	0.8544
90.19	0.8274
95.14	0.8109
100.00	0.7940

151. B = CH_5NO_2
Ammonium formate (276)
d_4^{25} = (1.2142 + 0.001479 × g-Mole B per l soln.) ± 0.1%

152. B = $C_2H_4O_2$
Acetic acid
(±0.05%)(157)
d_4^t =

100 Mol % B
1.0715(1 − 0.001026t)
95 Mol % B
1.0806(1 − 0.001020t)
75 Mol % B
1.1062(1 − 0.001040t)
50 Mol % B
1.1434(1 − 0.001030t)
25 Mol % B
1.1872(1 − 0.001002t)
0 Mol % B
1.2450(1 − 0.001001t)

153. B = C_2H_6O
Ethyl alcohol (168, 169)

154. B = C_7H_6O
Benzaldehyde (168, 169)

155. B = $C_7H_9NO_2$
Phenylammonium formate
(±0.1%)(276)

Wt. % A	d_4^{25}
88.05	1.213
92.81	1.214
95.33	1.215
96.20	1.215
98.18	1.215
99.07	1.214
100.00	1.214

156. B = $C_{10}H_{16}O$
Camphor (323, 342)
(±0.1%)(100)

Wt. % B	d_4^{20}
0.00	1.2201
8.44	1.1881
12.27	1.1579
26.56	1.1313
36.31	1.1026
46.54	1.0746

CH_3I

Methyl iodide

157. B = C_2H_5I
Ethyl iodide (254)
(±0.05%)(166)

Wt. % B	d_4^{15}
100	1.9433
90	1.9713
80	2.0003
70	2.0301
60	2.0607
50	2.0923
40	2.1250
30	2.1585
20	2.1933
10	2.2292
0	2.2661

158. B = C_2H_6O
Ethyl alcohol
(±0.01%)(132)

Wt. % B	d_4^{25}
0.000	2.25095
1.956	2.16755
4.916	2.09160
7.710	1.95955
14.648	1.74860
20.965	1.60897
25.418	1.51855
39.971	1.28333
100.000	0.78662

159. B = C_3H_6O
Acetone
(±0.01%)(132)

Wt. % B	d_4^{25}
0.000	2.2509
2.590	2.1438
4.780	2.0603
9.376	1.9050
17.084	1.6936
24.015	1.5410
28.378	1.4336
45.640	1.2059
100.000	0.7853

160. B = C_3H_8O
n-Propyl alcohol
(±0.01%)(132)

Wt. % B	d_4^{25}
0.000	2.25095
2.572	2.14550
4.680	2.06785
4.890	2.06047
9.642	1.90575
19.616	1.69215
24.116	1.54487
29.800	1.45180
45.120	1.23140
100.000	0.79972

161. B = $C_4H_8O_2$
Ethyl acetate
(±0.01%)(132)

Wt. % B	d_4^{25}
0.000	2.25095
3.768	2.11280
7.456	2.00230
12.906	1.85980
15.552	1.73610
23.708	1.63240
37.268	1.41803
100.000	0.89088

162. B = C_6H_6 (172)[1]

163. B = $C_8H_{14}O_6$
Ethyl tartrate
(±0.05%)(228)

a	10^3b
(18.22°–26.35°)	
0.00 Wt. % B	
2.2825	2.891 (t − 18.22)
(19.39°–26.62°)	
5.20 Wt. % B	
2.1703	2.681 (t − 19.39)
(18.86°–23.16°)	
10.45 Wt. % B	
2.0744	2.512 (t − 18.86)
(18.77°–25.12°)	
38.09 Wt. % B	
1.6884	1.811 (t − 18.77)

v. also 3, 34, 1271, 1272

CH_3NO

Formamide

164. B = CH_4O
Methyl alcohol
(±0.075%)(183)

Mol % B	d_4^{25}
0.00	1.1312
9.87	1.1252
19.96	1.1186
30.80	1.1112
40.03	1.1032
50.03	1.0939
60.11	1.0825
69.97	1.0686
80.02	1.0511
89.99	1.0276

Mol % B	d_4^{40}
9.87	1.0906
19.96	1.0605
30.80	1.0302
40.03	0.9978
50.03	0.9638
60.11	0.9285
69.97	0.8940
80.02	0.8562
89.99	0.8172
100.00	0.7749

164.5 B = CH_5NO_2
Ammonium formate
(±0.05%) (360)

Wt. % B	d_4^{25}
1.393	1.1324
0.558	1.1310
0.000	1.1303

165. B = $C_2H_4O_2$
Acetic acid
(±0.075%)(183)

Mol % B	d_4^{25}
0.00	1.1318
9.62	1.1284
20.39	1.1198
29.74	1.1146
40.56	1.1122
49.82	1.1015
59.89	1.0938
69.42	1.0847
78.95	1.0755
90.10	1.0621
100.00	1.0463
Mol % B	d_4^{40}
9.62	1.1151
20.39	1.1063
29.74	1.1011
40.56	1.0983
49.82	1.0873
59.89	1.0791
69.42	1.0687
78.95	1.0600
90.10	1.0462
100.00	1.0294

166. B = C_2H_6O
Ethyl alcohol
(±0.075%)(183, 360[1])

Mol % B	d_4^{25}
0.00	1.1314
10.00	1.0846
18.92	1.0457
29.76	1.0042
39.07	0.9678
50.09	0.9335
59.29	0.9022
69.86	0.8701
80.09	0.8401
89.95	0.8126
100.00	0.7857

(±0.01%)(33)

Wt. % B	d_4^{30}
100.000	0.78078
98.188	0.78560
94.225	0.79628
84.329	0.82371

(±0.075%)(183)

Mol % B	d_4^{40}
0.00	1.1190
10.00	1.0722
18.92	1.0332
29.76	0.9927
39.07	0.9573
50.09	0.9209
59.29	0.8896
69.86	0.8571
80.09	0.8271
89.95	0.7997
100.00	0.7727

167. B = $C_3H_6O_2$
Propionic acid
(±0.075%)(183)

Mol % A	d_4^{25}
100.00	1.1327
97.60	1.1297
91.01	1.1250
81.15	1.1185
73.38	1.1083
59.87	1.0852
49.76	1.0699
39.79	1.0549
29.92	1.0391
19.49	1.0222
10.02	1.0059
0.00	0.9885
Mol % A	d_4^{40}
91.01	1.1130
81.15	1.1056
73.38	1.0954
59.87	1.0711
49.76	1.0566
39.79	1.0408
29.92	1.0248
19.49	1.0074
10.02	0.9906
0.00	0.9725

168. B = C_3H_8O
n-Propyl alcohol
(±0.1%)(78)

Wt. % B	d_4^{25}
0.00	1.1314
11.23	1.0850
20.67	1.0472
29.94	1.0114
39.96	0.9753
49.99	0.9411

169. B = $C_4H_8O_2$
Butyric acid
(±0.075%)(183)

Mol % B	d_4^{25}
0.00	1.1320
4.90	1.1169
14.30	1.1100
20.10	1.0952
29.89	1.0711
40.04	1.0505
49.73	1.0324
59.69	1.0151
69.87	0.9988
79.56	0.9825
89.57	0.9677
100.00	0.9528

CH_3NO.—(*Continued*)

$B = C_4H_8O_2$.—(*Continued*)

Mol % B	d_4^{40}
4.90	1.1044
14.30	1.0975
20.10	1.0826
29.89	1.0584
40.04	1.0375
49.73	1.0191
59.69	1.0019
69.87	0.9849
79.56	0.9684
89.57	0.9536
100.00	0.9380

170. $B = C_4H_{10}O$

Isobutyl alcohol

(±0.1%)(**78**)

Wt. % B	d_4^{25}
0.00	1.1307
10.09	1.0854
19.95	1.0475
30.00	1.0091
39.81	0.9745
49.98	0.9398

171. $B = C_5H_5N$

Pyridine

(±0.05%)(**70**)

Wt. % B	d_4^{25}
100.00	0.9746
92.23	0.9871
88.90	0.9935
82.88	1.0070

172. $B = C_5H_{12}O$

Isoamyl alcohol

(±0.075%)(**68, 150**)

Wt. % B	d_4^{0}
100.00	0.8253
97.18	0.8315
90.01	0.8497
69.92	0.9041
49.84	0.9649
30.14	1.0335
10.38	1.1111
0.00	1.1549

(±0.1%)(**78**)

Wt. % B	d_4^{25}
0.00	1.1314
10.01	1.0870
19.94	1.0485
29.98	1.0115
39.95	0.9756
50.01	0.9413
60.00	0.9108

(±0.075%)(**68, 150**)

Wt. % B	$d_4^{76.5}$
100.00	0.7656
97.18	0.7731
90.01	0.7908
69.92	0.8440
49.84	0.9044
30.14	0.9726
10.38	1.0479
0.00	1.0901

173. $B = C_8H_{14}O_6$

Ethyl tartrate

(±0.05%)(**343**)

Wt. % B	d_4^{20}
74.671	1.1986
51.103	1.1806
25.687	1.1577
8.860	1.1425
5.345	1.1396
1.899	1.1365

174. $B = C_{10}H_{14}N_2$

Nicotine

(±0.05%)(**343**)

Wt. % A	d_4^{20}
0.00	1.0100
38.46	1.0610
61.67	1.0889
82.20	1.1139
88.68	1.2203

v. also 149

CH_3NO_2

Nitromethane

175. $B = C_2H_6O$

Ethyl alcohol (**192**,[1] **328**[1])

176. $B = C_4H_{12}IN$

Tetramethylammonium iodide (**330**)[1]

177. $B = C_8H_{20}IN$

Tetraethylammonium iodide (**330**,[1] **331**[1])

178. $B = C_{12}H_{28}IN$

Tetrapropylammonium iodide (**330**)[1]

CH_4N_2O

Urea

179. $B = CH_4O$

Methyl alcohol (**299**)[1]

180. $B = CH_5N$

Methylamine

(±0.25%)(**83**)

Wt. % B	d_4^{0}
74.19	0.773
86.11	0.755
92.26	0.724
96.75	0.704
98.24	0.694
98.81	0.693
99.25	0.691
99.49	0.689
99.71	0.689
99.90	0.690
99.94	0.692
99.98	0.685

181. $B = C_2H_6O$

Ethyl alcohol (**299**)[1,2]

(±0.01%)(**33**)

Wt. % B	d_4^{25}
100.000	0.78521
97.580	0.79419
97.249	0.79542
96.599	0.79795
94.848	0.80456

Wt. % B	d_4^{30}
100.000	0.78078
97.685	0.78939
95.853	0.79628

(±0.025%)(**247**)

Mol % B	d_4^{40}
100.00	0.77329
88.46	0.77865
76.88	0.78553
65.71	0.79176
54.47	0.79746

Mol % B	d_4^{50}
100.00	0.76329
88.42	0.77143
77.00	0.77722
65.37	0.78304
54.38	0.78845

Mol % B	d_4^{60}
100.00	0.75435
88.59	0.76261
77.12	0.76841
65.59	0.77417
54.45	0.77926

Mol % B	d_4^{70}
100.00	0.74650
88.39	0.75220
77.00	0.75780
65.42	0.76360
54.27	0.76878

183. $B = C_5H_5N$

Pyridine (**70**)[1]

CH_4N_2S

Thiourea

184. $B = CH_4N_2S$

Ammonium thiocyanate (**8**)

185. $B = C_5H_5N$

Pyridine

(±0.05%)(**70**)

Wt. % B	d_4^{25}
100.00	0.9746
94.48	0.9949
87.43	1.0190

CH_4N_2S

Ammonium thiocyanate

v. 184

CH_4O

Methyl alcohol

186. $B = C_2H_3N$

Methyl cyanide

(±0.5%)(**322**)

Wt. % A	d_4^{0}
0	0.8052
10	0.8063
20	0.8073
30	0.8083
40	0.8093
50	0.8102
60	0.8110
70	0.8115
80	0.8115
90	0.8109
100	0.8098

187. $B = C_2H_4O_2$

Acetic acid (**168**)

(±0.1%)(**108**)

Wt. % B	d_4^{18}
100.00	1.057
50.50	0.916
33.55	0.878
20.27	0.842
6.44	0.809
0.00	0.794

187.5. $B = C_2H_5I$

Ethyl iodide

(±0.1%) (**362**)

Wt. % A	d_4^{20}
0.0	1.9340
26.8	1.3480
68.7	0.9656
100.0	0.7932

188. $B = C_2H_6O$

Ethyl alcohol (**133, 351**); *cf.* (**358.5**)

(0–100 Wt. % A)

$d_4^{15} = (0.79367 + 0.0_4235 \times$ Wt. % A) ±0.025% (**65**)

(0–100 Wt. % A)

$d_4^{25} = (0.7867 + 0.0_413 \times$ Wt. % A) ±0.1% (**113, 117**)

189. $B = C_3H_6O$

Acetone (**144**)[1]

(±0.1%) (**359**)

Vol. % B	d_4^{0}
0	0.8110
25	0.8160
50	0.8180
75	0.8170
100	0.8132

(±0.025%)(**65**)

Wt. % B	d_4^{15}
0.00	0.7960
8.00	0.7976
31.63	0.8005
50.29	0.8015
76.03	0.8007
88.05	0.7992
100.00	0.7900

(±0.1%) (**359**)

Vol. % B	d_4^{25}
0	0.7875
25	0.7896
50	0.7916
75	0.7896
100	0.7856

190. $B = C_3H_7NO_2$

Urethane (**299**)[1]

191. $B = C_3H_8O$

n-Propyl alcohol

(±0.025%)(**65**)

Wt. % A	d_4^{15}
100.00	0.79602
95.63	0.79651
90.12	0.79692
79.72	0.79788
65.37	0.79936
59.10	0.80005

Wt. % A	d^{15}_4
49.71	0.80104
40.38	0.80215
31.88	0.80325
21.05	0.80466
11.97	0.80582
0.00	0.80753

(±0.075%)(113, 118)

Wt. % A	d^{25}_4
100.00	0.7878
88.89	0.7894
76.20	0.7907
34.80	0.7954
8.20	0.7992
6.25	0.7995
3.40	0.7999
0.00	0.8004

d^t_4 =
(±0.05%)(157)
100 Mol % A
$0.8105(1 - 0.001135t)$
75 Mol % A
$0.8137(1 - 0.001083t)$
50 Mol % A
$0.8162(1 - 0.001030t)$
25 Mol % A
$0.8197(1 - 0.001054t)$
0 Mol % A
$0.8210(1 - 0.001024t)$

192. B = $C_3H_8O_3$
Glycerol
(±0.25%)(38)

Wt. % A	d^{56}_4
0.00	1.2400
2.96	1.2227
9.72	1.1853
16.76	1.1399
23.89	1.1006
31.02	1.0620
34.99	1.0418
50.61	0.9642
56.22	0.9386
66.17	0.8942
90.40	0.7963
100.00	0.7604

193. B = $C_4H_2O_4$
Acetylene dicarboxylic acid
(0–100 Wt. % B)(125)
$d^{25}_4 = (0.7880 + 0.00419 \times$ Wt. % B) ±0.05%

194. B = $C_4H_4O_4$
Fumaric acid
(to 8.15 Wt. % B)(125)
$d^{25}_4 = (0.7880 + 0.00403 \times$ Wt. % B) ±0.05%

195. B = $C_4H_6O_4$
Succinic acid
(to 10.08 Wt. % B)(125)
$d^{25}_4 = (0.7880 + 0.00407 \times$ Wt. % B) ±0.05%

196. B = $C_4H_6O_5$
Malic acid
(±0.075%)(194)

Wt. % A	d^{20}_4
84.17	0.8942
75.00	0.9452
47.58	1.0860

197. B = $C_4H_8O_2$
Butyric acid
(±0.1%)(108)

Wt. % A	d^{18}_4
0.00	0.9607
56.34	0.8610
76.73	0.8334
88.12	0.8148
100.00	0.7940

198. B = $C_4H_{10}O$
Isobutyl alcohol
(±0.025%)(65)

Wt. % B	d^{15}_4
0.00	0.79602
5.34	0.79631
14.19	0.79679
19.72	0.79709
22.54	0.79731
39.47	0.79854
49.41	0.79943
70.93	0.80177
89.84	0.80423
100.00	0.80567

199. B = $C_4H_{10}O$
Ethyl ether (10, 41)
(±0.025%)(9)

Wt. % B	d^{25}_4
0.00	0.7882
23.12	0.7733
35.07	0.7650
47.40	0.7561
60.23	0.7461
73.08	0.7353
86.33	0.7230
100.00	0.7079

200. B = $C_4H_{12}IN$
Tetramethylammonium iodide
(330)[1]

201. B = $C_5H_{12}O$
Amyl alcohol (168, 169)

202. B = $C_6H_5NO_2$
Nitrobenzene
(±0.1%)(82)

Wt. % A	d^{25}_4
100	0.7860
75	0.8945
50	0.9984
25	1.1010
0	1.1980

203. B = C_6H_6 (81,[1] 133, 139, 233,[1] 238,[1] 351)
(±0.005%)(319)

Wt. % B	$d^{12.87}_4$
100.000	0.88619
98.135	0.88437
92.693	0.87914
85.930	0.87280
80.370	0.86766
78.573	0.86605
61.666	0.85073

(0–100 Mol % A)(82)
$d^{25}_4 = (0.8722 - 0.0_3836 \times$ Mol % A) ±0.1%

204. B = C_6H_7N
Aniline
(0–100 Wt. % A)(107, 132)
$d^{25}_4 = (1.0175 - 0.002298 \times$ Wt. % A) ±0.025%

205. B = C_7H_8O
Anisole (10)
(±0.025%)(9)

Wt. % A	d^{25}_4
100.00	0.7886
84.89	0.8149
70.60	0.8413
57.09	0.8672
44.40	0.8927
32.38	0.9178
21.00	0.9427
10.27	0.9655
0.00	0.9909

206. B = C_8H_9NO
Acetanilide (299)[1]

207. B = $C_8H_{10}O$
Phenetole
(±0.025%)(9)

Wt. % A	d^{25}_4
100.00	0.7881
85.17	0.8109
71.07	0.8333
57.76	0.8556
45.12	0.8772
33.00	0.8988
21.43	0.9213
0.00	0.9622

208. B = $C_8H_{12}O_6$
Dimethyl acetylmalate
(±0.05%)(227)

a	10^3b
	(15.4°–29.5°)
	96.04 Wt. % A
0.8079	0.9575(t − 15.4)
	(16.6°–29.3°)
	89.66 Wt. % A
0.8257	0.9340(t − 16.6)

209. B = $C_8H_{14}O_6$
Ethyl tartrate
(±0.05%)(170, 343)

Wt. % B	d^{20}_4
100.00	1.2044
77.46	1.0882
56.65	1.0007
39.92	0.9381
26.97	0.8946
15.31	0.8568
12.01	0.8324
5.13	0.8102
0.00	0.7938

(±0.05%)(203, 288, 344)

a	10^3b
	(16°–48°)
	0.00 Wt. % B
0.7955	0.959(t − 16)
	(20.2°–46.7°)
	5.00 Wt. % B
0.8070	0.955(t − 20.2)
	(22°–45.8°)
	10.00 Wt. % B
0.8212	0.967(t − 22)
	(14.1°–43.2°)
	25.01 Wt. % B
0.8800	0.976(t − 14.1)
	(19.8°–51°)
	50.00 Wt. % B
0.9707	1.000(t − 19.8)
	(18.3°–53.2°)
	75.00 Wt. % B
1.0841	1.015(t − 18.3)
	(16.8°–99.4°)
	100.00 Wt. % B
1.2085	1.016(t − 16.8)

210. B = $C_8H_{20}IN$
Tetraethylammonium iodide
(330)[1]

211. B = $C_9H_6O_2$
Phenylpropiolic acid
(±0.05%)(125)

Wt. % A	d^{25}_4
100.00	0.7880
94.79	0.8049
89.65	0.8194

212. B = $C_9H_8O_2$
Cinnamic acid
(to 11.06 Wt. % B)(125)
$d^{25}_4 = (0.7880 + 0.003075 \times$ Wt. % B) ±0.05%

213. B = $C_9H_{10}O$
Cinnamyl alcohol (148)[1]

214. B = $C_9H_{10}O_2$
β-Phenylpropionic acid
(to 9.32 Wt. % B)(125)
$d^{25}_4 = (0.7880 + 0.002825 \times$ Wt. % B) ±0.05%

215. B = $C_{10}H_8$
Naphthalene (148,[1] 299[1])
(±0.0075%)(54)

Wt. % A	d^{18}_4
100.000	0.79511
98.436	0.79914
96.131	0.80299

216. B = $C_{10}H_8O$
α-Naphthol (148)[1]

217. B = $C_{10}H_8O$
β-Naphthol (148)[1]

218. B = $C_{10}H_{12}$
Tetrahydronaphthalene
(to 50.6 Wt. % B)(121)
$d^{25}_4 = (0.7869 + 0.00157 \times$ Wt. % B) ±0.075%

219. B = $C_{10}H_{14}N_2$
Nicotine (93)[1]
(0–100 Wt. % B)(343)
$d^{20}_4 = (0.7938 + 0.002162 \times$ Wt. % B) ±0.05%

CH_4O.—(*Continued*)

220. B = $C_{10}H_{14}O$
Thymol (354)

221. B = $C_{10}H_{15}BrO$
Bromocamphor (148)[1]

222. B = $C_{10}H_{16}O$
Camphor (148,[1] 170, 175, 323, 342, 354)
(±0.1%)(100)

Wt. % B	d_4^{20}
0.00	0.7912
12.34	0.8102
24.14	0.8286
35.46	0.8472
46.26	0.8649
56.66	0.8827

223. B = $C_{10}H_{18}O$
l-Borneol (53, 1481)

224. B = $C_{10}H_{22}O_3$
Terpine hydrate (148)[1]

225. B = $C_{12}H_{10}$
Acenaphthene (299)[1]

226. B = $C_{12}H_{28}IN$
Tetrapropylammonium iodide (330)[1]

227. B = $C_{18}H_{34}O_2$
Oleic acid (57)

v. also 4, 81, 90, 150, 164, 179, 1265

CH_5N

Methylamine

228. B = $C_6H_5N_3O_4$
2, 4-Dinitroaniline
(±0.25%)(83)

Wt. % B	d_4^{0}
15.67	0.776
12.24	0.763
8.82	0.737
6.09	0.719
4.16	0.709
2.25	0.701
1.52	0.691
0.81	0.689
0.55	0.687
0.20	0.686
0.07	0.685

229. B = $C_7H_9NO_3S$
m-Methoxybenzenesulfonamide
(±0.25%)(83)

Wt. % B	d_4^{0}
52.83	1.103
33.98	0.917
24.82	0.845
23.73	0.829
13.73	0.767
9.61	0.738
7.18	0.728
3.94	0.709
2.68	0.700
1.36	0.694
0.73	0.693
0.49	0.691

v. also 180

CH_5NO_2

Ammonium formate
v. 151, 164.5

C_2Cl_4

Tetrachloroethylene

230. B = C_8H_8O
Acetophenone
(±0.1%)(270)

Mol % B	d_4^{25}
0.00	1.612
12.55	1.528
32.15	1.407
53.97	1.275
73.29	1.168
91.42	1.071
100.00	1.025

v. also 5

C_2HCl_3

Trichloroethylene

231. B = C_2HCl_5
Pentachloroethane
(±0.075%)(113, 120)

Wt. % B	d_4^{25}
100.0	1.6712
82.1	1.6242
69.6	1.5967
53.5	1.5631
36.5	1.5290
22.3	1.5031
0.0	1.4540

C_2HCl_3O

Chloral

232. B = C_2H_6O
Ethyl alcohol
(±0.05%)(162)

Wt. % B	d_4^{40}
100.00	0.7732
73.76	0.9234
63.84	0.9862
55.54	1.0225
48.37	1.1165
42.15	1.1754
31.90	1.2826
29.71	1.3083
27.63	1.3303
25.66	1.3525
24.53	1.3632
23.80	1.3703
20.35	1.3927
17.24	1.4093
11.80	1.4364
9.52	1.4490
7.24	1.4633
3.36	1.4868
0.00	1.4911
Wt. % B	**d_4^{45}**
100.00	0.7690
73.76	0.9135
63.84	0.9803
55.54	1.0471
48.37	1.1117
42.15	1.1693
31.90	1.2760
29.71	1.3000
27.63	1.3221
25.66	1.3441
24.53	1.3556
23.80	1.3620
20.35	1.3857
17.24	1.4026
11.80	1.4288
9.52	1.4421
7.24	1.4550
3.36	1.4783
0.00	1.4812
Wt. % B	**d_4^{50}**
100.00	0.7644
73.76	0.9086
63.84	0.9725
55.54	1.0417
48.37	1.1025
42.15	1.1632
31.90	1.2696
29.71	1.2908
27.63	1.3140
25.66	1.3334
24.53	1.3460
23.80	1.3537
20.35	1.3771
17.24	1.3915
11.80	1.4212
9.52	1.4348
7.24	1.4468
3.36	1.4682
0.00	1.4724
Wt. % B	**d_4^{60}**
100.00	0.7552
73.76	0.8989
63.84	0.9628
55.54	1.0310
48.37	1.0970
42.15	1.1515
31.90	1.2561
29.71	1.2787
27.63	1.3018
25.66	1.3205
24.53	1.3321
23.80	1.3380
20.35	1.3606
17.24	1.3782
11.80	1.4063
9.52	1.4196
7.24	1.4303
3.36	1.4511
0.00	1.4540
Wt. % B	**d_4^{70}**
100.00	0.7462
73.76	0.8901
63.84	0.9530
55.54	1.0200
48.37	1.0811
42.15	1.1396
31.90	1.2421
29.71	1.2667
27.63	1.2853
25.66	1.3049
24.53	1.3150
23.80	1.3214
20.35	1.3418
17.24	1.3586
11.80	1.3902
9.52	1.4032
7.24	1.4135
3.36	1.4346
0.00	1.4356
Wt. % B	**d_4^{85}**
73.76	0.8769
63.84	0.9426
55.54	1.0035
48.37	1.0661
42.15	1.1216
31.90	1.2221
29.71	1.2434
27.63	1.2606
25.66	1.2803
24.53	1.2904
23.80	1.2965
20.35	1.3225
17.24	1.3403
11.80	1.3692
9.52	1.3822
7.24	1.3888
0.00	1.4068

233. B = $C_5H_{12}O$
Dimethylethyl carbinol
(±0.05%)(75)

Wt. % A	d_4^{25}
0.00	0.8068
15.69	0.8879
29.51	0.9660
41.80	1.0506
52.76	1.1386
55.28	1.1676
57.81	1.1789
60.22	1.2000
62.62	1.2189
67.18	1.2572
71.51	1.2911
79.61	1.3569
83.31	1.3904
87.01	1.4225
93.77	1.4757
100.00	1.5043
Wt. % A	**d_4^{40}**
0.00	0.7922
15.69	0.8719
29.51	0.9500
41.80	1.0352
52.76	1.1204
55.28	1.1373
57.81	1.1587
60.22	1.1746
62.62	1.1984
67.18	1.2349
71.51	1.2686
79.61	1.3359
83.31	1.3671
87.01	1.3997
93.77	1.4557
100.00	1.4911

Wt. % A	d_4^{50}
0.00	0.7823
15.69	0.8614
29.51	0.9390
41.80	1.0204
52.76	1.1018
55.28	1.1208
57.81	1.1421
60.22	1.1550
62.62	1.1822
67.18	1.2160
71.51	1.2506
79.61	1.3171
83.31	1.3471
87.01	1.3834
93.77	1.4362
100.00	1.4724

Wt. % A	d_4^{70}
0.00	0.7607
15.69	0.8377
29.51	0.9135
41.80	0.9931
52.76	1.0729
55.28	1.0907
57.81	1.1081
60.22	1.1262
62.62	1.1434
67.18	1.1794
71.51	1.2076
79.61	1.2783
83.31	1.3093
87.01	1.3427
93.77	1.4003
100.00	1.4356

Wt. % A	d_4^{85}
0.00	0.7445
15.69	0.8154
29.51	0.8939
41.80	0.9689
52.76	1.0449
55.28	1.0625
57.81	1.0793
60.22	1.0974
62.62	1.1138
67.18	1.1502
71.51	1.1786
87.01	1.3133
93.77	1.3748
100.00	1.4068

$C_2HCl_3O_2$

Trichloroacetic acid

234. B = $C_2H_4O_2$

Acetic acid

(±0.1%)(151)

Mol % B	d_4^{25}
100.00	1.050
92.63	1.129
82.23	1.223
67.91	1.337
56.52	1.409
47.38	1.457
41.47	1.491
34.19	1.508

235. B = C_3H_6O

Acetone

(±0.1%)(151)

Mol % B	d_4^{25}
100.00	0.787
95.16	0.854
86.84	0.934
74.57	1.073
61.74	1.209
49.52	1.319
40.29	1.400
28.25	1.483

236. B = $C_4H_8O_2$

Ethyl acetate

(±0.1%)(151)

Wt. % B	d_4^{25}
100.00	0.895
88.82	0.997
81.50	1.045
71.93	1.123
61.54	1.202
51.22	1.295
38.58	1.386
29.92	1.454

237. B = $C_4H_{10}O$

Ethyl ether

(±0.25%)(316)

Wt. % B	d_4^{18}
100.00	0.717
82.37	0.812
68.82	0.899
57.24	0.893 *sic*
37.37	1.159
25.40	1.314

238. B = C_8H_8O

Acetophenone

(±0.1%)(151)

Mol % B	d_4^{25}
100.00	1.026
91.04	1.076
86.00	1.103
78.79	1.146
70.61	1.192
59.10	1.268
51.24	1.317
42.06	1.376
31.85	1.442

239. B = $C_9H_{10}O_2$

Ethyl benzoate

(±0.05%)(151)

Mol % B	d_4^{25}
100.00	1.0458
91.13	1.0864
79.04	1.1466
68.75	1.1915
60.18	1.2413
50.93	1.2922
42.05	1.3501
33.42	1.4027

C_2HCl_5

Pentachloroethane

240. B = C_3H_6O

Acetone

(±0.1%)(270)

Mol % B	d_4^{25}
0.00	1.672
14.76	1.594
31.78	1.487
51.03	1.340
70.37	1.157
90.68	0.918
100.00	0.787

241. B = $C_4H_{10}O$

Ethyl ether

(±0.1%)(270)

Mol % B	d_4^{0}
100.00	0.736
85.76	0.906
74.73	1.031
49.68	1.293
30.47	1.467
13.03	1.609
0.00	1.708

242. B = C_8H_8O

Acetophenone

(0–100 Mol % A)(270)

d_4^{25} = (1.0251 + 0.006471 × Mol % A) ±0.1%

243. B = $C_8H_{10}O$

Phenetole

(±0.1%)(270)

Mol % A	d_4^{25}
100.00	1.672
90.29	1.603
77.86	1.508
51.05	1.317
32.02	1.176
9.70	1.027
0.00	0.961

244. B = $C_{12}H_{10}O$

Diphenyl ether

(±0.1%)(270)

Mol % B	d_4^{25}
0.00	1.672
26.42	1.481
51.09	1.330
76.11	1.189
100.00	1.072

v. also 231

$C_2H_2Br_2$

Dibromoethylene

245. B = C_6H_6 (254)

246. B = C_8H_{10}

Xylene (254)

$C_2H_2Br_4$

Acetylene tetrabromide

247. B = $C_2H_2Cl_4$

Acetylene tetrachloride (324)

248. B = $C_2H_3Br_3$

Vinyl tribromide

(±0.1%)(5)

Wt. % A	$d_4^{17.5}$
100.00	2.971
73.08	2.869
72.52	2.866
45.57	2.769
0.00	2.619

Wt. % A	$d_4^{21.5}$
100.00	2.963
73.08	2.860
72.52	2.860
45.57	2.762
0.00	2.611

249. B = $C_8H_{14}O_6$

Ethyl tartrate (228)

a	10^3b
(20.87°–31.5°)	
0.00 Wt. % B	
2.9595	2.240(t − 20.87)
(19.99°–45.91°)	
5.67 Wt. % B	
2.7260	2.100(t − 19.99)
(19.82°–30.2°)	
9.96 Wt. % B	
2.5740	2.003(t − 19.82)
(17.76°–25.98°)	
20.11 Wt. % B	
2.2804	1.839(t − 17.76)

$C_2H_2Cl_2O_2$

Dichloroacetic acid

250. B = C_6H_6 (135)[1]

251. B = C_7H_8

Toluene (±0.05%)(135)

Wt. % B	d_4^{16}
100.00	0.8694
92.41	0.8980
75.30	0.9761
0.00	1.5488

$C_2H_2Cl_4$

Tetrachloroethane

252. B = C_3H_6O

Acetone (±0.1%)(270)

Mol % B	d_4^{0}
0.00	1.614
15.92	1.534
58.07	1.238
73.08	1.106
81.36	1.023
97.28	0.849
100.00	0.812

253. B = $C_4H_8O_3$

Methyl *l*-lactate

(±0.05%)(211)

a	10^3b
(−75° to +125°)	
100.00 Wt. % B	
1.2040	1.158(t + 75)
(−7.8° to +120°)	
9.94 Wt. % B	
2.5806	2.084(t + 7.8)

254. B = $C_4H_{10}O$

Ethyl ether (±0.1%)(270)

Mol % B	d_4^{0}
100.00	0.736
94.01	0.794
82.68	0.907
69.81	1.030
47.99	1.231
21.15	1.459
0.00	1.614

$C_2H_2Cl_4$.—(*Continued*)

255. B = $C_5H_{10}O_3$
Methyl *l*-α-methoxypropionate (211)
(10.06 Wt. % B)(±0.05%)

t	d_4^t
16.7	2.4842
39.8	2.4373
52.5	2.4118
77.0	2.3613
101.0	2.3124
119.0	2.2744

(−16.6° to +130.0°)
100.0 Wt. % B
$d_4^t = 1.0361 - 0.001143(t + 16.6)$

256. B = $C_6H_5NO_2$
Nitrobenzene
(±0.075%)(68, 150)

Wt. % B	d_4^5
0.00	1.6095
10.00	1.5567
30.05	1.4672
48.33	1.3915
69.26	1.3136
89.64	1.2475
100.00	1.2168
Wt. % B	$d_4^{76.5}$
0.00	1.4991
10.00	1.4537
30.05	1.3746
48.33	1.3053
69.26	1.2369
100.00	1.1476

257. B = $C_6H_{10}O_4$
Methyl *l*-α-acetoxypropionate (211)
(10.04 Wt. % B)(±0.05%)

t	d_4^t
17.6	2.5244
39.8	2.4799
54.7	2.4502
76.4	2.4061
91.3	2.3755
119.0	2.3204
139.3	2.2689

(−7.4° to +141.0°)
100.0 Wt. % B
$d_4^t = 1.1198 - 0.001144\ (t + 7.4)$

258. B = C_8H_8O
Acetophenone
(±0.075%)(68, 150)

Wt. % B	d_4^{10}
0.00	1.5995
10.19	1.5176
30.07	1.3751
50.00	1.2590
70.01	1.1595
90.00	1.0757
100.00	1.0358
Wt. % B	d_4^{80}
0.00	1.4932
10.02	1.4160
31.20	1.2867
69.93	1.0892
89.74	1.0122
100.00	0.9758

259. B = $C_8H_{10}O$
Phenetole
(±0.1%)(270)

Wt. % B	d_4^0
0.00	1.614
21.76	1.465
51.67	1.266
62.80	1.194
78.37	1.101
100.00	0.984

260. B = $C_8H_{14}O_6$
Ethyl tartrate
(±0.05%)(228)

a	10^3b
(18.2°–29.27°) 0.00 Wt. % B	
1.6023	1.555(t − 18.2)
(18.79°–27.44°) 4.96 Wt. % B	
1.5744	1.514(t − 18.79)
(21.68°–71.2°) 9.31 Wt. % B	
1.5478	1.488(t − 21.68)
(17.76°–28.27°) 38.06 Wt. % B	
1.4226	1.293(t − 17.76)

261. B = $C_{10}H_8$
Naphthalene (48, 49)
(to 35.02 Wt. % B)

$$\frac{1}{d_4^{30}} = (0.63269 + 0.003495 \times \text{Wt. \% B}) \pm 0.005\%$$

262. B = $C_{12}H_{22}O_6$
Isobutyl tartrate
(±0.05%)(209)

a	10^3b
(0°–99.7°) 33.362 Wt. % B	
1.4030	1.26t
(24.8°–99.65°) 48.150 Wt. % B	
1.2923	1.153(t − 24.8)

263. B = $C_{16}H_{26}O_8$
Isobutyl diacetyl-*d*-tartrate
(±0.05%)(209)

a	10^3b
(16.03°–99.75°) 20.034 Wt. % B	
1.4664	1.375(t − 16.03)
(−21° to +99.3°) 100.00 Wt. % B	
1.1220	0.936(t + 21)

v. also 6, 247

$C_2H_3Br_3$

Vinyl tribromide, *v.* 248

$C_2H_3ClO_2$

Chloroacetic acid

264. B = C_6H_6 (135)[1]
(±0.005%)(319)

Wt. % B	$d_4^{12.87}$
100.000	0.88638
96.035	0.89915
91.596	0.91404
89.139	0.92255

265. B = C_7H_8 (135)[1]
(±0.005%)(319)

Wt. % B	$d_4^{12.87}$
100.000	0.87233
97.452	0.88082
91.868	0.90010
89.002	0.91032

$C_2H_3Cl_3O_2$

Chloral hydrate

266. B = C_2H_6O
Ethyl alcohol (299)[1]
(±0.025%)(265)

Wt. % B	$d_4^{20.2}$
100.000	0.7910
99.500	0.7933
95.004	0.8119
90.008	0.8444
80.014	0.8946
60.021	1.0208
40.021	1.1845
20.014	1.4014
Wt. % B	d_4^{44}
100.000	0.7700
99.500	0.7724
95.004	0.7931
90.008	0.8227
80.014	0.8722
60.021	1.0023
40.021	1.1576
20.014	1.3705

267. B = C_7H_8 (299)[1]
(±0.025%)(265)

Wt. % B	$d_4^{20.2}$
100.00	0.86511
99.80	0.86584
98.00	0.87245
95.00	0.88413
90.00	0.90384
80.01	0.95073
60.02	1.07037
Wt. % B	d_4^{44}
100.00	0.84288
99.80	0.84351
98.00	0.84950
95.00	0.86069
90.00	0.87932
80.01	0.92480
60.02	1.04270
40.02	1.18594

v. also 91

C_2H_3N

Acetonitrile

268. B = C_2H_6O
Ethyl alcohol
(0–100 Wt. % B)(322)
$d_4^0 = (0.805 + 0.0_47 \times \text{Wt. \% A}) \pm 0.5\%$

269. B = C_3H_5NO
Lactonitrile
(±0.05%)(329)

Wt. % A	d_4^0
100.00	0.8173
78.80	0.8626
55.23	0.9095
27.23	0.9589
0.00	1.0062
Wt. % A	d_4^{25}
100.00	0.7896
78.80	0.8374
55.23	0.8865
27.23	0.9356
0.00	0.9845

270. B = $C_8H_{20}IN$
Tetraethylammonium iodide
(330,[1] 331[1])

271. B = $C_{12}H_{28}IN$
Tetrapropylammonium iodide
(330[1], 331[1])

v. also 186

C_2H_3NS

Methyl thiocyanate

272. B = $C_8H_{20}IN$
Tetraethylammonium iodide
(330)[1]

$C_2H_4Br_2$

Ethylene bromide

274. B = $C_2H_4Cl_2$
Ethylene chloride
(±0.025%)(23)

Wt. % A	d_4^{20}
100.000	2.1804
68.603	1.9064
42.726	1.6696
19.322	1.4455
0.000	1.2551

275. B = $C_2H_4O_2$
Acetic acid (14)
(±0.05%)(92)

Mol % B	d_4^{15}
0.00	2.1851
26.51	1.9559
36.23	1.8625
54.17	1.6736
63.21	1.5689
83.45	1.3065
100.00	1.0558

276. B = C_3H_8O
Propyl alcohol
(±0.01%) (286, 290)

Wt. % A	$d_4^{18.07}$
0.000	0.80659
10.008	0.86081
20.952	0.92908
29.835	0.99300
40.732	1.08453
49.948	1.17623
60.094	1.29695
70.012	1.44175
80.089	1.62640
90.191	1.86652
100.000	2.18300

277. B = $C_4H_5Cl_3O_2$
Ethyl trichloroacetate (158)

278. B = $C_4H_7ClO_2$
Ethyl chloroacetate (158)

279. B = $C_4H_{10}O$
Ethyl ether (61)

280. B = C_5H_{10}
Amylene (61)

281. B = $C_6H_4Br_2$
p-Dibromobenzene (158)

282. B = C_6H_5Cl (122)[1]

283. B = $C_6H_5NO_2$
Nitrobenzene
(±0.05%)(220)

Wt. % A	d_4^{20}
100.00	2.1800
54.54	1.5873
38.27	1.4466
0.00	1.2033

284. B = C_6H_6 (31,[1] 61, 158)
(±0.0075%)(171)

Wt. % B	d_4^{25}
0.000	2.16855
39.359	1.65077
66.066	1.30527
100.000	0.87793

285. B = $C_6H_{10}O_3$
Ethyl acetoacetate (158)

286. B = C_6H_{12}
Cyclohexane
(±0.25%)(15)

Mol % A	d_4^{15}
0	0.786
10	0.897
20	1.033
30	1.137
40	1.265
50	1.403
60	1.544
70	1.691
80	1.847
90	2.015
100	2.187

287. B = C_7H_8
(±0.025%)(285)

Wt. % A	d_4^{25}
0	0.8627
10	0.9196
20	0.9819
30	1.0518
40	1.1381
50	1.2323
60	1.3527
70	1.4922
80	1.6653
90	1.8822
100	2.1758

288. B = $C_7H_{14}O_2$
Isoamyl acetate (158)

289. B = C_7H_{16}
Heptane (61)

290. B = $C_8H_8O_2$
Methyl benzoate (158)

291. B = $C_8H_{14}O_6$
Ethyl tartrate (220)[1]
(±0.075%)(221, 228)

a	10^3b
(18.1°–30.55°)	
100.00 Wt. % A	
2.1842	$2.097(t - 18.1)$
(18.02°–27.82°)	
94.41 Wt. % A	
2.0828	$1.990(t - 18.02)$
(16°–60°)	
90.16 Wt. % A	
2.0416	$1.803(t - 16)$

292. B = $C_{10}H_8$
Naphthalene (158)
(±0.0075%)(54)

Wt. % A	d_4^{18}
100.000	2.18376
99.328	2.16715
98.662	2.15094

293. B = $C_{12}H_{10}N_2$
Azobenzene (158)

294. B = $C_{12}H_{18}O_8$
Diethyl diacetyltartrate (273)
(67.3° – 99.0°)(±0.25%)

a	10^3b
100.00 Mol % A	
2.080	$2.492(t - 67.3)$
94.37 Mol % A	
1.932	$1.956(t - 67.3)$
84.84 Mol % A	
1.739	$1.736(t - 67.3)$
57.01 Mol % A	
1.408	$1.357(t - 67.3)$
32.10 Mol % A	
1.244	$1.167(t - 67.3)$
11.35 Mol % A	
1.150	$1.042(t - 67.3)$
0.00 Mol % A	
1.109	$0.915(t - 67.3)$

295. B = $C_{14}H_{10}$
Phenanthrene (158)

296. B = $C_{18}H_{16}O_6$
act. Methyl dibenzoylglycerate (90)

297. B = $C_{20}H_{38}O_2$
Ethyl oleate (158)

298. B = $C_{26}H_{30}O_8$
Isobutyl dibenzoyl-*d*-tartrate (221)
(47°–100°)(±0.05%)
9.2 Wt. % B

a	10^3b
1.9584	$1.932(t - 47)$

v. also 7, 35, 92, 1266, 1273

$C_2H_4Cl_2$

Ethylidene chloride

300. B = $C_8H_{14}O_6$
Ethyl tartrate
(±0.05%)(228)

a	10^3b
(17.6°–29.25°)	
0.00 Wt. % B	
1.1790	$1.561(t - 17.6)$
(19.91°–27.87°)	
4.65 Wt. % B	
1.1764	$1.508(t - 19.91)$
(19.27°–28.97°)	
10.70 Wt. % B	
1.1790	$1.494(t - 19.27)$
(19.9°–27.71°)	
34.24 Wt. % B	
1.1853	$1.345(t - 19.9)$

$C_2H_4Cl_2$

Ethylene chloride

301. B = $C_2H_4O_2$
Acetic acid (92)[1]

302. B = $C_4H_{10}O$
Ethyl ether
$d_4^t =$
(±0.0075%)(101)

100.00 Wt. % B
$1.35729(1 + 0.0015006t + 0.0_5437t^2)$
85.041 Wt. % B
$1.26661(1 + 0.0014410t + 0.0_5399t^2)$
69.305 Wt. % B
$1.17291(1 + 0.0014007t + 0.0_5315t^2)$
50.125 Wt. % B
$1.06124(1 + 0.0013266t + 0.0_5280t^2)$
29.907 Wt. % B
$0.94649(1 + 0.0012439t + 0.0_5224t^2)$
14.798 Wt. % B
$0.86228(1 + 0.0011702t + 0.0_5212t^2)$
0.000 Wt. % B
$0.78046(1 + 0.0011109t + 0.0_5170t^2)$

303. B = C_6H_6 (35, 99, 351)
(±0.25%)(79)

Mol % B	d_4^0
0	1.270
30	1.159
60	1.047
100	0.884

Mol % B	d_4^{19}
0	1.252
30	1.130
60	1.020
100	0.870

(±0.025%)(31, 171)

Mol % B	d_4^{20}
100.000	0.8779
79.515	0.9452
59.890	1.0132
39.517	1.0881
20.470	1.1623
0.000	1.2472

(±0.025%)(23)

Wt. % B	d_4^{20}
0.000	1.2548
4.313	1.2360
16.154	1.1857
23.185	1.1570
38.945	1.0946
47.539	1.0618
56.776	1.0275
67.592	0.9884
78.397	0.9507
88.994	0.9149
94.882	0.8953
100.000	0.8787

(±0.25%)(79)

Mol % B	d_4^{50}
0	1.215
30	1.092
60	0.977
100	0.845

304. B = C_8H_8O
Acetophenone
(±0.1%)(270)

Mol % B	d_4^{25}
100.00	1.025
88.82	1.042
64.19	1.081
30.58	1.158
0.00	1.248

305. B = $C_8H_{14}O_6$
Ethyl tartrate
(±0.05%)(228)

a	10^3b
(18.5°–27.15°)	
0.00 Wt. % B	
1.2553	$1.468(t - 18.5)$
(18.66°–24.05°)	
5.87 Wt. % B	
1.2502	$1.428(t - 18.66)$
(18.76°–31.72°)	
11.73 Wt. % B	
1.2461	$1.398(t - 18.76)$
(18.15°–30.65°)	
22.04 Wt. % B	
1.2406	$1.344(t - 18.15)$
(18.15°–27.12°)	
49.72 Wt. % B	
1.2262	$1.216(t - 18.15)$

v. also 36, 274

C_2H_4O

Acetaldehyde

306. B = C_2H_6O
Ethyl alcohol
(±0.025%)(55)

Mol % B	d_4^0
0.0	0.8050
22.6	0.8704
33.3	0.8947
40.8	0.9080
49.7	0.9061
51.1	0.9044
58.0	0.8944
68.9	0.8751
84.3	0.8413
100.0	0.8063

C_2H_4O.—*(Continued)*

$B = C_2H_6O$.—*(Continued)*

(±0.025%)(55)

Mol % B	d_4^{18}
0.00	0.7834
15.72	0.8277
24.92	0.8474
33.14	0.8601
46.14	0.8715
49.68	0.8719
55.44	0.8709
63.50	0.8627
70.30	0.8501
81.52	0.8296
86.98	0.8200
100.00	0.7907

(±0.0025%)(201)

Wt. % B	d_4^{25}
100.000	0.785101
99.977	0.785144
99.860	0.785394
99.534	0.786030

307. $B = C_6H_6$ (278)
(0–100 Wt. % B)
$d_4^{15} = (0.797 + 0.0_387 \times \text{Wt. \% B}) \pm 0.25\%$

$C_2H_4O_2$

Acetic acid

308. $B = C_2H_5Br$
Ethyl bromide
(±0.05%)(92)

Mol % A	d_4^{15}
0.00	1.4564
31.31	1.3420
50.27	1.2685
63.41	1.2154
70.26	1.1872
83.10	1.1320
100.00	1.0558

309. $B = C_2H_5NO_3$
Ethyl nitrate (92)[1]

310. $B = C_2H_6O$
Ethyl alcohol
(±0.1%)(108)

Wt. % A	d_4^{18}
100.00	1.057
75.70	0.978
47.06	0.903
25.00	0.851
6.29	0.807
0.00	0.793

(±0.05%)(263)

Wt. % A	d_4^{20}
100.000	1.0476
84.805	1.0036
69.884	0.9614
49.923	0.9078
30.568	0.8593
15.142	0.8236

311. $B = C_3H_6Br_2$
n-Propylene bromide
(±0.05%)(92)

Mol % A	d_4^{15}
0.000	1.9612
47.396	1.6472
70.310	1.4349
88.255	1.2235
100.000	1.0558

312. $B = C_3H_6O$
Acetone (79)
(±0.05%)(151)

Mol % A	d_4^{25}
0.00	0.7874
9.96	0.8091
20.35	0.8353
30.25	0.8569
40.49	0.8848
49.86	0.9065
59.73	0.9334
69.68	0.9609
80.15	0.9907
90.37	1.0255
100.00	1.0499

(±0.025%)(178)
50 Wt. % A

t	d_4^t
0	0.93639
25	0.90840
40	0.89192
55	0.87518
70	0.85784

313. $B = C_3H_6O_2$
Propionic acid
(±0.1%)(327)

Wt. % A	d_4^{30}
0.00	0.983
23.04	0.995
49.41	1.012
64.62	1.020
78.78	1.026
100.00	1.046

314. $B = C_4H_6O_3$
Acetic anhydride
(±0.075%)(68, 150)

Wt. % A	d_4^{15}
0.00	1.0850
10.05	1.0816
30.05	1.0753
50.03	1.0689
69.93	1.0631
90.03	1.0570
100.00	1.0550

Wt. % A	$d_4^{76.5}$
0.00	1.0096
10.05	1.0058
30.05	1.0021
50.03	0.9961
69.93	0.9914
90.03	0.9860
100.00	0.9853

315. $B = C_4H_8O_2$
Butyric acid (168, 169)
(±0.075%)(32, 289)

Wt. % A	d_4^{20}
0.00	0.9723
24.11	0.9884
46.76	1.0056
73.97	1.0288
100.00	1.0524

316. $B = C_4H_8O_2$
Ethyl acetate
(±0.05%)(151)

Mol % A	d_4^{25}
0.00	0.8949
10.49	0.9093
20.70	0.9212
30.37	0.9309
39.90	0.9418
49.85	0.9557
59.96	0.9697
69.88	0.9850
80.11	1.0015
87.42	1.0165
100.00	1.0499

317. $B = C_4H_{10}O$
Ethyl ether (14)
(±0.25%)(316)

Wt. % A	d_4^{18}
0.00	0.717
27.09	0.796
49.36	0.867
59.63	0.902
69.04	0.935
84.85	0.995
88.45	1.011
100.00	1.055

318. $B = C_5H_5N$
Pyridine (266)
(±0.25%)(79)
(18.4°–99.0°)

a	10^3b
0.0 Mol % A	
0.988	1.005 $(t - 18.4)$
50.0 Mol % A	
1.037	0.966 $(t - 18.4)$
80.0 Mol % A	
1.079	1.005 $(t - 18.4)$
82.5 Mol % A	
1.082	1.012 $(t - 18.4)$
85.0 Mol % A	
1.083	1.073 $(t - 18.4)$
100.0 Mol % A	
1.056	1.142 $(t - 18.4)$

(±0.25%)(312)

Mol % A	d_4^{20}
0.00	0.976
26.20	1.000
42.10	1.018
51.90	1.032
59.90	1.046
61.70	1.050
77.95	1.076
89.60	1.081
100.00	1.051

319. $B = C_6H_5Br$ (92)[1]

320. $B = C_6H_5Cl$ (92)[1]

321. $B = C_6H_5NO_2$ (14)

322. $B = C_6H_6$ (14, 32, 91, 92, 99, 124, 133, 135, 233)
(±0.005%)(319)

Wt. % A	$d_4^{12.87}$
0.000	0.88638
4.049	0.89071
8.016	0.89522
19.394	0.90904
23.399	0.91434

(±0.1%) (361)

Wt. % B	d_4^{20}
0.000	1.0532
0.230	1.0512
0.523	1.0504
0.940	1.0496
2.620	1.0452
4.738	1.0409
13.360	1.0250

(±0.005%)(134)

Wt. % A	d_4^{25}
0.000	0.87368
11.634	0.88678
23.614	0.90153
34.008	0.91580
44.857	0.93198
54.459	0.94743
63.968	0.96439
73.819	0.98341
82.321	1.00142
91.338	1.02218
100.000	1.04390

Wt. % A	d_4^{50}
0.000	0.84680
11.634	0.85939
23.614	0.87387
34.008	0.88784
44.857	0.90385
54.459	0.91935
63.968	0.93614
73.819	0.95517
82.321	0.97299
91.338	0.99377
100.000	1.01561

323. $B = C_6H_7N$
Aniline (79, 266, 307)
(±0.005%)(319)

Wt. % A	$d_4^{12.87}$
100.000	1.02780
96.140	1.03118
94.234	1.03280
89.853	1.03733
87.447	1.03985

(±0.1%)(250)

Wt. % A	d_4^{21}
100	1.053
90	1.076
80	1.089
70	1.092
60	1.086
50	1.075
40	1.064
30	1.052
20	1.041
10	1.029
0	1.018

(±0.025%)(178)
56 Wt. % A

a	10^3b
1.0822	1.087(t − 25)

323.5. B = $C_6H_{12}O_3$
Paraldehyde
(±0.1%) (361)

Wt. % B	d_4^{15}
0.000	1.0466
0.327	1.0465
1.634	1.0460
4.572	1.0445
8.185	1.0416
23.120	1.0315
41.800	1.0190
70.315	1.0064
88.525	0.9981
94.000	0.9958
97.690	0.9915
98.705	0.9910
99.422	0.9905
100.000	0.9905
Wt. % B	d_4^{20}
0.000	1.0478
0.525	1.0476
0.895	1.0475
2.623	1.0473
4.482	1.0464
8.195	1.0416
13.200	1.0400
22.620	1.0355
41.600	1.0245
70.405	1.0100
88.570	1.0012
94.015	0.9978
97.701	0.9958
98.797	0.9953
99.425	0.9950
100.000	0.9948

324. B = C_6H_{14}
Hexane (14)

325. B = C_7H_8 (14)
(±0.005%)(319)

Wt. % A	$d_4^{12.87}$
0.000	0.87233
3.017	0.87617
7.018	0.88140
12.121	0.88820
14.429	0.89141

(±0.05%)(92)

Mol % A	d_4^{15}
0.000	0.8688
18.010	0.8854
28.879	0.8973
40.897	0.9127
43.583	0.9164
49.541	0.9255
58.264	0.9402
67.269	0.9578
82.039	0.9939
91.555	1.0234
100.000	1.0558

(±0.05%)(135)

Wt. % A	d_4^{16}
9.606	0.8813
27.446	0.9072
38.492	0.9248

326. B = C_8H_8O
Acetophenone
(±0.05%)(151)

Mol % A	d_4^{25}
0.00	1.0263
9.98	1.0272
21.07	1.0287
29.35	1.0300
42.53	1.0325
48.85	1.0338
60.03	1.0365
69.98	1.0390
80.02	1.0420
90.13	1.0453
100.00	1.0499

327. B = C_8H_{10}
Xylene, (±0.05%)(92)

Mol % A	d_4^{15}
0.000	0.8675
23.567	0.8874
32.443	0.8969
43.491	0.9106
49.624	0.9192
59.612	0.9357
70.037	0.9568
83.632	0.9924
100.000	1.0558

328. B = $C_9H_{10}O_2$
Ethyl benzoate (151)
(0–100 Mol % A)
d_4^{25} = (1.046 + 0.0₄4 × Mol % A) ±0.1%

329. B = $C_9H_{14}O_6$
Ethyl diacetylglycerate (active) (90)

330. B = $C_{10}H_{13}NO_2$
Phenacetine (292)[2]

331. B = $C_{10}H_{14}N_2$
Nicotine (93)[1]

332. B = $C_{10}H_{16}O$
Camphor (175, 323, 342)
(±0.05%)(100, 170, 343)

Wt. % A	d_4^{20}
100	1.0502
90	1.0340
80	1.0300
70	1.0204
60	1.0111
50	1.0021
40	0.9939
30	0.9862

333. B = $C_{12}H_{10}N_2$
Azobenzene (318)[1]

334. B = $C_{13}H_{10}O_3$
Salol (292)[2]

335. B = $C_{15}H_{18}O_7$
Diethyl monobenzoyltartrate (89)

336. B = $C_{16}H_{20}O_7$
Diethyl mono-*o*-toluyltartrate (89)

337. B = $C_{16}H_{20}O_7$
Diethyl mono-*m*-toluyltartrate (89)

338. B = $C_{16}H_{20}O_7$
Diethyl mono-*p*-toluyltartrate (89)

339. B = $C_{18}H_{16}O_6$
d-Methyl dibenzoylglycerate (90)

339.5. B = *l*-Turpentine
(0.05%)(170, 263, 342)

Wt. % A	d_4^{20}
100	1.0476
90	1.0120
80	0.9972
70	0.9748
60	0.9542
50	0.9351
40	0.9180
30	0.9027
20	0.8883
10	0.8756
0	0.8648

v. also 8, 37, 93, 152, 165, 187, 234, 275, 301, 1273.5, 1274

$C_2H_4O_2$

Methyl formate

340. B = $C_4H_5Cl_3O_2$
Ethyl trichloroacetate (158)

341. B = $C_4H_7ClO_2$
Ethyl chloroacetate (158)

342. B = $C_4H_8O_2$
Ethyl acetate (158)

343. B = $C_4H_{10}O$
Ethyl ether (158)

344. B = $C_6H_4Br_2$
p-Dibromobenzene (158)

345. B = C_6H_6 (142, 158)

346. B = $C_6H_{10}O_3$
Ethyl acetoacetate (158)

347. B = C_6H_{14}
Hexane (158)

348. B = $C_8H_8O_2$
Methyl benzoate (158)

349. B = $C_8H_{20}IN$
Tetraethylammonium iodide (331)[1]

350. B = $C_{10}H_8$
Naphthalene (158)

351. B = $C_{14}H_{10}$
Phenanthrene (158)

352. B = $C_{20}H_{38}O_2$
Ethyl oleate (158)

v. also 38

C_2H_5Br

Ethyl bromide

353. B = C_2H_5I (103)

354. B = C_5H_5N
Pyridine (14)

355. B = $C_6H_4Br_2$
p-Dibromobenzene (158)
(±0.005%)(318)

Wt. % B	d_4^{25}
0.000	1.43841
3.565	1.45332
3.854	1.45429

356. B = $C_8H_{14}O_6$
Dimethyl *d*-dimethoxysuccinate
(±0.075%)(222)

a	10^3b
(65.3°–153°)	
100.00 Wt. % B	
1.1250	1.052(t−65.3)
(15.8°–88.5°)	
9.02 Wt. % B	
2.0242	1.929(t−15.8)

357. B = $C_8H_{14}O_6$
Ethyl tartrate
(±0.05%)(228)

a	10^3b
(18.32°–22.5°)	
0.00 Wt. % B	
1.4631	2.033 (t−18.32)
(18.47°–21.6°)	
2.02 Wt. % B	
1.4558	2.959 (t−18.47)
(18.7°–20.93°)	
4.98 Wt. % B	
1.4460	1.974 (t −18.7)
(18.95°–27.20°)	
10.92 Wt. % B	
1.4278	1.928 (t−18.95)
(18.85°–20.10°)	
30.58 Wt. % B	
1.3720	1.681(t−18.85)
(19.57°–21.20°)	
65.28 Wt. % B	
1.2828	1.228(t−19.57)

(±0.05%)(343)

Wt. % B	d_4^{20}
69.600	1.3867
44.472	1.5899
22.494	1.8298
11.583	1.9814
5.532	2.0789
2.311	2.1362
1.197	2.1567
0.424	2.1713
0.000	2.1789

358. B = $C_{10}H_{14}N_2$
Nicotine
(±0.05%)(343)

Wt. % A	d_4^{20}
0.00	1.0100
41.88	1.3009
63.71	1.5310
82.58	1.8096
89.86	1.9467
100.00	2.1789

C_2H_5Br.—(*Continued*)

359. B = $C_{10}H_{16}O$
Camphor
(±0.05%)(343)

Wt. % B	d_4^{20}
0.00	2.1789
1.00	2.1513
1.86	2.1279
2.99	2.0983
3.87	2.0759
36.23	1.4929

360. B = $C_{10}H_{18}O_6$
Dipropyl tartrate
(±0.1%)(340)

a	10^3b
(20°–60°)	
0.00 Wt. % A	
1.1389	0.905 (t − 20)
(20°–70°)	
25.29 Wt. % A	
1.2916	1.116 (t − 20)
55.00 Wt. % A	
1.5293	1.324 (t − 20)
84.71 Wt. % A	
1.8868	1.698 (t − 20)

361. B = $C_{12}H_{28}IN$
Tetrapropylammonium iodide
(331)[1]

v. also 308

C_2H_5I

Ethyl iodide

362. B = $C_4H_8O_2$
Ethyl acetate (158, 1711)
(±0.025%)(23)

Wt. % B	d_4^{20}
100.000	0.9006
93.775	0.9525
87.072	1.0100
78.358	1.0868
70.902	1.1547
61.278	1.2454
52.337	1.3333
44.697	1.4114
30.202	1.5679
16.129	1.7316
0.000	1.9365

(±0.005%)(134, 290)

Wt. % B	d_4^{25}
100.000	0.89422
80.918	0.99263
64.993	1.09390
50.483	1.20707
40.259	1.30314
31.471	1.39950
25.434	1.47573
17.208	1.59373
10.907	1.69938
5.030	1.81215
0.000	1.92282

(±0.005%)(134, 290)

Wt. % B	d_4^{50}
100.000	0.86307
80.918	0.95824
64.993	1.05648
50.483	1.16636
40.259	1.25981
31.471	1.35355
25.434	1.42776
17.208	1.54288
10.907	1.64612
5.030	1.75664
0.000	1.86491

363. B = $C_4H_{10}O$
Ethyl ether (165)[1]

364. B = C_6H_6 (254)

365. B = C_8H_{10}
Xylene (254)

366. B = $C_8H_{10}O$
Phenetole
(±0.1%)(269)

Mol % A	d_4^0
100.00	1.9745
90.44	1.8026
66.02	1.5295
45.29	1.3207
26.15	1.1630
9.11	1.0366
0.00	0.9841

367. B = $C_8H_{14}O_6$
Ethyl tartrate
(±0.05%)(228)

a	10^3b
(19.25°–32.35°)	
0.00 Wt. % B	
1.9377	2.306 (t−19.25)
(18.58°–32.9°)	
5.17 Wt. % B	
1.8748	2.207(t−18.58)
(18.22°–26.01°)	
10.63 Wt. % B	
1.8143	2.080(t−18.22)
(18.07°–25.33°)	
32.77 Wt. % B	
1.6067	1.640(t−18.07)

368. B = $C_{10}H_8$
Naphthalene (54)[1]

v. also 39, 157, 187.5, 353, 1271, 1272

C_2H_5NO

Acetamide

369. B = C_2H_6O
Ethyl alcohol (299)[1]
(±0.01%)(33)

Wt. % B	d_4^{30}
100.000	0.78090
95.837	0.78972
93.429	0.79494
91.203	0.79985

370. B = C_5H_5N, Pyridine
(±0.05%)(70)

Wt. % B	d_4^{25}
100.00	0.9746
96.13	0.9794
94.35	0.9814
91.49	0.9826
83.73	0.9959

$C_2H_5NO_3$

Ethyl nitrate

371. B = C_7H_{16}
Heptane (236)[1]

372. B = $C_8H_{20}IN$
Tetraethylammonium iodide
(330)[1]

373. B = $C_{10}H_7Br$
α-Bromonaphthalene (236)[1]

374. B = $C_{12}H_{28}IN$
Tetrapropylammonium iodide
(330)[1]

v. also 40, 309

$C_2H_6N_2O$

Dimethylnitrosamine

375. B = $C_8H_{20}IN$
Tetraethylammonium iodide
(330)[1]

C_2H_6O

Ethyl alcohol

376. B = C_3H_6O
Acetone (33,[1] 139, 1441)
(±0.1%) (359)

Vol. % B	d_4^0
0	0.8082
25	0.8124
50	0.8139
75	0.8138
100	0.8132
Vol. % B	**d_4^{25}**
0	0.7872
25	0.7886
50	0.7879
75	0.7872
100	0.7856

(±0.1%) (361)

Wt. % B	d_4^{20}
0.000	0.7934
0.605	0.7932
0.929	0.7931
2.427	0.7928
4.655	0.7925
5.455	0.7924
12.130	0.7923
19.800	0.7921
23.290	0.7921

50 Wt. % A
(±0.025%)(178)

t	d_4^t
0	0.9363
25	0.9083
40	0.8918
55	0.8751
70	0.8577

377. B = $C_3H_6O_2$
Methyl acetate
(±0.025%)(to 55°)(178)
50 Wt. % A

a	10^3b
0.88174	1.052t

378. B = C_3H_7NO
Propionamide (180)
(±0.01%)(33)

Wt. % A	d_4^{30}
100.000	0.78078
96.897	0.78560
92.990	0.79628
89.705	0.82371

379. B = $C_3H_7NO_2$
Urethane (299)[1,2]
(±0.01%) (261.1)

Wt. % B	d_4^{20}
0	0.7892
1	0.7915
2	0.7928
3	0.7962
4	0.7986
5	0.8010
10	0.8130
20	0.8375
30	0.8628
40	0.8895
50	0.9177
60	0.9470

381. B = C_3H_8O
n-Propyl alcohol
(0–100 Wt. % A)(65)
d_4^{15} = (0.80753 − 0.0001386 × Wt. % A)
±0.025%
(±0.1%)(113, 118)

Wt. % A	d_4^{25}
100.0	0.7869
91.9	0.7888
82.1	0.7904
43.4	0.7928
11.4	0.7975
8.8	0.7981
4.8	0.7988
0.0	0.8006

382. B = $C_3H_8O_3$
Glycerol (200)[1]
(±0.005%)(319)

Wt. % A	$d_4^{12.87}$
100.000	0.79586
96.842	0.80659
95.393	0.81148
88.048	0.83723
73.275	0.89218

(±0.05%)(346)

a	10^3b
0.00 Wt. % A	
1.2507	0.630t
20.00 Wt. % A	
1.1416	0.660t
33.33 Wt. % A	
1.0742	0.725t
50.02 Wt. % A	
0.9975	0.750t
66.67 Wt. % A	
0.9371	0.805t
100.00 Wt. % A	
0.8128	0.850t

383. B = $C_4H_5NO_2$
Succinimide (299)[1,2]

384. B = C_4H_5NS
Allyl isothiocyanate (192,[1] 3281)

385. B = $C_4H_6O_4$
Succinic acid
(±0.0075%)(264)

Wt. % A	$d_4^{14.2}$
100.000	0.79595
99.844	0.79654
99.690	0.79710
99.382	0.79829
98.754	0.80020
97.553	0.80509

386. B = $C_4H_6O_5$
Malic acid (194)[1]

387. B = $C_4H_6O_6$
Tartaric acid (296,[1] 303)
(20°–50°)(±0.1%)(339)

a	10^3b
93.55 Wt. % A	
0.8199	0.873(t − 20)
88.37 Wt. % A	
0.8480	0.873(t − 20)
83.82 Wt. % A	
0.8736	0.873(t − 20)
80.27 Wt. % A	
0.8931	0.880(t − 20)

388. B = $C_4H_8O_2$
Butyric acid
(0–100 Wt. % B)(108)
d_4^{18} = (0.7928 + 0.001683 × Wt. % B)
±0.1%

389. B = $C_4H_8O_2$
Ethyl acetate
(±0.005%)(182)

Wt. % B	d_4^0
100.000	0.92455
94.897	0.91736
89.816	0.91033
84.338	0.90299
83.815	0.90227
80.080	0.89741
75.159	0.89107
69.692	0.88419
65.412	0.87889
58.900	0.87097
49.941	0.86036
39.489	0.84833
28.985	0.83662
14.250	0.82080
5.346	0.81167
0.000	0.80631

(±0.25%)(101.1)

Wt. % B	$d_4^{17.5}$
100.00	0.9060
95.63	0.9002
91.21	0.8942
86.71	0.8880
82.17	0.8817
77.75	0.8753
72.89	0.8685
68.20	0.8615
63.34	0.8572

(±0.025%)(178)
50 Wt. % B

t	d_4^t
0	0.86207
25	0.84424
40	0.82665
55	0.80860

390. B = C_4H_9NO
Butyramide
(±0.01%)(33)

Wt. % A	d_4^{30}
100.000	0.78090
97.374	0.78501
94.372	0.78991

391. B = $C_4H_{10}O$
Isobutyl alcohol
(±0.025%)(65)

Wt. % B	d_4^{15}
0.00	0.79367
6.30	0.79435
12.34	0.79488
29.06	0.79670
49.49	0.79905
59.09	0.80022
68.54	0.80142
89.80	0.80430
100.00	0.80567

392. B = $C_4H_{10}O$
Ethyl ether (10, 32, 37, 50, 103, 169, 201,[1] 240, 252,[1] 274, 289)
(±0.025%)(36)

Wt. % A	d_4^{15}
0.0	0.7194
9.6	0.7317
16.8	0.7404
18.0	0.7418
18.7	0.7427
20.8	0.7452
22.2	0.7468
22.7	0.7474
23.0	0.7478
24.9	0.7501
25.0	0.7502
25.4	0.7509
25.7	0.7511
25.8	0.7512
26.7	0.7524
27.4	0.7533
28.3	0.7544
29.7	0.7562
100.0	0.7934

(±0.025%)(9)

Wt. % A	d_4^{25}
100.00	0.7882
76.85	0.7726
52.57	0.7548
42.49	0.7468
35.52	0.7412
27.01	0.7340
21.63	0.7295
13.61	0.7222
0.00	0.7079

393. B = $C_4H_{12}IN$
Tetramethylammonium iodide (330)[1]

394. B = C_5H_5N
Pyridine
(±0.05%)(130)

Wt. % A	$d_4^{15.5}$
0.00	0.9873
10.48	0.9640
25.98	0.9321
45.61	0.8931
100.00	0.7934

(±0.05%)(73)

Wt. % A	d_4^{25}
100.00	0.7904
70.08	0.8432
50.03	0.8845
33.93	0.9242
30.04	0.9456
0.00	0.9783

395. B = C_5H_{10}
Amylene (103)

396. B = $C_5H_{12}O$
Amyl alcohol (168, 169)

396.5. B = $C_5H_{12}O$
Isoamyl alcohol
(±0.1%) (361)

Wt. % B	$d_4^{18.4}$
0.000	0.7963
0.915	0.8030
1.099	0.8033
0.395	0.8022
1.578	0.8036
3.665	0.8040
5.478	0.8048
7.860	0.8050
18.265	0.8065
27.350	0.8075

397. B = $C_6H_3N_3O_6$
Trinitrobenzene (129)[1,2]

398. B = $C_6H_3N_3O_7$
Picric acid (18)[1]
(to 2.22 Wt. % B)(34)
d_4^{30} = (0.78100 + 0.00474 × Wt. % B) ±0.01%

399. B = $C_6H_4Br_2$
p-Dibromobenzene (158)

400. B = C_6H_5Br
Bromobenzene
(±0.01%)(34)

Wt. % B	d_4^{30}
0.000	0.78081
3.208	0.79327
4.128	0.79694
5.668	0.80301
6.596	0.80666
100.000	1.48200

401. B = C_6H_5Cl
Chlorobenzene
(±0.01%)(34)

Wt. % B	d_4^{30}
0.000	0.78081
2.858	0.78773
4.985	0.79287
6.361	0.79623

402. B = C_6H_5ClO
o-Chlorophenol (305)[1]

403. B = C_6H_5ClO
m-Chlorophenol (305)[1]

404. B = C_6H_5ClO
p-Chlorophenol (305)[1]

405. B = $C_6H_5NO_2$
Nitrobenzene (34,[1] 192,[1] 328[1])
(±0.025%)(247)

Mol % A	d_4^{20}
100.00	0.79110
97.71	0.80855
95.13	0.82747
92.10	0.84878
88.87	0.86987
85.54	0.89052
82.03	0.91097
77.01	0.93824
70.41	0.97144
60.46	1.01192
48.16	1.06451
Mol % A	d_4^{30}
100.00	0.78063
97.63	0.79848
95.11	0.81688
92.04	0.83808
88.75	0.85960
81.99	0.90090
77.11	0.92775
70.31	0.96182
61.51	1.00178
47.86	1.05549
Mol % A	d_4^{40}
100.00	0.77329
97.61	0.79129
95.11	0.80913
92.05	0.83005
88.85	0.87075
81.86	0.89263
77.01	0.91900
70.44	0.95191
62.00	0.99072
47.49	1.04750
Mol % A	d_4^{50}
100.00	0.76329
97.58	0.78115
94.94	0.79952
92.12	0.81920
88.93	0.83988
85.42	0.86113
82.08	0.88118
77.13	0.90822
71.32	0.93802
61.96	0.98103
47.86	1.03619
Mol % A	d_4^{60}
100.00	0.74650
97.69	0.77210
95.07	0.79122
92.09	0.81110
88.90	0.83168
85.69	0.85235
82.43	0.87179
77.28	0.89960
70.59	0.93288
61.59	0.97346
47.29	1.02451

C_2H_6O.—(*Continued*)

406. B = $C_6H_5NO_3$
o-Nitrophenol
(±0.005%)(319)

Wt. % A	$d_4^{12.87}$
100.000	0.79586
97.570	0.80493
93.528	0.81903
89.008	0.83582
88.790	0.83660

(to 5.261 Wt. % B)(34)
d_4^{30} = (0.78100 + 0.003508 × Wt. % B) ±0.01%

407. B = $C_6H_5NO_3$
p-Nitrophenol
(to 1.834 Wt. % B)(34)
d_4^{30} = (0.78100 + 0.00368 × Wt. % B) ±0.01%

408. B = C_6H_6 (35, 81,[1] 95,[1] 103, 139, 233,[1] 238,[1] 240, 351, 361[1])
(±0.075%)(32)

Wt. % B	d_4^{20}
100.00	0.7930
78.88	0.8106
47.14	0.8356
20.90	0.8604
0.00	0.8814

(±0.025%)(178)
50 Wt. % B

t	d_4^t
0	0.86536
25	0.84060
40	0.82549
55	0.80955

409. B = C_6H_6BrN
p-Bromoaniline
(to 4.711 Wt. % B)(34)
d_4^{30} = (0.78100 + 0.00437 × Wt. % B) ±0.01%

410. B = C_6H_6ClN
p-Chloroaniline
(±0.01%)(34)

Wt. % A	d_4^{30}
100.000	0.78100
98.781	0.78506
98.638	0.78535

411. B = $C_6H_6N_2O_2$
m-Nitroaniline
(to 2.694 Wt. % B) (34)
d_4^{30} = (0.78100 + 0.003597 × Wt. % B) ±0.01%

412. B = $C_6H_6N_2O_2$
p-Nitroaniline
(to 0.964 Wt. % B) (34)
d_4^{30} = (0.78100 + 0.003696 × Wt. % B) ±0.01%

413. B = C_6H_6O
Phenol
(±0.005%)(319)

Wt. % A	$d_4^{12.87}$
100.000	0.79586
96.354	0.80650
94.284	0.81160
91.029	0.81959
85.354	0.83381
79.467	0.84882

414. B = $C_6H_6O_2$
Resorcinol (299)[1,2]

415. B = C_6H_7N
Aniline (140)
(±0.01%)(34)

Wt. % B	d_4^{30}
0.000	0.78081
2.234	0.78592
3.956	0.78976
7.223	0.79693
100.000	1.01300

416. B = $C_6H_8O_7$
Citric acid (296)[1,2]

417. B = $C_6H_{10}O_3$
Ethyl acetoacetate
(±0.05%)(71)

Wt. % A	d_4^{25}
100.00	0.7875
91.95	0.8025
63.72	0.8605
53.29	0.8832
35.98	0.9244
0.00	1.0222

418. B = $C_6H_{10}O_8$
Citric acid hydrate (296)[1,2]

418.5. B = $C_6H_{12}O_3$
Paraldehyde
(±0.1%) (361)

Wt. % B	d_4^{20}
0.000	0.7934
0.710	0.7948
1.047	0.7953
2.830	0.7972
5.200	0.8006
13.835	0.8152
25.000	0.8347

419. B = $C_6H_{13}NO$
Caproamide
(to 3.293 Wt. % B)(33)
d_4^{30} = (0.78090 + 0.001259 × Wt. % B) ±0.01%

420. B = C_7H_5N
Cyanobenzene (192,[1] 328[1])

421. B = $C_7H_6O_2$
Benzoic acid (293, 296[1,2])

422. B = $C_7H_6O_3$
Salicylic acid (293, 294, 296,[1,2] 303)

423. B = C_7H_7NO
Benzamide (129,[1] 299[1,2])

424. B = $C_7H_7NO_2$
o-Nitrotoluene (192,[1] 328[1])
(±0.01%)(34)

Wt. % A	d_4^{30}
100.000	0.78100
96.867	0.78972
85.787	0.82051
69.002	0.87101
48.032	0.94148

425. B = $C_7H_7NO_2$
m-Nitrotoluene (192,[1] 328[1])

426. B = $C_7H_7NO_2$
p-Nitrotoluene (34,[1] 192,[1] 328[1])
(0 – 100 Wt. % B)(149)

$$\frac{1}{d_4^{30}} = [1.28035 - 0.0043628 \times \text{Wt. \% B} + 0.0_5 3532 \times (\text{Wt. \% B})^2]$$
±0.025%

427. B = C_7H_8 (35, 139)
(±0.01%)(34)

Wt. % A	d_4^{30}
100.000	0.78081
96.891	0.78322
96.014	0.78386
94.655	0.78488
91.768	0.78689

428. B = C_7H_8O
o-Cresol (237)[1]

429. B = C_7H_8O
Anisole (±0.025%)(9)

Wt. % A	d_4^{25}
100.00	0.7881
84.79	0.8149
70.38	0.8407
57.00	0.8666
44.33	0.8919
32.32	0.9168
20.95	0.9416
10.02	0.9660
0.00	0.9960

430. B = $C_7H_8O_6$
Gallic acid hydrate (296)[1,2]

431. B = C_7H_9N
p-Toluidine (299)[1]
(to 3.952 Wt. % B)(34)
d_4^{30} = (0.78100 + 0.00212 × Wt. % B) ± 0.01%

432. B = C_7H_9N
2, 6-Lutidine
(±0.05%)(73)

Wt. % A	d_4^{25}
100.00	0.7904
90.03	0.8038
80.12	0.8197
60.23	0.8515
40.30	0.8803
20.57	0.9074
9.45	0.9210
0.00	0.9322

433. B = $C_7H_9NO_2$
Ammonium benzoate (296)[1,2]

434. B = $C_7H_9NO_3$
Ammonium salicylate (294, 296[1,2])

435. B = C_8H_8ClNO
p-Chloroacetanilide
(±0.01%)(34)

Wt. % A	d_4^{30}
100.000	0.78100
98.717	0.78515
97.843	0.78794

436. B = C_8H_9NO
Acetanilide (129,[1,2] 292, 299,[1,2] 303)

437. B = C_8H_{10}
Xylene (139)

438. B = $C_8H_{10}O$
Phenetole
(±0.025%)(9)

Wt. % A	d_4^{25}
100.00	0.7881
85.03	0.8108
71.11	0.8331
57.68	0.8552
45.03	0.8767
32.95	0.8982
21.50	0.9195
9.75	0.9422
0.00	0.9619

439. B = $C_8H_{14}O_3$
Ethyl ethylacetoacetate
(±0.05%)(71)

Wt. % A	d_4^{25}
100.00	0.7875
94.56	0.7953
76.20	0.8271
58.76	0.8588
28.69	0.9165
13.13	0.9495
0.00	0.9750

440. B = $C_8H_{14}O_6$
Ethyl tartrate (170,[1] 343[1])
(±0.05%)(203, 288, 344)

Range	Wt. % A	a	10^3b
(17.6° – 58.2°)	100.00 Wt. % A	0.7934	0.880(t−17.6)
(20.5°–54.4°)	95.00 Wt. % A	0.8058	0.891(t−20.5)
(17.4°–65.8°)	89.06 Wt. % A	0.8265	0.902(t−17.4)
(13.1°–69.0°)	80.00 Wt. % A	0.8596	0.932(t−13.1)
(16.7°–62.8°)	60.00 Wt. % A	0.9273	0.954(t−16.7)
(17.5°–59.1°)	39.99 Wt. % A	1.0079	0.988(t−17.5)
(16.8°–99.4°)	0.00 Wt. % A	1.2085	1.016(t−16.8)

441. B = $C_8H_{20}IN$
Tetraethylammonium iodide (330,[1] 331[1])

442. B = C_9H_8O
Cinnamaldehyde (353)

443. B = $C_9H_{10}O_2$
Ethyl benzoate (303)

444. B = $C_9H_{11}NO$
p-Acettoluide (129)[1,2]

445. B = $C_9H_{11}NO$
Methylacetanilide (180)

446. B = $C_{10}H_7Br$
Bromonaphthalene (353)

447. B = $C_{10}H_8$
Naphthalene (299)[1]
(to 2.711 Wt. % B)(54)
d_4^{18} = (0.79250 + 0.002089 × Wt. % B) ±0.0075%

448. B = $C_{10}H_{12}$
Tetrahydronaphthalene
(±0.075%)(121)

Wt. % A	d_4^{25}
100.0	0.7847
75.4	0.8245
51.7	0.8645
24.2	0.9158
7.7	0.9465
0.0	0.9656

449. B = $C_{10}H_{13}NO_2$
Phenacetine (292, 297[2])

450. B = $C_{10}H_{14}N_2$
Nicotine (93)[1]
(±0.05%)(170, 341)

Wt. % A	d_4^{20}
0.00	1.0110
9.91	0.9884
25.07	0.9536
40.07	0.9200
54.92	0.8875
69.97	0.8554
85.04	0.8251
100.00	0.7957

(±0.05%)(343, 344)
(to 30°)

a	10^3b
43.27 Wt. % A	
0.9283	0.84*t*
58.00 Wt. % A	
0.8955	0.83*t*
74.07 Wt. % A	
0.8615	0.84*t*
89.76 Wt. % A	
0.8288	0.83*t*

451. B = $C_{10}H_{15}BrO$
Bromocamphor
(±0.1%)(235)

Wt. % A	d_4^{25}
100.00	0.7874
99.49	0.7892
95.02	0.8040
90.23	0.8213
85.68	0.8379
81.27	0.8549

452. B = $C_{10}H_{16}O$
Camphor (175,[1] 323, 342)
(±0.1%)(100, 170)

Wt. % B	d_4^{20}
0	0.7948
10	0.8094
20	0.8240
30	0.8391
40	0.8548
50	0.8715
60	0.8892

(±0.1%)(235)

Wt. % B	d_4^{25}
0.00	0.7874
0.76	0.7886
3.05	0.7918
7.54	0.7987
14.82	0.8094
24.28	0.8239
37.83	0.8460
50.72	0.8671

453. B = $C_{10}H_{16}O_4$
Camphoric acid (293, 296[1,2])

454. B = $C_{10}H_{18}O$
Borneol (303)

455. B = $C_{10}H_{18}O_3$
Ethyl diethylacetoacetate
(±0.05%)(71)

Wt. % A	d_4^{25}
100.00	0.7875
84.34	0.8112
79.26	0.8200
71.44	0.8325
8.22	0.9491
0.00	0.9646

456. B = $C_{10}H_{20}O$
Menthol
(±0.05%)(226)

a	10^3b
(12.0°–27.9°)	
98.43 Wt. % A	
0.7994	0.856(*t*−12.0)
(12.0°–46.9°)	
91.73 Wt. % A	
0.8060	0.848(*t*−12.0)

457. B = $C_{12}H_{10}$
Acenaphthene (299)[1,2]

458. B = $C_{12}H_{10}O$
Phenyl ether (237)[1]

459. B = $C_{12}H_{10}NO$
α-Acetnaphthalide (129)[1,2]

460. B = $C_{12}H_{28}IN$
Tetrapropylammonium iodide
(330)[1]

461. B = $C_{13}H_{10}O$
Benzophenone
(±0.01%)(33)

Wt. % A	d_4^{30}
100.000	0.78090
92.849	0.79894
89.430	0.80778

462. B = $C_{13}H_{10}O_3$
Phenyl salicylate (294, 296[1,2])

463. B = $C_{13}H_{12}N_2O$
Benzoylphenylhydrazine
(129)[1,2]

464. B = $C_{14}H_{10}$
Phenanthrene (18,[1] 158, 299[1,2])

465. B = $C_{16}H_{24}O_3S$
Menthyl benzenesulfonate
(212)[1]

466. B = $C_{16}H_{32}O_2$
Palmitic acid (158)

467. B = $C_{18}H_{34}O_2$
Oleic acid (57)

468. B = $C_{18}H_{36}O_2$
Stearic acid (296)[1,2]

469. B = $C_{19}H_{17}N_3$
Triphenylguanidine (129)[1,2]

470. B = $C_{19}H_{22}N_2O$
Cinchonicine (234)

471. B = $C_{20}H_{13}N_3O_7$
Phenanthrene picrate (18)[1]

472. B = $C_{20}H_{16}Br_2O_8$
Methyl di-[*o*-bromobenzoyl]-tartrate (88)

473. B = $C_{20}H_{16}Br_2O_8$
Methyl di-[*m*-bromobenzoyl]-tartrate (88)

474. B = $C_{20}H_{16}Br_2O_8$
Methyl di-[*p*-bromobenzoyl]-tartrate (88)

475. B = $C_{20}H_{16}Cl_2O_8$
Methyl di-[*o*-chlorobenzoyl]-tartrate (88)

476. B = $C_{20}H_{16}Cl_2O_8$
Methyl di-[*m*-chlorobenzoyl]-tartrate (88)

477. B = $C_{20}H_{16}Cl_2O_8$
Methyl di-[*p*-chlorobenzoyl]-tartrate (88)

478. B = $C_{20}H_{20}O_6$ (87)
Methyl di-*p*-toluylglycerate

479. B = $C_{20}H_{26}O_3S$
Menthyl naphthalene-β-sulfonate (212)[1]

480. B = $C_{21}H_{22}O_6$
Ethyl di-*p*-toluylglycerate (87)

481. B = $C_{24}H_{42}O_6$
l-Menthyl *l*-tartrate
(±0.05%)(214)

a	10^3b
(19.55°–29.8°)	
97.58 Wt. % A	
0.7964	0.858(*t*−19.55)
(18.25°–38.6°)	
92.95 Wt. % A	
0.8054	0.860(*t*−18.25)

482. B = $C_{24}H_{42}O_6$
l-Menthyl *d*-tartrate
(±0.05%)(226)

a	10^3b
(12.8°–62.7°)	
93.30 Wt. % A	
0.8112	0.863(*t*−12.8°)
(9.7°–33.9°)	
92.07 Wt. % A	
0.8178	0.856(*t*−9.7)

483. B = $C_{26}H_{26}N_2O_2$
Benzoylcinchonicine (234)

484. B = $C_{26}H_{28}N_2O_3S$
p-Toluenesulfonylcinchonicine
(234)

485. B = $C_{27}H_{34}N_2O_7$
Quinine salicylate dihydrate
(294, 296[1,2])

486. B = $C_{28}H_{46}O_8$
l-Menthyl diacetyl-*l*-tartrate
(±0.05%)(214)

a	10^3b
(21.0°–39.4°)	
96.05 Wt. % A	
0.7982	0.870(*t* − 21.0)
(19.1°–37.2°)	
94.20 Wt. % A	
0.8035	0.857(*t*−19.1)

487. B = $C_{28}H_{46}O_8$
l-Menthyl diacetyl-*dl*-tartrate
(215)[1]

488. B = $C_{28}H_{46}O_8$
l-Menthyl diacetyl-*d*-tartrate
(±0.05%)(226)

a	10^3b
(18.7°–41.3°)	
98.21 Wt. % A	
0.7957	0.867(*t* − 18.7)
(13.0°–40.2°)	
92.74 Wt. % A	
0.8119	0.861(*t* − 13)

488.1. B = *d*-**Turpentine**
(0.05%)(170)

Wt. % A	d_4^{20}
0.00	0.9108
26.91	0.8765
53.49	0.8464
77.76	0.8186
100.00	0.7957

488.2 B = *l*-**Turpentine** (170,[1] 342[1])
(0.05%)(263)

Wt. % A	d_4^{20}
0.00	0.8648
10.31	0.8550
32.68	0.8368
49.01	0.8247
68.57	0.8108
79.90	0.8033
89.89	0.7969
100.00	0.7911

v. also 9, 41, 82, 94, 153, 158, 166, 175, 181, 188, 232, 266, 268, 306, 310, 369, 1265, 1275, 1276, 1277

$C_2H_6O_2$
Glycol

489. B = $C_4H_{12}IN$
Tetramethylammonium iodide
(330)[1]

490. B = $C_8H_{20}IN$
Tetraethylammonium iodide
(330)[1]

C_2H_7N

Dimethylamine

490.1. B = C_2H_8ClN

Dimethylamine hydrochloride

(±0.5%) (358)

Wt. % B	$d_4^{-33.5}$
0.00	0.727
2.01	0.728
3.99	0.734
8.66	0.740

C_2H_7N

Ethylamine

490.2. B = C_2H_8ClN

Ethylamine hydrochloride

(±0.5%) (358)

Wt. % B	$d_4^{-33.5}$
0.00	0.742
4.07	0.767
9.97	0.771
13.78	0.881

$C_3H_3N_3O_3$

Cyanuric acid

491. B = C_5H_5N

Pyridine (70)

C_3H_5ClO

Epichlorohydrin

492. B = $C_8H_{20}IN$

Tetraethylammonium iodide

(329)[1]

C_3H_5N

Propionitrile

493. B = $C_8H_{20}IN$

Tetraethylammonium iodide

(330,[1] 331[1])

494. B = $C_{12}H_{28}IN$

Tetrapropylammonium iodide

(330,[1] 331[1])

C_3H_5NO

Lactonitrile

v. 269

C_3H_5NS

Ethyl thiocyanate

495. B = $C_5H_{11}N$

Piperidine

(±0.05%)(165)

Mol % A	d_4^{50}
100	0.9672
95	0.9766
75	1.0151
55	1.0534
50	1.0633
45	1.0414
25	0.9474
5	0.8560
0	0.8338

496. B = $C_8H_{20}IN$

Tetraethylammonium iodide

(330)[1]

$C_3H_6Br_2$

n-Propylene bromide

v. 311

C_3H_6O

Allyl alcohol

497. B = C_3H_8O

Propyl alcohol (335)[1]

498. B = C_6H_6

(±0.05%)(335)

Wt. % B	d_4^0
100.00	0.9001
84.19	0.8933
81.23	0.8923
0.00	0.8690

499. B = $C_8H_{14}O_6$

Ethyl tartrate

(±0.05%)(223)

a	10^3b
(8.6°–55.5°)	
28.27 Wt. % B	
0.941	0.917(t − 8.6)
(11.5°–53.0°)	
49.81 Wt. % B	
1.009	0.917(t − 11.5)

C_3H_6O

Acetone

500. B = C_3H_7NO

Propionamide (180)

501. B = $C_4H_5NO_2$

Methyl cyanoacetate

(±0.05%)(329)

Wt. % A	d_4^0
0.00	1.1492
18.97	1.0697
41.28	0.9862
67.83	0.9030
100.00	0.8121
Wt. % A	d_4^{25}
0.00	1.1225
18.97	1.0437
41.28	0.9607
67.83	0.8739
100.00	0.7851

502. B = $C_4H_6O_4$

Succinic acid

(±0.0075%)(264)

Wt. % A	$d_4^{12.9}$
100.000	0.80009
99.847	0.80036
99.695	0.80095
99.387	0.80216
98.778	0.80458
97.571	0.80928

503. B = $C_4H_6O_5$

Malic acid (194)[1]

504. B = $C_4H_7ClO_2$

Ethyl chloroacetate (158)

505. B = C_4H_8O

Methyl ethyl ketone

(0–100 Wt. % A)

(±0.025%)(248)

d_4^{20} = (0.8052 − 0.0_3142 × Wt. % A)

d_4^{30} = (0.7946 − 0.0_3151 × Wt. % A)

d_4^{40} = (0.7841 − 0.0_3161 × Wt. % A)

d_4^{50} = (0.7734 − 0.0_3172 Wt. % A)

506. B = $C_4H_{10}O$

Ethyl ether

(±0.05)(281)

Mol % A	d_4^{20}
0	0.7106
20	0.7191
40	0.7312
50	0.7383
60	0.7461
80	0.7645
100	0.7877

(±0.05%)(274)

Mol % A	$d_4^{25.04}$
0.000	0.7080
10.764	0.7146
20.752	0.7209
31.186	0.7280
41.842	0.7356
45.646	0.7385
54.939	0.7456
56.104	0.7465
63.691	0.7525
72.850	0.7607
77.158	0.7640
85.858	0.7720
93.418	0.7792
100.000	0.7859

(0°–32°)(±0.25%)(79)

a	10^3b
0 Mol % A	
0.736	1.343t
30 Mol % A	
0.757	1.625t
70 Mol % A	
0.785	1.501t
100 Mol % A	
0.813	1.312t

507. B = $C_5H_{12}O$

Amyl alcohol (39)[1]

508. B = C_6H_5Br

(±0.1%)(270)

Mol % A	d_4^0
0.00	1.518
15.68	1.445
26.46	1.382
49.85	1.234
71.85	1.074
82.50	0.982
93.75	0.875
100.00	0.812

509. B = C_6H_5Cl

(±0.1%)(270)

Mol % A	d_4^0
0.00	1.127
15.30	1.094
49.12	1.003
60.30	0.948
84.74	0.878
95.97	0.834
100.00	0.812

510. B = C_6H_5ClO

o-Chlorophenol

(±0.01 %)(28)

Wt. % A	d_4^0
100.00	0.8148
81.51	0.8800
67.62	0.9364
50.05	1.0138
39.51	1.0638
28.99	1.1175
16.88	1.1824
8.27	1.2282
0.00	1.2737
Wt. % A	d_4^{10}
100.00	0.8032
81.51	0.8689
67.62	0.9256
50.05	1.0032
39.51	1.0532
28.99	1.1068
16.88	1.1716
8.27	1.2170
0.00	1.2622
Wt. % A	d_4^{20}
100.00	0.7914
81.51	0.8577
67.62	0.9148
50.05	0.9924
39.51	1.0427
28.99	1.0961
16.88	1.1607
8.27	1.2058
0.00	1.2508
Wt. % A	d_4^{30}
100.00	0.7795
81.51	0.8466
67.62	0.9040
50.05	0.9818
39.51	1.0321
28.99	1.0855
16.88	1.1499
8.27	1.1946
0.00	1.2397
Wt. % A	d_4^{40}
100.00	0.7676
81.51	0.8354
67.62	0.8931
50.05	0.9712
39.51	1.0215
28.99	1.0747
16.88	1.1392
8.27	1.1834
0.00	1.2282
Wt. % A	d_4^{50}
100.00	0.7557
81.51	0.8242
67.62	0.8822
50.05	0.9601
39.51	1.0109
28.99	1.0641
16.88	1.1284
8.27	1.1723
0.00	1.2170
Wt. % A	d_4^{60}
40.63	0.9948
31.77	1.0391
23.01	1.0847
15.36	1.1241
8.92	1.1579
0.00	1.2058

Wt. % A	d_4^{70}
40.63	0.9837
31.77	1.0280
23.01	1.0735
15.36	1.1129
8.92	1.1467
0.00	1.1945

511. B = $C_6H_5NO_2$
Nitrobenzene
(±0.1%) (361)

Wt. % A	d_4^{20}
0.000	1.2048
0.372	1.2016
0.600	1.1994
1.366	1.1996
1.864	1.1993
3.031	1.1868
7.083	1.1632
9.730	1.1494
16.100	1.1176

(±0.1%)(82)

Mol % B	d_4^{25}
100	0.7869
75	0.8970
50	0.9980
25	1.1005
0	1.1963

512. B = C_6H_6(33,[1] 59,[1] 82,[1] 139, 141,[1] 149, 176, 361[1])
(±0.1%) (355)

Wt. % B	d_4^{10}
0.00	0.8042
21.24	0.8323
49.34	0.8445
72.14	0.8645
100.00	0.8893
Wt. % B	d_4^{20}
0.00	0.7926
21.24	0.8102
49.34	0.8335
72.14	0.8534
100.00	0.8784

(±0.1%)(74)

Wt. % B	d_4^{25}
0.00	0.8736
9.33	0.8668
18.05	0.8565
24.70	0.8507
39.31	0.8381
43.28	0.8347
63.98	0.8179
74.81	0.8080
89.51	0.7948
100.00	0.7862

(±0.1%) (355)

Wt. % B	d_4^{30}
0.00	0.7810
21.24	0.7999
49.34	0.8227
72.14	0.8425
100.00	0.8677

513. B = C_6H_6O
Phenol
(±0.01%)(27)

Wt. % A	$d_4^{9.95}$
100.00	0.8033
85.81	0.8427
73.28	0.8769
61.94	0.9086
50.57	0.9407
42.21	0.9642
34.78	0.9851
26.26	1.0090
21.06	1.0237
14.61	1.0420
7.15	1.0622
0.00	1.0835
Wt. % A	$d_4^{20.05}$
100.00	0.7914
85.81	0.8317
73.28	0.8663
61.94	0.8984
50.57	0.9309
42.21	0.9547
34.78	0.9757
26.26	0.9998
21.06	1.0146
14.61	1.0334
7.15	1.0537
0.00	1.0751
Wt. % A	$d_4^{29.8}$
100.00	0.7801
90.43	0.8058
80.47	0.8338
72.30	0.8573
62.58	0.8856
55.33	0.9064
47.21	0.9331
39.76	0.9520
32.81	0.9724
25.75	0.9935
19.24	1.0115
12.02	1.0327
7.19	1.0466
0.00	1.0667
Wt. % A	$d_4^{40.1}$
100.00	0.7678
90.43	0.7942
80.47	0.8225
72.30	0.8462
62.58	0.8744
55.33	0.8953
47.21	0.9221
39.76	0.9417
32.81	0.9625
25.75	0.9837
19.24	1.0022
12.02	1.0237
7.19	1.0378
0.00	1.0583
Wt. % A	$d_4^{49.8}$
100.00	0.7561
90.43	0.7832
80.47	0.8118
72.30	0.8337
62.58	0.8637
55.33	0.8847
47.21	0.9116
39.76	0.9317
32.81	0.9530

Wt. % A	$d_4^{49.8}$
25.75	0.9733
19.24	0.9933
12.02	1.0150
7.19	1.0293
0.00	1.0502

514. B = C_6H_7N
Aniline
(±0.25%)(79)

Mol % A	d_4^{18}
0	1.021
30	0.978
70	0.886
100	0.810
Mol % A	d_4^{41}
0	1.002
30	0.966
70	0.863
100	0.765

(±0.025%)(178)
50 Wt. % A

t	d_4^t
0	0.93268
25	0.90893
40	0.89118
55	0.87720
70	0.86282

515. B = C_6H_{14}, Hexane
(±0.1%)(76)

Wt. % A	d_4^{15}
0.00	0.6744
22.84	0.6913
54.20	0.7272
63.94	0.7445
73.41	0.7558
82.55	0.7684
91.41	0.7836
100.00	0.7977

(±0.1%) (361)

Wt. % A	d_4^{20}
0.000	0.6872
0.402	0.6879
0.557	0.6881
9.985	0.6930
18.135	0.6990

516. B = $C_7H_7NO_2$
p-Nitrotoluene (136)[1]

517. B = C_7H_8(2, 102)
(0–100 Wt. % B)(±0.25%)

$d_4^{13} = (0.799 + 0.0_3762 \times \text{Wt. \% B})$

$d_4^{16} = (0.797 + 0.0_3731 \times \text{Wt. \% B})$

$d_4^{22} = (0.788 + 0.0_3727 \times \text{Wt. \% B})$

518. B = $C_7H_8O_6$
Gallic acid monohydrate (296)[1,2]

519. B = $C_7H_{14}O_2$
Amyl acetate (69)[1]

520. B = C_8H_9NO
Acetanilide (292)[2]

521. B = $C_8H_{10}N_4O_2$
Caffeine (292)

522. B = $C_8H_{14}O_6$
Ethyl tartrate
(±0.05%)(223)

a	10^3b
(13°–46°)	
89.99 Wt. % A	
0.8304	$1.085(t - 13)$
(11.5°–36°)	
74.94 Wt. % A	
0.8821	$1.102(t - 11.5)$

523. B = $C_8H_{20}IN$
Tetraethylammonium iodide
(330,[1] 331[1])

524. B = $C_9H_{11}NO$
Methylacetanilide (180)

525. B = $C_{10}H_8$
Naphthalene (354)

526. B = $C_{10}H_{14}N_2$
Nicotine (110, 341)

527. B = $C_{10}H_{14}O$
Thymol (354)

528. B = $C_{10}H_{15}BrO$
Bromocamphor
(±0.1%)(235)

Wt. % A	d_4^{25}
100.00	0.7874
99.23	0.7901
92.62	0.8117
77.07	0.8719
65.28	0.9219
51.42	0.9884

529. B = $C_{10}H_{16}O$
Camphor (354)
(±0.1%)(175)

Wt. % A	d_4^{20}
100	0.7970
90	0.8135
80	0.8303
70	0.8469
60	0.8635

(±0.1%)(235)

Wt. % A	d_4^{25}
100.00	0.7874
99.20	0.7887
96.95	0.7915
94.96	0.7949
90.01	0.8021
75.73	0.8241
62.17	0.8461
49.27	0.8673
33.06	0.8962

530. B = $C_{12}H_{10}O$
Diphenyl ether
(±0.1%)(270)

Mol % A	d_4^{25}
0.00	1.072
48.43	0.992
73.06	0.921
89.40	0.849
100.00	0.787

C_3H_6O.—(*Continued*)

531. B = $C_{12}H_{28}IN$
Tetrapropylammonium iodide
(330,[1] 331[1])

532. B = $C_{13}H_{10}O$
Benzophenone
(±0.01%)(33)

Wt. % A	d_4^{30}
100.000	0.78117
96.446	0.79017
92.988	0.79881
89.305	0.80846

533. B = $C_{16}H_{32}O_2$
Palmitic acid (158)

534. B = $C_{18}H_{34}O_2$
Oleic acid
(0 – 100 Wt. % A)(38)
d_4^{30} = (0.8859 – 0.0_3756 × Wt. % A) ± 0.25%

535. B = $C_{18}H_{36}O_2$
Stearic acid (158, 296,[1,2])

536. B = $C_{19}H_{22}N_2O$
Cinchonicine (234)

537. B = $C_{20}H_{20}O_6$
Methyl di-*p*-toluylglycerate (87)

538. B = $C_{21}H_{22}O_6$
Ethyl di-*p*-toluylglycerate (87)

539. B = $C_{25}H_{23}N_5O_7$
Picryl cinchonicine (234)

540. B = $C_{26}H_{26}N_2O_2$
Benzoyl cinchonicine (234)

541. B = $C_{26}H_{28}N_2O_3S$
p-Toluenesulfonylcinchonicine
(234)

v. also 10, 42, 83, 95, 143, 159, 189, 235, 240, 252, 312, 376, 1265, 1275, 1277.5, 1278

$C_3H_6O_2$
Propionic acid

542. B = C_6H_6
(±0.05%)(135)

Wt. % B	d_4^{16}
100.00	0.8842
84.97	0.8958
62.74	0.9183
0.00	0.9973

543. B = C_7H_8
(±0.05%)(135)

Wt. % B	d_4^{16}
100.00	0.8694
84.11	0.8856
70.03	0.9020
0.00	0.9973

544. B = $C_{10}H_{16}O$
Camphor (323, 342)
(to 50.96 Wt. % B)(100)
d_4^{20} = (0.9948 – 0.0_32708 × Wt. % B) ± 0.1%

v. also 167, 313

$C_3H_6O_2$
Ethyl formate

545. B = $C_3H_6O_2$
Methyl acetate
(0–100 Wt. % B)(23)
d_4^{20} = (0.9175 + 0.0_3171 × Wt. % B)
±0.025%

546. B = $C_4H_8O_2$
Ethyl acetate
(±0.025%)(23)

Wt. % B	d_4^{20}
0.000	0.9175
23.580	0.9125
46.094	0.9083
71.740	0.9042
100.000	0.9001

547. B = C_6H_6 (199)[1]

548. B = C_8H_{10}
Xylene (199)[1]

v. also 1265

$C_3H_6O_2$
Methyl acetate

549. B = $C_4H_7ClO_2$
Ethyl chloroacetate (158)

550. B = $C_4H_8O_2$
Ethyl acetate (133)
d_4^t =
(±0.05%)(157)
0 Mol % B
0.9559(1 – 0.001247*t*)
25 Mol % B
0.9500(1 – 0.001379*t*)
50 Mol % B
0.9384(1 – 0.001278*t*)
100 Mol % B
0.9230(1 – 0.001371*t*)
(±0.025%)(23)

Wt. % B	d_4^{20}
0.000	0.9346
21.036	0.9258
44.555	0.9171
71.008	0.9084
100.000	0.9001

551. B = $C_6H_4Br_2$
p-Dibromobenzene (158)

552. B = C_6H_6 (35, 158, 199[1])

553. B = $C_6H_{12}O_3$
Paraldehyde (158)

554. B = C_8H_{10}
Xylene (199)[1]

555. B = $C_{10}H_8$
Naphthalene (54,[1] 158)

556. B = $C_{12}H_{10}N_2$
Azobenzene (158)

557. B = $C_{14}H_{10}$
Phenanthrene (158)

v. also 11, 377, 545, 1265

C_3H_7NO
Methylacetamide

558. B = C_5H_5N
Pyridine
(±0.05%)(70)

Wt. % B	d_4^{25}
100.00	0.9746
93.41	0.9786
88.80	0.9819
83.56	0.9844

C_3H_7NO
Propionamide

559. B = C_5H_5N
Pyridine
(to 23.75 Wt. % A)(70)
d_4^{25} = (0.9746 + 0.00299 × Wt. % A) ±0.05%

560. B = C_6H_6 (180)

v. also 96, 378, 500

$C_3H_7NO_2$
Urethane

561. B = C_3H_8O
Propyl alcohol (299)[1]

562. B = $C_4H_{10}O$
Ethyl ether (±0.01%)(261.1)

Wt. % A	d_4^{20}
0	0.7137
1	0.7167
2	0.7197
3	0.7227
4	0.7258
5	0.7289
10	0.7442
20	0.7754
30	0.8083
40	0.8430

563. B = C_5H_5N
Pyridine
(±0.05%)(70)

Wt. % B	d_4^{25}
100.00	0.9746
90.91	0.9832
85.04	0.9899

564. B = C_6H_6 ±0.01%(261.1)

Wt. % A	d_4^{20}
0	0.8784
1	0.8800
2	0.8815
3	0.8831
4	0.8846
5	0.8862
10	0.8942

565. B = C_7H_8 (299)[1,2]

v. also 97, 190, 379

C_3H_8O
Propyl alcohol

566. B = $C_3H_8O_3$
Glycerol (200)[1]

567. B = $C_4H_6O_5$
Malic acid (194)[1]

568. B = $C_4H_{10}O$
Ethyl ether
(±0.025%)(9)

Wt. % B	d_4^{25}
0.00	0.8012
10.93	0.7920
22.99	0.7820
34.92	0.7732
47.16	0.7596
59.89	0.7477
72.97	0.7345
86.22	0.7204
100.00	0.7079

569. B = C_6H_6 (133, 233,[1] 238,[1] 351)

570. B = C_6H_7N
Aniline
d_4^t =
(±0.05%)(157)
100.0 Mol % B
1.0415(1 – 0.0_3844t)
65.0 Mol % B
0.9798(1 – 0.0_3878t)
20.3 Mol % B
0.8856(1 – 0.001014*t*)
0.0 Mol % B
0.8210(1 – 0.001024*t*)

571. B = $C_8H_{14}O_6$
Ethyl tartrate
(±0.05%)(203, 288)

a	10^3b
(20°–69.6°)	
0.00 Wt. % B	
0.8041	0.840 (*t* – 20)
(16.6°–32.5°)	
2.50 Wt. % B	
0.8148	0.811 (*t* – 16.6)
(16.7°–80.2°)	
5.00 Wt. % B	
0.8212	0.865 (*t* – 16.7)
(23.5°–79.6°)	
7.71 Wt. % B	
0.8238	0.844 (*t* – 23.5)
(17.7°–70.6°)	
25.00 Wt. % B	
0.8811	0.899 (*t* – 17.7)
(19.8°–80.2°)	
49.83 Wt. % B	
0.9678	0.958 (*t* – 19.8)
(21°–71.2°)	
74.99 Wt. % B	
1.0746	0.995 (*t* – 21)

572. B = $C_{10}H_8$
Naphthalene (299)[1]

573. B = $C_{10}H_{14}N_2$
Nicotine (110, 341)

574. B = $C_{10}H_{16}O$
Camphor (323, 342)
(±0.1%)(100)

Wt. % B	d_4^{20}
0.00	0.8046
12.19	0.8210
23.90	0.8380
35.10	0.8543
45.93	0.8709
56.37	0.8874

575. B = $C_{12}H_{10}$
Acenaphthene (299)[1]

v. also 43, 84, 160, 168, 191, 276, 381, 497, 561

$C_3H_8O_2$
Methylal
v. 44

$C_3H_8O_3$
Glycerol

576. B = $C_4H_6O_4$
Succinic acid (116)[1,2]

577. B = $C_5H_{12}O$
Isoamyl alcohol (200)[1]

578. B = $C_8H_{14}O_6$
Ethyl tartrate
(±0.01%)(131)

Wt. % B	d_4^{15}
100.000	1.20990
86.833	1.22034
77.577	1.22674
68.038	1.23262
60.224	1.23693
54.263	1.24028
47.663	1.24376
42.513	1.24636
37.676	1.24869
0.000	1.26396

(±0.05%)(203, 288, 344)

a	10^3b
(13.2°–99.5°)	
0.00 Wt. % B	
1.2647	0.642(t − 13.2)
(17.1°–99°)	
4.99 Wt. % B	
1.2616	0.664(t − 17.1)
(17.3°–99.5°)	
9.91 Wt. % B	
1.2597	0.678(t − 17.3)
(8.5°–100°)	
23.46 Wt. % B	
1.2596	0.717(t − 8.5)
(10°–100°)	
48.13 Wt. % B	
1.2478	0.812(t − 10)
(19°–100°)	
69.93 Wt. % B	
1.2287	0.882(t − 19)
(8°–100°)	
89.98 Wt. % B	
1.2269	0.972(t − 8)
(16.8°–99.4°)	
100.00 Wt. % B	
1.2085	1.016 (t − 16.8)

v. also 192, 382, 566, 1274

$C_4H_2O_4$
Acetylene dicarboxylic acid
v. 193

$C_4H_4O_4$
Fumaric acid
v. 194

$C_4H_5Cl_3O_2$
Ethyl trichloroacetate

579. B = $C_4H_8O_2$
Ethyl acetate (158)
d_4^t =
(±0.05%)(157)

0 Mol % B
1.4126(1 − 0.001016t)
25 Mol % B
1.3217(1 − 0.001059t)
50 Mol % B
1.2141(1 − 0.001132t)
75 Mol % B
1.0839(1 − 0.001200t)
100 Mol % B
0.9230(1 − 0.001371t)

580. B = $C_4H_{10}O$
Ethyl ether (158)

581. B = $C_6H_5NO_2$
Nitrobenzene (158)

582. B = C_6H_6 (158)

583. B = C_6H_{14}
Hexane (158)

584. B = $C_8H_8O_2$
Methyl benzoate (158)

585. B = $C_{14}H_{10}$
Phenanthrene (158)

v. also 277, 340

$C_4H_5NO_2$
Methyl cyanoacetate

586. B = $C_8H_{20}IN$
Tetraethylammonium iodide
(330)[1]

v. also 501

$C_4H_5NO_2$
Succinimide
v. 383

C_4H_5NS
Allyl thiocyanate

587. B = C_5H_5N
Pyridine (165)[1]

588. B = $C_5H_{11}N$
Piperidine
(±0.05%)(165)

Mol % A	d_4^{25}
100	1.0125
90	1.0200
75	1.0692
60	1.0768
55	1.0813
52	1.0818
50	1.0804
48	1.0708
45	1.0571
40	1.0382
25	0.9728
10	0.9032
0	0.8565
Mol % A	**d_4^{50}**
100	0.9885
55	1.0638
52	1.0666
50	1.0668
48	1.0577
45	1.0447
0	0.8338
Mol % A	**d_4^{80}**
100	0.9537
55	1.0450
52	1.0457
50	1.0451
48	1.0337
45	1.0249
10	0.8526
0	0.8035

589. B = C_7H_9N
Methylaniline
(±0.05%)(165)

Mol % A	d_4^{25}
100	1.0124
90	1.0362
75	1.0586
60	1.0845
52	1.0970
50	1.0978
48	1.0929
45	1.0821
40	1.0703
25	1.0294
10	1.0282
0	0.9841
Mol % A	**d_4^{50}**
100	0.9885
90	1.0170
75	1.0346
60	1.0620
52	1.0677
50	1.0770
48	1.0723
45	1.0697
40	1.0508
25	1.0093
10	0.9857
0	0.9634

v. also 384

$C_4H_6O_3$
Acetic anhydride

590. B = $C_6H_{12}O_3$
Paraldehyde
(±0.075%)(68, 150)

Wt. % A	d_4^{10}
100.00	1.0897
90.00	1.0813
70.04	1.0633
50.00	1.0474
30.01	1.0309
9.98	1.0104
0.00	1.0037
Wt. % A	**$d_4^{76.5}$**
100.00	1.0096
90.00	1.0019
70.04	0.9860
50.00	0.9702
30.01	0.9533
9.98	0.9367
0.00	0.9248

v. also 314

$C_4H_6O_4$
Succinic acid
v. 195, 385, 502, 576

$C_4H_6O_5$
Malic acid
v. 196, 386, 503, 567

$C_4H_6O_6$
Tartaric acid

591. B = $C_4H_{10}O$
Ethyl ether (296)[1,2]

592. B = $C_5H_{12}O$
Isoamyl alcohol (296)[1,2]

593. B = C_6H_6 (296)[1,2]

v. also 12, 387

$C_4H_7ClO_2$
Ethyl chloroacetate

594. B = $C_4H_8O_2$
Ethyl acetate (158)

595. B = $C_5H_{10}O_2$
Methyl butyrate (158)

596. B = $C_6H_4Br_2$
p-Dibromobenzene (158)

597. B = C_6H_6 (158)

598. B = $C_6H_{10}O_3$
Ethyl acetoacetate (158)

599. B = C_6H_{14}
Hexane (158)

600. B = $C_7H_{14}O_2$
Isoamyl acetate (158)

601. B = $C_7H_{14}O_2$
Propyl butyrate (158)

602. B = $C_8H_8O_2$
Methyl benzoate (158)

603. B = $C_{10}H_8$
Naphthalene (158)

604. B = $C_{10}H_{16}O$
d-Camphor
(14.23–54.22 Wt. % B)(170)
d_4^{20} = (1.1224 − 0.0021
(Wt. % B − 14.23)) ±0.1%

605. B = $C_{12}H_{10}N_2$
Azobenzene (158)

606. B = $C_{14}H_{10}$
Phenanthrene (158)

607. B = $C_{18}H_{36}O_2$
Stearic acid (158)

v. also 278, 341, 504, 549

C_4H_8O
Methyl ethyl ketone
v. 505

$C_4H_8O_2$
Butyric acid

608. B = C_5H_5N
Pyridine
(±0.25%)(312)

Mol % B	d_4^{20}
100.0	0.976
81.8	0.982
64.2	0.988
52.8	0.993
42.9	0.998
25.6	0.991
15.2	0.984
0.0	0.965

$C_4H_8O_2$.—(*Continued*)

609. B = C_6H_6
(±0.05%)(135)

Wt. % B	d_4^{16}
100.00	0.8842
93.97	0.8866
65.81	0.9059
0.00	0.9633

610. B = C_7H_8
(±0.05%)(135)

Wt. % B	d_4^{16}
100.00	0.8694
90.23	0.8771
64.09	0.8996
0.00	0.9633

611. B = $C_{10}H_{16}O$
Camphor (323, 342)

v. also 169, 197, 315, 388

$C_4H_8O_2$

Isobutyric acid

612. B = C_6H_6 (233)[1]

v. also 45

$C_4H_8O_2$

Ethyl acetate

613. B = $C_4H_8O_2$
Propyl formate
(to 40°)(±0.025%)(24)

a	10^3b
100.00 Wt. % A	
0.92425	1.218*t*
49.754 Wt. % A	
0.92360	1.183*t*
0.00 Wt. % A	
0.92335	1.153*t*

614. B = C_5H_5N
Pyridine
(to 55°)(±0.025%)(178)
50 Wt. % A

a	10^3b
0.9573	1.071*t*

615. B = $C_5H_{10}O_2$
Isobutyl formate
(to 40°)(±0.025%)(24)

a	10^3b
100.00 Wt. % A	
0.92425	1.218*t*
54.886 Wt. % A	
0.91535	1.145*t*
0.00 Wt. % A	
0.90660	1.075*t*

616. B = $C_5H_{10}O_2$
Ethyl propionate (351, 352[1])

617. B = $C_6H_4Br_2$
p-Dibromobenzene (158)
(±0.005%)(318)

Wt. % B	d_4^{25}
0.000	0.89450
3.165	0.91100
5.302	0.92152
7.100	0.93073
12.355	0.95939
20.100	1.00447

618. B = $C_6H_4N_2O_4$
m-Dinitrobenzene (158)
(±0.005%)(47, 187)

Wt. % A	d_4^{30}
100.00	0.88894
74.25	0.99199
72.36	1.00014
69.15	1.01473
68.14	1.01935
67.40	1.02287
65.78	1.03021
65.56	1.03118
60.86	1.05349
56.79	1.07333
0.00	1.56563

(±0.025%)(318)

a	10^3b
(15°–70°)	
100.00 Wt. % A	
0.90728	1.259(*t* − 15)
(20°–60°)	
96.411 Wt. % A	
0.91366	1.232(*t* − 20)
(15°–60°)	
93.971 Wt. % A	
0.92868	1.226(*t* − 15)
(20°–60°)	
85.831 Wt. % A	
0.95438	1.206(*t* − 20)

619. B = $C_6H_5NO_2$
Nitrobenzene (158)
(±0.075%)(122)

Wt. % A	d_4^{20}
0.00	1.2034
15.00	1.1500
29.24	1.1023
36.57	1.0780
55.55	1.0193
79.98	0.9499
92.02	0.9191
100.00	0.8976

(±0.0075%)(171)

Wt. % A	d_4^{25}
0.000	1.19824
24.466	1.11280
43.892	1.05007
77.100	0.95398
100.000	0.89415

(50 Wt. % A)(±0.025%) (178)

t	d_4^t
0	1.0578
25	1.0303
40	1.0135
55	0.9970
70	0.9791

620. B = C_6H_6 (122, 142, 158, 176, 263[1])
(±0.0075%)(171)

Wt. % B	d_4^{25}
0.000	0.89415
15.594	0.89036
51.404	0.88262
80.803	0.87738
100.000	0.87420

(±0.025%)(178)
50 Wt. % B

a	10^3b
0.9105	1.2*t*

621. B = $C_6H_6O_2$
Resorcinol (49)
0–100 Wt. % B

$$\frac{1}{d_4^{30}} = [1.12616 - 0.0_2 42025\ \text{Wt. \% B} + 0.0_4 12997(\text{Wt. \% B})^2 - 0.0_7 264(\text{Wt. \% B})^3](\pm 0.005\%)$$

622. B = C_6H_7N
Aniline
(±0.25%)(345)

Mol % B	d_4^0
100.0	1.034
93.9	1.033
88.9	1.028
85.5	1.024
84.2	1.022
77.6	1.015
74.9	1.012
67.2	1.004
50.8	0.985
42.8	0.978
22.3	0.952
15.2	0.944
0.0	0.923
Mol % B	d_4^{-9}
0.0	0.932
27.0	0.966
78.0	1.210
Mol % B	d_4^{-10}
0.0	0.933
14.4	0.955
20.0	0.960
Mol % B	$d_4^{-19.5}$
45.1	1.012
27.0	0.976
0.0	0.941

623. B = $C_6H_{10}O_8$
Citric acid monohydrate
(296)[1,2]

624. B = $C_6H_{12}O_3$
Paraldehyde (158)

625. B = C_6H_{14}
Hexane (158)

626. B = C_7H_8
Toluene (158)
(±0.0075%)(171)

Wt. % A	d_4^{25}
100.000	0.88909
84.292	0.88342
54.699	0.87292
28.745	0.86401
0.000	0.85448

627. B = $C_7H_8O_6$
Gallic acid monohydrate
(296)[1,2]

628. B = $C_7H_{14}O_2$
Isoamyl acetate (99, 133)

d_4^t =
(±0.05%)(157)
0 Mol % B
0.9230(1 − 0.001710*t*)
51 Mol % B
0.9005(1 − 0.001176*t*)
100 Mol % B
0.8864(1 − 0.001087*t*)

629. B = $C_8H_8O_2$
Methyl benzoate (158)

630. B = C_8H_{10}
Ethyl benzene
(to 40°)(±0.025%)(24)

a	10^3b
100 Wt. % A	
0.92425	1.218*t*
54.969 Wt. % A	
0.90635	1.033*t*
0.00 Wt. % A	
0.89130	0.886*t*

631. B = $C_8H_{11}N$
Dimethylaniline
(±0.075%)(122)

Wt. % A	d_4^{20}
100.00	0.8977
90.64	0.9038
81.57	0.9097
60.11	0.9215
49.92	0.9319
22.68	0.9431
9.93	0.9503
0.00	0.9558

632. B = $C_8H_{14}O_4$
Ethyl succinate
d_4^t =
(±0.05%)(157)
0 Mol % A
1.0607(1 − 0.0_3978*t*)
10 Mol % A
1.0534(1 − 0.0_3969*t*)
25 Mol % A
1.0301(1 − 0.0_21026*t*)
37.5 Mol % A
1.0294(1 − 0.0_21041*t*)
50 Mol % A
1.0171(1 − 0.0_21032*t*)
75 Mol % A
0.9816(1 − 0.0_21179*t*)
100 Mol % A
0.9230(1 − 0.0_21371*t*)

633. B = $C_9H_{10}O_2$
Ethyl benzoate
(±0.1%)(152)

Mol % A	d_4^{25}
100.00	0.8948
89.92	0.9204
79.77	0.9440
69.89	0.9598
59.98	0.9740
50.44	0.9866
39.73	0.9992
31.31	1.0101
20.88	1.0223
12.16	1.0320
0.00	1.0431

d_4^t =
(±0.05%)(157)
0 Mol % A
$1.0648(1 - 0.0_3856t)$
25 Mol % A
$1.0458(1 - 0.0_3893t)$
50 Mol % A
$1.0329(1 - 0.0_3964t)$
75 Mol % A
$0.9726(1 - 0.0_21104t)$
100 Mol % A
$0.9230(1 - 0.0_21371t)$

634. B = $C_{10}H_8$
Naphthalene (158)
(to 2.808 Wt. % B)(54)
d_4^{18} = (0.90299 + 0.001321 Wt. % B) ±0.0075%

635. B = $C_{10}H_{14}$
Durene
(to 12.531 Wt. % B)(318)
d_4^{25} = $(0.89450 - 0.0_31979$ Wt. % B) ±0.005%

636. B = $C_{10}H_{15}BrO$
Bromocamphor
(±0.1%)(235)

Wt. % A	d_4^{25}
100.00	0.8947
99.54	0.8959
95.61	0.9083
79.24	0.9630
68.11	1.0031
61.10	1.0286

637. B = $C_{10}H_{16}O$
d-Camphor
(to 50 Wt. % B)(170, 175, 263)
d_4^{20} = $(0.8966 + 0.0_3672$ Wt. % B)
±0.1%
(to 51.69 Wt. % B)(235)
d_4^{25} = $(0.8948 + 0.0_365$ Wt. % B)
±0.1%

638. B = $C_{10}H_{22}O$
Isoamyl ether
(±0.05%)(157)
d_4^t =
0 Mol % A
$0.8048(1 - 0.0_21017t)$
25 Mol % A
$0.8210(1 - 0.0_21056t)$
50 Mol % A
$0.8413(1 - 0.0_21096t)$
75 Mol % A
$0.8737(1 - 0.0_21202t)$
100 Mol % A
$0.9230(1 - 0.0_21371t)$

639. B = $C_{12}H_{10}$
Acenaphthene (158)
(±0.005%)(318)

Wt. % A	d_4^{25}
100.000	0.89450
96.368	0.90103
93.439	0.90642
89.090	0.91389

640. B = $C_{12}H_{10}$
Diphenyl (158)
(to 17.194 Wt. % B)(318)
d_4^{25} = $(0.89450 + 0.0_21382$ Wt. % B) ±0.005%

641. B = $C_{12}H_{10}N_2$
Azobenzene (158)

642. B = $C_{12}H_{28}IN$
Tetrapropylammonium iodide (330)[1]

643. B = $C_{14}H_8O_2$
Phenanthraquinone (297,[1] 317[1,2])

644. B = $C_{14}H_{10}$
Phenanthrene (158)
(±0.025%)(318)

a	10^3b
(15°–70°)	
100.000 Wt. % A	
0.90728	1.259(*t* − 15)
(15°–60°)	
93.526 Wt. % A	
0.91550	1.1213(*t* − 15)
91.616 Wt. % A	
0.92353	1.188(*t* − 15)
(20°–70°)	
84.152 Wt. % A	
0.93231	1.142(*t* − 20)

645. B = $C_{14}H_{10}O_2$
Benzil (158)
(±0.005%)(318)

Wt. % A	d_4^{25}
100.000	0.89450
98.006	0.89911
95.775	0.90415
93.009	0.91066
84.862	0.92978

646. B = $C_{14}H_{12}O_2$
Benzyl benzoate (±0.1%) (152)

Mol % A	d_4^{25}
100.00	0.8948
89.80	0.9394
79.90	0.9720
69.73	0.9988
58.63	1.0247
50.00	1.0454
40.01	1.0625
30.02	1.0778
23.47	1.0867
14.26	1.0975
7.84	1.1048
0.00	1.1121

647. B = $C_{16}H_{32}O_2$
Palmitic acid (158)

648. B = $C_{18}H_{36}O_2$
Stearic acid (158, 296[1,2])

649. B = $C_{19}H_{16}$
Triphenylmethane (158)
(±0.005%)(318)

Wt. % A	d_4^{25}
100.000	0.89450
98.222	0.89764
93.655	0.90481
90.506	0.90981

v. also 13, 46, 161, 236, 316, 342, 362, 389, 546, 550, 579, 594, 1265, 1279

$C_4H_8O_2$
Methyl propionate
650. B = $C_6H_4Br_2$
p-Dibromobenzene (158)

651. B = C_6H_6 (158)

652. B = $C_{10}H_8$
Naphthalene (158)

653. B = $C_{12}H_{10}N_2$
Azobenzene (158)

$C_4H_8O_2$
Propyl formate
654. B = $C_5H_{10}O_2$
Isobutyl formate
(0°–40°)(±0.025%)(24)

a	10^3b
0 Wt. % B	
0.9234	1.153*t*
46.265 Wt. % B	
0.9149	1.114*t*
100.00 Wt. % B	
0.9066	1.075*t*

v. also 613

$C_4H_8O_3$
Methyl *l*-lactate
655. B = $C_6H_5NO_2$
Nitrobenzene
(±0.05%)(211)

a	10^3b
(−75° to +125°)	
0 Wt. % B	
1.2040	1.158(*t* + 75)
(16°–141°)	
90.12 Wt. % B	
1.1918	1.000(*t* − 16)

v. also 253

C_4H_9NO
Butyramide
v. 390

$C_4H_9NO_2$
Methylurethane
656. B = $C_{10}H_{20}O$
Menthol
(55.6°–99°)(±0.25%)(273)

a	10^3b
0.00 Mol % B	
1.136	1.060(*t*−55.6)
14.12 Mol % B	
1.027	0.945(*t*−55.6)
38.72 Mol % B	
0.961	0.853(*t*−55.6)
58.13 Mol % B	
0.923	0.829(*t*−55.6)
72.21 Mol % B	
0.904	0.898(*t*−55.6)
85.50 Mol % B	
0.884	0.807(*t*−55.6)
100.00 Mol % B	
0.869	0.737(*t*−55.6)

$C_4H_{10}O$
n-Butyl alcohol
657. B = C_6H_6 (238)[1]

658. B = $C_{10}H_{12}$
Tetrahydronaphthalene
(±0.075%)(121)

Wt. % A	d_4^{25}
100.00	0.8037
71.66	0.8441
42.87	0.8878
28.70	0.9105
15.10	0.9335
0.00	0.9656

659. B = $C_{10}H_{18}$
Decahydronaphthalene
(±0.075%)(121)

Wt. % A	d_4^{25}
100.00	0.8037
67.62	0.8262
50.57	0.8385
32.88	0.8520
17.41	0.8640
10.20	0.8702
0.00	0.8790

$C_4H_{10}O$
Isobutyl alcohol
660. B = $C_6H_5NO_2$
Nitrobenzene (192, 328)

661. B = C_6H_6 (233,[1] 351)

662. B = C_7H_5N
Cyanobenzene (192, 328)

663. B = $C_8H_{14}O_6$
Ethyl tartrate (235,[1] 340,[1] 343[1])
(±0.1%)(204, 288)

a	10^3b
(16.9°–83.7°)	
100.00 Wt. % A	
0.8053	0.854(*t*−16.9)
(18.5°–80.1°)	
95.00 Wt. % A	
0.8174	0.854(*t*−18.5)
(19.7°–83.4°)	
90.00 Wt. % A	
0.8311	0.863(*t*−19.7)
(14.7°–77.2°)	
75.00 Wt. % A	
0.8812	0.896(*t*−14.7)
(16°–77.6°)	
49.99 Wt. % A	
0.9683	0.941(*t* − 16)
(17.4°–82.8°)	
37.16 Wt. % A	
1.0198	0.971(*t*−17.4)
(18.4°–78.8°)	
24.97 Wt. % A	
1.0738	0.986(*t*−18.4)
(16.8°–99.4°)	
0.00 Wt. % A	
1.2085	1.016(*t*−16.8)

664. B = $C_{10}H_{14}N_2$
Nicotine (343)[1]

$C_4H_{10}O$.—(*Continued*)

665. B = $C_{10}H_{16}O$
Camphor (323, 342)
(±0.1%)(235)

Wt. % A	d_4^{25}
100.00	0.7994
99.02	0.8007
95.06	0.8065
76.02	0.8330
53.85	0.8666
43.35	0.8825

666. B = $C_{10}H_{18}O_6$
Dipropyl tartrate
(20°–60°)(±0.1%)(340)

a	10^3b
0.00 Wt. % A	
1.1389	0.9050(t − 20)
21.21 Wt. % A	
1.0492	0.9125(t − 20)
41.24 Wt. % A	
0.9750	0.8800(t − 20)
59.15 Wt. % A	
0.9172	0.8425(t − 20)
76.84 Wt. % A	
0.8645	0.8200(t − 20)
84.69 Wt. % A	
0.8449	0.8100(t − 20)

v. also 47, 170, 198, 391

$C_4H_{10}O$

Trimethylcarbinol

667. B = C_6H_6O
Phenol
(±0.075%)(232)

Wt. % B	d_4^{25}
79.63	1.0032
49.25	0.9105
29.23	0.8571
24.87	0.8442
0.00	0.7825
Wt. % B	d_4^{46}
100.00	1.0455
79.63	0.9852
49.25	0.8918
29.23	0.8375
24.87	0.8238
0.00	0.7561

$C_4H_{10}O$

Ethyl ether

668. B = C_5H_{10}
Amylene (103)

669. B = C_5H_{12}
Pentane (61)

670. B = $C_6H_4Br_2$
p-Dibromobenzene (158)
(±0.005%)(318)

Wt. % B	d_4^{25}
0.000	0.70803
2.712	0.72129
7.492	0.74567
7.801	0.74708
15.710	0.79138

671. B = $C_6H_5NO_2$
Nitrobenzene
(±0.05%)(107)

Wt. % A	d_4^{20}
0.00	1.2037
10.35	1.1340
20.21	1.0729
34.34	0.9946
48.85	0.9212
65.87	0.8430
84.21	0.7710
100.00	0.7132

672. B = C_6H_6 (32,[1] 35, 59,[1] 61, 95,[1] 103, 158, 171,[1] 240, 280,[1] 282,[1] 355[1])
(to 40°)(±0.0075%)(101)

$\frac{1}{d_4^t}$ =

0.000 Wt. % B
$1.35729(1 + 0.0_215006t + 0.0_54370t^2)$
16.294 Wt. % B
$1.31370(1 + 0.0_214371t + 0.0_53355t^2)$
29.813 Wt. % B
$1.27993(1 + 0.0_213536t + 0.0_53660t^2)$
51.087 Wt. % B
$1.22752(1 + 0.0_212790t + 0.0_52570t^2)$
69.739 Wt. % B
$1.18308(1 + 0.0_212260t + 0.0_52380t^2)$
84.946 Wt. % B
$1.14745(1 + 0.0_211965t + 0.0_51850t^2)$
100.00 Wt. % B
$1.11235(1 + 0.0_211715t + 0.0_6155t^2)$

673. B = C_6H_7N
Aniline
(±0.05%)(107)

Wt. % B	d_4^{20}
100.00	1.0220
85.46	0.9732
69.22	0.9210
55.55	0.8785
45.80	0.8487
44.15	0.8437
37.81	0.8247
28.23	0.7961
19.62	0.7705
0.00	0.7131

674. B = $C_6H_8O_7$
Citric acid (296)[1,2]

675. B = $C_6H_{10}O_8$
Citric acid monohydrate (296)[1,2]

676. B = $C_7H_6O_2$
Benzoic acid (296,[1,2] 303)

677. B = $C_7H_6O_3$
Salicylic acid (296,[1,2] 303)

678. B = C_7H_8
Toluene
(15°–35°)(±0.05%)(95)

a	10^3b
71.30 Wt. % A	
0.7628	1.10(t − 15)
45.25 Wt. % A	
0.8012	0.99(t − 15)
21.60 Wt. % A	
0.8388	1.16(t − 15)

679. B = C_7H_8O
Benzyl alcohol (10)

680. B = $C_7H_8O_6$
Gallic acid monohydrate (296)[1,2]

681. B = $C_8H_8O_2$
Methyl benzoate (158)

682. B = $C_8H_{10}O$
Phenetole
(±0.1%)(152)

Mol % A	d_4^{25}
100.00	0.7139
90.04	0.7458
83.03	0.7656
75.85	0.7891
68.82	0.8059
60.48	0.8283
55.79	0.8387
51.06	0.8488
45.01	0.8628
35.16	0.8853
30.26	0.8970
25.23	0.9083
18.55	0.9230
9.75	0.9427
7.45	0.9471
0.00	0.9618

683. B = $C_{10}H_7Br$
α-Bromonaphthalene (61)

684. B = $C_{10}H_8$
Naphthalene (54,[1] 158, 303)
(±0.005%)(85)

Wt. % A	d_4^{18}
100.000	0.71640
94.759	0.73043
90.167	0.74298
84.903	0.75747
80.088	0.77094
74.490	0.78699
70.342	0.79939

685. B = $C_{10}H_{14}N_2$
Nicotine (110, 341)

686. B = $C_{10}H_{16}O$
d-Camphor (53)

687. B = $C_{10}H_{16}O_4$
Camphoric acid (296)[1,2]

688. B = $C_{10}H_{17}Cl$
Pinene hydrochloride (53)
(9.11–63.26 Wt. % B)
$d_4^{15} = (0.735 + 0.0_22825$ (Wt. % B − 9.11)) ±0.5%

689. B = $C_{12}H_{10}$
Acenaphthene (158)
(±0.005%)(318)

Wt. % A	d_4^{25}
100.000	0.70803
96.189	0.71935
93.607	0.72723
92.521	0.73034

690. B = $C_{12}H_{10}$
Diphenyl
(±0.005%)(318)

Wt. % A	d_4^{25}
100.000	0.70803
97.886	0.71351
96.350	0.71759
91.945	0.72962
88.797	0.73904

691. B = $C_{12}H_{10}N_2$
Azobenzene (158)
(±0.005%)(318)

Wt. % B	d_4^{25}
0.000	0.70803
2.014	0.71366
5.831	0.72486
7.691	0.73336
16.592	0.75798

692. B = $C_{12}H_{10}O$
Diphenyl ether
(±0.1%)(152)

Wt. % A	d_4^{25}
100.00	0.7139
90.92	0.7601
78.26	0.8213
70.88	0.8554
60.76	0.8974
51.02	0.9311
42.35	0.9583
32.97	0.9862
21.93	1.0181
13.18	1.0387
7.04	1.0542
0.00	1.0706

693. B = $C_{14}H_{10}$
Phenanthrene (158)

694. B = $C_{14}H_{10}O_2$
Benzil (158)
(±0.005%)(318)

Wt. % A	d_4^{25}
100.000	0.70803
97.900	0.71475
95.182	0.72378
89.507	0.74309

695. B = $C_{16}H_{32}O_2$
Palmitic acid (158)

696. B = $C_{18}H_{34}O_2$
Oleic acid
(±0.25%)(38)

Wt. % A	d_4^{30}
0.00	0.8859
9.52	0.8690
24.55	0.8429
40.91	0.8118
53.29	0.7896
100.00	0.7010

697. B = $C_{18}H_{36}O_2$
Stearic acid (296)[1,2]

698. B = $C_{19}H_{16}$
Triphenylmethane (158)
(±0.005%)(318)

Wt. % A	d_4^{25}
100.000	0.70803
98.453	0.71230
92.160	0.73048

698.5. B = **Turpentine**
(±0.025%)(123)

Wt. % A	d_4^{15}
100.00	0.7193
80.19	0.7465
59.88	0.7741
40.40	0.8015
20.57	0.8313
0.00	0.8617

v. also 14, 48, 85, 98, 199, 237, 241, 254, 279, 302, 317, 343, 363, 392, 506, 562, 568, 580, 591, 1265, 1274

$C_4H_{11}N$

Diethylamine

699. B = C_7H_5NS
Phenyl thiocyanate
(±0.05%)(165)

Mol % A	d_4^{25}
0.0	1.1287
10.0	1.1237
25.0	1.1167
40.0	1.1134
45.0	1.1113
48.0	1.1100
50.0	1.1090
52.0	1.0994
55.0	1.0874
60.0	1.0465
66.7	0.9959
75.0	0.9299
90.0	0.7888
100.0	0.7004
Mol % A	d_4^{35}
0.0	1.1201
10.0	1.1134
25.0	1.1087
40.0	1.1051
45.0	1.1034
48.0	1.1027
50.0	1.1018
52.0	1.0925
55.0	1.0792
60.0	1.0382
66.7	0.9875
75.0	0.9208
90.0	0.7799
100.0	0.6894
Mol % A	d_4^{50}
0.0	1.1060
10.0	1.1004
25.0	1.0958
40.0	1.0932
45.0	1.0921
48.0	1.0918
50.0	1.0909
52.0	1.0804
55.0	1.0677

$C_4H_{12}ClN$

Diethylammonium chloride

v. 99

$C_4H_{12}IN$

Tetramethylammonium iodide

700. B = $C_7H_6O_2$
Salicylaldehyde (330)[1]

v. also 176, 200, 393, 489

$C_4H_{12}N_2O_3$

Diethylammonium nitrate

v. 100

$C_5H_4O_2$, Furfural

701. B = $C_8H_{20}IN$
Tetraethylammonium iodide (330)[1]

C_5H_5N

Pyridine

702. B = C_6H_5ClO
o-Chlorophenol
(±0.01%)(28)

Wt. % A	d_4^{0}
100.00	1.0013
88.83	1.0288
78.38	1.0554
68.43	1.0820
57.69	1.1122
48.52	1.1401
39.85	1.1672
32.53	1.1892
27.50	1.2038
23.07	1.2160
18.94	1.2270
14.83	1.2382
7.49	1.2558
0.00	1.2737
Wt. % A	d_4^{10}
100.00	0.9916
88.83	1.0190
78.38	1.0459
68.43	1.0725
57.69	1.1029
48.52	1.1307
39.85	1.1578
32.53	1.1796
27.50	1.1939
23.07	1.2060
18.94	1.2169
14.83	1.2276
7.49	1.2451
0.00	1.2622
Wt. % A	d_4^{20}
100.00	0.9819
88.83	1.0093
78.38	1.0364
68.43	1.0630
57.69	1.0936
48.52	1.1212
39.85	1.1485
32.53	1.1699
27.50	1.1841
23.07	1.1961
18.94	1.2064
14.83	1.2175
7.49	1.2342
0.00	1.2508
Wt. % A	d_4^{30}
100.00	0.9723
88.83	0.9995
78.38	1.0267
68.43	1.0535
57.69	1.0842
48.52	1.1119
39.85	1.1391
32.53	1.1603
27.50	1.1741
23.07	1.1858
18.94	1.1959
14.83	1.2062
7.49	1.2234
0.00	1.2397
Wt. % A	d_4^{40}
100.00	0.9627
88.83	0.9896
78.38	1.0171
68.43	1.0441
57.69	1.0749
48.52	1.1026
39.85	1.1296
32.53	1.1507
27.50	1.1643
23.07	1.1757
18.94	1.1855
14.83	1.1956
7.49	1.2126
0.00	1.2282
Wt. % A	d_4^{60}
100.00	0.9425
88.83	0.9696
78.38	0.9976
68.43	1.0250
57.69	1.0560
48.52	1.0838
39.85	1.1109
32.53	1.1317
27.50	1.1446
23.07	1.1557
18.94	1.1652
14.83	1.1751
7.49	1.1913
0.00	1.2058
Wt. % A	d_4^{80}
100.00	0.9219
88.83	0.9499
78.38	0.9783
68.43	1.0058
57.69	1.0373
48.52	1.0650
39.85	1.0920
32.53	1.1123
27.50	1.1246
23.07	1.1357
18.94	1.1449
14.83	1.1546
7.49	1.1701
0.00	1.1832
Wt. % A	d_4^{110}
100.00	0.8901
88.83	0.9199
78.38	0.9493
68.43	0.9770
57.69	1.0080
48.52	1.0357
39.85	1.0621
32.53	1.0821
27.50	1.0941
23.07	1.1047
18.94	1.1138
14.83	1.1231
7.49	1.1375
0.00	1.1489

703. B = $C_6H_5NO_3$
o-Nitrophenol
(±0.01%)(28)

Wt. % A	d_4^{30}
100.00	0.9723
88.68	1.0047
79.26	1.0331
72.42	1.0543
60.38	1.0934
47.75	1.1361
39.76	1.1643
31.68	1.1927
23.21	1.2231
13.04	1.2574
8.75	1.2726
0.00	1.3041
Wt. % A	d_4^{40}
100.00	0.9627
88.68	0.9947
79.26	1.0231
72.42	1.0442
60.38	1.0830
47.75	1.1256
39.76	1.1535
31.68	1.1819
23.21	1.2123
13.04	1.2470
8.75	1.2618
0.00	1.2938
Wt. % A	$d_4^{60.1}$
100.00	0.9425
88.68	0.9740
79.26	1.0022
72.42	1.0232
60.38	1.0616
47.75	1.1036
39.76	1.1316
31.68	1.1597
23.21	1.1902
13.04	1.2248
8.75	1.2398
0.00	1.2708
Wt. % A	d_4^{80}
100.00	0.9219
88.68	0.9536
79.26	0.9816
72.42	1.0025
60.38	1.0407
47.75	1.0823
39.76	1.1102

C_5H_5N.—*(Continued)*

B = $C_6H_5NO_3$.—*(Continued)*

Wt. % A	d_4^{80}
31.68	1.1382
23.21	1.1684
13.04	1.2033
8.75	1.2183
0.00	1.2480

704. B = C_6H_6 (14)

(±0.05%)(73)

Wt. % B	d_4^{25}
100.00	0.8737
60.27	0.9144
40.65	0.9347
20.36	0.9556
10.23	0.9660
0.00	0.9783

705. B = C_6H_6O

Phenol

(±0.01%)(27)

Wt. % B	d_4^{10}
0.00	0.9916
17.26	1.0101
26.01	1.0196
35.14	1.0294
45.48	1.0412
51.89	1.0479
58.46	1.0543
66.99	1.0617
76.81	1.0699
82.86	1.0741
91.89	1.0786
100.00	1.0835
Wt. % B	**d_4^{20}**
0.00	0.9819
8.30	0.9916
16.12	1.0005
24.36	1.0096
32.58	1.0187
38.94	1.0258
47.13	1.0349
54.96	1.0429
63.81	1.0513
70.49	1.0567
77.94	1.0619
85.17	1.0667
92.45	1.0709
100.00	1.0751
Wt. % B	**d_4^{30}**
0.00	0.9723
8.30	0.9820
16.12	0.9909
24.36	1.0002
32.58	1.0096
38.94	1.0167
47.13	1.0260
54.96	1.0343
63.81	1.0426
70.49	1.0482
77.94	1.0533
85.17	1.0582
92.45	1.0624
100.00	1.0667
Wt. % B	**d_4^{40}**
0.00	0.9627
8.30	0.9724
16.12	0.9814
24.36	0.9909
32.58	1.0005
38.94	1.0077
47.13	1.0173
54.96	1.0257
63.81	1.0341
70.49	1.0397
77.94	1.0449
85.17	1.0498
92.45	1.0539
100.00	1.0583
Wt. % B	**d_4^{60}**
0.00	0.9425
8.30	0.9524
16.12	0.9620
24.36	0.9720
32.58	0.9821
38.94	0.9897
47.13	0.9995
54.96	1.0083
63.81	1.0168
70.49	1.0226
77.94	1.0279
85.17	1.0327
92.45	1.0369
100.00	1.0414
Wt. % B	**d_4^{80}**
0.00	0.9219
8.30	0.9325
16.12	0.9429
24.36	0.9532
32.58	0.9639
38.94	0.9718
47.13	0.9821
54.96	0.9910
63.81	0.9995
70.49	1.0053
77.94	1.0107
85.17	1.0155
92.45	1.0198
100.00	1.0242
Wt. % B	**d_4^{110}**
0.00	0.8901
8.30	0.9015
16.12	0.9120
24.36	0.9235
32.58	0.9348
38.94	0.9431
47.13	0.9535
54.96	0.9626
63.81	0.9719
70.49	0.9779
77.94	0.9833
85.17	0.9878
92.45	0.9923
100.00	0.9967

706. B = C_6H_7N

Aniline (267)[1]

(0°–100°)(±0.25%)(79)

a	10^3b
100 Mol % B	
1.033	0.800t
50 Mol % B	
1.025	0.885t
0 Mol % B	
1.001	0.964t

707. B = $C_6H_{10}O_3$

Ethyl acetoacetate

(±0.05%)(71)

Wt. % A	d_4^{25}
100.00	0.9782
82.89	0.9853
67.91	0.9916
49.00	0.9999
28.93	1.0091
0.00	1.0222

708. B = $C_7H_6O_2$

Benzoic acid

(±0.1%)(12)

Mol % A	d_4^{110}
100.0	0.8897
60.0	1.0122
50.0	1.0326
44.0	1.0455
38.0	1.0560
33.3	1.0626
28.0	1.0694
25.0	1.0713
18.0	1.0747
Mol % A	**d_4^{125}**
60.0	0.9999
50.0	1.0189
44.0	1.0325
38.0	1.0440
33.3	1.0494
28.0	1.0560
25.0	1.0581
18.0	1.0612
14.0	1.0698
8.0	1.0740
0.0	1.0769
Mol % A	**d_4^{140}**
50.0	1.0059
44.0	1.0182
38.0	1.0304
33.3	1.0362
28.0	1.0418
25.0	1.0447
18.0	1.0495
14.0	1.0560
8.0	1.0605

709. B = C_7H_7NO

Benzamide

(to 12.46 Wt. % B)(70)

$d_4^{25} = (0.9746 + 0.0_21087$ Wt. % B) ±0.05%

710. B = C_7H_7NO

Formanilide

(to 19.14 Wt. % B)(70)

$d_4^{25} = (0.9746 + 0.0_21537$ Wt. % B) ±0.05%

711. B = C_7H_8O

o-Cresol (±0.01%)(28)

Wt. % B	d_4^{0}
0.00	1.0013
12.05	1.0100
24.55	1.0197
33.60	1.0267
45.83	1.0364
55.91	1.0438
66.83	1.0513
77.73	1.0573
85.72	1.0605
91.85	1.0628
100.00	1.0653
Wt. % B	**d_4^{10}**
0.00	0.9916
12.05	1.0005
24.55	1.0104
33.60	1.0178
45.83	1.0279
55.91	1.0355
66.83	1.0430
77.73	1.0491
85.72	1.0521
91.85	1.0544
100.00	1.0567
Wt. % B	**d_4^{20}**
0.00	0.9819
12.05	0.9912
24.55	1.0012
33.60	1.0091
45.83	1.0196
55.91	1.0273
66.83	1.0348
77.73	1.0408
85.72	1.0439
91.85	1.0461
100.00	1.0483
Wt. % B	**d_4^{30}**
0.00	0.9723
12.05	0.9818
24.55	0.9928
33.60	1.0005
45.83	1.0112
55.91	1.0190
66.83	1.0265
77.73	1.0324
85.72	1.0356
91.85	1.0376
100.00	1.0399
Wt. % B	**d_4^{40}**
0.00	0.9627
12.05	0.9722
24.55	0.9835
33.60	0.9918
45.83	1.0026
55.91	1.0105
66.83	1.0180
77.73	1.0238
85.72	1.0270
91.85	1.0290
100.00	1.0312
Wt. % B	**d_4^{60}**
0.00	0.9425
12.05	0.9531
24.55	0.9653
33.60	0.9742
45.83	0.9855

Wt. % B	d_4^{60}
55.91	0.9937
66.83	1.0013
77.73	1.0070
85.72	1.0099
91.85	1.0117
100.00	1.0137
Wt. % B	d_4^{80}
0.00	0.9219
12.05	0.9341
24.55	0.9473
33.60	0.9565
45.83	0.9684
55.91	0.9767
66.83	0.9846
77.73	0.9901
85.72	0.9929
91.85	0.9946
100.00	0.9963
Wt. % B	d_4^{110}
0.00	0.8901
12.05	0.9041
24.55	0.9179
33.60	0.9277
45.83	0.9404
55.91	0.9491
66.83	0.9570
77.73	0.9623
85.72	0.9649
91.85	0.9664
100.00	0.9678

712. B = C_7H_8O
m-Cresol
(±0.1%)(28)

Wt. % B	d_4^{0}
0.00	1.0013
14.09	1.0098
27.45	1.0181
41.40	1.0264
46.92	1.0296
55.33	1.0345
61.80	1.0377
70.62	1.0418
75.90	1.0439
85.17	1.0467
91.41	1.0479
100.00	1.0493
Wt. % B	d_4^{10}
0.00	0.9916
14.09	1.0003
27.45	1.0088
41.40	1.0175
46.92	1.0209
55.33	1.0260
61.80	1.0294
70.62	1.0336
75.90	1.0357
85.17	1.0385
91.41	1.0399
100.00	1.0413
Wt. % B	d_4^{20}
0.00	0.9819
14.09	0.9908
27.45	0.9995
41.40	1.0086
46.92	1.0121
55.33	1.0174
61.80	1.0211
70.62	1.0254
75.90	1.0275
85.17	1.0303
91.41	1.0318
100.00	1.0333
Wt. % B	d_4^{30}
0.00	0.9723
14.09	0.9813
27.45	0.9902
41.40	0.9998
46.92	1.0033
55.33	1.0089
61.80	1.0128
70.62	1.0172
75.90	1.0193
85.17	1.0221
91.41	1.0237
100.00	1.0253
Wt. % B	d_4^{40}
0.00	0.9627
14.09	0.9718
27.45	0.9809
41.40	0.9909
46.92	0.9946
55.33	1.0003
61.80	1.0045
70.62	1.0089
75.90	1.0110
85.17	1.0139
91.41	1.0155
100.00	1.0173
Wt. % B	d_4^{60}
0.00	0.9425
14.09	0.9527
27.45	0.9630
41.40	0.9737
46.92	0.9778
55.33	0.9839
61.80	0.9882
70.62	0.9930
75.90	0.9951
85.17	0.9981
91.41	0.9997
100.00	1.0015
Wt. % B	d_4^{80}
0.00	0.9219
14.47	0.9344
26.75	0.9448
38.43	0.9545
50.72	0.9644
61.52	0.9721
70.94	0.9772
82.33	0.9817
90.88	0.9836
100.00	0.9853
Wt. % B	d_4^{110}
0.00	0.8901
14.47	0.9037
26.75	0.9155
38.43	0.9265
50.72	0.9376
61.52	0.9456
70.94	0.9511
82.33	0.9555
90.88	0.9576
100.00	0.9594

713. B = C_7H_8O
p-Cresol
(±0.01%)(28)

Wt. % B	d_4^{0}
0.00	1.0013
21.03	1.0145
29.61	1.0200
40.04	1.0265
46.71	1.0305
54.46	1.0351
60.37	1.0385
67.82	1.0419
75.36	1.0445
83.28	1.0464
91.01	1.0477
100.00	1.0487
Wt. % B	d_4^{10}
0.00	0.9916
21.03	1.0051
29.61	1.0108
40.04	1.0176
46.71	1.0219
54.46	1.0267
60.37	1.0302
67.82	1.0338
75.36	1.0365
83.28	1.0386
91.01	1.0400
100.00	1.0412
Wt. % B	d_4^{20}
0.00	0.9819
21.03	0.9957
29.61	1.0016
40.04	1.0087
46.71	1.0132
54.46	1.0182
60.37	1.0217
67.82	1.0254
75.36	1.0283
83.28	1.0306
91.01	1.0320
100.00	1.0335
Wt. % B	d_4^{30}
0.00	0.9723
21.03	0.9865
29.61	0.9926
40.04	1.0000
46.71	1.0046
54.46	1.0099
60.37	1.0133
67.82	1.0170
75.36	1.0200
83.28	1.0223
91.01	1.0239
100.00	1.0257
Wt. % B	d_4^{40}
0.00	0.9627
21.03	0.9773
29.61	0.9836
40.04	0.9913
46.71	0.9962
54.46	1.0014
60.37	1.0048
67.82	1.0086
75.36	1.0117
83.28	1.0140
91.01	1.0159
100.00	1.0177
Wt. % B	d_4^{60}
0.00	0.9425
21.03	0.9592
29.61	0.9661
40.04	0.9744
46.71	0.9795
54.46	0.9850
60.37	0.9888
67.82	0.9927
75.36	0.9959
83.28	0.9984
91.01	1.0005
100.00	1.0026
Wt. % B	d_4^{80}
0.00	0.9219
14.06	0.9344
27.48	0.9463
41.10	0.9575
54.03	0.9679
63.11	0.9741
71.88	0.9792
81.72	0.9828
89.95	0.9850
100.00	0.9868
Wt. % B	d_4^{110}
0.00	0.8901
14.06	0.9038
27.48	0.9166
41.10	0.9292
54.03	0.9411
63.11	0.9475
71.88	0.9527
81.72	0.9566
89.95	0.9588
100.00	0.9604

714. B = $C_8H_5NO_2$
Phthalimide
(to 11.93 Wt. % B)(70)
$d_4^{25} = (0.9746 + 0.0_2263$ Wt. % B) ±0.05%

715. B = $C_8H_{14}O_3$
Ethyl ethylacetoacetate
(±0.05%)(71)

Wt. % A	d_4^{25}
100.00	0.9742
87.30	0.9743
59.38	0.9750
36.01	0.9755
14.67	0.9751
0.00	0.9750

C_5H_5N.—(*Continued*)

716. B = $C_8H_{14}O_6$
Ethyl tartrate
(±0.05%)(209)
19.26 Wt. % B

t	d_4^t
0.0	1.0410
13.8	1.0277
15.7	1.0262
43.6	0.9981
58.6	0.9878
66.3	0.9742
91.6	0.9477
100.0	0.9387

717. B = $C_{10}H_8$
Naphthalene
(to 3.113 Wt. % A)(54)
d_4^{18} = (0.97112 + 0.0_35915 Wt. % A) ±0.0075%

718. B = $C_{10}H_{18}O_3$
Ethyl diethylacetoacetate
(±0.05%)(71)

Wt. % A	d_4^{25}
100.00	0.9782
97.17	0.9781
93.09	0.9777
78.90	0.9758
49.17	0.9719
0.00	0.9646

719. B = $C_{13}H_{11}NO$
Benzanilide
(to 12.75 Wt. % B)(70)
d_4^{25} = (0.9746 + 0.0_21709 Wt. % B) ± 0.05%

720. B = $C_{13}H_{12}N_2O$
Carbanilide
(to 7.18 Wt. % B)(70)
d_4^{25} = (0.9746 + 0.0_21615 Wt. % B) ± 0.05%

721. B = $C_{13}H_{12}N_2S$
Thiocarbanilide
(±0.05%)(70)

Wt. % A	d_4^{25}
100.00	0.9746
92.60	0.9919
85.49	1.0050

722. B = $C_{14}H_9NO_2$
Phthalanil (70)[1]

723. B = $C_{20}H_{16}Br_2O_8$
Methyl di-[*o*-bromobenzoyl]-tartrate (88)

v. also 15, 171, 183, 185, 318, 354, 370, 394, 491, 558, 559, 563, 587, 608, 614

$C_5H_7NO_2$

Ethyl cyanoacetate
724. B = $C_8H_{20}IN$
Tetraethylammonium iodide (330)[1]

C_5H_8O

Propargyl ethyl ether
725. B = $C_7H_{14}O_2$
Isoamyl acetate
(0–100 Wt. % A)(125)
d_4^{25} = (0.8664 − 0.0_334 Wt. % A) ± 0.05%

$C_5H_8O_2$

Acetylacetone
726. B = $C_8H_{20}IN$
Tetraethylammonium iodide (329)[1]

$C_5H_8O_3$

Methyl acetoacetate
727. B = $C_8H_{14}O_6$
Ethyl tartrate
(±0.05%)(223)

a	10^3b
(15.3°–54°)	
10.21 Wt. % B	
1.0919	1.033(t−15.3)
(16.9°–57.3°)	
25.23 Wt. % B	
1.1102	1.071(t−16.9)
(15.6°–56.2°)	
50.46 Wt. % B	
1.1429	1.011(t−15.6)

$C_5H_8O_4$

Dimethyl malonate
728. B = $C_8H_{20}IN$
Tetraethylammonium iodide (330)[1]

728.5. B = $C_{12}H_{28}IN$
Tetrapropylammonium iodide (330)[1]

C_5H_{10}

Amylene
729. B = C_6H_6 (103)

730. B = C_6H_7N
Aniline
(±0.25%)(314)

Wt. % B	d_4^{20}
0.0	0.658
27.8	0.743
61.1	0.857
76.0	0.913
100.0	1.022

v. also 49, 101, 280, 395, 668

$C_5H_{10}O$

Allyl ethyl ether
731. B = $C_7H_{14}O_2$
Isoamyl acetate
(±0.05%)(125)

Wt. % B	d_4^{25}
100.00	0.8664
94.36	0.8628
89.42	0.8591
0.00	0.7993

$C_5H_{10}O_2$

Valeric acid
732. B = $C_{10}H_{16}O$
Camphor (323, 342)

$C_5H_{10}O_2$

Isovaleric acid
v. 50

$C_5H_{10}O_2$

Isobutyl formate
733. B = $C_5H_{10}O_2$
Ethyl propionate
(0°–40°)(±0.025%)(24)

a	10^3b
100.00 Wt. % A	
0.9066	1.075t
49.875 Wt. % A	
0.9094	1.106t
0.000 Wt. % A	
0.9122	1.139t

734. B = $C_5H_{10}O_2$
Propyl acetate
(0°–40°)(±0.025%)(24)

a	10^3b
100.000 Wt. % A	
0.9066	1.075t
50.556 Wt. % A	
0.9076	1.094t
0.000 Wt. % A	
0.9084	1.111t

735. B = C_8H_{10}
Ethylbenzene
(0°–40°)(±0.025%)(24)

a	10^3b
0.000 Wt. % A	
0.8913	0.8863t
51.162 Wt. % A	
0.8983	0.9788t
100.000 Wt. % A	
0.9066	1.0750t

v. also 615, 654

$C_5H_{10}O_2$

Ethyl propionate
736. B = $C_5H_{10}O_2$
Propyl acetate
(to 40°)(±0.025%)(24)

a	10^3b
100.000 Wt. % A	
0.91220	1.139t
49.776 Wt. % A	
0.91020	1.124t
0.000 Wt. % A	
0.90835	1.111t

737. B = C_5H_{12}
Isopentane (24)[1]

738. B = $C_6H_4Br_2$
p-Dibromobenzene (158)

739. B = C_6H_6 (158)

740. B = C_9H_{12}
1, 2, 4-Trimethylbenzene
(to 40°)(±0.025%)(24)

a	10^3b
100.000 Wt. % A	
0.91220	1.1388t
53.579 Wt. % A	
0.90180	0.9675t
0.000 Wt. % A	
0.89260	0.8088t

741. B = $C_{10}H_8$
Naphthalene (158)

742. B = $C_{12}H_{10}N_2$
Azobenzene (158)

v. also 616, 733

$C_5H_{10}O_2$

Methyl butyrate
743. B = $C_6H_4Br_2$
p-Dibromobenzene (158)

744. B = C_6H_6 (158)

745. B = $C_{10}H_8$
Naphthalene (158)

746. B = $C_{12}H_{10}N_2$
Azobenzene (158)

747. B = $C_{14}H_{10}$
Phenanthrene (158)

v. also 595

$C_5H_{10}O_2$

Propyl acetate
748. B = $C_6H_{12}O_2$
Amyl formate
(±0.05%)(157)
d_4^t =
0 Mol % B
0.9049(1 − 0.0_21203t)
26 Mol % B
0.9029(1 − 0.0_21171t)
70 Mol % B
0.8999(1 − 0.0_21125t)
100 Mol % B
0.8971(1 − 0.0_21097t)

749. B = C_6H_{14}
Isohexane (24)[1]

750. B = C_9H_{12}
1, 2, 4-Trimethylbenzene
(to 40°)(±0.025%)(24)

a	10^3b
100.000 Wt. % A	
0.9084	1.1112t
53.615 Wt. % A	
0.9000	0.9575t
0.000 Wt. % A	
0.8926	0.8075t

v. also 734, 736

$C_5H_{10}O_3$

Methyl *l*-α-methoxypropionate
751. B = $C_6H_5NO_2$
Nitrobenzene
(±0.05%)(211)
(−16.6° to +130°)

a	10^3b
0.00 Wt. % B	
1.0361	1.143(t+16.6)
(16.6°–119°)	
90.10 Wt. % B	
1.1841	1.022(t − 16.6)

v. also 255

$C_5H_{11}Br$

l-Amyl bromide
752. B = $C_{10}H_{17}NO$
d-Camphoroxime (145)

753. B = $C_{10}H_{17}NO$
l-Camphoroxime (145)

$C_5H_{11}N$, Piperidine

754. B = C_6H_6 (142)

755. B = C_7H_8
Toluene (122, 251)
$d_4^{46.6}$ = (0.8380 − $0.0_4 17$ Mol % A) ±0.1%
(83.33 Mol % B)(±0.1%)

t	d_4^t
14.5	0.8684
46.6	0.8377
78.4	0.8077
132.5	0.7535

v. also 495, 588

C_5H_{12}

Pentane
v. 102, 669

C_5H_{12}

Isopentane
756. B = C_6H_{14}
n-Hexane (24)[1]

757. B = C_9H_{12}
Trimethylbenzene (24)[1]

v. also 737

$C_5H_{12}O$

Amyl alcohol
758. B = C_6H_6 (35, 39[1])

759. B = $C_8H_{20}IN$
Tetraethylammonium iodide (331)[1]

v. also 103, 201, 396, 507

$C_5H_{12}O$

Isoamyl alcohol
760. B = $C_6H_5NO_2$
Nitrobenzene
(±0.075%)(68, 150)

Wt. % A	d_4^0
100.00	0.8253
90.02	0.8541
70.01	0.9166
50.00	0.9866
29.98	1.0703
9.94	1.1664
0.00	1.2206

Wt. % A	d_4^{80}
100.00	0.7636
90.02	0.7914
70.03	0.8497
49.96	0.9151
30.03	0.9943
10.06	1.0875
0.00	1.1444

760.5. B = C_6H_6 (351)
(±0.1%) (361)

Wt. % A	$d_4^{18.4}$
0.000	0.8800
0.911	0.8800
1.727	0.8798
2.520	0.8792
3.655	0.8785
8.670	0.8754
12.670	0.8727
18.495	0.8686
36.000	0.8587

761. B = $C_6H_{10}O_8$
Citric acid monohydrate (296)[1,2]

762. B = $C_6H_{12}O_3$
Paraldehyde
(±0.075%)(68, 150)

Wt. % A	d_4^{10}
100.00	0.8183
90.00	0.8327
70.00	0.8659
50.00	0.9011
30.05	0.9401
10.00	0.9822
0.00	1.0037

Wt. % A	$d_4^{76.5}$
100.00	0.7656
89.98	0.7785
70.02	0.8061
50.00	0.8366
29.99	0.8719
9.96	0.9076
0.00	0.9248

762.5. B = C_6H_{14}
Hexane (±0.1%) (361)

Wt. % A	$d_4^{18.4}$ (?)
0.000	0.6660
1.208	0.6709
3.591	0.6778
4.770	0.6795
17.600	0.6918
23.060	0.7024
100.000	0.8116

763. B = $C_7H_6O_2$
Benzoic acid (296)[1,2]

764. B = $C_7H_6O_3$
Salicylic acid (296)[1,2]

765. B = $C_7H_8O_6$
Gallic acid monohydrate (296)[1,2]

766. B = $C_8H_{10}N_4O_2$
Caffeine (292)[2]

767. B = $C_{10}H_{13}NO_2$
Phenacetine (292)[2]

768. B = $C_{10}H_{15}N$
Diethylaniline
(±0.075%)(68, 150)

Wt. % A	d_4^0
100.00	0.8253
90.03	0.8367
70.52	0.8586
50.08	0.8834
30.52	0.9091
10.00	0.9367
0.00	0.9504

Wt. % A	$d_4^{76.5}$
100.00	0.7656
90.02	0.7764
70.00	0.7995
50.08	0.8218
30.15	0.8473
10.07	0.8741
0.00	0.8901

769. B = $C_{10}H_{16}O_4$
Camphoric acid (296)[1,2]

770. B = $C_{13}H_{10}O_3$
Salol (292)[2]

771. B = $C_{18}H_{34}O_2$
Oleic acid (57)

772. B = $C_{18}H_{36}O_2$
Stearic acid (296)[1,2]

v. also 86, 172, 396.5, 577, 592

$C_5H_{12}O$

Dimethylethyl carbinol, *v.* 233

$C_5H_{12}O$

n-Propyl ethyl ether
773. B = $C_7H_{14}O_2$
Isoamyl acetate
(0–100 Wt. % A)(125)
d_4^{25} = (0.8664 − $0.0_2 1052$ Wt. % A) ±0.05%

$C_6H_3N_3O_6$

1, 3, 5-Trinitrobenzene
774. B = $C_{10}H_8$
Naphthalene (163.1)
(±0.05%)(163)

Mol % B	d_4^{152}
0	1.4769
25	1.3676
40	1.2920
50	1.2370
60	1.1159
75	1.0883
100	0.9213

775. B = $C_{12}H_{11}N$
Diphenylamine
(±0.5%)(311)

Mol % B	d_4^{130}
100	1.065
80	1.100
60	1.140
40	1.200
20	1.265
0	1.333

v. also 397

$C_6H_3N_3O_7$

Picric acid
776. B = C_6H_6 (148)[1]

v. also 398, 1276, 1277

$C_6H_4Br_2$

p-Dibromobenzene
777. B = C_6H_6 (158)
(±0.005%)(318)

Wt. % B	d_4^{25}
100.000	0.87339
95.176	0.89724
91.022	0.91867
81.344	0.97381
72.520	1.02956

778. B = $C_6H_{12}O_2$
Ethyl butyrate (158)

779. B = $C_6H_{12}O_3$
Paraldehyde (158)

780. B = C_6H_{14}
Hexane (318)[1]

781. B = C_7H_8
Toluene (158)
(±0.005%)(318)

Wt. % A	d_4^{25}
0.000	0.86137
3.771	0.88001
7.744	0.90046
13.631	0.93323
23.644	0.99323

782. B = $C_7H_{14}O_2$
Isoamyl acetate (158, 318[1])

783. B = $C_7H_{14}O_2$
Propyl butyrate (158)

784. B = $C_8H_8O_2$
Methyl benzoate (158)

v. also 16, 51, 104, 281, 344, 355, 399, 551, 596, 617, 650, 670, 738, 743

$C_6H_4Br_3N$

2, 4, 6-Tribromoaniline
785. B = $C_7H_{14}O_2$
Isoamyl acetate (306)[1]

$C_6H_4ClNO_2$

o-Chloronitrobenzene
786. B = $C_{12}H_{11}N$
Diphenylamine
(±0.5%)(311)

Mol % A	d_4^{60}
0	1.060
10	1.075
20	1.100
30	1.130
40	1.145
50	1.170
60	1.200
70	1.230
80	1.260
90	1.290
100	1.335

$C_6H_4Cl_2$

p-Dichlorobenzene
787. B = C_6H_5Cl
Chlorobenzene
(±0.1%)(25)

Wt. % B	d_4^0
97.34	1.1323
94.87	1.1363
92.45	1.1402
90.07	1.1441
84.74	1.1528
82.69	1.1561
80.11	1.1605
74.84	1.1693
69.58	1.1782
67.80	1.1811
66.80	1.1830
0.00	1.1282

$C_6H_4Cl_2$.—(*Continued*)

B = C_6H_5Cl.—(*Continued*)

Wt. % B	$d_4^{13.5}$
100.00	1.1135
97.34	1.1176
94.87	1.1214
92.45	1.1253
90.07	1.1292
84.74	1.1377
82.69	1.1413
80.11	1.1415
74.84	1.1541
69.58	1.1632
67.80	1.1662
66.80	1.1679
64.98	1.1710
60.18	1.1797
55.36	1.1800

$C_6H_4Cl_2$

Dichlorobenzene

v. 17

$C_6H_4Cl_3N$

2, 4, 6-Trichloroaniline

788. B = $C_7H_{14}O_2$
Isoamyl acetate (**306**)[1]

$C_6H_4N_2O_4$

m-Dinitrobenzene

789. B = C_6H_6
(±0.01%)(**158, 318**)

a	10^3b
(15°–70°)	
100.000 Wt. % B	
0.88441	1.081(t − 15)
(15°–60°)	
95.399 Wt. % B	
0.90082	1.065(t − 15)
(20°–70°)	
91.795 Wt. % B	
0.90893	1.068(t − 20)
(15°–70°)	
86.036 Wt. % B	
0.93598	1.062(t − 15)

790. B = C_7H_8
Toluene (**158, 319**[1])
(±0.01%)(**318**)

a	10^3b
(15°–70°)	
0.000 Wt. % A	
0.8705	0.938(t − 15)
(20°–70°)	
3.931 Wt. % A	
0.8807	0.922(t − 20)
(15°–70°)	
7.128 Wt. % A	
0.8974	0.940(t − 15)
13.491 Wt. % A	
0.9225	0.940(t − 15)

791. B = $C_{10}H_8$
Naphthalene (**163.1**)
(±0.05%)(**163**)

Mol % A	d_4^{90}	d_4^{52}
0.0	1.3639	
25.0	1.2663	
42.5	1.1975	1.2180
50.0	1.1706	1.1955
54.0	1.1512	1.1751
60.0	1.1319	1.1613
75.0	1.0753	
100.0	0.9696	

v. also 105, 618, 1280

C_6H_5Br

Bromobenzene

792. B = C_6H_5Cl
Chlorobenzene (**35, 349**[1])
(±0.025%)(**23**)

Wt. % A	d_4^{20}
100.000	1.4960
80.603	1.4223
68.989	1.3777
45.179	1.2854
25.320	1.2074
10.723	1.1494
0.000	1.1065

(±0.05%)(**157**)

d_4^t =
0.0 Mol % A
$1.1257(1 - 0.0_3935t)$
20.2 Mol % A
$1.2114(1 - 0.0_3946t)$
67.4 Mol % A
$1.3770(1 - 0.0_3943t)$
100.00 Mol % A
$1.5158(1 - 0.0_3853t)$

793. B = C_6H_6 (**61, 186**)
(±0.01%)(**23**)

Wt. % B	d_4^{20}
0.000	1.4960
36.892	1.2918
53.614	1.1910
67.696	1.1016
82.230	1.0046
100.000	0.8790

(to 80°)(±0.1%)(**185**)

a	10^3b
100.00 Wt. % B	
0.9003	1.073t
75.26 Wt. % B	
1.0001	1.107t
49.73 Wt. % B	
1.1330	1.186t
25.26 Wt. % B	
1.2948	1.251t
0.00 Wt. % B	
1.5215	1.354t

794. B = C_7H_8
Toluene
(±0.025%)(**23**)

Wt. % A	d_4^{20}
100.000	1.4960
65.796	1.2801
41.048	1.1241
22.297	1.0061
0.000	0.8661

795. B = $C_8H_{14}O_6$
Ethyl tartrate
(±0.05%)(**217**)

Wt. % A	d_4^{20}
100.00	1.4938
95.00	1.4744
90.07	1.4567
52.03	1.3355
0.00	1.2052

a	10^3b
(14.3°–100.6°)	
100.00 Wt. % A	
1.5013	1.340(t − 14.3)
(18.6°–100.6°)	
90.07 Wt. % A	
1.4585	1.320(t − 18.6)
(19.4°–100.8°)	
75.06 Wt. % A	
1.4043	1.263(t − 19.4)
(19.1°–101.0°)	
52.03 Wt. % A	
1.3366	1.195(t − 19.1)
(16.8°–99.4°)	
0.00 Wt. % A	
1.2085	1.016(t − 16.8)

796. B = $C_8H_{20}IN$
Tetraethylammonium iodide
(**331**)[1]

v. also 18, 52, 106, 319, 400, 508

$C_6H_5Br_2N$

2, 4-Dibromoaniline

797. B = $C_7H_{14}O_2$
Isoamyl acetate (**306**)[1]

$C_6H_5Br_2N$

2, 6-Dibromoaniline

798. B = $C_7H_{14}O_2$
Isoamyl acetate (**306**)[1]

C_6H_5Cl

Chlorobenzene

799. B = C_6H_6 (**25, 135, 99, 186**)
(±0.025%)(**23**)

Wt. % B	d_4^{20}
0.000	1.1065
31.171	1.0419
57.896	0.9820
77.462	0.9357
100.000	0.8790

(to 80°)(±0.075%)(**185**)

a	10^3b
0.00 Wt. % B	
1.1283	1.080t
25.39 Wt. % B	
1.0592	1.073t
49.46 Wt. % B	
1.0020	1.081t
74.84 Wt. % B	
0.9483	1.081t
100.000 Wt. % B	
0.9002	1.073t

800. B = C_6H_6O
Phenol
(±0.01%)(**27**)

Wt. % A	d_4^{20}
100.00	1.1050
95.07	1.1033
90.22	1.1017
78.27	1.0979
69.57	1.0953
61.10	1.0929
50.10	1.0897
41.85	1.0873
28.59	1.0835
18.55	1.0805
0.00	1.0752

801. B = C_7H_8
Toluene (**158**)
(±0.025%)(**23**)

Wt. % A	d_4^{20}
100.000	1.1065
71.678	1.0369
45.779	0.9744
21.516	0.9167
13.803	0.8985
7.060	0.8826
0.000	0.8661

(±0.0075%)(**171**)

Wt. % A	d_4^{25}
100.000	1.10026
80.249	1.04460
46.646	0.95883
22.292	0.90535
20.427	0.90148
0.000	0.86053

802. B = C_7H_{16}
Heptane (**61**)

803. B = $C_7H_{16}O$
Ethyl amyl ether (**61**)

804. B = C_8H_{10}
m-Xylene (**61**)

805. B = $C_8H_{14}O_6$
Ethyl tartrate
(±0.05%)(**217**)

a	10^3b
(17.05°–38.53°)	
100.00 Wt. % A	
1.1096	1.080(t − 17.05)
(18.5°–31.87°)	
96.19 Wt. % A	
1.1106	1.084(t − 18.5)
(15°–99°)	
89.99 Wt. % A	
1.1202	1.101(t − 15)
(14.7°–99.0°)	
75.00 Wt. % A	
1.1342	1.101(t − 14.7)
(17.9°–101.3°)	
52.53 Wt. % A	
1.1516	1.078(t − 17.9)
(18.8°–49.5°)	
24.65 Wt. % A	
1.1795	1.081(t − 18.8)
(16.8°–99.4°)	
0.00 Wt. % A	
1.2085	1.016(t − 16.8)

806. B = $C_{10}H_8$
Naphthalene
(to 2.132 Wt. % B)(54)
d_4^{18} = (1.10864 − 0.0_3835 Wt. % B) ±0.0075%

807. B = $C_{10}H_{16}O$
Camphor
(±0.1%)(235)

Wt. % B	d_4^{25}
0.00	1.101
0.73	1.099
5.51	1.092
18.64	1.072
30.35	1.054
59.25	1.014

v. also 19, 53, 282, 320, 401, 509, 787, 792

C_6H_5ClO

o-Chlorophenol

808. B = C_6H_7N
Aniline (307)[1]
(±0.01%)(28)

Wt. % B	d_4^{10}
100.00	1.0350
84.46	1.0643
70.06	1.0956
59.84	1.1219
53.39	1.1374
48.32	1.1495
43.13	1.1615
39.39	1.1701
34.82	1.1809
31.50	1.1891
22.20	1.2105
10.35	1.2382
0.00	1.2623

Wt. % B	d_4^{20}
100.00	1.0218
84.46	1.0554
70.06	1.0864
59.84	1.1123
53.39	1.1277
48.32	1.1396
43.13	1.1515
39.39	1.1600
34.82	1.1707
31.50	1.1788
22.20	1.2000
10.35	1.2273
0.00	1.2509

Wt. % B	d_4^{30}
100.00	1.0131
84.46	1.0466
70.06	1.0772
59.84	1.1027
53.39	1.1180
48.32	1.1297
43.13	1.1416
39.39	1.1499
34.82	1.1605
31.50	1.1685
22.20	1.1895
10.35	1.2164
0.00	1.2397

Wt. % B	d_4^{40}
100.00	1.0045
84.46	1.0377
70.06	1.0680
59.84	1.0931
53.39	1.1083
48.32	1.1198
43.13	1.1316
39.39	1.1399
34.82	1.1503
31.50	1.1582
22.20	1.1790
10.35	1.2055
0.00	1.2282

Wt. % B	d_4^{60}
100.00	0.9872
84.46	1.0197
70.06	1.0496
59.84	1.0739
53.39	1.0888
48.32	1.1000
43.13	1.1116
39.39	1.1196
34.82	1.1300
31.50	1.1376
22.20	1.1580
10.35	1.1837
0.00	1.2058

Wt. % B	d_4^{80}
100.00	0.9700
84.46	1.0017
70.06	1.0311
59.84	1.0547
53.39	1.0693
48.32	1.0802
43.13	1.0916
39.39	1.0993
34.82	1.1096
31.50	1.1169
22.20	1.1371
10.35	1.1619
0.00	1.1832

Wt. % B	d_4^{110}
100.00	0.9431
84.46	0.9739
70.06	1.0019
59.84	1.0248
53.39	1.0389
48.32	1.0493
43.13	1.0603
39.39	1.0678
34.82	1.0774
31.50	1.0843
22.20	1.1038
10.35	1.1280
0.00	1.1489

Wt. % B	d_4^{150}
100.00	0.9053
84.46	0.9355
70.06	0.9620
59.84	0.9839
53.39	0.9972
48.32	1.0069
43.13	1.0177
39.39	1.0249
34.82	1.0339
31.50	1.0404
22.20	1.0589
10.35	1.0822
0.00	1.1027

809. B = $C_6H_8N_2$
Phenylhydrazine
(±0.1%)(307)

Wt. % A	d_4^{50}
100.0	1.203
85.2	1.187
64.0	1.166
53.5	1.154
50.7	1.145
25.0	1.108
0.0	1.068

810. B = $C_7H_{14}O_2$
Isoamyl acetate (305)[1]

811. B = $C_8H_{11}N$
Dimethylaniline
(to 80°)(±0.025%)(28)

a	10^3b
0.00 Wt. % A	
0.9726	0.8213*t*
14.67 Wt. % A	
1.0070	0.8700*t*
27.71 Wt. % A	
1.0432	0.9075*t*
40.65 Wt. % A	
1.0819	0.9475*t*
52.49 Wt. % A	
1.1191	0.9850*t*
60.40 Wt. % A	
1.1443	1.0050*t*
70.50 Wt. % A	
1.1761	1.0325*t*
75.41 Wt. % A	
1.1928	1.0550*t*
80.87 Wt. % A	
1.2108	1.0725*t*
83.81 Wt. % A	
1.2205	1.0825*t*
90.14 Wt. % A	
1.2414	1.1000*t*
100.00 Wt. % A	
1.2737	1.1338*t*

812. B = C_9H_7N
Quinoline
(±0.01%)(28)

Wt. % B	d_4^{0}
100.00	1.1077
83.21	1.1412
67.47	1.1728
57.61	1.1925
51.19	1.2045
49.69	1.2074
46.72	1.2128
45.06	1.2156
42.08	1.2203
36.58	1.2282
27.82	1.2403
13.34	1.2581
0.00	1.2737

Wt. % B	d_4^{10}
100.00	1.1001
83.21	1.1331
67.47	1.1643
57.61	1.1837
51.19	1.1956
49.69	1.1985
46.72	1.2038
45.06	1.2066
42.08	1.2112
36.58	1.2188
27.82	1.2304
13.34	1.2474
0.00	1.2622

Wt. % B	d_4^{20}
100.00	1.0925
83.21	1.1250
67.47	1.1557
57.61	1.1748
51.19	1.1867
49.69	1.1895
46.72	1.1948
45.06	1.1975
42.08	1.2021
36.58	1.2095
27.82	1.2205
13.34	1.2363
0.00	1.2508

Wt. % B	d_4^{30}
100.00	1.0849
83.21	1.1169
67.47	1.1472
57.61	1.1660
51.19	1.1777
49.69	1.1805
46.72	1.1858
45.06	1.1883
42.08	1.1930
36.58	1.2001
27.82	1.2106
13.34	1.2253
0.00	1.2397

Wt. % B	d_4^{40}
100.00	1.0772
83.21	1.1089
67.47	1.1387
57.61	1.1573
51.19	1.1688
49.69	1.1715
46.72	1.1768
45.06	1.1792
42.08	1.1838
36.58	1.1906
27.82	1.2006
13.34	1.2149
0.00	1.2282

Wt. % B	d_4^{60}
100.00	1.0614
83.21	1.0928
67.47	1.1220
57.61	1.1402
51.19	1.1510
49.69	1.1537
46.72	1.1588
45.06	1.1611

C_6H_5ClO.—(*Continued*)

$B = C_9H_7N$.—(*Continued*)

Wt. % B	d_4^{60}
42.08	1.1655
36.58	1.1718
27.82	1.1811
13.34	1.1941
0.00	1.2058
Wt. % B	d_4^{80}
100.00	1.0458
83.21	1.0767
67.47	1.1053
57.61	1.1230
51.19	1.1333
49.69	1.1360
46.72	1.1407
45.06	1.1433
42.08	1.1473
36.58	1.1531
27.82	1.1615
13.34	1.1732
0.00	1.1832
Wt. % B	d_4^{110}
100.00	1.0213
83.21	1.0517
67.47	1.0790
57.61	1.0952
51.19	1.1049
49.69	1.1072
46.72	1.1118
45.06	1.1139
42.08	1.1175
36.58	1.1232
27.82	1.1311
13.34	1.1413
0.00	1.1489
Wt. % B	d_4^{150}
100.00	0.9879
83.21	1.0178
67.47	1.0428
57.61	1.0574
51.19	1.0664
49.69	1.0681
46.72	1.0721
45.06	1.0741
42.08	1.0772
36.58	1.0822
27.82	1.0893
13.34	1.0976
0.00	1.1027

813. $B = C_{13}H_{13}N$

Diphenylmethylamine

(to 80°)(±0.025%)(28)

a	10^3b
0.00 Wt. % A	
1.0674	0.7888t
13.83 Wt. % A	
1.0923	0.8200t
25.90 Wt. % A	
1.1146	0.8575t
38.35 Wt. % A	
1.1391	0.8975t
50.52 Wt. % A	
1.1637	0.9350t
57.58 Wt. % A	
1.1788	0.9750t
68.76 Wt. % A	
1.2030	1.0150t
79.34 Wt. % A	
1.2261	1.0525t
89.62 Wt. % A	
1.2492	1.0925t
100.00 Wt. % A	
1.2737	1.1388t

v. also 402, 510, 702

C_6H_5ClO

m-Chlorophenol

814. $B = C_6H_7N$

Aniline

(±0.1%)(307)

Wt. % B	d_4^{25}
0.0	1.268
9.0	1.238
19.4	1.207
30.1	1.181
40.3	1.153
60.1	1.104
75.4	1.071
100.0	1.022
Wt. % B	d_4^{50}
0.0	1.237
9.0	1.210
19.4	1.180
30.1	1.153
40.3	1.126
60.1	1.077
75.4	1.045
100.0	0.992

815. $B = C_7H_{14}O_2$

Isoamyl acetate (305)[1]

v. also 403

C_6H_5ClO

p-Chlorophenol

816. $B = C_6H_7N$

Aniline

(±0.1%)(307)

Wt. % B	d_4^{25}
7.8	1.249
15.4	1.228
22.2	1.209
29.9	1.185
37.2	1.166
41.8	1.154
50.2	1.133
70.2	1.084
90.3	1.037
100.0	1.022
Wt. % B	d_4^{50}
0.0	1.244
7.8	1.223
15.4	1.199
22.2	1.179
29.9	1.158
37.2	1.140
41.8	1.128
50.2	1.107
70.2	1.058
90.3	1.012
100.0	0.992

817. $B = C_7H_{14}O_2$

Isoamyl acetate (305)[1]

v. also 404

$C_6H_5Cl_2N$

2, 4-Dichloroaniline

818. $B = C_7H_{14}O_2$

Isoamyl acetate (306)[1]

C_6H_5F

Fluorobenzene

818.5 $B = C_6H_6$

(to 80°)(±0.075%)(185)

a	10^3b
0.00 Wt. % B	
1.0468	1.216t
24.98 Wt. % B	
1.0052	1.159t
50.24 Wt. % B	
0.9687	1.159t
74.22 Wt. % B	
0.9345	1.125t
100.00 Wt. % B	
0.9002	1.073t

C_6H_5I

Iodobenzene

819. $B = C_6H_6$

(to 80°)(±0.075%)(185)

a	10^3b
0.00 Wt. % B	
1.8611	1.520t
25.16 Wt. % B	
1.4662	1.406t
50.05 Wt. % B	
1.2133	1.294t
100.00 Wt. % B	
0.9002	1.073t

820. $B = C_8H_{14}O_6$

Ethyl tartrate

(±0.05%)(217)

a	10^3b
(19.5°–38.5°)	
0.00 Wt. % B	
1.8316	1.575(t − 19.5)
(18.85°–51.6°)	
9.93 Wt. % B	
1.7313	1.495(t − 18.85)
(19.5°–50.6°)	
24.94 Wt. % B	
1.6148	1.413(t − 19.5)
(18.3°–53.2°)	
47.97 Wt. % B	
1.4502	1.259(t − 18.3)
(19.25°–36.2°)	
75.30 Wt. % B	
1.3135	1.132(t−19.25)

$C_6H_5I_2N$

2, 4-Diiodoaniline

821. $B = C_7H_{14}O_2$

Isoamyl acetate (306)

$C_6H_5NO_2$

Nitrobenzene

823. $B = C_6H_6$ (14, 122,[1] 142, 158, 240)

(50 Wt. % B)(±0.025%)(178)

t	d_4^t
0	1.03874
25	1.01248
40	0.99731
55	0.98282
70	0.96678

(±0.1%) (361)

Wt. % B	d_4^{20}
0.000	1.2048
0.282	1.2040
0.353	1.2032
0.773	1.2022
1.419	1.2000
3.118	1.1920
7.250	1.1734
16.335	1.1382
100.000	0.8800

(±0.0075%)(171)

Wt. % B	d_4^{25}
0.000	1.19823
14.391	1.13851
37.604	1.05304
80.049	0.92504
100.000	0.87421

824. $B = C_6H_6O$

Phenol

(±0.01%)(27)

Wt. % A	d_4^{20}
100.00	1.2019
95.84	1.1955
91.16	1.1886
81.88	1.1754
72.59	1.1633
62.04	1.1494
50.27	1.1345
41.36	1.1232
28.97	1.1084
15.32	1.0926
0.00	1.0751

825. $B = C_6H_7N$

Aniline (±0.075%)(112)

(25°–90°)

62.92 Wt. % B

a	10^3b
1.1343	0.903(t − 25)

(±0.25%)(156)

d_4^0 = (1.038 + $0.0_2$184 Mol % A)

d_4^{62} = (0.987 + $0.0_2$176 Mol % A)

826. $B = C_6H_{10}O_4$

Methyl *l*-α-acetoxypropionate

(±0.05%)(211)

a	10^3b
(−7.4° to +141°)	
0.00 Wt. % A	
1.1198	1.144(t + 7.4)
(0.3°–141°)	
89.86 Wt. % A	
1.2103	1.006(t − 0.3)

827. B = $C_6H_{10}O_6$
Methyl tartrate
(14°-41°)(±0.05%)(210)
95.06 Wt. % A

a	10^3b
1.214	$1.0(t - 14)$

828. B = $C_6H_{12}O_3$
Paraldehyde (158)
(±0.1%) (361)

Wt. % B	d_4^{20}
0.000	1.2048
0.443	1.2032
0.685	1.2024
0.906	1.2020
1.778	1.2000
3.442	1.1968
4.555	1.1944
9.000	1.1852
17.630	1.1670
23.650	1.1530

829. B = $C_7H_6O_2$
Benzoic acid (296)[1,2]

830. B = $C_7H_6O_3$
Salicylic acid (296)[1,2]

831. B = C_7H_8
Toluene (158, 348)
(±0.0075%)(171)

Wt. % A	d_4^{25}
100.000	1.19848
84.606	1.13195
62.598	1.04733
29.050	0.93966
12.207	0.89218
0.000	0.86036

(±0.075%)(122)

Wt. % A	d_4^{55}
0.00	0.8330
16.92	0.8775
31.62	0.9192
57.61	1.0019
71.48	1.0517
82.03	1.0926
91.70	1.1324
100.00	1.1691

(±0.075%)(112)

a	10^3b
(25°–75°) 0.00 Wt. % A	
0.8599	$0.890(t - 25)$
(25°–90°) 73.70 Wt. % A	
1.0869	$0.944(t - 25)$

832. B = C_7H_8O
o-Cresol
(±0.005%)(319)

Wt. % B	$d_4^{12.87}$
0.000	1.21065
3.080	1.20504
9.545	1.19320
16.221	1.18142

833. B = C_7H_9N
Methylaniline
(±0.05%)(157)
d_4^t =
100 Mol % A
$1.2220(1 - 0.0_37804t)$
75 Mol % A
$1.1618(1 - 0.0_37930t)$
50 Mol % A
$1.1060(1 - 0.0_38040t)$
25 Mol % A
$1.0521(1 - 0.0_38060t)$
0 Mol % A
$1.0028(1 - 0.0_37980t)$

834. B = C_7H_9N
o-Toluidine
(±0.05%)(157)
d_4^t =
100 Mol % A
$1.2220(1 - 0.0_37804t)$
75 Mol % A
$1.1677(1 - 0.0_38040t)$
50 Mol % A
$1.1159(1 - 0.0_38160t)$
0 Mol % A
$1.0647(1 - 0.0_38160t)$

835. B = $C_8H_8O_2$
Methyl benzoate (158)

836. B = $C_8H_9Cl_3O_7$
Methyl mono(trichloro-acetyl)tartrate
(17°–48.7°)(±0.05%)(210)
95.25 Wt. % A

a	10^3b
1.2163	$0.0_3963(t - 17)$

837. B = $C_8H_{11}N$
Dimethylaniline
(±0.05%)(157)
d_4^t =
100 Mol % A
$1.2220(1 - 0.0_37804t)$
75 Mol % A
$1.1582(1 - 0.0_38190t)$
50 Mol % A
$1.0868(1 - 0.0_38190t)$
25 Mol % A
$1.0266(1 - 0.0_38410t)$
0 Mol % A
$0.9742(1 - 0.0_38680t)$

838. B = $C_8H_{11}N$
Ethylaniline
(±0.05%)(157)
d_4^t =
100 Mol % A
$1.2220(1 - 0.0_37804t)$
75 Mol % A
$1.1493(1 - 0.0_38100t)$
50 Mol % A
$1.0853(1 - 0.0_38220t)$
25 Mol % A
$1.0278(1 - 0.0_38260t)$
0 Mol % A
$0.9792(1 - 0.0_38740t)$

839. B = $C_8H_{14}O_6$
Dimethyl *d*-dimethoxy-succinate
(±0.075%)(222)

a	10^3b
(65.3°–153°) 0.00 Wt. % A	
1.1250	$1.052(t - 65.3)$
(15.6°–150°) 90.90 Wt. % A	
1.2039	$0.993(t - 15.6)$

840. B = $C_8H_{14}O_6$
Ethyl tartrate (220)
(±0.075%)(208)

a	10^3b
(19.1°–100.0°) 0.00 Wt. % B	
1.2042	$0.978(t - 19.1)$
(20.0°–99.0°) 2.00 Wt. % B	
1.2030	$0.987(t - 20.0)$
(19.0°–98.5°) 5.00 Wt. % B	
1.2037	$0.995(t - 19.0)$
(18.0°–100.0°) 10.00 Wt. % B	
1.2041	$0.989(t - 18.0)$
(17.3°–100.0°) 19.94 Wt. % B	
1.2042	$0.998(t - 17.3)$
(18.7°–100.0°) 50.02 Wt. % B	
1.2029	$1.013(t - 18.7)$
(19.3°–131.2°) 100.00 Wt. % B	
1.2062	$1.023(t - 19.3)$

841. B = $C_8H_{20}IN$
Tetraethylammonium iodide (331)[1]

842. B = $C_{10}H_8$
Naphthalene (158, 163.1)
(±0.0075%)(54)

Wt. % B	d_4^{18}
0.000	1.20538
1.032	1.20322
2.037	1.20106

(±0.05%)(163)

Mol % B	d_4^{80}
0	1.1439
20	1.1135
30	1.0959
50	1.0626
70	1.0300
80	1.0120
90	0.9951
100	0.9790

843. B = $C_{10}H_8Cl_6O_8$
Methyl di(trichloro-acetyl)tartrate
(±0.05%)(210)

a	10^3b
(17°–48.7°) 95.25 Wt. % A	
1.2163	$0.963(t - 17.0)$
(14°–90.2°) 95.10 Wt. % A	
1.2779	$1.006(t - 14.0)$

844. B = $C_{10}H_{14}$
Durene
(±0.005%)(318)

Wt. % A	d_4^{25}
100.000	1.19761
97.984	1.18915
94.225	1.17376

845. B = $C_{10}H_{15}N$
Diethylaniline
(±0.05%)(157)
d_4^t =
100.00 Mol % A
$1.2220(1 - 0.0_37804t)$
66.67 Mol % A
$1.1071(1 - 0.0_37910t)$
33.33 Mol % A
$1.0147(1 - 0.0_37720t)$
0.00 Mol % A
$0.9508(1 - 0.0_38455t)$

846. B = $C_{10}H_{16}O_4$
Camphoric acid (296)[1,2]

847. B = $C_{10}H_{20}O$
l-Menthol
(±0.05%)(226)

a	10^3b
(19.25°–43.2°) 98.55 Wt. % A	
1.1978	$0.981(t - 19.25)$
(8.5°–41.7°) 97.94 Wt. % A	
1.2061	$0.988(t - 8.5)$
(9.8°–78.7°) 93.35 Wt. % A	
1.1853	$0.953(t - 9.8)$
(19.1°–54.1°) 69.51 Wt. % A	
1.0891	$0.917(t - 19.1)$

(±0.25%)(273)

a	10^3b
(55.6°–99.0°) 100.00 Mol % A	
1.1655	$0.922(t - 55.6)$
90.85 Mol % A	
1.1215	$0.988(t - 55.6)$
69.16 Mol % A	
1.0374	$0.934(t - 55.6)$
54.83 Mol % A	
0.9915	$0.852(t - 55.6)$
36.73 Mol % A	
0.9442	$0.868(t - 55.6)$
16.26 Mol % A	
0.9011	$0.826(t - 55.6)$
0.00 Mol % A	
0.8690	$0.733(t - 55.6)$

848. B = $C_{12}H_{10}$
Acenaphthene (158)
(±0.005%)(318)

Wt. % A	d_4^{25}
100.000	1.19761
97.166	1.19385
96.135	1.19249

849. B = $C_{12}H_{10}$
Diphenyl (158)
(±0.005%)(318)

Wt. % A	d_4^{25}
100.000	1.19761
98.103	1.19389
95.751	1.18902

$C_6H_5NO_2$.—(*Continued*)

850. B = $C_{12}H_{10}N_2$
Azobenzene (158)
(±0.005%)(318)

Wt. % B	d_4^{25}
0.000	1.19761
1.844	1.19490
4.479	1.19134

851. B = $C_{12}H_{12}Cl_6O_8$
Ethyldi(trichloroacetyl)tartrate
(±0.05)(210)

a	10^3b
(15.2°–131°) 0.00 Wt. % A	
1.4764	1.222(t − 15.2)
(12.5°–74.2°) 95.01 Wt. % A	
1.2218	0.998(t − 12.5)

852. B = $C_{12}H_{18}O_8$
Diethyl diacetyltartrate
(±0.25%)(273)

a	10^3b
(55.6°–99.0°) 100.00 Mol % A	
1.1655	0.922(t − 55.6)
(67.3°–99.0°) 87.73 Mol % A	
1.1435	0.997(t − 67.3)
68.13 Mol % A	
1.1248	0.820(t − 67.3)
50.12 Mol % A	
1.1310	0.997(t − 67.3)
32.90 Mol % A	
1.1198	1.019(t − 67.3)
15.59 Mol % A	
1.1439	1.133(t − 67.3)
0.00 Mol % A	
1.1086	0.896(t − 67.3)

853. B = $C_{12}H_{28}IN$
Tetrapropylammonium iodide (330)[1]

854. B = $C_{14}H_{10}$
Phenanthrene (158)

855. B = $C_{14}H_{10}O_2$
Benzil (158)
(±0.005%)(318)

Wt. % A	d_4^{25}
100.000	1.19761
98.197	1.19660
95.357	1.19529

856. B = $C_{16}H_{20}Cl_6O_8$
Isobutyl di(trichloroacetyl)-tartrate
(±0.05%)(210)

a	10^3b
(18.2°–157°) 0.00 Wt. % A	
1.3584	1.044(t − 18.2)
(13.6°–91.9°) 94.98 Wt. % A	
1.2164	0.991(t − 13.6)

857. B = $C_{16}H_{24}O_3S$
Menthyl benzenesulfonate
(±0.05%)(212)

a	10^3b
(15.7°–70.5°) 92.14 Wt. % A	
1.1973	0.972(t − 15.7)
(16.0°–78.4°) 81.23 Wt. % A	
1.1863	0.954(t − 16.0)

858. B = $C_{16}H_{26}O_8$
Isobutyl diacetyl-*d*-tartrate
(±0.05%)(216)
(−4.2° to +141°)
90.32 Wt. % A

a	10^3b
1.2146	0.977(t + 4.2)

859. B = $C_{18}H_{16}O_6$
act.-Methyl dibenzoyl-glycerate (90)

860. B = $C_{18}H_{36}O_2$
Stearic acid (296)[1,2]

861. B = $C_{20}H_{26}O_3S$
Menthyl naphthalene-β-sulfonate
(±0.05%)(212)

a	10^3b
(12.5°–61.7°) 97.05 Wt. % A	
1.2058	0.939(t − 12.5)
(12.7°–61.4°) 91.36 Wt. % A	
1.2028	0.958(t − 12.7)

862. B = $C_{24}H_{42}O_6$
l-Menthyl *d*-tartrate
(±0.05%)(226)

a	10^3b
(16.7°–43.3°) 98.57 Wt. % A	
1.2038	0.974(t − 16.7)
(10.1°–56.9°) 93.51 Wt. % A	
1.2012	0.969(t − 10.1)

863. B = $C_{24}H_{42}O_6$
Di-*l*-menthyl *l*-tartrate
(±0.05%)(214)

a	10^3b
(17.85°–29.30°) 98.02 Wt. % A	
1.2006	1.004(t − 17.85)
(17.50°–43.50°) 94.65 Wt. % A	
1.1932	0.981(t − 17.50)

864. B = $C_{28}H_{46}O_8$
l-Menthyl diacetyl-*l*-tartrate
(±0.05%)(214)

a	10^3b
(15°–142°) 0.00 Wt. % A	
1.0557	0.802(t − 15)
(16.66°–32.80°) 97.41 Wt. % A	
1.2017	0.991(t − 16.66)
(17.75°–48.40°) 94.64 Wt. % A	
1.1957	0.973(t − 17.75)

865. B = $C_{28}H_{46}O_8$
l-Menthyl diacetyl-*dl*-tartrate
(±0.05%)(215)

a	10^3b
(19.85°–34.8°) 95.62 Wt. % A	
1.1958	0.963(t − 19.85)

v. also 54, 87, 202, 256, 283, 321, 405, 511, 581, 619, 655, 660, 671, 751, 760, 1273

$C_6H_5NO_3$

o-Nitrophenol

866. B = C_6H_6 (±0.005%)(319)

Wt. % B	$d_4^{12.87}$
100.000	0.88619
96.908	0.89533
93.380	0.90617
88.562	0.92127
74.895	0.96695

867. B = C_6H_7N, Aniline
(±0.01%)(28)

Wt. % B	d_4^{30}
100.00	1.0131
89.12	1.0376
77.64	1.0654
67.23	1.0923
58.00	1.1174
48.72	1.1444
39.48	1.1715
31.68	1.1966
22.89	1.2261
14.96	1.2527
8.51	1.2741
0.00	1.3041
Wt. % B	d_4^{40}
100.00	1.0045
89.12	1.0288
77.64	1.0565
67.23	1.0832
58.00	1.1079
48.72	1.1349
39.48	1.1618
31.68	1.1865
22.89	1.2160
14.96	1.2426
8.51	1.2638
0.00	1.2938
Wt. % B	d_4^{60}
100.00	0.9872
89.12	1.0109
77.64	1.0382
67.23	1.0644
58.00	1.0887
48.72	1.1149
39.48	1.1418
31.68	1.1661
22.89	1.1952
14.96	1.2214
8.51	1.2427
0.00	1.2708
Wt. % B	d_4^{80}
100.00	0.9700
89.12	0.9933
77.64	1.0202
67.23	1.0460
58.00	1.0698
48.72	1.0954
39.48	1.1221
31.68	1.1461
22.89	1.1746
14.96	1.2006
8.51	1.2216
0.00	1.2480

868. B = C_7H_9N
p-Toluidine
(±0.1%)(307)

Wt. % A	d_4^{50}
0.0	0.958
35.3	1.050
79.6	1.220
100.0	1.282

869. B = $C_7H_{14}O_2$
Isoamyl acetate (305)[1]

870. B = $C_8H_{14}O_6$
Ethyl tartrate
(±0.05%)(224)

a	10^3b
(47.7°–78.1°) 23.89 Wt. % B	
1.2599	1.014(t − 47.7)
(56.8°–97.3°) 51.12 Wt. % B	
1.2321	1.099(t − 56.8)
(12.5°–72.5°) 74.95 Wt. % B	
1.2554	1.081(t − 12.5)

871. B = C_9H_7N
Quinoline
(±0.01)(28)

Wt. % B	d_4^{30}
100.00	1.0849
89.20	1.1071
78.57	1.1311
69.31	1.1518
58.39	1.1758
50.84	1.1938
41.80	1.2140
32.96	1.2339
22.44	1.2549
17.59	1.2655
13.24	1.2746
8.82	1.2842
4.46	1.2939
0.00	1.3041
Wt. % B	d_4^{40}
100.00	1.0772
89.20	1.0988
78.57	1.1223
69.31	1.1429
58.39	1.1665
50.84	1.1842
41.80	1.2043
32.96	1.2240
22.44	1.2454
17.59	1.2557

Wt. % B	d_4^{40}
13.24	1.2647
8.82	1.2742
4.46	1.2838
0.00	1.2938
Wt. % B	d_4^{60}
100.00	1.0614
89.20	1.0822
78.57	1.1049
69.31	1.1248
58.39	1.1478
50.84	1.1649
41.80	1.1844
32.96	1.2036
22.44	1.2244
17.59	1.2346
13.24	1.2433
8.82	1.2521
4.46	1.2613
0.00	1.2708
Wt. % B	d_4^{80}
100.00	1.0458
89.20	1.0656
78.57	1.0878
69.31	1.1068
58.39	1.1290
50.84	1.1457
41.80	1.1647
32.96	1.1834
22.44	1.2036
17.59	1.2136
13.24	1.2218
8.82	1.2304
4.46	1.2391
0.00	1.2480

v. also 107, 406, 703

$C_6H_5NO_3$

m-Nitrophenol

872. B = $C_7H_{14}O_2$
Isoamyl acetate (305)[1]

$C_6H_5NO_3$

p-Nitrophenol

873. B = $C_7H_{14}O_2$
Isoamyl acetate (305)[1]

v. also 407

$C_6H_5N_3O_4$

2, 4-Dinitroaniline, *v.* 228

C_6H_6

874. B = C_6H_6O
Phenol (±0.01%) (27)

Wt. % A	d_4^{20}
100.00	0.8773
93.96	0.8881
90.16	0.8950
79.99	0.9134
67.60	0.9371
57.91	0.9549
46.98	0.9766
36.35	0.9976
25.89	1.0194
17.80	1.0383
0.00	1.0751

875. B = C_6H_7N
Aniline (14, 142)
(±0.075%)(122)

Wt. % B	d_4^{20}
100.00	1.0208
89.59	1.0034
66.65	0.9712
11.40	0.8934
0.00	0.8783

876. B = $C_6H_{10}O_3$
Ethyl acetoacetate (142, 158)
(±0.05%)(71)

Wt. % A	d_4^{25}
100.00	0.8736
97.22	0.8770
89.53	0.8869
56.44	0.9324
6.12	1.0126
0.00	1.0222

877. B = $C_6H_{10}O_4$
Ethyl oxalate (199)[1]

878. B = $C_6H_{12}O_2$
Amyl formate (199)[1]

879. B = $C_6H_{12}O_2$
Butyl acetate (199)[1]

880. B = $C_6H_{12}O_2$
Ethyl butyrate (158, 199[1])

881. B = $C_6H_{12}O_3$
Paraldehyde (142, 158)
(±0.1%) (361)

Wt. % A	d_4^{20}
0.000	0.9948
0.442	0.9940
0.660	0.9935
1.770	0.9910
3.480	0.9892
8.915	0.9846
15.485	0.9730
81.150	0.8980
89.325	0.8892
96.160	0.8814
97.849	0.8808
99.231	0.8805
99.962	0.8803
100.000	0.8800

882. B = C_6H_{14}
n-Hexane (14, 35, 158, 351)
(±0.025%)(138)

Wt. % A	d_4^{0}
0.00	0.67743
1.24	0.67939
1.52	0.67995
9.27	0.69249
12.31	0.69759
15.07	0.70232
16.95	0.70570
21.57	0.71377
22.41	0.71535
24.22	0.71855
31.87	0.73290
33.23	0.73548
36.51	0.74197
38.38	0.74558
40.40	0.74966
41.39	0.75183
41.54	0.75214
47.03	0.76355
55.30	0.78166
63.58	0.80081
69.18	0.81417
70.78	0.81819
77.38	0.83512
79.85	0.84161
81.34	0.84566
86.27	0.85933
88.61	0.86602
91.58	0.87452
92.80	0.87816
95.20	0.88527
100.00	0.90017

883. B = $C_7H_5N_3O_6$
Trinitrotoluene
(±0.005%)(319)

Wt. % A	$d_4^{12.87}$
100.000	0.88619
95.959	0.90238
92.736	0.91559
88.621	0.92751
86.608	0.94176

884. B = C_7H_6O
Benzaldehyde (142)

885. B = $C_7H_6O_2$
Benzoic acid (148,[1] 296,[1] 303)
(25°–75°)(±0.1%)(112)

4.81 Wt. % B

a	10^3b
0.8818	1.062(*t* − 25)

(to 6.785 Wt. % B)(319)
$d_4^{12.87}$ = (0.88638 + $0.0_{2}1504$ Wt. % B) ±0.005%

886. B = $C_7H_6O_3$
Salicylic acid (296)[1,2]

887. B = C_7H_8
(24,[1] 95,[1] 99, 105,[1] 112,[1] 133, 158, 178,[1] 186.1,[1] 283,[1] 351, 352[1])
(±0.025%)(23)

Wt. % A	d_4^{20}
0.00	0.8661
28.22	0.8687
52.93	0.8715
78.16	0.8751
100.00	0.8790

(±0.0075%)(171)

Wt. % A	d_4^{25}
0.000	0.86054
10.990	0.86198
30.588	0.86400
51.920	0.86682
66.576	0.86906
91.556	0.87288
100.000	0.87420

(±0.05%)(157)
d_4^t =
100 Mol % A
$0.8995(1 - 0.0_{2}1325t)$
75 Mol % A
$0.8957(1 - 0.0_{2}1163t)$
50 Mol % A
$0.8903(1 - 0.0_{2}1100t)$
25 Mol % A
$0.8866(1 - 0.0_{2}1052t)$
0 Mol % A
$0.8825(1 - 0.0_{3}982t)$

888. B = C_7H_8O
Benzyl alcohol (233)[1]

889. B = C_7H_8O
o-Cresol
(±0.005%)(319)

Wt. % A	$d_4^{12.87}$
100.000	0.88638
96.379	0.89155
94.827	0.89433
88.954	0.90245
77.725	0.91935

890. B = C_7H_8O
m-Cresol
(±0.05%)(157)
d_4^t =
0 Mol % A
$1.0493(1 - 0.0_{3}711t)$
25 Mol % A
$1.0180(1 - 0.0_{3}967t)$
50 Mol % A
$0.9795(1 - 0.0_{3}878t)$
75 Mol % A
$0.9382(1 - 0.0_{3}980t)$
100 Mol % A
$0.8994(1 - 0.0_{2}1192t)$

891. B = $C_7H_8O_6$
Gallic acid monohydrate (296)[1,2]

892. B = $C_7H_{12}O_4$
Ethyl malonate (199)[1]

893. B = $C_7H_{14}O_2$
Isoamyl acetate (158, 199[1])

894. B = $C_7H_{14}O_2$
Ethyl valerate (199)[1]

895. B = $C_7H_{14}O_2$
Propyl butyrate (158)

896. B = C_7H_{16}
Heptane (236)[1]

897. B = $C_7H_{16}O$
Diethylisopropyl alcohol (233)[1]

898. B = C_8H_8O
Acetophenone
(16°–55°)(±0.1%)(29)

a	10^3b
100.00 Wt. % A	
0.8832	1.06(*t* − 16)
84.49 Wt. % A	
0.9050	1.037(*t* − 16)
50.83 Wt. % A	
0.9523	0.954(*t* − 16)
32.12 Wt. % A	
0.9809	0.908(*t* − 16)
15.35 Wt. % A	
1.0070	0.9125(*t* − 16)
0.00 Wt. % A	
1.0317	0.867(*t* − 16)

899. B = $C_8H_8O_2$
Methyl benzoate (158)

C_6H_6—(*Continued*)

900. B = C_8H_9NO
Acetanilide (292)[2]

901. B = C_8H_{10}
Ethylbenzene
(to 40°)(±0.025%)(24)

a	10^3b
100.000 Wt. % A	
0.89993	1.0658t
57.367 Wt. % A	
0.89455	0.9725t
0.000 Wt. % A	
0.89130	0.8863t

902. B = C_8H_{10}
m-Xylene
(±0.05%)(157)
d_4^t =
100 Mol % A
$0.8995(1 - 0.0_21325t)$
75 Mol % A
$0.8931(1 - 0.0_21107t)$
50 Mol % A
$0.8883(1 - 0.0_21053t)$
25 Mol % A
$0.8851(1 - 0.0_21016t)$
0 Mol % A
$0.8828(1 - 0.0_3957t)$

903. B = $C_8H_{10}N_4O_2$
Caffeine (292)[2]

904. B = $C_8H_{10}O_4$
Diallyl oxalate (148)[1]

905. B = $C_8H_{12}O_6$
Dimethyl acetylmalate
(16.5°–45.8°)(±0.05%)
(227)
4.039 Wt. % B

a	10^3b
0.8909	$1.051(t - 16.5)$

906. B = $C_8H_{14}O_3$
Ethyl ethylacetoacetate (158)
(±0.05%)(71)

Wt. % A	d_4^{25}
100.00	0.8736
82.25	0.8907
75.02	0.8974
63.87	0.9086
0.00	0.9754

907. B = $C_8H_{14}O_4$
Ethyl succinate (199)[1]

908. B = $C_8H_{14}O_6$
Ethyl tartrate (340,[1] 343,[1] 344[1])
(±0.05%)(205)

a	10^3b
(17.95°–58.90°)	
100.000 Wt. % A	
0.8812	$1.085(t-17.95)$
(19.65°–26.53°)	
98.999 Wt. % A	
0.8817	$1.075(t-19.65)$
(18.6°–24.53°)	
98.647 Wt. % A	
0.8835	$1.063(t - 18.6)$
(20°–24.22°)	
97.955 Wt. % A	
0.8836	$1.068(t - 20)$
(19.61°–45.05°)	
97.479 Wt. % A	
0.8851	$1.117(t-19.61)$
(18.1°–24.03°)	
96.983 Wt. % A	
0.8879	$1.079(t - 18.1)$
(18.15°–45.8°)	
95.003 Wt. % A	
0.8924	$1.074(t-18.15)$
(19.7°–25.63°)	
92.466 Wt. % A	
0.8969	$1.062(t - 19.7)$
(17.6°–61.28°)	
89.998 Wt. % A	
0.9053	$1.089(t - 17.6)$
(16.33°–25.60°)	
82.582 Wt. % A	
0.9254	$1.068(t-16.33)$
(17.5°–60.6°)	
75.022 Wt. % A	
0.9443	$1.093(t - 17.5)$
(19.3°–62.8°)	
49.996 Wt. % A	
1.0165	$1.079(t - 19.3)$
(20.7°–60.2°)	
24.801 Wt. % A	
1.1026	$1.061(t - 20.7)$
(16.8°–99.4°)	
0.000 Wt. % A	
1.2085	$1.016(t - 16.8)$

909. B = $C_8H_{18}O$
Capryl alcohol (233)[1]

910. B = $C_9H_{10}O_2$
Ethyl benzoate (199)[1]

911. B = $C_9H_{10}O_3$
Ethyl salicylate (199)[1]

912. B = $C_9H_{11}NO$
Methylacetanilide (180)

913. B = C_9H_{12}
1, 2, 4-Trimethylbenzene
(to 40°)(±0.025%)(24)

a	10^3b
100.000 Wt. % A	
0.8999	1.0650t
61.954 Wt. % A	
0.8925	0.9238t
0.000 Wt. % A	
0.8926	0.8075t

914. B = $C_9H_{13}N$
Dimethyl-*o*-toluidine
(±0.075%)(122)

Wt. % A	$d_4^{54.6}$
100.00	0.8427
88.50	0.8488
76.64	0.8553
55.93	0.8667
36.81	0.8775
23.01	0.8855
10.44	0.8930
0.00	0.8992

915. B = $C_9H_{14}O$
Phorone (148)[1]

916. B = $C_9H_{14}O_6$
Ethyl *l*-diacetylglycerate (90)

917. B = $C_{10}H_6Cl_2$
Dichloronaphthalene (148)[1]

918. B = $C_{10}H_7NO_2$
Nitronaphthalene (148)[1]

919. B = $C_{10}H_8$
Naphthalene (106, 148,[1] 158, 172,[1] 354)
(±0.005%)(319)

Wt. % A	$d_4^{12.87}$
100.000	0.88638
97.634	0.88946
91.206	0.89805

(±0.005%)(336)

Wt. % A	d_4^{25}
100.000	0.87166
92.863	0.88132
83.893	0.89378
80.090	0.89906
72.852	0.90930
65.188	0.92028

$\frac{1}{d_4^{30}} = (1.15338 - 0.0_218196$ Wt. % B $+ 0.0_51076$ (Wt. % B$)^2) \pm 0.005\%$
(48, 49)

920. B = $C_{10}H_{12}O$
Anethole
(±0.075%)(233)

Wt. % A	$d_4^{19.43}$
100.00	0.8795
96.57	0.8826
89.66	0.8911
78.86	0.9073
0.00	0.9987

921. B = $C_{10}H_{13}NO_2$
Phenacetine (292)[2]

922. B = $C_{10}H_{14}$
Durene
(±0.005%)(318)

Wt. % A	d_4^{25}
100.000	0.87339
97.405	0.87294
92.962	0.87267
90.439	0.87233
86.366	0.87208
84.068	0.87242
76.732	0.87217

923. B = $C_{10}H_{14}N_2$
Nicotine (93,[1] 110, 341, 343[1])

924. B = $C_{10}H_{14}O$
Thymol (354)
(15°–65°)(±0.075%)(172)

a	10^3b
100.00 Wt. % A	
0.8846	$1.036(t - 15)$
87.86 Wt. % A	
0.8943	$1.022(t - 15)$

925. B = $C_{10}H_{15}BrO$
Bromocamphor (148)[1]
(±0.1%)(235)

Wt. % A	d_t^{25}
100.00	0.8728
99.53	0.8743
95.49	0.8871
78.79	0.9431
67.50	0.9848
53.88	1.0409

926. B = $C_{10}H_{16}O$
Camphor (148,[1] 354)
(to 54.20 Wt. % B) (100, 170, 175, 263, 343)
$d_4^{18.5} = (0.8814 + 0.0_37801$ Wt. % B) ± 0.1%
(to 50.00 Wt. % B)(100, 170, 175, 263, 343)
$d_4^{20} = (0.8795 + 0.0_37980$ Wt. % B) ±0.1%
(to 52.37 Wt. % B)(235)
$d_4^{25} = (0.8728 + 0.0_38325$ Wt. % B) ±0.1%

927. B = $C_{10}H_{16}O_4$
Camphoric acid (296)[1,2]

928. B = $C_{10}H_{17}Cl$
Terpine hydrochloride (148)[1]

929. B = $C_{10}H_{18}O_3$
Ethyl diethylacetoacetate (158)
(±0.05%)(71)

Wt. % A	d_4^{25}
100.00	0.8736
96.35	0.8766
85.84	0.8851
50.48	0.9171
31.81	0.9345
0.00	0.9646

930. B = $C_{10}H_{18}O_6$
Dipropyl tartrate
(±0.1%)(340)

a	10^3b
(20°–60°)	
0.00 Wt. % A	
1.1389	$0.905(t - 20)$
(20°–40°)	
24.09 Wt. % A	
1.0648	$0.94(t - 20)$
54.49 Wt. % A	
0.9811	$0.96(t - 20)$
83.64 Wt. % A	
0.9128	$1.00(t - 20)$

931. B = $C_{10}H_{20}O$
Menthol (148)[1]
(±0.05%)(226)

a	10^3b
(9.1°–32.6°)	
98.544 Wt. % A	
0.8915	$1.111(t - 9.1)$
(7.1°–34.2°)	
92.503 Wt. % A	
0.8917	$0.997(t - 7.1)$

932. B = $C_{10}H_{20}O_2$
Amyl valerate (199)[1]

933. B = $C_{10}H_{20}O_2$
d-β-Octyl acetate (242)
$d_4^{17} = (0.8794 - 0.0_32073$ Wt. % B) ±0.1%

934. B = $C_{12}H_{10}$
Acenaphthene (158)
(±0.005%)(318)

Wt. % A	d_4^{25}
100.000	0.87338
98.131	0.87678
95.807	0.88140
92.183	0.88752
87.436	0.89598

935. B = $C_{12}H_{10}$
Diphenyl (158)
(±0.005%)(318, 336)

Wt. % A	d_4^{25}
100.000	0.87253
98.036	0.87600
94.794	0.88037
92.054	0.88240
90.305	0.88678
87.051	0.89146
84.823	0.89256
84.661	0.89495
76.870	0.90578
70.205	0.91138
60.653	0.92786

936. B = $C_{12}H_{10}N_2$
Azobenzene (158)
(±0.005%)(318)

Wt. % B	d_4^{25}
0.000	0.87339
1.946	0.87673
3.819	0.88009
7.292	0.88600
13.643	0.89750

937. B = $C_{12}H_{14}O_5$
Ethyl monobenzoylglycerate
(90)

938. B = $C_{12}H_{16}O_2$
Amyl benzoate (199)[1]

939. B = $C_{13}H_{10}O$
Benzophenone
(±0.01%)(33)

Wt. % A	d_4^{30}
100.000	0.86833
98.516	0.87119
95.899	0.87640
88.941	0.89052

940. B = $C_{13}H_{10}O_3$
Salol (292)[2]

941. B = $C_{14}H_8O_2$
Anthraquinone
(±0.01%)(297, 317)

Wt. % A	d_4^t	t
99.89	0.8900	0
99.74	0.8794	20
99.65	0.8692	30
99.51	0.8591	40
99.30	0.8439	50
99.04	0.8389	60
98.66	0.8288	70
98.25	0.8190	80

942. B = $C_{14}H_8O_2$
Phenanthraquinone (297,[1,2] 317[1,2])

943. B = $C_{14}H_{10}$
Anthracene
(±0.01%)(297, 317)

Wt. % A	d_4^t	t
99.40	0.9008	0
99.03	0.8909	10
98.59	0.8812	20
98.01	0.8717	30
97.29	0.8627	40
96.38	0.8541	50
95.11	0.8460	60
93.46	0.8374	70
92.30	0.8347	75

944. B = $C_{14}H_{10}$
Phenanthrene (158)
(±0.01%)(318)

a	10^3b
(15°–70°)	
100.00 Wt. % A	
0.88441	1.081(t − 15)
95.970 Wt. % A	
0.89174	1.058(t − 15)
(15°–60°)	
92.770 Wt. % A	
0.89807	1.046(t − 15)
(20°–70°)	
86. 285 Wt. % A	
0.90588	1.019(t − 20)

945. B = $C_{14}H_{10}O_2$
Benzil (158)
(±0.005%)(318)

Wt. % A	d_4^{25}
100.000	0.87338
98.106	0.87764
94.313	0.88646
94.052	0.88690
87.748	0.90169
82.948	0.91334

946. B = $C_{14}H_{12}O_2$
Benzyl benzoate
(±0.01%)(22)

t	d_4^t
100 Wt. % A	
5	0.8939
15	0.8832
25	0.8725
40	0.8565
60	0.8347
75	0.8083
75 Wt. % A	
5	0.9468
15	0.9363
25	0.9263
40	0.9106
60	0.8904
75	0.8750
50 Wt. % A	
5	1.0016
10	0.9980
15	0.9925
25	0.9825
40	0.9687
60	0.9560
75	0 9359
25 Wt. % A	
5	1.0640
15	1.0550
25	1.0454
40	1.0325
60	1.0148
75	1.0015
0 Wt. % A	
5	1.1134
15	1.1249
25	1.1163
40	1.0780
60	1.0870
80	1.0546
90	1.0604
100	1.0571

947. B = $C_{15}H_{18}O_7$
Diethyl monobenzoyltartrate
(89)

948. B = $C_{16}H_{11}N_3O_7$
Naphthalene picrate (148)[1]

949. B = $C_{16}H_{22}O_4$
d-Octyl hydrogen phthalate
(±0.05%)(72)

Wt. % A	d_4^{25}
93.82	0.8836
89.29	0.8837?
88.84	0.8866
80.71	0.9046
80.56	0.9054

950. B = $C_{16}H_{22}O_4$
l-Octyl hydrogen phthalate
(72)[1]

951. B = $C_{16}H_{22}O_4$
dl-Octyl hydrogen phthalate
(5.86–18.29 Wt. % B)(72)
d_4^{25} = (0.8826 + 0.0_21537 (Wt. % B − 5.86)) ± 0.05%

952. B = $C_{16}H_{24}O_3S$
Menthyl benzenesulfonate
(212)[1]

953. B = $C_{16}H_{32}O_2$
Palmitic acid (158)

954. B = $C_{18}H_{16}O_6$
Methyl *d*-dibenzoylglycerate
(90)

955. B = $C_{18}H_{36}O_2$
Stearic acid (158)

956. B = $C_{19}H_{16}$
Triphenylmethane (158)
(±0.005%)(318)

Wt. % A	d_4^{25}
100.000	0.87339
98.447	0.87612
97.499	0.87774
93.205	0.88488

957. B = $C_{20}H_{26}O_3S$
Menthyl naphthalene-β-sulfonate (212)[1]

958. B = $C_{20}H_{38}O_2$
Ethyl oleate (158)

959. B = $C_{24}H_{42}O_6$
Di-*l*-menthyl *l*-tartrate
(±0.05%)(214)

a	10^3b
(18.5°–27.0°)	
97.269 Wt. % A	
0.8821	1.012(t−18.5)
(17.75°–30.15°)	
94.606 Wt. % A	
0.8860	1.040(t−17.75)

960. B = $C_{24}H_{42}O_6$
l-Menthyl *d*-tartrate
(±0.05%)(226)

a	10^3b
(10.50°–39.75°)	
98.363 Wt. % A	
0.8911	1.060(t−10.50)
(9.4°–37.2°)	
92.583 Wt. % A	
0.8993	1.004(t − 9.4)

961. B = $C_{28}H_{46}O_8$
l-Menthyl diacetyl-*l*-tartrate
(±0.05%)(214)

a	10^3b
(17.75°–30.50°)	
97.938 Wt. % A	
0.8833	1.090(t−17.75)
(17.85°–30.10°)	
94.781 Wt. % A	
0.8878	1.053(t−17.85)
(15°–142°)	
0.000 Wt. % A	
1.0557	0.802(t − 15)

962. B = $C_{28}H_{46}O_8$
l-Menthyl diacetyl-*dl*-tartrate
(19°–28.8°)(±0.05%)(215)
5.204 Wt. % B

a	10^3b
0.8865	1.041 (t − 19)

963. B = $C_{51}H_{98}O_6$
Tripalmitin
(±0.05%)(332)

a	10^3b
(18.1°–41.0°)	
100.00 Wt. % A	
0.8799	1.057(t − 18.1)
(25°–50°)	
98.02 Wt. % A	
0.8735	1.036(t − 25)
95.93 Wt. % A	
0.8745	1.048(t − 25)
92.22 Wt. % A	
0.8753	1.036(t − 25)
(70°–107.2°)	
0.00 Wt. % A	
0.8752	0.710(t − 70)

964. B = $C_{57}H_{110}O_6$
Tristearin
(±0.05%)(332)

a	10^3b
(18.1°–41.0°)	
100.00 Wt. % A	
0.8799	1.057(t − 18.1)

C_6H_6.—(*Continued*)

B = $C_{57}H_{110}O_6$.—(*Continued*)

a	10^3b
(25°–50°)	
97.92 Wt. % A	
0.8734	0.968(t − 25)
(70°–113.2°)	
0.00 Wt. % A	
0.8689	0.628(t − 70)

964.5 B = *l*-Turpentine

(0.025%)(**123, 124, 289**)

Wt. % A	d_4^8
0.000	0.86723
20.077	0.86975
39.999	0.87272
60.027	0.87774
79.573	0.88390
100.000	0.89144
Wt. % A	d_4^{15}
0.000	0.86153
20.077	0.86351
39.999	0.86625
60.027	0.87087
79.573	0.87660
100.000	0.88369

(0.05%)(**60, 170, 342**)

Wt. % A	d_4^{20}
0.00	0.8629
10.08	0.8634
22.07	0.8644
34.94	0.8656
48.95	0.8677
63.10	0.8705
77.04	0.8738
90.02	0.8771
100.00	0.8803

(0.025%)(**123, 124, 289**)

Wt. % A	d_4^{22}
0.000	0.85590
20.077	0.85767
39.999	0.85987
60.027	0.86412
79.573	0.86944
100.000	0.87611

v. also 20, 55, 88, 108, 145, 162, 203, 245, 250, 264, 284, 303, 307, 322, 345, 364, 408, 498, 512, 542, 547, 552, 560, 564, 569, 582, 593, 597, 609, 612, 620, 651, 657, 661, 672, 704, 729, 739, 744, 754, 758, 760.5, 776, 777, 789, 793, 799, 819, 818.5, 823, 866, 1267, 1269, 1271, 1278, 1279, 1281

C_6H_6BrN

o-Bromoaniline

965. B = $C_7H_{14}O_2$

Isoamyl acetate (**306**)[1]

C_6H_6BrN

p-Bromoaniline

966. B = $C_7H_{14}O_2$

Isoamyl acetate (**306**)[1]

v. also 409

C_6H_6ClN

o-Chloroaniline

967. B = $C_7H_{14}O_2$

Isoamyl acetate (**306**)[1]

C_6H_6ClN

m-Chloroaniline

968. B = $C_7H_{14}O_2$

Isoamyl acetate (**306**)[1]

C_6H_6ClN

p-Chloroaniline

969. B = $C_7H_{14}O_2$

Isoamyl acetate (**306**)[1]

v. also 410

C_6H_6IN

p-Iodoaniline

970. B = $C_7H_{14}O_2$

Isoamyl acetate (**306**)[1]

$C_6H_6N_2O_2$

o-Nitroaniline

971. B = $C_7H_{14}O_2$

Isoamyl acetate (**306**)[1]

$C_6H_6N_2O_2$

m-Nitroaniline

972. B = $C_7H_{14}O_2$

Isoamyl acetate (**306**)[1]

v. also 411

$C_6H_6N_2O_2$

p-Nitroaniline, *v.* 412

C_6H_6O, Phenol

973. B = C_6H_7N

Aniline (**156, 307**[1])

(±0.01%)(**27**)

Wt. % B	d_4^{20}
100.00	1.0219
92.06	1.0276
84.69	1.0326
76.66	1.0380
68.72	1.0434
60.61	1.0485
52.44	1.0531
46.19	1.0568
37.50	1.0610
30.48	1.0643
22.98	1.0674
14.98	1.0703
7.72	1.0728
0.00	1.0749
Wt. % B	d_4^{30}
100.00	1.0131
92.42	1.0185
84.04	1.0242
76.67	1.0292
68.35	1.0347
60.86	1.0394
52.83	1.0442
46.00	1.0448
38.16	1.0520
30.72	1.0556
23.14	1.0589
15.20	1.0616
7.50	1.0645
0.00	1.0667
Wt. % B	d_4^{40}
100.00	1.0045
92.42	1.0099
84.04	1.0156
76.67	1.0206
68.35	1.0260
60.86	1.0307
52.83	1.0355
46.00	1.0394
38.16	1.0434
30.72	1.0470
23.14	1.0503
15.20	1.0530
7.50	1.0560
0.00	1.0583
Wt. % B	d_4^{60}
100.00	0.9872
92.42	0.9925
84.04	0.9982
76.67	1.0032
68.35	1.0086
60.86	1.0133
52.83	1.0180
46.00	1.0220
38.16	1.0259
30.72	1.0296
23.14	1.0330
15.20	1.0358
7.50	1.0388
0.00	1.0414
Wt. % B	d_4^{80}
100.00	0.9700
92.42	0.9752
84.04	0.9809
76.67	0.9858
68.35	0.9911
60.86	0.9959
52.83	1.0005
46.00	1.0047
38.16	1.0085
30.72	1.0122
23.14	1.0156
15.20	1.0185
7.50	1.0215
0.00	1.0242
Wt. % B	d_4^{125}
100.00	0.9289
92.06	0.9343
84.69	0.9391
76.66	0.9437
68.72	0.9483
60.61	0.9527
52.44	0.9571
46.19	0.9606
37.50	0.9648
30.48	0.9690
22.98	0.9727
14.98	0.9762
7.72	0.9795
0.00	0.9828

974. B = $C_6H_8N_2$

Phenylhydrazine

(±0.1%)(**307**)

Wt. % A	d_4^{50}
100.0	1.048
79.8	1.056
59.8	1.065
49.9	1.068
46.3	1.069
37.2	1.069
19.6	1.069
0.0	1.068

975. B = C_7H_8

Toluene

(±0.005%)(**319**)

Wt. % A	$d_4^{12.87}$
0.000	0.87233
2.091	0.87603
4.257	0.87985
9.841	0.88987
18.727	0.90640
28.789	0.92552

976. B = C_7H_8O

o-Cresol

(to 45 Wt. % A)(**86**)

$d_4^{15.5}$ = (1.052 + $0.0_3$2675 Wt. % A) ±0.25%

977. B = C_7H_8O

m-Cresol

(to 40 Wt. % A)(**86**)

$d_4^{15.5}$ = (1.039 + $0.0_3$3625 Wt. % A) ±0.25%

978. B = C_7H_8O

p-Cresol

(to 55 Wt. % A)(**86**)

$d_4^{15.5}$ = (1.039 + $0.0_3$372 Wt. % A) ±0.25%

979. B = C_7H_9N

p-Toluidine (**307**)[1]

(±0.01%)(**27**)

Wt. % A	$d_4^{39.9}$
0.00	0.9703
9.85	0.9808
20.67	0.9913
29.86	1.0004
38.57	1.0087
46.25	1.0160
55.09	1.0239
62.70	1.0305
71.11	1.0372
80.19	1.0441
89.76	1.0511
100.00	1.0584
Wt. % A	$d_4^{59.9}$
0.00	0.9534
9.85	0.9640
20.67	0.9744
29.86	0.9835
38.57	0.9919
46.25	0.9991
55.09	1.0069
62.70	1.0135
71.11	1.0201
80.19	1.0270
89.76	1.0340
100.00	1.0414

Wt. % A	$d_4^{79.8}$
0.00	0.9366
9.85	0.9471
20.67	0.9574
29.86	0.9665
38.57	0.9750
46.25	0.9820
55.09	0.9898
62.70	0.9965
71.11	1.0031
80.19	1.0099
89.76	1.0170
100.00	1.0243

Wt. % A	$d_4^{99.9}$
0.00	0.9190
9.85	0.9296
20.67	0.9399
29.86	0.9489
38.57	0.9575
46.25	0.9645
55.09	0.9723
62.70	0.9795
71.11	0.9856
80.19	0.9924
89.76	0.9995
100.00	1.0065

Wt. % A	d_4^{125}
0.00	0.8963
9.85	0.9069
20.67	0.9173
29.86	0.9262
38.57	0.9349
46.25	0.9419
55.09	0.9496
62.70	0.9567
71.11	0.9628
80.19	0.9696
89.76	0.9766
100.00	0.9833

Wt. % A	d_4^{150}
0.00	0.8735
16.62	0.8899
23.11	0.8962
34.42	0.9070
38.24	0.9106
45.61	0.9173
56.31	0.9265
65.69	0.9342
76.25	0.9422
79.43	0.9444
86.34	0.9492
100.00	0.9572

Wt. % A	d_4^{175}
0.00	0.8503
16.62	0.8669
23.11	0.8733
34.42	0.8843
38.24	0.8879
45.61	0.8944
56.31	0.9035
65.69	0.9111
76.25	0.9189
79.43	0.9211
86.34	0.9257
100.00	0.9338

980. B = $C_7H_{14}O_2$
Isoamyl acetate (305)[1]

981. B = $C_8H_{11}N$
Dimethylaniline
(±0.01%)(27)

Wt. % A	d_4^{10}
0.00	0.9647
9.07	0.9752
17.30	0.9851
23.94	0.9932
33.08	1.0041
40.39	1.0136
48.27	1.0236
55.75	1.0327
62.82	1.0413
69.97	1.0499
78.14	1.0594
85.39	1.0677
92.76	1.0758
100.00	1.0834

Wt. % A	d_4^{20}
0.00	0.9564
9.07	0.9670
17.30	0.9768
23.94	0.9849
33.08	0.9959
40.39	1.0053
48.27	1.0150
55.75	1.0243
62.82	1.0330
69.97	1.0416
78.14	1.0511
85.39	1.0594
92.76	1.0675
100.00	1.0751

Wt. % A	$d_4^{29.8}$
0.00	0.9483
7.93	0.9574
16.61	0.9677
24.60	0.9772
32.71	0.9872
41.46	0.9981
49.19	1.0076
56.14	1.0158
63.95	1.0252
70.99	1.0329
78.83	1.0431
86.08	1.0515
93.19	1.0593
100.00	1.0667

Wt. % A	$d_4^{40.2}$
0.00	0.9401
7.93	0.9493
16.61	0.9593
24.60	0.9688
32.71	0.9788
41.46	0.9895
49.19	0.9990
56.14	1.0073
63.95	1.0166
70.99	1.0243
78.83	1.0346
86.08	1.0431
93.19	1.0508
100.00	1.0583

Wt. % A	$d_4^{59.9}$
0.00	0.9235
7.93	0.9326
16.61	0.9426
24.60	0.9520
32.71	0.9619
41.46	0.9724
49.19	0.9818
56.14	0.9899
63.95	0.9991
70.99	1.0069
78.83	1.0171
86.08	1.0256
93.19	1.0335
100.00	1.0414

Wt. % A	d_4^{80}
0.00	0.9071
7.93	0.9160
16.61	0.9259
24.60	0.9353
32.71	0.9450
41.46	0.9553
49.19	0.9645
56.14	0.9726
63.95	0.9817
70.99	0.9895
78.83	0.9997
86.08	1.0082
93.19	1.0162
100.00	1.0242

Wt. % A	d_4^{126}
0.00	0.8680
9.07	0.8777
17.30	0.8864
23.94	0.8940
33.08	0.9041
40.39	0.9128
48.27	0.9217
55.75	0.9303
62.82	0.9388
69.97	0.9472
78.14	0.9564
85.39	0.9648
92.76	0.9734
100.00	0.9815

Wt. % A	d_4^{177}
0.00	0.8227
9.07	0.8320
17.30	0.8405
23.94	0.8474
33.08	0.8569
40.39	0.8648
48.27	0.8734
55.75	0.8818
62.82	0.8896
69.97	0.8979
78.14	0.9070
85.39	0.9153
92.76	0.9238
100.00	0.9316

982. B = $C_8H_{14}O_6$
Ethyl tartrate
(±0.075%)(224)

a	10^3b
(38.5°–78.8°)	
14.79 Wt. % B	
1.0786	$0.883(t - 38.5)$
(21.4°–99.8°)	
23.85 Wt. % B	
1.1049	$0.916(t - 21.4)$
(11.9°–99.2°)	
48.20 Wt. % B	
1.1403	$0.875(t - 11.9)$
(14.6°–83.4°)	
64.78 Wt. % B	
1.1663	$0.972(t - 14.6)$
(16.1°–64.7°)	
74.39 Wt. % B	
1.1753	$0.969(t - 16.1)$
(13.5°–82.1°)	
79.24 Wt. % B	
1.1835	$0.963(t - 13.5)$

983. B = C_9H_7N
Quinoline (±0.01%)(27)

Wt. % A	$d_4^{9.8}$
0.00	1.1003
7.54	1.1020
14.56	1.1036
22.73	1.1055
29.76	1.1070
37.52	1.1077
45.08	1.1073
53.20	1.1056
60.30	1.1029
68.21	1.0993
76.88	1.0949
83.37	1.0915
92.06	1.0874
100.00	1.0835

Wt. % A	$d_4^{20.1}$
0.00	1.0924
7.54	1.0943
14.56	1.0959
22.73	1.0976
29.76	1.0991
37.52	1.0998
45.08	1.0993
53.20	1.0976
60.30	1.0949
68.21	1.0913
76.88	1.0868
83.37	1.0834
92.06	1.0790
100.00	1.0749

Wt. % A	$d_4^{29.9}$
0.00	1.0850
7.77	1.0869
14.92	1.0885
21.96	1.0903
29.82	1.0916
37.14	1.0923
44.62	1.0916
52.31	1.0900
59.89	1.0873
67.92	1.0836
75.75	1 0794
83.49	1.0755
91.79	1.0710
100.00	1.0667

C_6H_6O.—(*Continued*)
B = **C_9H_7N.**—(*Continued*)

Wt. % A	d_4^{40}
0.00	1.0772
7.77	1.0791
14.92	1.0807
21.96	1.0822
29.82	1.0837
37.14	1.0842
44.62	1.0836
52.31	1.0819
59.89	1.0792
67.92	1.0754
75.75	1.0712
83.49	1.0671
91.79	1.0627
100.00	1.0583

Wt. % A	d_4^{60}
0.00	1.0614
7.77	1.0634
14.92	1.0650
21.96	1.0665
29.82	1.0678
37.14	1.0681
44.62	1.0674
52.31	1.0657
59.89	1.0628
67.92	1.0589
75.75	.0547
83.49	1.0502
91.79	1.0457
100.00	1.0414

Wt. % A	d_4^{80}
0.00	1.0458
7.77	1.0478
14.92	1.0494
21.96	1.0508
29.82	1.0517
37.14	1.0520
44.62	1.0513
52.31	1.0496
59.89	1.0465
67.92	1.0425
75.75	1.0382
83.49	1.0335
91.79	1.0288
100.00	1.0242

Wt. % A	d_4^{125}
0.00	1.0085
7.54	1.0103
14.56	1.0119
22.73	1.0133
29.76	1.0140
37.52	1.0139
45.08	1.0127
53.20	1.0099
60.30	1.0065
68.21	1.0021
76.88	0.9969
83.37	0.9927
92.06	0.9876
100.00	0.9828

Wt. % A	d_4^{175}
0.00	0.9673
7.54	0.9687
14.56	0.9698
22.73	0.9707
29.76	0.9705
37.52	0.9696
45.08	0.9678
53.20	0.9643
60.30	0.9602
68.21	0.9550
76.88	0.9492
83.37	0.9445
92.06	0.9389
100.00	0.9337

984. B = **$C_{10}H_9N$**
α-Naphthylamine
(±0.1%)(**307**)

Wt. % A	d_4^{30}
100.0	1.067
48.0	1.094
43.5	1.097
20.9	1.106
Wt. % A	d_4^{50}
100.0	1.048
48.0	1.075
43.5	1.076
20.9	1.092
7.5	1.102
0.0	1.108

985. B = **$C_{12}H_{11}N$**
Diphenylamine (**307**)[1]
(±0.01%)(**27**)

$d_4^{30} = (1.0799 - 0.0_3133$ Wt. % A)

$d_4^{40} = (1.0721 - 0.0_3138$ Wt. % A)

$d_4^{61} = (1.0542 - 0.0_3138$ Wt. % A)

$d_4^{81} = (1.0377 - 0.0_3144$ Wt. % A)

986. B = **$C_{12}H_{18}O_8$**
Diethyl diacetyltartrate
(±0.25%)(**273**)

a	10^3b
(55.6°–99.0°)	
100.00 Mol % A	
1.045	0.9194(t − 55.6)
87.36 Mol % A	
1.070	0.8986(t − 55.6)
71.25 Mol % A	
1.117	0.9701(t − 55.6)
58.80 Mol % A	
1.098	0.9677(t − 55.6)
36.35 Mol % A	
1.111	0.9837(t − 55.6)
15.02 Mol % A	
1.121	1.0410(t − 55.6)
(67.3°–99.0°)	
0.00 Mol % A	
1.109	0.8958(t − 67.3)

987. B = **$C_{13}H_{13}N$**
Diphenylmethylamine
(±0.01%)(**27**)

Wt. % A	$d_4^{9.8}$
0.00	1.0594
4.92	1.0604
9.48	1.0614
17.18	1.0631
27.69	1.0656
36.92	1.0678
48.42	1.0707
56.87	1.0727
67.10	1.0752
78.79	1.0781
89.30	1.0808
100.00	1.0838
Wt. % A	$d_4^{20.1}$
0.00	1.0514
4.92	1.0522
9.48	1.0531
17.18	1.0547
27.69	1.0571
36.92	1.0592
48.42	1.0620
56.87	1.0640
67.10	1.0664
78.79	1.0692
89.30	1.0719
100.00	1.0749
Wt. % A	d_4^{30}
0.00	1.0438
4.98	1.0449
10.21	1.0461
20.04	1.0483
35.34	1.0518
49.87	1.0551
62.12	1.0580
73.58	1.0606
82.22	1.0626
90.05	1.0644
100.00	1.0667
Wt. % A	d_4^{40}
0.00	1.0359
4.98	1.0369
10.21	1.0379
20.04	1.0401
35.34	1.0435
49.87	1.0467
62.12	1.0495
73.58	1.0520
82.22	1.0541
90.05	1.0559
100.00	1.0583
Wt. % A	d_4^{60}
0.00	1.0198
4.98	1.0207
10.21	1.0217
20.04	1.0237
35.34	1.0269
49.87	1.0301
62.12	1.0328
73.58	1.0354
82.22	1.0373
90.05	1.0391
100.00	1.0414
Wt. % A	d_4^{80}
0.00	1.0040
4.98	1.0048
10.21	1.0058
20.04	1.0076
35.34	1.0104
49.87	1.0136
62.12	1.0164
73.58	1.0188
82.22	1.0206
90.05	1.0223
100.00	1.0242

v. also 109, 413, 513, 667, 705, 800, 824, 874, 1282, 1283

$C_6H_6O_2$

Resorcinol, *v.* 414, 621

C_6H_7N

Aniline

988. B = **C_6H_8IN**
Aniline hydroiodide
(to 20.48 Wt. % B)(**266**)

$d_4^{25} = (1.018 + 0.0_25225$ Wt. % B) ± 0.25%

989. B = **$C_7H_6O_2$**
Benzoic acid
(±0.005%)(**319**)

Wt. % A	$d_4^{12.87}$
100.000	1.02780
98.222	1.03044
94.694	1.03581
91.005	1.04158
87.831	1.04665

990. B = **C_7H_8**
Toluene
(±0.075%)(**122**)

Wt. % A	d_4^{20}
100.00	1.0208
87.45	0.9989
80.84	0.9878
60.07	0.9541
40.95	0.9241
25.43	0.9007
0.00	0.8654

(±0.075%)(**112**)

a	10^3b
(25°–90°)	
100.00 Wt. % A	
1.0170	0.838(t − 25)
70.28 Wt. % A	
0.9658	0.867(t − 25)
37.14 Wt. % A	
0.9133	0.898(t − 25)
(25°–75°)	
0.00 Wt. % A	
0.8599	0.890(t − 25)

991. B = **C_7H_8O**
m-Cresol
(±0.25%)(**156**)

Mol % A	d_4^{0}
0	1.049
25	1.050
45	1.049
50	1.048
55	1.048
75	1.044
100	1.039

(±0.25%)(312)

Mol % A	d_4^{25}
100.0	1.018
70.0	1.022
62.6	1.024
53.9	1.026
45.1	1.029
36.9	1.030
22.2	1.030
0.0	1.031

(±0.25%)(156)

Mol % A	$d_4^{61.5}$
0	1.003
25	1.002
45	1.001
50	1.000
55	0.999
75	0.995
100	0.987

992. B = C_7H_8O
p-Cresol (±0.1%)(307)

Wt. % A	d_4^{25}
100.0	1.020
70.0	1.022
46.4	1.027
37.3	1.028
20.5	1.028
10.0	1.029
Wt. % A	d_4^{50}
100.0	0.992
70.0	0.997
46.4	1.001
37.3	1.004
20.5	1.005
10.0	1.005
0.0	1.005

993. B = C_7H_9N
o-Toluidine
(0–100 Wt. % A)(122)
$d_4^{54} = (0.9700 + 0.0_3216$ Wt. % A) ±0.075%

994. B = $C_7H_{14}O_2$
Isoamyl acetate (306)[1]

995. B = C_8H_9NO
Acetanilide (292)[2]

996. B = C_8H_{10}
Xylene (149) (±0.25%)(46)

Wt. % A	d_4^{0}
100.0	1.039
87.0	1.014
63.6	0.975
54.4	0.960
37.4	0.938
19.4	0.917
0.0	0.909

997. B = $C_8H_{10}N_4O_2$
Caffeine (292)[2]

998. B = $C_8H_{10}O$
Phenetole
(0 – 100 Wt. % B)(±0.01%)(27)

$d_4^0 = (1.0390 - 0.0_3538$ Wt. % B)

$d_4^{9.9} = (1.0303 - 0.0_3543$ Wt. % B)

$d_4^{20.2} = (1.0214 - 0.0_3548$ Wt. % B)

$d_4^{29.6} = (1.0134 - 0.0_3554$ Wt. % B)

$d_4^{40} = (1.0045 - 0.0_3561$ Wt. % B)

$d_4^{60} = (0.9872 - 0.0_3573$ Wt. % B)

$d_4^{80} = (0.9700 - 0.0_3589$ Wt. % B)

999. B = $C_8H_{11}N$
Dimethylaniline
(±0.1%)(122)

Wt. % A	$d_4^{54.7}$
100.00	0.9916
92.01	0.9858
80.41	0.9776
53.92	0.9598
35.58	0.9484
17.40	0.9377
11.76	0.9344
0.00	0.9278

1000. B = $C_8H_{14}O_6$
Ethyl tartrate
(±0.05%)(225)

a	10^3b
(15.1°–25.1°) 0.00 Wt. % B	
1.0262	0.86(t − 15.1)
(17.2°–70.7°) 7.66 Wt. % B	
1.0373	0.878(t − 17.2)
(12.7°–81.8°) 23.98 Wt. % B	
1.0699	0.915(t − 12.7)
(12.2°–86.1°) 66.29 Wt. % B	
1.1474	0.959(t − 12.2)

1001. B = $C_{10}H_{13}NO_2$
Phenacetine (292)

1002. B = $C_{10}H_{14}N_2$
Nicotine (343)[1]

1003. B = $C_{12}H_{11}N$
Diphenylamine
(±0.075%)(112)
93.55 Wt. % A

t	d_4^t
25	1.0212
60	0.9922
90	0.9644

v. also 21, 56, 204, 323, 415, 514, 570, 622, 673, 706, 730, 808, 814, 816, 825, 867, 875, 973

C_6H_8IN

Aniline hydroiodide
v. 988

$C_6H_8N_2$

o-Phenylenediamine
1004. B = $C_7H_{14}O_2$
Isoamyl acetate (306)[1]

$C_6H_8N_2$

m-Phenylenediamine
1005. B = $C_7H_{14}O_2$
Isoamyl acetate (306)[1]

$C_6H_8N_2$

Phenylhydrazine
v. 809, 974

$C_6H_8O_7$

Citric acid
1006. B = $C_7H_{14}O_2$
Amyl acetate (296)[1,2]

v. also 416, 674

$C_6H_{10}O$

Mesityl oxide
1007. B = $C_7H_{14}O_2$
Isoamyl acetate
(±0.05%)(69)

Wt. % B	d_4^{25}
100.00	0.8664
91.42	0.8644
86.85	0.8635
0.00	0.8549

$C_6H_{10}O_3$

Ethyl acetoacetate
1008. B = C_6H_{14}
Hexane (158)

1009. B = C_7H_9N
2, 6-Lutidine
(±0.05%)(71)

Wt. % A	d_4^{25}
0.00	0.9324
10.90	0.9413
32.63	0.9598
52.01	0.9769
88.55	1.0112
100.00	1.0222

1010. B = $C_8H_{14}O_6$
Ethyl tartrate
(±0.05%)(223)

a	10^3b
(14°–71.5°) 10.47 Wt. % B	
1.0509	1.018(t − 14)
(14°–50.5°) 25.08 Wt. % B	
1.0749	1.013(t − 14)
(15.2°–54.2°) 50.19 Wt. % B	
1.1169	1.026(t − 15.2)

1011. B = $C_{10}H_8$
Naphthalene (158)

1012. B = $C_{12}H_{10}N_2$
Azobenzene (158)

1013. B = $C_{14}H_{10}$
Phenanthrene (158)

1014. B = $C_{16}H_{32}O_2$
Palmitic acid (158)

v. also 57, 285, 346, 417, 598, 707, 876

$C_6H_{10}O_4$

Ethyl oxalate
1015. B = C_8H_{10}
Xylene (199)[1]

v. also 146, 877

$C_6H_{10}O_4$

Methyl *l*-α-acetoxypropionate
v. 257, 826

$C_6H_{10}O_6$

Methyl tartrate
v. 827

$C_6H_{10}O_8$

Citric acid monohydrate
1016. B = $C_7H_{14}O_2$
Amyl acetate (296)[1,2]

v. also 110, 418, 623, 675, 761

C_6H_{12}

Cyclohexane
v. 286

$C_6H_{12}O_2$

Caproic acid
1017. B = $C_{10}H_{16}O$
Camphor (323, 342)

$C_6H_{12}O_2$

Amyl formate
1018. B = C_8H_{10}
Xylene (199)[1]

v. also 748, 878

$C_6H_{12}O_2$

Butyl acetate
1019. B = C_8H_{10}
Xylene (199)[1]

v. also 879

$C_6H_{12}O_2$

d-β-Butyl acetate
v. 58

$C_6H_{12}O_2$

Isobutyl acetate
1020. B = $C_6H_{12}O_2$
Ethyl butyrate
(0°–40°)(±0.025%)(24)

a	10^3b
100.00 Wt. % A	
0.8920	1.049t
50.63 Wt. % A	
0.8959	1.050t
0.00 Wt. % A	
0.8997	1.053t

1021. B = $C_6H_{12}O_2$
Ethyl isobutyrate
(0°–40°)(±0.025%)(24)

a	10^3b
100.00 Wt. % A	
0.8920	1.049t
50.711 Wt. % A	
0.8914	1.067t
0.00 Wt. % A	
0.8906	1.075t

$C_6H_{12}O_2$.—(*Continued*)

1022. B = $C_7H_{14}O_2$
Ethyl isovalerate
(0°–40°)(±0.025%)(24)

a	10^3b
100.000 Wt. % A	
0.8920	1.049*t*
53.512 Wt. % A	
0.8888	1.023*t*
0.00 Wt. % A	
0.8854	0.994*t*

$C_6H_{12}O_2$

Ethyl butyrate
1023. B = $C_6H_{12}O_2$
Ethyl isobutyrate

a	10^3b
(to 40°)(±0.025%)(24)	
0.000 Wt. % A	
0.89060	1.075*t*
51.368 Wt. % A	
0.89530	1.065*t*
100.000 Wt. % A	
0.89970	1.053*t*

1024. B = C_6H_{14}
n-Hexane
(to 40°)(±0.025%)(24)

a	10^3b
100.000 Wt. % B	
0.68720	0.9025*t*
49.961 Wt. % B	
0.79305	0.9913*t*
0.000 Wt. % B	
0.89970	1.0525*t*

1025. B = C_8H_{10}
Xylene (199)[1]

1026. B = $C_{10}H_8$
Naphthalene (158)

1027. B = $C_{12}H_{10}N_2$
Azobenzene (158)

v. also 778, 880, 1020, 1265

$C_6H_{12}O_2$

Ethyl isobutyrate
1028. B = C_6H_{14}
n-Hexane
(to 40°)(±0.025%)(24)

a	10^3b
100.000 Wt. % B	
0.68720	0.9025*t*
50.289 Wt. % B	
0.78760	1.0050*t*
0.000 Wt. % B	
0.89060	1.0750*t*

1029. B = C_6H_{14}
Isohexane
(to 40°)(±0.025%)(24)

a	10^3b
100.000 Wt. % B	
0.67790	0.9125*t*
50.405 Wt. % B	
0.78250	1.0050*t*
0.000 Wt. % B	
0.89060	1.0750*t*

v. also 1021, 1023

$C_6H_{12}O_3$

Paraldehyde
1030. B = $C_8H_{14}O_6$
Ethyl tartrate
(±0.05%)(223)
(20°–67.5°)
49.99 Wt. % B

a	10^3b
1.0974	1.189(*t* − 20)

1031. B = $C_8H_{20}IN$
Tetraethylammonium iodide
(331)[1]

1032. B = $C_{10}H_8$
Naphthalene (158)

1033. B = $C_{12}H_{10}N_2$
Azobenzene (158)

1034. B = $C_{16}H_{32}O_2$
Palmitic acid (158)

v. also 59, 323.5, 418.5, 553, 590, 624, 762, 779, 828, 881

$C_6H_{13}NO$

Caproamide
v. 419

C_6H_{14}

Hexane
1035. B = C_6H_{14}
Isohexane
(to 40°)(±0.025%)(24)

a	10^3b
100.000 Wt. % A	
0.68720	0.9025*t*
50.805 Wt. % A	
0.68260	0.9075*t*
0.000 Wt. % A	
0.67790	0.9125*t*

1036. B = $C_7H_{14}O_2$
Propyl butyrate (158)

1037. B = C_8H_{18}
n-Octane (351, 352[1])

1038. B = $C_{10}H_8$
Naphthalene (158)

1039. B = $C_{10}H_{14}$
Durene
(±0.005%)(318)

Wt. % A	d_4^{25}
100.000	0.67207
97.435	0.67642
90.168	0.68869
86.070	0.68918

1040. B = $C_{10}H_{16}O$
d-Camphor (53)

1041. B = $C_{10}H_{17}Cl$
Pinene hydrochloride
(31.6–70.87 Wt. % B)(53)
$d_4^{15} = (0.756 + 0.0_2341$ (Wt. % B − 31.6)) ±0.5%

1042. B = $C_{12}H_{10}$
Acenaphthene (158)
(to 4.712 Wt. % B)(318)
$d_4^{25} = (0.67207 + 0.0_22825$ Wt. % B) ±0.005%

1043. B = $C_{12}H_{10}$
Diphenyl (158)
(to 6.434 Wt. % B)(318)
$d_4^{25} = (0.67207 + 0.0_22556$ Wt. % B) ±0.005%

1044. B = $C_{12}H_{10}N_2$
Azobenzene (158)
(to 3.671 Wt. % B)(318)
$d_4^{25} = (0.67207 + 0.0_22711$ Wt. % B) ±0.005%

1045. B = $C_{16}H_{32}O_2$
Palmitic acid (158)

1046. B = $C_{18}H_{36}O_2$
Stearic acid (158)

1047. B = $C_{19}H_{16}$
Triphenylmethane (158)
(to 3.011 Wt. % B)(318)
$d_4^{25} = (0.67207 + 0.0_22729$ Wt. % B) ±0.005%

v. also 324, 347, 515, 583, 599, 625, 756, 762.5, 780, 882, 1008, 1024, 1028

C_6H_{14}

Isohexane
v. 749, 1029, 1035

$C_6H_{16}ClN$

Triethylammonium iodide
v. 111

C_7H_5N

Benzonitrile
1048. B = $C_8H_{20}IN$
Tetraethylammonium iodide
(329,[1] 331[1])

1049. B = $C_{12}H_{28}IN$
Tetrapropylammonium iodide
(330,[1] 331[1])

v. also 420, 662

C_7H_5NS

Phenyl thiocyanate
1050. B = $C_{10}H_7Br$
α-Bromonaphthalene (289, 353)

1051. B = $C_{10}H_{12}O$
Anethole (289, 353)

v. also 60, 699

$C_7H_5N_3O_6$

Trinitrotoluene
v. 112, 883, 1281

$C_7H_6N_2O_4$

2, 4-Dinitrotoluene
1052. B = $C_8H_{14}O_6$
Ethyl tartrate
(±0.05%)(208)

a	10^3b
(72.3°–100.0°)	
24.94 Wt. % B	
1.2706	1.000(*t* − 72.3)
(19.3°–131.2°)	
100.00 Wt. % B	
1.2062	1.023(*t* − 19.3)

$C_7H_6N_2O_4$

2, 6-Dinitrotoluene
1053. B = $C_8H_{14}O_6$
Ethyl tartrate
(±0.05%)(208)

a	10^3b
(63.3°–80.5°)	
24.75 Wt. % B	
1.2788	1.023(*t* − 63.3)
(19.3°–131.2°)	
100.00 Wt. % B	
1.2062	1.023(*t* − 19.3)

C_7H_6O

Benzaldehyde
1054. B = C_8H_9NO
Acetanilide (292)[2]

1055. B = $C_8H_{10}N_4O_2$
Caffeine (292)[2]

1056. B = $C_8H_{14}O_6$
Ethyl tartrate (209)
(±0.05%)(218)

a	10^3b
(18.5°–31.65°)	
0.00 Wt. % B	
1.0516	0.905(*t* − 18.5)
(18.05°–42.4°)	
9.97 Wt. % B	
1.0649	0.904(*t* − 18.05)
(17.7°–31.15°)	
35.50 Wt. % B	
1.1049	0.967(*t* − 17.7)

1057. B = $C_{10}H_{13}NO_2$
Phenacetine (292)[2]

1058. B = $C_{12}H_{28}IN$
Tetrapropylammonium iodide
(330)[1]

v. also 61, 154, 884

$C_7H_6O_2$

Salicylaldehyde
1059. B = $C_7H_{14}O_2$
Isoamyl acetate (305)[1]

1060. B = $C_8H_{14}O_6$
Ethyl tartrate
(±0.05%)(209)

a	10^3b
(−23° to + 223.5°)	
100.00 Wt. % B	
1.2482	1.007(*t* + 23)
(18.5°–100°)	
20.21 Wt. % B	
1.1750	0.987(*t* − 18.5)

v. also 700

$C_7H_6O_2$

Benzoic acid
1061. B = C_7H_8
Toluene (296)[1,2]

1062. B = $C_7H_{14}O_2$
Amyl acetate (296)[1,2]

1063. B = C_8H_{10}
Xylene (296)[1,2]

1064. B = C_9H_7N
Quinoline
(±0.1 %)(12)

a	10^3b
(99°–125°)	
100.0 Mol % B	
1.031	0.847(t − 99)
80.0 Mol % B	
1.052	0.847(t − 99)
50.0 Mol % B	
1.082	0.808(t − 99)
33.4 Mol % B	
1.096	0.847(t − 99)

1065. B = C_9H_{12}
Cumene (296)[1,2]

1065.5. B = Turpentine (296)[1]

v. also 22, 62, 113, 421, 676, 708, 763, 829, 885, 989

$C_7H_6O_3$

Salicylic acid

1066. B = C_7H_8
Toluene (296)[1,2]

1067. B = $C_7H_{14}O_2$
Amyl acetate (296)[1,2]

1068. B = C_8H_{10}
Xylene (296)[1,2]

1069. B = C_9H_{12}
Cumene (296)[1,2]

1069.5. B = Turpentine (296)[1]

v. also 23, 63, 114, 422, 677, 764, 830, 886

C_7H_7NO

Benz-*anti*-aldoxime

1070. B = $C_8H_{14}O_6$
Ethyl tartrate
(±0.05%)(219)

a	10^3b
(44.6°–74.0°)	
79.90 Wt. % B	
1.1645	1.017(t − 44.6)
(18°–40.0°)	
49.62 Wt. % B	
1.1603	0.937(t − 18)
(22°–77.7°)	
22.82 Wt. % B	
1.1312	0.880(t − 22)
(21.5°–44.5°)	
10.37 Wt. % B	
1.1197	0.848(t − 21.5)
(18°–38.0°)	
0.00 Wt. % B	
1.1122	0.830(t − 18)

C_7H_7NO

Benz-*syn*-aldoxime

1071. B = $C_8H_{14}O_6$
Ethyl tartrate
(±0.05%)(219)

a	10^3b
(21.1°–43.50°)	
90.11 Wt. % B	
1.1973	1.023(t − 21.1)

C_7H_7NO

Benzamide
v. 423, 709

C_7H_7NO

Formanilide
v. 710

$C_7H_7NO_2$

o-Nitrotoluene

1072. B = $C_8H_{14}O_6$
Ethyl tartrate
(±0.05%)(208)

a	10^3b
(16.0°–100.5°)	
0.00 Wt. % B	
1.1672	0.943(t − 16.0)
(12.0°–101.0°)	
5.00 Wt. % B	
1.1717	0.950(t − 12.0)
(14.1°–101.0°)	
10.00 Wt. % B	
1.1711	0.961(t − 14.1)
(15.0°–101.0°)	
25.01 Wt. % B	
1.1749	0.972(t − 15.0)
(19.4°–101.6°)	
50.21 Wt. % B	
1.1799	0.999(t − 19.4)
(19.3°–131.2°)	
100.00 Wt. % B	
1.2062	1.023(t − 19.3)

1073. B = $C_{16}H_{26}O_8$
Isobutyl diacetyl-*d*-tartrate
(±0.05%)(209)

a	10^3b
(16.6°–99.7°)	
24.694 Wt. % B	
1.1453	0.959(t − 16.6)
(16.05°–99.3°)	
58.860 Wt. % B	
1.1187	0.941(t − 16.05)
(−21° to +99°)	
100.000 Wt. % B(±0.1%)	
1.1220	0.936(t + 21)

v. also 64, 424

$C_7H_7NO_2$

m-Nitrotoluene

1074. B = $C_8H_{14}O_6$
Ethyl tartrate
(±0.05%)(208)

a	10^3b
(17.5°–99.6°)	
0.00 Wt. % B	
1.1598	0.936(t − 17.5)
(15.5°–99.0°)	
5.00 Wt. % B	
1.1625	0.942(t − 15.5)
(18.3°–99.4°)	
9.99 Wt. % B	
1.1612	0.948(t − 18.3)
(18.4°–99.6°)	
25.00 Wt. % B	
1.1667	0.970(t − 18.4)
(20.4°–99.4°)	
51.19 Wt. % B	
1.1764	1.000(t − 20.4)
(19.3°–131.2°)	
100.00 Wt. % B	
1.2062	1.023(t − 19.3)

1075. B = $C_{12}H_{18}O_8$
Diethyl diacetyltartrate
(±0.25%)(273)
(67.3°–99.0°)

a	10^3b
0.00 Mol % B	
1.100	0.852(t − 67.3)
14.18 Mol % B	
1.073	0.820(t − 67.3)
31.49 Mol % B	
1.109	0.978(t − 67.3)
49.80 Mol % B	
1.107	0.915(t − 67.3)
66.49 Mol % B	
1.110	0.978(t − 67.3)
84.77 Mol % B	
1.111	0.978(t − 67.3)
100.00 Mol % B	
1.109	0.915(t − 67.3)

v. also 425

$C_7H_7NO_2$

p-Nitrotoluene

1076. B = $C_8H_{14}O_6$
Ethyl tartrate
(±0.05%)(208)

a	10^3b
(53.9°–93.4°)	
20.3 Mol % B	
1.1297	0.960(t − 53.9)
(45.7°–77.0°)	
48.5 Mol % B	
1.1486	1.006(t − 45.7)
(19.3°–131.2°)	
100.00 Mol % B	
1.2062	1.023(t − 19.3)

v. also 65, 426, 516

$C_7H_7NO_3$

o-Nitroanisole

1077. B = $C_8H_{14}O_6$
Ethyl tartrate
(±0.05%)(224)

a	10^3b
(17.7°–59.7°)	
9.79 Wt. % B	
1.2469	1.001(t − 17.7)
(14.9°–66.4°)	
21.17 Wt. % B	
1.2440	1.017(t − 14.9)

$C_7H_7NO_3$

p-Nitroanisole

1078. B = $C_8H_{14}O_6$
Ethyl tartrate (224)

C_7H_8

1079. B = C_7H_8O
m-Cresol
(±0.05%)(157)
d_4^t =
0 Mol % B
$0.8825(1 - 0.0_3982t)$
25 Mol % B
$0.9272(1 - 0.0_3991t)$
50 Mol % B
$0.9676(1 - 0.0_3881t)$
75 Mol % B
$1.0088(1 - 0.0_3928t)$
100 Mol % B
$1.0493(1 - 0.0_3711t)$

1080. B = C_7H_9N
o-Toluidine
(±0.075%)(122)

Wt. % A	$d_4^{54.5}$
0.00	0.9700
7.49	0.9588
17.69	0.9437
35.88	0.9177
58.59	0.8867
79.34	0.8592
88.84	0.8478
100.00	0.8340

1081. B = C_7H_9N
p-Toluidine (299)[1,2]

1082. B = C_7H_{16}
Heptane (61)

1083. B = $C_8H_8O_2$
Phenylacetic acid
(±0.075%)(172)
(15°–100°)

a	10^3b
86.04 Wt. % A	
0.8998	0.912(t − 15)
100.00 Wt. % A	
0.8706	0.912(t − 15)

1084. B = C_8H_9NO
Acetanilide (292)[2]

1085. B = C_8H_{10}
Ethylbenzene (351, 352[1])
(±0.025%)(24)
(to 40°)

a	10^3b
0.000 Wt. % A	
0.89130	0.8863t
52.670 Wt. % A	
0.88805	0.9075t
100.000 Wt. % A	
0.88450	0.9300t

1086. B = $C_8H_{10}N_4O_2$
Caffeine (292)[2]

1087. B = $C_8H_{11}N$
Dimethylaniline
(±0.075%)(122)

Wt. % A	d_4^{20}
0.00	0.9558
12.95	0.9436
20.86	0.9363
39.81	0.9188
59.53	0.9011
79.24	0.8836
86.12	0.8775
100.00	0.8655

C_7H_8.—(*Continued*)

1088. B = $C_8H_{14}O_6$
Ethyl tartrate
(±0.05%)(**205**)

a	10^3b
(18.77°–28.65°)	
0.00 Wt. % B	
0.8663	0.931(*t* − 18.77)
(20.72°–31.02°)	
2.01 Wt. % B	
0.8691	0.932(*t* − 20.72)
(20.15°–41.65°)	
5.02 Wt. % B	
0.8768	0.939(*t* − 20.15)
(19.80°–50.60°)	
9.98 Wt. % B	
0.8895	0.952(*t* − 19.80)
(21.32°–48.85°)	
24.99 Wt. % B	
0.9284	0.977(*t* − 21.32)
(18°–99°)	
49.18 Wt. % B	
1.0064	1.002(*t* − 18)
(20.5°–82.6°)	
59.91 Wt. % B	
1.0409	0.997(*t* − 20.5)
(19°–99°)	
69.99 Wt. % B	
1.0792	1.010(*t* − 19)

1089. B = $C_9H_{10}O_2$
Ethyl benzoate (**158**)
(±0.0075%)(**171**)

Wt. % A	d_4^{25}
0.000	1.04528
15.279	1.01164
47.316	0.94666
76.166	0.89419
100.000	0.85448

1090. B = C_9H_{12}
1, 2, 4-Trimethylbenzene
(±0.025%)(**24**)
(to 40°)

a	10^3b
0.000 Wt. % A	
0.89260	0.8088*t*
55.381 Wt. % A	
0.88760	0.8638*t*
100.000 Wt. % A	
0.88450	0.9300*t*

1091. B = $C_9H_{13}N$
Dimethyl-*o*-toluidine
(±0.05%)(**122**)

Wt. % A	$d_4^{54.6}$
100.00	0.8342
90.88	0.8400
71.56	0.8518
46.70	0.8644
39.88	0.8725
19.78	0.8858
14.06	0.8895
0.00	0.8990

1092. B = $C_{10}H_8$
Naphthalene (**54,**[1] **2991**)
(±0.005%)(**319**)

Wt. % B	$d_4^{12.87}$
0.000	0.87233
1.243	0.87416
5.064	0.88968
7.257	0.88289
20.286	0.90208

(±0.075%)(**172**)

Wt. % A	d_4^{15}
100.00	0.8712
93.59	0.8802
90.80	0.8837
88.03	0.8883
77.13	0.9046

(±0.005%)(**85**)

Wt. % B	d_4^{18}
0.000	0.86701
4.953	0.87416
9.090	0.88022
14.660	0.88850
20.133	0.89672
25.093	0.90424

1093. B = $C_{10}H_{13}NO_2$
Phenacetine (**292**)[2]

1094. B = $C_{10}H_{14}$
Durene
(±0.005%)(**318**)

Wt. % A	d_4^{25}
100.000	0.86137
97.057	0.86145
93.388	0.86197
93.229	0.86213
83.597	0.86387

1095. B = $C_{10}H_{16}O_4$
Camphoric acid (**296**)[1,2]

1096. B = $C_{12}H_{10}$
Acenaphthene (**158, 2991**)
(±0.005%)(**318**)

Wt. % A	d_4^{25}
100.000	0.86137
97.902	0.86526
94.657	0.87144
90.754	0.87858
82.571	0.89481

1097. B = $C_{12}H_{10}$
Diphenyl (**158**)
(±0.005%)(**318**)

Wt. % A	d_4^{25}
100.000	0.86137
97.372	0.86528
95.680	0.86777
91.063	0.87496
88.072	0.87911
75.834	0.89864

1098. B = $C_{12}H_{10}N_2$
Azobenzene
(±0.005%)(**318**)

Wt. % B	d_4^{25}
0.000	0.86137
2.841	0.86680
4.462	0.86968
8.547	0.87739
10.719	0.88128

1099. B = $C_{13}H_{10}O_3$
Salol (**292**)[2]

1100. B = $C_{14}H_{10}$
Phenanthrene (**158, 2991**)
(±0.01%)(**318**)
(to 70°)

a	10^3b
100.000 Wt. % A	
0.87047	0.938(*t* − 15)
96.902 Wt. % A	
0.87665	0.929(*t* − 15)
94.793 Wt. % A	
0.88121	0.926(*t* − 15)
89.516 Wt. % A	
0.89230	0.912(*t* − 15)
78.557 Wt. % A	
0.91592	0.884(*t* − 15)

1101. B = $C_{14}H_{10}O_2$
Benzil (**158**)
(±0.005%)(**318**)

Wt. % A	d_4^{25}
100.000	0.86137
97.217	0.86787
95.824	0.87124
93.451	0.87744
83.056	0.90238
77.966	0.91521

1102. B = $C_{18}H_{36}O_2$
Stearic acid (**296**)[1,2]

1103. B = $C_{19}H_{16}$
Triphenylmethane (**158**)
(±0.005%)(**318**)

Wt. % A	d_4^{25}
100.000	0.86137
96.147	0.86858
92.613	0.87462
88.843	0.88138
82.114	0.89433

1103.5. B = **Turpentine**
(0.0075%)(**171**)

Wt. % A	d_4^{25}
0.000	0.85720
6.791	0.85698
20.654	0.85588
53.701	0.85432
75.091	0.85404
100.000	0.85430

v. also 24, 66, 115, 251, 265, 267, 287, 325, 427, 517, 543, 565, 610, 626, 678, 755, 781, 790, 794, 801, 831, 887, 975, 990, 1061, 1066, 1266, 1280

C_7H_8O

Benzyl alcohol

1104. B = $C_7H_{14}O_2$
Isoamyl acetate (**305**)[1]

1105. B = $C_8H_{14}O_6$
Ethyl tartrate
(±0.05%)(**225**)

a	10^3b
(17.0°–46.9°)	
10.00 Wt. % B	
1.0635	0.763 (*t*−17.0)
(20°–101.1°)	
23.38 Wt. % B	
1.0818	0.833(*t* − 20)

v. also 679, 888, 1265

C_7H_8O, *o*-Cresol

1106. B = C_7H_8O
m-Cresol
(0–100 Wt. % A)
$d_4^{15.5}$ = (1.039 + 0.0_3129 Wt. % A) ± 0.25% (**86**)

1107. B = $C_7H_{14}O_2$
Isoamyl acetate (**305**)[1]

v. also 428, 711, 832, 889, 976, 1282

C_7H_8O, *m*-Cresol

1108. B = C_7H_8O
p-Cresol (**86**)

1109. B = C_7H_9N
o-Toluidine (**312**)
(±0.05%)(**157**)
d_4^t =
100 Mol % A
$1.0493(1 - 0.0_3711t)$
75 Mol % A
$1.0452(1 - 0.0_3782t)$
50 Mol % A
$1.0386(1 - 0.0_3802t)$
25 Mol % A
$1.0276(1 - 0.0_3794t)$
0 Mol % A
$1.0151(1 - 0.0_3808t)$

1110. B = $C_7H_{14}O_2$
Isoamyl acetate (**305**)[1]

1111. B = $C_8H_{11}N$
Dimethylaniline
(±0.05%)(**157**)
d_4^t =
0 Mol % A
$0.9742(1 - 0.0_3868t)$
25 Mol % A
$0.9925(1 - 0.0_3846t)$
50 Mol % A
$1.0113(1 - 0.0_3815t)$
75 Mol % A
$1.0313(1 - 0.0_3795t)$
100 Mol % A
$1.0493(1 - 0.0_3711t)$

v. also 712, 890, 977, 991, 1079, 1106, 1282, 1283

C_7H_8O, *p*-Cresol

1112. B = $C_7H_{14}O_2$
Isoamyl acetate (**305**)[1]

v. also 713, 978, 992, 1108, 1283

C_7H_8O

Anisole

1113. B = $C_7H_{14}O_2$
Isoamyl acetate (**305**)[1]

1114. B = $C_8H_{14}O_6$
Ethyl tartrate
(±0.05%)(224)

t	d_4
9.99 Wt. % B	
17.5	1.0142
25.4	1.0064
24.62 Wt. % B	
14.9	1.0424
32.5	1.0261
45.5	1.0130
55.5	1.0033
49.85 Wt. % B	
15.8	1.0932
25.6	1.0834

v. also 205, 429, 1265

$C_7H_8O_6$
Gallic acid monohydrate

1115. B = $C_7H_{14}O_2$
Amyl acetate (296)[1,2]

v. also 67, 430, 518, 627, 680, 765, 891

C_7H_9N
2, 6-Lutidine
v. 432, 1009

C_7H_9N
Methylaniline

1116. B = $C_8H_{14}O_6$
Ethyl tartrate
(±0.05%)(225)

a	10^3b
(14.9°–65.0°)	
9.94 Wt. % B	
1.0069	$0.812(t-14.9)$
(15.3°–20.0°)	
30.89 Wt. % B	
1.0486	$0.872(t-15.3)$

v. also 589, 833

C_7H_9N
o-Toluidine

1117. B = C_7H_9N
p-Toluidine
(to 50 Wt.% B)(173)
d_4^{15} = (1.0030 − 0.0_3126 Wt. % B) ±0.1%
(50–56 Wt. % B)
d_4^{20} = (0.9930 − 0.0_3216 (Wt. % B − 50)) ±0.1%

1118. B = $C_7H_{14}O_2$
Isoamyl acetate (306)[1]

1119. B = $C_8H_{14}O_6$
Ethyl tartrate
(±0.05%)(225)

a	10^3b
(12.6°–47.4°)	
10.93 Wt. % B	
1.0250	$0.851(t-12.6)$
(15°–58°)	
25.10 Wt. % B	
1.0501	$0.889(t-15)$
(14.9°–50.5°)	
50.30 Wt. % B	
1.1006	$0.927(t-14.9)$

v. also 834, 993, 1080, 1109

C_7H_9N
m-Toluidine

1120. B = $C_7H_{14}O_2$
Isoamyl acetate (306)[1]

1121. B = $C_8H_{14}O_6$
Ethyl tartrate
(±0.05%)(225)

a	10^3b
(15.5°–43.2°)	
11.66 Wt. % B	
1.0154	$0.845(t-15.5)$
(16.3°–64.3°)	
24.96 Wt. % B	
1.0407	$0.837(t-16.3)$

C_7H_9N
p-Toluidine

1122. B = $C_7H_{14}O_2$
Isoamyl acetate (306)[1]

1123. B = $C_8H_{14}O_6$
Ethyl tartrate
(±0.05%)(225)

a	10^3b
(20°–67.8°)	
24.93 Wt. % B	
1.0350	$0.836(t-20)$
(16.8°–58.2°)	
49.98 Wt. % B	
1.0919	$0.925(t-16.8)$

1124. B = $C_{10}H_8$
Naphthalene
(±0.1%)(159)

Mol % B	d_4^{80}
0	0.9365
10	0.9399
20	0.9434
29	0.9466
40	0.9510
60	0.9592
80	0.9681
90	0.9730
100	0.9777
Mol % B	d_4^{90}
0	0.9283
10	0.9316
20	0.9350
29	0.9384
40	0.9428
60	0.9513
80	0.9596
90	0.9648
100	0.9701

v. also 116, 431, 868, 979, 1081, 1117

C_7H_9NO
o-Anisidine

1125. B = $C_7H_{14}O_2$
Isoamyl acetate (306)[1]

$C_7H_9NO_2$
Ammonium benzoate
v. 433

$C_7H_9NO_2$
Phenylammonium formate
v. 155

$C_7H_9NO_3$
Ammonium salicylate
v. 434

$C_7H_9NO_3S$
m-Methoxybenzenesulfonamide
v. 229

$C_7H_{12}O_3$
Ethyl methylacetoacetate

1128. B = $C_8H_{14}O_6$
Ethyl tartrate
(±0.05%)(223)
(13°–41°)(10.23 Wt. % B)

a	10^3b
1.0225	$1.008(t-13)$

$C_7H_{12}O_4$
Ethyl malonate

1127. B = C_8H_{10}
Xylene (199)[1]

v. also 892

$C_7H_{14}O_2$
Amyl acetate

1129. B = C_8H_9NO
Acetanilide (292)[2]

1130. B = C_8H_{10}
Xylene (199)[1]

1131. B = $C_8H_{10}N_4O_2$
Caffeine (292)[2]

1132. B = $C_{10}H_{13}NO_2$
Phenacetine (292)[2]

1133. B = $C_{13}H_{10}O_3$
Salol (292)[2]

1134. B = $C_{18}H_{36}O_2$
Stearic acid (296)[1,2]

v. also 519, 1006, 1016, 1062, 1067, 1115, 1265

$C_7H_{14}O_2$
Isoamyl acetate

1136. B = C_8H_6
Phenylacetylene (69,[1] 125[1])

1137. B = C_8H_8
Phenylethylene
(±0.05%)(69, 125)

Wt. % A	d_4^{25}
100.00	0.8664
95.30	0.8684
91.61	0.8702
0.00	0.8998

1138. B = C_8H_8O
Acetophenone
(±0.05%)(69)

Wt. % A	d_4^{25}
100.00	0.8664
95.69	0.8731
91.72	0.8744

1139. B = $C_8H_8O_2$
Phenyl acetate (305)[1]

1140. B = $C_8H_8O_3$
l-Mandelic acid
(±0.05%)(72)

Wt. % A	d_4^{25}
100.00	0.8664
95.28	0.8722
92.07	0.8823
91.45	0.8843
88.61	0.8933

1141. B = $C_8H_8O_3$
dl-Mandelic acid
(±0.05%)(72)

Wt. % A	d_4^{25}
100.00	0.8664
93.88	0.8764
92.36	0.8813
90.14	0.8880
87.12	0.8976

1142. B = C_8H_{10}
Phenylethane (69,[1] 125[1])

1143. B = $C_8H_{10}O$
Benzyl methyl ether (305)[1]

1144. B = $C_8H_{10}O$
Phenetole (305)[1]

1145. B = $C_8H_{10}O$
o-Tolyl methyl ether (305)[1]

1146. B = $C_8H_{10}O$
m-Tolyl methyl ether (305)[1]

1147. B = $C_8H_{10}O$
p-Tolyl methyl ether (305)[1]

1148. B = $C_9H_6O_2$
Phenylpropiolic acid
(to 7.16 Wt. % B)(125)
d_4^{25} = (0.8664 + 0.0_2375 Wt. % B) ±0.05%

1149. B = $C_9H_8O_2$
Cinnamic acid
(±0.05%)(125)

Wt. % A	d_4^{25}
100.00	0.8664
96.11	0.8748
94.98	0.8782

1150. B = $C_9H_{10}O_2$
β-Phenylpropionic acid
(±0.05%)(125)

Wt. % A	d_4^{25}
100.00	0.8664
95.99	0.8754
94.25	0.8776

1151. B = $C_9H_{10}O_2$
Benzyl acetate (305)[1]

1152. B = $C_9H_{10}O_3$
Ethyl salicylate (305)[1]

1153. B = $C_9H_{10}O_3$
Ethyl *m*-hydroxybenzoate (305)[1]

1154. B = $C_9H_{11}NO_2$
Ethyl *p*-aminobenzoate (306)[1]

1155. B = $C_9H_{11}NO_2$
Ethyl anthranilate (306)[1]

$C_7H_{14}O_2$.—*(Continued)*

1156. B = $C_9H_{14}O$
Phorone
(±0.05%)(69)

Wt. % A	d_4^{25}
100.00	0.8664
91.26	0.8680
85.10	0.8698
0.00	0.8964

1157. B = $C_{10}H_8$
Naphthalene (158)

1158. B = $C_{10}H_8O$
α-Naphthol (305)[1]

1159. B = $C_{10}H_8O$
β-Naphthol (305)[1]

1160. B = $C_{10}H_9N$
α-Naphthylamine (306)[1]

1161. B = $C_{10}H_9N$
β-Naphthylamine (306)[1]

1162. B = $C_{10}H_{10}O$
Benzylideneacetone
(to 9.12 Wt. % B)(69)
d_4^{25} = (0.8664 + 0.0_21623 Wt. % B) ±0.05%

1163. B = $C_{10}H_{10}O_2$
Safrole
(±0.05%)(69)

Wt. % A	d_4^{25}
100.00	0.8664
93.46	0.8790
72.70	0.9212
0.00	1.0950

1164. B = $C_{10}H_{10}O_2$
Isosafrole (69)[1]

1165. B = $C_{10}H_{12}O$
Benzylacetone
(±0.05%)(69)

Wt. % A	d_4^{25}
100.00	0.8664
96.35	0.8714
92.08	0.8760

1166. B = $C_{10}H_{12}O_2$
Eugenol
(±0.05%)(69)

Wt. % A	d_4^{25}
100.00	0.8664
87.74	0.8864
80.39	0.9019
0.00	1.0620

1167. B = $C_{10}H_{12}O_2$
Isoeugenol
(±0.05%)(69)

Wt. % A	d_4^{25}
100.00	0.8664
92.34	0.8810
85.49	0.8940
0.00	1.0791

1168. B = $C_{12}H_{10}$
Diphenyl (69,[1] 158)
(±0.05%)(318)

Wt. % A	d_4^{25}
100.00	0.86208
93.052	0.87276
88.565	0.88972

1169. B = $C_{12}H_{11}N$
Diphenylamine (306)[1]

1170. B = $C_{12}H_{10}N_2$
Azobenzene (158)

1171. B = $C_{12}H_{12}O$
Cinnamylideneacetone
(to 2.47 Wt. % B)(69)
d_4^{25} = (0.8664 + 0.0_21539 Wt. % B) ±0.05%

1172. B = $C_{13}H_{10}O$
Benzophenone
(to 6.48 Wt. % B)(69)
d_4^{25} = (0.8664 + 0.0_22127 Wt. % B) ± 0.05%

1173.5 B = $C_{13}H_{12}O$
Diphenylcarbinol (305)[1]

1173. B = $C_{13}H_{20}O_2$
Menthyl propiolate (125)[1]

1174. B = $C_{14}H_{10}$
Phenanthrene (158)

1175. B = $C_{14}H_{10}$
Diphenylacetylene (125)[1]

1176. B = $C_{14}H_{12}$
Diphenylethylene
(to 4.70 Wt. % B)(125)
d_4^{25} = (0.8664 + 0.0_2149 Wt. % B) ±0.05%

1177. B = $C_{14}H_{14}$
Diphenylethane
(to 5.29 Wt. % B) (125)
d_4^{25} = (0.8664 + 0.0_21247 Wt. % B) ± 0.05%

1178. B = $C_{15}H_{12}O$
Benzylideneacetophenone
(±0.05%)(69)

Wt. % A	d_4^{25}
100.00	0.8664
96.00	0.8768
94.55	0.8790

1179. B = $C_{15}H_{14}O$
Diphenylacetone
(to 4.84 Wt. % B)(69)
d_4^{25} = (0.8664 + 0.0_21838 Wt. % B) ±0.05 %

1180. B = $C_{15}H_{14}O$
Benzylacetophenone
(to 5.10 Wt. % B)(69)
d_4^{25} = (0.8664 + 0.0_21883 Wt. % B) ±0.05%

1181. B = $C_{16}H_{14}$
Diphenylbutadiene (125)[1]

1182. B = $C_{16}H_{18}$
Diphenylbutane
(±0.05%)(125)

Wt. % A	d_4^{25}
100.00	0.8664
98.56	0.8698
96.60	0.8730

1183. B = $C_{17}H_{14}O$
Dibenzylideneacetone
(to 2.76 Wt. % B)(69)
d_4^{25} = (0.8664 + 0.0_2239 Wt. % B) ±0.05%

1184. B = $C_{17}H_{14}O$
Cinnamylideneacetophenone
(±0.05%)(69)

Wt. % A	d_4^{25}
100.00	0.8664
97.90	0.8715
96.69	0.8734

1185. B = $C_{18}H_{36}O_2$
Stearic acid (158)

1186. B = $C_{19}H_{16}O$
Triphenylcarbinol (305)[1]

1187. B = $C_{19}H_{26}O_2$
Menthyl cinnamate
(±0.05%)(125)

Wt. % A	d_4^{25}
100.00	0.8664
98.80	0.8684
93.92	0.8732
81.52	0.9101

1188. B = $C_{19}H_{28}O_2$
Menthyl β-phenylpropionate
(±0.05%)(125)

Wt. % A	d_4^{25}
100.00	0.8664
94.12	0.8713
90.62	0.8755

1189. B = $C_{21}H_{18}O$
Dicinnamylideneacetone
(±0.05%)(69)

Wt. % A	d_4^{25}
100.00	0.8664
99.11	0.8675
98.99	0.8688

v. also 288, 600, 628, 725, 731, 773, 782, 785, 788, 797, 798, 810, 815, 817, 818, 821, 869, 872, 873, 893, 965, 966, 967, 968, 969, 970, 971, 972, 980, 994, 1004, 1005, 1007, 1059, 1104, 1107, 1110, 1112, 1113, 1118, 1120, 1122, 1125

$C_7H_{14}O_2$
Ethyl valerate
1190. B = C_8H_{10}
Xylene (199)[1]

v. also 894

$C_7H_{14}O_2$
Ethyl isovalerate
v. 1022

$C_7H_{14}O_2$
Propyl butyrate
1191. B = $C_{10}H_8$
Naphthalene (158)

1192. B = $C_{12}H_{10}N_2$
Azobenzene (158)

1193. B = $C_{14}H_{10}$
Phenanthrene (158)

1194. B = $C_{16}H_{32}O_2$
Palmitic acid (158)

1195. B = $C_{18}H_{36}O_2$
Stearic acid (158)

v. also 601, 783, 895, 1036

C_7H_{16}
Heptane
1196. B = $C_{10}H_7Br$
α-Bromonaphthalene (61, 236[1])

1197. B = $C_{10}H_8$
Naphthalene
(to 2.483 Wt. % A)(54)
d_4^{18} = (0.73383 + 0.0_22186 Wt. % A) ± 0.0075%

v. also 68, 117, 289, 371, 802, 896, 1082

$C_7H_{16}O$
Diethylisopropyl alcohol
v. 897
Ethyl amyl ether
v. 25, 118, 803

$C_8H_5NO_2$
Phthalimide
v. 714

C_8H_6
Phenylacetylene
v. 1136

C_8H_7N
Benzyl cyanide
1198. B = $C_8H_{10}O$
Phenetole (236)[1]

1199. B = $C_8H_{20}IN$
Tetraethylammonium iodide (329)[1]

C_8H_8
Phenylethylene
v. 1137

C_8H_8ClNO
p-Chloroacetanilide
v. 435

C_8H_8O
Acetophenone
1200. B = $C_8H_{20}IN$
Tetraethylammonium iodide (331)[1]

v. also 119, 230, 238, 242, 258, 304, 326, 898, 1138

$C_8H_8O_2$
Anisaldehyde
1201. B = $C_{12}H_{28}IN$
Tetrapropylammonium iodide (330)[1]

$C_8H_8O_2$
Phenylacetic acid
v. 1083

$C_8H_8O_2$
Methyl benzoate

1202. B = $C_9H_{10}O_2$
Ethyl benzoate
(±0.01%)(**255**)

Wt. % B	d_4^{25}
100.00	1.04171
81.57	1.04917
64.20	1.05637
53.45	1.06081
38.71	1.06732
22.53	1.07420
0.00	1.08433

1203. B = $C_{10}H_8$
Naphthalene (**158**)

1204. B = $C_{12}H_{10}N_2$
Azobenzene (**158**)

1205. B = $C_{14}H_{10}$
Phenanthrene (**158**)

v. also 290, 348, 584, 602, 629, 681, 784, 835, 899

$C_8H_8O_2$
Phenyl acetate
v. 1139

$C_8H_8O_3$
l-Mandelic acid
v. 1140
dl-Mandelic acid
v. 1141

$C_8H_9Cl_3O_7$
Methyl mono (trichloroacetyl)-tartrate
v. 836

C_8H_9NO
Acetanilide
1206. B = C_8H_{10}
Xylene (**292**)[2]

v. also 120, 206, 436, 520, 900, 995, 1054, 1084, 1129

$C_8H_9NO_3$
o-Nitrophenetole
1207. B = $C_8H_{14}O_6$
Ethyl tartrate
(±0.05%)(**224**)

a	10^3b
(17.1°–54.3°)	
25.09 Wt. % B	
1.1894	$1.000(t-17.1)$
(14.6°–41.0°)	
39.43 Wt. % B	
1.1946	$1.016(t-14.6)$

C_8H_{10}
Ethylbenzene
1208. B = C_9H_{12}
Trimethylbenzene
(to 40°)(±0.025%)(**24**)

a	10^3b
0.000 Wt. % A	
0.89260	$0.8088t$
51.999 Wt. % A	
0.89100	$0.8450t$
100.000 Wt. % A	
0.89130	$0.8863t$

v. also 630, 735, 901, 1085, 1142

C_8H_{10}
o-Xylene
1209. B = C_8H_{10}
m-Xylene
(±0.05%)(**157**)
d_4^t =
100.0 Mol % A
$0.8975(1 - 0.0_3937t)$
72.9 Mol % A
$0.8941(1 - 0.0_3955t)$
26.9 Mol % A
$0.8862(1 - 0.0_3907t)$
0.0 Mol % A
$0.8828(1 - 0.0_3957t)$

1210. B = C_8H_{10}
p-Xylene
(±0.05%)(**157**)
d_4 =
100.0 Mol % A
$0.8975(1 - 0.0_3937t)$
81.5 Mol % A
$0.8936(1 - 0.0_3929t)$
31.9 Mol % A
$0.8861(1 - 0.0_3981t)$
0.0 Mol % A
$0.8787(1 - 0.0_3989t)$

1211. B = $C_8H_{14}O_6$
Ethyl tartrate
(±0.05%)(**205**)

a	10^3b
(19.12°–36.34°)	
0.00 Wt. % B	
0.8809	$0.842(t-19.12)$
(19.2°–31.7°)	
2.00 Wt. % B	
0.8852	$0.848(t-19.2)$
(19.21°–33.47°)	
5.00 Wt. % B	
0.8920	$0.848(t-19.21)$
(19.23°–35.85°)	
9.96 Wt. % B	
0.9038	$0.860(t-19.23)$
(18.97°–37.76°)	
25.01 Wt. % B	
0.9426	$0.910(t-18.97)$
(18.86°–41.90°)	
49.99 Wt. % B	
1.0157	$0.955(t-18.86)$
(18.75°–45.58°)	
74.99 Wt. % B	
1.1023	$0.991(t-18.75)$

C_8H_{10}
m-Xylene
1212. B = C_8H_{10}
p-Xylene
d_4^t =
(±0.05%)(**157**)
100.0 Mol % A
$0.8828(1 - 0.0_3957t)$
75.4 Mol % A
$0.8819(1 - 0.0_3956t)$
29.2 Mol % A
$0.8798(1 - 0.0_3979t)$
0.0 Mol % A
$0.8787(1 - 0.0_3989t)$

1213. B = $C_8H_{10}N_4O_2$
Caffeine (**292**)[2]

1214. B = $C_8H_{11}N$
Dimethylaniline
(±0.05%)(**157**)
d_4^t =
0.0 Mol % A
$0.9742(1 - 0.0_3868t)$
28.7 Mol % A
$0.9475(1 - 0.0_3862t)$
73.4 Mol % A
$0.9095(1 - 0.0_3938t)$
100.0 Mol % A
$0.8828(1 - 0.0_3957t)$

1215. B = $C_8H_{14}O_4$
Ethyl succinate (**199**)[1]

1216. B = $C_8H_{14}O_6$
Ethyl tartrate
(±0.05%)(**205**)

a	10^3b
(21.37°–42.10°)	
0.00 Wt. % B	
0.8630	$0.873(t-21.37)$
(18.42°–30.42°)	
2.00 Wt. % B	
0.8699	$0.858(t-18.42)$
(18.35°–33.75°)	
2.41 Wt. % B	
0.8710	$0.864(t-18.35)$
(18.4°–33.89°)	
5.10 Wt. % B	
0.8772	$0.872(t-18.4)$
(18.80°–31.20°)	
10.00 Wt. % B	
0.8890	$0.887(t-18.80)$
(18.01°–32.27°)	
18.82 Wt. % B	
0.9128	$0.898(t-18.01)$
(17.66°–30.26°)	
33.12 Wt. % B	
0.9533	$0.928(t-17.66)$
(17.8°–100°)	
39.99 Wt. % B	
0.9743	$0.942(t-17.8)$
(21.6°–100°)	
59.98 Wt. % B	
1.0371	$0.977(t-21.6)$
(18.18°–39.12°)	
74.09 Wt. % B	
1.0931	$0.995(t-18.18)$

1217. B = $C_9H_{10}O_2$
Ethyl benzoate (**199**)[1]

1218. B = $C_9H_{10}O_3$
Ethyl salicylate (**199**)[1]

1219. B = $C_{10}H_8$
Naphthalene
(to 17.99 Wt. % A)(**172**)
d_4^{15} = (0.8678 + 0.001401 Wt. % A) ±0.075%

1220. B = $C_{10}H_{13}NO_2$
Phenacetine (**292**)[2]

1221. B = $C_{10}H_{16}O_4$
Camphoric acid (**296**)[1,2]

1222. B = $C_{10}H_{20}O_2$
Amyl valerate (**199**)[1]

1223. B = $C_{12}H_{16}O_2$
Amyl benzoate (**199**)[1]

v. also 26, 147, 246, 327, 365, 437, 548, 554, 804, 902, 996, 1015, 1018, 1019, 1025, 1063, 1068, 1127, 1130, 1190, 1206, 1209, 1268, 1270, 1272

C_8H_{10}
p-Xylene
1224. B = $C_8H_{14}O_6$
Ethyl tartrate
(±0.05%)(**205**)

a	10^3b
(19.50°–40.65°)	
0.00 Wt. % B	
0.8614	$0.869(t-19.50)$
(18.8°–30.33°)	
2.00 Wt. % B	
0.8667	$0.877(t-18.8)$
(18.1°–37.27°)	
5.00 Wt. % B	
0.8745	$0.882(t-18.1)$
(17.95°–42.97°)	
10.10 Wt. % B	
0.8874	$0.900(t-17.95)$
(18.42°–31.00°)	
24.98 Wt. % B	
0.9270	$0.915(t-18.42)$
(18.59°–43.21°)	
50.09 Wt. % B	
1.0044	$0.971(t-18.59)$
(18.43°–34.75°)	
74.99 Wt. % B	
1.0957	$0.998(t-18.43)$

v. also 1210, 1212

$C_8H_{10}N_4O_2$
Caffeine
v. 521, 766, 903, 997, 1055, 1086, 1131, 1213

$C_8H_{10}O$
Benzyl methyl ether
v. 1143

$C_8H_{10}O$
Phenetole
1225. B = $C_8H_{14}O_6$
Ethyl tartrate
(±0.05%)(**224**)

t	d_4
9.99 Wt. % B	
18.6	0.9862
25.8	0.9794
24.96 Wt. % B	
17.9	1.0161
28.1	1.0071
38.3	0.9969
48.4	0.9869
51.73 Wt. % B	
17.7	1.0771
26.5	1.0682

$C_8H_{10}O$.—(*Continued*)

1226. B = $C_{12}H_{10}O$
Diphenyl ether
(±0.1%)(152)

Mol % B	d_4^{25}
0.00	0.9618
9.94	0.9755
18.73	0.9870
29.63	0.9993
39.98	1.0111
48.95	1.0206
62.69	1.0346
67.47	1.0396
79.28	1.0510
86.33	1.0573
100.00	1.0706

v. also 121, 207, 243, 259, 366, 438, 682, 998, 1144, 1198

$C_8H_{10}O$

o-Tolyl methyl ether
v. 1145
m-Tolyl methyl ether
v. 1146
p-Tolyl methyl ether
v. 1147

$C_8H_{10}O_4$

Diallyl oxalate
v. 904

$C_8H_{11}N$

Dimethylaniline
1227. B = $C_8H_{14}O_6$
Ethyl tartrate
(±0.05%)(225)

a	10^3b
(16.4°–43.0°)	
9.40 Wt. % B	
0.9774	0.850(t−16.4)
(15.6°–50.9°)	
24.84 Wt. % B	
1.0100	0.892(t−15.6)

1228. B = $C_{10}H_{16}O$
d-Camphor
(to 60 Wt. % B)(170, 175)
d_4^{20} = (0.9576 + 0.0₄45 Wt. % B) ±0.025%

v. also 631, 811, 837, 981, 999, 1087, 1111, 1214

$C_8H_{11}N$

Ethylaniline
v. 838

$C_8H_{12}O_4$

Ethyl maleate
1229. B = $C_8H_{14}O_6$
Ethyl tartrate
(±0.05%)(213)

a	10^3b
(10°–44.2°)	
0.00 Wt. % B	
1.0789	1.009(t − 10)
(20.3°–44.4°)	
20.68 Wt. % B	
1.0942	1.017(t−20.3)

$C_8H_{12}O_4$

Ethyl fumarate
1230. B = $C_8H_{14}O_6$
Ethyl tartrate
(±0.05%)(213)

a	10^3b
(19.05°–48.8°)	
79.98 Wt. % B	
1.1716	1.039(t−19.05)
(15.95°–42.05°)	
20.68 Wt. % B	
1.0843	1.039(t−15.95)
(20.6°–33.25°)	
0.00 Wt. % B	
1.0518	1.019(t−20.6)

$C_8H_{12}O_6$

Dimethyl acetylmalate
v. 122, 208, 905

$C_8H_{14}O_3$

Ethyl dimethylacetoacetate
1231. B = $C_8H_{14}O_6$
Ethyl tartrate
(±0.05%)(223)

a	10^3b
(11.9°–35.8°)	
10.28 Wt. % B	
1.0350	0.984(t−11.9)
(13.2°–57.1°)	
25.17 Wt. % B	
1.0601	1.006(t−13.2)
(12.6°–51.0°)	
50.31 Wt. % B	
1.1069	0.989(t−12.6)

$C_8H_{14}O_3$

Ethyl ethylacetoacetate
v. 439, 715, 906

$C_8H_{14}O_4$

Ethyl succinate
1232. B = $C_8H_{14}O_6$
Ethyl tartrate
(±0.05%)(213)

a	10^3b
(19°–31.75°)	
0.00 Wt. % B	
1.0416	1.036(t − 19)
(19.35°–43.3°)	
20.67 Wt. % B	
1.0719	1.040(t−19.35)
(20.1°–42.9°)	
79.93 Wt. % B	
1.1682	1.027(t−20.1)

v. also 632, 907, 1215

$C_8H_{14}O_6$

Dimethyl *d*-dimethoxysuccinate, *v.* 356, 839

$C_8H_{14}O_6$

Ethyl tartrate
1233. B = $C_8H_{18}O$
Methylhexylcarbinol
(±0.075%)(204, 288)

a	10^3b
(18.1°–79.3°)	
0.00 Wt. % A	
0.8214	0.792(t−18.1)
(17.8°–81.0°)	
5.00 Wt. % A	
0.8344	0.803(t−17.8)
(18.4°–78.8°)	
10.00 Wt. % A	
0.8473	0.810(t−18.4)
(18.4°–80.3°)	
25.00 Wt. % A	
0.8896	0.842(t−18.4)
(19.1°–81.0°)	
50.02 Wt. % A	
0.9728	0.904(t−19.1)
(17.0°–81.6°)	
75.01 Wt. % A	
1.0776	0.953(t−17.0)

1234. B = C_9H_7N
Quinoline
(±0.05%)(209, 218)

a	10^3b
(14.3°–96.0°)	
4.97 Wt. % A	
1.1048	0.820(t−14.3)
(19.5°–99.0°)	
10.05 Wt. %A	
1.1089	0.817(t−19.5)
(−13° to +116°)	
13.60 Wt. % A	
1.1392	0.825(t+13.0)
(19.8°–99.0°)	
25.40 Wt. % A	
1.1292	0.876(t−19.8)
(20.7°–30.6°)	
49.98 Wt. % A	
1.1585	0.778(t−20.7)
(−23° to +223.5°)	
100.00 Wt. % A	
1.2482	1.007(t + 23)

1235. B = C_9H_8O
Cinnamic aldehyde
(9.64 Wt. % A)(±0.05%)
(15°–100°)(221)

a	10^3b
1.0684	0.81(t − 15)

1236. B = C_9H_{12}
Mesitylene
(±0.05%)(205)

a	10^3b
(19.9°–60.05°)	
0.00 Wt. % A	
0.8598	0.824(t−19.9)
(19.44°–28.25°)	
2.07 Wt. % A	
0.8649	0.818(t−19.44)
(18.22°–62.30°)	
5.00 Wt. % A	
0.8727	0.836(t−18.22)
(17.97°–64.32°)	
10.01 Wt. % A	
0.8852	0.852(t−17.97)
(19.57°–62.9°)	
24.98 Wt. % A	
0.9235	0.895(t−19.57)
(17.05°–39.3°)	
36.23 Wt. % A	
0.9586	0.908(t−17.05)
(17.6°–24.82°)	
50.00 Wt. % A	
1.0017	0.938(t−17.6)

1237. B = $C_{10}H_7Br$
α-Bromonaphthalene
(±0.05%)(217)

Wt. % A	d_4^{20}
0.00	1.4881
2.08	1.4777
5.00	1.4710
20.26	1.4189
49.69	1.3305

1238. B = $C_{10}H_7NO_2$
α-Nitronaphthalene
(±0.05%)(208)

a	10^3b
(63.9°–101°)	
10.21 Wt. % A	
1.2111	0.836(t−63.9)
(62.4°–98.7°)	
25.15 Wt. % A	
1.2021	0.896(t−62.4)
(48.9°–100°)	
49.57 Wt. % A	
1.1999	0.948(t−48.9)
(19.3°–131.2°)	
100.00 Wt. % A	
1.2062	1.023(t−19.3)

1239. B = $C_{10}H_8$
Naphthalene (±0.05%)(206)

t	d_4^t
10.02 Wt. % A	
84.1	0.9897
99.0	0.9780
25.02 Wt. % A	
82.5	1.0117
99.0	0.9980
49.77 Wt. % A	
73.8	1.0582
82.0	1.0508
90.0	1.0445
98.5	1.0349
74.98 Wt. % A	
57.30	1.1182
70.65	1.1055
80.65	1.0955
97.70	1.0788

v. also 27, 89, 123, 144, 148, 163, 173, 209, 249, 260, 291, 300, 305, 357, 367, 440, 499, 522, 571, 578, 663, 716, 727, 795, 805, 820, 840, 870, 908, 982, 1000, 1010, 1030, 1052, 1053, 1056, 1060, 1070, 1071, 1072, 1074, 1076, 1077, 1078, 1088,

1105, 1114, 1116, 1119, 1121, 1123, 1128, 1207, 1211, 1216, 1224, 1225, 1227, 1229, 1230, 1231, 1232, 1273

C_8H_{18}

n-Octane, *v.* 1037

$C_8H_{18}O$

Octyl alcohol
v. 909
Methylhexylcarbinol
v. 1233

$C_8H_{20}BrN$

Tetraethylammonium bromide
v. 124

$C_8H_{20}ClN$

Tetraethylammonium chloride
v. 125

$C_8H_{20}IN$

Tetraethylammonium iodide
1240. B = $C_{11}H_{12}O_3$
Ethyl benzoylacetate (330)[1]

v. also 177, 210, 270, 272, 349, 372, 375, 441, 490, 492, 493, 496, 523, 586, 701, 724, 726, 728, 759, 796, 841, 1031, 1048, 1199, 1200

$C_9H_6O_2$

Phenylpropiolic acid
v. 211, 1148

C_9H_7N

Quinoline
1241. B = $C_{10}H_8$
Naphthalene (172)[1]

1242. B = $C_{12}H_{22}O_6$
Isobutyl tartrate
(79.93 Wt. % A)(±0.05%)
(209)

t	d_4^t
18.00	1.1002
39.95	1.0831
69.55	1.0579
99.55	1.0330
151.00	0.9880

1243. B = $C_{16}H_{26}O_8$
Isobutyl diacetyl-*d*-tartrate
(±0.05%)(209)

a	10^3b
(15.55°–100.0°) 79.52 Wt. % A	
1.0969	0.8175 (t − 15.55)
(16.50°–99.6°) 25.04 Wt. % A	
1.0926	0.9030 (t − 16.50)
(17.25°–98.9°) 0.00 Wt. % A	
1.0863	0.9290 (t − 17.25)

v. also 812, 871, 983, 1064, 1234

C_9H_8O

Cinnamic aldehyde
1244. B = $C_{10}H_{12}O$
Anethole (353)

1245. B = $C_{26}H_{30}O_8$
Isobutyl dibenzoyl-*d*-tartrate
(0°–100°)(±0.05%)(221)
9.458 Wt. % B

a	10^3b
1.0737	0.763t

v. also 69, 442, 1235

$C_9H_8O_2$

Cinnamic acid
v. 212, 1149

$C_9H_9BrO_2$

Ethyl *p*-bromobenzoate
1246. B = $C_9H_{10}O_2$
Ethyl benzoate
(±0.025%)(255)

Wt. % B	d_4^{25}
100.00	1.0417
61.52	1.1635
39.05	1.2485
38.28	1.2517
22.43	1.3203
0.00	1.4307

$C_9H_{10}O$

Cinnamyl alcohol
v. 213

$C_9H_{10}O_2$

β-Phenylpropionic acid
v. 214, 1150
Benzyl acetate
v. 1151

$C_9H_{10}O_2$

Ethyl benzoate
1247. B = $C_{14}H_{12}O_2$
Benzyl benzoate
(±0.1%)(152)

Mol % B	d_4^{25}
0.00	1.043
10.37	1.052
19.77	1.060
30.94	1.068
40.59	1.076
49.46	1.083
60.55	1.091
70.27	1.097
75.25	1.101
84.50	1.105
95.35	1.110
100.00	1.112

v. also 239, 328, 443, 633, 910, 1089, 1202, 1217, 1246

$C_9H_{10}O_3$

Ethyl salicylate
v. 911, 1152, 1218
Ethyl *m*-hydroxybenzoate
v. 1153

$C_9H_{11}NO$

p-Acettoluide
v. 444
Methylacetanilide
v. 126, 445, 524, 912

$C_9H_{11}NO_2$

Ethyl *p*-aminobenzoate
v. 1154
Ethyl anthranilate
v. 1155

C_9H_{12}

Cumene
1148. B = $C_{10}H_{16}O_4$
Camphoric acid (296)[1,2]
v. also 1065, 1069

C_9H_{12}

Mesitylene
v. 1236
Trimethylbenzene
v. 740, 750, 757, 913, 1090, 1208

$C_9H_{13}N$

Dimethyl-*o*-toluidine
v. 914, 1091

$C_9H_{14}O$

Phorone
v. 915, 1156

$C_9H_{14}O_6$

Ethyl diacetylglycerate
v. 329, 916

$C_{10}H_4Cl_4$

Naphthalene tetrachloride
v. 127

$C_{10}H_6Cl_2$

Dichloronaphthalene
v. 917

$C_{10}H_7Br$

Bromonaphthalene
v. 70, 373, 446, 683, 1050, 1196, 1237

$C_{10}H_7NO_2$

Nitronaphthalene
1249. B = $C_{12}H_{11}N$
Diphenylamine
(±0.25%)(13)

Wt. % B	d_4^0
0.00	1.375
9.10	1.348
33.33	1.278
50.00	1.240
66.67	1.211
75.00	1.190
89.90	1.175
100.00	1.156
Wt. % B	**d_4^{18}**
0.00	1.368
9.10	1.341
33.33	1.272
50.00	1.234
66.67	1.205
75.00	1.185
89.90	1.171
100.00	1.152
Wt. % B	**d_4^{60}**
0.00	1.223
9.10	1.202
33.33	1.157
50.00	1.139
66.67	1.105
75.00	1.084
89.90	1.071
100.00	1.057

v. also 918, 1238

$C_{10}H_8$, Naphthalene

1250. B = $C_{10}H_9N$
Naphthylamine
(±0.25%)(13)

Wt. % A	d_4^0
100.00	1.179
88.89	1.161
50.00	1.151
33.33	1.154
25.00	1.156
11.11	1.160
5.80	1.170
0.00	1.189
Wt. % A	**d_4^{18}**
100.00	1.175
88.89	1.156
50.00	1.146
33.33	1.145
25.00	1.146
11.11	1.148
5.80	1.159
0.00	1.177
Wt. % A	**d_4^{91}**
100.00	0.971
88.89	0.980
50.00	1.017
33.33	1.028
25.00	1.038
11.11	1.053
5.80	1.062
0.00	1.071

1251. B = $C_{10}H_{20}O$
l-Menthol
(±0.25%)(273)

Mol % A	$d_4^{82.2}$
100.00	0.9766
83.51	0.9683
68.55	0.9260
50.48	0.8958
34.37	0.8830
17.98	0.8666
8.84	0.8584
0.00	0.8498
Mol % A	**$d_4^{99.0}$**
100.00	0.9635
83.51	0.9399
68.55	0.9127
50.48	0.8877
34.37	0.8687
17.98	0.8519
8.84	0.8452
0.00	0.8372

$C_{10}H_8$.—(*Continued*)

1252. B = $C_{12}H_{18}O_8$
Diethyl diacetyltartrate
(±0.25%)(273)

Mol % A	$d_4^{82.2}$
100.00	0.9766
82.97	1.0142
66.87	1.0321
49.88	1.0593
32.70	1.0377
16.60	1.0869
0.00	1.0976

Mol % A	$d_4^{99.0}$
100.00	0.9635
82.97	0.9997
66.87	1.0217
49.88	1.0433
32.70	1.0221
16.60	1.0705
0.00	1.0802

1253. B = $C_{14}H_{10}$
Phenanthrene (158)

1254. B = $C_{16}H_{32}O_2$
Palmitic acid (158)

v. also 28, 71, 128, 215, 261, 292, 350, 368, 447, 525, 555, 572, 603, 634, 652, 684, 717, 741, 745, 774, 791, 806, 842, 919, 1011, 1026, 1032, 1038, 1092, 1124, 1157, 1191, 1197, 1203, 1219, 1239, 1241, 1280, 1281

$C_{10}H_8Cl_6O_8$
Methyl di(trichloroacetyl)-tartrate
v. 843

$C_{10}H_8O$
α-Naphthol
v. 216, 1158
β-Naphthol
v. 217, 1159

$C_{10}H_9N$
Naphthylamine
v. 984, 1160, 1161, 1250

$C_{10}H_{10}O$
Benzylideneacetone
v. 1162

$C_{10}H_{10}O_2$
Safrole
v. 1163, 1164

$C_{10}H_{12}$
Tetrahydronaphthalene
v. 218, 448, 658

$C_{10}H_{12}O$
Anethole
1255. B = $C_{10}H_{20}O$
l-Menthol
(55.6°–99.0°)(±0.25%)(273)

a	10^3b
0.00 Mol % A	
0.961	0.8778($t-55.6$)
9.44 Mol % A	
0.951	0.8802($t-55.6$)
33.41 Mol % A	
0.923	0.8271($t-55.6$)
51.69 Mol % A	
0.907	0.8570($t-55.6$)
66.71 Mol % A	
0.894	0.8179($t-55.6$)
84.94 Mol % A	
0.881	0.7879($t-55.6$)
100.00 Mol % A	
0.869	0.7326($t-55.6$)

v. also 72, 920, 1051, 1244

$C_{10}H_{12}O$
Benzylacetone
v. 1165

$C_{10}H_{12}O_2$
Eugenol
v. 1166, 1167

$C_{10}H_{13}NO_2$
Phenacetine
v. 330, 449, 767, 921, 1001, 1057, 1093, 1132, 1220

$C_{10}H_{14}$
Durene
v. 129, 635, 844, 922, 1039, 1094

$C_{10}H_{14}N_2$
Nicotine
v. 130, 174, 219, 331, 358, 450, 526, 573, 664, 685, 923, 1002

$C_{10}H_{14}O$
Thymol, *v.* 220, 527, 924

$C_{10}H_{15}BrO$
Bromocamphor
1256. B = $C_{57}H_{110}O_6$
Tristearin
(±0.25%)(13)

Wt. % A	d_4^0
100.00	1.520
88.88	1.459
66.67	1.335
50.00	1.240
33.33	1.156
20.00	1.090
0.00	0.995

Wt. % A	d_4^{18}
100.00	1.516
88.88	1.453
66.67	1.325
50.00	1.228
33.33	1.145
20.00	1.076
0.00	0.982

Wt. % A	d_4^{91}
100.00	1.272
88.88	1.222
66.67	1.123
50.00	1.044
33.33	0.974
20.00	0.916
0.00	0.829

v. also 221, 451, 528, 636, 925

$C_{10}H_{15}N$
Diethylaniline, *v.* 768, 845

$C_{10}H_{16}$
d-Pinene
1257. B = $C_{10}H_{16}O$
d-Camphor (145)[2]

1258. B = $C_{10}H_{16}O$
l-Camphor (145)[2]

$C_{10}H_{16}O$
d-Camphor
v. 29, 73, 131, 156, 222, 332, 359, 452, 529, 544, 574, 604, 611, 637, 665, 686, 732, 807, 926, 1017, 1040, 1228, 1257, 1279
l-Camphor
v. 1258

$C_{10}H_{16}O_4$
Camphoric acid
1258.1. B = **Turpentine** (296)[1]
v. also 74, 132, 453, 687, 769, 846, 927, 1095, 1221, 1248

$C_{10}H_{17}Cl$
Pinene hydrochloride
v. 688, 1041
Terpine hydrochloride
v. 928

$C_{10}H_{17}NO$
d-Camphoroxime
1258.2. B = **Turpentine** (145, 297[2])

v. also 752

$C_{10}H_{17}NO$
l-Camphoroxime
1258.3. B = **Turpentine** (145, 297[2])

v. also 753

$C_{10}H_{18}$
Decahydronaphthalene
v. 659

$C_{10}H_{18}O$
Borneol
v. 223, 454

$C_{10}H_{18}O_3$
Ethyl diethylacetoacetate
v. 455, 718, 929

$C_{10}H_{18}O_6$
Dipropyl tartrate
v. 360, 666, 930

$C_{10}H_{20}O$
Menthol
v. 456, 656, 931
l-Menthol
v. 847, 1251, 1255

$C_{10}H_{20}O_2$
Amyl valerate
v. 932, 1222
d-β-Octyl acetate
v. 75, 933

$C_{10}H_{22}O$
Isoamyl ether
v. 638

$C_{10}H_{22}O_3$
Terpine hydrate
v. 224

$C_{10}H_{24}ClN$
Diamylammonium chloride
v. 133

$C_{11}H_{12}O_3$
Ethyl benzoylacetate
v. 1240

$C_{11}H_{15}NO$
Acetoethyl-*o*-toluide
v. 1265

$C_{12}H_{10}$
Acenaphthene
v. 134, 225, 457, 575, 639, 689, 848, 934, 1042, 1096
Diphenyl
v. 76, 135, 640, 690, 849, 935, 1043, 1097, 1168

$C_{12}H_{10}NO$
α-Acenaphthalide
v. 459

$C_{12}H_{10}N_2$
Azobenzene
1258.4. B = $C_{14}H_{12}$
Stilbene (356)

1258.5. B = $C_{14}H_{14}$
Dibenzyl (356)

1259. B = $C_{16}H_{32}O_2$
Palmitic acid (158)

1259.5. B = $C_{13}H_{11}N$
Benzalaniline (356)

v. also 77, 136, 293, 333, 556, 605, 641, 653, 691, 742, 746, 850, 936, 1012, 1027, 1033, 1044, 1098, 1170, 1192, 1204

$C_{12}H_{10}O$
Diphenyl ether
v. 137, 244, 458, 530, 692, 1226

$C_{12}H_{11}N$
Diphenylamine
v. 775, 786, 985, 1003, 1169, 1249

$C_{12}H_{12}Cl_6O_8$
Ethyl di(trichloroacetyl)tartrate
v. 851

$C_{12}H_{12}O$
Cinnamylideneacetone
v. 1171

$C_{12}H_{14}O_4$
Ethyl phthalate
v. 1265

$C_{12}H_{14}O_5$
Ethyl monobenzoylglycerate
v. 937

$C_{12}H_{16}O_2$
Amyl benzoate
v. 938, 1223

$C_{12}H_{17}NO_2$
Ethyl *o*-tolylethylcarbamate
v. 1265

$C_{12}H_{18}O_8$
Diethyl diacetyltartrate
v. 294, 852, 986, 1075, 1252

$C_{12}H_{22}O_6$
Isobutyl tartrate
v. 262, 1242

$C_{12}H_{24}O_2$
Lauric acid

1260. B = $C_{16}H_{32}O_2$
Palmitic acid
(±0.1%)(327)

Wt. % A	d_4^{75}
0.00	0.8457
14.92	0.8468
27.88	0.8477
40.64	0.8484
54.28	0.8493
59.84	0.8497
72.83	0.8507
84.47	0.8514
100.00	0.8527

1261. B = $C_{18}H_{36}O_2$
Stearic acid
(±0.1%)(327)

Wt. % A	d_4^{75}
100.00	0.8527
84.19	0.8510
65.96	0.8494
51.37	0.8481
38.73	0.8470
25.14	0.8455
0.00	0.8436

$C_{12}H_{28}IN$
Tetrapropylammonium iodide
v. 178, 226, 271, 361, 374, 460, 494, 531, 642, 728.5, 853, 1049, 1058, 1201

$C_{13}H_{10}O$
Benzophenone
v. 461, 532, 939, 1172, 1275, 1278

$C_{13}H_{10}O_3$
Salol
v. 334, 462, 770, 940, 1099, 1133

$C_{13}H_{11}N$
Benzalaniline
v. 1259.5, 1261.5, 1262.2

$C_{13}H_{11}NO$
Benzanilide
v. 719

$C_{13}H_{12}N_2O$
Benzoylphenylhydrazine
v. 463
Carbanilide
v. 720

$C_{13}H_{12}N_2S$
Thiocarbanilide
v. 721

$C_{13}H_{12}O$
Diphenylcarbinol
v. 1173.5

$C_{13}H_{13}N$
Benzylaniline

1261.5. B = $C_{13}H_{11}N$
Benzalaniline (356)

$C_{13}H_{13}N$
Diphenylmethylamine
v. 813, 987

$C_{13}H_{20}O_2$
Menthyl propiolate
v. 1173

$C_{14}H_8O_2$
Anthraquinone
v. 138, 941
Phenanthraquinone
v. 643, 942

$C_{14}H_9NO_2$
Phthalanil
v. 722

$C_{14}H_{10}$
Anthracene
v. 943
Diphenylacetylene
v. 1175

$C_{14}H_{10}$
Phenanthrene

1262. B = $C_{16}H_{32}O_2$
Palmitic acid (158)

v. also 30, 295, 351, 464, 557, 585, 606, 644, 693, 747, 854, 944, 1013, 1100, 1174, 1193, 1205, 1253, 1276

$C_{14}H_{10}O_2$
Benzil
v. 139, 645, 694, 855, 945, 1101

$C_{14}H_{12}$
Diphenylethylene
v. 1176

$C_{14}H_{12}$
Stilbene

1262.1. B = $C_{14}H_{14}$
Dibenzyl (356)

1262.2. B = $C_{13}H_{11}N$
Benzalaniline (356)

v. also 1258.4

$C_{14}H_{12}O_2$
Benzyl benzoate
v. 646, 946, 1247

$C_{14}H_{14}$
Dibenzyl
v. 1258.5, 1262.1
Diphenylethane
v. 1177

$C_{14}H_{14}N_2O_3$
p-Azoxyanisole

1263. B = $C_{16}H_{18}N_2O_3$
p-Azoxyphenetole
(0 − 100 Wt. % A)(241)
$d_4^{136} = (1.100 + 0.0_347$ Wt. % A) ±0.1%

$C_{15}H_{12}O$
Benzylideneacetophenone
v. 1178

$C_{15}H_{14}O$
Benzylacetophenone
v. 1180
Diphenylacetone
v. 1179

$C_{15}H_{18}O_7$
Diethyl monobenzoyltartrate
v. 335, 947

$C_{16}H_{11}N_3O_7$
Naphthalene picrate
v. 948

$C_{16}H_{14}$
Diphenylbutadiene
v. 1181

$C_{16}H_{18}$
Diphenylbutane
v. 1182

$C_{16}H_{18}N_2O_3$
p-Azoxyphenetole
v. 1263

$C_{16}H_{20}Cl_6O_8$
Isobutyl di(trichloroacetyl)-tartrate
v. 856

$C_{16}H_{20}O_7$
Diethyl mono-*o*-toluyltartrate
v. 336
Diethyl mono-*m*-toluyltartrate
v. 337
Diethyl mono-*p*-toluyltartrate
v. 338

$C_{16}H_{22}O_4$
d-Octyl hydrogen phthalate
v. 949
l-Octyl hydrogen phthalate
v. 950
dl-Octyl hydrogen phthalate
v. 951

$C_{16}H_{24}O_3S$
Menthyl benzenesulfonate
v. 465, 857, 952

$C_{16}H_{26}O_8$
Isobutyl diacetyl-*d*-tartrate
v. 263, 858, 1073, 1243

$C_{16}H_{32}O_2$
Palmitic acid

1264. B = $C_{18}H_{36}O_2$
Stearic acid
(0 − 100 Wt. % A)(327)
$d_4^{75} = (0.8436 + 0.0_421$ Wt. % A) ±0.1%

v. also 466, 533, 647, 695, 953, 1014, 1034, 1045, 1194, 1254, 1259, 1260, 1262

$C_{17}H_{14}O$
Dibenzylideneacetone
v. 1183
Cinnamylideneacetophenone
v. 1184

$C_{18}H_{16}O_6$
Methyl dibenzoylglycerate
v. 296, 339, 859, 954

$C_{18}H_{34}O_2$
Oleic acid
v. 227, 467, 534, 696, 771

$C_{18}H_{36}O_2$
Stearic acid
v. 31, 78, 140, 468, 535, 607, 648, 697, 772, 860, 955, 1046, 1102, 1134, 1185, 1195, 1261, 1264

$C_{19}H_{16}$
Triphenylmethane
v. 141, 649, 698, 956, 1047, 1103

$C_{19}H_{16}O$
Triphenyl carbinol
v. 1186

$C_{19}H_{17}N_3$
Triphenylguanidine
v. 469

$C_{19}H_{22}N_2O$
Cinchonicine
v. 470, 536

$C_{19}H_{26}O_2$
Menthyl cinnamate
v. 1187

$C_{19}H_{28}O_2$
Menthyl β-phenylpropionate
v. 1188

$C_{20}H_{13}N_3O_7$
Phenanthrene picrate
v. 471, 1277

$C_{20}H_{16}Br_2O_8$
Methyl di (*o*-bromobenzoyl)-tartrate
v. 472, 723
Methyl di (*m*-bromobenzoyl)-tartrate
v. 473
Methyl di (*p*-bromobenzoyl)-tartrate
v. 474

$C_{20}H_{16}Cl_2O_8$
Methyl di (*o*-chlorobenzoyl)-tartrate
v. 475
Methyl di (*m*-chlorobenzoyl)-tartrate
v. 476
Methyl di (*p*-chlorobenzoyl)-tartate
v. 477

$C_{20}H_{20}O_6$
Methyl di-*p*-toluylglycerate
v. 478, 537

$C_{20}H_{26}O_3S$
Menthyl naphthalene-β-sulfonate
v. 479, 861, 957

$C_{20}H_{38}O_2$
Ethyl oleate
v. 297, 352, 958

$C_{21}H_{18}O$
Dicinnamylideneacetone
v. 1189

$C_{21}H_{22}O_6$
Ethyl di-*p*-toluylglycerate
v. 480, 538

$C_{24}H_{42}O_6$
l-Menthyl *l*-tartrate
v. 481, 863, 959
dl-Menthyl *d*-tartrate
v. 482, 862, 960

$C_{25}H_{23}N_5O_7$
Picryl cinchonicine
v. 539

$C_{26}H_{26}N_2O_2$
Benzoyl cinchonicine
v. 483, 540

$C_{26}H_{28}N_2O_3S$
p-Toluenesulfonyl cinchonicine
v. 484, 541

$C_{26}H_{30}O_8$
Isobutyl dibenzoyl-*d*-tartrate
v. 298, 1245

$C_{27}H_{34}N_2O_7$
Quinine salicylate dihydrate
v. 485

$C_{27}H_{46}O$
Cholesterol
v. 142

$C_{28}H_{46}O_8$
l-Menthyl diacetyl-*l*-tartrate
v. 486, 864, 961
l-Menthyl diacetyl-*dl*-tartrate
v. 487, 865, 962
l-Menthyl diacetyl-*d*-tartrate
v. 488

$C_{51}H_{98}O_6$
Tripalmitin
v. 963

$C_{57}H_{110}O_6$
Tristearin
v. 964, 1256

Turpentine
v. 78.5, 339.5, 488.1, 488.2, 698.5, 964.5, 1065.5, 1069.5, 1103.5, 1273.5, 1258.1, 1258.2, 1258.3

Nitrocellulose (Blasting Soluble) (10)
1265. B =
(1) C_3H_6O
Acetone
(2) $C_3H_6O_2$
Ethyl formate
(3) $C_3H_6O_2$
Methyl acetate
(4) $C_4H_8O_2$
Ethyl acetate
(5) $C_5H_{10}O_2$
Propyl acetate
(6) $C_6H_{12}O_2$
Ethyl butyrate
(7) $C_7H_{14}O_2$
Amyl acetate
(8) $C_{11}H_{15}NO$
Acetoethyl-*o*-toluide
(9) $C_{12}H_{14}O_4$
Ethyl phthalate
(10) $C_{12}H_{17}NO_2$
Ethyl *o*-toluylethylcarbamate

B =	C =
CH_4O Methyl alcohol	$C_4H_{10}O$ Ethyl ether
CH_4O Methyl alcohol	C_7H_8O Anisole
C_2H_6O Ethyl alcohol	$C_4H_{10}O$ Ethyl ether
$C_4H_{10}O$ Ethyl ether	C_7H_8O Benzyl alcohol

Nitrocellulose (guncotton) (10)
B = C_3H_6O
Acetone

Nitrocellulose (highly soluble) (10)
B =
C_3H_6O
Acetone
$C_4H_8O_2$
Ethyl acetate

Three-Component Systems

CCl_4
Carbon tetrachloride
1266. B = $C_2H_4Br_2$
Ethylene bromide
C = C_7H_8
Toluene
(±0.025%)(285)

Wt. % A/Wt. % C	$1/d_4^{25}$
0 Wt. % B	
0/100	1.1593
10/90	1.1043
20/80	1.0530
30/70	1.0000
40/60	0.9463
50/50	0.8932
60/40	0.8420
70/30	0.7873
80/20	0.7349
90/10	0.6820
100/0	0.6300
10 Wt. % B	
0/100	1.0890
10/90	1.0405
20/80	0.9940
30/70	0.9463
40/60	0.8977
50/50	0.8502
60/40	0.8035
70/30	0.7550
80/20	0.7072
90/10	0.6599
100/0	0.6130
20 Wt. % B	
0/100	1.0190
10/90	0.9765
20/80	0.9348
30/70	0.8922
40/60	0.8496
50/50	0.8067
60/40	0.7654
70/30	0.7222
80/20	0.6800
90/10	0.6378
100/0	0.5958
30 Wt. % B	
0/100	0.9489
10/90	0.9124
20/80	0.8755

Wt. % A/Wt. % C	$1/d_4^{25}$
30 Wt. % B.—(*Continued*)	
30/70	0.8382
40/60	0.8012
50/50	0.7638
60/40	0.7278
70/30	0.6897
80/20	0.6527
90/10	0.6155
100/0	0.5789
40 Wt. % B	
0/100	0.8790
10/90	0.8484
20/80	0.8164
30/70	0.7847
40/60	0.7529
50/50	0.7205
60/40	0.6893
70/30	0.6572
80/20	0.6249
90/10	0.5933
100/0	0.5620
50 Wt. % B	
0/100	0.8092
10/90	0.7844
20/80	0.7572
30/70	0.7309
40/60	0.7043
50/50	0.6772
60/40	0.6510
70/30	0.6246
80/20	0.5971
90/10	0.5711
100/0	0.5450
60 Wt. % B	
0/100	0.7395
10/90	0.7194
20/80	0.6979
30/70	0.6770
40/60	0.6558
50/50	0.6337
60/40	0.6125
70/30	0.5918
80/20	0.5696
90/10	0.5489
100/0	0.5280
70 Wt. % B	
0/100	0.6701
10/90	0.6545
20/80	0.6381
30/70	0.6222
40/60	0.6065
50/50	0.5903
60/40	0.5740
70/30	0.5585
80/20	0.5421
90/10	0.5262
100/0	0.5109
80 Wt. % B	
0/100	0.6002
10/90	0.5896
20/80	0.5788
30/70	0.5680
40/60	0.5575

Wt. % A/Wt. % C	$1/d_4^{25}$
50/50	0.5470
60/40	0.5360
70/30	0.5257
80/20	0.5146
90/10	0.5040
100/0	0.4939
90 Wt. % B	
0/100	0.5305
10/90	0.5244
20/80	0.5190
30/70	0.5139
40/60	0.5086
50/50	0.5031
60/40	0.4980
70/30	0.4923
80/20	0.4870
90/10	0.4816
100/0	0.4768
100 Wt. % B	
0/0	0.4596

$CHBr_3$

Bromoform
1267. B = CHI_3
Iodoform
C = C_6H_6 (254)

1268. B = CHI_3
Iodoform
C = C_8H_{10}
Xylene (254)

CHI_3

Iodoform
1269. B = CH_2I_2
Methylene iodide
C = C_6H_6 (260)

1270. B = CH_2I_2
Methylene iodide
C = C_8H_{10}
Xylene (260)

CH_3I

Methyl iodide
1271. B = C_2H_5I
Ethyl iodide
C = C_6H_6 (254)

1272. B = C_2H_5I
Ethyl iodide
C = C_8H_{10}
Xylene (254)

CH_3NO

Formamide
1272.5. B = C_2H_6O
Ethyl alcohol
C = $C_8H_{20}IN$
Tetraethylammonium iodide
(360)

$C_2H_4Br_2$

Ethylene bromide
1273. B = $C_6H_5NO_2$
Nitrobenzene
C = $C_8H_{14}O_6$
Ethyl tartrate (220)[1]

$C_2H_4O_2$

Acetic acid
1273.5. B = $C\ H_6O$
Ethyl alcohol
C = Turpentine (263)[1]

1274. B = $C_3H_8O_3$
Glycerol
C = $C_4H_{10}O$
Ethyl ether (44)[1]

C_2H_6O

Ethyl alcohol
1275. B = C_3H_6O
Acetone
C = $C_{13}H_{10}O$
Benzophenone (33)[1]

1276. B = $C_6H_3N_3O_7$
Picric acid
C = $C_{14}H_{10}$
Phenanthrene (18)[1]

1277. B = $C_6H_3N_3O_7$
Picric acid
C = $C_{20}H_{13}N_3O_7$
Phenanthrene picrate (18)[1]

C_3H_6O

Acetone
1277.5. B = $C_4H_{10}O$
Ethyl ether
C = C_6H_6 (355)[1]

1278. B = C_6H_6
C = $C_{13}H_{10}O$
Benzophenone (33)[1]

$C_4H_8O_2$

Ethyl acetate
1279. B = C_6H_6
C = $C_{10}H_{16}O$
Camphor (263)[1]

$C_6H_4N_2O_4$

m-Dinitrobenzene
1280. B = C_7H_8
Toluene
C = $C_{10}H_8$
Naphthalene (319)[1]

C_6H_6

1281. B = $C_7H_5N_3O_6$
Trinitrotoluene
C = $C_{10}H_8$
Naphthalene (319)[1]

C_6H_6O

Phenol
1282. B = C_7H_8O, *o*-Cresol
C = C_7H_8O, *m*-Cresol
(±0.25%)(86)

Wt. % A	Wt. % B	Wt. % C	$d_4^{15.5}$
0	79.9	20.1	1.0403
5	75.9	19.1	1.0421
10	71.9	18.1	1.0439
15	67.9	17.1	1.0457
20	63.9	16.1	1.0476
25	59.9	15.1	1.0494
30	55.9	14.1	1.0511
35	51.9	13.1	1.0530
40	47.9	12.1	1.0549

1283. B = C_7H_8O, *m*-Cresol
C = C_7H_8O, *p*-Cresol
(±0.25%)(86)

Wt. % A	Wt. % B	Wt. % C	$d_4^{15.5}$
0	49.3	50.7	1.0384
5	46.8	48.2	1.0403
10	44.4	45.6	1.0422
15	41.9	43.1	1.0441
20	39.4	40.6	1.0460
25	37.0	38.0	1.0479
30	47.5	35.5	1.0497
35	32.1	32.9	1.0517
40	29.6	30.4	1.0537
45	27.1	27.9	1.0556
50	24.6	25.4	1.0576

LITERATURE

(For a key to the periodicals see end of volume)

(1) Alexander, *Diss.*, Giessen, 1899. (2) Andersin and Hirn, *60*, **51**: No. 11; 08. (3) Andrews and Carlton, *1*, **29**: 688; 07. (4) Andrews and Ende, *7*, **17**: 136; 95. (5) Anschütz, *13*, **221**: 133; 83. (6) Arndt and Kunze, *9*, **18**: 994; 12. (7) Aten, *7*, **88**: 321; 14. (8) Atkins and Werner, *4*, **101**: 1167; 12. (9) Baker, *4*, **101**: 1409; 12.

(10) Baker, *4*, **103**: 1653; 13. (11) Ballo and Dittler, *93*, **76**: 39; 12. (12) Baskov, *53*, **50**: 589; 18. *10*, **5**: 40; 25. (13) Battelli and Martinetti, *22*, **2 II**: 247; 86. (14) Baud, *27*, **7**: 117; 10. (15) Baud, *27*, **17**: 329; 15. (16) Beckmann and Faust, *93*, **84**: 103; 14. (17) Becquerel, *6*, **12**: 5; 77. (18) Behrend, *7*, **10**: 265; 02. (19) Beilby, *4*, **43**: 388; 83.

(20) Beijerinck, *136*, **21**: 853; 97. (21) Bezold, *Diss.*, Giessen, 1906. (22) Bingham and Sarver, *1*, **42**: 2011; 20. (23) Biron, *53*, **41**: 469; 09. (24) Biron, *53*, **42**: 167; 10. (25) Bourion, *14*, **14**: 215; 20. (26) Bousfield, *4*, **115**: 45; 19. (27) Bramley, *4*, **109**: 10; 16. (28) Bramley, *4*, **109**: 434; 16. (29) Bregman, *Thèse*, Lausanne, 1914. *10*, **4**: 42; 21.

(30) Brown, *4*, **35**: 547; 79. (31) Brown, *4*, **39**: 202, 304; 81. (32) Buchkremer, *7*, **6**: 161; 90. (33) Burrows, *461*, **53**: 74; 19. (34) Burrows and Eastwood, *461*, **57**: 118; 23. (35) Burwinkel, *Diss.*, Münster, 1914. (36) Busnikov, *53*, **33**: 128; 01. (37) Bussy and Buignet, *6*, **4**: 5; 65. *34*, **59**: 673; 64. (38) Campbell, *83*, **11**: 91; 15. (39) Carnazzi, *59*, **9**: 161; 05.

(40) Cederburg, *42*, **9**: 3; 11. (41) Centnerszwer and Zoppi, *7*, **54**: 689; 06. (42) Chauvenet, *14*, **13**: 59; 20. (43) Chauvenet and Gueylard, *34*, **167**: 24; 18. (44) Cheneveau, *Sur les propriétés optiques des solutions*, p. 80. Paris, Gauthier, 1913. (45) Christomanos, *93*, **45**: 132; 05. (46) Clarke, *63*, **6**: 154; 05. (47) Cohen and Moesveld, *7*, **93**: 385; 19. (48) Cohen, de Meester and Moesveld, *70*, **42**: 779; 23. (49) Cohen, de Meester and Moesveld, *7*, **108**: 103; 24.

(50) Cox, *173*, **44**: 26; 19. (51) Curtis and Titus, *50*, **19**: 738; 15. (52) Darby, *1*, **40**: 347; 18. (53) Darmois, *6*, **22**: 495; 11. (54) Dawson, *4*, **97**: 1041; 10. (55) De Leeuw, *7*, **77**: 284; 11. (56) Delépine, *49*, **25**: 496; 92. (57) Dennhardt, *8*, **67**: 325; 99. *Diss.*, Erlangen, 1899. (58) de Pauw, *Diss.*, Utrecht, 1922. *10*, **5**: 39; 25. (59) Deutschmann, *Diss.*, Berlin, 1911, p. 23, 37.

(60) Deutschmann, *7*, **96**: 428; 20. (61) Dobroserdov, *53*, **44**: 679; 12. (62) Dolezalek, *7*, **64**: 727; 08. (63) Dolezalek and Schulze, *7*, **83**: 45; 13. (64) Dolezalek and Schulze, *7*, **98**: 395; 21. (65) Doroschewski, *53*, **43**: 46; 11. (66) Doroschewski, *53*, **43**: 655; 11. (67) Drecker, *8*, **20**: 870; 83. (68) Drucker and Kassel, *7*, **76**: 367; 11. (69) Dunstan and Hilditch, *9*, **18**: 185; 12.

(70) Dunstan and Mussell, *4*, **97**: 1935; 10. (71) Dunstan and Stubbs, *4*, **93**: 1919; 08. (72) Dunstan and Thole, *4*, **97**: 1249; 10. (73) Dunstan, Thole and Hunt, *4*, **91**: 1728; 07. (74) Ebersole, *50*, **5**: 239; 01. (75) Efremov, *53*, **50**: 338; 18. (76) Ehrenhaft, *75*, **111 IIA**: 1549; 02. (77) Eidmann, *Diss.*, Giessen, 1899. (78) English and Turner, *4*, **105**: 1656; 14. (79) Faust, *7*, **79**: 97; 12.

(80) Ferguson and Buddington, *12*, **50**: 131; 20. (81) Findlay, *7*, **69**: 203; 09. (82) Fischler, *9*, **19**: 123; 13. (83) Fitzgerald, *50*, **16**: 621; 12. (84) Foote and Langley, *12*, **30**: 393; 10. (85) Forch, *8*, **Boltzmann Festschrift**: 696; 04. (86) Fox and Barker, *54*, **36**: 842; 17. (87) Frankland and Aston, *4*, **75**: 493; 99. (88) Frankland, Carter and Adams, *4*, **101**: 2470; 12. (89) Frankland and McRae, *4*, **73**: 307; 98.

(90) Frankland and Pickard, *4*, **69**: 123; 96. (91) Friedländer, *7*, **38**: 385; 01. (92) Gay, *16*, **6**: 36; 16. *Thèse*, Paris, 1914. (93) Gennari, *7*, **19**: 130; 96. (94) Georgiewski, *427*, **27**: 516; 03. *53*, **34**: 565; 02. (94.1) Germann, *50*, **29**: 138; 25. (95) Getman, *42*, **4**: 386; 06. (96) Getman, *1*, **30**: 1077; 08. (97) Getman and Gibbons, *1*, **37**: 1990; 15. (98) Glaser, *8*, **22**: 694; 07. (99) Goerdt, *Diss.*, Münster, 1911.

(100) Golse, *Thèse*, Bordeaux, 1911. (101) Götz, *7*, **94**: 181; 20. (101.1) Gradenwitz, *136*, **42**: 221; 18. (102) Granquist, *60*, **54**: No. 20; 12. (103) Guthrie, *3*, **18**: 495; 84. (104) Haffner, *63*, **2**: 739; 01. (105) Haissig,

136, 21: 939; 97. (106) Harden, 427, 18: 695; 94. (107) Hartung, 83, 12: 66; 16. (108) Hartwig, 8, 33: 58; 88. (109) Hedvall, 19, 5: No. 6; 13. 93, 86: 201; 13.
(110) Hein, Diss., Berlin, 1896. (111) Henninger, Diss., Giessen, 1907. (112) Herz, 7, 87: 63; 14. (113) Herz, 93, 104: 47; 18. (114) Herz and Anders, 93, 52: 164; 07. (115) Herz and Anders, 93, 55: 271; 07. (116) Herz and Knoch, 93, 45: 262; 05. (117) Herz and Kuhn, 93, 58: 159; 08. (118) Herz and Kuhn, 93, 60: 152; 08. (119) Herz and Martin, 93, 132: 41; 24.
(120) Herz and Rathmann, 9, 19: 589; 13. (121) Herz and Schuftan, 7, 101: 269; 22. (122) Herzen, 149, 14: 232; 02. Thèse, Lausanne, 1902. (123) Hess, 75, 114 IIA: 1231; 05. (124) Hess, 75, 117: 947; 08. 8, 27: 589; 08. (125) Hilditch and Dunstan, 9, 17: 929; 11. (126) Hill, 1, 44: 1163; 22. (127) Hill and Macy, 1, 46: 1132; 24. (128) Hill, 4, 101: 2467; 12. (129) Holleman and Antusch, 70, 13: 277; 94.
(130) Holmes, 4, 89: 1774; 06. (131) Holmes, 4, 103: 2147; 13. (132) Holmes and Sageman, 4, 95: 1919; 09. (133) Hovelman, Diss., Münster, 1914. (134) Hubbard, 7, 74: 207; 10. 2, 30: 740; 10. (135) Humburg, 7, 12: 401; 93. (136) Hyde, 1, 34: 1507; 12. (137) Isbekov and Plotnikov, 53, 43: 18; 11. 93, 71: 328; 11. (138) Jackson and Young, 4, 73: 922; 98. (139) Jahn, 8, 43: 280; 91.
(140) Johst, 8, 20: 47; 83. (141) Jokela and Valanto, 60, 54: No. 18; 12. (142) Jones, 135, 72: 279; 95. (143) Jones and Hartmann, 78, 30: 295; 16. (144) Jones, Bingham and McMaster, 11, 34: 481; 05. (145) Jones, 201, 14: 27; 08. (146) Jones, Lapworth and Lingford, 4, 103: 252; 13. (147) Joseph, 4, 107: 1; 15. (148) Kanonnikov, 52, 31: 321; 85. (149) Karhi and Suikkanen, 60, 54: No. 19; 12.
(150) Kassel, Diss., Leipzig, 1910. (151) Kendall and Brakeley, 1, 43: 1826; 21. (152) Kendall and Wright, 1, 42: 1776; 20. (153) Keyes and Winninghoff, 1, 38: 1178; 16. (153.1) King and Smedley, 50, 28: 1265; 24. (153.2) King and Partington, 4, 129: 20; 26. (154) Kohlmeyer, 187, 10: 483; 13. (155) Kohlmeyer and Hilpert, 192, 7: 225; 10. (156) Kremann and Ehrlich, 57, 28: 831; 07. 75, 116 IIB: 753; 07. (157) Kremann, Meingast and Gugl, 57, 35: 1235; 14. (158) Kröber, Diss., Leipzig, 1914. (159) Kultasev, Diss., Dorpat, 1915.
(160) Kunze, Diss., Berlin, 1912. (161) Kurnakov and Beketov, 53, 48: 1697; 16. 134, 9: 1381; 15. 10, 5: 39; 25. (162) Kurnakov and Efremov, 7, 85: 401; 13. 169, 18: 386; 13. (163) Kurnakov, Krotkov and Oksmann, 53, 47: 583; 15. 134, 9: 45; 15. 10, 4: 43; 21. (163.1) Kurnakov, Krotkov, Oksmann, Beketov, Perelmutter, Kanov and Finkel, 93, 135: 81; 24. (164) Kurnakov, Perelmutter and Kanov, 53, 48: 1680; 16. 169, 24: 399; 15. 10, 5: 39; 25. (165) Kurnakov and Zhemchuzhnui, 7, 83: 481; 13. 53, 44: 1975; 12. 169, 18: 125; 13. (166) Lam, 92, 11: 125; 98. (167) Lamme, Diss., Columbia, 1909. (168) Landolt, 8, 123: 595; 64. (169) Landolt, 13 Supp., 4: 1; 66.
(170) Landolt, 13, 189: 241; 77. Optische Drehungsvermögen, p. 154. Braunschweig, F. Vieweg und Sohn, 1898. 25, 9: 914; 76. (170.1) Lewis, 1, 47: 626; 25. (171) Linebarger, 12, 2: 226, 331; 96. 11, 18: 429; 96. (172) Lumsden, 4, 91: 24; 07. (173) Lunge, 317, 8: 74; 85. (174) Macagno, 135, 43: 192; 81. (174.1) Macy, 1, 47: 1031; 25. (174.2) Macy and Thomas, 1, 48: 1547; 26. (175) Malosse, 34, 154: 1697; 12. (176) Marden and Dover, 1, 38: 1235; 16. (177) Martin, Diss., Breslau, 1923. (178) Matthews and Cooke, 50, 18: 559; 14. (179) McBain and Coleman, 83, 15: 27; 19.
(180) Meldrum and Turner, 4, 97: 1605; 10. (181) Menschutkin, On Etherates and Other Molecular Combinations of Magnesium Bromide and Iodide. St. Petersburg, 1907. 93, 49: 34, 207; 06. 52: 9, 152; 07. 53: 26; 07. 61: 100, 113; 09. 62: 40, 45; 09. (182) Merriman, 4, 103: 1774; 13. (183) Merry and Turner, 4, 105: 748; 14. (184) Metzger and Lamme, 173, 40: 204; 15. (185) Meyer and Mylius, 7, 95: 349; 20. (186) Michailenko, 136, 26: 135; 02. (186.1) Mitsukuri and Nakatsuchi, 142, 29: 25; 26. (187) Moesveld, Thèse, Utrecht, 1918. (188) Morgan and Lammert, 1, 46: 1117; 24. (189) Muchin and Tarle, 181, 43: 54; 16. 10, 4: 39; 21.
(190) Müller and Abegg, 7, 57: 513; 06. (191) Müller, Diss., Breslau, 1905. (192) Mühlenbein, Diss., Cöthen, 1901. (193) Müller, Diss., Giessen, 1904. (194) Nasini and Gennari, 7, 19: 113; 96. (195) Naumann, 25, 37: 3600; 04. (196) Naumann, 25, 37: 4328; 04. (197) Naumann, 25, 42: 3789; 09. (198) Naumann, 25, 43: 313; 10. (199) Nicol, 4, 69: 142; 96.
(200) Öholm, 147, 2: No. 26; 13. (201) Osborne, McKelvy and Bearce, 31A, 9: 327; 13. (202) Otin, 192, 9: 92; 12. (203) Patterson, 4, 79: 167; 01. (204) Patterson, 4, 79: 477; 01. (205) Patterson, 4, 81: 1097; 02. (206) Patterson, 4, 81: 1134; 01. (207) Patterson, 4, 87: 313; 05. (208) Patterson, 4, 93: 1836; 08. (209) Patterson, 4, 109: 1139; 16.
(210) Patterson and Davidson, 4, 101: 374; 12. (211) Patterson and Forsyth, 4, 103: 2263; 13. (212) Patterson and Frew, 4, 89: 332; 06. (213) Patterson, Henderson and Fairlie, 4, 91: 1838; 07. (214) Patterson and Kaye, 4, 89: 1884; 06. (215) Patterson and Kaye, 4, 91: 705; 07. (216) Patterson and McArthur, 4, 107: 814; 15. (217) Patterson and McDonald, 4, 93: 936; 08. (218) Patterson and McDonald, 4, 95: 321; 09. (219) Patterson and McMillan, 4, 91: 504; 07.
(220) Patterson and Montgomerie, 4, 95: 1128; 09. (221) Patterson and Moudgill, 68, 39: 18; 19. (222) Patterson and Patterson, 4, 107: 142; 15. (223) Patterson and Pollack, 4, 105: 2322; 14. (224) Patterson and Stevenson, 4, 97: 2110; 10. (225) Patterson and Stevenson, 4, 101: 241; 12. (226) Patterson and Taylor, 4, 87: 122; 05. (227) Patterson and Thomson, 25, 40: 1243; 07. (228) Patterson and Thomson, 4, 93: 355; 08. (229) Pascal and Garnier, 27, 25: 142; 19.
(230) Pascal and Garnier, 27, 25: 309; 19. (231) Pascal and Jouniaux, 27, 15: 312; 14. 9, 22: 71; 16. (232) Paterno and Mieli, 22, 17 I: 396; 08. (233) Paterno and Montemartini, 36, 24 II: 179; 94. 22, 3 II: 139; 94. (234) Peacock, 182, 30: 274; 14. (235) Peacock, 4, 107: 1547; 15. (236) Perkin, 4, 77: 267; 00. (237) Perrakis, 34, 178: 703; 24. (238) Perrakis, 34, 178: 1482; 24. (239) Pfeiffer, 93, 15: 194; 97.
(240) Philip, 7, 24: 18; 97. (241) Pick, 7, 77: 577; 11. (242) Pickard and Kenyon, 4, 105: 830; 14. (243) Plotnikov and Rokotjan, 7, 84: 367; 13. 53, 45: 193; 13. (244) Plotnikov and Rokotjan, 53, 47: 723; 15. 10, 4: 35; 21. (245) Posnjak, Allen and Merwin, Economic Geology, 10: 491; 15. (246) Pound, 4, 99: 698; 11. (247) Price, 4, 107: 188; 15. (248) Price, 4, 115: 1116; 19. (249) Pulfrich, 7, 4: 561; 89.
(250) Rabinowitsch, 7, 99: 434; 21. (251) Ramsay and Aston, 7, 15: 89; 94. 5, 56: 182; 94. (252) Ramsay and Young, 4, 51: 755; 87. (253) Ramstedt, 199, 8: 253; 11. (254) Recueil de constantes physiques, p. 148. Paris, Gauthier-Villars, 1913. (255) Reid, 11, 45: 479; 11. (256) Reinitzer, 92, 26: 456; 13. (257) Retgers, 93, 3: 252; 93. (258) Retgers, 93, 3: 343; 93. (259) Retgers, 7, 3: 497; 89.
(260) Retgers, 190, 1889 II: 185. (261) Retgers, 190, 1896 I: 212. (261.1) Richards and Chadwell, 1, 47: 2283; 25. (262) Rill, Diss., Giessen, 1907. (263) Rimbach, 7, 9: 698; 92. (264) Röhrs, 8, 37: 289; 12. Diss., Rostock, 1910. (265) Rudolphi, 7, 37: 426; 01. (266) Sachanov, 7, 83: 129; 13. (267) Sachanov and Przeborovski, 53, 47: 849; 15. 10, 4: 42; 21. (268) Sachanov and Rabinovic, 53, 47: 859; 15. 10, 4: 42; 21. (269) Sachanov and Rjachovski, 53, 46: 78; 14. 10, 4: 42; 21.
(270) Sachanov and Rjachovski, 53, 47: 113; 15. 10, 4: 42; 21. (271) Sackur, 7, 83: 297; 13. (272) Sameshima, 1, 40: 1482; 18. (273) Scheuer, 7, 72: 513; 10. (274) Schiff, 13, 111: 373; 59. (275) Schlesinger and Coleman, 1, 38: 271; 16. (276) Schlesinger and Martin, 1, 36: 1589; 14. (277) Schlundt, 50, 7: 194; 03. (278) Schroeder, 53, 49: 647; 17. 10, 5: 40; 25. (279) Schulz, Diss., Giessen, 1901.
(280) Schulze, 9, 18: 77; 12. (281) Schulze, 63, 22: 177; 21. (282) Schulze, 7, 97: 388; 21. (283) Schulze, 7, 97: 417; 21. (284) Schulze and Hock, 7, 86: 445; 14. (285) Schulze, 1, 36: 498; 14. (286) Schütt, 7, 9: 349; 92. (287) Schwarz and Haacke, 93, 115: 87; 21. (288) Schwers, 42, 9: 15; 11. 294, 1911: 117. (289) Schwers, 186, 1912: 55.
(290) Schwers, 186, 1912: 252. (291) Schwers, 4, 101: 1889; 12. (292) Seidell, 1, 29: 1088; 07. (293) Seidell, 78, 13: 319; 08. (294) Seidell, 1, 31: 1164; 09. (295) Seidell, 11, 48: 453; 12. (296) Seidell, 464, No. 67: 1910. (297) Seidell, Solubilities of Inorganic and Organic Compounds. New York, Van Nostrand, 1919. (298) Smith and Menzies, 68, 30: 432; 10. (299) Speyers, 12, 14: 293; 02.
(300) Stortenbeker, 70, 32: 226; 13. (301) Stortenbeker, 70, 33: 85; 14. (302) Swinne, 7, 84: 348; 13. (303) Tammann and Hirschberg, 7, 13: 543; 94. (304) Tammann and Krings, 93, 130: 229; 23. (305) Thole, 4, 97: 2596; 10. (306) Thole, 4, 103: 317; 13. (307) Thole, Mussell and Dunstan, 4, 103: 1108; 13. (308) Thomas and Yu, 1, 45: 113; 23. (309) Thorpe and Rodger, 4, 71: 360; 97.
(310) Tillotson, 38, 1: 76; 18. (311) Tinkler, 4, 103: 2171; 13. (312, 313) Tsakalotos, 27, 3: 234; 08. (314) Tsakalotos, 7, 68: 32; 10. (315) Tsakalotos, 7, 74: 743; 10. (316) Tsakalotos, 27, 9: 519; 11. (317) Tyrer, 4, 97: 1778; 10. (318) Tyrer, 4, 97: 2620; 10. (319) Tyrer, 4, 99: 871; 11.
(320) Van Klooster, 1, 35: 145; 13. (321) Van Nest, 94, 47: 263; 10. Diss., München, 1909. (322) Vincent and Delachanal, 6, 20: 207; 80. 34, 90: 747; 80. (323) Vogel, Diss., Berlin, 1892. (324) Vogel, 92, 19: 49; 06. (325) Vogt, Diss., Giessen, 1903. (326) Wade and Finnemore, 4, 85: 938; 04. (327) Waentig and Pescheck, 7, 93: 529; 19. (328) Wagner, 7, 46: 867; 03. (329) Walden, 7, 55: 207; 06.
(330) Walden, 7, 55: 683; 06. (331) Walden, 7, 61: 633; 08. (332) Walden, 7, 75: 555; 10. (333) Walden, 134, 9: 789; 15. 10, 4: 42; 21. (334) Walden, 134, 9: 1021; 15. 10, 4: 42; 21. (335) Wallace and Atkins, 4, 101: 1958; 12. (336) Washburn and Read, 1; 41: 729; 19. (337) Willard and Smith, 1, 44: 2816; 22. (338) Willard and Smith, 1, 45: 286; 23. (339) Winther, 7, 41: 161; 02.
(340) Winther, 7, 45: 331; 03. (341) Winther, 7, 55: 257; 06. (342) Winther, 7, 56: 703; 06. (343) Winther, 7, 60: 563; 07. (344) Winther, 7, 60: 590; 07. (345) Wroczynski and Guye, 42, 8: 189; 10. (346) Wüllner, 8, 133: 1; 68. (347) Yamaguchi, 41, 34: 691; 13. 10, 4: 42; 21. (348) Ylönen, 138, 1: No. 7; 22. (349) Young, 4, 81: 768; 02.
(350) Young, 4, 83: 77; 03. (351) Young, Fractional Distillation. New York, Macmillan, 2nd ed., 1922. (352) Young and Fortey, 4, 83: 45; 03. (353) Zecchini, 36, 27 I: 358; 97. (354) Zoppellari, 36, 35 I: 355; 05. (355) Bingham and Brown, Thesis, Lafayette, 1921. (356) Brinkman, Diss., Leipzig, 1903. (357) Dancaster, 4, 125: 2036, 24. (358) Elsey, 1, 42: 2454; 20. (358.1) Ewart and Raikes, 4, 1926: 1907. (358.5) Goldsmith and Aarflot, 7, 122: 371; 26. (359) Jones and Bingham, 11, 34: 481; 06.
(360) Jones, Davis and Johnson, 152, No. 260: 71; 18. (361) Muchin, 9, 19: 819; 13. (362) Tsakalotos, 7, 71: 667; 10.

PHASE EQUILIBRIUM DATA

VAPOR PRESSURES OF P, S, SE, TE AND THE HALOGENS

ALAN W. C. MENZIES

THE CRYSTALLINE STATE

$$\log_{10} p = \frac{0.05223\text{A}}{T} + \text{B}; p \text{ in mm} \left(= \frac{1}{760} \text{A}_n\right); t \text{ in } ^\circ\text{C}, T = t + 273.1$$

BR, BROMINE (16, 18, 31)

t, °C	p, mm	t, °C	p, mm
	±5%		±5%
(−95)	(0.0022)	−45	1.83
−90	0.0052		±3%
−85	0.0117	−40	2.98
−80	0.0251	−35	4.77
−75	0.0513	−30	7.45
−70	0.102	−25	11.4
−65	0.192	−20	17.1
−60	0.357	−15	25.2
−55	0.628	−10	36.6
−50	1.09	− 7.3*	44.4

* M. P.

CL, CHLORINE (16)

A = −29 293; B = 9.950; accuracy, ±10%; range, −154 to −103°C

I, IODINE (1, 2, 14, 31)

t, °C	p, mm	t, °C	p, mm
	±5%		±1%
−50	0.0_437	40	1.03
−40	0.0_319	50	2.16
−30	0.0_380	60	4.31
−20	0.0030	70	8.22
−10	0.0099	80	15.1
	±1%	90	26.8
0	0.0299	100	45.5
+10	0.0808	110	74.9
20	0.202	114.15*	90.1
30	0.471		

* M. P.

P, PHOSPHORUS (7, 24, 36)

For white P: A = −63 123; B = 9.6511; range, 20 to 44.1°C (M. P.); error ± <10%.

For violet P: A = −108 510; B = 11.0842; range, 380 to *ca.* 590°C; accuracy ±5% above 500°C.

S, SULFUR (13, 34)

t, °C	p, mm	t, °C	p, mm
50	0.0002	90	0.0049
60	0.0004	100	0.010
70	0.0010	110	0.021
80	0.0023	114.5*	0.028†

* M. P. † ±10%.

SE, SELENIUM (10)

Hexagonal form

t, °C	p, mm	t, °C	p, mm
	±10%		±10%
195	0.0010	210	0.0032
200	0.0015	215	0.0047
205	0.0022	217.4*	0.0055

* M. P.

THE LIQUID STATE UP TO ONE ATMOSPHERE

BR, BROMINE (4, 18, 28, 31)

t, °C	p, mm	t, °C	p, mm
	±2%		±2%
−7.3*	44.4	30	264
−5	50.5	35	324
0	65.9	40	392
+5	85.3	45	472
10	109	50	564
15	138	55	670
20	173	58.78†	760
25	214	(60)	(793)
		302‡	

* M. P. † ± 0.03°. ‡ Crit.

CL, CHLORINE (16, 19, 21, 29, 38)

t, °C	p, mm	t, °C	p, mm
	±5%		±3%
−103*	8.9	−50	363
−100	11.8	−40	594
−90	27.8		±1%
−80	58.7	−34.6	760
	±3%		±2%
−70	115	−30	935
−60	211	−20	1398

* M. P.

I, IODINE (31, 32, 37)

t, °C	p, mm	t, °C	p, mm
	±2%		±2%
114.15	90.1	160	394
115	92.9	170	521
120	111	180	679
130	157	184.35*	760
140	217	190	(869)
150	294	**553.4**†	

* ±0.1°. † ±3°crit.

P, PHOSPHORUS (20, 24, 25, 30, 36)

$\log_{10} p,\text{mm} = 11.5694 - \frac{2898.1}{T} - 1.2566 \log_{10} T$; range, 44.1 to 635°C; accuracy of p = ±7% except near the B. P., 279.7°C, where it is ±2% (equivalent to ±1°).

S, SULFUR (3, 5, 6, 8, 9, 12, 13, 15, 17, 26, 27, 32, 33, 34, 39)

t, °C	p, mm	t, °C	p, mm
	±10%	250	12
114.5 M. P.	0.028	260	16
120	0.040	270	21
130	0.074	280	28
140	0.13	290	37
150	0.22	300	48
160	0.37	310	60
	±7%	320	76
170	0.59	330	95
180	0.91		±5%
190	1.4	340	118
200	2.1	350	146
210	3.1	360	179
220	4.4	370	218
230	6.3	380	263
240	8.7		

S.—(*Continued*)

t, °C	p, mm	t, °C	p, mm
	±3%		± <0.1%
390	325	444.6$_0$	760.0
400	376		±0.3%
410	446	450	821
	±1%		±3%
420	525	460	948
430	613	470	109$_3$
	±0.3%	480	125$_7$
440	711		±5%
		490	144$_1$

$t = 444.6_0 + 0.0910(p - 760) - 0.0_449(p - 760)^2$, for $p = 695$ to 805 mm (±1–2 mm). Relative accuracy, ±0.1–0.2 mm (40).

Se, Selenium (10, 23, 30)

t, °C	p, mm	t, °C	p, mm
	±10%		±10%
217.4 M. P.	0.0055	480	28
220	0.0062	500	42
225	0.0078		±3%
230	0.0097	620	313
235	0.0120	640	420
390	3.0	660	550
400	4.0	680	700
420	7.0	688	760
440	11	700	865
460	17	710	970

Te, Tellurium (11, 35)

t, °C	p, mm	t, °C	p, mm
488	0.464	671	14.1
578	3.34	1390	760

VAPOR PRESSURES AND ORTHOBARIC DENSITIES ABOVE ONE ATMOSPHERE

d_l (resp. d_v) = density of saturated liquid (resp. vapor) in g per cm³; $d_m = \frac{1}{2}(d_l + d_v)$.

All values at the critical point are given in bold-face type.

The latent heat of vaporization (l) in joules per g is given by the equation:

$$l = 0.10133\left(\frac{1}{d_v} - \frac{1}{d_l}\right)T.\frac{dp}{dT} = \frac{0.10133}{0.4343}\left(\frac{1}{d_v} - \frac{1}{d_l}\right)pT\frac{d\log_{10}p}{dT}$$

Cl, Chlorine (16, 19, 21, 22, 29, 38)

t, °C	p, atm.	d_l	d_v
	±1%		±0.5%
−34.6	1.00	1.561	
	±2%		
−30	1.23	1.550	
−20	1.84	1.524	
−10	2.61	1.496	
0	3.65	1.468	0.0128
+10	4.96	1.438	0.0175
20	6.57	1.408	0.0226
30	8.60	1.377	0.0300

Cl.—(*Continued*)

t, °C	p, atm.	d_l	d_v
	±?%		
40	11.1	1.344	0.0384
50	14.1	1.310	0.0486
60	17.6	1.375	0.0600
70	21.6	1.240	0.0740
80	26.2	1.199	0.0910
90	31.5	1.156	0.1125
100	37.6	1.109	0.136
110	44.4	1.059	0.164
120	52.4	0.998	0.206
130	61.4	0.920	0.258
140	71.4	0.750	0.405
144 ±1	(76.1)	**0.573**	

$d_m = 0.7403 - 0.0011618t$.

P, Phosphorus (20, 24, 25, 30, 36)

For white and violet P: $\log_{10} p$, mm = $11.5694 - 2898.1/T - 1.2566 \log_{10} T$; ($p$ ± 7%) range, 44.1 to 635°C (±2% near B. P., 279.7°C); t, crit. = 720.6 ± 3°C; p, crit. = 100 ± 10 atm. (calc. from equation).

S, Sulfur (5, 6, 8, 9, 12, 13, 15, 17, 26, 27, 32, 33, 34, 39)

t, °C	p, mm	t, °C	p, mm
	± <0.1%		±5%
444.6	760	500	164$_7$
	±0.3%	510	187$_6$
450	821	520	213$_0$
	±3%	530	241$_0$
460	948	540	271$_8$
470	109$_3$	550	305$_5$
480	125$_7$	560	342$_3$
	±5%	570	382$_4$
490	144$_1$	**1040** ± 5°	

LITERATURE

(For key to the periodicals see end of volume)

(1) Baxter and Grose, *1*, **37**: 1061; 15. (2) Baxter, Hickey and Holmes, *1*, **29**: 127; 07. (3) Bodenstein, *7*, **30**: 113; 99. (4) Bouzat and Leluan, *34*, **178**: 635; 24. (5) Callendar and Griffiths, *62*, **182A**: 119; 91. (6) Callendar and Moss, *5*, **84**: 595; 10. (7) Centnerszwer, *7*, **85**: 99; 13. (8) Chappuis, *238*, **16**; 14. (9) Day and Sosman, *12*, **38**: 517; 12.

(10) Dodd, *1*, **42**: 1579; 20. (11) Doolan and Partington, *83*, **20**: 342; 24. (12) Eumorfopoulos, *5*, **90**: 189; 14. (13) Gruener, *1*, **29**: 1396; 07. (14) Haber and Kerschbaum, *9*, **20**: 296; 14. (15) Harker and Sexton, *133*, **1908**: 621. (16) Henglein, Rosenberg and Muchlinski, *96*, **11**: 1; 22. (17) Holborn and Henning, *8*, **35**: 761; 11. (18) Isnardi, *8*, **61**: 264; 20. (19) Johnson and McIntosh, *1*, **31**: 1138; 09.

(20) Jolibois, *34*, **149**: 287; 09. (21) Knietsch, *13*, **259**: 100; 90. (22) Lange, *92*, **1900**: 683. (23) LeChatelier, *34*, **121**: 323; 95. (24) MacRae and Van Voorhis, *1*, **43**: 547; 21. (25) Marckwald and Helmholtz, *93*, **124**: 81; 22. (26) Matthies, *63*, **7**: 395; 06. (27) Mueller and Burgess, *31*, No. **339**; 19. (28) Nadeždin, *Kiev Univ. Unters.*, **6**: 32; 85. **9**: 721; 85. (29) Pellaton, *42*, **13**: 426; 15.

(30) Preuner and Brockmoeller, *7*, **81**: 129; 12. (31) Ramsay and Young, *4*, **49**: 453; 86. (32) Rassow, *93*, **114**: 117; 20. (33) Regnault, *151*, **26**: 339; 62. (34) Ruff and Graf, *93*, **58**: 209; 08. (35) Saint-Claire Deville and Troost, *34*, **91**: 83; 80. (36) Smits and Bokhorst, *7*, **91**: 249; 16. (37) Stelzner and Niederschulte, *96*, **7**: 159; 05. (38) Trautz and Gerwig, *93*, **134**: 417; 24. (39) Waidner and Burgess, *31A*, No. **6**: 149; 10.

VAPOR PRESSURES OF THE ATMOSPHERIC GASES

C. A. Crommelin

I. VAPOR PRESSURES UP TO TWO ATMOSPHERES

p, in mm Hg (=1/760 A_n); t, in °C (Leiden scale, *v.* Vol. I, p. 54); the following equation applies over the range covered by the tabulated data, except as otherwise indicated:

$$\log_{10} p_{mm} = \frac{0.05223A}{T} + B + CT + DT^2 + ET^3$$

Trp. = triple point.

1. Two-Phase, Crystal—Vapor, Sublimation Pressures

Argon	$t°$	−189.19 Trp.	−207.62	A = −7 814.5	(1)
	p	512.17	21.97	B = +7.5741	
Kr	$t°$	−169 Trp.	−188.7	A = −10 065	(31)
	p	132.5	9.0	B = +7.1770	
N_2	$t°$	−209.86 Trp.	−215.20	A = −6 881.3	(2); *cf.*
	p	96.4	28.82	B = +7.66558	(10, 35)

Neon (39)

t, °C	p_{mm}	t, °C	p_{mm}
−248.56	317	−253.64	20.0
−248.84	279	−254.07	14.9
−249.09	250	−254.63	9.8
−249.62	195	−254.92	7.8
−250.22	148	−255.43	5.1
−250.84	111	−255.79	3.7
−251.24	91	−256.46	2.1
−252.62	40	−256.79	1.3
−253.16	28.2	−257.62	0.55
−253.30	25.3		

Rn	$t°$	−70.5 Trp.	−78	−101	−127
	p	500	250*	50*	9*
	Lit.	(9)		(34)	

* These pressures probably too high, possibly on account of impurities.

2. Two-Phase, Liquid—Vapor

Argon (1)

t, °C	p_{mm}
−182.82	1026.0
−185.66	(760)
−189.19	512.17 Trp.

A = −6826.0
B = 6.9605

H_2 (3, 11, 28)

−248.50	2199.2
−252.45	823.7
−252.74	760.0
−254.73	397.6
−256.61	191.9
−258.46	79.9
−259.14	51.4 Trp.

A = −849.48
B = 4.5331
C = 0.03240
D = -0.0_34189
E = 0.0_5484

Helium (18, 19, 29)

t, °C	p_{mm}
−268.88	760
−269.20	565
−269.57	359.5
−269.92	197
−270.85	51
−271.61	4.15
−271.74	3

$\log_{10} p = 4.7290 - 7.9780/T - 0.13628/T^2 + 4.3634/T^3$.
Range, 5.19 to 1.475°K

Kr (31)

−149.9	898.20
−152.1	760.0
−160.3	386.4
−169 Trp.	(132.5)

A = −9377.0
B = 6.92387

N_2 (2)

t, °C	p_{mm}
−188.88	1591.1
−193.91	938.6
−195.78	760.0
−198.26	561.3
−204.69	228.37
−208.58	120.90
−209.86	96.4 Trp.

A = −6407.0
B = 7.5777
C = −0.00476

Neon (4, 24, 39)

−228.66	19 797
−229.26	18 472
−231.71	13 245
−233.60	10 042
−236.82	6 057.2
−240.25	3 171.5
−241.77	2 264.8
−243.69	1 434.9
−245.68	816.2
−245.79	791.0
−245.88	767.1
−246.66	605.2
−247.33	486.0
−247.49	451.6
−247.82	410
−248.10	373
−248.29	350
−248.51	325.0

A = −1615.5
B = 5.69991
C = 0.0111800

O_2 (2, 10, 21, 22, 35)

t, °C	p_{mm}
−182.62	786.63
−182.95	760.00
−186.91	493.30
−192.01	263.19
−195.50	162.15
−201.38	64.01
−204.52	36.11
−210.72	9.59
−218.4	±2 Trp.

A = −8028.1
B = 8.1173
C = −0.00648
Range, −182 to −211°C

Rn Radon (9)

−38.6	2000
−61.8	(760)
−70.5 Trp.	500

A = −17 153
B = 7.12128

O_3 Ozone* (14, 32, 33)

t, °C ±1	p_{mm}
−193.1	0.015
−183.1	0.17
−173.1	1.3
−163.1	6.87
−153.1	25.4
−143.1	74.6
−133.1	182.8
−123.1	387.7
−112.4	760
−5	**17** atm. (critical)
−182	1.78 g/cm³ (d_l)

* Evaluated by C. S. Cragoe, cooperating expert.

Xenon (31)
Trp. = *ca.* −140°C

II. VAPOR PRESSURES AND ORTHOBARIC DENSITIES ABOVE ONE ATMOSPHERE

p = vapor pressure in normal atmospheres.
t = temperature, °C, Leiden scale (*v.* Vol. I, p. 54).
$T = t + 273.1°$.
d_l (resp. d_v) = density of saturated liquid (resp. vapor) in grams per cm³.
$d_m = \frac{1}{2}(d_l + d_v)$.
All values at the critical point are given in bold-face type.

Argon (1, 5, 6, 16)

t, °C	p, atm.
−122.44	**47.996**
−125.49	42.457
−129.83	35.846
−134.72	29.264
−140.80	22.185
−150.57	13.707
−161.23	7.4332
−185.66	1.0000

$\log_{10} p = 4.85033 - 634.391/T + 30\,769.09/T^2 - 1\,076\,464/T^3$; for $p > 1$.

t, °C	d_l	d_v
−122.44	**0.53078**	
−125.17	0.77289	0.29534
−135.51	0.97385	0.15994
−150.76	1.13851	0.06785
−161.23	1.22414	0.03723*
−175.39	1.32482	0.01457*
−183.15	1.37396	0.00801*

$d_m = 0.20956 - 0.0026235t$.
* Calculated from equation of state.

H_2 (3, 11, 12, 23, 26)

t, °C	p, atm.
−239.91	**12.80**
−240.49	11.752
−245.68	5.0566
−248.50	2.8937
−252.74	1.0000

$T \log_{10} p = -56.605 + 3.8015T - 0.10458T^2 + 0.003321T^3 - 0.0_43219T^4$; for $p > 1$

t, °C	d_l	d_v
−239.91	**0.03102**	
−240.57	0.04316	0.01922
−243.03	0.05402	0.01081
−245.73	0.06050	0.00613
−249.89	0.06724	0.00264
−253.24	0.07134	0.00116*
−256.75	0.07494	0.00038*
−258.27	0.07631	0.00020*

$d_m = -0.063510 - 0.00039402t$.
* Calculated from equation ot state.

Helium (19, 20, 29, 36)

T, °K	p, atm.
5.19	**2.261**
5.16	2.195
4.90	1.749
4.21	1.000

$\log_{10} p = 1.8482 - 7.9780/T - 0.13628/T^2 + 4.3634/T^3$ (from critical point to T = 1.475°).

T, °K	d_l	d_v
5.19	**0.06930**	
4.71	0.1139	0.02699
4.59	0.1165	0.02389
4.23	0.1253	0.01637

Helium.—(*Continued*)

T, °K	d_l	d_v
4.22	0.1255	0.01618*
3.90	0.1311	0.01176*
3.30	0.1395	0.006435*
2.56	0.1457	0.002079*
2.37	0.1466	0.001368*
2.30	0.1469†	0.001159*
2.21	0.1466	
2.10	0.1464	
1.92	0.1462	
1.59	0.1460	
1.20	0.1459	

$d_m = -0.40263 - 0.0017616t.$

* Calculated from equation of state.
† Maximum.

Kr (31)

t, °C	p, atm.
− 62.6	**54.24**
− 70	41.12
− 90	24.27
−110	11.32
−130	4.315
−150	1.175
−151.8	1.000

d_l at −146° = 2.155.

N_2 (2, 7, 17, 27)

t, °C	p, atm.
−147.13	**33.490**
−152.11	25.889
−161.31	15.949
−173.58	7.3705
−182.47	3.7248
−195.78	1.0000

$\log_{10} p = 5.76381 - 853.522/T + 54\,372.3/T^2 - 1\,783\,500/T^3$; for $p > 1$.

A new series of determinations and discussion of all available data are given in (38).

t, °C	d_l	d_v
−147.13	**0.31096**	
−148.08	0.4314	0.2000
−153.65	0.5332	0.1177
−161.20	0.6071	0.06987
−173.73	0.6922	0.02962

N_2.—(*Continued*)

t, °C	d_l	d_v
−182.51	0.7433	0.01576*
−195.09	0.8043	0.00498*
−208.36	0.8622	0.000868*

$d_m = 0.022904 - 0.0019577t.$

* Calculated from equation of state.

Neon (4, 8, 13, 24, 25)

t, °C	p, atm.
−228.71	**26.86**
−231.71	17.428
−236.82	7.970
−241.77	2.980
−245.92	1.000

$T \log_{10} p = -84.380 + 2.81910T + 0.0111800T^2.$

t, °C	d_l	d_v
−228.71	**0.4835**	
−230.07	0.74866	0.23935
−234.01	0.92803	0.11592
−237.04	1.01750	0.06742
−242.96	1.14960	0.02013
−247.92	1.23824	0.00534*

$d_m = -1.154406 - 0.00716146t.$

* Calculated from equation of state.

O_2 (2, 15, 27)

t, °C	p, atm.
−118.82	**49.713**
−118.88	49.640
−125.28	38.571
−135.96	24.528
−149.25	12.506
−154.87	9.096
−182.95	1.000

A new series of determinations and discussion of all available data are given in (38).

t, °C	d_l	d_v
−118.82	**0.4299**	
−120.4	0.6032	0.2701
−123.3	0.6779	0.2022
−129.9	0.7781	0.1320
−140.2	0.8742	0.0805
−154.5	0.9758	0.0385

O_2.—(*Continued*)

t, °C	d_l	d_v
−182.0	1.1415	0.00490*
−210.4	1.2746	0.0000865*

$d_m = 0.1608 - 0.002265t.$

* Calculated from equation of state.

Rn, Radon (9)

t, °C	p, atm.
+104.4	**62.44**
100	59.43
70	37.67
40	13.64
+ 10	11.40
− 20	5.260
− 50	2.065
− 60	1.361
− 61.8	1.000

Xenon (30, 31)

t, °C	p, atm.
+ 16.6	**58.22**
0.0	41.24
− 20	26.73

Xenon.—(*Continued*)

t, °C	p, atm.
− 40	15.85
− 60	8.570
− 80	4.064
−100	1.629
−109.1	1.000

t, °C	d_l	d_v
+16.6	**1.154**	
16	1.468	0.844
15	1.528	0.791
+10	1.745	0.602
0	1.987	0.421
−10	2.169	0.313
−20	2.292	0.238
−30	2.410	0.180
−40	2.511	0.137
−50	2.605	0.108
−60	2.699	0.079
−70	2.792	0.048

$d_m = 1.205 - 0.003055t.$

LITERATURE

(For a key to the periodicals see end of volume)

(1) Born, *8*, **69:** 473; 22. (2) Cath, *64P*, **21:** 656; 19. *168*, No. **152d.** (3) Cath and Onnes, *64P*, **20:** 991, 1155; 18. *168*, No. **152a.** (4) Cath and Onnes, *64P*, **20:** 1160; 18. *168*, No. **152b.** (5) Crommelin, *64P*, **13:** 54; 10. *168*, No. **115.** (6) Crommelin, *64P*, **16:** 477; 13. *168*, No. **138c.** (7) Crommelin, *64P*, **17:** 959; 15. *168*, No. **145d.** (8) Crommelin, *70*, **42:** 814; 23. (9) Gray and Ramsay, *4*, **95:** 1073; 09.

(10) Holst, *64P*, **18:** 829; 16. *168*, No. **148a.** (11) Martinez and Onnes, *18*, **6:** 31; 22. *168*, No. **156b.** (12) Mathias, Crommelin and Onnes, *64P*, **23:** 1175; 22. *34*, **172:** 261; 21. *168*, No. **154b.** (13) Mathias, Crommelin and Onnes, *34*, **175:** 933; 22. *168*, No. **162b.** (14) Mathias, Crommelin, Onnes and Swallow, *64V*, **34:** 334; 25. *168*, No. **172b.** (15) Mathias and Onnes, *64P*, **13:** 939; 11. *168*, No. **117.** (16) Mathias, Onnes and Crommelin, *64P*, **15:** 667, 960; 13. *168*, No. **131a.** (17) Mathias, Onnes and Crommelin, *64P*, **17:** 953; 15. *168*, No. **145c.** (18) Onnes, *64P*, **13:** 1093; 11. *168*, No. **119.** (19) Onnes, *64P*, **14:** 678; 12. *168*, No. **124b.**

(20) Onnes and Boks, *B60*, 215. *168*, No. **170b.** (21) Onnes and Braak, *64P*, **11:** 333; 08. *168*, No. **107a.** (22) Onnes and Crommelin, *64P*, **14:** 163; 11. *168*, No. **121c.** (23) Onnes and Crommelin, *64P*, **16:** 245; 13. *168*, No. **137a.** (24) Onnes and Crommelin, *64P*, **18:** 515; 15. *168*, No. **147d.** (25) Onnes, Crommelin and Cath, *64P*, **19:** 1058; 17. *168*, No. **151b.** (26) Onnes, Crommelin and Cath, *64P*, **20:** 178; 17. *168*, No. **151c.** (27) Onnes, Dorsman and Holst, *64P*, **17:** 950; 15. *168*, No. **145b.** (28) Onnes and Keesom, *64P*, **16:** 440; 13. *168*, No. **137d.** (29) Onnes and Weber, *64P*, **18:** 493; 15. *168*, No. **147b.**

(30) Patterson, Cripps and Gray, *5*, **86:** 579; 12. (31) Ramsay and Travers, *62*, **197:** 47; 01. (32) Riesenfeld and Beja, *147*, **6:** No. 7; 23. *93*, **132:** 179; 24. (33) Riesenfeld and Schwab, *25*, **55:** 2088; 22. *96*, **11:** 12; 22. (34) Rutherford, *3*, **17:** 723; 09. (35) von Siemens, *8*, **42:** 871; 13. (36) Spangenberg, *7*, **119:** 419; 26. (37) Travers, Senter and Jacquerod, *62*, **200:** 155; 03. (38) Dodge and Davis, *1*, **49:** 610; 27. (39) Crommelin and Gibson, *64V*, **36:** 173; 27. *168*, No. **185b.**

VAPOR PRESSURES OF THE METALS

J. Johnston, F. Fenwick and H. G. Leopold

The value, for the several metals, of the coefficient A (in kilojoules) and of B (for pressures p in mm of mercury) in the equation $\log_{10} p = -52.23\ A/T + B$, together with the values (calculated from the equation) of the temperatures corresponding to the pressures 760, 1, and 0.001 mm Hg. (l) = liquid, (s) = solid.

Substance	State	Range covered by equation, °C	A (kilo-joule)	B (for p in mm Hg)	°C at which p in mm Hg equals 760	1	0.001	Lit.
Ag	(l)	1650–1950	250	8.762	1948	(1218)	(837)*	(22, 23, 24, 25, 54, 63, 73, 85, 88, 90)
Al	(l)				1800			(22, 25, 88)
As	(l)	800– 860	47.1	6.692	Calculated triple point 36.0 atm., 820°C			(34)
	(s)	440– 815	133	10.800	604.3	(370.2)	(230.3)	(20, 21, 29, 30, 34, 38, 40, 47, 66, 68, 73, 81)
Au	(l)	2315–2500	385	9.853	(2611)	(1768)	(1292)	(54, 73, 85, 88)
Ba	(l)	930–1130	350	15.765	(1146)	(887)	(701.1)*	(77)
Bi	(l)	1210–1420	200	8.876	(1470)	(904)	(606.8)	(22, 23, 24, 25, 54, 73, 81)
C	(l)	3880–4430	540	9.596	(3927)	(2666)*	(2018)*	(1, 14, 15, 45, 46, 55, 56, 57, 69, 84, 92)
Ca†	(l)	960–1110	370	16.240	(1174)	(917)	(731)*	(77, 79)
	(s)	500– 700	195	9.697	(1221)‡	(777)	529	(64)
Cd	(l)	500– 840	99.9	7.897	767			(4, 5, 18, 32, 36, 54, 59, 73)
	(l)	320.9– 525	111–0.01T§	12.107	p = 10	5	1	
					°C = 485.3	454.6	392.2	
	(s)	150– 320.9	109.0	8.564		(391.7)‡	219.1	(9, 10, 13, 59)
Co‖	(l)	2375	309	7.571	(3168)	(1859)	(1254)*	(80)
Cr	(l)	2200			2200			(22, 25)
Cs	(l)	200– 350	73.4	6.949	(669.3)	278.6	(112.3)	(2, 12, 28, 45, 48, 52, 78, 82)
Cu	(l)	2100–2310	468	12.344	2310	(1707)	(1320)	(16, 22, 23, 24, 25, 54, 58, 73, 81, 85)
Fe	(l)	2220–2450	309	7.482	(3235)	(1884)	(1267)*	(22, 25, 76)
Hg	(l)	400–1300	58.7	7.752	$p = 10^4$	10^5	5×10^5	(3, 6, 7, 9, 10, 12, 19, 26, 31, 32, 33, 36, 37, 41, 43, 44, 49,
					°C = 544.1	841	1220	
	(l)	−38.87–400			356.70	*See* special table, p. 206		60, 61, 62, 65, 67, 73, 82, 83, 86, 87, 94)
	(s)	(−80)–(−38.87)	73.0	10.383	$p = 10^{-9}$	10^{-8}	10^{-7} 10^{-6}	(65)
					°C = −76.4	−65.7	−53.6 −40.4	
K	(l)	260– 760	84.9	7.183	758	344.2	(162.3)	(17, 28, 32, 42, 48, 78, 82)
Mg	(l)	900–1070	260	12.993	1070	(772)	(576.0)*	(8, 22, 25, 77, 88)
Mn	(l)	1510–1900	267	9.300	1900	(1227)*	(861)*	(22, 25, 74)
Mo	(s)	1800–2240	680	10.844	(4188)‡	(3003)‡	(2293)	(39, 53, 54, 93)
Na	(l)	180– 883	103.3	7.553	882	441.2	238.1	(19, 27, 28, 32, 37, 50, 70, 78, 91)
Ni‖	(l)	2360	309	7.600	(3147)	(1851)	(1250)*	(75)
Pb	(l)	525–1325	188.5	7.827	(1718)	985	636.2	(11, 12, 22, 23, 24, 25, 35, 54, 71, 72, 73, 88, 90)
Pt	(s)	1425–1765	486	7.786	(4901)‡	(2987)‡	(2080)‡	(39, 53, 54)
Rb	(l)	250– 370	76	6.976	(696.0)	295.8	(124.8)	(12, 28, 42, 78, 82)
Sb	(l)	1070–1325	189	9.051	1327	(818)	(546.0)*	(22, 25, 54, 73, 81)
Si	(s)	1200–1320	170	5.950	(2620)‡	1219	(719.2)	(89); *cf.* (96)
Sn	(l)	1950–2270	328	9.643	(2260)	(1503)	(1282)	(22, 23, 24, 25, 54, 73, 88)
Sr	(l)	940–1140	360	16.056	(1154)	(899)	(713.4)*	(77)
Tl	(l)	950–1200	120	6.140	(1650)	(748)	(412.7)	(20, 47, 88, 90)
W	(s)	2230–2770	897	9.920	(6383)‡	(4450)‡	(3353)	(39, 51, 54, 95)
Zn	(l)	600– 985	118.0	8.108	906			(4, 5, 12, 23, 24, 32, 36, 54, 59, 71, 73)
	(l)	419.4– 625	127–0.01T§	12.184	p = 20	10	5 1	
					°C = (632.3)	594.1	558.9 487.7	
	(s)	250– 419.4	133	9.200		(532.0)‡	296.3	(9, 10)

( ) Extrapolated beyond experimental range.

* Extrapolated below freezing point.

† These two curves are mutually inconsistent.

‡ Extrapolated above melting point.

§ These are the only two cases in which the accuracy of the present data seems to justify the use of a curved line. The equations of these curves are respectively:

$$\log_{10} p_{Cd} = -111 \times 52.23/T - 1.203 \log_{10} T + 12.107$$

and

$$\log_{10} p_{Zn} = -127 \times 52.23/T - 1.203 \log_{10} T + 12.184$$

‖ Slope made equal to that of iron.

THE VAPOR PRESSURE OF MERCURY FROM −39 TO +400°C
Unit, mm of Hg = 1/760 A_n

t, °C	0°	1°	2°	3°	4°	5°	6°	7°	8°	9°
−30	0.0_5478	0.0_5415	0.0_5359	0.0_5309	0.0_5266	0.0_5229	0.0_5197	0.0_5169	0.0_5145	0.0_5124
−20	$.0_4181$	$.0_4159$	$.0_4140$	$.0_4123$	$.0_4108$	$.0_5947$	$.0_5828$	$.0_5723$	$.0_5630$	$.0_5549$
−10	$.0_4606$	$.0_4540$	$.0_4481$	$.0_4428$	$.0_4380$	$.0_4337$	$.0_4298$	$.0_4263$	$.0_4232$	$.0_4205$
− 0	$.0_3185$	$.0_3166$	$.0_3149$	$.0_3133$	$.0_3119$	$.0_3107$	$.0_4954$	$.0_4853$	$.0_4762$	$.0_4680$
+ 0	$.0_3185$	$.0_3206$	$.0_3228$	$.0_3251$	$.0_3276$	$.0_3304$	$.0_3335$	$.0_3369$	$.0_3406$	0_3446
+10	$.0_3490$	$.0_3537$	$.0_3588$	$.0_3644$	$.0_3706$	$.0_3773$	$.0_3846$	$.0_3925$	.001009	.001101
20	.001201	.001309	.001426	.001553	.001691	.001840	.002000	.002173	.002359	.002560
30	.002777	.003010	.003261	.003532	.003823	.004135	.004471	.004832	.005219	.005634
40	.006079	.006556	.007067	.007614	.008200	.008827	.009497	.01021	.01098	.01180
50	.01267	.01360	.01459	.01565	.01677	.01797	.01925	.02061	.02206	.02360
60	.02524	.02698	.02883	.03079	.03287	.03507	.03740	.03988	.04251	.04530
70	.04825	.05138	.05469	.05819	.06189	.06580	.06993	.07429	.07889	.08375
80	.08880	.09430	.1000	.1060	.1124	.1191	.1261	.1335	.1413	.1495
90	.1582	.1673	.1769	.1870	.1976	.2086	.2202	.2324	.2453	.2588
100	.2729	.2877	.3032	.3195	.3366	.3544	.3731	.3927	.4132	.4347
110	.4572	.4807	.5052	.5308	.5576	.5857	.6150	.6456	.6776	.7109
120	.7457	.7820	.8198	.8592	.9004	.9434	.9882	1.035	1.084	1.134
130	1.186	1.241	1.298	1.357	1.419	1.484	1.551	1.620	1.692	1.767
140	1.845	1.926	2.010	2.097	2.188	2.282	2.379	2.480	2.585	2.694
150	2.807	2.924	3.046	3.172	3.303	3.438	3.578	3.723	3.873	4.028
160	4.189	4.356	4.528	4.706	4.890	5.080	5.277	5.480	5.689	5.905
170	6.128	6.358	6.596	6.842	7.095	7.356	7.626	7.905	8.193	8.490
180	8.796	9.111	9.436	9.711	10.116	10.472	10.839	11.217	11.607	12.009
190	12.423	12.849	13.287	13.738	14.203	14.681	15.173	15.679	16.200	16.736
200	17.287	17.854	18.437	19.036	19.652	20.285	20.936	21.605	22.292	22.998
210	23.723	24.468	25.233	26.019	26.826	27.654	28.504	29.376	30.271	31.190
220	32.133	33.100	34.092	35.110	36.153	37.222	38.318	39.442	40.595	41.777
230	42.989	44.231	45.503	46.806	48.141	49.509	50.909	52.343	53.812	55.316
240	56.855	58.431	60.044	61.695	63.384	65.113	66.882	68.692	70.543	72.437
250	74.375	76.356	78.381	80.451	82.568	84.732	86.944	89.206	91.518	93.881
260	96.296	98.763	101.28	103.85	106.48	109.17	111.91	114.71	117.57	120.49
270	123.47	126.51	129.62	132.79	136.02	139.34	142.69	146.13	149.64	153.22
280	156.87	160.59	164.39	168.26	172.21	176.24	180.34	184.52	188.79	193.14
290	197.57	202.09	206.70	211.39	216.17	221.04	226.00	231.06	236.21	241.46
300	246.80	252.24	257.78	263.42	269.17	275.02	280.98	287.04	293.21	299.49
310	305.89	312.40	319.02	325.76	332.62	339.60	346.70	353.92	361.26	368.73
320	376.33	384.06	391.92	399.91	408.04	416.31	424.71	433.25	441.94	450.77
330	459.74	468.86	478.13	487.55	497.12	506.85	516.74	526.79	537.00	547.37
340	557.90	568.59	579.45	590.48	601.69	613.08	624.64	636.38	648.30	660.40
350	672.69	685.17	697.83	710.68	723.73	736.98	750.43	764.08	777.92	791.97
360	806.23	820.70	835.38	850.26	865.36	880.68	896.23	912.01	928.02	944.27
370	960.66	977.38	994.34	1011.5	1028.9	1046.5	1064.4	1082.5	1100.9	1119.5
380	1138.4	1157.6	1177.0	1196.6	1216.6	1236.8	1257.3	1278.1	1299.1	1320.3
390	1341.9	1363.9	1386.1	1408.6	1431.3	1454.3	1477.7	1501.3	1525.2	1549.5
400	1574.1	(For continuation use the equation, $\log_{10} p = \frac{-52.23 \times 58.7}{T} + 7.75_2$, valid up to 1300°C)								

LITERATURE

(For a key to the periodicals see end of volume)

(1) Alterthum, *97*, **6**: 540; 25. (2) Bartels, *8*, **65**: 143; 21. (3) Bernhardt, *63*, **26**: 265; 25. (4) Berthelot, *34*, **131**: 380; 00. (5) Braune, *93*, **111**: 109; 20. (6) Cailletet, Colardeau and Rivière, *34*, **130**: 1585; 00. (7) Callendar and Griffiths, *62*, **182**: 119; 92. (8) Ditte, *34*, **73**: 108; 71. (9) Egerton, *3*, **33**: 33; 17.

(10) Egerton, *3*, **39**: 1; 20. (11) Egerton, *5*, **103**: 469; 23. (12) Egerton, *3*, **48**: 1048; 24. (13) Egerton and Raleigh, *4*, **123**: 3024; 23. (14) Fajans, *9*, **31**: 63; 25. (15) Fajans and Rishkevich, *218*, **12**: 304, 578; 24. (16) Fèry, *6*, **29**: 428; 03. (17) Fiock and Rodebush, *1*, **48**: 2522; 26. (18) Fogler and Rodebush, *1*, **45**: 2080; 23. (19) Gebhardt, *26*, **3**: 184; 05.

(20) Gibson, *Diss.*, Breslau, 1911. (21) Goubau, *34*, **158**: 121; 14. (22) Greenwood, *5*, **82**: 396; 09. (23) Greenwood, *5*, **8**: 483; 10. (24) Greenwood, *7*, **76**: 484; 11. (25) Greenwood, *9*, **18**: 319; 12. (26) Haber and Kerschbaum, *9*, **20**: 296; 14. (27) Haber and Zisch, *96*, **9**: 302; 22. (28) Hackspill, *34*, **154**: 877; 12. (29) Heike, *93*, **118**: 254; 21.

(30) Heike and Leroux, *93*, **92**: 119; 15. (31) Hertz, *8*, **17**: 193; 82. (32) Heycock and Lamplough, *182*, **28**: 3; 12. (33) Hill, *2*, **20**: 259; 22. (34) Horiba, *7*, **106**: 295; 23. (35) Ingold, *4*, **121**: 2419; 22. (36) Jenkins, *5*, **110**: 456; 26. (37) Jewett, *3*, **4**: 546; 02. (38) Jolibois, *34*, **152**: 1767; 11. (39) Jones, Langmuir, Dushman and Mackay, *0*. The General Electric Co., Schenectady, N. Y.

(40) Jonker, *93*, **62**: 89; 09. (41) Kahlbaum, *7*, **13**: 14; 94. (42) Killian, *2*, **27**: 578; 26. (43) Knudsen, *8*, **29**: 179; 09. (44) Knudsen, *8*, **32**: 809; 10. (45) Kohn, *96*, **3**: 143; 20. (46) Kohn and Guckel, *96*, **27**: 305; 24. (47) Krafft and Knocke, *25*, **42**: 202; 09. (48) Kröner, *8*, **40**: 438; 13. (49) Laby, *3*, **16**: 789; 08.

(50) Ladenburg and Minkowski, *96*, **6**: 153; 21. (51) Langmuir, *2*, **2**: 329; 13. (52) Langmuir and Kingdon, *5*, **107**: 61; 25. (53) Langmuir and Mackay, *2*, **4**: 377; 14. (54) van Liempt, *93*, **114**: 105; 20. (55) van Liempt, *93*, **115**: 218; 20. (56) van Liempt, *176*, **21**: 517; 24. (57) van Liempt, *218*, **12**: 578; 24. (58) Mack, Osterhof and Kraner, *1*, **45**: 617; 23. (59) Maier, *1*, **48**: 356; 26.

(60) Menzies, *1*, **41**: 1783; 19. (61) Morley, *3*, **7**: 662; 04. (62) Pfaundler, *8*, **63**: 36; 97. (63) Piersol, *2*, **23**: 785; 25. (64) Pilling, *2*, **18**: 362; 21. (65) Poindexter, *2*, **26**: 859; 25. (66) Preuner and Brockmöller, *7*, **81**: 129; 12. (67) Ramsay and Young, *4*, **49**: 37; 86. (68) Rassow, *93*, **114**: 117; 20. (69) Rishkevich, *9*, **31**: 54; 25.
(70) Rodebush and DeVries, *1*, **47**: 2488; 25. (71) Rodebush and Dixon, *1*, **47**: 1036; 25. (72) Rodebush and Dixon, *2*, **26**: 851; 25. (73) Ruff and Bergdahl, *93*, **106**: 76; 19. (74) Ruff and Bormann, *93*, **88**: 365; 14. (75) Ruff and Bormann, *93*, **88**: 386; 14. (76) Ruff and Bormann, *93*, **88**: 397; 14. (77) Ruff and Hartmann, *93*, **133**: 29; 24. (78) Ruff and Johannsen, *25*, **38**: 3601; 05. (79) Ruff and Josephy, *93*, **153**: 17; 26.
(80) Ruff and Keilig, *93*, **88**: 410; 14. (81) Ruff and Mugdan, *93*, **117**: 147; 21. (82) Scott, *3*, **47**: 32; 24. (83) Smith and Menzies, *1*, **32**: 1434; 10. (84) Thiel and Ritter, *93*, **132**: 125; 23. (85) Tiede and Birnbräuer, *93*, **87**: 129; 14. (86) Villiers, *6*, **30**: 588; 13. (87) Volmer and Estermann, *96*, **7**: 1; 21. (88) von Wartenberg, *93*, **56**: 320; 07. (89) von Wartenberg, *93*, **79**: 71; 12.
(90) von Wartenberg, *9*, **19**: 482; 13. (91) von Wartenberg, *9*, **20**: 443; 14. (92) Wertenstein and Jedrzejewski, *34*, **177**: 316; 23. (93) Worthing, *2*, **28**: 190; 26. (94) Young, *4*, **59**: 629; 91. (95) Zwikker, *208*, **5**: 249; 25. (96) Ruff and Konschak, *9*, **32**: 515; 26.

VAPOR PRESSURE OF CHEMICAL COMPOUNDS IN THE CRYSTALLINE STATE

A. C. Egerton and W. Edmondson

This section covers the pressure-temperature relations for systems composed of a single crystalline phase in contact with its own vapor. In the case of substances which dissociate on vaporization the value given is the total pressure. The literature references given first are to data to which most weight has been given.

𝔅-TABLE, STANDARD ARRANGEMENT (*v.* p. viii)

$$\log_{10} p_{mm} = \frac{-0.05223A}{T} + B$$

Key No.	Formula	Range, °C	A, joule	B	Lit.
2	H_2O	*v.* p. 210			
	HCl*	−158 to −110	19 58$_8$	8.443$_0$	(29, 32, 45); *cf.* (20, 52)
	HBr†	−114 to − 86	22 42$_0$	8.734	(29, 52, 93); *cf.* (20)
	HI‡	− 97 to − 51	24 16$_0$	8.259	(29, 52, 93); *cf.* (92)
8	SO_2	− 95 to − 75	35 82$_7$	10.591$_6$	(6, 13, 14); *cf.* (92)
	SO_3	4 crystalline forms			(50)
	H_2S	−110 to − 83	20 69$_0$	7.880	(52); *cf.* (93)
	SeO_2§	*t*, °C	*p*, mm		(38)
		72.0	13.43		
		112.5	21.28		
		180.9	39.00		
		213.5	50.12		
		236.9	66.07		
		259.9	109.6		
		289.2	316.2		
		319.9	849.0		
		317.0	760.0		
	H_2Se	−78.11	82.5		(12)
		−70.27	157.3		
		−70.15	158.1		
	H_2SeO_4	25 to 56	82 40$_0$	14.130	(38)
		t, °C	*p*, mm		
10	TeH_2	−60	34		(11)
		−50	79		
		−45.4	102		
	N_2O	−144 to − 90	23 59$_0$	9.579	(13, 14)
	NO	−200 to −161	16 423	10.048	(26, 30); *cf.* (57, 61)
	N_2O_4‖	−100 to − 40	55 16$_0$	13.400	(23); *cf.* (76)
		− 40 to − 10	45 44$_0$	11.214	(76); *cf.* (27, 74)
	N_2O_5	− 30 to + 30	57 18$_0$	12.647	(17, 75)
	NH_3¶	−127 to − 78	31 21$_1$	9.997$_4$	(15, 45, 53, 88); *cf.* (7, 13, 14, 57)
	$NOCl$	*p* = 55.0 mm at −68.6°			(10)
	NH_4Cl**	100 to 400	83 486	10.0164	(40, 41, 67, 85, 86, 87); *cf.* (34, 66)
		t, °C	*p*, mm		
		338.0	760		
		427	4 560		
		459	8 360		(67)
		490	15 200		
		520	26 220		
	NH_4Br	250 to 400	90 208	9.9404	(41, 85)
		760 mm at 394.2°			
	NH_4I††	300 to 400	95 730	10.270$_0$	(41, 85)
		760 mm at 403.5°			
	NH_4HS	6 to 40	46 02$_5$	10.750$_0$	(35, 109)
		760 mm at 32.7°			
12	PCl_5	*t*, °C	*p*, mm		
		156.1	562.3		(85)
		143.6	354.8		
		136.7	266.1		
		122.2	133.4		
		101.4	37.58		
	PH_4Cl	−78.2	10.0		(102)
		−63.0	39.81		
		−41.1	251.2		
		−26.8	760.0		
		−23.1	1 000.$_0$		
		+ 0.9	5 623.$_0$		
		29.9	38 90$_0$.$_0$		
	PH_4Br	−80 to +40	48 11$_5$	10.956$_1$	(43)
		760 mm at 38.1°			
	PH_4I	10 to 60	51 85$_4$	10.950$_0$	(43, 85)
		760 mm at 62.5°			
	As_2O_3	100 to 310	111 35$_0$	12.127	(59, 84); *cf.* (94)
		355.8° at 760.0 mm			
	$SbCl_3$	50.3° at 1.1 mm			(54)
		59.9° at 3.4 mm			
	$BiCl_3$	91 to 213	13 12$_5$	2.681	(54)
		t, °C	*p*, mm		
16	CO	−220.6	4		(24, 33, 60)
		−209.1	50		
		−205.70	111.33 ±0.04		
	CO_2‡‡	−135 to −56.7	26 179.$_8$	9.9082	(31, 32, 47, 62, 83, 96); *cf.* (33, 107, 116)
		p = 760.0 at −78.5$_2$°			
		$\log_{10} p = -\frac{1275.6_2}{T} + 0.00683_8 T + 8.307_1$ (−183° to −135°)			
	CCl_4	−70 to −50	34 608	8.05	(57)
		−36.53° at 3.52 mm			
		−27.19° at 6.17 mm			(68)
	$(CN)_2$	−72 to −28	32 437	9.653$_9$	(63, 103)
	NH_4CN	7 to 17	41 48$_4$	9.97$_8$	(36)
	$NH_2CO_2NH_4$	Data conflicting			(9, 37)
	$(NH_4)_2CO_3$				(8)
		t, °C	*p*, mm		
	$CNCl$	−32.69	58.6		(68)
		−30.65	60.1		
		−24.7	101.71		
		−11.41	250.67		
	$CNBr$	−17 to +35	47 05$_1$	10.32$_8$	(5)

For other C-compounds, *see* the ℭ-table, p. 208

Key No.	Formula	Range, °C	A, joule	B	Lit.
18	$SiCl_4$	1.0 mm at −70°			(100)
		t, °C	*p*, mm		
	SiH_3Cl	−125.3	0.5		(99)
		−119.0	1.0		
	SiH_3Br	−94.0	2.5		(98)
	$SnCl_4$	−52 to −38	46 74$_0$	9.824	(57)
		t, °C	*p*, mm		
	$PbCl_2$	400	0.00174		(22)
		425	.0058		
		450	.0178		
		475	.051		

Key No.	Formula	Range, °C	A, joule	B	Lit.
23	PbS	*t*, °C	*p*, mm		(77)
		850	2.0		
		917	4.0		
		968	10.5		
		995	17.0		
	HgF_2	Data unreliable			(71)
	Hg_2Cl_2	*t*, °C	*p*, mm		(54)
		90	0.004 (Less accurate)		
		100	0.0089 (Less accurate)		
		110	0.011 (Less accurate)		
		120	0.016 (Less accurate)		
		130	0.0227 (Less accurate)		
		140	0.038		
		150	0.07		
		160	0.15		
		170	0.27		
		180	0.45		
	$HgCl_2$	60 to 130	85 030	10.888	(42, 95); *cf.* (3)
		130 to 270	78 850	10.094	
	$HgBr_2$	111 to 235	79 800	10.181	(42, 95); *cf.* (3)
	HgI_2	100 to 250	82 340	10.057	(42, 95); *cf.* (3, 19)
	HgS	760 mm at 580°			(2)
31		*t*, °C	*p*, mm		
	CuO	600	1.34×10^{-7}		(55)
		800	1.15×10^{-4}		
		950	6.8×10^{-4}		
	$CuCl_2$	487.6	223.9		(54)
		470.5	128.8		
		407.2	22.39		
		335.2	5.0		
		318.6	3.55		
	Ag_2O	1 435	3.4		(110)
		1 316	0.46		
	$AuCl_3$§§	100	7.0		(64)
		138.5	11.0		
		181	61.2		
		202	154.5		
		229	424.2		
		251	808.7		
	OsO_4	−38 to 40.1	56 500	10.7100	(111)
	$FeCl_2$	700 to 930	135 200	8.33	(54)
		t, °C	*p*, mm		
	$FeCl_3$	245.0	19.95		(54)
		256.0	35.48		
		292.3	316.2		

Key No.	Formula	Range, °C	A, joule	B	Lit.
	$Co_2(CO)_8$	15	0.072 mm		(56)
49	UF_6	0 to 69	41 730	9.521	(72)
		t, °C	*p*, mm		
	NbF_5	184.5	303.1		(73)
		191.6	329.7		
		194.5	358.9		
	BBr_3	−50	0.7		(97)
	BN	*v.* Vol. IV, p. 84			
	$B(CH_3)_3NH_3$§§	0 to 40	53 184	10.172	(101)
	$AlCl_3$	70 to 190	115 000	16.24	(54)
82	$NaCl$	2.4 mm at 746.9°			(54)

* Over the range −150 to −114°C, Karwat gives the equation:

$$\log p = -\frac{1171.62}{T} - 2.3577 \log T + 14.57497,$$

the coefficient of log *T* being obtained from specific heat measurements at low temperatures.

† Henglein gives the equation:

$$\log p = -\frac{2202.0}{T^{1.1602}} + 7.5030,$$

over the range of his measurements from −130 to −95°C.

‡ Henglein gives the equation:

$$\log p = -\frac{1435.9}{T^{1.0496}} + 7.5030$$

§ The results when plotted give an unusual curve.

‖ For amount of dissociation see (76).

¶ Karwat gives the equation: $\log p = -\frac{1790.00}{T} - 1.81630 \log T + 14.97593,$ the coefficient of log *T* being obtained from specific heat measurements at low temperatures.

** Smith and Calvert give the equation:

$$\log p = -\frac{1920.357}{T} + 9.778609 \log T - 21.21708.$$

†† Smith and Calvert give the equation:

$$\log p = -\frac{7714.591}{T} + 10.04345 \log T + 42.69560.$$

‡‡ Over the range −110 to −80°C Henning, to express his experimental results, gives the equation:

$$\log p = -\frac{1279.11}{T} + 1.75 \log T - 0.0020757T + 5.85242.$$

The simpler equation:

$$\log p = -\frac{1352.6}{T} + 9.8318$$

expresses his experimental results closely.

§§ The vapor is strongly dissociated.

C-TABLE

$$\log_{10} p_{mm} = \frac{-0.05223A}{T} + B$$

Formula	Name	Range, °C	A	B	Lit.
CH_4	Methane*	−194 to −184	9 896.2	7.6509	(16, 32, 45); *cf.* (33, 61)
C_2H_2	Acetylene	−140 to −82	21 914	8.933	(13); *cf.* (106)
$C_2H_2O_4$	Oxalic acid	55 to 105	90 502.6	12.2229	(112)
$C_2H_4O_2$	Acetic acid	·35 to 10	41 689	8.502	(57, 79, 113, 114); *cf.* (49)
C_6H_4BrCl	*p*-Bromochlorobenzene	23 to 63	69 755	11.629	(91)
$C_6H_4Cl_2$	*p*-Dichlorobenzene	30 to 50	72 218	12.480	(91); *cf.* (46, 48)
C_6H_6	Benzene	−58 to −30	42 904	9.556	(25, 57); *cf.* (4, 68, 114)
		−30 to +5	44 222	9.846	
		0.018 mm at −77.5°			
C_6H_{12}	Cyclohexane	−5 to +5	37 394	8.594	(115)
$C_7H_6O_2$	Benzoic acid	60 to 110	63 820	9.033	(59)
$C_{10}H_8$	Naphthalene	0 to 80	71 401	11.450	(1, 4, 78, 104); *cf.* (70, 90)
$C_{10}H_{16}O$	Camphor	0 to 180	53 559	8.799	(1, 65, 94, 105); *cf.* (18, 59)
$C_{14}H_8O_2$	Anthraquinone	224 to 286	110 040	12.305	(58, 94)
$C_{14}H_{10}$	Anthracene	100 to 160	70 390	8.706	(59)

* Using specific heats at low temperatures, for log *T* coefficient, Karwat gives:

$$\log_{10} p_{mm} = \frac{-554.518}{T} - 1.0831 \log_{10} T + 10.1840$$

VALUES OF p AND t

CH_2O_2, Formic acid ([44])

t, °C	p, mm
1	8.8
2	9.7
3	10.6
4	11.6
5	12.8
6	14.1
7	15.5
8	17.4

$C_2H_4Br_2$, Ethylene bromide* (M. P., 9.55°) ([69])

−28.21	1.51
−23.16	1.90
−12.30	2.65
− 7.18	3.24
0	3.47
+ 5.62	5.53
6.54	6.16

* M. P. of pure $C_2H_4Br_2$, 7.7°.

C_2H_9NS, $NH_3(C_2H_5)HS$ ([109])

5.0	33
13.4	55
17.0	73
23.2	109
31.4	183
35.0	228
37.2	264
40.5	322

C_3H_4, Allylene ([51])

−110	1_0

C_3H_4, Allene ([51])

−146	1_0

C_3H_6O, Acetone ([21])

−94.8	0.017

$C_3H_6O_2$, Methyl acetate ([39])

−135	0.00354

$C_4H_{10}O$, Ethyl ether ([21])

−119.8	0.0027
−117.3	0.0065

$C_4H_{12}ClN$, Tetramethylammonium chloride ([85])

231.5	690
227.1	567
222.5	430
213.3	312
202.4	187
186.6	108

$C_4H_{12}IN$, Tetramethylammonium iodide ([85])

306.2	781
303.0	698
295.8	547
287.4	421
276.6	298
260.6	166
242.6	83

$C_6H_3N_3O_7$, Picric acid ([81])

100.4	0.00249

$C_6H_4Br_2$, p-Dibromobenzene ([46, 48, 91])

t, °C	p, mm
84.0	7.58_6
69.4	2.63
52.8	0.660_7
32.8	.0794
21.0	.0158

$C_6H_4N_2O_5$, 2, 4-Dinitrophenol ([81])

100	0.228

$C_6H_6N_2O_2$, p-Nitroaniline ([82])

100	0.0136

$C_6H_6O_2$, Hydroquinol ([94])

155.0	5.9
157.6	7.1
164.3	1.0

$C_7H_5ClO_2$, Chlorobenzoic acid ([80])

o-	100	0.1803
m-	100.63	.197
p-	100	.045

$C_7H_5NO_4$, p-Nitrobenzoic acid ([80])

100	0.0096

$C_7H_6O_3$, Hydroxybenzoic acid ([80])

o-	100	0.397
m-	101.06	.00149
p-	100.91	.00030

$C_8H_8N_2O_3$, Nitroacetanilide ([82])

m-	100	0.0042
p-	100	.0021

$C_8H_8O_2$, p-Toluic acid ([80])

100	0.216

$C_8H_8O_3$, Hydroxytoluic acid ([80])

o-3	100	0.235
o-4	100	.121
o-5	100	.182
m-4	100	.0176
p-3	100.17	.00072

$C_{10}H_{18}O$, Borneol ([105])

154.3	114.8
129.1	38.9
107.1	12.88
90.5	5.012
79.0	2.455

$C_{13}H_{10}O$, Benzophenone ([108])

0	2.03×10^{-5}
8	6.94×10^{-5}
26	6.859×10^{-4}
	7.614×10^{-4}
32	1.418×10^{-3}
40	3.198×10^{-3}
	3.933×10^{-3}

LITERATURE

(For a key to the periodicals see end of volume)

([1]) Allen, *4*, **77**: 400, 413; 00. ([2]) Allen and Crenshaw, *93*, **79**: 125; 12. *12*, **34**: 341; 12. ([3]) Arctowski, *93*, **12**: 413; 96. ([4]) Barker, *7*, **71**: 235; 10. ([5]) Baxter, Bezzenberger and Wilson, *1*, **42**: 1386; 20. ([6]) Bergstrom, *50*, **26**: 358; 22. ([7]) Brill, *8*, **21**: 170; 06. ([8]) Briner, *34*, **142**: 1416; 06. ([9]) Briner, *42*, **4**: 276; 06.

([10]) Briner and Pylkoff, *42*, **10**: 640; 12. ([11]) Bruylants, *186*, **1920**: 472. ([12]) Bruylants and Dondeyne, *186*, **8**: 387; 22. ([13]) Burrell and Robertson, *30*, No. **142**; 15. ([14]) Burrell and Robertson, *1*, **37**: 2691; 15. ([15]) Cragoe, Meyers and Taylor, *1*, **42**: 206; 20. ([16]) Crommelin, *64V*, **21**: 684; 12. ([17]) Daniels and Bright, *1*, **42**: 1131; 20. ([18]) Datin, *6*, **5**: 218; 16. ([19]) Ditte, *34*, **140**: 1162; 05.

([20]) Drozdowski and Pietrzak, *165*, **1913**: 219. ([21]) Drucker, Jiméno and Kangro, *7*, **90**: 513; 15. ([22]) Eastman and Duschak, *30*, No. **225**; 19. ([23]) Egerton, *4*, **105**: 647; 14. ([24]) Estreicher and Bobotek, *165*, **1913**: 451. ([25]) Ferche, *8*, **44**: 265; 91. ([26]) Goldschmidt, *96*, **20**: 159; 23. ([27]) Guye and Drouginine, *42*, **8**: 473; 10. ([28]) Ham, Churchill and Ryder, *143*, **186**: 15; 18. ([29]) Henglein, *96*, **18**: 64; 23.

([30]) Henglein and Krüger, *93*, **130**: 181; 23. ([31]) Henning, *8*, **43**: 282; 14. ([32]) Henning and Stock, *96*, **4**: 226; 21. ([33]) Homfray, *7*, **74**: 129; 10. ([34]) Horstman, *25*, **2**: 137; 69. ([35]) Isambert, *34*, **92**: 919; 81. ([36]) Isambert, *34*, **94**: 958; 82. ([37]) Isambert, *34*, **102**: 1313; 86. ([38]) Jannek and Meyer, *93*, **83**: 51; 13. ([39]) Jiméno Gil, *132*, **12**: 469; 14.

([40]) Johnson, *7*, **61**: 457; 08. ([41]) Johnson, *7*, **65**: 36; 09. ([42]) Johnson, *1*, **35**: 777; 11. ([43]) Johnson, *1*, **34**: 877; 12. ([44]) Kahlbaum, *7*, **13**: 14; 94. ([45]) Karwat, *7*, **112**: 486; 24. ([46]) Kruyt, *7*, **79**: 657; 12. ([47]) Kuenen and Robson, *3*, **3**: 149; 02. ([48]) Küster, *7*, **51**: 222; 05. ([49]) Landolt, *13 Suppl.*, **6**: 129; 68.

([50]) Le Blanc and Rühle, *221*, **74**: 106; 22. ([51]) Lespieau, *6*, **27**: 137; 12. ([52]) Maass and McIntosh, *69*, **8 IV**: 65; 14. ([53]) McKelvy and Taylor, *31A*, **18**: 655; 23. ([54]) Maier, *30*, No. **360**; 25. ([55]) Mack, Osterhof and Kraner, *1*, **45**: 617; 23. ([56]) Mond, Hirtz and Cowap, *4*, **97**: 798; 10. ([57]) Mundel, *7*, **85**: 435; 13. ([58]) Nelson and Senseman, *45*, **14**: 58; 22. ([59]) Niederschulte, *Diss.*, Erlangen, 1903.

([60]) Olszewski, *34*, **99**: 706; 84. ([61]) Olszewski, *34*, **100**: 940; 85. ([62]) Onnes and Weber, *64P*, **16**: 215; 13. ([63]) Perry and Bardwell, *1*, **47**: 2629; 25. ([64]) Petit, *27*, **37**: 615; 25. ([65]) Ramsay and Young, *62*, **175**: 37; 84. ([66]) Ramsay and Young, *62*, **177**: 71; 87. ([67]) Rassow, *93*, **114**: 117; 20. ([68]) Regnault, *151*, **26**: 339; 62. ([69]) Regnault, *151*, **26**: 462; 62.

([70]) Rolla, *59*, **19**: 318; 10. *22*, **18 II**: 365; 09. ([71]) Ruff and Bahlau, *25*, **51**: 1752; 18. ([72]) Ruff and Heinzelmann, *93*, **72**: 63; 11. ([73]) Ruff and Schiller, *93*, **72**: 329; 11. ([74]) Russ, *7*, **82**: 217; 13. ([75]) Russ and Pokorny, *57*, **34**: 1027; 13. ([76]) Scheffer and Treub, *7*, **81**: 308; 12. ([77]) Schenk and Albers, *93*, **105**: 145; 18. ([78]) Schlumberger, *397*, **55**: 1257; 12. ([79]) Schmidt, *7*, **7**: 433; 91.

([80]) Sidgwick, *4*, **117**: 396; 20. ([81]) Sidgwick and Aldous, *4*, **119**: 1001; 21. ([82]) Sidgwick and Rubie, *4*, **119**: 1013; 21. ([83]) Siemens, *8*, **42**: 871; 13. ([84]) Smellie, *54*, **42**: 466T; 23. ([85]) Smith and Calvert, *1*, **36**: 1363; 14. ([86]) Smith and Lombard, *1*, **37**: 38; 15. ([87]) Smith and Menzies, *1*, **32**: 1448; 10. ([88]) Smits and Postma, *64P*, **17**: 182; 14. ([89]) Smits and Schoenmaker, *4*, **1926**: 1108.

([90]) Speranski, *7*, **46**: 70; 03. ([91]) Speranski, *7*, **51**: 45; 05. ([92]) Steele and Bagster, *4*, **97**: 2607; 10. ([93]) Steele, McIntosh and Archibald, *7*, **55**: 129; 06. ([94]) Stelzner, *Diss.*, Erlangen, 1901. ([95]) Stelzner and Niederschulte, *88*, **7**: 159; 05. ([96]) Stock, Henning and Kuss, *25*, **54**: 1119; 21. ([97]) Stock and Kuss, *25*, **47**: 3113; 14. ([98]) Stock and Somieski, *25*, **50**: 1739; 17. ([99]) Stock and Somieski, *25*, **52**: 695; 19.

([100]) Stock, Somieski and Wintgen, *25*, **50**: 1754; 17. ([101]) Stock and Zeidler, *25*, **54**: 531; 21. ([102]) Tammann, *B57*, p. 289. ([103]) Terwen, *7*, **91**: 469; 16. ([104]) Thomas, *54*, **35**: 506; 16. ([105]) Vanstone, *4*, **97**: 429; 10. ([106]) Villard, *34*, **120**: 1262; 95. ([107]) Villard and Jarry, *34*, **120**: 1413; 95. ([108]) Volmer and Kirchhoff, *7*, **115**: 233; 25. ([109]) Walker and Lumsden, *4*, **71**: 428; 97.

([110]) von Wartenberg, *9*, **19**: 489; 13. ([111]) von Wartenberg, *13*, **440**: 97; 24. ([112]) Wobbe and Noyes, *1*, **48**: 2856; 26. ([113]) Young, *4*, **59**: 903; 91. ([114]) Young, *117*, **12**: 374; 10. ([115]) Young and Fortey, *4*, **75**: 873; 99. ([116]) Zeleny and Smith, *63*, **7**: 667; 06.

THE VAPOR PRESSURES OF ICE AND WATER UP TO 100°C

E. W. Washburn

In the following tables, the values given are the vapor pressures for the condition that the solid or liquid phase is under its own vapor pressure. If the solid or liquid phase is in contact with the atmosphere, the corresponding vapor pressures will be somewhat higher, and can be obtained by adding to the value given in the table a small increment, Δp, computed by means of the following equations:

Dans les tables suivantes, les valeurs données sont les tensions de vapeur dans la condition de la phase solide ou liquide se trouvant sous la pression de sa propre vapeur. Si la phase liquide ou la phase solide se trouve en contact avec l'atmosphère, les tensions de vapeur correspondantes seront un peu plus élevées, et elles peuvent être obtenues en additionnant aux valeurs données dans les tables un petit accroissement, Δp, calculé au moyen des équations suivantes:

Die in den folgenden Tafeln angegebenen Werte für die Dampfdrucke gelten für den Zustand, dass die feste oder flüssige Phase unter dem eigenen Dampfdruck steht. Ist die feste oder flüssige Phase mit der Atmosphäre in Verbindung, so werden die entsprechenden Dampfdrucke etwas höher sein. Man erhält sie, wenn man zu dem in der Tafel angegebenen Wert das Inkrement Δp addiert, das sich nach den Gleichungen berechnen lässt:

Nelle tabelle seguenti le tensioni riportate sono quelle del solido o del liquido a contatto col solo vapore proprio. Quando il solido o il liquido si trovano in contatto con l'atmosfera, le tensioni di vapore corrispondenti sono un po'più alte e si possono avere aggiungendo al valore della tabella, un incremento Δp, calcolato per mezzo della seguente equazione:

For ice and for water below 0°C:

$$\frac{100\Delta p}{p} = \frac{20}{t + 273}$$

For water above 0°C:

$$100\,\frac{\Delta p}{p} = 0.0775 - 3.13 \times 10^{-4}t \text{ (valid up to } t = 40°\text{C)}$$

and

$$100\,\frac{\Delta p}{p} = 0.0652 - 8.75 \times 10^{-5}p \text{ (valid above 50°C)}$$

The Vapor Pressure of Ice

Computed from the equation

$$\log_{10}p = \frac{-2445.5646}{T} + 8.2312\log_{10}T - 0.01677006T + 1.20514 \times 10^{-5}T^2 - 6.757169, \text{ mm Hg}$$

Based upon the measurements of Weber (2) and Scheel and Heuse (1); *see* Washburn (3).

$T = 273.1 + t$

−90° to −30°; unit, 0.001 mm Hg

t, °C	0	1	2	3	4	5	6	7	8	9
−90	0.07_0	0.05_8	0.04_8	0.04_0	0.03_3	0.02_7	0.02_2	0.01_8	0.01_5	0.01_2
−80	0.40	0.34	0.29	0.24	0.20	0.17	0.14	0.12	0.10	0.08_4
−70	1.94	1.67	1.43	1.23	1.05	0.90	0.77	0.66	0.56	0.47
−60	8.0_8	7.0_3	6.1_4	5.3_4	4.6_4	4.0_3	3.4_9	3.0_2	2.6_1	2.2_5
−50	29.5_5	26.1	23.0	20.3	17.8	15.7	13.8	12.1	10.6	9.2_5
−40	96.6	86.2	76.8	68.4	60.9	54.1	48.1	42.6	37.8	33.4
−30	285.9	257.5	231.8	208.4	187.3	168.1	150.7	135.1	120.9	108.1

−30° to 0°; mm Hg

t, °C	0.0	0.1	0.2	0.3	0.4	0.5	0.6	0.7	0.8	0.9
−29	0.317	0.314	0.311	0.307	0.304	0.301	0.298	0.295	0.292	0.289
−28	0.351	0.348	0.344	0.341	0.337	0 334	0.330	0.327	0.324	0.320
−27	0.389	0.385	0.381	0.377	0.374	0.370	0.366	0.362	0.359	0.355
−26	0.430	0.426	0.422	0.418	0.414	0.409	0.405	0.401	0.397	0.393
−25	0.476	0.471	0.467	0.462	0.457	0.453	0.448	0.444	0.439	0.435
−24	0.526	0.520	0.515	0.510	0.505	0.500	0.495	0.490	0.486	0.481
−23	0.580	0.574	0.569	0.563	0.558	0.552	0.547	0.541	0.536	0.531
−22	0.640	0.633	0.627	0.621	0.615	0.609	0.603	0.597	0.592	0.586
−21	0.705	0.698	0.691	0.685	0.678	0.672	0.665	0.659	0.652	0.646
−20	0.776	0.769	0.761	0.754	0.747	0.740	0.733	0.726	0.719	0.712
−19	0.854	0.846	0.838	0.830	0.822	0.814	0.806	0.799	0.791	0.783
−18	0.939	0.930	0.921	0.912	0.904	0.895	0.887	0.879	0.870	0.862
−17	1.031	1.021	1.012	1.002	0.993	0.984	0.975	0.966	0.956	0.947
−16	1.132	1.121	1.111	1.101	1.091	1.080	1.070	1.060	1.051	1.041
−15	1.241	1.230	1.219	1.208	1.196	1.186	1.175	1.164	1.153	1.142

−30° to 0°; mm Hg.—(*Continued*)

t, °C	0.0	0.1	0.2	0.3	0.4	0.5	0.6	0.7	0.8	0.9
−14	1.361	1.348	1.336	1.324	1.312	1.300	1.288	1.276	1.264	1.253
−13	1.490	1.477	1.464	1.450	1.437	1.424	1.411	1.399	1.386	1.373
−12	1.632	1.617	1.602	1.588	1.574	1.559	1.546	1.532	1.518	1.504
−11	1.785	1.769	1.753	1.737	1.722	1.707	1.691	1.676	1.661	1.646
−10	1.950	1.934	1.916	1.899	1.883	1.866	1.849	1.833	1.817	1.800
−9	2.131	2.112	2.093	2.075	2.057	2.039	2.021	2.003	1.985	1.968
−8	2.326	2.306	2.285	2.266	2.246	2.226	2.207	2.187	2.168	2.149
−7	2.537	2.515	2.493	2.472	2.450	2.429	2.408	2.387	2.367	2.346
−6	2.765	2.742	2.718	2.695	2.672	2.649	2.626	2.603	2.581	2.559
−5	3.013	2.987	2.962	2.937	2.912	2.887	2.862	2.838	2.813	2.790
−4	3.280	3.252	3.225	3.198	3.171	3.144	3.117	3.091	3.065	3.039
−3	3.568	3.539	3.509	3.480	3.451	3.422	3.393	3.364	3.336	3.308
−2	3.880	3.848	3.816	3.785	3.753	3.722	3.691	3.660	3.630	3.599
−1	4.217	4.182	4.147	4.113	4.079	4.045	4.012	3.979	3.946	3.913
−0	4.579	4.542	4.504	4.467	4.431	4.395	4.359	4.323	4.287	4.252

The Vapor Pressure of Liquid Water from −16 to 0°C (in mm Hg)

Computed from the above table with the aid of the thermodynamic equation

$$\log_{10}\frac{p_w}{p_i} = \frac{-1.1489t}{273.1 + t} - 1.330 \times 10^{-5}t^2 + 9.084 \times 10^{-8}t^3 \quad (3)$$

t, °C	0.0	0.1	0.2	0.3	0.4	0.5	0.6	0.7	0.8	0.9
−15	1.436	1.425	1.414	1.402	1.390	1.379	1.368	1.356	1.345	1.334
−14	1.560	1.547	1.534	1.522	1.511	1.497	1.485	1.472	1.460	1.449
−13	1.691	1.678	1.665	1.651	1.637	1.624	1.611	1.599	1.585	1.572
−12	1.834	1.819	1.804	1.790	1.776	1.761	1.748	1.734	1.720	1.705
−11	1.987	1.971	1.955	1.939	1.924	1.909	1.893	1.878	1.863	1.848
−10	2.149	2.134	2.116	2.099	2.084	2.067	2.050	2.034	2.018	2.001
−9	2.326	2.307	2.289	2.271	2.254	2.236	2.219	2.201	2.184	2.167
−8	2.514	2.495	2.475	2.456	2.437	2.418	2.399	2.380	2.362	2.343
−7	2.715	2.695	2.674	2.654	2.633	2.613	2.593	2.572	2.553	2.533
−6	2.931	2.909	2.887	2.866	2.843	2.822	2.800	2.778	2.757	2.736
−5	3.163	3.139	3.115	3.092	3.069	3.046	3.022	3.000	2.976	2.955
−4	3.410	3.384	3.359	3.334	3.309	3.284	3.259	3.235	3.211	3.187
−3	3.673	3.647	3.620	3.593	3.567	3.540	3.514	3.487	3.461	3.436
−2	3.956	3.927	3.898	3.871	3.841	3.813	3.785	3.757	3.730	3.702
−1	4.258	4.227	4.196	4.165	4.135	4.105	4.075	4.045	4.016	3.986
−0	4.579	4.546	4.513	4.480	4.448	4.416	4.385	4.353	4.320	4.289

The Vapor Pressure of Liquid Water from 0°C to 100°C (in mm Hg)

From the Physikalisch-Technische Reichsanstalt "Wärmetabellen," Holborn, Scheel and Henning, Vieweg und Sohn, Braunschweig, 1909. By permission

t, °C	0.0	0.1	0.2	0.3	0.4	0.5	0.6	0.7	0.8	0.9
0	4.579	4.613	4.647	4.681	4.715	4.750	4.785	4.820	4.855	4.890
1	4.926	4.962	4.998	5.034	5.070	5.107	5.144	5.181	5.219	5.256
2	5.294	5.332	5.370	5.408	5.447	5.486	5.525	5.565	5.605	5.645
3	5.685	5.725	5.766	5.807	5.848	5.889	5.931	5.973	6.015	6.058
4	6.101	6.144	6.187	6.230	6.274	6.318	6.363	6.408	6.453	6.498
5	6.543	6.589	6.635	6.681	6.728	6.775	6.822	6.869	6.917	6.965
6	7.013	7.062	7.111	7.160	7.209	7.259	7.309	7.360	7.411	7.462
7	7.513	7.565	7.617	7.669	7.722	7.775	7.828	7.882	7.936	7.990
8	8.045	8.100	8.155	8.211	8.267	8.323	8.380	8.437	8.494	8.551
9	8.609	8.668	8.727	8.786	8.845	8.905	8.965	9.025	9.086	9.147
10	9.209	9.271	9.333	9.395	9.458	9.521	9.585	9.649	9.714	9.779
11	9.844	9.910	9.976	10.042	10.109	10.176	10.244	10.312	10.380	10.449
12	10.518	10.588	10.658	10.728	10.799	10.870	10.941	11.013	11.085	11.158
13	11.231	11.305	11.379	11.453	11.528	11.604	11.680	11.756	11.833	11.910
14	11.987	12.065	12.144	12.223	12.302	12.382	12.462	12.543	12.624	12.706

THE VAPOR PRESSURE OF LIQUID WATER FROM 0°C TO 100°C (IN MM HG).—(*Continued*)

t, °C	0.0	0.1	0.2	0.3	0.4	0.5	0.6	0.7	0.8	0.9
15	12.788	12.870	12.953	13.037	13.121	13.205	13.290	13.375	13.461	13.547
16	13.634	13.721	13.809	13.898	13.987	14.076	14.166	14.256	14.347	14.438
17	14.530	14.622	14.715	14.809	14.903	14.997	15.092	15.188	15.284	15.380
18	15.477	15.575	15.673	15.772	15.871	15.971	16.071	16.171	16.272	16.374
19	16.477	16.581	16.685	16.789	16.894	16.999	17.105	17.212	17.319	17.427
20	17.535	17.644	17.753	17.863	17.974	18.085	18.197	18.309	18.422	18.536
21	18.650	18.765	18.880	18.996	19.113	19.231	19.349	19.468	19.587	19.707
22	19.827	19.948	20.070	20.193	20.316	20.440	20.565	20.690	20.815	20.941
23	21.068	21.196	21.324	21.453	21.583	21.714	21.845	21.977	22.110	22.243
24	22.377	22.512	22.648	22.785	22.922	23.060	23.198	23.337	23.476	23.616
25	23.756	23.897	24.039	24.182	24.326	24.471	24.617	24.764	24.912	25.060
26	25.209	25.359	25.509	25.660	25.812	25.964	26.117	26.271	26.426	26.582
27	26.739	26.897	27.055	27.214	27.374	27.535	27.696	27.858	28.021	28.185
28	28.349	28.514	28.680	28.847	29.015	29.184	29.354	29.525	29.697	29.870
29	30.043	30.217	30.392	30.568	30.745	30.923	31.102	31.281	31.461	31.642
30	31.824	32.007	32.191	32.376	32.561	32.747	32.934	33.122	33.312	33.503
31	33.695	33.888	34.082	34.276	34.471	34.667	34.864	35.062	35.261	35.462
32	35.663	35.865	36.068	36.272	36.477	36.683	36.891	37.099	37.308	37.518
33	37.729	37.942	38.155	38.369	38.584	38.801	39.018	39.237	39.457	39.6772
34	39.898	40.121	40.344	40.569	40.796	41.023	41.251	41.480	41.710	41.94
35	42.175	42.409	42.644	42.880	43.117	43.355	43.595	43.836	44.078	44.320
36	44.563	44.808	45.054	45.301	45.549	45.799	46.050	46.302	46.556	46.811
37	47.067	47.324	47.582	47.841	48.102	48.364	48.627	48.891	49.157	49.424
38	49.692	49.961	50.231	50.502	50.774	51.048	51.323	51.600	51.879	52.160
39	52.442	52.725	53.009	53.294	53.580	53.867	54.156	54.446	54.737	55.030
40	55.324	55.61	55.91	56.21	56.51	56.81	57.11	57.41	57.72	58.03
41	58.34	58.65	58.96	59.27	59.58	59.90	60.22	60.54	60.86	61.18
42	61.50	61.82	62.14	62.47	62.80	63.13	63.46	63.79	64.12	64.46
43	64.80	65.14	65.48	65.82	66.16	66.51	66.86	67.21	67.56	67.91
44	68.26	68.61	68.97	69.33	69.69	70.05	70.41	70.77	71.14	71.51
45	71.88	72.25	72.62	72.99	73.36	73.74	74.12	74.50	74.88	75.26
46	75.65	76.04	76.43	76.82	77.21	77.60	78.00	78.40	78.80	79.20
47	79.60	80.00	80.41	80.82	81.23	81.64	82.05	82.46	82.87	83.29
48	83.71	84.13	84.56	84.99	85.42	85.85	86.28	86.71	87.14	87.58
49	88.02	88.46	88.90	89.34	89.79	90.24	90.69	91.14	91.59	92.05
50	92.51	97.20	102.09	107.20	112.51	118.04	123.80	129.82	136.08	142.60
60	149.38	156.43	163.77	171.38	179.31	187.54	196.09	204.96	214.17	223.73
70	233.7	243.9	254.6	265.7	277.2	289.1	301.4	314.1	327.3	341.0
80	355.1	369.7	384.9	400.6	416.8	433.6	450.9	468.7	487.1	506.1
90	525.76	527.76	529.77	531.78	533.80	535.82	537.86	539.90	541.95	544.00
91	546.05	548.11	550.18	552.26	554.35	556.44	558.53	560.64	562.75	564.87
92	566.99	569.12	571.26	573.40	575.55	577.71	579.87	582.04	584.22	586.41
93	588.60	590.80	593.00	595.21	597.43	599.66	601.89	604.13	606.38	608.64
94	610.90	613.17	615.44	617.72	620.01	622.31	624.61	626.92	629.24	631.57
95	633.90	636.24	638.59	640.94	643.30	645.67	648.05	650.43	652.82	655.22
96	657.62	660.03	662.45	664.88	667.31	669.75	672.20	674.66	677.12	679.59
97	682.07	684.55	687.04	689.54	692.05	694.57	697.10	699.63	702.17	704.71
98	707.27	709.83	712.40	714.98	717.56	720.15	722.75	725.36	727.98	730.61
99	733.24	735.88	738.53	741.18	743.85	746.52	749.20	751.89	754.58	757.29
100	760.00	762.72	765.45	768.19	770.93	773.68	776.44	779.22	782.00	784.78
101*	787.57	790.37	793.18	796.00	798.82	801.66	804.50	807.35	810.21	813.08

* For higher temperatures, *v.* p. 233.

LITERATURE

(For a key to the periodicals see end of volume)

(1) Scheel and Heuse, *16*, **29**: 731; 09. (2) Weber, *168*, No. **150**: 37; 15. (3) Washburn, *406*, **52**: 488; 24.

VAPOR PRESSURES OF CHEMICAL COMPOUNDS IN THE LIQUID STATE FOR PRESSURES UP TO TWO ATMOSPHERES

Otto Maass

In addition to the vapor-pressure data for the compounds given, the 𝔅-Table is a complete index to the vapor-pressure data for all pure chemical compounds in the liquid state. The literature references given first are those upon which the values given are based; confirmatory references are marked *cf.*

𝔅-TABLE, STANDARD ARRANGEMENT (*v.* p. viii)

$$\log_{10} p_{\mathrm{mm}} = \frac{-0.05223\mathrm{A}}{T} + \mathrm{B}$$

The tables contain either the values of A and B in the above equation (together with the range of applicability of the equation), tabulated values of *t* and *p*, or both.

The values in the B. P. column are based on the best available direct determinations of the boiling point. These values not infrequently differ considerably from those interpolated from the vapor-pressure data, a situation which can be cleared up only by further research.

Formula	Range, °C	A, joule	B	Normal B. P., °C	Lit.
H_2O	*v.* p. 210				
H_2O_2	10 to 90	48530	8.853		(31)
HF	−83 to +48	25180	7.370		(60)
ClO_2	−59 to +11	27260	7.893		(29)
HCl				−85.0	(25); *cf.* (32, 64)
	t, °C	*p*, mm			
	−108	168.5			
	−104	226.2			
	−100	329.8			
	− 96	503.4			
	− 88	640.3			
HBr	−86 to −66	17960	7.427		(32); *cf.* (63, 64)
HI	−50 to −34	21580	7.630		(32); *cf.* (63)
SO_2				−10.02	(7, 25, 37)
	t, °C	*p*, mm	*t*, °C	*p*, mm	
	−70	19.9	−30	286.0	
	−65	30.0	−25	373.0	
	−60	42.8	−20	478.0	
	−55	61.8	−15	607.0	
	−50	86.7	−10	761.0	
	−45	119.6	− 5	947.0	
	−40	162.3	0	1164.0	
	−35	217.1			
SO_3	24 to 48	43450	10.022		(8)
H_2S				−59.4	(32); *cf.* (63, 64)
	t, °C	*p*, mm	*t*, °C	*p*, mm	
	−82	172	−66	535	
	−78	235	−62	660	
	−74	339	−58	830	
	−70	432			
S_2Cl_2	0 to 138	35990	7.455		(23)
$SOBr_2$					(85)
H_2Se	−66 to −26	20210	7.431		(11)
H_2SeO_3	70 to 110	43000	8.150		(27)
$SeOCl_2$				176.4	(30)
	t, °C	*p*, mm	*t*, °C	*p*, mm	
	85	22.0	135	213.0	
	95	37.4	145	304.0	
	105	58.9	155	418.0	
	115	94.4	165	560.0	
	125	114.0			
H_2Te	−46 to 0	22760	7.260		(10)
N_2O	−90.1 to −88.7	16440	7.535		(12); *cf.* (7, 46)
NO	−163.7 to −148	13040	8.440		(21, 24)
N_2O_3	−25 to 0	39400	10.80		(22)
N_2O_4	−8 to +43.2	33430	8.814		(5, 56); *cf.* (45, 85.5)

Formula	Range, °C	A, joule	B	Normal B. P., °C	Lit.
H_3N				−33.35	(13, 25); *cf.* (7, 12, 43)
	t, °C	*p*, mm	*t*, °C	*p*, mm	
	−77	47.8	−47	365.5	
	−74	60.5	−44	432.9	
	−71	76.7	−41	510.3	
	−68	94.7	−38	598.6	
	−65	117.1	−35	699.1	
	−62	143.8	−32	812.9	
	−59	175.5	−29	941.3	
	−56	212.7	−26	1085.0	
	−53	256.3	−23	1247.0	
	−50	307.0	−20	1427.0	
$NOCl$	−61.5 to −5.4	25500	7.870		(80); *cf.* (9)
P_2O_3	*t*, °C	*p*, mm	*t*, °C	*p*, mm	(57)
	30	3	70	60	
	50	9.0	80	150	
	60	20	90	300	
PH_3				−87.4	(25); *cf.* (64)
	t, °C	*p*, mm	*t*, °C	*p*, mm	
	−133	29.3	−109	209.9	
	−129	43.0	−105	274.6	
	−125	61.3	−101	354.2	
	−121	85.7	− 97	450.4	
	−117	117.5	− 93	564.5	
	−113	158.3	− 89	699.5	
PCl_3	0–70	31860	7.681	73.5	(46)
As_2O_3	315 to 490	52120	6.513		(55)
$AsCl_3$	50 to 100	39110	7.953		(6)
$SbCl_3$	170 to 253	49440	8.090		(49)
	t, °C	*p*, mm			
	120	29			
	130	43			
	140	64			
	150	92			
	160	127			
$SbBr_3$	235 to 324	55000	8.005		(49)
	t, °C	*p*, mm	*t*, °C	*p*, mm	
	180	42	210	111	
	190	59	220	148	
	200	82	230	195	
SbI_3	330 to 445	64150	7.831		(49)
	t, °C	*p*, mm	*t*, °C	*p*, mm	
	250	23	295	80	
	265	35	310	115	
	280	53	325	166	
CO	−290 to −206	6354	6.976		(18); *cf.* (3, 39)
CO_2, *v.* p. 235					
C_3O_2	−100 to +6	25460	7.640	6.3	(77)
CCl_4, *see also* p. 215	*t*, °C	*p*, mm	*t*, °C	*p*, mm	(16, 84)
	−20	9.9	60	439.0	
	0	33.1	90	1112	
	+30	139.5	110	1880	
CCl_2O	−15 to +22	25390	7.595	*v.* p. 215	(41)
CS_2				46.25	(4, 25, 37, 59); *cf.* (46, 47)
	t, °C	*p*, mm	*t*, °C	*p*, mm	
	−70	1.6	+10	198.1	
	−60	3.5	20	297.5	
	−50	7.1	30	432.7	
	−40	14.0	40	616.7	
	−30	26.2	50	854.0	
	−20	46.5	60	1173.0	
	−10	78.8	70	1570.0	
	0	127.3			
COS	−80 to −50	19220	7.383		(68)
	t, °C	*p*, mm			
	−130	1.5			
	−110	13.0			
	− 90	73.0			

Formula	Range, °C	A, joule	B	Normal B. P., °C	Lit.
$CSSe$	t, °C	p, mm		84.5	(78)
	0	26			
	+15	55			
	30	112			
	50	246			
	70	485			
$(CN)_2$	−32 to − 6	23750	7.808		(79)
HCN	− 8 to +27	27830	7.7446		(42); cf. (87)
$CNCl$	− 5 to +40	27100	7.840		(46)
For other C-compounds, v. the C-Table, p. 215					
SiO_2	1860 to 2230	506000	13.43	2230	(52)
H_4Si	−160 to −112	12690	6.996		(71); cf. (1)
H_6Si_2	−115 to −14.6	21700	7.258		(71)
H_8Si_3	−70 to +52	29850	7.676		(71, 76)
$(SiH_3)_2O$	−110 to −15	23590	7.686		(75)
$SiCl_4$	−70 to +5	30100	7.644		(46, 75)
Si_2Cl_6	40 to 103	45900	8.700	139	(33)
Si_3Cl_8	124 to 149	50500	8.300	213	(33)
$(SiCl_3)_2O$	30 to 137	39850	7.980		(75)
	t, °C	p, mm			
	0	1.5			
	10	3.0			
	20	6.0			
SiH_3Cl	−110 to −30	21400	7.483		(73)
SiH_2Cl_2	−100 to + 8	25500	7.613		(73)
SiH_3Br	− 90 to + 2	24430	7.524		(71)
SiH_2Br_2	− 65 to +18	31010	7.654		(72)
$(SiH_3)_3N$	− 60 to +15	30620	7.883		(74)
For methylsilicanes, v. p. 215					
Ge_2H_6	− 98 to +30	26400	7.444		(14)
Ge_3H_8	0 to 111	31900	7.224		(14)
$GeCl_4$	10.4 to 86	38500	7.340		(38)
SnH_4	−148 to −49	19140	7.400		(40)
$SnCl_4$	t, °C	p, mm	t, °C	p, mm	(84)
	−10	2.8	90	360.5	
	+10	10.3	120	895.0	
	30	31.3	140	1497.0	
	60	112.0			
PbF_2	1078 to 1289	165100	8.391	1292	(82)
$PbCl_2$	500 to 950	141900	8.961	945	(17); cf. (82)
$PbBr_2$	735 to 918	118000	8.064	916	(82)
TlF	282 to 298	105000	12.52	298	(82)
$TlCl$	665 to 807	105200	7.974	806	(82)
$TlBr$	634 to 817	105400	7.940	815	(82)
TlI	693 to 822	105400	7.902	824	(82)
CdI_2	385 to 450	122200	9.269		(58)
$HgCl$				383	(61); cf. (2, 48)
	t, °C	p, mm			
	310	103.0			
	330	189.2			
	350	329.9			
	370	548.9			
$HgCl_2$	275 to 309	61020	8.409		(28, 44, 65)
$HgBr_2$	238 to 331	61250	8.284		(28, 44, 65)
HgI_2	266 to 360	62770	8.115		(28, 44, 65)
Cu_2Cl_2	878 to 1369	80700	5.454	1366	(82)
Cu_2Br_2	997 to 1351	79900	5.460	1345	(82)
Cu_2I_2	991 to 1154	80700	5.570	1293	(82)
$AgCl$	1255 to 1442	185500	8.179	1554	(82)
OsF_8	38 to 47.3	29200	7.650		(54)
$Co(CO)_3NO$	14 to 66	30210	7.366		(36)
$Ni(CO)_4$	2 to 40	29800	7.780	43	(15); cf. (34)
CrO_2Cl_2	79 to 116	36230	7.735	116.7	(35)
NbF_5				219	(51)
	t, °C	p, mm			
	182	290			
	200	420			
	210	540			

Formula	Range, °C	A, joule	B	Normal B. P., °C	Lit.
	t, °C	p, mm	t, °C	p, mm	
TaF_5	182	370	218	580	(51)
	200	460	229	750	
B_2H_6	−112 to −87	13050	6.556		(66)
B_5H_{11}					(86)
BCl_3				+12.7	(70)
	t, °C	p, mm			
	−80	4.0			
	−60	18.0			
	−30	116.0			
	−15	251.0			
	0	477.0			
BBr_3	−40 to +90	33320	7.655		(67)
B_2H_5Br	−80 to −5	26260	7.640		(69)
$B_3N_3H_6$					(86)
For $B(C_aH_b)_x$, v. p. 215					
Al_2O_3	1840 to 2200	540000	14.22	2210	(52)
LiF	1398 to 1666	218400	8.753	1670	(53); cf. (83)
$LiCl$	1045 to 1325	155900	7.939	1337	(50); cf. (83)
$LiBr$	1010 to 1265	152700	8.068	1265	(50); cf. (83)
LiI	940 to 1140	143600	8.011	1189	(50); cf. (83)
$NaOH$	1010 to 1402	132000	7.030	1390	(81)
NaF	1562 to 1701	218200	8.640	1705	(53); cf. (83)
$NaCl$	1156 to 1430	185800	8.548	1439	(81); cf. (50)
	976 to 1155	180300	8.3297		(19)
$NaBr$	1138 to 1394	161600	7.948	1393	(81); cf. (50)
NaI	1063 to 1307	165100	8.371	1297	(81); cf. (50)
$NaCN$	800 to 1360	155520	7.472	1496	(26)
KOH	1170 to 1327	136000	7.330	1322	(81)
KF	1278 to 1500	207500	9.000	1498	(53); cf. (83)
KCl	1116 to 1418	169700	8.130	1416	(81); cf. (50)
	906 to 1105	174500	8.3526		(19)
KBr	1095 to 1375	163800	7.936	1381	(81); cf. (50)
	906 to 1063	168100	8.2470		(19)
KI	1063 to 1333	155700	7.949	1331	(81); cf. (50)
	843 to 1028	157600	8.0957		(19)
RbF	1142 to 1400	183200	8.570	1408	(53); cf. (83)
$RbCl$	1142 to 1395	198600	9.111	1388	(50); cf. (83)
$RbBr$	1050 to 1365	165000	8.223	1340	(50); cf. (83)
RbI	1075 to 1325	156600	8.067	1304	(50); cf. (83)
CsF	1033 to 1255	140900	7.703	1253	(53); cf. (83)
$CsCl$	986 to 1295	163200	8.340	1289	(50); cf. (83)
$CsBr$	978 to 1305	153600	7.990	1297	(50); cf. (83)
CsI	1052 to 1280	185700	9.124	1280	(50); cf. (83)

LITERATURE

(For a key to the periodicals see end of volume)

(1) Adwentowski and Drozdowski, *180*, **1911 A**: 330. (2) Arctowski, *93*, **12**: 417; 96. (3) Baly and Donnan, *4*, **81**: 907; 02. (4) Battelli, *Mem. della Accad. di Torino*, **41**: 1; 90. (5) Baume and Robert, *34*, **168**: 1201; 19. (6) Baxter, Bezzenberger and Wilson, *1*, **42**: 1386; 20. (7) Bergström, *50*, **26**: 358, 876; 22. (8) Berthoud, *42*, **20**: 77; 23. (9) Briner and Pylkoff, *42*, **10**: 640; 12.

(10) Bruylants, *186*, **6**: 472; 20. (11) Bruylants and Dondeyne, *186*, **8**: 387; 22. (12) Burrell and Robertson, *1*, **37**: 2482; 15. (13) Cragoe, Meyers and Taylor, *1*, **42**: 206; 20. (14) Dennis, Corey and Moore, *1*, **46**: 657; 24. (15) Dewar and Jones, *5*, **71**: 434; 03. (16) Drucker, Jiméno and Kangro, *7*, **90**: 513; 15. (17) Eastman and Duschak, *30*, No. **225**: 19. (18) Estreicher and Bobotek, *165*, **7**: 451; 13. (19) Fiock and Rodebush, *1*, **48**: 2522; 26.

(20) Germann and Taylor, *1*, **48**: 1154; 26. (21) Goldschmidt, *96*, **20**: 159; 23. (22) Guye and Drouguinine, *42*, **8**: 473; 10. (23) Harvey and Schuette, *1*, **48**: 2065; 26. (24) Henglein and Krüger, *93*, **130**: 181; 23. (25) Henning and Stock, *96*, **4**: 226; 21. (26) Ingold, *4*, **123**: 885; 23. (27) Jannek and Meyer, *93*, **83**: 51; 13. (28) Johnson, *1*, **33**: 771; 11. (29) King and Partington, *4*, **1926**: 925.

(30) Lenher, Smith and Town, *50*, **26**: 156; 22. (31) Maass and Hiebert, *1*, **46**: 2693; 24. (32) Maass and McIntosh, *69*, **8 III**: 65; 14. (33) Martin, *4*, **105**: 2836; 14. (34) Mittasch, *7*, **40**: 3; 02. (35) Moles and Gómez, *7*, **80**: 513; 12. (36) Mond and Wallis, *4*, **121**: 32; 22. (37) Mund, *186*, **1919**: 529. (38) Nilson and Petterson, *7*, **1**: 38; 87. (39) Olszewski, *34*, **99**: 706; 84.

(40) Paneth, Haken and Rabinowitsch, *25*, **57**: 1891; 24. (41) Paternò and Mazzuchelli, *36*, **50 I**: 30; 20. (42) Perry and Porter, *1*, **48**: 299; 26. (43) Postma, *70*, **39**: 515; 20. (44) Prideaux, *4*, **97**: 2032; 10. (45) Ramsay and Young, *62*, **177**: 71; 86. (46) Regnault, *151*, **26**: 339; 62. (47) Rex, *7*, **55**: 358; 06. (48) von Richter, *25*, **19**: 1057; 86. (49) Rotinyanz and Suchodskii, *7*, **87**: 635; 14.
(50) Ruff and Mugdan, *93*, **117**: 147; 21. (51) Ruff and Schiller, *93*, **72**: 329; 11. (52) Ruff and Schmidt, *93*, **117**: 172; 21. (53) Ruff, Schmidt and Mugdan, *93*, **123**: 83; 22. (54) Ruff and Tschirch, *25*, **46**: 929; 13. (55) Rushton and Daniels, *1*, **48**: 384; 26. (56) Scheffer and Treub, *7*, **81**: 308; 13. (57) Schenck, Mihr and Bauthien, *25*, **39**: 1506; 06. (58) Schmidt and Walter, *8*, **72**: 565; 23. (59) Siemens, *8*, **42**: 871; 13.
(60) Simons, *1*, **46**: 2179; 24. (61) Smith and Calvert, *1*, **38**: 801; 16. (62) Smits and Schoenmaker, *4*, **1926**: 1108. (63) Steele and Bagster, *4*, **97**: 2607; 11. (64) Steele and McIntosh, *7*, **55**: 136; 06. (65) Stelzner, Niederschulte and Priess, *88*, **7**: 159; 06. (66) Stock and Friederici, *25*, **46**: 1959; 13. (67) Stock and Kuss, *25*, **47**: 3115; 14. (68) Stock and Kuss, *25*, **50**: 159; 17. (69) Stock, Kuss and Priess, *25*, **47**: 3115; 14.
(70) Stock and Priess, *25*, **47**: 3109; 14. (71) Stock and Somieski, *25*, **49**: 111; 16. (72) Stock and Somieski, *25*, **50**: 1739; 17. (73) Stock and Somieski, *25*, **52**: 695; 19. (74) Stock and Somieski, *25*, **54**: 740; 21. (75) Stock, Somieski and Wintgen, *25*, **50**: 1754; 17. (76) Stock, Stiebeler and Zeidler, *25*, **56**: 1695; 23. (77) Stock and Stolzenberg, *25*, **50**: 498; 17. (78) Stock and Willfroth, *25*, **47**: 144; 14. (79) Terwen, *7*, **91**: 469; 16.
(80) Trautz and Gerwig, *93*, **134**: 409; 24. (81) Wartenberg and Albrecht, *9*, **27**: 162; 21. (82) Wartenberg and Bosse, *9*, **28**: 384; 22. (83) Wartenberg and Schulz, *9*, **27**: 568; 21. (84) Young, *117*, **12**: 428; 10. (85) Mayes and Partington, *4*, **1926**: 2594. (85.5) Mittasch, Kuss and Schlueter, *93*, **159**: 1; 26. (86) Stock and Pohland, *25*, **59**: 2210; 26. (87) Sinozaki, Hara and Mitsukuri, *505*, **6**: 157; 26.

VAPOR PRESSURES OF ORGANIC LIQUIDS

H. R. Raikes and E. J. Bowen

ℭ-TABLE

The ℭ-arrangement, *v.* p. viii

$$\log_{10} p_{mm} = -\frac{0.05223}{T} A + B$$

The values in the B. P. column are based upon the best available direct determinations of the boiling point. These values not infrequently differ considerably from those interpolated from the vapor-pressure data, a situation which can be cleared up only by further research.

Range, °C (or t, °C)	A, joule (or p_{mm})	B (for p in mm)	Normal B. P., °C
CCl_2O Carbonyl chloride ([3, 76, 78]); *cf.* ([80])			
−90 to +25	24 684	7.460	8.45
CCl_3NO_2 Chloropicrin ([5, 124])			
−20	1.5		111.91
−10	3.0		
0	5.7		
+10	10.4		
20	13.8		
25	18.3		
30	31.1		
35	40.15		
CCl_4 Carbon tetrachloride ([28, 44, 72, 87, 124, 126, 136])			
−70 to −19	36 585	8.540	76.75
−19 to +20	33 914	8.004	
20	91		
25	114.5		
30	143.0		
35	176.2		
40	215.8		
45	262.5		
50	317.1		
55	379.3		
60	450.8		
65	530.9		
70	622.3		
80	843		
90	1 122		
100	1 463		
CN_4O_8 Tetranitromethane ([65])			
40	26.6		125.7
50	44.2		
60	70.6	t, °C	p_{mm}
70	109	100	339
80	164	110	470
90	239	120	640
$CHBr_3$ Bromoform, 9.4 mm at 25.0° ([97])			
$CHCl_3$ Chloroform ([7, 28, 44, 89]); *cf.* ([87, 126])			
−60	0.81		61.20
−50	2.06		
−40	4.7		
−30	10.0		
−20	19.6		
−10	34.75	t, °C	p_{mm}
0	61.0	45	439.0
+10	100.5	50	526.0
20	159.6	55	625.2
25	199.1	60	739.6
30	246.0	60.9	760.0
35	301.3	70	1 019
40	366.4	80	1 403
HCN Hydrocyanic acid ([41]); *cf.* ([80, 140])			
0 to 46	27 875	7.7526	25.75
CH_2Br_2 Methylene bromide ([89])			
0	11.5		
10	20.4		
20	34.7		
30	56.4		
CH_2Cl_2 Methylene chloride ([89, 116])			
0	147		
10	229.7		
20	348.9		
30	511.4		
CH_2O_2 Formic Acid ([29, 34, 53, 55, 57, 92]); *cf.* ([96])			
10	18.9		100.5
20	33.1		
30	52.2		
40	82.6		
50	125.9		
60	189.7		
70	279.6		
80	398.1		
90	552.1		
100	753.4		
CH_3AsCl_2 Methylarsine dichloride ([5])			
−17 to +35	43 686	8.6944	
CH_3Cl Methyl chloride ([47, 100]); *cf.* ([87])			
−47 to −10	21 988	7.481	−23.47

Range, °C (or t, °C)	A, joule (or p_{mm})	B (for p in mm)	Normal B. P., °C
CH_3F Methyl fluoride (69)			
−102 to −76	17 053	7.445	−77.96
CH_3I Methyl iodide (15, 89, 93)			
0	141.2		42.35
10	220.2		
20	331.4		
30	483.4		
CH_3NO_2 Nitromethane (131)			
47 to 100	36 914	8.033	101.1
CH_4 Methane (25, 48, 113)			
−174 to −163	8 516.9	6.8626	−161.4
−176	190.5		
−178	152.1		
−182	94.0		
−183.15	70		
CH_4Cl_2Si Methyl dichlorosilicane (114)			
−70	1.2		
−60	3.0		
−40	14.3		
−20	49.0		
0	140.0		
+10	210.0		
20	309.0		
CH_4O Methyl alcohol (2, 28, 72, 91, 92, 106, 112, 126, 129, 136, 137)			
−62 to −44	39 234	8.9547	64.6
−10 to +80	38 324	8.8017	
CH_4S Methylmercaptan (13)			
0	595		6.8
10	855		
20	1 270		
CH_5ClSi Methyl chlorosilicane (114)			
−90	2.0		
−80	4.5		
−60	23.2		
−40	84.3		
−30	146.6		
−20	237.1		
−10	363.0		
CH_5N Methylamine, 720 mm at −7.55° (12)			
CH_6Si Methylsilicane (114)			
−130	4.15		−56.9
−110	28.8		
− 90	131.8		
− 80	234.4		
− 70	411.2		
− 60	660.7		
C_2Cl_4 Tetrachloroethylene (44)			
40	41		118.8
50	67		
60	104		
70	155.3		
80	226		
90	319.2		
100	438.5		
110	591.6		
C_2N_2 Cyanogen (21, 79); *cf.* (30, 123)			
−25	629.8		−21.2
−20	800.0		
−15	1 005.0		
−10	1 230.0		

Range, °C (or t, °C)	A, joule (or p_{mm})	B (for p in mm)	Normal B. P., °C
C_2HCl_3 Trichloroethylene (44)			
25	73		87.15
30	94		
40	149		
50	224		
60	324.5		
70	453.0		
80	618.0		
C_2HCl_5 Pentachloroethane (44, 109)			
70	39		161.75
90	90		
100	130		
110	176.2		
120	236.6		
130	316.2		
140	421.7		
150	555.9		
160	724.4		
170	929		
180	1 183		
$C_2H_2Cl_2$ *cis*-Dichloroethylene (45)			
23 to 49	29 216	7.624	48.35
$C_2H_2Cl_2$ *trans*-Dichloroethylene (45)			
27 to 59	31 006	7.752	60.25
$C_2H_2Cl_4$ 1, 1, 2, 2-Tetrachloroethane (44)			
26 to 145	39 729	7.846	145.0
$C_2H_2Cl_4$ 1, 1, 1, 2-Tetrachloroethane (109)			
105 to 145	36 508	7.605	130.5
C_2H_3ClO Acetyl chloride, 760 mm at 50.92° (124)			
$C_2H_3Cl_3$ 1, 1, 1-Trichloroethane (109)			
55 to 85	31 142	7.564	74.2
$C_2H_3Cl_3$ 1, 1, 2-Trichloroethane (109)			
90 to 130	35 371	7.656	113.7
C_2H_3N Acetonitrile, 760 mm at 81.60° (126)			
C_2H_4 Ethylene (17, 60, 113)			
−160 to −104	14 396	7.330	−103.9
C_2H_4BrCl 1-Bromo-1-chloroethane (109)			
75 to 95	33 051	7.7325	82.7
$C_2H_4Br_2$ Ethylene bromide (87, 127)			
10 to 150	38 082	7.792	131.70
−10	2.5		
0	3.9		
$C_2H_4Cl_2$ 1, 1-Dichloroethane (88, 109)			
0 to 30	31 706	7.909	57.65
40 to 70	30 625	7.7165	
$C_2H_4Cl_2$ 1, 2-Dichloroethane (89, 109, 126)			
0 to 30	35 598	8.126	83.70
64 to 86	32 996	7.705	
C_2H_4O Acetaldehyde (35)			
−24.3 to +27.5	27 707	7.8206	19.8
C_2H_4O Ethylene oxide (59)			
−60	15.3		10.75
−40	64.1		
−20	196.4		
−10	316.3		
0	493.1		
+10	738.0		

Range, °C (or t, °C)	A, joule (or p_{mm})	B (for p in mm)	Normal B. P., °C
$C_2H_4O_2$ Acetic acid (53, 57, 92, 136); *cf.* (96)			
20	11.7		118.5
30	20.6		
40	34.8		
50	56.6		
60	88.9		
70	136.0		
80	202.3		
90	293.7		
100	417.1		
110	580.8		
120	794.0		
130	1 067.6		
140	1 414		
$C_2H_4O_2$ Methyl formate (126, 136)			
−20	67.7		31.75
−10	117.6		
0	195.0		
+10	309.4		
20	476.4		
30	707.9		
40	1 029		
50	1 451		
C_2H_5Br Ethyl bromide (87, 89, 90, 126, 129)			
−20	59		38.40
−10	101		
0	165		
+10	257		
20	386		
30	564		
40	802		
50	1 113		
60	1 512		
C_2H_5Cl Ethyl chloride (12, 52)			
−30 to +30	26 319	7.691	12.7
C_2H_5I Ethyl iodide (87, 89, 93, 125, 129)			
0	41.5		72.5
10	68.5		
20	108.5		
30	167.5		
40	251.5		
50	364.0		
60	512.0		
C_2H_6 Ethane (57.5); *cf.* (17, 60, 115)			
−140	14.1		−88.63
−130	39.5		
−120	94.7		
−110	202.8		
−100	393.8		
− 90	705.2		
− 80	1 182		
− 75	1 499		
C_2H_6O Ethyl alcohol (16, 28, 58, 59, 67, 71, 78, 129, 136, 137); *cf.* (87)			
−65	0.021		78.32
−60	0.045		
−55	0.087		
−50	0.12		
−45	0.24		
−40	0.39		
−35	0.63		

Range, °C (or t, °C)	A, joule (or p_{mm})	B (for p in mm)	Normal B. P., °C
−30	1.04	t, °C	p_{mm}
−25	1.63	35	103.7
−20	2.5	40	135.3
−15	3.65	45	174.0
−10	5.6	50	222.2
− 5	8.3	55	280.6
0	12.2	60	352.7
+ 5	17.3	65	448.8
10	23.6	70	542.5
15	32.2	75	666.1
20	43.9	80	812.6
25	59.0	85	986.3
30	78.8	90	1 187
C_2H_6O Methyl ether (59); *cf.* (87)			
−70 to −20	23 025	7.720	−24.6
$C_2H_6O_2$ Glycol (32)			
120	39		197.0
130	62		
140	96.8		
150	147.9		
160	218.8		
170	316.2		
180	446.2		
190	615.9		
C_2H_6S Methyl sulfide (13)			
0	172		35.9
10	275.4		
20	418.8		
30	616.6		
40	873		
C_2H_6S Ethylmercaptan (13)			
8 to 45	28 210	7.672	34.4
C_2H_7N Dimethylamine (12)			
6.05	724		
15.6	1 216		
C_2H_7N Ethylamine (12, 126)			
15.45	724		16.55
C_2H_8Si Dimethylsilicane (114)			
−110	1.6		−20
− 80	29.5		
− 50	187.5		
− 40	316.2		
− 30	510.0		
C_3H_4 Allylene (60)			
−73 to −13	21 372	7.4295	−27.5
$C_3H_4Br_2$ 2, 3-Dibromopropylene (54)			
40	17.2		141.2
60	46.8		
80	105.0		
100	218.8		
120	415.9		
130	555.9		
C_3H_5Cl 3-Chloropropylene, 760 mm at 44.60° (127)			
C_3H_5ClO α-Epichlorohydrin, 760 mm at 116.56° (124)			
C_3H_5N Propionitrile, 760 mm at 97.20° (127)			

Range, °C (or t, °C)	A, joule (or p_{mm})	B (for p in mm)	Normal B. P., °C
C_3H_6 Propylene (**18, 60**)			
−95 to −48	19 693	7.446$_3$	−47.7
−127.4	3		
−110.4	15		
− 34.4	1 307		
$C_3H_6Br_2$ 1, 3-Dibromopropane (**54**)			
60	18.5		164.4
80	45.8		
100	101.9		
120	205.1		
140	384.6		
150	515.2		
C_3H_6O Acetone (**6, 28, 50, 82, 91, 95, 112, 126**); *cf.* (**87, 121**)			
−90	0.021		56.10
−70	0.34	t, °C	p_{mm}
−50	2.4	35	346.4
−30	11.2	40	421.5
−10	38.7	45	510.5
5	89.1	50	612.6
+10	115.6	56.30	760
15	147.1	60	860.6
20	184.8	70	1 190
25	229.2	80	1 611
30	282.7		
$C_3H_6O_2$ Propionic acid (**53, 54, 96**)			
20 to 140	46 150	8.715	140.0
$C_3H_6O_2$ Ethyl formate (**136**)			
−20	22.5		54.5
−10	41.5		
0	72.4		
+10	120.3		
20	192.5		
30	297.5		
40	446.7		
50	649.4		
60	917.9		
70	1 266		
$C_3H_6O_2$ Methyl acetate (**136**)			
−20	19		57.1
−10	35.1		
0	62.1		
+10	104.8		
20	169.8		
30	265.8		
40	400.4		
50	588.2		
60	837.5		
70	1 167		
C_3H_7Br Propyl bromide (**89, 127**)			
0 to 30	32 430	7.821	71.00
C_3H_7Br Isopropyl bromide (**89**)			
0 to 30	30 760	7.722	
C_3H_7Cl Propyl chloride (**12, 43, 89**)			
0 to 50	28 894	7.593	47.2
64.2	1 414		
C_3H_7Cl Isopropyl chloride (**89**)			
0 to 30	27 242	7.493	
C_3H_7I Propyl iodide (**89**)			
0 to 30	35 334	7.826	

Range, °C (or t, °C)	A, joule (or p_{mm})	B (for p in mm)	Normal B. P., °C
C_3H_7I Isopropyl iodide (**89**)			
0 to 30	32 978	7.629	
$C_3H_7NO_2$ Urethane (**118**)			
103	54		
120	103		
130	146		
140	203		
150	283		
160	392		
170	551		
176.8	697		
$C_3H_7NO_5$ Nitroglycerol (**63**); *cf.* (**22**)			
20	0.00025		
30	0.00083		
40	0.0024		
50	0.0073		
60	0.0188		
70	0.043		
80	0.098		
90	0.23 (some decomposition)		
C_3H_8 Propane (**18, 60, 139**)			
−136 to −40	19 037	7.217	−44.5
−38.4	1 050		
−30.85	1 368		
C_3H_8O *n*-Propyl alcohol (**16, 72, 136, 137**)			
−45 to −10	47 274	9.518$_0$	97.19
0	3.44	t, °C	p_{mm}
+5	5.04	65	186.8
10	7.26	70	239.0
15	10.3	75	301.0
20	14.5	80	376.0
25	20.1	85	466
30	27.6	90	574
35	37.4	95	697
40	50.2	100	842.5
45	66.4	105	1 097
50	87.2	110	1 206
55	113.6	115	1 428
60	147.0		
C_3H_8O Isopropyl alcohol, 760 mm at 82.26° (**16**)			
C_3H_8O Methyl ethyl ether (**13**)			
0 to 25	26 262	7.769	7.5
$C_3H_8O_2$ Methylal, 760 mm at 42.30° (**126**)			
C_3H_9B Boron trimethyl (**117**)			
−118 to −20	22 171	7.459$_5$	−20.2
C_3H_9N Propylamine, 726 mm at 47.05° (**12**)			
$C_4H_2O_3$ Maleic anhydride (**130**)			
60 to 160	46 340	7.825	
$C_4H_6O_3$ Acetic anhydride (**8, 77**)			
100 to 140	45 585	8.688	139.55
150	1 171		
C_4H_7N Butyronitrile, 760 mm at 117.00° (**127**)			
C_4H_8O Methyl ethyl ketone (**79, 126**)			
20	77.5		79.60
30	121.4		
40	188.4		
50	300.0		

Range, °C (or *t*, °C)	A, joule (or p_{mm})	B (for *p* in mm)	Normal B. P., °C
$C_4H_8O_2$ Butyric acid (53, 54, 85, 96)			
80 to 165	51 103	9.010	162.4
20	0.75		
30	1.5		
40	3.0		
50	5.25		
60	9.35		
$C_4H_8O_2$ Isobutyric acid (53, 54, 92, 126); *cf.* (96)			
30 to 155	48 498	8.8193	153.45
10	0.7		
$C_4H_8O_2$ Ethyl acetate (126, 128, 136)			
−20	6.5		77.15
−10	12.9	*t*, °C	p_{mm}
0	24.2	50	282.3
+10	42.8	60	415.3
20	72.8	70	596.3
30	118.7	80	832.8
40	186.3	90	1 133
		100	1 520
$C_4H_8O_2$ Methyl propionate (136)			
−20	5.6		79.75
−10	11.5	*t*, °C	p_{mm}
0	21.9	60	380.3
+10	38.8	70	548.0
20	66.2	80	771.0
30	107.8	90	1 048
40	169.3	100	1 408
50	256.7		
$C_4H_8O_2$ Propyl formate (136)			
−10	11.4		81.1
0	21.4		
+10	37.8		
20	63.9		
30	104.1		
40	163.6		
60	364.9		
70	523.9		
80	734.5		
90	1 003		
100	1 343		
C_4H_9Br Butyl bromide, 760 mm at 101.60° (127)			
C_4H_{10} Butane (18, 139)			
−100 to +12	23 450	7.395	−0.3
C_4H_{10} Isobutane (19, 98, 139)			
−115 to −34	21 273	7.25	−13.4
−30	463		
−25	544		
−20	646		
−15	745		
$C_4H_{10}O$ *n*-Butyl alcohol (16, 54, 127)			
75 to 117.5	4 6774	9.1362	117.71
20	4.39	*t*, °C	p_{mm}
25	6.44	55	44.9
30	9.52	60	59.2
35	13.1	65	77.7
40	18.6	70	112.3
45	24.9	75	131.3
50	33.7		

Range, °C (or *t*, °C)	A, joule (or p_{mm})	B (for *p* in mm)	Normal B. P., °C
$C_4H_{10}O$ Isobutyl alcohol (16, 68); *cf.* (96, 138)			
60	99.1		107.89
70	158.5		
80	248.9		
90	384.6		
100	583.5		
110	845.3		
120	1 197		
130	1 668		
$C_4H_{10}O$ *sec.*-Butyl alcohol, 760 mm at 99.53° (16) *tert.*-Butyl alcohol, 760 mm at 82.55° (137)			
$C_4H_{10}O$ Ethyl ether (28, 58, 72, 126, 136)			
−100	0.05		34.60
− 80	0.6	*t*, °C	p_{mm}
− 60	4.1	20	442.2
− 40	19.0	25	537.0
− 30	37.6	30	647.3
− 10	112.3	35	775.5
0	185.3	40	921.3
+ 5	233.2	45	1 090
10	291.7	50	1 277
15	360.7		
$C_4H_{10}O$ Methyl propyl ether (14)			
−0.5 to +40	28 952	7.729	38.8
$C_4H_{10}S$ Ethyl sulfide (13)			
10	43.1		91.6
20	63.8		
30	94.0		
40	137.0		
50	199.5		
60	283.5		
70	393.6		
80	539.5		
90	724.4		
$C_4H_{11}N$ Diethylamine (12)			
54.0	724		
75.2	1 345		
$C_5H_4O_2$ Furfural, 760 mm at 161.7° (61)			
C_5H_5N Pyridine, 760 mm at 115.50° (126)			
C_5H_9N Valeronitrile, 760 mm at 140.65° (127)			
$C_5H_{10}O_2$ Valeric acid (53, 54)			
60	2.07		184.4
80	9.3		
100	28.2		
120	70.5		
130	106.9		
140	159.6		
150	234.5		
160	336.1		
170	475.3		
180	660.7		
$C_5H_{10}O_2$ Isovaleric acid (53, 96)			
10	0.2		
30	0.75		
50	2.9		
70	9.4		
90	27.3		
110	69.8		
130	159.8		
150	338.3		

Range, °C (or t, °C)	A, joule (or p_{mm})	B (for p in mm)	Normal B. P., °C
$C_5H_{10}O_2$ Isobutyl formate [64]			
35	62		98.2
40	84		
50	139		
60	200		
70	294		
80	417		
90	586		
95	687		
$C_5H_{10}O_2$ Ethyl propionate [64, 126, 136]			
−10	4.05		99.10
0	8.3		
+10	15.55		
20	27.75		
40	77.9		
60	188.0		
80	403.6		
100	785.0		
120	1383		
$C_5H_{10}O_2$ Methyl n-butyrate [136]			
−10	3.5		102.65
0	7.3	t, °C	p_{mm}
+10	13.8	70	250.3
20	24.5	80	361.4
30	41.9	90	507.0
40	69.2	100	700.7
50	109.6	110	941.0
60	167.5	120	1 247
$C_5H_{10}O_2$ Methyl isobutyrate [136]			
−10	6.2		92.2
0	12.1	t, °C	p_{mm}
+10	22.4	70	355.2
20	38.9	80	505.0
30	65.4	90	707.0
40	104.7	100	956.0
50	162.0	110	1 269
60	243.8		
$C_5H_{10}O_2$ Propyl acetate [1, 136]			
−10	3.6		101.7
0	7.0		
+20	25.0		
40	70.9		
60	171.9		
80	373.0		
90	525.0		
100	723.8		
110	976.1		
120	1 291		
C_5H_{12} n-Pentane [136]			
−20 to +50	27 691	7.558	36.1
C_5H_{12} Isopentane [126, 136]			
−30	58.55		27.95
−20	100.00		
−10	164.05		
0	257.35		
+10	390.4		
20	572.2		
30	819.0		
40	1 140.5		
50	1 535.7		

Range, °C (or t, °C)	A, joule (or p_{mm})	B (for p in mm)	Normal B. P., °C
$C_5H_{12}O$ Amyl alcohol [38, 127]			
0	0.6		137.75
10	1.3		
20	2.8		
40	10.6		
60	34.1		
80	95.1		
100	233.3		
110	350.3		
120	512.3		
130	730.8		
$C_5H_{12}O$ Isoamyl alcohol [96, 137]			
10	1.0		132.05
20	2.3		
40	9.7		
60	33.3		
80	95.9		
100	238.6		
110	358.6		
120	523.3		
130	743.2		
140	1 033		
150	1 400		
$C_5H_{12}O$ Ethyl propyl ether [14]			
0	52.5		64.0
10	89.1		
20	143.3		
30	219.8		
40	326.6		
50	472.1		
60	666.0		

$C_6H_4N_2O_5$ 2, 3-Dinitrophenol, 0.128 mm at 100° [101]
2, 4-Dinitrophenol, 0.294 mm at 100° [101]
2, 5-Dinitrophenol, 0.506 mm at 100° [101]
2, 6-Dinitrophenol, 0.117 mm at 100° [101]
3, 4-Dinitrophenol, 0.00664 mm at 100° [101]
3, 5-Dinitrophenol, 0.0098 mm at 100° [105]

Range, °C (or t, °C)	A, joule (or p_{mm})	B (for p in mm)	Normal B. P., °C
$C_6H_5AsCl_2$ Phenylarsine dichloride [5]			
0 to 45	60 578	9.150	
C_6H_5Br Bromobenzene [72, 94, 126, 136]; *cf.* [54]			
−26 to −15	42 500	8.075	156.15
+30	5.67	t, °C	p_{mm}
40	9.99	120	274.9
50	16.96	130	372.65
60	27.61	140	495.8
70	43.55	150	649.05
80	66.22	160	846.0
90	97.72	170	1 077
100	141.1	180	1 351
110	198.7	190	1 684
C_6H_5Cl Chlorobenzene [72, 126, 136]			
−35 to −15	42 250	8.500	132.00
0	2.52	t, °C	p_{mm}
+10	4.86	90	208.35
20	8.76	100	292.75
30	15.45	110	402.55
40	26.00	120	542.80
50	41.98	130	718.95
60	65.54	140	939.4
70	97.90	150	1 206
80	144.75	160	1 534

Range, °C (or *t*, °C)	A, joule (or p_{mm})	B (for *p* in mm)	Normal B. P., °C
C_6H_5F Fluorobenzene (136)			
−20	6.15		85.2
−10	11.55	*t*, °C	p_{mm}
0	20.92	60	325.1
+10	36.40	70	463.5
20	60.54	80	644.9
30	96.61	90	883
40	149.6	100	1 177
50	223.9	110	1 542
C_6H_5I Iodobenzene (28, 72, 94, 136)			
−30 to +18	43 000	7.500	188.45
30	1.48	*t*, °C	p_{mm}
40	2.24	140	204.9
50	4.85	150	276.7
60	8.30	160	367.3
70	13.65	170	479.7
80	21.78	180	618.7
90	33.50	190	793.0
100	50.23	200	991.0
110	73.88	210	1 232.0
120	105.4	220	1 520.0
130	148.3		
$C_6H_5NO_2$ Nitrobenzene (54, 126)			
112 to 209	48 955	8.192	210.85
80	7.5		
90	12.9		
100	20.85		
110	32.5		
$C_6H_5NO_3$ *o*-Nitrophenol, 2.92 mm at 100° (101); *m*-Nitrophenol, 0.196 mm at 100° (101); *p*-Nitrophenol, 0.828 mm at 100° (101)			
C_6H_6 Benzene (2, 26, 31, 54, 62, 91, 107, 127, 136)			
0 to 42	34 172	7.9622	80.25
42 to 100	32 295	7.6546	80.10
			80.15
			79.71*
			80.12

* Known to be very pure by freezing point.

Range, °C (or *t*, °C)	A, joule (or p_{mm})	B (for *p* in mm)	Normal B. P., °C
C_6H_6ClN *o*-Chloroaniline (54, 104)			
80	7.7		208.8
90	13.0	*t*, °C	p_{mm}
100	20.7	160	199.1
110	32.1	170	269.8
120	48.4	180	358.5
130	71.0	190	472.1
140	101.9	200	608.2
150	144.6	210	778.0
C_6H_6ClN *m*-Chloroaniline (54, 104)			
95	7.0		228.5
100	9.0	*t*, °C	p_{mm}
110	14.8	180	203.5
120	23.1	190	274.2
130	35.1	200	363.1
140	52.1	210	476.4
150	75.9	220	616.6
160	107.2	230	783.4
170	149.6		
C_6H_6ClN *p*-Chloroaniline, 8.03 mm at 100° (104)			

Range, °C (or *t*, °C)	A, joule (or p_{mm})	B (for *p* in mm)	Normal B. P., °C
$C_6H_6N_2O_2$ *o*-Nitroaniline (11, 104)			
150 to 260	63 881	8.8684	284.11
100	0.73		
265	466.7	(Some decomposition occurs)	
270	538.5		
275	627.4		
280	743.6		
285	922.0		
$C_6H_6N_2O_2$ *m*-Nitroaniline (11, 104)			
170 to 260	65 880	8.8188	306
100	0.16		
265	265.6	(Some decomposition occurs)	
270	304.2		
280	433.4		
290	653.2		
$C_6H_6N_2O_2$ *p*-Nitroaniline (11, 104)			
190 to 260	77 345	9.5595	
100	0.032		
265	116.8	(Rapid decomposition occurs)	
270	155.0		
275	210.6		
$C_6H_6N_3$ Phenyl azoimide (20)			
75	33.8		
80	41.8		
85	52.0		
90	63.6		
95	79.1		
C_6H_6O Phenol (9); *cf.* (54)			
116 to 180	49 644	8.587	181.2
$C_6H_6O_2$ Hydroquinol (110)			
150	4.0		
170	15.2		
190	37.7		
200	55.7		
210	79.8		
230	158.5		
250	291.8		
270	509.3		
C_6H_7N Aniline (9, 42, 126); *cf.* (84)			
145 to 185	45 951.6	8.1278	184.3
50	2.4		184.07
60	5.7		
70	10.6		
80	18.0		
90	29.2		
100	45.7		
110	69.2		
120	96.6		
130	144.5		
140	204.0		
$C_6H_{10}O_4$ Glycol diacetate (122)			
100	24		190.6
110	45	*t*, °C	p_{mm}
120	70	160	315
130	106	170	425
140	158	180	573
150	225	190	748
$C_6H_{10}O_6$ Methyl tartrate (38)			
155 to 175	50 670	7.36	

Range, °C (or t, °C)	A, joule (or p_{mm})	B (for p in mm)	Normal B. P., °C
C_6H_{12} Butylethylene (**132**)			
0	52.6		65.9
10	86.9		
20	138.8		
30	212.7		
40	314.9		
50	452.1		
60	631.3		
65	738.9		
C_6H_{12} Cyclohexane (**27, 127, 136**)			
0	27.55		80.75
10	47.05		
20	76.9		
30	121.3		
40	181.6		
50	269.2		
60	385.0		
70	540.8		
80	741.3		
90	992		
100	1 304		
$C_6H_{12}O_2$ Caproic acid (**53**)			
80	2.5		
90	5.3		
100	10.6		
110	18.9		
120	31.4		
130	51.0		
135	62.6		
$C_6H_{12}O_2$ Isocaproic acid (**53, 54**)			
70	1.9		198.6
80	4.0	t, °C	p_{mm}
100	13.9	160	204.2
120	39.3	170	290.4
140	94.4	180	407.4
150	141.0	190	564.9
$C_6H_{12}O_2$ Amyl formate, 760 mm at 123.25° (**135**)			
$C_6H_{12}O_2$ Isoamyl formate (**64**)			
50	49		123.5
60	79		
70	121		
80	180		
90	258		
100	360		
110	493		
120	679		
$C_6H_{12}O_2$ Ethyl butyrate (**64**)			
45 to 121	39 318	8.093	121.0
$C_6H_{12}O_2$ Isobutyl acetate, 25 to 115° (**138**)			
$C_6H_{12}O_2$ Propyl propionate (**64**)			
45 to 125	39 221	8.0525	123.0
C_6H_{14} Diisopropyl (**136**)			
−10	44.7		57.95
0	76.0	t, °C	p_{mm}
+10	123.5	50	584.8
20	190.5	60	807
30	285.1	70	1 093
40	411.6	80	1 444

Range, °C (or t, °C)	A, joule (or p_{mm})	B (for p in mm)	Normal B. P., °C
C_6H_{14} Hexane (**30, 72, 132, 136**)			
−83 to −50	36 702	8.782	68.95
−50 to −10	35 162.7	8.399	
−10 to +90	31 679	7.724	
$C_6H_{14}O$ Methylisobutyl carbinol, 760 mm at 131.82° (**16**)			
$C_6H_{14}O$ Dipropyl ether (**14**)			
8 to 90	34 295	7.821	89.5
$C_6H_{15}B$ Boron triethyl (**117**)			
0	12.5		
20	39.8		
40	104.7		
60	236.6		
70	331.9		
80	455.0		
$C_7H_4Cl_2O$ *o*-Chlorobenzoyl chloride (**49**)			
100 to 122	52 742	8.396	
$C_7H_4Cl_2O$ *m*-Chlorobenzoyl chloride (**49**)			
94 to 117	49 870	8.086	
$C_7H_4Cl_2O$ *p*-Chlorobenzoyl chloride (**49**)			
97 to 120	53 848	8.619	
C_7H_5ClO Benzoyl chloride (**49, 54**)			
140 to 200	45 416	7.9245	197.3
40	1.1	t, °C	p_{mm}
50	2.4	100	33.9
60	4.8	110	51.4
70	8.2	120	75.1
80	13.6	130	107.8
90	21.8	140	152.0
$C_7H_5ClO_2$ *o*-Chlorobenzoic acid, 0.298 mm at 100° (**103**)			
m-Chlorobenzoic acid, 0.333 mm at 100° (**103**)			
p-Chlorobenzoic acid, 0.94 mm at 100° (**103**)			
C_7H_5N Benzonitrile (**54, 126**)			
60	6.3		191.30
70	10.5	t, °C	p_{mm}
80	17.0	150	254.7
90	27.2	160	338.8
100	42.7	170	445.7
110	65.0	180	582.1
120	94.2	190	748.2
130	135.5		
140	187.3		
C_7H_5NO Phenyl isocyanate (**20**)			
75	36.3		
80	45.3		
85	55.9		
90	68.2		
95	83.9		
$C_7H_5NO_3$ *o*-Nitrobenzaldehyde, 0.0188 mm at 100° (**102**)			
m-Nitrobenzaldehyde, 0.0132 mm at 100° (**102**)			
p-Nitrobenzaldehyde, 0.0090 mm at 100° (**102**)			
$C_7H_5NO_4$ *o*-Nitrobenzoic acid, 0.0605 mm at 100° (**103**)			
m-Nitrobenzoic acid, 0.0212 mm at 100° (**103**)			
p-Nitrobenzoic acid, 0.0059 mm at 100° (**103**)			
$C_7H_5N_3O_6$ Trinitrotoluene (**66**)			
80	0.042		
85	0.053		
90	0.067		
95	0.085		
100	0.106		

Range, °C (or t, °C)	A, joule (or p_{mm})	B (for p in mm)	Normal B. P., °C
C_7H_6O Benzaldehyde (54)			
30	1.1		178.3
40	2.3	t, °C	p_{mm}
50	5.0	120	132
60	8.9	130	188
70	15.3	140	263
80	27.7	150	353
90	39.8	160	469
100	60.5	170	614
110	90.7	180	790
$C_7H_6O_2$ Benzoic acid (54, 103)			
100	1.79 (Steam distillation)		249
140	14.6	t, °C	p_{mm}
150	23.6	210	239
160	36.3	220	331.5
170	55.8	230	451
180	81.6	240	597
190	119.1	250	780
200	171.3		

$C_7H_6O_3$ *o*-Hydroxybenzoic acid, 0.862 mm at 100° (103)
m-Hydroxybenzoic acid, 0.257 mm at 100° (103)
p-Hydroxybenzoic acid, 0.025 mm at 100° (103)

Range, °C (or t, °C)	A, joule (or p_{mm})	B (for p in mm)	Normal B. P., °C
$C_7H_7NO_2$ *o*-Nitrotoluene (11.5); *cf.* (54)			
50 to 225	48 114	7.9728	220.38
$C_7H_7NO_2$ *m*-Nitrotoluene (11.5)			
55 to 235	50 128	8.0655	231.87
$C_7H_7NO_2$ *p*-Nitrotoluene (11.5); *cf.* (54)			
80 to 240	49 950	7.9815	238.34
C_7H_8 Toluene (4, 28, 91, 126); *cf.* (54)			
−92 to +15	39 198	8.330	110.70
30	36.7	t, °C	p_{mm}
40	59.1	80	289.7
50	92.6	90	404.6
60	139.5	100	557.2
70	202.4		
C_7H_8O Benzyl alcohol (54)			
100 to 135	59 491	9.5152	203.9
135 to 205	53 118	8.6977	
61	1		
80	4.7		
90	8.7		
C_7H_8O *o*-Cresol (33); *cf.* (54)			
50	1.87		190.5
60	3.55	t, °C	p_{mm}
70	6.5	130	109.4
80	11.5	140	158.1
90	19.4	150	222.9
100	31.6	160	308.3
110	49.2	170	421.2
120	74.1	180	566.9
C_7H_8O *m*-Cresol (33); *cf.* (54)			
60	1.76		202.2
70	3.4	t, °C	p_{mm}
80	6.37	140	106.9
90	11.3	150	154.2
100	19.05	160	219.3
110	31.0	170	302.7
120	48.6	180	411.2
130	72.5	190	549.6

Range, °C (or t, °C)	A, joule (or p_{mm})	B (for p in mm)	Normal B. P., °C
C_7H_8O *p*-Cresol (33); *cf.* (54)			
60	1.7		202.1
70	3.3	t, °C	p_{mm}
80	6.17	140	105.0
90	10.8	150	152.1
100	18.3	160	216.8
110	30.1	170	300.0
120	47.4	180	407.4
130	71.0	190	548.3

C_7H_8O Anisole, 760 mm at 153.80° (126)

Range, °C (or t, °C)	A, joule (or p_{mm})	B (for p in mm)	Normal B. P., °C
C_7H_9N Methylaniline (74); *cf.* (54)			
40	1.0		195.70
50	2.5	t, °C	p_{mm}
60	4.4	140	147.6
70	7.5	150	207.1
80	12.1	160	286.0
90	19.6	170	380.9
100	31.5	180	502.6
110	49.3	190	654.5
120	72.8	200	843.5
130	104.0		
C_7H_9N *o*-Toluidine (11.5); *cf.* (54)			
40	1.1		199.84
50	2.1	t, °C	p_{mm}
60	3.7	140	129.9
70	6.4	150	180.5
80	10.5	160	250.2
90	17.3	170	338.0
100	27.2	180	450.2
110	41.7	190	590.7
120	62.3	200	762.9
130	91.2	205	863.9
C_7H_9N *m*-Toluidine (11.5); *cf.* (54)			
45	1.3		202.86
50	1.9	t, °C	p_{mm}
60	3.4	150	162.6
70	5.7	160	224.9
80	9.4	170	305.9
90	15.2	180	410.6
100	23.9	190	541.9
110	36.7	200	706.7
120	54.8	205	803.4
130	80.4		
140	115.5		
C_7H_9N *p*-Toluidine (11.5); *cf.* (54)			
40	1.1		200.35
50	2.0	t, °C	p_{mm}
60	3.7	150	177.2
70	6.3	160	244.0
80	10.5	170	330.6
90	16.9	180	441.3
100	26.6	190	580.4
110	40.6	200	753.0
120	60.6	205	854.2
130	88.4		
140	126.3		

C_7H_{14} Methylcyclohexane, 760 mm at 101.20° (127)

$C_7H_{14}O_2$ Heptylic acid (53, 54)

Range, °C (or t, °C)	A, joule (or p_{mm})	B (for p in mm)	Normal B. P., °C
90	1.9		221.0
100	4.1	t, °C	p_{mm}
120	15.1	190	288.4
140	42.3	200	400.9
160	97.5	210	549.6
170	141.7	220	741.3
180	204.2		

$C_7H_{14}O_2$ Isopropyl isobutyrate (135)

Range, °C (or t, °C)	A, joule (or p_{mm})	B (for p in mm)	Normal B. P., °C
10	6.5		120.75
20	11.9		
40	35.0		
60	89.0		
80	201.1		
100	406.0		
120	743.9		
140	1 290		

C_7H_{16} Heptane (72, 136)

Range, °C (or t, °C)	A, joule (or p_{mm})	B (for p in mm)	Normal B. P., °C
−63 to −40	37 358	8.2585	98.42
0	11.45	t, °C	p_{mm}
+10	20.5	80	426.6
20	35.5	90	588.8
30	58.35	100	795.2
40	92.05	110	1 047
50	140.9	120	1 367
60	208.9		
70	302.3		

$C_8H_4O_3$ Phthalic anhydride (56, 57, 70); *cf.* (86)

Range, °C (or t, °C)	A, joule (or p_{mm})	B (for p in mm)	Normal B. P., °C
160 to 285	54 920	8.022	284.6

C_8H_8ClNO *o*-Chloroacetanilide, 0.94 mm at 100° (104)
m-Chloroacetanilide, 0.078 mm at 100° (104)
p-Chloroacetanilide, 0.92 mm at 100° (104)

$C_8H_8N_2O_3$ *o*-Nitroacetanilide, 0.12 mm at 100° (104)
m-Nitroacetanilide, 0.007 mm at 100° (104)
p-Nitroacetanilide, 0.008 mm at 100° (104)

C_8H_8O Acetophenone (10, 39, 54)

Range, °C (or t, °C)	A, joule (or p_{mm})	B (for p in mm)	Normal B. P., °C
30 to 100	55 117	9.1352	198.5
100 to 194	49 141	8.3170	(at 715 mm)

$C_8H_8O_2$ Phenylacetic acid, 0.541 mm at 100° (103)

$C_8H_8O_2$ Methyl benzoate (54)

Range, °C (or t, °C)	A, joule (or p_{mm})	B (for p in mm)	Normal B. P., °C
60	3.9		197.5
70	6.8	t, °C	p_{mm}
80	11.5	140	136.2
90	18.6	150	190.5
100	29.2	160	260.9
110	45.0	170	351.6
120	66.7	180	472.1
130	96.3	190	625.9

$C_8H_8O_3$ 3-Hydroxytoluene-2-carboxylic acid, 0.982 mm at 100° (103)
3-Hydroxytoluene-4-carboxylic acid, 0.507 mm at 100° (103)
4-Hydroxytoluene-3-carboxylic acid, 0.462 mm at 100° (103)
5-Hydroxytoluene-3-carboxylic acid, 0.151 mm at 100° (103)
4-Hydroxytoluene-2-carboxylic acid, 0.0073 mm at 100° (103)

$C_8H_8O_3$ Methyl salicylate (84)

Range, °C (or t, °C)	A, joule (or p_{mm})	B (for p in mm)	Normal B. P., °C
175 to 215	48 670	8.008	222.89
216	645.5		
218	677.2		
220	710.2		
222	744.3		
224	779.8		
225	798.1		

C_8H_9FO *p*-Fluorophenetole, 762 mm at 172.70° (120)

C_8H_{10} Ethylbenzene (132)

Range, °C (or t, °C)	A, joule (or p_{mm})	B (for p in mm)	Normal B. P., °C
0	5.9		133.91
10	9.6	t, °C	p_{mm}
20	15.3	90	223.1
30	23.75	100	307.0
40	36.1	110	414.15
50	53.8	120	545.9
60	78.65	130	695.95
70	113.0		
80	160.0		

C_8H_{10} *o*-Xylene (132)

Range, °C (or t, °C)	A, joule (or p_{mm})	B (for p in mm)	Normal B. P., °C
0	4.0		143.61
10	6.4	t, °C	p_{mm}
20	10.05	90	153.5
30	15.55	100	213.1
40	23.7	110	291.7
50	35.5	120	393.85
60	52.4	130	524.6
70	76.15	140	689.9
80	108.9		

C_8H_{10} *m*-Xylene (127, 132)

Range, °C (or t, °C)	A, joule (or p_{mm})	B (for p in mm)	Normal B. P., °C
0	1.75		139.00
10	3.45	t, °C	p_{mm}
20	6.43	90	168.05
30	11.43	100	238.22
40	19.48	110	330.33
50	31.94	120	448.85
60	50.59	130	598.59
70	77.62	140	784.64
80	115.72		

C_8H_{10} *p*-Xylene (127, 132)

Range, °C (or t, °C)	A, joule (or p_{mm})	B (for p in mm)	Normal B. P., °C
0	8.29		138.30
10	11.52	t, °C	p_{mm}
20	16.35	90	197.48
30	23.52	100	270.46
40	34.00	110	364.23
50	49.22	120	481.33
60	70.64	130	624.93
70	100.76	140	794.84
80	142.04		

$C_8H_{10}O$ Phenetole, 760 mm at 172.00° (119)

$C_8H_{11}N$ Dimethylaniline (74); *cf.* (54)

Range, °C (or t, °C)	A, joule (or p_{mm})	B (for p in mm)	Normal B. P., °C
40	2.5		193.50
50	4.1	t, °C	p_{mm}
60	6.8	140	163.9
70	10.0	150	227.1
80	15.4	160	307.0
90	24.3	170	408.1
100	37.9	180	536.0
110	56.8	190	695.4
120	81.8	195	787.5
130	116.2		

$C_8H_{11}N$ Ethylaniline (**74**); *cf.* (**54**)

Range, °C (or *t*, °C)	A, joule (or p_{mm})	B (for *p* in mm)	Normal B. P., °C
40	1.1		204.72
50	2.4	*t*, °C	p_{mm}
60	4.0	150	158.0
70	6.1	160	218.8
80	10.0	170	296.0
90	16.0	180	394.2
100	24.0	190	518.0
110	36.4	200	674.4
120	54.5	210	867.0
130	79.0		
140	112.0		

$C_8H_{16}O_2$ *n*-Caprylic acid (**53**)

Range, °C (or *t*, °C)	A, joule (or p_{mm})	B (for *p* in mm)	Normal B. P., °C
95	0.8		
100	1.6		
110	3.8		
120	7.6		
130	14.2		
140	24.3		
150	39.0		
160	61.0		

C_8H_{18} 2, 5-Dimethylhexane (**124, 136**)

Range, °C (or *t*, °C)	A, joule (or p_{mm})	B (for *p* in mm)	Normal B. P., °C
10	13.0		108.53
20	23.0		
30	38.5		
40	61.8		
50	95.9		
70	213.3		
90	426.6		
100	578.8		
120	1 020		
130	1 319		

C_8H_{18} *n*-Octane (**72, 132, 136**)

Range, °C (or *t*, °C)	A, joule (or p_{mm})	B (for *p* in mm)	Normal B. P., °C
−35	0.17		125.8
−30	0.28	*t*, °C	p_{mm}
−20	0.64	80	174.8
−10	1.39	90	253.4
0	2.94	100	353.6
+10	5.62	110	481.9
20	10.45	120	646.4
30	18.40	130	859
40	30.85	140	1 114
50	49.35	150	1 425
60	77.55		
70	117.9		

C_9H_7N Quinoline (**133**)

Range, °C (or *t*, °C)	A, joule (or p_{mm})	B (for *p* in mm)	Normal B. P., °C
180 to 240	49 720	7.969	237.2
80	3.1		
90	5.2		
100	8.5		
110	13.4		
120	20.7		
130	31.0		
140	45.3		
150	65.3		
160	91.4		
170	127.0		

$C_9H_{10}O_2$ Hydratropic acid, 0.293 mm at 100° (**103**)

C_9H_{12} Cumene (**132**)

Range, °C (or *t*, °C)	A, joule (or p_{mm})	B (for *p* in mm)	Normal B. P., °C
0	6.45		154.73
10	8.65	*t*, °C	p_{mm}
20	11.8	90	124.45
30	16.45	100	170.5
40	23.05	110	230.95
50	32.5	120	309.0
60	45.8	130	407.55
70	64.35	140	530.1
80	89.9	150	679.7

C_9H_{12} *n*-Propylbenzene (**132**)

Range, °C (or *t*, °C)	A, joule (or p_{mm})	B (for *p* in mm)	Normal B. P., °C
0	6.25		156.28
10	7.7	*t*, °C	p_{mm}
20	10.0	90	110.05
30	13.55	100	154.4
40	18.8	110	213.6
50	26.6	120	291.0
60	38.0	130	389.6
70	54.4	140	511.9
80	77.65	150	659.1

C_9H_{12} Pseudocumene (**132**)

Range, °C (or *t*, °C)	A, joule (or p_{mm})	B (for *p* in mm)	Normal B. P., °C
0	5.9		169.33
10	7.0	*t*, °C	p_{mm}
20	8.7	100	105.95
30	11.3	110	145.8
40	15.05	120	198.55
50	20.5	130	267.6
60	28.3	140	355.9
70	39.4	150	466.8
80	54.9	160	603.9
90	76.45		

C_9H_{12} Mesitylene (**132**)

Range, °C (or *t*, °C)	A, joule (or p_{mm})	B (for *p* in mm)	Normal B. P., °C
0	15.6		161.94
10	20.45	*t*, °C	p_{mm}
20	27.15	100	247.25
30	36.4	110	309.55
40	48.9	120	381.1
50	65.55	130	461.7
60	87.35	140	550.05
70	115.45	150	643.55
80	150.8	160	740.35
90	194.45		

$C_9H_{13}N$ Dimethyl-*o*-toluidine (**54**)

Range, °C (or *t*, °C)	A, joule (or p_{mm})	B (for *p* in mm)	Normal B. P., °C
105 to 185	45 260	8.043	184.8
60	7.0		
70	12.3		
80	20.2		
90	32.1		
100	49.4		

$C_9H_{13}N$ Dimethyl-*p*-toluidine (**54**)

Range, °C (or *t*, °C)	A, joule (or p_{mm})	B (for *p* in mm)	Normal B. P., °C
135 to 211	48 502	8.124	210.0
80	6.9		
90	12.0		
100	19.5		
110	30.8		
120	46.6		
130	68.55		

Range, °C (or t, °C)	A, joule (or p_{mm})	B (for p in mm)	Normal B. P., °C
$C_9H_{18}O_2$ Pelargonic acid (53)			
100	0.3	t, °C	p_{mm}
110	1.2	150	20.5
120	3.0	160	32.5
130	6.3	170	51.5
140	12.2		
$C_9H_{18}O_2$ Isobutyl valerate (64)			
90 to 170	44 482	8.143	168.4
$C_{10}H_7Br$ α-Bromonaphthalene (54, 84)			
110	3.55		281.1
120	5.55	t, °C	p_{mm}
130	8.5	230	232.6
140	12.8	240	300.3
150	18.9	250	381.5
160	27.4	260	482.0
180	54.95	270	604.0
200	102.4	280	743.0
220	178.7		
$C_{10}H_7Cl$ α-Chloronaphthalene (54)			
100	3.8		259.3
110	6.5	t, °C	p_{mm}
120	10.5	200	178.2
130	16.3	220	304.8
140	24.5	230	390.4
150	35.7	240	497.7
160	51.05	250	622.0
180	98.5		
$C_{10}H_8$ Naphthalene (9, 23, 51, 71, 73, 108, 111)			
120 to 200	47 362	7.927	218.0
85	9.8	t, °C	p_{mm}
90	12.5	235	1 098
100	18.9	240	1 218
110	28.3	245	1 347
225	887	250	1 487
230	988		
$C_{10}H_8O$ α-Naphthol (11.5)			
110	1.7		288.01
120	2.8	t, °C	p_{mm}
130	4.6	220	139.0
140	7.4	230	185.2
150	11.5	240	243.2
160	17.9	250	315.4
170	25.8	260	403.7
180	37.5	270	511.3
190	53.5	280	639.6
200	74.7	290	797.3
210	02.9	295	879.1
$C_{10}H_8O$ β-Naphthol (11.5)			
130	3.6		294.85
140	5.8	t, °C	p_{mm}
150	9.0	230	149.8
160	13.6	240	198.5
170	20.2	250	259.9
180	29.5	260	336.2
190	42.1	270	430.0
200	59.2	280	544.3
210	81.9	290	685.1
220	111.5	300	848.7
$C_{10}H_{12}$ Tetrahydronaphthalene (46)			
100	26.3	t, °C	p_{mm}
140	118	200	646
160	219	207	753

Range, °C (or t, °C)	A, joule (or p_{mm})	B (for p in mm)	Normal B. P., °C
$C_{10}H_{14}$ Cymene (132)			
0	4.65		174.98
10	5.2	t, °C	p_{mm}
20	6.3	100	87.85
30	8.15	110	122.85
40	10.95	120	169.25
50	15.15	130	229.45
60	21.4	140	304.65
70	30.45	150	398.0
80	43.55	160	519.6
90	62.1	170	672.7
$C_{10}H_{14}$ Isobutylbenzene (132)			
0	2.55		167.41
10	3.65	t, °C	p_{mm}
20	5.3	100	104.5
30	7.75	110	145.7
40	11.4	120	200.35
50	16.8	130	271.85
60	24.6	140	363.2
70	35.85	150	478.3
80	51.75	160	627.1
90	74.0		
$C_{10}H_{15}N$ Diethylaniline (74); *cf.* (54)			
50	1.6		216.27
60	2.7	t, °C	p_{mm}
70	4.2	150	113.5
80	6.8	160	158.0
90	10.0	170	216.0
100	16.2	180	291.7
110	25.1	190	386.9
120	38.2	200	504.0
130	56.2	210	651.0
140	80.6	220	837.0
$C_{10}H_{16}O$ Camphor (83, 110)			
180	380		208.25
190	490		
200	624		
$C_{10}H_{18}$ Decahydronaphthalene (46)			
100	49.5	t, °C	p_{mm}
130	140	170	459
150	261		
$C_{10}H_{20}O_2$ Capric acid (53)			
120	0.5	t, °C	p_{mm}
130	1.9	170	25.4
140	4.5	180	40.2
150	8.8	190	62.9
160	15.4		
$C_{10}H_{22}$ 2, 6-Dimethyloctane (136)			
0	0.6		158.6
15	1.9	t, °C	p_{mm}
30	5.0	90	87.3
45	11.7	105	150.1
60	24.7	120	247.0
75	48.0	140	453.2
$C_{12}H_9N$ Carbazole (71, 99)			
244 to 352	64 715	8.280	354.76
250	65.0	t, °C	p_{mm}
260	87.9	290	191.2
270	115.7	300	242.0
280	149.7	310	303.8

Range, °C (or *t*, °C)	A, joule (or p_{mm})	B (for *p* in mm)	Normal B. P., °C
$C_{12}H_9N$ Carbazole.—(*Continued*)			
320	378.5	*t*, °C	p_{mm}
330	467.7	350	695.8
340	573.0		
$C_{12}H_{10}$ Acenaphthene (71)			
147 to 288	54 279	8.033	277.0
$C_{12}H_{10}$ Diphenyl (51)			
210	243		255
220	330	*t*, °C	p_{mm}
225	376.5	240	542.9
230	426.6	245	609.5
235	482	250	681.6
$C_{12}H_{10}AsCl$ Diphenylarsine chloride (5)			
25 to 75	62 952	7.8930	
$C_{12}H_{10}O$ Phenyl ether (14.5)			
153.0	42.6		259
158.0	51.8	*t*, °C	p_{mm}
165.0	66.8	168.0	73.3
$C_{12}H_{11}N$ Diphenylamine (43)			
278 to 284	57 350	8.088	
286	544	*t*, °C	p_{mm}
287	565	288	600
$C_{12}H_{24}O_2$ Lauric acid (40, 88)			
164 to 205	74 386	9.768	
100	0.058		
$C_{13}H_{10}$ Fluorene (71)			
161 to 300	56 615	8.059	297.9
$C_{13}H_{10}O$ Benzophenone (51)			
260 to 308	58 221	8.137	305.4
$C_{13}H_{12}$ Diphenylmethane (24)			
217 to 283	52 360	7.967	264.5
$C_{14}H_8O_2$ Anthraquinone (73); *cf.* (110)			
285 to 370	63 985	8.002	379.8
380	763.4		
$C_{14}H_{10}$ Anthracene (71, 73); *cf.* (75)			
100 to 160	72 000	8.91	342
223 to 342	59 219	7.910	
$C_{14}H_{10}$ Phenanthrene (71, 73)			
203 to 347	57 247	7.771	338.4
$C_{14}H_{28}O_2$ Myristic acid (40, 88)			
190 to 224	75 783	9.541	
100	0.033		
$C_{15}H_{14}O$ Dibenzyl ketone (134)			
285 to 325	62 118	8.257	330.6
280	245.2	*t*, °C	p_{mm}
285	277.5	310	495.2
290	313.3	315	551.8
295	352.7	320	613.2
300	396.0	325	679.9
305	443.3	330	752.0

LITERATURE

(For a key to the periodicals see end of volume)

(1) Ariès, *34*, **168**: 1188; 19. (2) Atkins and Wallace, *4*, **103**: 146; 13. (3) Atkinson, Heycock and Pope, *4*, **117**: 1410; 20. (4) Barker, *7*, **71**: 235; 10. (5) Baxter, Bezzenberger and Wilson, *1*, **42**: 1386; 20. (6) Beckmann and Faust, *7*, **89**: 235; 15. (7) Beckmann and Liesche, *7*, **88**: 23; 14. (8) Beckmann and Liesche, *7*, **88**: 419; 14. (9) Beckmann and Liesche, *7*, **89**: 111; 15.

(10) Bergman, *Thesis*, Lausanne, 1914. (11) Berliner and May, *1*, **47**: 2350; 25. (11.5) Berliner and May, U. S. Dept. of Agriculture, *O*. (12) Berthoud, *42*, **15**: 3; 17. (13) Berthoud and Brum, *42*, **21**: 143; 24. (14) Bingham, *11*, **43**: 287; 10. (14.5) Britton, The Dow Chemical Co., Midland, Mich., *O*. (15) Brown and Acree, *1*, **38**: 2145; 16. (16) Brunel, Grenshaw and Tobin, *1*, **43**: 561; 21. (17) Burrell and Robertson, *1*, **37**: 1883; 15. (18) Burrel and Robertson, *1*, **37**: 2188; 15. (19) Burrell and Robertson, *1*, **37**: 2482; 15.

(20) Carothers, *1*, **45**: 1734; 23. (21) Chappuis and Rivière, *34*, **104**: 1504; 87. (22) Chiaraviglio and Corbino, *22*, **23 I**: 37; 14. (23) Crafts, *42*, **11**: 429; 13. (24) Crafts, *42*, **13**: 105; 15. (25) Crommelin, *64V*, **21**: 684; 12. *64P*, **15**: 666; 12. (26) Déjardin, *8*, **11**: 253; 19. (27) Dittmar and Fawsitt, *174*, **33**: 509; 88. (28) Drucker, Jiméno and Kangro, *7*, **90**: 513; 15. (29) Ewins, *4*, **105**: 354; 14.

(30) Faraday, *62*, **135**: 155; 1845. (31) Ferche, *8*, **44**: 265; 91. (32) de Forcrand, *34*, **132**: 688; 01. (33) Fox and Barker, *54*, **36**: 842; 17. **37**: 265; 18. (34) Garner, Saxton and Parker, *11*, **46**: 236; 11. (35) Gilmour, *54*, **41**: 293; 22. (36) Graebe and Zschokke, *25*, **17**: 1175; 84. (37) Grassi, *59*, **24**: 109; 88. (38) Gróh, *25*, **45**: 1441; 12. (39) Ham, Churchill and Ryer, *143*, **186**: 15; 18.

(40) Hansen, *7*, **74**: 65; 10. (41) Hara and Sinozaki, Tohoku Imperial University, Sendai, Japan, *O*. (42) Harlow, *67*, **24**: 30; 11. (43) Hein, *7*, **86**: 385; 14. (44) Herz and Rathmann, *136*, **36**: 1417; 12. (45) Herz and Rathmann, *136*, **37**: 621; 13. (46) Herz and Schuftan, *7*, **101**: 269; 22. (47) Holst, *168*, No. **144**; 14. (48) Homfray, *7*, **74**: 129; 10. (49) Hope and Riley, *4*, **121**: 2510; 22.

(50) Jacob, *Recherches et Inventions*, No. **12**: 460; 24. (51) Jaquerod and Wassmer, *25*, **37**: 2531; 04. (52) Jenkin and Shorthose, *B67*. (53) Kahlbaum, *7*, **13**: 14; 94. (54) Kahlbaum, *7*, **26**: 577; 98. (55) Konovalov, *8*, **14**: 34; 81. (56) Küster, *7*, **51**: 222; 05. (57) Landolt, *13*, Supp. **6**: 129; 68. (58) Louder, Briggs and Browne, *45*, **16**: 932; 24. (59) Maass and Boomer, *1*, **44**: 1709; 22.

(60) Maass and Wright, *1*, **43**: 1098; 21. (61) Mains, *33*, **26**: 779, 841; 22. (62) Mangold, *75*, **102 IIa**: 1071; 93. (63) Marshall and Peace, *4*, **109**: 298; 16. (64) Mathews and Faville, *50*, **22**: 1; 18. (65) Menzies, *1*, **41**: 1336; 19. (66) Menzies, *1*, **42**: 2218; 20. (67) Merriman, *4*, **103**: 628; 13. (68) Michels, *64V*, **31**: 53; 22. (69) Moles and Batuecas, *42*, **17**: 537; 19.

(70) Monroe, *45*, **12**: 969; 20. (71) Mortimer and Murphy, *45*, **15**: 1140; 23. (72) Mündel, *7*, **85**: 435; 13. (73) Nelson and Senseman, *45*, **14**: 58; 22. (74) Nelson and Wales, *1*, **47**: 867; 25. (75) Niederschultze, *Diss.*, Erlangen, 1903. (76) Nikitin, *53*, **52**: 247; 20. *10*, **5**: 234; 25. (77) Orton and Jones, *133*, **1912**: 122. (78) Paterno and Mazzucchelli, *36*, **50 I**: 30; 20. (79) Perry and Bardwell, *1*, **47**: 2629; 25.

(80) Perry and Porter, *1*, **48**: 299; 26. (81) Price, *4*, **107**: 188; 15. (82) Price, *4*, **115**: 1116; 19. (83) Ramsay and Young, *62*, **175**: 37; 84. (84) Ramsay and Young, *4*, **47**: 640; 85. (85) Ramsay and Young, *25*, **19**: 2107; 86. (86) Ramsay and Young, *62*, **177**: 123; 87. (87) Regnault, *151*, **26**: 339; 62. (88) Reilly and Hickinbottom, *117*, **16**: 131; 20. (89) Rex, *7*, **55**: 355; 06.

(90) Richards and Mathews, *1*, **30**: 8; 08. (91) Richards and Shipley, *1*, **38**: 989; 16. (92) Richardson, *4*, **49**: 761; 86. (93) Robertson and Acree, *11*, **49**: 474; 13. (94) Rolla, *59*, **19**: 323; 09. (95) Sameshima, *1*, **40**: 1482; 18. (96) Schmidt, *7*, **7**: 433; 91. (97) Schulze, *7*, **97**: 388; 21. (98) Seibert and Burrell, *1*, **37**: 2683; 15. (99) Senseman and Nelson, *45*, **15**: 382; 23.

(100) Shorthose, *B40*. (101) Sidgwick and Aldous, *4*, **119**: 1001; 21. (102) Sidgwick and Dash, *4*, **121**: 2586; 22. (103) Sidgwick and Ewbank, *4*, **119**: 979; 21. (104) Sidgwick and Rubie, *4*, **119**: 1013; 21. (105) Sidgwick and Taylor, *4*, **121**: 1853; 22. (106) Smith, Balliol College, Oxford, England, *O*. (107) Smith and Menzies, *1*, **32**: 1448; 10. (108) Speranski, *7*, **46**: 70; 03. (109) Städel, *25*, **15**: 2559; 82.

(110) Stelzner, *Diss.*, Erlangen, 1901. (111) Stelzner, *Diss.*, Erlangen, 1903. (112) Stern, *Jahres. Schles. Vaterl. Kult.*, **90**: 29; 13. (113) Stock, Henning and Kuss, *25*, **54**: 1119; 21. (114) Stock and Somieski, *25*, **52**: 695; 19. (115) Stock and Somieski, *25*, **54**: 524; 21. (116) Stock and Stiebeler, *25*, **56**: 1087; 23. (117) Stock and Zeidler, *25*, **54**: 531; 21. (118) Stuckgold, *42*, **15**: 502; 17. (119) Swarts, *186*, **1912**: 481.

(120) Swarts, *70*, **32**: 58; 13. (121) Taylor, *50*, **4**: 355; C0. (122) Taylor and Rinkenbach, U. S. Bureau of Mines, Pittsburgh, Pa., *O*. (123) Terwen, *7*, **91**: 469; 16. (124) Thorpe, *4*, **37**: 141; 80. (125) Thorpe and Rodger, *62*, **185**: 397; 95. (126) Timmermans, *28*, **24**: 244; 10. (127) Timmermans, University of Brussels, *O*. (128) Tyrer, *4*, **101**: 81; 12. (129) Tyrer, *4*, **105**: 2534; 14.

(130) Weiss and Downs, *1*, **45**: 1003; 23. (131) Williams, *1*, **47**: 2644; 25. (132) Woringer, *7*, **34**: 257; 00. (133) Young, *4*, **55**: 483; 89. (134) Young, *4*, **59**: 621; 91. (135) Young, *4*, **81**: 777; 02. (136) Young, *117*, **12**: 374; 10. (137) Young and Fortey, *4*, **81**: 717; 02. (138) *Paint Manufacturers Association*, Circ. No. 237. (139) Dana, Jenkins, Burdick and Timm, *382*, **12**: 387; 26.

(140) Sinozaki, Hara and Mitsukuri, *505*, **6**: 157; 26.

VAPOR PRESSURES AND ORTHOBARIC DENSITIES ABOVE ONE ATMOSPHERE

C. S. Cragoe

The available data on the compounds in this section are expressed within the experimental errors by an equation which may be written in either of the following forms:

$$\log_{10} p = \frac{T - T_B}{T}\left[A - B\left(\frac{T - T_B}{T_B}\right) + C\left(\frac{T - T_B}{T_B}\right)^2\right]$$

$$\log_{10} p = (A + 2B + 3C) - \frac{T_B}{T}(A + B + C) - \frac{T}{T_B}(B + 3C) + \frac{CT^2}{T_B^2}$$

where p is the vapor pressure in normal atmospheres, T the temperature and T_B the normal boiling point in °K, and A, B and C are constants.

The latent heat of vaporization in joules per g at T°K is given by

$$l = 0.2333p\frac{T_B}{T}\left(\frac{1}{d_v} - \frac{1}{d_l}\right)\left[A - B\left(\frac{T - T_B}{T_B}\right)\left(\frac{T + T_B}{T_B}\right) + C\left(\frac{T - T_B}{T_B}\right)^2\left(\frac{2T + T_B}{T_B}\right)\right]$$

t = °C; d_l(resp. d_v) = density of saturated liquid (resp. vapor) in g/cm³; $d_m = \frac{1}{2}(d_l + d_v)$. Critical-point values are in boldface type. T_c = Critical temperature, °K.

The literature references are arranged in the order of their relative importance.

B-TABLE, STANDARD ARRANGEMENT

H_2O, *v.* p. 233

HCl Hydrogen Chloride (p), (**79, 46, 53, 57, 58, 51, 104, 107, 163, 164, 21, 96, 98, 55, 179, 180, 50, 7, 8, 61, 62**); (d) (**107, 145, 163, 164, 7, 8, 156**)

t, °C	p, atm.	g/cm³ d_l	g/cm³ d_v
−85.03	1.00	1.191	0.0025
−80	1.32	1.178	.0032
−70	2.19	1.151	.0052
−60	3.45	1.122	.0083
−50	5.20	1.093	.012
−40	7.55	1.063	.017
−30	10.62	1.031	.023
−20	14.53	0.997	.032
−10	19.43	.962	.042
0	25.46	.924	.054
+10	32.78	.881	.072
20	41.58	.831	.097
30	52.08	.772	.130
40	64.52	.697	.180
50	79.19	.592	.260
51.5	**81.6**	**0.424**	
T_B	A	B	C
188.07	4.630	0.48	0.50

$$d_m = 0.424\left[1 + 0.97\left(1 - \frac{T}{T_c}\right)\right].$$

HBr Hydrogen Bromide (p) (**114, 53, 104, 57, 58, 162, 163, 164, 107, 96, 55**); (d) (**156, 163, 164, 56**)

t	p	t	p
−67.0	1.00	0	12.3
−60	1.41	+10	16.0
−50	2.20	20	20.6
−40	3.31	30	26.1
−30	4.79	40	32.5
−20	6.72	50	40.2
−10	9.19	60	49.0

HBr.—(*Continued*)

t	p	t	d_l
70	59.4	−67	2.152
80	71.4	+10	1.630
90	**85**	20	1.589
T_B	A	B	C
206.1	4.540	0.48	0.50

HI Hydrogen Iodide (p) (**104, 53, 57, 58, 107, 163, 164, 162, 96, 55, 61, 62**); (d) (**156, 107, 163, 164, 19**)

t	p	t	p
−35.5	1.00	80	25.8
−30	1.26	90	31.0
−20	1.86	100	37.0
−10	2.66	110	43.9
0	3.70	120	51.6
+10	5.01	130	60.4
20	6.65	140	70.4
30	8.65	**150.5**	**82**
40	11.1	t	d_l
50	13.9	−35.5	2.798
60	17.3	+12	2.270
70	21.2	20	2.230
T_B	A	B	C
237.6	4.430	0.48	0.50

SO_2 Sulfur Dioxide, *v.* p. 236

SO_3 Sulfur Trioxide (p) (**17, 18, 99, 151, 154, 155**); (d) (**17, 18, 99, 88, 151, 115**)

t	p	d_l	d_v
44.6	1.00	1.807	0.003
60	2.0	1.732	.006
80	4.3	1.639	.013
100	8.0	1.547	.025
110	10.4	1.506	.031
120	13.3	1.465	.037
130	16.7	1.424	.045
140	20.6	1.382	.056
150	25.1	1.340	.069
160	30.3	1.296	.086
170	36.4	1.249	.107
180	43.4	1.196	.137
190	51.5	1.134	.177
200	61.1	1.058	.233
210	72.5	0.960	.313
218.3	**83.6**	**0.630**	
T_B	A	B	C
317.7	6.860	5.50	5.30

$$d_m = 0.630\left[1 + 0.60\left(1 - \frac{T}{T_c}\right) + 1.8\left(1 - \frac{T}{T_c}\right)^2\right].$$

H_2S Hydrogen Sulfide (p) (**41, 42, 147, 148, 125, 104, 57, 58, 162, 163, 164, 107, 96, 98, 50, 143**); (d) (**163, 164, 107, 19**)

t	p	t	p
−59.5	1.00	−20	5.39
−50	1.60	−10	7.53
−40	2.50	0	10.2
−30	3.74	+10	13.6

H_2S.—(*Continued*)

t	p	t	p
20	17.7	80	62.6
30	22.6	90	74.5
40	28.3	**100.4**	**88.9**
50	35.1		
60	43.0		
70	52.1		

t	d_l
−59.5	0.965
+18.5	.91

T_B	A	B	C
213.6	4.820	0.83	0.63

H_2Se Hydrogen Selenide (p) (25, 64, 65, 125); (d) (64, 65)

t	p	t	p
−41.2	1.00	40	15
−40	1.06	60	23
−30	1.64	80	34
−20	2.45	100	48
−10	3.54	120	67
0	4.9	**138**	**88**
+10	6.7		
20	8.9		
30	11.6		

t	d_l
−41.2	2.12

T_B	A	B	C
231.9	4.725	0.83	0.63

NO Nitric Oxide (69, 78, 1, 173, 96, 121)

t	p	t	p
−151.0	1.0	−120	14.3
−150	1.1	−110	27
−140	3.0	−100	46
−130	7.0	**− 93**	**65**

T_B	A	B	C
122.1	5.780	0.30	0.00

N_2O Nitrous Oxide (p) (15, 42, 71, 175, 177, 174, 91, 92, 141, 84, 132, 133, 29, 82, 34, 50, 143, 185, 61, 62); (d) (70, 175, 35, 3, 4)

t	p	d_l	d_v
−89.5	1.00	1.226	0.0031
−80	1.70	1.199	.0050
−70	2.81	1.170	.0080
−60	4.40	1.140	.0122
−50	6.6	1.108	.018
−40	9.5	1.075	.025
−30	13.3	1.040	.035
−20	18.1	1.001	.048
−10	24.0	0.958	.066
0	31.3	.910	.087
+10	40.0	.856	.115
20	50.3	.784	.161
30	62.6	.679	.240
36.5	**71.7**	**0.451**	

T_B	A	B	C
183.6	4.725	0.57	0.48

$$d_m = 0.451\left[1 + 0.89\left(1 - \frac{T}{T_c}\right)\right].$$

N_2O_4 Nitrogen Peroxide (14, 72, 142, 149, 150)

t	p	t	p
21.3	1.00	60	5.03
30	1.48	70	7.26
40	2.28	80	10.3
50	3.42	90	14.4

N_2O_4.—(*Continued*)

t	p	t	p
100	19.8	140	62.2
110	26.8	150	80.7
120	35.9	**158**	**99**
130	47.5		

T_B	A	B	C
294.4	5.945	−0.74	0.00

Partial dissociation in vapor phase ($N_2O_4 \rightarrow 2NO_2$).

NH_3 Ammonia, *v.* p. 234

N_2H_4 Hydrazine (100, 101)

t	p	t	p
113.5	1.0	250	26
140	2.3	300	56
170	5	350	104
200	10	**380**	**145**

T_B	A	B	C
386.6	5.720	1.00	0.56

NOCl Nitrosyl Chloride (22, 172)

t	p	d_l	d_v
− 5.7	1.00	1.364	0.003
0	1.27	1.350	.004
+10	1.86	1.325	.006
20	2.67	1.300	.008
30	3.7	1.27	.010
40	5.1	1.24	.014

T_B	A	B	C
267.4	4.900	0.50	0.50

PH_3 Phosphine (p) (79, 21, 97, 98, 107, 163, 164, 122, 161); (d) (161, 163, 164, 107, 19)

t	p	d_l	d_v
−87.5	1.00	0.746	0.0023
−80	1.46	.738	.0032
−70	2.30	.725	.0050
−60	3.47	.712	.0073
−50	5.0	.698	.010
−40	7.1	.684	.014
−30	9.7	.668	.019
−20	12.9	.651	.025
−10	16.8	.633	.033
0	21.6	.613	.042
+10	27.4	.591	.053
20	34.2	.566	.067
30	42.3	.537	.086
40	51.9	.50	.11
51	**64**	**0.30**	

T_B	A	B	C
185.6	4.225	0.35	0.48

$$d_m = 0.30\left[1 + 0.58\left(1 - \frac{T}{T_c}\right)\right].$$

PF_3 Phosphorus Trifluoride (111, 112)

t	p	t	p
−95	1.0	−40	15
−80	2.4	−20	30
−60	7	−10	40

T_B	A	B	C
178.1	4.970	0.00	0.00

PF_5 Phosphorus Pentafluoride (110, 112)

t	p	t	p
−75	1.0	0	28
−60	2.4	+10	38
−30	9	16	46
T_B	A	B	C
198.1	5.280	0.00	0.00

PH_4Cl Phosphonium Chloride (21, 161, 169)

t	p	t	p
28.5*	48	40	61
30	50	45	68
35	55	**49**	**73**
T_B	A	B	C
188.1	4.480	0.00	0.00

* Triple point. (Partial decomposition in vapor phase, $PH_4Cl \rightarrow PH_3 + HCl$).

PSF_3 Phosphorus Sulfofluoride (171)

t	p	t	p
−10	4.6	+10	9.4
0	6.7	20	12.8
T_B	A	B	C
228.1	5.000	0.00	0.00

AsH_3 Arsine (61, 62, 118)

t	p	t	p
−55	1.00	−10	6.1
−40	2.0	0	8.4
−30	3.0	+10	11
−20	4.3	20	15
T_B	A	B	C
218.1	4.650	0.35	0.48

CO Carbon Monoxide (*p*) (39, 40, 56, 9, 120, 189, 191); (*d*) (9, 39)

t	p	d_l	d_v
−192.0	1.0	0.803	0.0044
−190	1.2	.794	.0054
−180	3.2	.748	.013
−170	6.7	.697	.027
−160	12.4	.639	.046
−150	20.9	.560	.088
−140	33.2	.420	.190
−139	**35**	**0.303**	
T_B	A	B	C
81.1	3.990	0.60	0.70

$$d_m = 0.303\left[1 + 0.84\left(1 - \frac{T}{T_c}\right)\right].$$

CO_2 Carbon Dioxide, *v.* p. 235

CH_4 Methane (*p*) (27, 87, 39, 38, 173, 96, 121, 190, 50, 82); (*d*) (27, 87, 39, 38, 13, 123)

t	p	d_l	d_v
−161.5	1.00	0.4245	0.0018
−160	1.13	.4222	.0020
−150	2.35	.4075	.0039
−140	4.38	.3916	.0068
−130	7.45	.3742	.0112
−120	11.84	.3547	.0175
−110	17.83	.3324	.0269
−100	25.7	.3050	.0413
− 90	35.9	.2668	.0665
− 82.1	**45.8**	**0.1615**	
T_B	A	B	C
111.6	4.000	0.22	0.30

$$d_m = 0.1615\left[1 + 0.77\left(1 - \frac{T}{T_c}\right)\right].$$

C_2H_2 Acetylene (*p*) (43, 106, 92, 93, 176, 177, 5, 6, 96, 82, 31); (*d*) (105, 106, 108, 109, 5)

t	p	d_l	d_v
−84.0*	1.00		
−81.5†	1.20	0.618	0.0021
−70	2.20	.601	.0036
−60	3.48	.585	.0056
−50	5.3	.568	.0085
−40	7.7	.551	.012
−30	10.9	.532	.017
−20	14.9	.512	.024
−10	20.0	.490	.033
0	26.3	.464	.045
+10	33.9	.435	.060
20	43.1	.400	.082
30	54.1	.346	.122
36.0	**61.7**	**0.230**	
T_B	A	B	C
188.1	4.675	0.48	0.50

$$d_m = 0.230\left[1 + 0.915\left(1 - \frac{T}{T_c}\right)\right].$$

* Normal sublimation point.
† Triple point.

C_2H_4 Ethylene (*p*) (79, 105, 28, 42, 177, 82, 173, 96, 188, 33, 32, 119, 127, 50, 183, 61, 62); (*d*) (103, 105, 96, 35, 36, 19)

t	p	d_l	d_v
−103.8	1.00	0.569	0.0022
−100	1.24	.564	.0026
− 90	2.10	.549	.0041
− 80	3.35	.534	.0063
− 70	5.07	.517	.0093
− 60	7.38	.500	.0133
− 50	10.4	.481	.019
− 40	14.2	.461	.025
− 30	18.9	.439	.034
− 20	24.8	.414	.046
− 10	31.9	.384	.062
0	40.6	.345	.088
+ 9.6	**50.6**	**0.210**	
T_B	A	B	C
169.3	4.330	0.59	0.70

$$d_m = 0.210\left[1 + 0.90\left(1 - \frac{T}{T_c}\right)\right].$$

C_2H_6 Ethane (*p*) (102, 138, 139, 28, 103, 45, 37, 94, 91, 126, 73, 124, 127, 96, 50); (*d*) (138, 105, 103, 91)

t	p	d_l	d_v
−88.62	1.000	0.546	0.00206
−80	1.556	.535	.00311
−70	2.471	.522	.00478
−60	3.743	.509	.00707
−50	5.449	.496	.0101
−40	7.672	.482	.0141
−30	10.50	.468	.0193
−20	14.02	.453	.0260
−10	18.34	.435	.0348
0	23.56	.416	.0463
+10	29.83	.393	.0619

C_2H_6.—(*Continued*)

t	p	d_l	d_v
20	37.28	0.363	0.085
30	46.1	.30	.14
32.2	**48.2**	**0.220**	
T_B	A	B	C
184.48	4.325	0.45	0.52

$$d_m = 0.220\left[1 + 0.43\left(1 - \frac{T}{T_c}\right) + 0.48\left(1 - \frac{T}{T_c}\right)^2\right].$$

For other hydrocarbons, *v.* p. 244.

CH_3Cl Methyl Chloride (p) (**81, 80, 158, 12, 68, 128, 23, 47, 76, 90, 143, 178, 179**); (d) (**158, 81, 80, 47, 90, 181, 182**)

t	p	d_l	d_v
−24.0	1.00	0.997	0.00255
−20	1.18	.990	.00297
−10	1.74	.973	.00427
0	2.50	.955	.00599
+10	3.49	.937	.00820
20	4.75	.918	.0110
30	6.35	.898	.0145
40	8.33	.878	.0189
50	10.7	.856	.0242
60	13.6	.832	.032
70	17.1	.809	.039
80	21.2	.783	.049
90	25.9	.756	.060
100	31.4	.725	.075
110	37.8	.690	.094
120	45.0	.647	.120
130	53.2	.592	.159
140	62.6	.497	.238
143.2	**65.8**	**0.365**	
T_B	A	B	C
249.1	4.540	0.22	0.30

$$d_m = 0.365\left[1 + 0.92\left(1 - \frac{T}{T_c}\right)\right].$$

C_2H_5Cl Ethyl Chloride (p) (**27, 86, 16, 146, 143, 135, 134, 179, 180, 52**); (d) (**27, 187, 59, 60, 195, 129, 140, 136**)

t	p	d_l	d_v
12.2	1.00	0.9060	0.00285
20	1.33	.8943	.00372
30	1.86	.8790	.00513
40	2.55	.8633	.00692
50	3.42	.8472	.00917
60	4.50	.8306	.0120
70	5.82	.8134	.0152
80	7.41	.7958	.0190
90	9.31	.7770	.0236
100	11.5	.7575	.0294
110	14.2	.737	.035
120	17.2	.715	.043
130	20.7	.691	.052
140	24.7	.665	.064
150	29.2	.636	.079
160	34.3	.602	.099
170	40.1	.559	.128
180	46.6	.494	.178
187	**51.6**	**0.331**	
T_B	A	B	C
285.3	4.615	0.48	0.50

$$d_m = 0.331\left[1 + 1.006\left(1 - \frac{T}{T_c}\right) - 0.064\left(1 - \frac{T}{T_c}\right)^2\right].$$

For other halogen substitution products of hydrocarbons, *v.* p. 245.

CS_2 Carbon Disulfide (p) (**79, 167, 159, 160, 144, 10, 11, 66, 74, 192, 146, 143**); (d) (**89, 63, 157, 54, 10, 192, 136**)

t	p	d_l	d_v
46.25	1.00	1.225	
50	1.13	t, °C	
60	1.54	52.17	0.003559
70	2.05	53.53	.003709
80	2.69	57.08	.004064
90	3.47	59.95	.004452
100	4.42	64.24	.005000
110	5.55	66.96	.005376
120	6.90	70.10	.005797
130	8.47	75.55	.006658
140	10.3	78.82	.007288
150	12.4	85.03	.008361
160	14.9	99.24	.01167
170	17.6	130.48	.02166
180	20.8	159.10	.03484
190	24.3	171.52	.04185
200	28.3	183.48	.05846
210	32.8	193.05	.07309
220	37.8	209.32	.09907
230	43.4	217.35	.1163
240	49.6	229.46	.1420
250	56.5	262.8	.2570
260	64.1	271.6	.3215
270	72.5	273.0	.3679
273	**75**		
T_B	A	B	C
319.35	4.525	0.35	0.48

COS Carbon Oxysulfide (**165, 77, 83**)

t	p	t	p
−50.2	1.0	40	18
−20	3	60	27
0	6	80	40
+20	11	**105**	**61**
T_B	A	B	C
222.9	4.465	0.65	0.70

C_2N_2 Cyanogen (p) (**130, 170, 43, 48, 50, 61, 62, 26**); (d) (**61, 62**)

t	p	t	p
−21.17	1.000	70	18.7
−20	1.055	80	23.4
−10	1.626	90	28.9
0	2.414	100	35.3
+10	3.47	110	42.8
20	4.85	120	51.5
30	6.61	**128.3**	**59.7**
40	8.80	t	d_l
50	11.5		
60	14.8	17	0.866
T_B	A	B	C
251.93	5.010	0.94	0.90

HCN Hydrogen Cyanide (p) (**131, 20, 75, 30**); *cf.* (**196**); (d) (**20, 19, 30, 67**)

t	p	d_l	d_v
25.65	1.00	0.695	0.0011
30	1.14	t	p
40	1.67		
50	2.31	60	3.15

HCN.—*(Continued)*

t	p	t	p
70	4.20	120	14.5
80	5.52	130	18.0
90	7.16	140	22.1
100	9.16	150	27.0
110	11.6	d_l	d_v
160	32.7	0.420	0.050
170	39.3	.365	.077
180	47.1	.290	.120
183.5	**50**	**0.20**	
T_B	A	B	C
298.75	4.840	0.22	0.70

ClCN Cyanogen Chloride (**143**)

t	p	t	p
12.7	1.00	50	3.58
20	1.32	60	4.80
30	1.88	70	6.33
40	2.62	80	8.22
T_B	A	B	C
285.8	4.800	0.00	0.00

For other C-compounds, *v.* p. 237.

SiH_4 Silane (**168, 2, 117**)

t	p	t	p
−112	1.00	−50	13
−100	1.9	−40	18
−90	3.0	−30	24
−80	4.6	−20	31
−70	6.7	−10	40
−60	9.5	**−3.5**	**48**
T_B	A	B	C
161.1	4.050	0.38	0.82

SiF_4 Silicon Tetrafluoride (**61, 62, 113**)

t	p	t	p
−77*	2	−30	19
−70	3	−20	27
−60	5	−10	38
−50	8	**−1.5**	**50**
−40	13		
T_B	A	B	C
185.1	5.335	0.00	0.00

* Triple point.

$GeCl_4$ Germanium Tetrachloride (**49, 116, 186**)

t	p	t	p
86.5	1.0	200	12
100	1.5	220	17
120	2.5	240	23
140	4.0	260	30
160	6.1	270	35
180	8.9	**277**	**38**
T_B	A	B	C
359.6	4.735	0.76	0.82

$SnCl_4$ Tin Tetrachloride (p) (**24, 152, 184, 193, 194**); (d) (**153, 193, 194**)

t	p	d_l	d_v
114.1	1.00	1.978	0.0085
120	1.18	1.963	.0099
130	1.53	1.935	.0127
140	1.96	1.907	.0162
150	2.48	1.878	0.0202
160	3.10	1.849	.0251
170	3.82	1.819	.0308
180	4.67	1.787	.0374
190	5.66	1.755	.0454
200	6.79	1.721	.0546
220	9.55	1.649	.0773
240	13.07	1.569	.108
260	17.48	1.476	.152
280	22.92	1.363	.216
300	29.56	1.21	.32
318.7	**37.0**	**0.742**	
T_B	A	B	C
387.2	4.710	0.76	0.82

$$d_m = 0.742\left[1 + 0.98\left(1 - \frac{T}{T_c}\right)\right].$$

BF_3 Boron Trifluoride (**61, 62, 113**)

t	p	t	p
−101	1.00	−70	5.4
−90	2.0	−60	8.4
−80	3.4	−50	12
T_B	A	B	C
172.1	4.930	0.76	0.82

BCl_3 Boron Trichloride (**137, 143, 166**)

t	p	t	p
12.4	1.00	50	3.2
20	1.3	60	4.2
30	1.8	70	5.4
40	2.4	80	6.8
T_B	A	B	C
285.5	4.480	0.76	0.82

LITERATURE

(For a key to the periodicals see end of volume)

(1) Adwentowski, *474*, **13:** 19; 10. (2) Adwentowski and Drozdowski, *165*, **1911:** 330. (3) Andréeff, *6*, **56:** 317; 59. (4) Andréeff, *13*, **110:** 1; 59. (5) Ansdell, *5*, **29:** 209; 79. (6) Ansdell, *135*, **40:** 136; 79. (7) Ansdell, *5*, **30:** 117; 80. (8) Ansdell, *135*, **41:** 75; 80. (9) Baly and Donnan, *4*, **81:** 907; 02.

(10) Battelli, *Mem. accad. sci. Torino*, **41:** 1; 90. (11) Battelli, *Mem. accad. sci. Torino*, **44:** 1; 93. (12) Baume, *42*, **6:** 1; 08. (13) Baume and Perrot, *34*, **148:** 39; 09. (14) Baume and Robert, *34*, **168:** 1199; 19. (15) Bergström, *50*, **26:** 876; 22. (16) Berthoud, *42*, **15:** 3; 17. (17) Berthoud, *37*, **5:** 513; 22. (18) Berthoud, *42*, **20:** 77; 23. (19) Bleekrode, *5*, **37:** 339; 84.

(20) Bredig and Teichmann, *9*, **31:** 449; 25. (21) Briner, *42*, **4:** 476; 06. (22) Briner and Pylkoff, *42*, **10:** 640; 12. (23) Brinkman, *Diss.*, Amsterdam, 1904. (24) Briscoe, *4*, **107:** 63; 15. (25) Bruylants and Dondeyne, *186*, **8:** 387; 22. (26) Bunsen, *8*, **46:** 97; 39. (27) Bureau of Standards, Washington, D. C., *0*. (28) Burrell and Robertson, *1*, **37:** 1893; 15. (29) Burrell and Robertson, *1*, **37:** 2691; 15.

(30) Bussy and Buignet, *6*, **3:** 231; 64. (31) Cailletet, *34*, **85:** 851; 77. (32) Cailletet, *34*, **94:** 1224; 82. (33) Cailletet, *34*, **99:** 213; 84. (34) Cailletet and Colardeau, *34*, **106:** 1489; 88. (35) Cailletet and Mathias, *51*, **5:** 549; 86. (36) Cailletet and Mathias, *34*, **102:** 1202; 86. (37) Cardoso, *149*, **30:** 432; 10. (38) Cardoso, *149*, **36:** 97; 13. (39) Cardoso, *42*, **13:** 312; 15.

(40) Cardoso, *149*, **39:** 400; 15. (41) Cardoso, *36*, **51 I:** 153; 21. (42) Cardoso and Arni, *42*, **10:** 504; 12. (43) Cardoso and Baume, *34*, **151:** 141; 10. (44) Cardoso and Baume, *42*, **10:** 509; 12. (45) Cardoso and Bell, *42*, **10:** 497; 12. (46) Cardoso and Germann, *42*, **11:** 632; 13. (47) Centnerszwer, *7*, **49:** 199; 04. (48) Chappuis and Rivière, *34*, **104:** 1504; 87. (49) Dennis and Hance, *93*, **122:** 265; 22.

(50) Dewar, *3*, **18:** 210; 84. (51) Dorsmann, *Diss.*, Amsterdam, 1908. (52) Drion, *6*, **56:** 221; 59. (53) Drozdowski and Pietrzak, *165*, **1913:** 219. (54) Erdmann and Unruh, *93*, **32:** 413; 02. (55) Estreicher, *7*, **20:** 605; 96. (56) Estreicher and Bobotek, *165*, **1913:** 451. (57) Estreicher and Schnerr, *Diss.*, Amsterdam, 1910. (58) Estreicher and Schnerr, *474*, **15:** 161; 13. (59) Eversheim, *8*, **8:** 539; 02.

(60) Eversheim, *Diss.*, Bonn, 1902. (61) Faraday, *62*, **135:** 155; 45. (62) Faraday, *6*, **15:** 257; 45. (63) Faust, *7*, **79:** 97; 12. (64) de Forcrand and Fonzes-

Diacon, *34*, **134**: 171, 229; 02. (65) de Forcrand and Fonzes-Diacon, *6*, **26**: 247; 02. (66) Galitzine, *8*, **41**: 588; 90. (67) Gay-Lussac, *8*, **53**: 138; 1816. (68) Gibbs, *1*, **27**: 851; 05. (69) Goldschmidt, *96*, **20**: 159; 23.

(70) Grunmach, *76*, **1901**: 914. (71) Grunmach, *76*, **1904**: 1198. (72) Guye and Drouginine, *42*, **8**: 473; 10. (73) Hainlen, *13*, **282**: 229; 94. (74) Hannay, *5*, **33**: 294; 82. (75) Hara and Shinozaki, *41*, **26**: 884; 23. (76) Hartman, *18*, **5**: 636; 00. *168*, No. **64**. (77) Hempel, *92*, **14**: 865; 01. (78) Henglein and Krüger, *93*, **130**: 181; 23. (79) Henning and Stock, *96*, **4**: 226; 21.

(80) Holst, *Diss.*, Zurich, 1914. (81) Holst, *475*, **6**: 48; 15. (82) Hunter, *50*, **10**: 330; 06. (83) Ilosvay, *27*, **37**: 294; 82. (84) Janssen, *133*, **1876**: 211. (85) Janssen, *Diss.*, Leiden, 1877. (86) Jenkin and Shorthose, *B67*. (87) Keyes, Taylor and Smith, *285*, **1**: 211; 22. (88) Knietsch, *25*, **34**: 4069; 01. (89) Körber, *8*, **37**: 1014; 12.

(90) Kuenen, *18*, **26**: 354; 93. (91) Kuenen, *3*, **40**: 173; 95. *168*, No. **16**. (92) Kuenen, *3*, **44**: 174; 97. (93) Kuenen, *7*, **24**: 667; 97. (94) Kuenen and Robson, *3*, **3**: 149; 02. (95) Ladenburg and Krügel, *25*, **32**: 1415; 99. (96) Ladenburg and Krügel, *25*, **32**: 1818; 99. (97) Leduc, *6*, **15**: 1; 98. (98) Leduc and Sacerdote, *34*, **125**: 397; 97. (99) Lichty, *1*, **34**: 1440; 12.

(100) Lobry de Bruyn, *25*, **28**: 3085; 95. (101) Lobry de Bruyn, *70*, **15**: 174; 96. (102) Loomis and Walters, *1*, **48**: 2051; 26. (103) Maass and McIntosh, *1*, **36**: 737; 14. (104) Maass and McIntosh, *69*, **8 III**: 65; 14. (105) Maass and Wright, *1*, **43**: 1098; 21. (106) McIntosh, *50*, **11**: 306; 07. (107) McIntosh and Steele, *5*, **73**: 450; 04. (108) Mathias, *34*, **148**: 1102; 09. (109) Mathias, *Recueil de Constants Physiques*, **1913**: 161.

(110) Moissan, *34*, **101**: 1490; 85. (111) Moissan, *6*, **6**: 433; 85. (112) Moissan, *34*, **138**: 789; 04. (113) Moissan, *34*, **139**: 711; 04. (114) Moles, *42*, **17**: 415; 19. (115) Nasini, *25*, **15**: 2878; 82. (116) Nilson and Pettersson, *7*, **1**: 27; 87. (117) Ogier, *34*, **88**: 236; 79. (118) Olszewski, *57*, **5**: 127; 84. (119) Olszewski, *34*, **99**: 133; 84.

(120) Olszewski, *34*, **99**: 706; 84. (121) Olszewski, *34*, **100**: 940; 85. (122) Olszewski, *57*, **7**: 371; 86. (123) Olszewski, *8*, **31**: 58; 87. (124) Olszewski, *165*, **1889**: No. 1, xxvii. (125) Olszewski, *165*, **1890**: 57. (126) Olszewski, *25*, **27**: 3305; 94. (127) Olszewski, *3*, **39**: 188; 95. (128) Onnes and Zakrzewski, *64P*, **7**: 233, 285, 377; 04. *168*, No. **92**: (129) Perkin, *52*, **31**: 481; 85.

(130) Perry and Bardwell, *1*, **47**: 2629; 25. (131) Perry and Porter, *1*, **48**: 299; 26. (132) Pictet, *149*, **61**: 16; 78. (133) Pictet, *6*, **13**: 145; 78. (134) Pictet, *34*, **120**: 43; 95. (135) Pictet and Altschul, *7*, **16**: 26; 95. (136) Pierre, *6*, **15**: 325; 45. (137) Podszus, *93*, **99**: 123; 17. (138) Porter, *1*, **48**: 2055; 26. (139) Prins, *64P*, **17**: 1095; 15.

(140) Ramsay, *4*, **35**: 463; 79. (141) Ramsay and Shields, *4*, **63**: 833; 93. (142) Ramsay and Young, *62*, **177**: 71; 87. (143) Regnault, *151*, **26**: 1862. (144) Rex, *7*, **55**: 355; 06. (145) Rupert, *1*, **31**: 851; 09. (146) Sajotschewsky, *427*, **3**: 741; 79. (147) Scheffer, *7*, **71**: 671; 10. (148) Scheffer, *64P*, **13**: 829; 11. (149) Scheffer and Treub, *7*, **81**: 308; 12.

(150) Scheffer and Treub, *64P*, **14**: 536; 12. (151) Schenck, *13*, **316**: 1; 01. (152) Schlundt, *50*, **5**; 503; 01. (153) Schulze and Hock, *7*, **86**: 445; 14. (154) Schultz-Sellack, *25*, **3**: 215; 70. (155) Schultz-Sellack, *27*, **14**: 154; 70. (156) Schwers, *42*, **9**: 325; 11. (157) Schwers, *4*, **101**: 1889; 12. (158) Shorthose, *B40*. (159) von Siemens, *8*, **42**: 871; 13.

(160) von Siemens, *Diss.*, Berlin, 1913. (161) Skinner, *5*, **42**: 283; 87. (162) Steele and Bagster, *4*, **97**: 2607; 10. (163) Steele, McIntosh and Archibald, *5*, **205**: 99; 05. (164) Steele, McIntosh and Archibald, *7*, **55**: 129; 06. (165) Stock and Kuss, *25*, **50**: 159; 17. (166) Stock and Priess, *25*, **47**: 3109; 14. (167) Stock and Seelig, *25*, **52**: 672; 19. (168) Stock and Somieski, *25*, **49**: 111; 16. (169) Tammann, *B57*.

(170) Terwen, *7*, **91**: 469; 16. (171) Thorpe and Rodger, *4*, **55**: 306; 89. (172) Trautz and Gerwig, *93*, **134**: 409; 24. (173) Travers, *The Experimental Study of Gases*, p. 243. London, Macmillan, 1901. (174) Villard, *51*, **3**: 441; 94. (175) Villard, *34*, **118**: 1096; 94. (176) Villard, *34*, **120**: 1262; 95. (177) Villard, *6*, **10**: 387; 97. (178) Vincent and Chappuis, *34*, **100**: 1216; 85. (179) Vincent and Chappuis, *51*, **5**: 58; 86.

(180) Vincent and Chappuis, *34*, **103**: 379; 86. (181) Vincent and Delachanal, *6*, **16**: 427; 79. (182) Vincent and Delachanal, *27*, **31**: 11; 79. (183) van der Waals, *Verslagen en Medeelingen der Koninklijke Akademie van Wetenschappen te Amsterdam, Afd. Natuurk.*, **15**: 426; 80. (184) Walden, *7*, **70**: 569; 10. (185) Wills, *4*, **27**: 21; 74. (186) Winkler, *52*, **34**: 177; 86. (187) Wismer, *50*, **26**: 301; 22. (188) Witkowski, *3*, **42**: 1; 96. (189) Wroblewski, *34*, **98**: 982; 84.

(190) Wroblewski, *34*, **99**: 136; 84. (191) Wroblewski, *8*, **25**: 371; 85. (192) Wüllner and Grotrian, *8*, **11**: 544; 80. (193) Young, *4*, **59**: 911; 91. (194) Young, *3*, **34**: 510; 92. (195) Zuk, *53*, **16**: 304; 84. (196) Sinozaki, Hara and Mitsukuri, *505*, **6**: 157; 26.

VAPOR PRESSURES AND ORTHOBARIC VOLUMES FOR H_2O, NH_3, CO_2 AND SO_2 ABOVE ONE ATMOSPHERE

F. G. Keyes

H_2O: Vapor Pressures of Water in Atm.

Reichsanstalt values corrected to I. C. T. temperature scale

t, °C	0	1	2	3	4	5	6	7	8	9
100	1.0000	1.0362	1.0735	1.1120	1.1514	1.1922	1.2341	1.2771	1.3216	1.3670
110	1.4139	1.4621	1.5115	1.5624	1.6148	1.6684	1.7236	1.7802	1.8384	1.8982
120	1.9594	2.0221	2.0869	2.1531	2.2208	2.2907	2.3620	2.4353	2.5103	2.5873
130	2.6660	2.7466	2.8295	2.9140	3.0010	3.0885	3.1794	3.2739	3.3693	3.4669
140	3.567	3.669	3.773	3.880	3.989	4.101	4.215	4.332	4.451	4.574
150	4.698	4.825	4.956	5.088	5.224	5.363	5.505	5.649	5.796	5.947
160	6.100	6.257	6.417	6.579	6.746	6.916	7.088	7.265	7.445	7.629
170	7.817	8.007	8.202	8.399	8.603	8.808	9.017	9.231	9.448	9.670
180	9.895	10.124	10.358	10.596	10.838	11.084	11.337	11.592	11.852	12.116
190	12.386	12.658	12.936	13.220	13.507	13.801	14.099	14.401	14.710	15.023
200	15.341	15.665	15.994	16.327	16.666	17.012	17.365	17.721	18.082	18.451
210	18.823	19.204	19.590	19.980	20.379	20.780	21.190	21.606	22.029	22.457
220	22.889	23.331	23.780	24.234	24.693	25.162	25.635	26.117	26.605	27.101
230	27.603	28.112	28.628	29.150	29.682	30.221	30.767	31.319	31.881	32.449
240	33.027	33.610	34.203	34.802	35.411	36.028	36.652	37.284	37.926	38.575
250	39.234	39.900	40.576	41.259	41.954	42.655	43.365	44.086	44.815	45.551
260	46.300	47.055	47.820	48.595	49.381	50.175	50.977	51.792	52.614	53.447
270	54.291	55.145	56.008	56.881	57.766	58.659	59.565	60.479	61.407	62.345
280	63.295	64.255	65.224	66.206	67.201	68.208	69.226	70.257	71.299	72.354
290	73.42	74.49	75.59	76.69	77.81	78.94	80.08	81.24	82.40	83.59
300	84.78	85.99	87.21	88.44	89.68	90.94	92.20	93.49	94.80	96.09
310	97.40	98.74	100.10	101.47	102.85	104.25	105.65	107.07	108.51	109.96
320	111.43	112.92	114.42	115.94	117.47	119.01	120.57	122.14	123.74	125.36
330	126.99	128.63	130.29	131.97	133.66	135.37	137.10	138.85	140.62	142.40
340	144.20	146.01	147.84	149.67	151.55	153.44	155.36	157.28	159.23	161.19
350	163.16	165.16	167.17	169.21	171.26	173.33	175.43	177.56	179.71	181.88
360	184.07	186.28	188.52	190.78	193.07	195.42	197.79	200.17	202.58	205.02
370	207.49	209.98	212.51	215.09	217.72 (crit.)					

Saturated Specific Volumes

Liquid water (23, 40, 50)				Liquid water (23, 40, 50)				Water vapor (32)*				Water vapor (32)*			
t, °C	cm³/g	t, °C	cm³/g	t, °C	cm³/g	t, °C	cm³/g	t, °C	cm³/g	t, °C	cm³/g	t, °C	cm³/g	t, °C	cm³/g
100	1.0434	150	1.0881	200	1.1569	250	1.252	100	1677	125	768.9	150	392.4	175	217.2
110	1.0510	160	1.0997	210	1.1739	260	1.274	105	1420	130	667.1	155	346.6	180	194.9
120	1.0592	170	1.1124	220	1.1919	270	1.297	110	1208	135	581.0	160	307.1		
130	1.0680	180	1.1262	230	1.211			115	1034	140	508.0	165	272.8		
140	1.0776	190	1.1410	240	1.231			120	889.8	145	445.8	170	243.1		

* In view of the fact that the values (24) are obtained by calculation from vapor pressure and latent heat measurements, not as much consideration was given to them as to the direct measurements (32). The values given in the table are, however, in essential agreement with those (24); *cf. also* (5, 17, 38).

NH_3

Vapor Pressure of Liquid Ammonia, Atm. ± 0.05% (8, 10, 16, 19, 22, 28, 29, 30, 37, 39, 41, 48, 54)

From −78 to +70°

$$\log_{10}P = 27.376004 - \frac{1914.9569}{T} - 8.4598324\log_{10}T + 2.39309 \times 10^{-3}T + 2.955214 \times 10^{-6}T^2$$

or

$$\log_{10}P = 9.584586 - \frac{1648.6068}{T} - 1.638646 \times 10^{-2}T + 2.403276 \times 10^{-5}T^2 - 1.168708 \times 10^{-8}T^3$$

From +50 to +132.9°

$$\log_{10}P = 2.050418 - \frac{T_c - T}{T}[2.9771 - 1.492414 \times 10^{-3}(T_c - T) + 1.36142 \times 10^{-5}(T_c - T)^2 - 5.47917 \times 10^{-8}(T_c - T)^3]$$

$$T_c = (132.9 + 273.1) = 406$$

t, °C	0	1	2	3	4	5	6	7	8	9
−70	0.1078	0.1001	0.0929	0.0861	0.0797	0.0738	0.0683	0.0631	0.0582	0.0537
−60	0.2161	0.2022	0.1891	0.1767	0.1651	0.1541	0.1437	0.1339	0.1246	0.1159
−50	0.4034	0.3800	0.3578	0.3367	0.3167	0.2977	0.2796	0.2624	0.2461	0.2307
−40	0.7083	0.6712	0.6357	0.6017	0.5693	0.5383	0.5087	0.4805	0.4536	0.4279
−30	1.1799	1.1236	1.0695	1.0175	0.9676	0.9197	0.8738	0.8297	0.7875	0.7471
−20	1.8774	1.7956	1.7166	1.6405	1.5671	1.4963	1.4281	1.3624	1.2992	1.2384
−10	2.8703	2.7555	2.6443	2.5368	2.4328	2.3322	2.2349	2.1408	2.0499	1.9621
− 0	4.2380	4.0818	3.9303	3.7832	3.6405	3.5020	3.3677	3.2375	3.1112	2.9888
+ 0	4.2380	4.3985	4.5640	4.7340	4.9090	5.0895	5.2750	5.4655	5.6610	5.8620
10	6.0685	6.2805	6.4985	6.7225	6.9520	7.1875	7.4290	7.6770	7.9310	8.1915
20	8.4585	8.7320	9.0125	9.3000	9.5940	9.8955	10.2040	10.5195	10.8430	11.1735
30	11.512	11.858	12.212	12.574	12.943	13.321	13.708	14.103	14.507	14.919
40	15.339	15.770	16.209	16.656	17.113	17.580	18.056	18.542	19.038	19.543
50	20.059	20.585	21.121	21.667	22.224	22.793	23.372	23.962	24.562	25.174
60	25.797	26.432	27.079	27.737	28.407	29.089	29.784	30.491	31.211	31.942
70	32.687	33.454	34.227	35.013	35.813	36.626	37.453	38.294	39.149	40.018
80	40.902	41.799	42.712	43.640	44.582	45.539	46.511	47.500	48.503	49.522
90	50.558	51.609	52.677	53.760	54.860	55.977	57.111	58.261	59.429	60.613
100	61.816	63.037	64.274	65.530	66.804	68.096	69.406	70.736	72.084	73.451
110	74.837	76.244	77.668	79.114	80.578	82.064	83.570	85.097	86.644	88.212
120	89.802	91.413	93.045	94.700	96.376	98.075	99.796	101.541	103.309	105.099
130	106.913	108.751	110.613							
132.9	112.3 (crit.)									

Specific Volume of Liquid Ammonia under Saturation Pressure, cm³/g (7, 15, 18, 20, 27, 34)

$$V = \frac{4.2830 + 0.813055(133 - t)^{1/2} - 0.0082861(133 - t)}{1 + 0.424805(133 - t)^{1/2} + 0.015938(133 - t)};\ \text{range, } -70 \text{ to } 130°\text{C}$$

t, °C	0	1	2	3	4	5	6	7	8	9
−70	1.3788	1.3766	1.3745	1.3724	1.3702	1.3681	1.3660	1.3639	1.3618	1.3597
−60	1.4010	1.3988	1.3965	1.3942	1.3920	1.3898	1.3876	1.3854	1.3832	1.3810
−50	1.4245	1.4221	1.4197	1.4173	1.4150	1.4126	1.4103	1.4079	1.4056	1.4033
−40	1.4493	1.4468	1.4442	1.4417	1.4392	1.4367	1.4342	1.4318	1.4293	1.4269
−30	1.4757	1.4730	1.4703	1.4676	1.4649	1.4623	1.4597	1.4571	1.4545	1.4519
−20	1.5037	1.5008	1.4980	1.4951	1.4923	1.4895	1.4867	1.4839	1.4811	1.4784
−10	1.5338	1.5307	1.5276	1.5245	1.5215	1.5185	1.5155	1.5125	1.5096	1.5066
− 0	1.5660	1.5627	1.5594	1.5561	1.5528	1.5496	1.5464	1.5432	1.5400	1.5369
+ 0	1.5660	1.5694	1.5727	1.5761	1.5796	1.5831	1.5866	1.5901	1.5936	1.5972
10	1.6008	1.6045	1.6081	1.6118	1.6156	1.6193	1.6231	1.6270	1.6308	1.6347
20	1.6386	1.6426	1.6466	1.6506	1.6547	1.6588	1.6630	1.6672	1.6714	1.6757
30	1.6800	1.6844	1.6888	1.6932	1.6977	1.7023	1.7069	1.7115	1.7162	1.7209
40	1.7257	1.7305	1.7354	1.7404	1.7454	1.7504	1.7555	1.7607	1.7659	1.7712

Specific Volume of Liquid Ammonia under Saturation Pressure, cm^3/g.—(*Continued*)

t, °C	0	1	2	3	4	5	6	7	8	9
50	1.7766	1.7820	1.7875	1.7931	1.7987	1.8044	1.8102	1.8160	1.8220	1.8280
60	1.8341	1.8403	1.8465	1.8529	1.8593	1.8658	1.8725	1.8792	1.8860	1.8930
70	1.9000	1.9072	1.9145	1.9219	1.9294	1.9370	1.9448	1.9528	1.9608	1.9690
80	1.9774	1.9859	1.9946	2.0034	2.0124	2.0217	2.0311	2.0407	2.0505	2.0605
90	2.0708	2.0813	2.0920	2.1030	2.1143	2.1258	2.1377	2.1498	2.1623	2.1752
100	2.1885	2.2021	2.2162	2.2307	2.2510	2.2612	2.2773	2.2940	2.3112	2.3292
110	2.3478	2.3674	2.3877	2.4080	2.4314	2.4548	2.4796	2.5058	2.5393	2.5632
120	2.5948	2.6288	2.6656	2.7055	2.7495	2.7979	2.8523	2.9142	2.9851	3.0710
130	3.1769	3.3175	3.5315	4.2830 (crit.)						

Specific Volume of Saturated NH_3 Vapor, cm^3/g (7, 18, 21, 25, 29, 51, 55)

$$\log_{10} v = \frac{1939.032}{T} - 32.0661 + 10.70409 \log_{10} T + 8.62366 \times 10^{-2}(406.1 - T)^{1/2} + 2.667 \times 10^{-3}(406.1 - T);\ T = (273.1 + t);$$

range, − 70 to +50°C

t, °C	0	1	2	3	4	5	6	7	8	9
−70	8 976.2	9 617.9	10 314	11 069	11 889	12 781	13 752	14 809		
−60	4 690.3	4 988.9	5 310.0	5 655.8	6 028.3	6 429.9	6 863.3	7 331.2	7 837.0	8 384.1
−50	2 620.7	2 770.3	2 929.9	3 100.7	3 283.4	3 479.0	3 688.5	3 913.1	4 154.0	4 412.5
−40	1 550.2	1 630.0	1 714.7	1 804.8	1 900.5	2 002.4	2 110.8	2 226.3	2 349.4	2 480.7
−30	962.82	1 007.8	1 055.3	1 105.5	1 158.7	1 214.8	1 274.4	1 337.4	1 404.2	1 475.1
−20	623.48	650.06	678.03	707.45	738.44	771.06	805.44	841.69	879.92	920.25
−10	418.46	434.84	452.02	470.02	488.88	508.68	529.45	551.25	574.15	598.20
− 0	289.62	300.10	311.04	322.47	334.42	346.90	359.95	373.59	387.87	402.82
+ 0	289.62	279.58	269.95	260.73	251.88	243.39	235.25	227.43	219.92	212.71
10	205.79	199.13	192.73	186.58	180.66	174.97	169.49	164.22	159.14	154.25
20	149.53	144.99	140.61	136.39	132.33	128.40	124.61	120.96	117.43	114.02
30	110.73	107.55	104.48	101.51	98.640	95.865	93.181	90.586	88.074	85.643
40	83.290	81.012	78.806	76.670	74.600	72.594	70.650	68.766	66.939	65.167
50	63.448									

50 to 100° (53, 55)

t, °C	50	60	70	80	90	100
cm³/g	63.49	48.8	37.7	29.3	22.8	17.6

CO_2

Vapor Pressure of the Liquid in Atm. (1, 2, 4, 12, 19, 31, 33, 36, 43, 45, 46, 48, 49, 52)

$$\log_{10} P = 1.8630096 - \frac{T_c - T}{T}[3.0067 - 9.03453 \times 10^{-3}(T_c - T) + 2.37353 \times 10^{-4}(T_c - T)^2 - 3.7788 \times 10^{-6}(T_c - T)^3 + 3.27304 \times 10^{-8}(T_c - T)^4 - 1.11383 \times 10^{-10}(T_c - T)^5];\ T_c = (273.1 + 31.1);$$

range, − 56.6 to 31.1°C

t, °C	0	1	2	3	4	5	6	7	8	9
−56.6	5.1148									
−50	6.7446	6.4751	6.2139	5.9608	5.7156	5.4782	5.2485			
−40	9.9251	9.5650	9.2147	8.8740	8.5426	8.2207	7.9078	7.6039	7.3089	7.0225
−30	14.099	13.631	13.176	12.733	12.299	11.877	11.466	11.065	10.675	10.295
−20	19.437	18.845	18.267	17.702	17.150	16.611	16.084	15.569	15.067	14.577
−10	26.129	25.393	24.673	23.967	23.277	22.601	21.940	21.293	20.661	20.042
− 0	34.379	33.478	32.595	31.728	30.879	30.046	29.231	28.431	27.648	26.881
+ 0	34.379*	35.298	36.235	37.190	38.163	39.155	40.166	41.197	42.247	43.316
10	44.406	45.517	46.648	47.800	48.974	50.170	51.388	52.629	53.895	55.182
20	56.495	57.833	59.197	60.588	62.006	63.452	64.928	66.434	67.971	69.540
30	71.143	72.780								
31.1	72.947									

* A new determination by Bridgeman (9) gives 34.4009 ± 0.0013 atm. at 0° and this value is recommended as a fixed point for the calibration of pressure gages.

Specific Volume of Liquid Carbon Dioxide under Saturation Pressure, cm^3/g (1, 6, 13, 26)

$$\frac{1}{V} = 0.925 - 5.8836 \times 10^{-3}t - 4.4189 \times 10^{-5}t^2 - 1.3486 \times 10^{-6}t^3 - 3.64025 \times 10^{-8}t^4 - 3.2475 \times 10^{-10}t^5;$$

range, −40 to +20°C

t, °C	0	1	2	3	4	5	6	7	8	9
−56.6	0.8482									
−50	0.8658	0.8636	0.8606	0.8576	0.8554	0.8525	0.8496			
−40	0.8961	0.8929	0.8897	0.8865	0.8834	0.8803	0.8780	0.8749	0.8718	0.8688
−30	0.9302	0.9268	0.9226	0.9191	0.9158	0.9124	0.9091	0.9058	0.9025	0.8993

Specific Volume of Liquid Carbon Dioxide under Saturation Pressure, cm^3/g.—(*Continued*)

t, °C	0	1	2	3	4	5	6	7	8	9
−20	0.9699	0.9653	0.9615	0.9579	0.9533	0.9497	0.9452	0.9416	0.9381	0.9337
−10	1.0194	1.0142	1.0091	1.0040	0.9990	0.9940	0.9892	0.9843	0.9794	0.9747
− 0	1.0810	1.0753	1.0683	1.0616	1.0548	1.0482	1.0428	1.0362	1.0309	1.0256
+ 0	1.0811	1.0881	1.0953	1.1025	1.1099	1.1186	1.1261	1.1350	1.1442	1.1534
10	1.1628	1.1737	1.1834	1.1947	1.2063	1.2195	1.2330	1.2469	1.2626	1.2788
20	1.2953	1.3141	1.3351	1.3587	1.3831	1.4104	1.4430	1.4815	1.5267	1.5873
30	1.6722	1.8692								
31.1	2.1547									

Specific Volume of Saturated CO_2 Vapor, cm^3/g (1, 6, 13)

$$\frac{1}{v} = 0.09743 + 2.854 \times 10^{-3}t + 4.419 \times 10^{-5}t^2 + 1.349 \times 10^{-6}t^3 + 3.640 \times 10^{-8}t^4 + 3.25 \times 10^{-10}t^5;$$ range, −40 to + 20°C

t, °C	0	1	2	3	4	5	6	7	8	9
−30	27.19									
−20	19.22	19.91	20.62	21.36	22.11	22.89	23.71	24.53	25.40	26.26
−10	13.83	14.27	14.73	15.21	15.70	16.23	16.78	17.35	17.95	18.57
− 0	10.26	10.57	10.88	11.21	11.54	11.89	12.25	12.62	13.01	13.41
+ 0	10.26	9.97	9.68	9.41	9.13	8.85	8.59	8.33	8.06	7.81
10	7.57	7.30	7.04	6.80	6.58	6.33	6.14	5.92	5.68	5.46
20	5.26	5.05	4.83	4.61	4.39	4.35	3.97	3.76	3.53	3.28
30	3.00	2.54								
31.1	2.15									

SO_2

Vapor Pressure of the Liquid in Atm. (8, 11, 19, 39, 42, 44, 47, 48) T_B = B. P., °K

$$\log_{10} P = \frac{T - T_B}{T}[5.0762 - 4.03843 \times 10^{-3}(T - T_B) + 1.79492 \times 10^{-5}(T - T_B)^2 + 1.27073 \times 10^{-7}(T - T_B)^3 - 8.50057 \times 10^{-10}(T - T_B)^4];$$ $T_B = (273.1 + 9.99)$; range, − 70 to + 40°C

t, °C	0	2	4	6	8	t, °C	0	5
−70	0.02635	0.02236	0.02145*			50	8.176	9.385
−60	.05699	.04916	.04227	0.03623	0.03095	60	10.729	12.219
−50	.11411	.09989	.08719	.07589	.06586	70	13.867	15.684
−40	.2135	.1893	.1674	.1477	.1300	80	17.682	19.872
−30	.3759	.3371	.3018	.2695	.2401	90	22.268	24.878
−20	.6274	.5686	.5142	.4641	.4181	100	27.714	30.784
−10	.9995	.9138	.8340	.7599	.6911	110	34.091	37.641
− 0	1.529	1.408	1.295	1.190	1.091	120	41.432	45.457
+ 0	1.529	1.657	1.793	1.938	2.092	130	49.705	54.157
10	2.256	2.429	2.613	2.807	3.012	140	58.783	63.549
20	3.228	3.456	3.697	3.951	4.217	150	68.405	73.296
30	4.498	4.793	5.102	5.427	5.768	157	75.245	
40	6.125	6.499	6.890	7.300	7.729			

* At −72.5°.

Specific Volume of the Liquid under Saturation Pressure (3, 13, 14, 35)

$$\frac{1}{V} = 1.434 - 2.486 \times 10^{-3}t - 2.63 \times 10^{-6}t^2 - 5.591 \times 10^{-8}t^3 + 8.1 \times 10^{-11}t^4;$$ range, −50 to + 90°C

t	cm^3/g	t	cm^3/g	t	cm^3/g	t	cm^3/g	t	cm^3/g	t	cm^3/g
		2	0.6998	26	0.7315	50	0.7722	74	0.8230	98	0.8913
−50	0.6423	4	0.7022	28	0.7348	52	0.7758	76	0.8278	100	0.8977
−45	0.6472	6	0.7047	30	0.7375	54	0.7794	78	0.8333	105	0.9158
−40	0.6523	8	0.7072	32	0.7407	56	0.7837	80	0.8382	110	0.9355
−35	0.6575	10	0.7097	34	0.7440	58	0.7874	82	0.8432	115	0.9570
−30	0.6627	12	0.7123	36	0.7474	60	0.7918	84	0.8489	120	0.9823
−25	0.6680	14	0.7153	38	0.7508	62	0.7962	86	0.8547	125	1.0111
−20	0.6739	16	0.7179	40	0.7536	64	0.8000	88	0.8606	130	1.0449
−15	0.6798	18	0.7205	42	0.7570	66	0.8046	90	0.8658	135	1.0858
−10	0.6859	20	0.7231	44	0.7610	68	0.8091	92	0.8718	140	1.1363
− 5	0.6916	22	0.7262	46	0.7646	70	0.8137	94	0.8780	145	1.2019
0	0.6974	24	0.7289	48	0.7680	72	0.8183	96	0.8850	150	1.3038
										157.2	1.9305

Specific Volume of the Vapor under Saturation Pressure, cm^3/g (13, 14)

t, °C	0	2	4	6	8
0					156.3
10	147.1	137.0	128.2	119.0	111.1
20	103.1	97.09	90.91	86.21	81.30
30	75.76	70.92	66.67	62.50	58.14
40	54.64	51.02	48.08	45.25	42.74
50	40.65	38.61	36.76	34.84	33.33
60	31.85	30.49	29.15	28.01	26.88
70	25.77	24.81	23.81	22.88	21.93
80	20.92	19.96	19.01	18.15	17.24
90	16.39	15.60	14.88	14.20	13.51
100	12.94	12.32	11.76	11.25	10.79
110	10.31	9.833	9.381	8.937	8.503
120	8.078	7.669	7.267	6.878	6.502
130	6.146	5.800	5.473	5.147	4.845
140	4.554	4.274	4.008	3.755	3.509
150	3.256	2.990	2.670		

LITERATURE

For a key to the periodicals see end of volume)

(1) Amagat, *34*, **114**: 1093; 92. (2) Amagat, *34*, **114**: 1322; 92. (3) Andréeff, *13*, **110**: 1; 59. (4) Andrews, *5*, **24**: 455; 76. (5) Battelli, *6*, **26**: 394; 92. **3**: 408; 94. (6) Behn, *8*, **3**: 733; 00. (7) Berthoud, *37*, **1**: 84; 18. (8) Blümcke, *8*, **34**: 10; 88. (9) Bridgeman, *1*, **49**: 1174; 27.

(10) Burrell and Robertson, *1*, **37**: 2482; 15. (11) Burrell and Robertson, *1*, **37**: 2691; 15. (12) Cailletet, *34*, **112**: 1170; 91. (13) Cailletet and Mathias, *51*, **5**: 549; 86. (14) Cardoso, *149*, **34**: 127; 12. (15) Cragoe and Harper, *31A*, **17**: 287; 21. (16) Cragoe, Meyers and Taylor, *1*, **42**: 206; 20. (17) Dieterici, *8*, **38**: 1; 89. (18) Dieterici, *148*, **11**: 21; 04. (19) Faraday, *62*, **135**: 155; 45.

(20) Fitzgerald, *50*, **16**: 621; 12. (21) Goodenough and Mosher, *86*, **10**: No. 66; 13. (22) Henning and Stock, *96*, **4**: 226; 21. (23) Hirn, *6*, **10**: 32; 67. (24) Holborn, Scheel and Henning, *Wärmetabellen*, Braunschweig, Vieweg, 1919. (25) Holst, *462*, **6**: 48; 15. (26) Jenkin, *5*, **98**: 170; 20. (27) Keyes, *382*, **1**: No. 1, 9; 14. (28) Keyes, *382*, **7**: 371; 21. (29) Keyes and Brownlee, *Thermodynamic Properties of Ammonia.* New York, Wiley, 1916.

(30) Keyes and Brownlee, *1*, **40**: 25; 18. (31) Keyes and Kenney, *382*, **3**: No. 4, 17; 17. (32) Knoblauch, Linde and Klebe, *414*, **21**: 33; 05. (33) Kuenen and Robson, *3*, **3**: 149; 02. (34) Lange, *317*, **21**: 191; 98. (35) Lange, *92*, **12**: 275; 99. (36) Meyer and Van Dusen, *382*, **13**: 180; 26. (37) Mündel, *7*, **85**: 435; 13. (38) Perot, *6*, **13**: 145; 88. (39) Pictet, *Nouvelles machines frigorifiques.* Paris, Gauthier-Villars, 1885.

(40) Ramsay and Young, *62*, **183**: 107; 93. (41) Regnault, *151*, **26**: 506; 62. (42) Regnault, *151*, **26**: 581; 62. (43) Regnault, *151*, **26**: 615; 62. (44) Sajotschewski, *427*, **3**: 741; 79. (45) Scheffer, *64P*, **21**: 664; 19. (46) von Siemans, *8*, **42**: 871; 13. (47) Steele and Bagster, *4*, **97**: 2607; 10. (48) Stock, Henning and Kuss, *25*, **54**: 1119; 21. (49) Villard, *6*, **10**: 387; 97.

(50) Waterston, *3*, **26**: 116; 63. (51) Wobsa, *148*, **15**: 11; 08. (52) Zeleny and Smith, *63*, **7**: 667; 06. (53) Keyes, *O.* (54) Cragoe, Myers and Taylor, *31A*, **16**: 1; 20. (55) Cragoe, McKelvy and O'Connor, *31A:* **18**: 707: 23.

VAPOR PRESSURES AND ORTHOBARIC DENSITIES ABOVE ONE ATMOSPHERE, TWO-PHASE, LIQUID—VAPOR, ORGANIC COMPOUNDS[1]

ALBERT F. O. GERMANN

p = vapor pressure in normal atmospheres.

d_l (resp. d_v) = density of saturated liquid (resp. vapor) in g per cm^3.

$d_m = \frac{1}{2}(d_l + d_v)$.

Accuracy, *ca.* ±5 in last figure given.

All values at the critical point are given in bold-face type.

C-TABLE, THE C-ARRANGEMENT

CCl_2O Phosgene (1, 10, 11, 17)

t, °C	$p_{atm.}$	d_l	d_v
7.95	1.00	1.409	0.005
10	1.08	1.405	0.005
20	1.55	1.381	0.007
30	2.17	1.357	0.009
40	2.97	1.332	0.012
50	3.99	1.306	0.016
60	5.25	1.280	0.020
70	6.81	1.252	0.024
80	8.68	1.224	0.030
90	10.94	1.195	0.037
100	13.6	1.165	0.046
110	16.7	1.134	0.057
120	20.3	1.100	0.072
130	24.4	1.062	0.090
140	29.1	1.017	0.112
150	34.4	0.966	0.142
160	40.4	0.903	0.182
170	47.0	0.826	0.239
180	54.4	0.685	0.359
182	**56**	**0.520**	

$d_m = 0.715 - 1070 \times 10^{-6}t$.

CH_4O Methyl Alcohol (25, 37)

t, °C	$p_{atm.}$	d_l	d_v
64.7	1.000	0.7510	0.001222
70	1.220	.7460	.001465
80	1.764	.7355	.002084
90	2.494	.7250	.002907
100	3.452	.7140	.003984
110	4.688	.7020	.005376
120	6.255	.6900	.007142
130	8.213	.6770	.009379
140	10.63	.6640	.01216
150	13.57	.6495	.01562
160	17.11	.6340	.01994
170	21.34	.6160	.02526
180	26.35	.5980	.03186
190	32.23	.5770	.04010
200	39.08	.5530	.05075
210	47.03	.5255	.06521
220	56.18	.4900	.08635
225	61.25	.4675	.1003
230	66.67	.4410	.1187
235	72.47	.4054	.1438
240.0	**78.67**	**0.2722**	

$d_m = 0.4050 - 447.9 \times 10^{-6}t + 133 \times 10^{-9}t^2 - 2376 \times 10^{-12}t^3$.

[1] Except hydrocarbons and their halogen derivatives for which *v.* p. 244.

CH_4S Methylmercaptan (3)

t, °C	$p_{atm.}$	d_l	d_v
6.0	1.000	0.888	0.002
10	1.16	.882	.002
20	1.68	.868	.003
30	2.36	.854	.004
40	3.22	.840	.004
50	4.33	.827	.005
60	5.68	.813	.005
70	7.36	.799	.006
80	9.33	.783	.008
90	11.7	.768	.011
100	14.5	.752	.015
110	17.6	.734	.020
120	21.3	.714	.027
130	25.5	.692	.036
140	30.3	.669	.048
150	35.7	.643	.062
160	41.6	.612	.079
170	48.6	.577	.102
180	56.2	.535	.131
190	65.0	.477	.179
196.8	**71.4**	**0.323**	

$d_m = 0.449 - 675 \times 10^{-6}t + 180 \times 10^{-9}t^2$.

CH_5N Methylamine (2)

t, °C	$p_{atm.}$	t, °C	$p_{atm.}$
− 6.6	1.000	80	16.7
0	1.33	90	20.9
+10	2.00	100	25.9
20	2.92	110	31.9
30	4.16	120	38.5
40	5.93	130	46.3
50	7.70	140	55.1
60	10.15	150	65.5
70	13.12	**156.9**	**73.6**

C_2H_3N Acetonitrile (31); *cf.* (29, 32)

t, °C	$p_{atm.}$	d_l	d_v
80		0.717	0.001
90		.706	002
100		.694	002
110		.682	.003
120		.670	.004
130		.658	.005
140		.646	.007
150		.633	.009
160		.620	.011
170		.605	.013
180		.590	.015
190		.573	.018
200		.555	.022
210		.536	.027
220		.514	.034
230		.492	.042
240		.467	.053
250		.439	.068

C_2H_3N.—(*Continued*)

t, °C	$p_{atm.}$	d_l	d_v
260		0.399	0.091
270		.342	.139
274.7		**0.240**	

$d_m = 0.402 - 495 \times 10^{-6}t - 350 \times 10^{-9}t^2$.

$C_2H_4O_2$ Acetic Acid (**21, 22, 36, 37**)

t, °C	$p_{atm.}$	d_l	d_v
118.5	1.000	0.9380	0.003150
120	1.058	.9362	.003271
130	1.426	.9235	.004275
140	1.884	.9091	.005515
150	2.452	.8963	.00703
160	3.149	.8829	.00887
170	3.994	.8694	.01084
180	5.014	.8555	.01370
190	6.233	.8413	.01681
200	7.682	.8265	.02052
210	9.391	.8109	.02488
220	11.39	.7941	.03021
230	13.73	.7764	.03626
240	16.42	.7571	.04327
250	19.52	.7364	.05163
260	23.07	.7136	.06165
270	27.11	.6900	.07365
280	31.67	.6629	.0883
290	36.79	.6334	.1073
300	42.54	.5950	.1331
310	48.93	.5423	.1718
320	56.01	.4615	.2417
321.6	**57.21**	**0.3506**	

$d_m = 0.5355 - 536.6 \times 10^{-6}t - 119.1 \times 10^{-9}t^2$.

$C_2H_4O_2$ Methyl Formate (**39**); *cf.* (**37**)

t, °C	$p_{atm.}$	d_l	d_v
31.9	1.000	0.9569	0.002468
40	1.355	.9447	.003236
50	1.903	.9294	.004456
60	2.608	.9133	.006039
70	3.500	.8968	.008032
80	4.610	.8803	.01049
90	5.969	.8634	.01350
100	7.614	.8452	.01723
110	9.582	.8264	.02160
120	11.91	.8070	.02688
130	14.64	.7860	.03344
140	17.83	.7638	.04124
150	21.46	.7403	.05063
160	25.64	.7136	.06231
170	30.40	.6844	.07634
180	35.76	.6521	.09434
190	41.78	6148	.1178
200	48.50	5658	.1524
210	55.95	.4857	.2188
214.0	**59.15**	**0.3489**	

$d_m = 0.5020 - 701.3 \times 10^{-6}t - 66.5 \times 10^{-9}t^2$.

C_2H_6O Ethyl Alcohol (**23, 37**)

t, °C	$p_{atm.}$	d_l	d_v
78.3	1.000	0.7365	0.00165
80	1.069	.7348	.00174
90	1.562	.7251	.00250
100	2.228	.7157	.00351
110	3.107	.7057	.00486
120	4.243	.6925	.00658

C_2H_6O.—(*Continued*)

t, °C	$p_{atm.}$	d_l	d_v
130	5.685	0.6789	0.00877
140	7.486	.6631	.01152
150	9.700	.6489	.01488
160	12.39	.6329	.01916
170	15.61	.6165	.02446
180	19.44	.5984	.03115
190	23.94	.5782	.0397
200	29.20	.5568	.0508
210	35.31	.5291	.0655
220	42.38	.4958	.0854
230	50.53	.4550	.1135
240	59.92	.3825	.1715
243.1	**63.11**	**0.2755**	

$d_m = 0.4028 - 382.7 \times 10^{-6}t - 594.0 \times 10^{-9}t^2 + 65.1 \times 10^{-12}t^3$.

C_2H_6O Methyl Ether (p) (**5, 27**); (d) (**6**)

t, °C	$p_{atm.}$	d_l	d_v
−23.7	1.000	0.7222	0.0024
−20	1.17	.7174	.0027
−10	1.74	.7040	.0039
0	2.54	.6905	.0055
+10	3.59	.6759	.0076
20	4.95	.6610	.0104
30	6.62	.6455	.0142
40	8.69	.6292	.0188
50	11.25	.6116	.0241
60	14.27	.5932	.0306
70	17.90	.5735	.0385
80	22.10	.5517	.0484
90	26.9	.5257	.0623
100	32.6	.4950	.0810
110	39.0	.4575	.1060
115	42.5	.4350	.1222
120	46.3	.4040	.1465
125	50.3	.3510	.1930
126.9	**52.0**	**0.2714**	

$d_m = 0.3480 - 604.0 \times 10^{-6}t$.

C_2H_6S Methyl Sulfide (p) (**3**); (d) (**3, 12**)

t, °C	$p_{atm.}$	d_l	d_v
35.8	1.000	0.831	0.002
40	1.15	.826	.003
50	1.60	.814	.003
60	2.15	.803	.003
70	2.84	.791	.004
80	3.68	.777	.006
90	4.70	.764	.008
100	5.97	.750	.010
110	7.45	.736	.013
120	9.14	.721	.016
130	11.1	.706	.020
140	13.4	.689	.026
150	16.0	.671	.032
160	19.1	.652	.040
170	22.4	.632	.050
180	26.2	.610	.063
190	30.6	.585	.076
200	35.6	.559	.092
210	41.5	.528	.113
220	47.0	.486	.146
229.9	**54.6**	**0.306**	

$d_m = 0.437 - 570 \times 10^{-6}t$.

C_2H_6S Ethylmercaptan (3)

t, °C	$p_{atm.}$	d_l	d_v
34.4	1.000	0.822	0.002
40	1.21	.815	.003
50	1.66	.803	.003
60	2.22	.790	.004
70	2.95	.777	.006
80	3.84	.762	.007
90	4.92	.749	.009
100	6.24	.735	.012
110	7.80	.721	.015
120	9.64	.706	.019
130	11.8	.689	.023
140	14.3	.672	.029
150	17.2	.653	.036
160	20.5	.634	.044
170	24.2	.613	.054
180	28.2	.590	.065
190	33.0	.564	.079
200	38.2	.534	.095
210	44.1	.499	.117
220	50.5	.444	.161
225.5	**54.2**	**0.301**	

$d_m = 0.432 - 580 \times 10^{-6}t - 50.0 \times 10^{-9}t^2$.

C_2H_7N Dimethylamine (2)		**C_2H_7N** Ethylamine (2)	
t, °C	$p_{atm.}$	t, °C	$p_{atm.}$
7.2	1.000	16.6	1.000
10	1.12	20	1.14
20	1.66	30	1.65
30	2.38	40	2.34
40	3.32	50	3.23
50	4.55	60	4.35
60	6.04	70	5.77
70	7.93	80	7.48
80	10.2	90	9.57
90	12.9	100	12.1
100	16.0	110	15.0
110	19.7	120	18.5
120	23.9	130	22.5
130	28.8	140	27.0
140	34.4	150	32.4
150	40.8	160	38.4
160	48.0	170	44.9
164.6	**51.7**	180	52.9
		183.2	**55.5**

C_3H_5N Propionitrile (31); *cf.* (29)

t, °C	$p_{atm.}$	d_l	d_v
90		0.711	0.002
100		.700	.002
110		.689	.003
120		.678	.003
130		.666	.004
140		.654	.005
150		.642	.006
160		.629	.007
170		.615	.008
180		.602	.010
190		.588	.012
200		.573	.015
210		.557	.019
220		.541	.025
230		.524	.033
240		.505	.041

C_3H_5N.—(*Continued*)

t, °C	$p_{atm.}$	d_l	d_v
250		0.483	0.051
260		.458	.063
270		.428	.080
280		.388	.108
290		.311	.171
291.2		**0.241**	

$d_m = 0.400 - 475 \times 10^{-6}t - 250 \times 10^{-9}t^2$.

C_3H_6O Acetone (p) (14, 27); *cf.* (32); (d) (12); *cf.* (28, 29, 33, 35)

t, °C	$p_{atm.}$	d_l	d_v
56.1	1.000	0.750	0.002
60	1.14	.746	.003
70	1.58	.734	.003
80	2.12	.719	.004
90	2.81	.706	.005
100	3.67	.693	.007
110	4.74	.679	.009
120	6.01	.665	.011
130	7.53	.650	.013
140	9.33	.634	.016
150	11.5	.618	.020
160	13.9	.601	.024
170	16.6	.588	.030
180	20.0	.568	.039
190	23.8	.540	.050
200	28.0	.514	.065
210	32.7	.482	.085
220	38.1	.443	.110
230	44.1	.393	.152
235	**47.0**	**0.268**	

$d_m = 0.405 - 525 \times 10^{-6}t - 250 \times 10^{-9}t^2$.

$C_3H_6O_2$ Propionic Acid (13); *cf.* (7, 9, 18, 19)

t, °C	$p_{atm.}$	d_l	d_v
140		0.860	0.004
150		.848	.004
160		.837	.005
170		.825	.006
180		.813	.008
190		.800	.010
200		.786	.012
210		.772	.015
220		.757	.019
230		.740	.024
240		.722	.029
250		.703	.035
260		.683	.043
270		.663	.051
280		.642	.060
290		.619	.071
300		.595	.083
339.5		**0.315**	

$d_m = 0.508 - 530 \times 10^{-6}t - 110 \times 10^{-9}t^2$.

$C_3H_6O_2$ Ethyl Formate (39); *cf.* (37)

t, °C	$p_{atm.}$	d_l	d_v
54.35	1.000	0.8767	0.002843
60	1.208	.8689	.003370
70	1.667	.8552	.004570
80	2.251	.8409	.006098
90	2.983	.8262	.007994
100	3.883	.8112	.01032
110	4.978	.7955	.01312
120	6.290	.7796	.01657
130	7.846	.7628	.02073

$C_3H_6O_2$.—(*Continued*)

t, °C	$p_{atm.}$	d_l	d_v
140	9.674	0.7448	0.02564
150	11.80	.7257	.03164
160	14.26	.7058	.03876
170	17.07	.6843	.04739
180	20.28	.6610	.05747
190	23.91	.6355	.07018
200	28.00	.6066	.08621
210	32.59	.5724	.1073
220	37.70	.5290	.1379
225	40.47	.5014	.1587
230	43.39	.4635	.1890
235.3	**46.65**	**0.3232**	

$d_m = 0.4741 - 625.1 \times 10^{-6}t - 69.4 \times 10^{-9}t^2$.

$C_3H_6O_2$ Methyl Acetate (39); *cf.* (37)

t, °C	$p_{atm.}$	d_l	d_v
57.15	1.000	0.8840	0.002830
60	1.104	.8800	.003076
70	1.537	.8662	.004193
80	2.092	.8519	.005618
90	2.791	.8374	.007440
100	3.659	.8221	.009671
110	4.719	.8060	.01239
120	5.998	.7893	.01570
130	7.523	.7715	.01970
140	9.325	.7532	.02454
150	11.43	.7339	.03026
160	13.88	.7133	.03731
170	16.71	.6907	.04598
180	19.95	.6671	.05682
190	23.64	.6410	.06993
200	27.84	.6100	.08658
210	32.56	.5741	.1091
220	37.92	.5281	.1416
230	43.92	.4527	.2028
233.7	**46.31**	**0.3252**	

$d_m = 0.4799 - 628.0 \times 10^{-6}t - 146.7 \times 10^{-9}t^2$

C_3H_8O Propyl Alcohol (26, 37)

t, °C	$p_{atm.}$	d_l	d_v
97.4	1.000	0.7351	0.00208
100	1.100	.7325	.00226
110	1.577	.7220	.00320
120	2.208	.7110	.00443
130	3.022	.6995	.00605
140	4.055	.6875	.00805
150	5.341	.6740	.01060
160	6.915	.6600	.01380
170	8.817	.6450	.01770
180	11.08	.6285	.0225
190	13.75	.6110	.0282
200	16.86	.5920	.0353
210	20.46	.5715	.0442
220	24.57	.5485	.0556
230	29.26	.5230	.0704
240	34.57	.4920	.0904
250	40.55	.4525	.1180
260	47.27	.3905	.1610
263.7	**49.95**	**0.2734**	

$d_m = 0.4095 - 379.0 \times 10^{-6}t - 375.0 \times 10^{-9}t^2 - 553.3 \times 10^{-12}t^3$.

C_3H_8O Methyl Ethyl Ether (3)

t, °C	$p_{atm.}$	d_l	d_v
7.5	1.000	0.716	0.003
10	1.10	.713	.004
20	1.61	.700	.006
30	2.29	.687	.008
40	3.14	.672	.010
50	4.24	.658	.013
60	5.56	.644	.016
70	7.21	.628	.019
80	9.16	.612	.023
90	11.4	.596	.029
100	14.2	.579	.034
110	17.3	.560	.040
120	20.9	.540	.050
130	25.0	.516	.064
140	29.6	.487	.082
150	34.7	.450	.109
160	40.5	.401	.153
164.7	**43.4**	**0.270**	

$d_m = 0.364 - 570 \times 10^{-6}t$.

C_3H_9N Propylamine (2)

t, °C	$p_{atm.}$	*t*, °C	$p_{atm.}$
48.4	1.000	140	11.8
50	1.06	150	14.4
60	1.49	160	17.2
70	2.06	170	20.3
80	2.79	180	24.2
90	3.71	190	28.4
100	4.82	200	32.9
110	6.17	210	38.1
120	7.76	220	43.9
130	9.64	**223.8**	**46.3**

$C_4H_6O_4$ Dimethyl Oxalate (27, 34)

t, °C	$p_{atm.}$	*t*, °C	$p_{atm.}$
163.3	1.000	220	4.17
170	1.20	230	5.19
180	1.59	240	6.37
190	2.06	250	7.76
200	2.62	**260**	**9.48**
210	3.32		

$C_4H_8O_2$ *n*-Butyric Acid (13); *cf.* (7, 8, 28, 40)

t, °C	$p_{atm.}$	d_l	d_v
160		0.818	0.003
170		.807	.003
180		.796	.004
190		.784	.005
200		.771	.007
210		.758	.009
220		.744	.012
230		.730	.015
240		.715	.018
250		.700	.022
260		.685	.027
270		.669	.032
280		.652	.038
290		.633	.045
300		.612	.053
355		**0.302**	

$d_m = 0.487 - 450 \times 10^{-6}t - 200 \times 10^{-9}t^2$.

$C_4H_8O_2$ Isobutyric Acid (13); *cf.* (20, 28)

t, °C	$p_{atm.}$	d_l	d_v
150		0.812	0.003
160		.801	.004
170		.789	.005
180		.777	.007
190		.764	.009
200		.751	.012
210		.737	.015
220		.723	.018
230		.708	.022
240		.692	.026
250		.675	.032
260		.657	.039
270		.638	.047
280		.617	.056
290		.594	.067
300		.569	.080
336		**0.304**	

$d_m = 0.485 - 500 \times 10^{-6}t - 120 \times 10^{-9}t^2$.

$C_4H_8O_2$ Propyl Formate (39); *cf.* (37)

t, °C	$p_{atm.}$	d_l	d_v
80.9	1.000	0.8330	0.003136
90	1.320	.8214	.004107
100	1.769	.8080	.005432
110	2.327	.7947	.007047
120	3.010	.7811	.009033
130	3.836	.7670	.01140
140	4.821	.7523	.01422
150	5.984	.7369	.01770
160	7.343	.7209	.02179
170	8.921	.7045	.02667
180	10.74	.6873	.03236
190	12.82	.6691	.03891
200	15.20	.6487	.04717
210	17.90	.6259	.05698
220	20.94	.6024	.06897
230	24.39	.5757	.08403
240	28.27	.5438	.1045
250	32.63	.5025	.1340
260	37.54	.4404	.1848
264.85	**40.13**	**0.3093**	

$d_m = 0.4647 - 574.8 \times 10^{-6}t - 45.9 \times 10^{-9}t^2$.

$C_4H_8O_2$ Methyl Propionate (39); *cf.* (37)

t, °C	$p_{atm.}$	d_l	d_v
79.7	1.000	0.8412	0.003173
80	1.006	.8408	.003199
90	1.379	.8273	004301
100	1.851	.8137	005714
110	2.440	.7996	007446
120	3.165	.7852	.009569
130	4.043	.7705	.01214
140	5.096	.7553	.01529
150	6.345	.7390	01905
160	7.812	.7221	.02356
170	9.523	.7045	.02907
180	11.50	.6856	.03552
190	13.78	.6657	.04320
200	16.38	.6445	.05236
210	19.33	.6207	.06390
220	22.68	.5938	.07812
230	26.46	.5635	.09662
240	30.70	.5220	.1236

$C_4H_8O_2$.—(*Continued*)

t, °C	$p_{atm.}$	d_l	d_v
245	33.01	0.4976	0.1418
250	35.46	.4655	.1675
255	38.04	.4151	.2118
257.4	**39.34**	**0.3124**	

$d_m = 0.4696 - 592.1 \times 10^{-6}t - 72.9 \times 10^{-9}t^2$.

$C_4H_8O_2$ Ethyl Acetate (39); *cf.* (37)

t, °C	$p_{atm.}$	d_l	d_v
77.15	1.000	0.8283	0.003230
80	1.093	.8245	.003495
90	1.494	.8112	.004677
100	2.000	.7972	.006158
110	2.630	.7831	.008006
120	3.404	.7683	.01030
130	4.340	.7533	.01314
140	5.461	.7378	.01650
150	6.789	.7210	.02070
160	8.349	.7033	.02577
170	10.17	.6848	.03165
180	12.27	.6653	.03883
190	14.68	.6441	.04751
200	17.45	.6210	.05797
210	20.59	.5944	.07128
220	24.15	.5648	.08905
230	28.16	.5281	.1131
240	32.68	.4778	.1499
245	35.14	.4401	.1802
250	37.74		
250.1	**37.80**	**0.3077**	

$d_m = 0.4624 - 599.2 \times 10^{-6}t - 76.4 \times 10^{-9}t^2$.

$C_4H_{10}O$ Ethyl Ether (24, 37)

t, °C	$p_{atm.}$	d_l	d_v
34.6	1.000	0.6962	0.003162
40	1.212	.6894	.003731
50	1.680	.6764	.005079
60	2.275	.6658	.006771
70	3.021	.6532	.00892
80	3.939	.6402	.01155
90	5.054	.6250	.01477
100	6.394	.6105	.01867
110	7.987	.5942	.02349
120	9.861	.5764	.02934
130	12.05	.5580	.03638
140	14.58	.5385	.04488
150	17.48	.5179	.05551
160	20.80	.4947	.06911
170	24.57	.4658	.08731
180	28.81	.4268	.1135
185	31.12	.4018	.1320
190	33.57	.3663	.1620
193.8	**35.52**	**0.2625**	

$d_m = 0.3685 - 537.7 \times 10^{-6}t - 47.5 \times 10^{-9}t^2$.

$C_4H_{10}S$ Ethyl Sulfide (3)

t, °C	$p_{atm.}$	d_l	d_v
90.3	1.000	0.765	0.003
100	1.32	.755	.003
110	1.75	.744	.004
120	2.26	.732	.005
130	2.90	.721	.006
140	3.66	.709	.008
150	4.58	.697	.009
160	5.68	.684	.011

$C_4H_{10}S$.—(*Continued*)

t, °C	$p_{atm.}$	d_l	d_v
170	6.93	0.671	0.013
180	8.36	.656	.017
190	10.00	.641	.022
200	12.0	.625	.027
210	14.2	.608	034
220	16.6	.590	.041
230	19.3	.571	.050
240	22.3	.549	.061
250	25.6	.524	.075
260	29.3	.494	.094
270	33.2	.457	.121
280	37.6	.395	.175
283.8	**39.1**	**0.279**	

$d_m = 0.428 - 470 \times 10^{-6}t - 200 \times 10^{-9}t^2$.

$C_4H_{11}N$ Diethylamine (*p*) (2); (*d*) (12, 16)

t, °C	$p_{atm.}$	d_l	d_v
55.4	1.000	0.668	0.003
60	1.16	.663	.003
70	1.59	.652	.004
80	2.13	.640	.005
90	2.82	.628	.006
100	3.67	.616	.008
110	4.70	.604	.011
120	5.92	.591	.014
130	7.39	.577	.018
140	9.10	.562	.022
150	11.1	.546	.028
160	13.4	.528	.035
170	15.9	.510	.043
180	18.9	.489	.053
190	22.2	.466	.065
200	25.8	.438	.080
210	30.0	.400	.103
220	34.4	.339	.150
223.5	**36.2**	**0.246**	

$d_m = 0.364 - 515 \times 10^{-6}t - 50.0 \times 10^{-9}t^2$.

$C_5H_{10}O_2$ Isobutyl Formate (15, 30)

t, °C	$p_{atm.}$	*t*, °C	$p_{atm.}$
97.9	1.000	190	9.62
100	1.067	200	11.5
110	1.44	210	13.8
120	1.92	220	16.3
130	2.52	230	19.1
140	3.25	240	22.3
150	4.14	250	25.8
160	5.19	260	29.8
170	6.37	270	34.3
180	7.89	**278**	**38**

$C_5H_{10}O_2$ Propyl Acetate (39); *cf.* (37)

t, °C	$p_{atm.}$	d_l	d_v
101.55	1.000	0.7938	0.003495
110	1.284	.7830	.004405
120	1.703	.7702	.005760
130	2.223	.7571	.007440
140	2.851	.7435	.009497
150	3.611	.7297	.01195
160	4.518	.7149	.01489
170	5.581	.6997	.01848
180	6.832	.6835	.02268
190	8.276	.6667	02778
200	9.947	.6488	.03390

$C_5H_{10}O_2$.—(*Continued*)

t, °C	$p_{atm.}$	d_l	d_v
210	11.86	0.6301	0.04115
220	14.05	.6087	.05025
230	16.54	.5855	.06154
240	19.36	.5586	.07576
250	22.54	.5289	.09390
260	26.13	.4908	.1205
270	30.16	.4333	.1661
275	32.36	.3769	.2169
276.2	**32.91**	**0.2957**	

$d_m = 0.4553 - 546.9 \times 10^{-6}t - 112.4 \times 10^{-9}t^2$.

$C_5H_{10}O_2$ Ethyl Propionate (39); *cf.* (37)

t, °C	$p_{atm.}$	d_l	d_v
99.0	1.000	0.7964	0.003489
100	1.027	.7951	.003580
110	1.383	.7823	.004748
120	1.828	.7692	.00620
130	2.376	.7548	.00800
140	3.042	.7413	.01024
150	3.840	.7267	.01292
160	4.788	.7115	.01615
170	5.904	.6958	.02004
180	7.206	.6795	.02469
190	8.727	.6625	.03012
200	10.45	.6443	.03676
210	12.45	.6243	.04464
220	14.73	.6027	.05435
230	17.33	.5784	.06667
240	20.28	.5501	.08230
250	23.62	.5181	.1030
260	27.40	.4744	.1337
265	29.48	.4459	.1562
270	31.69	.4018	.1957
272.9	**33.03**	**0.2965**	

$d_m = 0.4564 - 564.4 \times 10^{-6}t - 78.4 \times 10^{-9}t^2$.

$C_5H_{10}O_2$ Methyl Butyrate (39); *cf.* (37)

t, °C	$p_{atm.}$	d_l	d_v
102.75	1.000	0.8035	0.003595
110	1.245	.7945	.004374
120	1.649	.7816	.005708
130	2.148	.7685	.007353
140	2.756	.7551	.009294
150	3.488	.7415	.01168
160	4.359	.7270	.01459
170	5.386	.7122	.01807
180	6.587	.6964	.02215
190	7.982	.6800	.02699
200	9.593	.6633	.03268
210	11.44	.6448	.03968
220	13.55	.6251	.04831
230	15.96	.6018	.05848
240	18.69	.5773	.07143
250	21.77	.5505	.08696
260	25.25	.5166	.1091
270	29.17	.4721	.1416
275	31.31	.4386	.1691
280	33.58	.3812	.2201
281.3	**34.19**	**0.3002**	

$d_m = 0.4601 - 543.0 \times 10^{-6}t - 90.6 \times 10^{-9}t^2$.

$C_5H_{10}O_2$ Methyl Isobutyrate ([39]), *cf.* ([37])

t, °C	$p_{atm.}$	d_l	d_v
92.3	1.000	0.8040	0.003617
100	1.257	.7945	.004472
110	1.675	.7815	.005882
120	2.193	.7680	.007628
130	2.826	.7539	.009718
140	3.588	.7396	.01224
150	4.497	.7248	.01533
160	5.569	.7095	.01903
170	6.825	.6933	.02345
180	8.280	.6767	.02869
190	9.960	.6593	.03490
200	11.89	.6411	.04228
210	14.09	.6200	.05141
220	16.59	.5961	.06289
230	19.43	.5690	.07722
240	22.64	.5386	.09615
250	26.25	.5021	.1218
260	30.32	.4495	.1623
265	32.54	.4036	.2033
267.55	**33.72**	**0.3012**	

$d_m = 0.4558 - 559.3 \times 10^{-6}t - 68.9 \times 10^{-9}t^2$.

$C_5H_{12}O$ Ethyl Propyl Ether ([3])

t, °C	$p_{atm.}$	d_l	d_v
61.4	1.000	0.682	0.008
70	1.30	.672	.010
80	1.73	.659	.013
90	2.27	.646	.015
100	2.94	.633	.018
110	3.76	.620	.021
120	4.72	.607	.025
130	5.89	.593	.029
140	7.28	.579	.032
150	8.89	.564	.036
160	10.7	.548	.041
170	12.9	.530	.047
180	15.2	.511	.055
190	18.0	.491	.067
200	21.2	.462	.082
210	24.8	.433	.104
220	28.8	.385	.142
227.4	**32.1**	**0.258**	

$d_m = 0.3785 - 530.0 \times 10^{-6}t$.

$C_6H_{12}O_2$ Isobutyl Acetate ([15])

t, °C	$p_{atm.}$	t, °C	$p_{atm.}$
116.4	1.000	210	9.0
120	1.12	220	10.8
130	1.48	230	12.8
140	1.93	240	15.1
150	2.50	250	17.7
160	3.16	260	20.6
170	3.94	270	23.9
180	4.96	280	27.5
190	6.12	**288**	**31**
200	7.43		

$C_6H_{12}O_2$ Ethyl Isobutyrate ([15])

t, °C	$p_{atm.}$	t, °C	$p_{atm.}$
110	1.000	140	2.25
120	1.33	150	2.89
130	1.75	160	3.63

$C_6H_{12}O_2$.—(*Continued*)

t, °C	$p_{atm.}$	t, °C	$p_{atm.}$
170	4.49	230	14.2
180	5.60	240	16.7
190	6.85	250	19.5
200	8.31	260	22.6
210	10.05	270	26
220	12.0	**280**	**30**

$C_6H_{15}N$ Triethylamine ([12])

t, °C	$p_{atm.}$	d_l	d_v
90		0.661	0.005
100		.650	.006
110		.638	.008
120		.626	.010
130		.614	.013
140		.603	.016
150		.591	.019
160		.578	.022
170		.565	.026
180		.552	.030
190		.538	.035
200		.523	.040
210		.507	.046
220		.488	.056
230		.466	.071
240		.437	.090
250		.399	.115
260		.335	.175
262		**0.251**	

$d_m = 0.373 - 440 \times 10^{-6}t - 100 \times 10^{-9}t^2$.

$C_7H_{14}O_2$ Isopropyl Isobutyrate ([38])

t, °C	$p_{atm.}$	d_l	d_v
120.76	1.000	0.7377	
130	1.298	.7264	
140	1.689	.7140	
150	2.163	.7014	
160	2.758	.6683	
170	3.443	.6751	
180	4.222	.6610	
190	5.165	.6468	
200	6.259	.6311	
210	7.507	.6145	
220	8.965	.5965	
230	10.58	.5770	0.0475
240	Begins to decompose		

$C_{12}H_{10}O$ Diphenyl Ether ([4])

$\log_{10} p_{mm} = 7.771 - \frac{2600}{T}$; range 259.0 (B. P.) to 360°C

LITERATURE

(For a key to the periodicals see end of volume)

(1) Atkinson, Heycock and Pope, *4*, **117**: 1410; 20. (2) Berthoud, *42*, **15**: 3; 17. (3) Berthoud and Brum, *42*, **21**: 143; 24. (4) Britton, The Dow Chemical Co., Midland, Mich., *0*. (5) Cardoso and Bruno, *42*, **20**: 347; 23. (6) Cardoso and Coppola, *42*, **20**: 337; 23. (7) Eijkman, *70*, **12**: 157; 93. (8) Falk, *1*, **31**: 86; 09. (9) Faucon, *34*, **146**: 691; 08.

(10) Germann and Taylor, *1*, **48**: 1154; 26. (11) Hackspill and Mathieu, *27*, **25**: 482; 19. (12) Herz and Neukirch, *7*, **104**: 433; 23. (13) von Hirsch, *8*, **69**: 456; 99. (14) Kuenen and Robson, *3*, **4**: 116; 02. (15) Nadejdine, *Exner Repertorium der Physik*, **23**: 759; 87. (16) Oudemans, *70*, **1**: 56; 82. (17) Paternò and Mazzucchelli, *36*, **50 I**: 30; 20. (18) Perkin, *4*, **65**: 402; 94. (19) Perkin, *4*, **69**: 1169; 96.

(20) Pierre and Puchot, *6*, **28**: 363; 73. (21) Ramsay and Young, *62*, **175**: 461; 85. (22) Ramsay and Young, *4*, **49**: 790; 86. (23) Ramsay and Young, *62*, **177**: 123; 87. (24) Ramsay and Young, *62*, **178**: 57; 88. (25) Ramsay and Young, *62*, **178**: 313; 88. (26) Ramsay and Young, *62*, **180**: 137; 90. (27) Regnault, *151*, **26**: 335; 62. (28) Schiff, *13*, **220**: 71; 83. (29) Schiff, *25*, **19**: 560; 86.

([30]) Schumann, *8*, **12**: 40; 81. ([31]) Ter-Gazarian, *42*, **4**: 140; 06. ([32]) Timmermans, *28*, **24**: 244; 10. ([33]) Walden, *7*, **60**: 87; 07. ([34]) Weger, *13*, **221**: 61; 83. ([35]) Wüllner and Grotrian, *8*, **11**: 545; 80. ([36]) Young, *4*, **59**: 903; 91. ([37]) Young, *117*, **12**: 374; 10. ([38]) Young and Fortey, *4*, **81**: 783; 02. ([39]) Young and Thomas, *4*, **63**: 1191; 93. ([40]) Zander, *13*, **224**: 56; 84.

VAPOR PRESSURES AND ORTHOBARIC DENSITIES OF HYDROCARBONS AND THEIR HALOGEN DERIVATIVES

Jean Timmermans

p = vapor pressures in mm Hg ($=\frac{1}{760}$A$_n$)
d_l (resp. d_v) = density of saturated liquid (resp. vapor) in g per cm³
$d_m = \frac{1}{2}(d_l + d_v)$; range, B. P. to t_c

Accuracy: Young's data, 0.1 % for the pressures and 0.0001 for the densities. Other authors' accuracy usually less, and indicated by the number of significant figures given.

All values at the critical point are given in bold-face type.

HYDROCARBONS

The ℭ-Arrangement

C₁ and C₂ Hydrocarbons, *v.* p. 230

$CH_3.CH{:}CH_2$ (3, 10, 17)

t, °C	p_{mm}	d_l
−47.8	760	
−40	1110	0.599
−30	1575	0.587
−20	2280	0.574
−10	3235	0.560
0	4400	0.546
+10	5800	0.531
20	7700	0.516
30	9900	
40	1240_0	
50	1550_0	
60	1890_0	
70	2280_0	

t, °C	p_{mm}
80	2740_0
90	3400_0
92.6	**3450_0**

$$\log_{10} p = 7.340 - \frac{1066.1}{T}$$

C_4H_{10} (3, 10, 14)

t, °C	p_{mm}	t, °C	p_{mm}
−44.5	760	+20	6690
−20	1980	50	1475_0
0	3800	**97.5**	**3420_0**

$\log_{10}p = 7.3402 - \dfrac{983.7}{T}$; range, −125° to t_c.

n-C_4H_{10} (3, 7, 17, 19)

t, °C	p_{mm}	t, °C	p_{mm}
− 0.3	760	100	1280_0
+30	2550	130	2060_0
70	6700	**153.2***	**2710_0**
		150.8†	**2850_0**
		*(7)	†(17)

$\log_{10}p = 7.3948 - \dfrac{1224.5}{T}$; range, M. P. to t_c.

For d_l up to 35°, *see* (8).

iso-C_4H_{10} (3, 13, 17)

t, °C	p_{mm}	t, °C	p_{mm}
−11.5	760	90	1290_0
+30	3400	120	2170_0
60	7000	**133.7**	**2775_0**

$\log_{10} p = 6.98 - \dfrac{1056.3}{T}$; range, M. P. to t_c.

n-C_5H_{12} (18, 20)

t, °C	p_{mm}	d_l	d_v
36.15	760		
40	873	0.6062	0.0034
50	1193	0.5957	0.0045
60	1605	0.5850	0.0060
70	2119	0.5739	0.0079
80	2735	0.5624	0.0101
90	3500	0.5503	0.0129
100	4410	0.5377	0.0163
110	5485	0.5248	0.0202
120	6740	0.5107	0.0250
130	8190	0.4957	0.0310
140	9890	0.4787	0.0386
150	1181_0	0.4604	0.0476
160	1405_0	0.4394	0.0591
170	1655_0	0.4162	0.0735
180	1935_0	0.3867	0.0935
190	2250_0	0.3485	0.1269
195	2425_0	0.3065	0.1609
197.2	**2510_0**	**0.2323**	

$d_m = 0.4402 - 0.0_343413T - 0.0_73477T^2$; range, M. P. to t_c.
$d_m = 0.3283 - 0.0_34610t$; range, 0° to t_c.

iso-C_5H_{12} (18, 20)

t, °C	p_{mm}	d_l	d_v
27.95	760		
30	819	0.6092	0.0033
40	1140	0.5988	0.0045
50	1535	0.5881	0.0060
60	2036	0.5769	0.0078
70	2656	0.5656	0.0101
80	3385	0.5540	0.0129
90	4280	0.5413	0.0162
100	5345	0.5278	0.0202
110	6585	0.5140	0.0251
120	8020	0.4991	0.0311
130	9685	0.4826	0.0383
140	1163_0	0.4642	0.0473
150	1380_0	0.4445	0.0583
160	1630_0	0.4206	0.0729
170	1911_0	0.3914	0.0934
180	2227_0	0.3498	0.1258
185	2400_0	0.3142	0.1574
187.8	**2500_0**	**0.2343**	

$d_m = 0.44806 - 0.0_347586T + 0.0_72664T^2$; range, M. P. to t_c.
$d_m = 0.3202 - 0.0_34658t + 0.0_7463t^2$; range, 0° to t_c.

C_6H_6 (20)

t, °C	p_{mm}	d_l	d_v
80.2	760		
90	1008	0.8041	0.0036
100	1335	0.7927	0.0047
110	1740	0.7809	0.0060
120	2230	0.7692	0.0077
130	2820	0.7568	0.0096
140	3520	0.7440	0.0118
150	4335	0.7310	0.0144
160	5300	0.7185	0.0173
170	6385	0.7043	0.0209
180	7620	0.6906	0.0249
190	9040	0.6758	0.0298
200	1065_0	0.6605	0.0355
210	1245_0	0.6432	0.0421
220	1452_0	0.6255	0.0502
230	1682_0	0.6065	0.0598
240	1935_0	0.5851	0.0714
250	2220_0	0.5609	0.0855
260	2535_0	0.5328	0.1038
270	2885_0	0.4984	0.1287
280	3280_0	0.4514	0.1660
288.5	**3640_0**	**0.3045**	

$d_m = 0.4501 - 0.0_35248t + 0.0_7693t^2$; range, M. P. to t_c.

C_6H_{12}, Cyclohexane (12, 20)

t, °C	p_{mm}	d_l	d_v
80.75	760	0.7199	0.0029*
90	992*	0.7098	0.0038*
100	1304*	0.6988	0.0049*
110	1687*	0 6883	0.0063*
120	2140	0.6775	0.0080*
130	2695	0.6667	0.0100*
140	3355	0.6553	0.0123
150	4140	0.6435	0.0150
160	5040	0.6313	0.0184
170	6095		
180	7285	0.6060	0.0265
190	8630	0.5917	0.0317
200	1013_0	0.5773	0.0380
210	1182_5	0.5614	0.0450
220	1369_0	0.5443	0.0534
230	1581_0	0.5257	0.0632
240	1814_0	0.5058	0.0746
250	2070_0	0.4824	0.0896
260	2359_0	0.4537	0.1097
270	2683_0	0.4154	0.1401
281.0	**3083_5**	**0.2703**	

* Values from Young, who used C_6H_{12} which was not absolutely pure it melted at 4.7° instead of 6.5° and its density ($\frac{15}{4}$) was 0.7826 instead of 0.7832.

$d_m = 0.3942 - 0.000433t$; range, M. P. to t_c.

n-C_6H_{14} (20)

t, °C	p_{mm}	d_l	d_v
68.95	760		
70	787	0.6122	0.0034
80	1062	0.6022	0.0045
90	1407	0.5918	0.0058
100	1836	0.5814	0.0075
110	2358	0.5703	0.0096
120	2980	0.5588	0.0120
130	3720	0.5467	0.0150
140	4605	0.5343	0.0187
150	5610	0.5207	0.0230
160	6790	0.5063	0.0283
170	8120	0.4913	0.0347
180	9650	0.4751	0.0423
190	1038_0	0.4570	0.0516
200	1335_0	0.4365	0.0633
210	1558_0	0.4124	0.0790
220	1810_0	0.3810	0.1011
230	2095_0	0.3329	0.1405
234.8	**2250_0**	**0.2344**	

$d_m = 0.3388 - 0.0_34445t$; range, 0° to t_c.

$(C_3H_7)_2$, Diisopropyl (20)

t, °C	p_{mm}	d_l	d_v
58.1	760		
60	807	0.6243	0.0035
70	1093	0.6144	0.0046
80	1444	0.6039	0.0060
90	1876	0.5931	0.0078
100	2410	0.5821	0.0099
110	3045	0.5708	0.0125
120	3790	0.5589	0.0155
130	4675	0.5464	0.0193
140	5715	0.5334	0.0236
150	6885	0.5199	0.0285
160	8255	0.5049	0.0352
170	9805	0.4885	0.0429
180	1153_0	0.4705	0.0522
190	1347_5	0.4508	0.0636
200	1570_0	0.4274	0.0783
210	1820_0	0.3988	0.0986
220	2100_0	0.3565	0.1321
225	2260_0	0.3198	0.1649
227.35	**2335_0**	**0.2411**	

$d_m = 0.3401 - 0.0_34445t + 0.0_7413t^2$; range, 0° to t_c.

$C_6H_5CH_3$ (1, 6)

t, °C	$p_{atm.}$	d_l	d_v
190		0.687	0.022
200		0.672	0.026
210		0.658	0.030
220		0.644	0.035
230		0.630	0.040
240		0.614	0.048
250		0.594	0.057
260		0.574	0.066
270		0.554	0.076
280		0.534	0.085
320.6	**41.6**		

$d_m = 0.4464 - 0.0_3483t$; range, 190° to t_c.

n-C_7H_{16} (20)

t, °C	p_{mm}	d_l	d_v
98.4	760		
100	795	0.6124	0.0036
110	1047	0.6027	0.0047
120	1367	0.5926	0.0061
130	1753	0.5821	0.0078
140	2229	0.5711	0.0098
150	2785	0.5598	0.0122
160	3450	0.5481	0.0151
170	4210	0.5359	0.0185
180	5090	0.5232	0.0224
190	6095	0.5066	0.0271
200	7260	0.4952	0.0330
210	8595	0.4793	0.0401
220	1011_0	0.4616	0.0489
230	1181_0	0.4414	0.0600
240	1379_0	0.4177	0.0745
250	1598_0	0.3882	0.0954
260	1847_0	0.3457	0.1287
266.85	**2040_0**	**0.2341**	

$d_m = 0.3504 - 0.0_34102t - 0.0_7621t^2$; range, 0° to t_c.

o-$C_6H_4(CH_3)_2$ (6)

t, °C	p_{mm}	d_l	d_v
190		0.716	0.014
200		0.705	0.016
210		0.694	0.019
220		0.682	0.021
230		0.670	0.024
240		0.656	0.028
250		0.641	0.034
260		0.625	0.040
270		0.609	0.046
280		0.593	0.052

$d_m = 0.4578 - 0.0_3481t$; range, 190° to t_c.

m-$C_6H_4(CH_3)_2$ (6)

t, °C	p_{mm}	d_l	d_v
190		0.690	0.020
200		0.678	0.023
210		0.666	0.026
220		0.654	0.030
230		0.642	0.034
240		0 629	0.038
250		0.615	0.043
260		0.600	0.048
270		0.585	0.054
280		0.570	0.060

$d_m = 0.4385 - 0.0_3438t$; range, 190° to t_c.

p-$C_6H_4(CH_3)_2$ (6)

t, °C	p_{mm}	d_l	d_v
190		0.620	0.028
200		0.612	0.030
210		0.603	0.032
220		0.594	0.035
230		0.585	0.038
240		0.575	0.041
250		0.562	0.045
260		0.548	0.051
270		0.534	0.057
280		0.520	0.062

$d_m = 0.3902 - 0.0_3344t$; range, 190° to t_c.

n-C_8H_{18} (20)

t, °C	p_{mm}	d_l	d_v
125.8	760		
130	859	0.6071	0.0042
140	1114	0.5973	0.0054
150	1425	0.5875	0.0068
160	1807	0.5772	0.0085
170	2255	0.5667	0.0107
180	2775	0.5556	0.0132
190	3385	0.5441	0.0161
200	4100	0.5317	0.0196
210	4925	0.5189	0.0236
220	5875	0.5053	0.0287
230	6950	0.4901	0.0348
240	8200	0.4732	0.0424
250	9600	0.4554	0.0512
260	1118_0	0.4364	0.0622
270	1298_0	0.4123	0.0772
280	1500_0	0.3818	0.0983
290	1715_0	0.3365	0.1346
296.2	**1870_0**	**0.2327**	

$d_m = 0.3592 - 0.0_33986t - 0.0_7960t^2$; range, 0° to t_c.

$(C_4H_9)_2$, Diisobutyl (20)

t, °C	p_{mm}	d_l	d_v
109.2	760		
110	777	0.6143	0.0040
120	1020	0.6046	0.0052
130	1320	0.5945	0.0067
140	1685	0.5841	0.0085
150	2115	0.5732	0.0107
160	2645	0.5620	0.0132
170	3245	0.5503	0.0161
180	3940	0.5383	0.0196
190	4740	0.5255	0.0237
200	5670	0.5117	0.0287
210	6730	0.4970	0.0348
220	7940	0.4810	0.0420
230	9310	0.4633	0.0509
240	1090_0	0.4434	0.0622
250	1267_0	0.4199	0.0768
260	1465_0	0.3912	0.0970
270	1690_0	0.3482	0.1321
276.8	**1865_0**	**0.2366**	

$d_m = 0.3550 - 0.0_34115t - 0.0_7592t^2$; range, 0° to t_c.

HALOGEN DERIVATIVES

CH_3Cl and C_2H_5Cl, *v.* p. 231

CH_3F (4, 11)

t, °C	p_{mm}	t, °C	p_{mm}
−78.2	760	30	3275_0
0	1470_0	40	4050_0
+10	2009_0	**44.9**	**4710_0**
20	2560_0		

C_6H_5F (20)

t, °C	p_{mm}	d_l	d_v
85.2	760		
90	883	0.9366	0.0038
100	1177	0.9233	0.0050
110	1542	0.9096	0.0065
120	1950	0.8955	0.0083
130	2530	0.8811	0.0105
140	3170	0.8665	0.0131
150	3930	0.8519	0.0163
160	4825	0.8363	0.0199
170	5840	0.8203	0.0241
180	7010	0.8037	0.0291
190	8375	0.7857	0.0350
200	9900	0.7671	0.0418
210	1161_5	0.7480	0.0497
220	1355_0	0.7265	0.0591
230	1572_5	0.7036	0.0704
240	1816_0	0.6789	0.0840
250	2090_0	0.6504	0.1008
260	2395_0	0.6163	0.1226
270	2735_0	0.5739	0.1535
280	3120_0	0.5133	0.2034
286.5	**3390_0**	**0.3541**	

$d_m = 0.5236 - 0.0_36000t + 0.0_7293t^2$; range, 0° to t_c.

CCl_4 (20)

t, °C	p_{mm}	d_l	d_v
76.75	760		
80	838	1.4765	0.0061
90	1112	1.4554	0.0080
100	1457	1.4343	0.0103
110	1880	1.4124	0.0131
120	2390	1.3902	0.0164
130	3000	1.3680	0.0204
140	3725	1.3450	0.0250
150	4555	1.3215	0.0304
160	5535	1.2983	0.0365
170	6640	1.2734	0.0437
180	7900	1.2470	0.0525
190	9315	1.2192	0.0625
200	1094_0	1.1888	0.0742
210	1276_0	1.1566	0.0879
220	1480_0	1.1227	0.1040
230	1706_0	1.0857	0.1232
240	1960_0	1.0444	0.1464
250	2241_0	0.9980	0.1754
260	2553_0	0.9409	0.2146
270	2900_0	0.8666	0.2710
280	3280_0	0.7634	0.3597
283.15	**3420_0**	**0.5576**	

$d_m = 0.8165 - 0.0_39564t + 0.0_6148t^2$; range, 0° to t_c.

$CHCl_3$ (5, 15, 20)

t, °C	p_{mm}	t, °C	p_{mm}
61.2	760	130	4860
90	1880	140	5950
100	2430	150	7080
110	3100	160	8800
120	3890		

$d_m = 0.546 - 0.0009\ (t - 230)$; range, 230° to t_c. For d_l and d_v to 4 decimals between 195° and t_c, *see* (5). $d_c = 0.516$ at $t_c = 262.9°$.

n-C_3H_7Cl (2, 18)

t, °C	p_{mm}	t, °C	p_{mm}
46.65	760	140	8500
50	859	150	1020_0
60	1233	160	1210_0
70	1680	170	1445_0
80	2210	180	1690_0
90	2870	190	1960_0
100	3670	200	2265_0
110	4600	210	2505_0
120	5700	220	2970_0
130	7000	**230.05**	**3437_0**

C_6H_5Cl (20)

t, °C	p_{mm}	d_l	d_v
132	760		
140	939.5	0.9723	0.0043
150	1206	0.9599	0.0054
160	1535	0.9480	0.0068
170	1920	0.9354	0.0084
180	2370	0.9224	0.0102
190	2900	0.9091	0.0125
200	3520	0.8955	0.0151
210	4230	0.8815	0.0181
229	5055	0.8672	0.0214
230	5990	0.8518	0.0254
240	7050	0.8356	0.0300
250	8270	0.8196	0.0354
260	9650	0.8016	0.0417
270	1119_0	0.7834	0.0492
359.2	**3390_0**	**0.3654**	

$d_m = 0.5640 - 0.0_35337t + 0.0_7509t^2$; range, 0° to t_c.

C_2H_5Br (5, 15, 20)

t, °C	p_{mm}	t, °C	p_{mm}
38.4	760	90	3420
40	794	100	4330
50	1110	110	5400
60	1500	120	6650
70	2010	130	8100
80	2630		

$d_m = 0.521 - 0.040\ (t - 210)$; range, 210° to t_c. For d_l and d_v to 3 decimals, 195° to t_c, *see* (5). $d_c = 0.513$ at $t_c = 230.9°$.

C_6H_5Br (16, 20)

t, °C	p_{mm}	d_l	d_v
156.15	760		
160	846	1.2994	0.0052
170	1077	1.2847	0.0066
180	1350	1.2697	0.0081
190	1685	1.2534	0.0099
200	2075	1.2385	0.0121
210	2525	1.2210	0.0146
220	3055	1.2037	0.0174
230	3660	1.1876	0.0208
240	4360	1.1689	0.0248
250	5160	1.1510	0.0293
260	6080	1.1310	0.0343
270	7105	1.1099	0.0402
397	**3390_0**	**0.4859**	

$d_m = 0.7609 - 0.0_36655t - 0.0_7725t^2$; range, 0° to t_c.

C_6H_5I (20)

t, °C	p_{mm}	d_l	d_v
188.45	760		
190	793	1.5639	0.0059
200	991	1.5470	0.0073
210	1232	1.5297	0.0089
220	1520	1.5124	0.0108
230	1855	1.4941	0.0130
240	2245	1.4764	0.0156
250	2700	1.4581	0.0185
260	3220	1.4384	0.0220
270	3815	1.4190	0.0260
448	**3390_0**	**0.5814**	

$d_m = 0.9303 - 0.0_37556t + 0.0_7519t^2$; range, 0° to t_c.

LITERATURE

(For a key to the periodicals see end of volume)

(1) Altschul, *7*, **2**: 577; 93. (2) Berthoud, *42*, **15**: 3; 17. (3) Burrell and Robertson, *1*, **37**: 2188; 15. *30*, No. **142**; 16. (4) Collie, *4*, **55**: 110; 89. (5) Herz and Neukirch, *7*, **104**: 433; 23. (6) von Hirsch, *8*, **69**: 456; 99. (7) Kuenen, *64V*, **20**: 725; 11. *3*, **6**: 637; 03. (8) Kuenen and Visser, *64V*, **22**: 330; 13. (9) Lebeau, *34*, **140**: 1454; 05. *186*, **1908**: 300.
(10) Maass and Wright, *1*, **43**: 1098; 21. (11) Moles and Batuecas, *42*, **17**: 537; 19. (12) Nagornov and Rotinjanz, *Ann. Inst. Anal. phys-chim.*, **2**: 371; 24. (13) Noyes, *1*, **30**: 142; 08. (14) Olszewski, *25*, **27**: 3305; 94. (15) Regnault, *151*, **26**: 403; 62. (16) Rolla, *59*, **19**: 327; 10. *22*, **18 II**: 365; 09. (17) Seibert and Burrell, *1*, **37**: 2683; 15. (18) Timmermans, *117*, **13**: 310; 12. (19) Visser, *Thesis*, Leiden, 1913. *168*, No. **136**; 13.
(20) Young, *117*, **12**: 374; 10. *3*, **50**: 291; 00.

CORRECTION OF BOILING POINTS TO NORMAL ATMOSPHERIC PRESSURE

C. S. Cragoe

This correction can be made most accurately and conveniently by means of the following equation:

$$\Delta t = \frac{273.1 + t}{\Phi}(2.8808 - \log_{10} p_{mm}) \qquad (1)$$

where Δt is the correction in degrees centigrade which must be added to the boiling point, t, determined at the pressure, p, mm of mercury, in order to obtain the normal boiling point.

Equation (1) is merely another way of writing

$$\log_{10} p_{mm} = -A/T + B \qquad (2)$$

which is known to express vapor-pressure data accurately over a considerable range. For the range near the normal boiling point, T_B, equation (2) may be written in the form

$$\log_{10}\frac{p_{mm}}{760} = \Phi\left(1 - \frac{T_B}{T}\right) \qquad (3)$$

where Φ in equations (1) and (3) is related to A and B in equation (2) by

$$\Phi = B - 2.8808 = \frac{0.05223\ A\ (\text{joule})}{T_B} = \frac{0.2186\ A\ (\text{calorie})}{T_B}$$

where A is the molal heat of vaporization at the normal boiling point.

For small pressure differences, equation (1) reduces to Craft's equation: $\Delta t = C\ T_B\ (760 - p)$; where $C = \dfrac{5.714 \times 10^{-4}}{\Phi}$.

In accordance with Trouton's rule and also Craft's rule, Φ is roughly constant for most substances and approximately constant for substances of a given class. Values of Φ are given in Tables 1, 2 and 3 and Fig. 1 for pressures near the normal boiling point. The compounds or classes of compounds given in Table 3 have been divided, for convenience, into eight groups, the values of Φ for each group being represented within about 2% by the lines indicated in Fig. 1.

To obtain a value of Φ for a substance, X, which is not listed in Tables 1, 2, or 3, proceed as follows:

(*a*) *Elementary Substances.*—Graph values of Φ given in Table 1 for elements in the column to which X belongs, against their normal boiling points (*v.* Vol. I, p. 102) and interpolate or extrapolate to approximate normal boiling point of X.

(*b*) T_B, *400 to 2250 C.*—Estimate Φ as well as possible from the values given in Table 2 or by moderate extrapolation from Fig. 1 to the normal boiling point of X.

(*c*) T_B, *−200 to +400°C.*—Determine the probable group by selection of compounds in Table 3 most analogous to X in constitution and obtain value of Φ for that group from Fig. 1 at approximate normal boiling point of X.

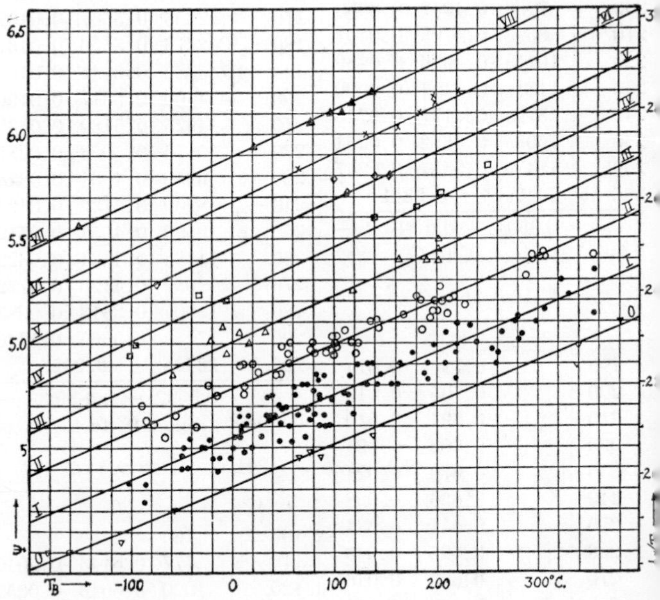

Fig. 1.—Entropy of vaporization at normal boiling point for 240 organic and inorganic compounds. (Roman numerals indicate groups listed in Table 3.)

It should be noted that the higher members of a series of compounds are usually in the same group and, almost without exception, the first (and frequently the second and third) member of the series is in a different group.

Wide extrapolations can be made with moderate accuracy since Φ changes only slightly over the entire range from the triple point to the critical point as is illustrated by the typical curves of Fig. 2.

Example.—The vapor pressure of benzene at 20°C is found to be 75.0 mm. What is its normal boiling point? Table 3 indicates this compound is in Group I. Figure 1 gives $\Phi = 4.60$ at 20°C for

Group I. Substituting this value in equation (1) gives $\Delta t = 64.1°$ or $t_B = 84.1°C$ as a first approximation. Figure 1 gives values of Φ for $T/T_B = 1.0$, or $\Phi = 4.73$ at 84° for Group I. The typical curves in Fig. 2 indicate that Φ is greater at $T/T_B = 293.1/357.2 = 0.82$ by about 3%, yielding $\Phi = 4.87$. Substituting this value in equation (1), $\Delta t = 60.5°$ or $t_B = 80.5°C$ as a second approximation.

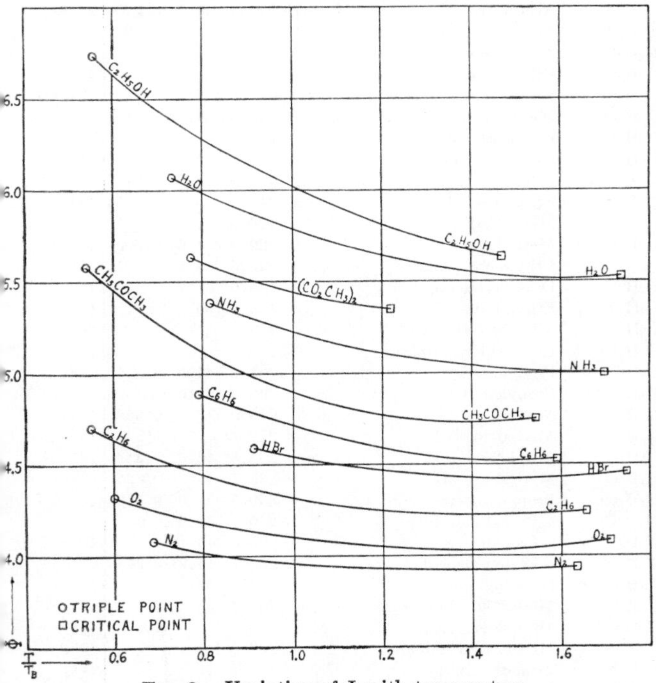

FIG. 2.—Variation of Φ with temperature.

TABLE 1.—Φ FOR ELEMENTARY SUBSTANCES

Figures in parentheses denote extrapolations beyond experimental range

0	I	II	III	IV	V	VI	VII	
He	H			C	N	O		
1.70	2.61			(6.7)	3.96	4.08		
Ne					P	S	Cl	
3.54					4.70	4.515	4.60	
A	Na	Mg					Mn	Fe
4.18	4.6	10.1					6.42	(4.6)
	K	Ca					Br	
	4.3	(13.3)					4.74	
Kr	Cu	Zn				Se		
4.04	9.5	5.23				4.80		
	Rb	Sr						
	(4.1)	(13.1)						
	Ag	Cd		Sn	Sb		I	
	5.9	5.02		(6.7)	6.17		5.06	
	Cs	Ba						
	(4.0)	(12.9)						
Rn	Au	Hg		Pb	Bi			
4.34	(7.0)	4.925		(4.9)	(6.0)			

TABLE 2.—Φ FOR COMPOUNDS WITH NORMAL BOILING POINTS BETWEEN 400 AND 2250°C

2.5	Cu_2Cl_2; Cu_2Br_2; Cu_2I_2
3.6	As_2O_3
4.1–4.6	NaOH; KOH; NaCN
4.8–5.5	Halides (13) of Li, Na, K, Rb, Cs, Pb, and Tl (except those given below)
5.6–6.0	LiF; NaF; NaCl; RbF
6.0–6.4	KF; CsI; RbCl; $PbCl_2$
10.5	SiO_2

TABLE 3.—COMPOUNDS WITH NORMAL BOILING POINTS BETWEEN −200 AND +400°C

Figures in parentheses denote number of compounds of that class

Inorganic	Organic	
	Group 0	
SiH_4	Methane	Butylethylene
S_2Cl_2	Carbon monoxide	Anthracene
$Co(CO)_3NO$	Methylsilicane	Phenanthrene
	Trichloroethylene	Anthraquinone
	Group I	
HF; PH_3	Hydrocarbons (34)	Benzonitrile
H_2Se; H_2Te	$C_aH_bX_c$* (30)	Benzaldehyde
Si_2H_6; Si_3H_8	Ethers (5)	Phthalic anhydride
Ge_2H_6; Ge_3H_8	C_aH_bS* (4)	Methyl salicylate
SnH_4	COS; CSSe	Quinoline
$H_aX_bY_c$* (17)	C_3O_2; $COCl_2$	Camphor
Si_2OCl_6	Dimethylsilicane	Benzophenone
$SeOCl_2$	*o, m, p*-Nitrotoluidines	Methyl ethyl ketone
CrO_2Cl_2	*o, m, p*-Nitrotoluenes	Dibenzyl ketone
	Group II	
HCl; HBr; HI	Esters (17)	Acetone
ClO_2; N_2O	Amines (14)	Methyl ether
AsH_3	HCN; CNCl	Methyl ethyl ether
$(SiH_3)_2O$; $(SiCl_3)_2O$	CH_3F; CH_3NO_2	Nitrobenzene
Si_3H_9N; $(SiH_3)_3N$	Tetranitromethane	*o, m*-Chloroanilines
$HgCl_2$	Formic acid	Methyl benzoate
	Ethylene oxide	α, β-Naphthols
	Acetaldehyde	
	Group III	
SO_2	Acetic acid	Dimethyl oxalate
H_2S	Cyanogen	*o, m, p*-Cresols
NOCl	Methyl formate	Acetophenone
	Glycol diacetate	Dimethylamine
		Ethylamine
	Group IV	
NH_3	Methylamine	Benzyl alcohol
PF_3	Propionic acid	Benzoic acid
BF_3	Phenol	
	Group V	
H_2O	Acetic anhydride	
N_2H_4	Isobutyric acid	
PF_5		
	Group VI	
	Methyl alcohol	Butyric acid
	Isoamyl alcohol	Valeric acid
	Glycol	Isocaproic acid
		Heptylic acid
	Group VII	
NO; N_2O_4	Ethyl alcohol	
HgCl	*n*-Propyl alcohol	
	Isobutyl alcohol	
	n-Amyl alcohol	

* a = 0, 1, 2, 3, etc.; b and c = 1, 2, 3, etc.; X = Halogen; Y = P, As, Sb, Si, Ge, Sn, Hg, Os, or B.

CRITICAL-POINT DATA

A. F. O. Germann and S. F. Pickering

In the following tables the values, for which no literature reference is given, have been compiled from the vapor pressure and orthobaric density sections of this volume, *q. v.* for the literature citations.

A-Table, Elementary Substances and Atmospheric Air

Formula	t_c, °C	p_c, atm.	d_c, g/cm³	Lit.
A	− 122	48	0.531	(21)
Br_2	302			
Cl_2	144.0	76.1	0.573	(21)
H_2	− 239.9	12.8	0.0310	(21)
He	− 267.9	2.26	0.0693	(21)
Hg	>1550	>200	4–5	
I_2	553			
Kr	− 63	54	0.78	(21)
N_2	− 147.1	33.5	0.3110	(21)
Ne	− 228.7	25.9	0.484	(21)
O_2	− 118.8	49.7	0.430	(21)
Rn	104	62		
S	1040			
Xe	16.6	58.2	1.155	(21)
Air	− 140.7	37.2	0.35*	(21)
			0.31†	

* Plait point.
† Critical point of contact.

B-Table, Chemical Compounds

Formula	t_c, °C	p_c, atm.	d_c, g/cm³	Lit.
H_2O	374.0	217.72	0.4	
HCl	51.4	81.6	0.42	(21)
HBr	90	84		(21)
HI	151	82		(21)
SO_2	157.2	77.7	0.52	(21)
SO_3	218.3	83.6	0.630	
H_2S	100.4	88.9		(21)
H_2Se	138	88		
N_2O	36.5	71.7	0.45	(21)
NO	−94	65	0.52	(21)
N_2O_4	158	99		
NH_3	132.4	111.5	0.235	(21)
N_2H_4	380	145		
PH_3	51	64	0.30	
PH_4Cl	49	73		
SiH_4	− 3.5	48		
SiF_4	− 1.5	50		
$GeCl_4$	277	38		
$SnCl_4$	318.7	37.0	0.742	

C-Table, Carbon Compounds

Formula	Name	t_c, °C	p_c, atm.	d_c, g/cm³	Lit.
CCl_2O	Phosgene	182	56	0.52	(7, 9, 17)
CCl_4	Carbon tetrachloride	283.1	45.0	0.558	
CO	Carbon monoxide	−139	35	0.311	(21)
COS	Carbon oxysulfide	105	61		
CO_2	Carbon dioxide	31.1	73.0	0.460	(21)
CS_2	Carbon disulfide	273	76		
$CHCl_3$	Chloroform	263		0.516	
HCN	Hydrogen cyanide	183.5	50	0.20	
CH_3Cl	Methyl chloride	143.1	65.8	0.37	(21)
CH_3F	Methyl fluoride	44.9	62.0		
CH_4	Methane	− 82.5	45.8	0.162	(21)
CH_4O	Methyl alcohol	240.0	78.7	0.272	(27, 33)
CH_4S	Methylmercaptan	196.8	71.4	0.323	(2)
CH_5N	Methylamine	156.9	73.6		(1)
C_2N_2	Cyanogen	128	59		(21)
C_2H_2	Acetylene	36	62	0.231	(21)
C_2H_3N	Acetonitrile	274.7	47.7	0.240	(8, 29)
C_2H_4	Ethylene	9.7	50.9	0.22	(21)
C_2H_4O	Acetaldehyde	188			(13)
C_2H_4O	Ethylene oxide	192.0			(14)
$C_2H_4O_2$	Acetic acid	321.6	57.2	0.351	(23, 24, 34)
$C_2H_4O_2$	Methyl formate	214.0	59.1_5	0.349	(34, 35)
C_2H_5Br	Ethyl bromide	231		0.513	
C_2H_5Cl	Ethyl chloride	187.2	52	0.33	(21)
C_2H_6	Ethane	32.1	48.8	0.21	(21)
C_2H_6O	Ethyl alcohol	243.1	63.1	0.275_5	(25, 33)
C_2H_6O	Methyl ether	126.9	52.0	0.271	(4, 5)
C_2H_6S	Methyl sulfide	229.9	54.6	0.306	(2)
C_2H_6S	Ethylmercaptan	225.5	54.2	0.301	(2)
C_2H_7N	Dimethylamine	164.6	51.7		(1)
C_2H_7N	Ethylamine	183.2	55.5		(1)
C_3H_4	Allylene $CH_3C\vdots CH$	128			(21)
$C_3H_5ClO_2$	Ethyl chloroformate	<235			(8)
C_3H_5N	Propionitrile	291.2	41.3	0.241	(29)
C_3H_6	Propylene $CH_3CH{:}CH_2$	92.3	45.0		(21)
C_3H_6O	Acetone	235.0	47	0.268	(11)
C_3H_6O	Allyl alcohol	272			(15)
$C_3H_6O_2$	Ethyl formate	235.3	46.6_5	0.323	(34, 35)
$C_3H_6O_2$	Methyl acetate	233.7	46.3	0.325	(34, 35)
$C_3H_6O_2$	Propionic acid	339.5	53.0	0.315	(12, 19, 30)
C_3H_7Cl	*n*-Propyl chloride	230	45.2		
C_3H_8	*n*-Propane	95.6	43		(21)
C_3H_8O	*n*-Propyl alcohol	263.7	49.9_5	0.273	(28, 33)
C_3H_8O	Isopropyl alcohol	235	53		(15)
C_3H_8O	Methyl ethyl ether	164.7	43.4	0.270	(2)
$C_3H_8O_2$	Methylal	224			(19)
C_3H_8S	Methyl ethyl sulfide	260	42		(30)
C_3H_9N	Trimethylamine	161	41		(31)
C_3H_9N	Propylamine	223.8	46.3		(1)
C_4H_4S	Thiophene	317	48		(20)
$C_4H_6O_3$	Acetic anhydride	296	46		(30)
$C_4H_6O_4$	Methyl oxalate	260	9.48		
C_4H_7N	Butyronitrile	309	37.4		(8)
$C_4H_8O_2$	Methyl propionate	257.4	39.3	0.312	(34, 35)
$C_4H_8O_2$	Ethyl acetate	250.1	37.8	0.308	(34, 35)
$C_4H_8O_2$	Propyl formate	264.8_5	40.1	0.309	(34, 35)
$C_4H_8O_2$	*n*-Butyric acid	355		0.302	(3, 12)
$C_4H_8O_2$	Isobutyric acid	336		0.304	(3, 12)
C_4H_{10}	*n*-Butane	153	36		(21)
C_4H_{10}	Isobutane	134	37		(21)
$C_4H_{10}O$	Ethyl ether	193.8	35.5	0.262_5	(26, 34)
$C_4H_{10}O$	*n*-Butyl alcohol	287	48.4		(11, 19)
$C_4H_{10}O$	Isobutyl alcohol	265	48		(15)
$C_4H_{10}O$	*sec.*-Butyl alcohol	265			(3)
$C_4H_{10}O$	*tert.*-Butyl alcohol	235			(19)
$C_4H_{10}S$	Ethyl sulfide	283.8	39.1	0.279	(2)
$C_4H_{10}S_2$	Ethyl disulfide	369			(6)
$C_4H_{11}N$	Diethylamine	223.5	36.2	0.246	(1, 11)
C_5H_5N	Pyridine	344	60.0		(8, 11)
$C_5H_{10}O$	Ethyl allyl ether	245			(19)
$C_5H_{10}O_2$	Ethyl propionate	272.9	33.0	0.296_5	(34, 35)
$C_5H_{10}O_2$	Isobutyl formate	278	38	0.288	(16)
$C_5H_{10}O_2$	Methyl butyrate	281.3	34.2	0.300	(34, 35)
$C_5H_{10}O_2$	Methyl isobutyrate	267.5_5	33.7	0.301	(34, 35)
$C_5H_{10}O_2$	Propyl acetate	276.2	32.9	0.296	(34, 35)
$C_5H_{10}O_2$	*n*-Valeric acid	379			(3)
$C_5H_{10}O_2$	Isovaleric acid	361			(3)
C_5H_{12}	*n*-Pentane	197.2	33.0	0.232	
C_5H_{12}	Isopentane	187.8	32.8	0.234	
$C_5H_{12}O$	Ethyl propyl ether	227.4	32.1	0.258	(2)
$C_5H_{12}O$	Isoamyl alcohol	307			(19)
$C_5H_{12}O$	*tert.*-Amyl alcohol	272			(3)
$C_5H_{12}O_2$	Methylene diethyl ether	254			(19)
$C_5H_{12}S$	Isoamylmercaptan	321			(6)
C_6H_5Br	Bromobenzene	397	44.6	0.486	
C_6H_5Cl	Chlorobenzene	359	44.6	0.365	
C_6H_5F	Fluorobenzene	286	44.6	0.354	
C_6H_5I	Iodobenzene	448	44.6	0.581	
C_6H_6	Benzene	288.5	47.7	0.304	

Formula	Name	t_c, °C	p_c, atm.	d_c, g/cm³	Lit.
C_6H_6O	Phenol	419	60.5		(8, 11)
C_6H_7N	Aniline	426	52.4		(8)
$C_6H_{10}O_2$	Ethyl crotonate	326			(19)
$C_6H_{10}S$	Allyl sulfide	380			(6)
$C_6H_{11}N$	Capronitrile	349	32.2		(8)
C_6H_{12}	Cyclohexane	281.0	40.4	0.270	
$C_6H_{12}O_2$	*n*-Butyl acetate	306			(18)
$C_6H_{12}O_2$	Ethyl butyrate	293	30	0.276	(16)
$C_6H_{12}O_2$	Ethyl isobutyrate	280	30	0.276	(16)
$C_6H_{12}O_2$	Isoamyl formate	303	34	0.282	(16)
$C_6H_{12}O_2$	Isobutyl acetate	288	31	0.281	(16)
$C_6H_{12}O_2$	Methyl valerate	294 d	32	0.279	(8, 16, 22)
$C_6H_{12}O_2$	Propyl propionate	305			(18)
$C_6H_{12}O_3$	Paraldehyde	290			(13)
C_6H_{14}	Diisopropyl	227.4	30.6	0.241	
C_6H_{14}	*n*-Hexane	234.8	29.5	0.234	
$C_6H_{15}N$	Triethylamine	262	30	0.251	(11, 32)
$C_6H_{15}N$	Dipropylamine	277	31		(32)
C_7H_5N	Benzonitrile	426	41.6		(8)
C_7H_8	Toluene	320.6	41.6	0.292	
C_7H_8O	*o*-Cresol	422	49.4		(8, 11, 22)
C_7H_8O	*m*-Cresol	432	45.0		(8)
C_7H_8O	*p*-Cresol	426	50.8		(8, 11, 22)
C_7H_8O	Anisole	369	41.3		(8)
C_7H_9N	Methylaniline	429	51.3		(8, 11, 22)
$C_7H_{14}O_2$	Isoamyl acetate	326			(3)
$C_7H_{14}O_2$	Isobutyl propionate	319			(18)
$C_7H_{14}O_2$	Ethyl isovalerate	315			(3)
$C_7H_{14}O_2$	Ethyl valerate	297			(10)
$C_7H_{14}O_2$	Propyl butyrate	327			(18)
$C_7H_{14}O_2$	Propyl isobutyrate	316			(18)
C_7H_{16}	*n*-Heptane	266.8	26.8	0.234	
$C_7H_{16}O$	*n*-Heptyl alcohol	365			(3)
C_8H_7N	Tolunitrile	450			(8, 22)
$C_8H_{10}O$	Phenetole	374	33.8		(8)
$C_8H_{11}N$	Dimethylaniline	415	35.8		(8)
$C_8H_{16}O_2$	Isoamyl propionate	338			(3)
$C_8H_{16}O_2$	Isobutyl butyrate	338			(3)
$C_8H_{16}O_2$	Isobutyl isobutyrate	329			(3)
$C_8H_{16}O_2$	Propyl isovalerate	336			(3)
C_8H_{18}	Diisobutyl	277	24.5	0.237	
C_8H_{18}	*n*-Octane	296	24.6	0.234	
$C_8H_{18}O$	*n*-Octyl alcohol	385			(3)
$C_8H_{18}O$	*sec.*-Octyl alcohol	364			(3)
C_9H_7N	Quinoline	> 520			(8, 22)
$C_9H_{13}N$	Dimethyl-*o*-toluidine	395	30.8		(8)
$C_9H_{18}O_2$	Isoamyl butyrate	346			(3)
$C_9H_{18}O_2$	Isobutyl isovalerate	348			(3)
$C_{10}H_{14}O$	Thymol	425			(8, 22)
$C_{10}H_{20}O_2$	Ethyl caprylate	386			(3)
$C_{10}H_{22}S$	Isoamyl sulfide	391			(6)
$C_{11}H_{22}O_2$	Ethyl nonylate	400			(3)

LITERATURE

(For a key to the periodicals see end of volume)

(1) Berthoud, *42*, **15**: 3; 17. (2) Berthoud and Brum, *42*, **21**: 143; 24. (3) Brown, *4*, **89**: 311; 06. (4) Cardoso and Bruno, *42*, **20**: 347; 23. (5) Cardoso and Coppola, *42*, **20**: 337; 23. (6) Ferretto, *36*, **30 I**: 296; 00. (7) Germann and Taylor, *1*, **48**: 1154; 26. (8) Guye and Mallet, *149*, **13**: 30, 129, 274, 462; 02. (9) Hackspill and Mathieu, *27*, **25**: 482; 19.

(10) de Heen, *Recherches, Partie Expérimentale*, p. 102. Paris, 1888. (11) Herz and Neukirch, *7*, **104**: 433; 23. (12) von Hirsch, *8*, **69**: 456; 99. (13) Hollmann, *7*, **43**: 129; 03. (14) Maass and Boomer, *1*, **44**: 1709; 22. (15) Nadejdine, *53*, **14**: 157, 536; 82. **15**: 25; 83. *427*, **7**: 678; 83. (16) Nadejdine, *428*, **23**: 617; 87. (17) Paternò and Mazzucchelli, *36*, **50 I**: 30; 20. (18) Pawlewski, *25*, **15**: 2460; 82. (19) Pawlewski, *25*, **16**: 2633; 83.

(20) Pawlewski, *25*, **21**: 2141; 88. (21) Pickering, *31*, No. **541**; 26. (22) Radice, *Thesis*, Geneva, 1899. (23) Ramsay and Young, *62*, **175**: 461; 85. (24) Ramsay and Young, *4*, **49**: 790; 86. (25) Ramsay and Young, *62*, **177**: 123; 87. (26) Ramsay and Young, *62*, **178**: 57; 88. (27) Ramsay and Young, *62*, **178**: 313; 88. (28) Ramsay and Young, *62*, **180**: 137; 90. (29) Ter-Gazarian, *42*, **4**: 140; 06.

(30) Vespignani, *36*, **33 I**: 73; 03. (31) Vincent and Chappuis, *34*, **101**: 427; 85. (32) Vincent and Chappuis, *34*, **103**: 379; 86. (33) Young, *4*, **59**: 903; 91. (34) Young, *117*, **12**: 374; 10. (35) Young and Thomas, *4*, **63**: 1191; 93.

ADSORPTION AT SOLID SURFACES AND SOLUBILITY OF GASES IN METALS OF THE PLATINUM GROUP

E. K. Rideal

INTRODUCTION

Adsorption of gases, vapors and liquids at solid surfaces is dependent not only on the chemical natures and potentials of the adsorbents and the nature of the adsorbate but also on the physical state of the adsorbing surface. Perfectly uniform solid surfaces have as yet not been constructed. In general, the surfaces of solids are composite, consisting of areas of different chemical potentials and adsorptive powers. Equations connecting the amount adsorbed and the chemical potential of the adsorbate hold only for the particular heterogeneous solid surface under investigation and are not rigidly applicable to other preparations of the same material.

The adsorption per g of adsorbing material varies not only on account of the inhomogeneity of the surface of the adsorbate but is also dependent on the specific surface of the material. The use of sieves for grading material is no guide to the specific surface. Charcoals may readily be prepared having specific surfaces varying from 20 to 200 m² per g although apparently similar in passage through graded sieves. Adsorption is likewise complicated by actual solution of the adsorbate in the adsorbent to form solid solutions or chemical compounds. Gel-like adsorbents may likewise change in specific surface during the process of adsorption, whilst condensation of vapor undoubtedly occurs in the micropores at pressures which vary with the mean diameters of the micropores.

1. For a great number of systems adsorption is complete when the adsorbate is completely covered with a unimolecular layer of adsorbent. For these the general equation of ([59]), and ([85]), is applicable in which the amount x adsorbed per g is related to the concentration c (or pressure p) of the adsorbent by the expression $x = \frac{\mathrm{abc}}{\mathrm{a} + \mathrm{bc}}$, $\left(\text{or } x = \frac{\mathrm{a'b'}p}{\mathrm{a'} + \mathrm{b'}p}\right)$, where a (a′) and b (b′) are constants.

2. For a few systems discrete areas of homogeneity with different properties in the adsorbing surface have been detected. Saturation for each homogeneous fraction of the surface is not attained at identical bulk concentrations but saturation is complete when a unimolecular layer of adsorbate covers the whole surface. The modified equation of Langmuir, $x = \sum \frac{\mathrm{abc}}{\mathrm{a} + \mathrm{bc}}$, is here applicable, one such term being applicable to the area of the integrated fractions of the equally uniform parts of the non-uniform surface.

3. For a few systems, especially for those in which vapors are present as adsorbate and where the adsorbent is a gel-like solid, multimolecular layers are formed in the pores of the gel. Over certain ranges of concentration at least, the relationship between the amount x adsorbed per g of adsorbent and the bulk concentration c (or pressure p) may be expressed by the equation of Freundlich, $x = \mathrm{a}c^{1/\mathrm{n}}$ (or $\mathrm{a'}p^{1/\mathrm{n'}}$) where a (a′) and n (n′) are constants.

For these reasons it is thought desirable to give only a few typical x, c and x, p relationships for diverse materials in detail and to indicate in a brief manner the results for other important systems investigated.

Gases on Charcoal

The Specific Surface.—The specific surface varies with the nature of the charcoal and with its preparation as well as with its subsequent treatment. The surface is not uniform in adsorbing power but areas of different adsorbing powers can be differentiated. The extent of these again varies with the mode of preparation. A comparison of "norite" and blood charcoal ([55]). Dense charcoals ([45]). Activation ([93]). Gas mask material ([58]). Activity ([23]). Service time and influence of O_2 ([66]). Others ([11, 13, 65, 82]).

Adsorption of Gases.—O_2, N_2 mixtures on coconut shell carbon ([60, 61]). Air by various charcoals ([46]). H_2, Ne, He, N_2 ([12]). Others ([6, 50, 86]). Theory ([8]).

Gases by Wood Charcoal ([50])

T = Temp. °K, p = pressure in cm Hg, x = cm³ adsorbed per 2.964 g at T and p reduced to 0° and 760

He, 83°K

p	x
12.0	1.00
17.1	1.38
23.5	2.40
42.76	3.46
70.5	5.45

A, Argon

p	x
83°K	
0.46	47.28
1.70	196.7
37.9	230.4
41.0	277.0
145°K	
0.40	11.32
0.60	15.2
1.28	29.42
1.34	38.65
1.94	47.14
2.70	57.00
3.60	74.35
9.7	144.6
22.8	171.2
36.0	190.7
79.0	228.0
236°K	
30.96	35.51
41.70	42.70
56.84	51.07
81.5	65.64
351°K	
29.16	2.55
72.24	5.70
86.80	8.51

N_2

p	x
83°K	
1.3	155.4
2.2	183.2
3.3	239.3
34.3	267.8
194.7°K	
1.4	15.0
4.6	42.3
13.5	70.0
25.3	96.5
51.8	121.0
273°K	
7.2	4.53
17.3	10.7
22.9	13.0
31.2	17.6
51.0	25.4

CO

p	x
194.7°K	
0.6	18.5
3.0	51.26
4.0	62.0
7.2	82.0
11.7	101.0
14.8	101.7
18.7	120.0
22.8	138.5
44.2	157.5
239.4°K	
10.1	27.3
18.8	42.0
32.0	58.0
43.0	67.0
54.0	76.0
67.0	84.0
273°K	
7.3	7.5
18.0	16.5
30.9	25.1
54.0	38.1
71.3	51.66
88.2	52.3
293°K	
12.3	7.0
30.0	15.4
49.5	23.2
85.6	35.0

CO_2

p	x
273°K	
6.0	62.8
8.7	78.2
12.3	95.5
17.9	114.5
24.2	113.0
293°K	
2.0	14.4
2.9	19.5
6.3	38.0
8.5	46.4
12.8	62.3
18.6	77.5
28.8	94.5
37.4	113.2
50.0	131.2
319°K	
7.0	19.2
12.1	28.2
15.1	37.4
20.0	45.7
31.5	61.2
43.6	75.8
59.7	97.2
84.2	110.0
351°K	
7.2	9.4
11.7	13.8
17.6	18.6
25.5	27.3
36.5	36.1
47.9	44.0
72.6	58.5
373°K	
6.1	9.8
12.1	9.1
18.8	13.4
27.2	18.0

CO_2, 373°K

p	x
42.1	26.4
60.6	34.7
455°K	
25.1	3.9
48.8	7.4
73.6	10.8

Gases adsorbed by 2.786 g charcoal

CH_4, Methane

p	x
240°K	
3.6	35.21
5.3	44.64
7.6	55.36
10.2	64.65
13.2	73.77
17.1	83.22
21.5	92.12
27	100.9
255°K	
7.0	34.8
10.3	44.1
15.1	54.53
19.0	63.7
24.2	72.58
31.1	81.9
39.3	90.16
48.4	98.62
273°K	
6.7	20.56
13.4	34.2
19.1	42.2
27.4	53.3
35.8	62.0
45.1	70.46
57.8	79.1
70.2	87.1
293°K	
4.0	7.53
6.9	11.98
12.7	20.0
24.8	33.10
35.5	41.65
49.7	51.20
64.0	59.36
79.5	67.26
319°K	
9.2	7.08
14.0	11.47
27.8	18.67
34.7	23.2
51.1	30.83
67.6	38.90

C_2H_4, Ethylene

p	x
273°K	
7.0	110.0
9.3	119.3
16.8	139.0
31.9	157.3
61.6	179.5

C_2H_4	
p	x
293°K	
1.5	28.9
3.2	58.0
5.2	71.4
7.9	84.9
17.1	109.1
22.0	118.1
38.8	136.8
68.5	153.8

C_2H_4	
p	x
333°K	
20.7	70.0
34.8	82.6
43.6	88.9
69.7	104.5
373°K	
3.4	9.2
8.1	17.3
15.2	29.0
23.0	37.2

C_2H_4, 373°K	
p	x
32.4	45.6
44.8	55.0
66.8	66.5
405°K	
47.7	35.4
67.8	43.1
88.7	51.7

CO_2 by blood charcoal at 20°C. $x/c = 4.4$. x = millimols adsorbed, per g charcoal, c = moles CO_2 per ml (51). CO_2 by blood charcoal at 31°C obeys the equation $x = Kp^{1/n}$ where x = cm³ adsorbed (n = 1.77) (29). Volume of gases adsorbed by coconut charcoal at 0°C (x_1) and at −185°C (x_2), reduced to S. T. P (2).

Gas	He	H_2	$(2H_2, O_2)$	A	N_2	O_2	CO	$CO + O_2$
x_1	2	4	12	12	15	18	21	30
x_2	15	135	150	175	155	230	190	195

Adsorption of air by charcoals from various woods (83). Adsorption of H_2, CH_4, C_2H_4, N_2 (47). Adsorption of vapors on charcoal, H_2O (9, 53, 84). $COCl_2$ by beechwood charcoal (10). Chloropicrin and CCl_4, velocity of adsorption (44). NH_3 by coconut charcoal (22). C_6H_6 by wood charcoal (3). SO_2 at 10°C (100).

$CH_3COOC_2H_5$, $CHCl_3$, C_6H_6, CS_2, H_2O. Weights of vapors adsorbed by 100 g bone charcoal divided by the bulk density of the charcoal = constant, 32.7 to 36.6. The same for blood charcoal = 105.2 to 106.1 (34). Others (17, 37).

NH_3 at 0° (94)

p_{mm}	2.9	28.8	78.7	161.0	319.2	440.0	636.4	746.7
x, cm³/g	5.4	30.2	60.4	90.3	115.7	127.0	132.4	135.9

NH_3 at 151.5°C (94)

p_{mm}	2.8	16.6	64.8	176.2	285.0	432.7	576.8	721.8
x, cm³/g	0.3	1.0	2.1	4.0	5.5	7.2	8.9	10.5

H_2 at −185°C (15)

p_{atm}	1	5	10	15	20	25
x, cm³/g	92	138	156	149	145	138

Gases on Glass and Silicates

H_2O, molecules per cm², 5.6×10^{16} on glass; 4.3×10^{16} on quartz (59); 20.2×10^{16} on anorthite (52); 8.7×10^{16} on glass at 30°C in saturated air (7).

MOLECULAR FILM THICKNESS ON GLASS FOR DIFFERENT WATER VAPOR PRESSURES (69)

298°K, p_{mm}	22.73	22.80	23.08	23.76
Number molecular layers	51.8	56.1	83	184

308°K, p	30.65	31.47	34.26	43.07	314°K, p	31.97	32.91	47.02
Number	5.9	5.5	15.5	46.3	Number	1.4	0.4	24.0

CO_2, 3.7×10^{16} molecules per cm² on glass (59).

N_2, 5.14 to 5.94 = number molecular layers at p = 121.68 mm and 273°K (21). 6.0×10^{14} molecules per cm² on glass (59).

MOLECULAR THICKNESS AT p = 121.68 MM AND 273°K (18, 21)

SO_2	NH_3	N_2O	C_2H_2
32.1	39.9	4.5	3.5

Gases on Silica Gel

The adsorption varies with the method of preparation. Gases: SO_2 (68); butane (79); C_6H_6, CCl_4, C_2H_5OH (80); NH_3 (14); CO_2, N_2O (81).

Adsorption of Liquids

A variation in apparent density of charcoal is noted when different immersion liquids are employed. This variation has been ascribed to (*a*) the presence of a compressed liquid film on the surface or to (*b*) variable penetration into the micropores (13, 42, 43, 101).

Adsorption on Charcoal, from Solutions

NON- OR WEAK ELECTROLYTES

Values of the constants in the equation $x = ac^{1/n}$ are given as follows:

Aqueous Solutions.—C_2H_5OH (16).

Isoamyl alcohol (19)

c, mols/l	0.0125	0.0225	0.1100
x, millimols/g	2.52	2.95	4.45

CH_3COCH_3, acetone 291°K (72)

x, millimols/g	0.208	0.618	1.075	1.50	2.08	2.88
c, millimols/l	2.34	14.65	41.03	88.62	177.69	268.97

Acetic acid, n = 2; succinic acid, n = 2; oxalic acid, n = 10 (88).

Acetic acid by bone charcoal (89)

x, g/g	0.406	0.456	0.492	0.562	0.60	0.626
c, g/100 ml	4.46	5.88	8.34	12.48	12.78	22.18
x, g/g	0.654	0.656	0.668	0.688	0.698	0.692
c, g/100 ml	29.27	35.26	40.38	50.62	63.69	91.56

Urea, n = 3 (62).

Sugars by Sugar Charcoal.—Lactose $\left(a = 1.737; \frac{1}{n} = 0.2221\right)$; saccharose $\left(a = 1.257; \frac{1}{n} = 0.1124\right)$ (98); glucose (74).

Dyes (5)

Methylene blue by animal charcoal (n = 5.0 to 8.9). Ponceau red by animal charcoal, n = 10.5 at 288°K, 6.6 at 323°, 4.9 at 343°. Ponceau red by blood charcoal, n = 21 at 288°K, 19.2 at 323°, 11.9 at 343°.

Night blue on blood charcoal (5)

c, mg/l	0	2	61	89	144	146	352	460
x, mg/g	100	143	128	122	112	108	96	80

Iodine (67)

Bromine, T = 273°K (26)

x, millimols/g	2.07	3.10	4.27	5.44	6.80
c, mols/l × 10⁴	9.2	25.9	66.9	170.8	297.5

Non-aqueous Solutions.—

Solvent	Solute	x, millimols/g	0.437	0.780	1.04	1.44
Benzene	Benzoic acid	c, millimols/l	6.18	25.0	53.13	117.7
		a	1/n	Lit.		
Acetone	o-$C_6H_4(OH)_2$	6.255	0.5762	(28)		
Acetone	m-$C_6H_4(OH)_2$	0.8072	0.2281			
Acetone	C_6H_5COOH	1.999	0.525			
Acetone	$C_6H_4(OH)COOH$	2.148	0.4173			
Acetone	m-$C_6H_4(NO_2)COOH$	3.599	0.5318			
Acetone	$C_6H_5COCH(OH)C_6H_5$	1.944	0.3201			
Acetone	Picric acid	0.9867	0.2373			
Alcohol	Benzoic acid			(35)		

Iodine in Various Solvents.—In C_2H_5OH and C_6H_6, n = 4 (88, 89). Values of the constant k in the equation $k = \frac{v}{m} \log_{10} \frac{C_0}{C}$; v = volume of solution in ml, m = mass of charcoal in g, C_0 = total weight of iodine present, C = equilibrium weight of iodine in solution (88, 89).

Solvent	$CHCl_3$	C_2H_5OH	C_2H_5OH
Charcoal	sugar	sugar	animal
k	38.4	35.6	26.2

I_2 in $CHCl_3$ (24).

Acetic acid from toluene, on animal charcoal (90)

x, g/g	+0.10	+0.13	+0.04	−0.04	−0.09	−0.13	−0.16
c, g solute per g, solution	0.1	0.2	0.3	0.4	0.5	0.6	0.7

Preferential adsorption of solvent.

Phenol from ethyl alcohol, on animal charcoal (36)

x, g/g...	+0.14	+0.185	+0.205	+0.21	+0.202	+0.175	+0.11
c, g solute per g solution....	0.1	0.2	0.3	0.4	0.5	0.6	0.7

Strong Electrolytes

Approximate values of exponent n in the equation $x = ac^{1/n}$ are indicated thus (n).

Literature.—Methylene blue hydrochloride (73). $NaAuCl_4$ (54). $K_2Cr_2O_7$ by bone charcoal (n = 2) (63).

Adsorption, positive and negative, of KCl, NH_4Cl, $MgSO_4$, $BaCl_2$, $CuSO_4$ from aqueous solutions; 5 g charcoal at 25°C (99).

c = millimols/l, x = mg adsorbed

KCl	c	0.44	2.66	6.16	20.5	39.8	56.3	68.0	72.1	101	128	170
	x	+0.32	+1.25	+2.30	+2.50	+1.10	+1.70	−1.70	−1.80	−1.20	−2.6	−7.7
NH_4Cl	c	12.2	22.9	48.9	99.2	152	191					
	x	+1.5	+3.4	+11.9	+7.4	+4.5	+3.3					
$MgSO_4$	c	0.43	1.23	25.7	51.6	52.8	100.1	153.8				
	x	+0.89	+2.4	−4.4	−14	−16	−34	−39				
$BaCl_2$	c	95	153	220								
	x	+26	+28	+36								
$CuSO_4$	c	67	114									
	x	+33	+24									

Salts from solution (76)

Order of Adsorption.—$I^- > NO_3^- > Br^- > Cl^- > SO_4^{--}$. N solutions of the following give % adsorption, KI, 28; KNO_3, 16; KBr, 14; KCl, 7; K_2SO_4, 5.

(87) gives $OH^- > CNS^- > I^- > NO_3^- > Br^- > Cl^- > HPO_4^{--} > SO_4^{--}$; $H^+ > Al^{+++} > Cu^{++} > Zn^{++} > Mg^{++} > Ca^{++} > NH_4^+$, K^+, Na^+.

Uranium salts (27).

Cl^- from KCl by blood charcoal at 21° (57); $c = Cl^-$, millimol/l; x = millimol/l Cl^- adsorbed by 1 g charcoal.

c	7.24	7.36	8.33	9.09	9.34	9.43	9.52
x	0.47	0.46	0.59	0.70	1.2	1.4	1.9

NH_4IO_3, KIO_3, $(NH_4)_2CrO_4$ in H_2O, KOH aq., and H_2SO_4 aq. (20).

Adsorption on Crystalline Substances

On AgI; KI from Aqueous Solution at 25.4°C (64)

c, mols per 1 × 10^4	x, millimols per g AgI × 10^3	c, mols per 1 × 10^4	x, millimols per g AgI × 10^3
1.31	4.6	44.38	9.0
4.10	7.8	56.83	8.5
11.02	8.4	69.26	7.7
18.19	8.7	86.89	5.5
27.01	9.0	94.83	4.0

On Uric Acid (71)

Bismarck brown		Methyl violet	
c, g/100 cm³	x, g/100 g	c, g/100 cm³	x, g/100 g
0.005	0.0070	0.00043	0.068
.008	.0095	.00074	.093
.009	.0120	.00085	.137
.0017	.0115	.00224	.109

On As_2S_3 (25)

In the equation, $x/m = ac^{1/n}$, x = millimols adsorbed per g adsorbent, c = concentration in mols per l, range of equilibrium concentrations examined c_1 to c_2.

Adsorbate	c_1	c_2	a	1/n
$C_6H_5NH_3Cl$..................	0.0012	0.0096	0.079	0.208
p-$C_6H_4ClNH_3Cl$...............	.0016	.014	.080	.194
New fuchsin..................	.00002	.00137	.229	.1937
NH_4Cl......................	.00053	.00204	.0484	.2034
$\frac{1}{2}(NH_4)_2SO_4$...................	.00015	.00194	.0421	.1831
$UO_2(NO_3)_2$...................	.000221	.00223	.0314	.0769
Morphine-HCl...............	.0009	.0027	.696	.3531

Adsorption of fatty acids on minerals, from aqueous solutions (95).

Adsorption on Glass

Dyes from aqueous solutions (3.5)

c, g/ml × 10^6..............	1	5	10	50
x, g/cm² × 10^8.............	2	8.7	14	40

Adsorption on Gels from Solution

On Ferric Oxide (70)

Chloride ions; x = millimols Cl^- adsorbed per 100 cm³ solution containing m g Fe_2O_3; c = millimols Cl^- per cm³ solution

m	x	c	m	x	c
1.2960	1.37	0.00257	1.207	1.873	0.00304
0.8640	1.891(?)	0.00194	1.207	1.830	0.00230
0.6483	0.646	0.00169	1.207	1.769	0.00176
0.5190	0.508	0.00144	1.207	1.744	0.00152
0.4321	0.417	0.00127	1.207	1.718	0.00130
0.3245	0.299	0.00110	1.207	1.693	0.00109
0.2595	0.234	0.00093	1.207	1.660	0.00095
0.2162	0.191	0.00079	1.207	1.628	0.00080

On Aluminium Hydroxide

Order of ionic adsorption: ferrocyanide > ferricyanide > oxalate > sulfate > chromate > dithionate > dichromate (96).

From solution (78): Formic, acetic and butyric acids, and I_2 from various solvents; $C_6H_5NO_2$ from kerosene; CH_3COOH from CS_2.

Invertin on alumina (102)

Dilution	% adsorption	Wt. Al_2O_3
1:400	9	0.186
1:400	19	0.1395
1:20 000	93	0.1395

Adsorption on Fibers

On Wool

HCl in H_2O (32)		H_2SO_4 in H_2O (32)	
x = g acid per 100 g wool	c = % acid in solution	x = g acid per 100 g wool	c = % acid in solution
0.616	0.0077	0.892	0.0021
1.118	.0176	1.658	.0068
1.958	.0608	2.87	.0426
2.38	.1524	3.471	.1305
2.732	.3453	4.456	.3107
3.194	.7361	5.818	.6838
3.465	1.1306	6.97	1.0606

Approximate relationship $\frac{\sqrt[5]{c}}{x} = 0.293$; $\frac{\sqrt[3]{c}}{x} = 0.140$.

Potash alum from aqueous solutions (77)

% potash alum on weight of wool	c, millimols/l		x, millimols/g	
	Al_2O_3	SO_3	Al_2O_3	SO_3
5.12	0.137	1.120	0.377	0.068
10.25	0.395	2.550	0.607	0.113
15.37	0.842	4.075	0.597	0.139
20.50	1.362	5.705	0.500	0.153
25.62	1.863	7.305	0.421	0.168
30.75	2.403	9.055	0.303	0.165

On Mercerized Cotton, Diamine Blue (92)

x, mg/g	c, mg/100 cm³	x, mg/g	c, mg/100 cm³
6.65	12.7	18.4	91.4
8.4	19.0	20.6	125.8
10.5	26.3	25.2	157.1
12.25	42.75	30.6	241.6
14.8	58.4	36.2	330.6

On Cotton Fibers (92)

Orange G at 100°C		Oxamine blue XX		Benzoblue 4B	
x, mg/g	c, mg/300 cm³	x, mg/g	c, mg/300 cm³	x, mg/g	c, mg/300 cm³
1.33	11	1.58	10.25	1.43	15.3
1.97	18.6	2.00	16.5	2.03	21.9
2.23	23.3	2.48	22.55	2.43	30.3
2.80	36.6	3.07	35.8	2.90	48.4
3.23	50.3	3.77	48.7	3.45	66.2
3.97	78.1	14.5	75.5	4.18	103.3
4.53	106.4	16.4	103.6	4.70	141.2
5.00	135	19.7	130.3	5.00	180.0
6.00	207	23.3	201.7	6.73	273.1
7.07	278.8	28.4	271.6	7.28	380.9

On Silk, Picric Acid (31, 48)

x = g acid per 100 g silk	c = % acid in solution	Solution	Nature of silk	Mole ratio, of adsorbed oxide to adsorbed acid
0.14	0.36	$SnCl_4$	Raw	$155(SnO_2):1$
0.28	0.72		Boiled off	$143(SnO_2):1$
1.0	1.0	Basic ferric sulfate	Raw	$111(Fe_2O_3):1$
			Boiled off	$91(Fe_2O_3):1$
2.29	1.71	$CrCl_3$	Raw	$40(Cr_2O_3):1$
3.8	6.19		Boiled off	$44(Cr_2O_3):1$
5.9	14.1	$Al(CH_3COO)_3$	Raw	Al_2O_3 only adsorbed
7.0	33		Boiled off	

Adsorption on Miscellaneous Materials

On Cellulose, Methylene Blue from H_2O $(x/m)^2 = Kc$ (30)

On Starch, I_2 from H_2O $(x/m)^5 = Kc$ (56)

On Soils (97); $x/m = ac^{1/n}$

Adsorbent	Solute	a	1/n
Garden soil	NH_4Cl	0.0948	0.039
Garden soil	NH_4Cl	.131	.424
Nile sediment	NH_4Cl	.489	.399
Permutite	NH_4Cl	2.823	.398
Sodium zeolite (Artificial)	$CaCl_2$	2.487	.317
Zeolite	LiCl	24.419	.414
"Soil"	NH_4OH	0.0994	.434
"Soil"	NH_4OH	.147	.461
"Soil"	NH_4OH	.054	.386

For a comprehensive discussion of the adsorption behavior of soils and their constituents for gases and for dissolved substances *see* Anderson and Mattson (1) and the literature cited by them.

ADSORPTION AND SOLUBILITY OF GASES IN METALS OF THE PLATINUM SERIES

H_2, Hydrogen

cm³ (at S. T. P.) adsorbed per 4.269 g Pt black at 25°C (4)

p_{H_2}, mm	1.1	23.5	67.8	162.4	393	577	768
cm³	6.06	6.63	6.83	6.97	7.12	7.21	7.34

cm³ (S. T. P.) adsorbed by 1 cm³ Pd black (d = 11.4) at 760 mm (40)

t, °C	−50	−21	0	+20	40	60	80	105
cm³	917	887	880	661	735	742	750	754

cm³ (at S. T. P.) adsorbed by 1 g of reduced Pd at p, mm Hg (33)

0°C		0°C		0°C	
p, mm	cm³	p, mm	cm³	p, mm	cm³
0.20	0.21	4.10*	3.13	43.8	68.00
1.10	0.85	4.20	57.30	51.9	70.18
2.6	1.27	4.30	62.00	95.7	71.51
3.80	1.87	5.30	63.70	407.0	71.85
	2.21	9.13	65.02	496.6	72.16
4.00	2.77	12.6	66.4	640	72.55

30°C		80°C		160°C	
p, mm	cm³	p, mm	cm³	p, mm	cm³
1.58	0.92	140.1	6.15	1508	53.51
4.0	0.98	131.6	7.43	1541	53.81
7.4	1.31	140.1*	6.15	1577	54.67
12.5	1.97	152	12.09	1657	55.08
15.6	2.44		50.5	2000	58.10
17.8	3.15	157.8	52.6	2434	60.11
18.6	4.00	169.6	55.0	180°C	
18.8*	3.50	171.6	55.4	101	0.97
	7.65	212.6	58.10	336	2.15
	49.40	670.1	68.81	919	4.52
24.8	60.8	160°C		1218	5.82
27.7	62.65	488	3.43	1363	6.42
29.9	63.0	700	4.65	1458	6.98
43.0	65.4	888	5.87	1695	8.45
52.5	66.0	1016	7.56	1733	8.53
109.3	68.2	1153	8.69	1896	11.15
80°C		1244	10.39	1929	32.39
30.1	1.31	1313	12.82	1955*	14.31
46.2	1.75		21	1960	29.61
78.6	2.43	1320*	41	1966	50.20
85.2	2.98		49	1970	51.78
115.4	3.41	1331	46.77	2006	52.53
127.9	4.79	1460	53.50	2130	54.50
135.6	5.23	1463	52.80	2788	56.95

* Unstable range.

cm³ (at t and p) adsorbed by 1 cm³ Rh black (ppt. by NH_4OH, d = 12.1) at p = 736 mm Hg (39)

t, °C	−20	0	+50	97	200
cm³	11	260	180	168	174

cm³ (at t and p) adsorbed by 1 cm³ Ir black (ppt. by NH_4OH, d = 22.4) at p = *ca.* 740 mm Hg (40)

°C	cm³	°C	cm³	°C	cm³	°C	cm³
−20	113	+20	140	0	48	60	67
−12	96	+49	38	+24	132	80	37
0	75	−21	69	40	103	100	0

Pd alloys saturated with H_2 electrolytically; cm³ (at t and atm. pressure) adsorbed by 1 g of alloy in which the mole fraction of Pd is x_{Pd} (75)

Pd-Cu			Pd-Ag		
x_{Pd}	cm³ 25°	cm³ 100°	x_{Pd}	cm³ 25°	cm³ 100°
1.0	70.7	61.4	1.0	70.7	61.3
0.95	53.6	48.4	0.8	81.1	72.0
.86	38.4	32.4	0.7	78.2	70.2
.77	31.3	27.4	0.6	43.2	30.1
.73	27.7	22.1	0.52	13.5	10.9
.53	6.3	4.3	0.51	5.9	2.9
.52	3.7	2.0	0.49	0	0
.48	0	0	0.48	0	0
.13	0	0			

O_2 and CO

cm³ (at S. T. P.) adsorbed per 4.269 g Pt black at 25°C (4)

p, mm	O_2	688	728	CO	770.5
cm³		4.38	4.96		7.72

LITERATURE

(For a key to the periodicals see end of volume)

(1) Anderson and Mattson, *157*, No. 1452; 26. (2) Armstrong, *325*, **19**: 354; 08. (3) Bakr and King, *4*, **119**: 454; 21. (3.5) Bancelin, *34*, **158**: 791; 19. (4) Benton, *1*, **48**: 1850; 26. (5) Biltz and Steiner, *55*, **7**: 113; 10. (6) Bohart and Adams, *1*, **42**: 523; 20. (7) Briggs, *50*, **9**: 617; 05. (8) Briggs, *5*, **100**: 88; 21. (9) Brown, *2*, **17**: 700; 21.

(10) Bunbury, *4*, **121**: 1525; 22. (11) Chaney, *78*, **36**: 91; 19 (12) Claude, *34*, **158**: 861; 14. (13) Cude and Hulett, *1*, **42**: 391; 20. (14) Davidheiser and Patrick, *1*, **44**: 1; 22. (15) Dewar, *325*, **18**: 433; 06. (16) Driver and Firth, *4*, **119**: 1126; 21. (17) Driver and Firth, *4*, **121**: 2409; 22. (18) Drucker, *7*, **74**: 567; 10. (19) van Duin, *55*, **17**: 123; 15.

(20) Estrup, *55*, **11**: 8; 12. (21) Evans and George, *5*, **103**: 190; 23. (22) Firth, *4*, **119**: 926; 21. (23) Firth, *54*, **42**: 242T; 23. (24) Firth and Watson, *4*, **123**: 1219; 23. (25) Freundlich, *7*, **73**: 385; 10. (26) Freundlich, *Kapillarchemie*, p. 234. Leipzig, Akadem. Verlagsges., 1923. (27) Freundlich and Kaempfer, *7*, **90**: 581; 15. (28) Freundlich and Posnjak, *7*, **79**: 168; 12. (29) Geddes, *8*, **29**: 797; 09.

(30) Georgievics, *Z. Farben-Ind.*, **2**: 253; 03. (31) Georgievics, *57*, **32**: 1075; 11. (32) Georgievics and Pollak, *57*, **32**: 655; 11. (33) Gillespie and Hall, *1*, **48**: 1207; 26. (34) Gurvich, *53*, **47**: 808; 15. (35) Gustafson, *9*, **21**: 459; 15. (36) Gustafson, *7*, **91**: 385; 16. (37) Gustafson, *19*, **7**: No. 22; 19. (38) Gutbier, Gebhardt and Ottenstein, *25*, **46**: 1453; 13. (39) Gutbier and Maisch, *25*, **52**: 2275; 19.

(40) Gutbier, Ottenstein and Weise, *25*, **52**: 1366; 19. (41) Halla, *7*, **86**: 496; 14. (42) Harkins and Ewing, *197*, **6**: 49; 20. (43) Harkins and Ewing, *1*, **43**: 1787; 21. (44) Harned, *1*, **42**: 372; 20. (45) Hawley, *45*, **13**: 301; 21. (46) Hayashi, *41*, **43**: 535; 22. (47) Hempel and Vater, *9*, **18**: 724; 12. (48) Heermann, *Färber-Ztg.*, **15**: 325, 345; 04. (49) Holt, Edgar and Firth, *7*, **82**: 513; 13.

(50) Homfray, *7*, **74**: 129; 10. (51) Jorissen, *Gedenkboek aangeboden aan J. M. van Bemmelen*, 1910. (52) Katz, *64V*, **21**: 230; 12. (53) Katz, *64P*, **26**: 548; 23. (54) Koch, *Thesis*, Zurich, 1918. (55) Kruyt and van Duin, *70*, **39**: 679; 20. (56) Küster, *13*, **283**: 360; 94. (57) Lacks and Michaelis, *55*, **9**: 275; 12. (58) Lamb, Wilson and Chaney, *45*, **11**: 420; 19. (59 Langmuir, *1*, **40**: 1361; 18.

(60) Lemon, *2*, **14**: 281; 19. (61) Lemon and Blodgett, *2*, **14**: 394; 19. *197* **5**: 289; 19. (62) Levites, *55*, **8**: 129; 10. (63) Levites, *55*, **9**: 1, 11. (64 Lottermoser, *55*, **9**: 135; 11. (65) Lowry, *1*, **46**: 824; 24. (66) Lowry an Hulett, *1*, **42**: 1393; 20. (67) McBain, *83*, **14**: 202; 19. (68) McGavac and Patrick, *1*, **42**: 946; 20. (69) McHaffie and Lehner, *4*, **127**: 1559; 25.

(70) Maffia, *287*, **3**: 85; 12. (71) Marc, *7*, **75**: 710; 10 (72) Michaelis and Rona *205*, **15**: 196; 08. (73) Miller, *1*, **46**: 1150; 24. (74) Morton, *1*, **36**: 1832; 1 (75) Nowack, *93*, **113**: 1; 20. (76) Osaka, *451*, **1**: 257; 15. (77) Paddon *50*, **26**: 790; 22. (78) Patrick and Jones, *50*, **29**: 1; 25. (79) Patrick an Long, *50*, **29**: 336; 25.

(80) Patrick and Opdycke, *50*, **29**: 601; 25. (81) Patrick, Preston and Owens *50*, **29**: 421; 25. (82) Philip, Dunnill and Workman, *4*, **117**: 362; 20. (83 Piutti, *172*, (7th), **2**: 83; 09. (84) Rakovskii, *53*, **49**: 371; 17. *10*, **5**: 1265 26. (85) Reichinstein, *7*, **107**: 119; 23. (86) Richardson, *1*, **39**: 1828; 17 (87) Rona and Michaelis, *205*, **94**: 240; 19. (88) Schmidt, *7*, **15**: 56; 94 (89) Schmidt, *7*, **74**: 689; 10.

(90) Schmidt-Walter, *55*, **14**: 242; 14. (91) Sieverts, *7*, **88**: 103, 451; 14. (92 Sapožhnikov, *7*, **78**: 209; 11. (93) Sheldon, *2*, **16**: 165; 20. (94) Titov *7*, **74**: 641; 10. (95) Traube and Nishizawa, *55*, **32**: 383; 23. (96) Weise and Middleton, *50*, **24**: 630; 20. (97) Wiegner, *J. Landw.*, **40**: 111, 197; 12 (98) Wiegner and Burmeister, *55*, **8**: 126; 11. (99) Williams, *83*, **10**: 167 14.

(100) Williams, *68*, **37**: 161; 16. (101) Williams, *5*, **98**: 223; 20. (102) Will stätter and Wasserman, *205*, **16**: 81; 09.

SOLUBILITIES OF GASES IN LIQUIDS

	Definitions, Abbreviations, Symbols and Units	**Définitions, Abréviations, Symboles et Unités**	**Definitionen, Abkürzungen, Zeichen und Einheiten**	**Definizioni, Abbreviazioni, Simboli e Unità**
α	The Bunsen absorption coefficient. The volume of gas (reduced to 0°C, 760 mm) which, at the temperature of the experiment, is dissolved in one volume of the solvent when the partial pressure of the gas is 760 mm.	Coefficient d'absorption de Bunsen. C'est le volume de gaz (réduit à 0°C, 760 mm) qui est dissout à la température de l'expérience dans un volume du solvant, lorsque la pression partielle du gaz est de 760 mm.	Der Bunsen-Absorptionskoeffizient. Dieser ist das Volumen eines Gases (reduziert auf 0°C und 760 mm) welches in einem Volumteil des Lösungsmittels bei der Versuchstemperatur gelöst ist, wenn der Partialdruck des Gases 760 mm beträgt.	Coefficiente di assorbimento di Bunsen Volume di gas (a 0°C e 760 mm) che, alla temperatura dell esperienza, si scioglie in un volume d solvente quando la pressione parziale del gas è di 760 mm
β	The same as α, except that the total pressure is 760 mm.	Le même que α, excepté que la pression totale est de 760 mm.	So wie α nur ist der Totaldruck 760 mm.	Lo stesso coefficiente α, con la differenza che la pressione totale è di 760 mm.
γ	The Kuenen absorption coefficient The same as α, except that the amount of the solvent is one g.	Coefficient d'absorption de Künen. Le même que α, excepté que la quantité du solvant est un gramme.	Der Künen-Absorptionskoeffizient. Dieser ist gleich α nur beträgt die Menge des Lösungsmittels 1 Gramm.	Coefficiente di assorbimento di Künen. Lo stesso coefficiente α riferito però ad un g di solvente.
δ	The Raoult absorption coefficient. The number of g of the gas dissolved by 100 cm³ of the solvent at the temperature of experiment when the	Coefficient d'absorption de Raoult. C'est le nombre de grammes du gaz dissout dans 100 cm³ du solvant à la température de l'expérience	Der Raoult-Absorptionskoeffizient. Ist die Anzahl der Gramme des Gases welche von 100 cm³ des Lösungsmittels bei der Versuchs-	Coefficiente di assorbimento di Raoult. Numero di grammi di gas disciolti da 100 cm³ di solvente alla temperatura dell'esperienza, quando

English	Français	Deutsch	Italiano
partial pressure of the gas is 760 mm.	lorsque la pression partielle du gaz est de 760 mm.	temperatur gelöst werden und wenn der Partialdruck des Gases 760 mm beträgt.	la pressione parziale del gas è di 760 mm.
λ The Ostwald absorption coefficient. The ratio of the concentration of the gas in the liquid to its concentration in the gas phase.	λ Coefficient d'absorption d'Ostwald. C'est le rapport de la concentration du gaz dans le liquide à sa concentration dans la phase gazeuse.	λ Der Ostwald-Absorptionskoeffizient. Dieser ist das Verhältnis der Konzentration des Gases in der Lösung zu der in der Gasphase.	λ Coefficiente di assorbimento di Ostwald. Rapporto tra la concentrazione del gas nel liquido e nella fase gassosa.
B Barometric pressure.	B Pression barométrique.	B Barometerdruck.	B Pressione barometrica.
K Henry's law constant. $K = \frac{p_A}{x_A}$.	K Constante de la loi de Henry. $K = \frac{p_A}{x_A}$	K Konstante des Henry'schen Gesetzes. $K = \frac{p_A}{x_A}$.	K Costante della legge di Henry. $K = \frac{p_A}{x_A}$.
p_A (resp. P) Partial pressure of A (resp. total pressure).	p_A (resp. P) Pression partielle de A (resp. pression totale).	p_A (bezw. P) Partialdruck von A (bzw. Totaldruck).	p_A (oppure P) Pressione parziale di A (oppure pressione totale).
S. T. P. Under standard conditions, 0°C, 1 atm.	S. T. P. Dans les conditions standard, 0°C, 1 atm.	S. T. P. Unter Normal (Standard)-Bedingungen, 0°C, 1 Atmosphäre.	S. T. P. Condizioni normali, 0°C, 1 atm.
t (resp. T) Centigrade (resp. absolute) temperature.	t (resp. T) Température centigrade (resp. absolue).	t (bezw. T) Zentigrad (bzw. absolute)-Temperatur.	t (oppure T) Temperatura centigrada (o assoluta).
x_A Mole fraction of A in the solution.	x_A Fraction moléculaire de A dans la solution.	x_A Molenbruch von A in der Lösung.	x_A Frazione di grammimolecole di A nella soluzione.

MATHEMATICAL RELATIONS AND CONVENTIONS

In all cases where interconversion of g of gas and cm³ at S. T. P. has been made, the normal molecular volume has been taken as 22 411.5 cm³ and the coefficient of thermal expansion as 1/273.1 per degree.

$$\alpha = \frac{\text{g/cm}^3\text{, liq.}}{\text{g/cm}^3\text{, gas}} \div \left(1 + \frac{t}{273.1}\right) = \frac{273.1\lambda}{T}.$$

$$\gamma = \frac{\lambda}{\left(1 + \frac{t}{273.1}\right)} d, \text{ where } d \text{ is the density of the solvent.}$$

$$\lambda = \frac{C_A}{C_A'} = \frac{\text{concentration, liq.}}{\text{concentration, gas}}.$$

According to the Henry-Dalton laws, λ is independent of the partial pressure of the gas.

$$\log_{10} K = \frac{0.05223(-A)}{T} + B.$$

The quantities A and B are given in the tables. The quantity (A) is the partial latent heat of vaporization of the gas from the solution, in joules per g mole, *i.e.*, the heat absorbed when one g-mole of the gas is vaporized reversibly from an infinite amount of the solution.

To compute K from α:

$$K = \frac{17\,032\,400d\,(1 + a)}{M\alpha},$$

where d is the density and M the molecular weight of the solvent; a is small in comparison with unity and is given by

$$a = \frac{Mp_A\alpha}{17\,032\,400d}$$

where p_A is the partial pressure of the dissolving gas in mm Hg.

SOLUBILITIES OF GASES IN WATER

A. G. Loomis

Index / Index / Index / Indice — Page

A-Table.—Elementary Gases and Atmospheric Air

A, Argon; *cf. also* (46, 111)

t, °C	0	10	20	30	40	Lit.
$10^{-7} \times K$	1.79	2.25	2.70	3.14	3.47	(101, 105)

t, °C	$10^{-7} \times K$	t, °C	$10^{-7} \times K$	t, °C	$10^{-7} \times K$
0	1.635	20	2.511	40	3.265
5	1.861	25	2.708	45	3.447
10	2.089	30	2.895	50	3.632
15	2.304	35	3.084	Lit.	(21)

An, Actinon (Ac. Em.); *v.* (36)

Br, Bromine (Br_2); *cf. also* (17, 18, 46)

$$\log_{10} K = \frac{0.05223}{T} \times (-33780) + 10.674; \text{ range, 0 to 10°C}$$

t, °C	$10^{-4} \times K$	t, °C	$10^{-4} \times K$
12	3.07	20	4.51
14	3.39	22	4.94
16	3.74	24	5.39
18	4.12	26	5.85

Br.—(*Continued*)

t, °C	$10^{-4} \times K$	t, °C	$10^{-4} \times K$
28	6.37	60	19.1
30	6.88	70	24.4
40	10.1	80	30.7
50	14.5	Lit.	(102, 103)

Cl, Chlorine (Cl_2); *cf. also* (2, 46, 66)

t, °C	β	t, °C	β	t, °C	β	t, °C	β
10	3.148	18	2.440	26	1.970	50	1.216
11	3.047	19	2.368	27	1.923	60	1.025
12	2.950	20	2.299	28	1.880	70	0.862
13	2.856	21	2.238	29	1.839	80	0.683
14	2.767	22	2.180	30	1.799	90	0.39
15	2.680	23	2.123	35	1.608	100	0.00
16	2.597	24	2.070	40	1.450	Lit.	(106)
17	2.517	25	2.019	45	1.320		

t, °C	0	3	6	9	12	Lit.
β	4.61	3.93	3.42	3.03	2.77	(3)

H, Hydrogen, (H_2); *cf. also* (46)

p_{H_2}, mm	560	600	650	700	727	Lit.
$10^6\alpha$, 25°C	1814	1807	1798	1790	1786	(20)

t, °C	20	25	Lit.
K	5.07×10^7	5.18×10^7	(39)

t, °C	$10^{-7} \times K$	t, °C	$10^{-7} \times K$
0	4.391	14	4.928
1	4.430	15	4.964
2	4.470	16	4.998
3	4.509	17	5.034
4	4.548	18	5.070
5	4.587	19	5.107
6	4.625	20	5.138
7	4.664	21	5.170
8	4.703	22	5.203
9	4.742	23	5.234
10	4.778	24	5.265
11	4.818	25	5.296
12	4.854	26	5.325
13	4.891	Lit.	(91)

t, °C (97, 99, 100)	$10^{-7} \times K$	t, °C	$10^{-7} \times K$
0	4.401	20	5.192
1	4.447	21	5.228
2	4.491	22	5.264
3	4.537	23	5.302
4	4.580	24	5.340
5	4.623	25	5.374
6	4.669	26	5.408
7	4.710	27	5.443
8	4.753	28	5.477
9	4.797	29	5.510
10	4.834	30	5.540
11	4.871	35	5.638
12	4.909	40	5.709
13	4.947	45	5.765
14	4.982	50	5.809
15	5.017	60	5.810
16	5.052	70	5.78
17	5.087	80	5.74
18	5.120	90	5.71
19	5.155	100	5.66

t = 19.5°C (15)				t = 23°C (15)			
p_{H_2}, mm	$10^3\alpha$	p_{H_2}, mm	$10^3\alpha$	p_{H_2}, mm	$10^3\alpha$	p_{H_2}, mm	$10^3\alpha$
900	16.76	5000	16.41	1100	16.01	5000	15.76
1000	16.76	5500	16.28	1500	16.00	5500	15.65
1500	16.75	6000	16.14	2000	16.00	6000	15.52
2000	16.75	6500	15.97	2500	15.99	6500	15.38
2500	16.73	7000	15.80	3000	15.98	7000	15.23
3000	16.71	7500	15.59	3500	15.96	7500	15.06
3500	16.67	8000	15.36	4000	15.92	8000	14.86
4000	16.61	8250	15.23	4500	15.85	8200	14.78
4500	16.52						

He, Helium; *cf. also* (46, 111)

$$\log_{10} K = \frac{0.05223}{T} \times (-3053) + 8.584;$$ range, 2 to 30°C (13)

t, °C (1)	0	10	20	30	40	50
$10^{-7} \times K$	9.78	9.54	9.50	9.39	9.19	8.73

Kr, Krypton; *cf. also* (46, 111)

t, °C	0	10	20	30	40	50	60	Lit.
$10^{-7} \times K$	0.945	1.170	1.510	1.850	2.182	2.471	2.649	(1)

N, Nitrogen (N_2); *cf. also* (16, 46)

t, °C	20	25	Lit.
K	5.939×10^7	6.297×10^7	(39)

p_{N_2}, mm	$10^3\alpha$, 25°C	p_{N_2}, mm	$10^3\alpha$, 25°C	p_{N_2}, mm	$10^3\alpha$, 25°C
270	14.38	500	14.26	800	14.36
300	14.37	601.6	14.20	830	14.38
400	14.31	700	14.28	Lit.	(20)

Atmospheric N_2, = 98.815 vol. % N_2 + 1.185 vol. % A (30)

t, °C	$10^{-7} \times K$	t, °C	$10^{-7} \times K$	t, °C	$10^{-7} \times K$	t, °C	$10^{-7} \times K$
0	4.007	9	4.893	18	5.731	27	6.493
1	4.103	10	4.988	19	5.816	28	6.573
2	4.200	11	5.084	20	5.906	29	6.655
3	4.299	12	5.178	21	5.991	30	6.730
4	4.395	13	5.273	22	6.076	35	7.120
5	4.496	14	5.365	23	6.160	40	7.493
6	4.593	15	5.457	24	6.244	45	7.874
7	4.694	16	5.548	25	6.331	50	8.244
8	4.794	17	5.638	26	6.411		

Argon-free N_2, computed from the above values

t, °C	$10^{-7} \times K$	t, °C	$10^{-7} \times K$	t, °C	$10^{-7} \times K$	t, °C	$10^{-7} \times K$
0	4.077	15	5.550	30	6.846	45	7.988
5	4.572	20	6.004	35	7.235	50	8.371
10	5.074	25	6.435	40	7.608		

Atmospheric N_2 (98, 99, 100)

t, °C	$10^{-7} \times K$	t, °C	$10^{-7} \times K$	t, °C	$10^{-7} \times K$	t, °C	$10^{-7} \times K$
0	4.016	10	5.079	20	6.109	30	7.022
1	4.116	11	5.184	21	6.203	35	7.483
2	4.219	12	5.291	22	6.298	40	7.923
3	4.323	13	5.399	23	6.394	45	8.285
4	4.428	14	5.497	24	6.485	50	8.586
5	4.535	15	5.606	25	6.574	60	9.087
6	4.641	16	5.710	26	6.670	70	9.462
7	4.753	17	5.811	27	6.759	80	9.591
8	4.861	18	5.912	28	6.845	90	9.61
9	4.970	19	6.013	29	6.932	100	9.54

Argon-free N_2, computed from the above values

t, °C	$10^{-7} \times K$	t, °C	$10^{-7} \times K$	t, °C	$10^{-7} \times K$	t, °C	$10^{-7} \times K$
0	4.089	15	5.704	30	7.149	45	8.427
5	4.609	20	6.217	35	7.614	50	8.722
10	5.168	25	6.686	40	8.051		

t = 19.4°C (15)				t = 24.9°C (15)			
p_{N_2}, mm	$10^3\alpha$	p_{N_2}, mm	$10^3\alpha$	p_{N_2}, mm	$10^3\alpha$	p_{N_2}, mm	$10^3\alpha$
900	15.10	5000	14.45	900	13.70	5000	13.08
1000	15.08	5500	14.35	1000	13.69	5500	12.99
1500	15.01	6000	14.24	1500	13.63	6000	12.90
2000	14.93	6500	14.13	2000	13.58	6500	12.81
2500	14.86	7000	14.02	2500	13.50	7000	12.73
3000	14.79	7500	13.90	3000	13.42	7500	12.64
3500	14.71	8000	13.77	3500	13.33	8000	12.55
4000	14.63	8100	13.75	4000	13.25	8200	12.52
4500	14.54			4500	13.16		

Ne, Neon; *cf. also* (46, 92, 111)

t, °C	0	10	20	30	40	50	Lit.
$10^{-7} \times K$	8.67	7.69	6.76	5.71	4.37	2.94	(1)

O, Oxygen (O_2); *cf. also* (46)

Results obtained by measuring volume of O_2 absorbed by H_2O (98, 105)

t, °C	$10^{-7} \times K$	t, °C	$10^{-7} \times K$	t, °C	$10^{-7} \times K$	t, °C	$10^{-7} \times K$
20	3.043	25	3.330	30	3.610	60	4.777
21	3.100	26	3.386	35	3.852	70	5.043
22	3.157	27	3.444	40	4.068	80	5.224
23	3.215	28	3.500	45	4.281	90	5.31
24	3.273	29	3.555	50	4.470	100	5.33

Results obtained by titrating O_2 in air-saturated water (96, 99, 100)

t, °C	$10^{-7} \times K$	t, °C	$10^{-7} \times K$	t, °C	$10^{-7} \times K$	t, °C	$10^{-7} \times K$
0	1.9336	8	2.3734	16	2.8211	24	3.259
1	1.9870	9	2.4294	17	2.8764	25	3.314
2	2.0407	10	2.4860	18	2.9322	26	3.368
3	2.0955	11	2.5420	19	2.9863	27	3.425
4	2.1502	12	2.5983	20	3.0415	28	3.481
5	2.2053	13	2.6550	21	3.095	29	3.540
6	2.2618	14	2.7103	22	3.150	30	3.599
7	2.3171	15	2.7661	23	3.205		

t, °C	$10^{-7} \times K$	t, °C	$10^{-7} \times K$	t, °C	$10^{-7} \times K$	t, °C	$10^{-7} \times K$
0	1.9206	9	2.4056	18	2.8928	27	3.369
1	1.9745	10	2.4602	19	2.9472	28	3.420
2	2.0284	11	2.5142	20	3.001	29	3.471
3	2.0825	12	2.5687	21	3.054	30	3.522
4	2.1362	13	2.6226	22	3.107	35	3.771
5	2.1901	14	2.6764	23	3.160	40	4.009
6	2.2436	15	2.7310	24	3.213	45	4.234
7	2.2975	16	2.7852	25	3.265	50	4.445
8	2.3516	17	2.8392	26	3.317	Lit.	(30)

t = 23°C (15)				t = 25.9°C (15)			
p_{O_2}, mm	$10^3\alpha$	p_{O_2}, mm	$10^3\alpha$	p_{O_2}, mm	$10^3\alpha$	p_{O_2}, mm	$10^3\alpha$
900	27.11	5000	26.24	800	26.00	5000	25.27
1000	27.10	5500	26.05	1000	26.00	5500	25.13
1500	27.09	6000	25.86	1500	25.98	6000	24.97
2000	27.06	6500	25.66	2000	25.93	6500	24.81
2500	27.00	7000	25.46	2500	25.85	7000	24.63
3000	26.89	7500	25.25	3000	25.76	7500	24.45
3500	26.74	8000	25.04	3500	25.65	8000	24.24
4000	26.57	8150	24.98	4000	25.53	8200	24.15
4500	26.41			4500	25.40		

For a graphical representation of the amount of O_2, saturated with water vapor, dissolved in H_2O from air, between 32 to 210°F and 0 to 30 in. Hg, *v.* (84).

O_3, Ozone; *cf. also* (46)

At 0°C, K = 1.915 × 10^6 (75); at 18°C, K = 2.080 × 10^6 (27)

t, °C	$10^{-6} \times K$	t, °C	$10^{-6} \times K$	t, °C	$10^{-6} \times K$	t, °C	$10^{-6} \times K$
0	1.475	20	2.856	40	9.110	60	∞
5	1.660	25	3.475	45	13.58	Lit.	(55)
10	1.884	30	4.548	50	20.85		
15	2.191	35	6.220	55	36.14		

Rn, Radon; *cf. also* (46, 111)

The following data are from Meyer (60), and are based upon (10, 44, 51, 52, 71, 90). They are in agreement also with (80).

t, °C	$10^{-6} \times K$	t, °C	$10^{-6} \times K$	t, °C	$10^{-6} \times K$	t, °C	$10^{-6} \times K$
0	1.855	20	3.97	50	7.92	80	10.6
5	2.295	30	5.26	60	8.94	90	11.1
10	2.805	40	6.63	70	9.84	100	11.6

The following data are by Szeparowicz (88.5):

$$\log_{10} K = \frac{0.05223}{T} \times (-25598) + 11.157; \text{ range, 0 to 16°C}$$

t, °C	$10^{-6} \times K$	t, °C	$10^{-6} \times K$	t, °C	$10^{-6} \times K$	t, °C	$10^{-6} \times K$
17	3.53	23	4.33	29	5.13	60	9.05
18	3.66	24	4.46	30	5.27	70	10.26
19	3.79	25	4.59	35	5.92	80	10.9
20	3.93	26	4.73	40	6.57	90	11.2
21	4.06	27	4.87	45	7.20	97	11.5
22	4.19	28	5.00	50	7.83		

Tn, Thoron (Th. Em.); *v.* (10, 36, 42)

Xe, Xenon; *cf. also* (46, 111)

$$\log_{10} K = \frac{0.05223}{T} \times (-21384) + 10.681; \text{ range, 0 to 20°C}$$

t, °C	30	40	45.45	Lit.
$10^{-6} \times K$	9.629	11.76	12.95	(1)

Air (104); *cf. also* (46)

t, °C	$10^{-7} \times K_1$*	$10^{-7} \times K_2$†	t, °C	$10^{-7} \times K_1$*	$10^{-7} \times K_2$†
0	3.277	3.220	20	5.044	4.938
1	3.361	3.303	21	5.130	5.019
2	3.450	3.392	22	5.216	5.102
3	3.536	3.477	23	5.297	5.182
4	3.624	3.564	24	5.379	5.265
5	3.712	3.653	25	5.468	5.351
6	3.803	3.738	26	5.544	5.428
7	3.894	3.826	27	5.625	5.512
8	3.985	3.913	28	5.702	5.597
9	4.076	4.002	29	5.781	5.683
10	4.168	4.088	30	5.858	5.765
11	4.257	4.176	35	6.249	
12	4.347	4.262	40	6.611	
13	4.438	4.348	45	6.916	
14	4.525	4.436	50	7.188	
15	4.612	4.520	60	7.645	
16	4.701	4.605	70	7.981	
17	4.789	4.689	80	8.166	
18	4.874	4.773	90	8.22	
19	4.964	4.856	100	8.16	

* K_1 is calculated from the absorption coefficients of O_2 and N_2, taking into consideration the correction for constant argon content. *See* Fox (30).

† K_2 is calculated from the O_2-content of water saturated with air, and from O_2-content of the air expelled by heating the solution.

The following table gives content of 1000 cm^3 of water, saturated with air at normal barometric pressure. The air is free of CO_2 and NH_3 (107).

t, °C	cm³ at 0°C and 760 mm		Total	O_2-content of the dissolved air, Vol. %
	O_2	N_2, A, etc.		
0	10.19	18.99	29.18	34.91
1	9.91	18.51	28.42	34.87
2	9.64	18.05	27.69	34.82
3	9.39	17.60	26.99	34.78
4	9.14	17.18	26.32	34.74
5	8.91	16.77	25.68	34.69
6	8.68	16.38	25.06	34.65
7	8.47	16.00	24.47	34.60
8	8.26	15.64	23.90	34.56
9	8.06	15.30	23.36	34.52
10	7.87	14.97	22.84	34.47
11	7.69	14.65	22.34	34.43
12	7.52	14.35	21.87	34.38
13	7.35	14.06	21.41	34.34
14	7.19	13.78	20.97	34.30
15	7.04	13.51	20.55	34.25
16	6.89	13.25	20.14	34.21
17	6.75	13.00	19.75	34.17
18	6.61	12.77	19.38	34.12
19	6.48	12.54	19.02	34.08
20	6.36	12.32	18.68	34.03
21	6.23	12.11	18.34	33.99
22	6.11	11.90	18.01	33.95
23	6.00	11.69	17.69	33.90
24	5.89	11.49	17.38	33.86
25	5.78	11.30	17.08	33.82
26	5.67	11.12	16.79	33.77
27	5.56	10.94	16.50	33.73
28	5.46	10.75	16.21	33.68
29	5.36	10.56	15.92	33.64
30	5.26	10.38	15.64	33.60

ℬ-Table.—Standard Arrangement

HF, Hydrogen fluoride (59)

HCl, Hydrogen chloride; *cf. also* (46, 110)

t, °C	β	t, °C	β	t, °C	β	t, °C	β
0	507	10	474	20	442	30	412
2	500	12	468	22	435	40	386
4	494	14	461	24	429	50	362
6	487	16	455	26	423	60	339
8	481	18	448	28	417	Lit. (74)	

t, °C	g HCl* / g H_2O	t, °C	β	g HCl* / g H_2O
−24	101.2	−10	550.4	89.8
−21	98.3	− 5	532.7	86.8
−18	95.7	0	517.0	84.2
−15	93.3		Lit. (4)	

* P = 1 atm. (total P of HCl).

p_{HCl}, mm at 25°C (6)	g HCl / g H_2O	cm³ HCl (S. T. P.) per cm³ H_2O
0.0182	0.1458	89.38
0.0530	0.1823	111.73
0.140	0.2188	134.08
0.348	0.2552	156.42
0.844	0.2917	178.77
1.93	0.3282	201.11
4.20	0.3646	223.46

HBr, Hydrogen bromide (5); *cf. also* (46, 69)

t, °C	β	g HBr* / g H_2O	t, °C	β	g HBr* / g H_2O
−25		255.0	0	612	221.2
−20		247.3	+ 10	580	209.6
−15		240.0	25	533	193.9
−10	645	233.5	50	469	171.3
− 5	629	227.5	75	406	150.5
			100	345	130.0

* P = 1 atm.

p_{HBr}, mm at 25°C (6)	g HBr / g H_2O	cm³ HBr (S. T. P.) per cm³ H_2O
0.000151	0.4855	134.08
0.00370	0.5665	156.42
0.0089	0.6474	178.77
0.0226	0.7283	201.11
0.059	0.8092	223.46
0.151	0.8902	245.80

HI, Hydrogen iodide; *cf. also* (46)

p_{HI}, mm at 25°C (6)	g HI / g H_2O	cm³ HI (S. T. P.) per cm³ H_2O
0.00057	0.7676	134.08
0.00182	0.8956	156.42
0.0065	1.0235	178.77
0.0295	1.1515	201.11
0.132	1.2794	223.46

At 10°C, β = 416 (8).

SO_2, Sulfur dioxide; *cf. also* (46, 54)

$$\log_{10} K = \frac{0.05223}{T} \times (-24619) + 8.805;$$ range, 10 to 30°C (38)

t, °C	$10^{-4} \times K$	t, °C	$10^{-4} \times K$	t, °C	$10^{-4} \times K$	t, °C	$10^{-4} \times K$
30	3.640	50	6.53	70	10.43	90	15.05
35	4.259	55	7.43	75	11.60	Lit. (38)	
40	4.954	60	8.39	80	12.76		
45	5.716	65	9.38	85	13.90		

t, °C	β	t, °C	β	t, °C	β	t, °C	β
0	79.79	17	43.91	22	36.59	35	22.49
4	69.78	18	42.35	23	35.30	40	18.78
10	56.65	19	40.78	24	33.94	Lit. (31)	
15	47.28	20	39.37	25	32.76		
16	45.57	21	37.98	30	27.18		

t = 0°C (50)		t = 25°C (50)		t = 50°C (50)	
p_{SO_2}, mm	mg SO_2 per cm³ solution	p_{SO_2}, mm	mg SO_2 per cm³ solution	p_{SO_2}, mm	mg SO_2 per cm³ solution
0.4	0.537	1.4	0.534	4.9	0.525
1.0	1.000	5.0	1.16	10.0	0.920
5.0	3.092	10.0	2.03	50.0	3.46
25.0	10.78	50.0	8.28	100.0	6.23
50.0	19.35	100.0	14.98	200.0	11.59
75.0	27.55	150.0	21.03	300.0	16.77
100.0	35.27	200.0	26.48	400.0	21.72
110.0	38.24	250.0	31.52	500.0	26.64
		300.0	36.27	600.0	31.56
		313.0	37.50	700.0	36.47

t, °C......	40	50	60	70	80	90	95	Lit.
mg*......	53	38.3	26.3	16.6	9.8	5.8	4.2	(65)

* mg SO_2 per cm³ solution at p_{SO_2} = 760 mm.

t, °C	p_{SO_2}, mm	mg*	t, °C	p_{SO_2}, mm	mg*
10	155	33.5	50	457	20.8
	455	89.1	60	157	0.3
30	157	13.7		457	13.4
	457	45.7	80	457	3.3
50	156	4.1		655	8.9

* mg SO_2 per cm³ solution at p_{SO_2} = 760 mm.

H_2S, Hydrogen sulfide; *cf. also* (**46, 79**). At 25°C, $K = 4.168 \times 10^5$ (**40**)

t, °C	$10^{-4} \times K$	t, °C	$10^{-4} \times K$	t, °C	$10^{-4} \times K$
0	20.318	14	31.276	28	44.30
1	20.982	15	32.14	29	45.32
2	21.665	16	33.01	30	46.29
3	22.409	17	33.94	35	51.40
4	23.138	18	34.84	40	56.59
5	23.896	19	35.74	45	61.83
6	24.640	20	36.66	50	67.19
7	25.408	21	37.56	60	78.19
8	26.202	22	38.53	70	90.53
9	27.023	23	39.50	80	102.6
10	27.825	24	40.47	90	109
11	28.715	25	41.38	100	112
12	29.549	26	42.36		
13	30.432	27	43.35	Lit. (**106**)	

H_2Se, Hydrogen selenide; *cf. also* (**46**)

$$\log_{10} K = \frac{0.05223}{T} \times (-10072) + 7.466; \text{ range, 14.6 to 35°C (53)}$$

NO, Nitric oxide (**100, 104**); *cf. also* (**46**)

t, °C	$10^{-6} \times K$	t, °C	$10^{-6} \times K$	t, °C	$10^{-6} \times K$	t, °C	$10^{-6} \times K$
0	12.808	10	16.540	20	20.055	30	23.511
1	13.160	11	16.918	21	20.402	35	25.170
2	13.520	12	17.284	22	20.756	40	26.750
3	13.886	13	17.639	23	21.112	45	28.277
4	14.247	14	17.996	24	21.455	50	29.638
5	14.634	15	18.353	25	21.806	60	31.779
6	15.012	16	18.707	26	22.155	70	33.215
7	15.398	17	19.030	27	22.497	80	34.031
8	15.770	18	19.396	28	22.841	90	34.33
9	16.170	19	19.728	29	23.176	100	34.45

N_2O, Nitrous oxide; *cf. also* (**43, 46**)

$$\log_{10} K = \frac{0.05223}{T} \times (-23298) + 10.3313; \text{ range, 5 to 16°C (32)}$$

t, °C	20	25	Lit.
K	1.5000×10^6	1.7323×10^6	(**32**)

t, °C	$10^{-6} \times K$*	t, °C	$10^{-6} \times K$*	t, °C	$10^{-6} \times K$*
18	1.431	26	1.756	34	2.213
20	1.501	28	1.855	36	2.361
22	1.581	30	1.966	Lit. (**45**)	
24	1.664	32	2.091		

* In the original the volume of dissolved gas (in cm³ at $t°$ under atmospheric pressure) per 1 cm³ of solvent is given. Since the gas was saturated with the solvent the volume of dissolved gas is independent of the pressure (assuming Henry's Law). *See* Manchot (**57**).

p_{N_2O}, mm	758–1362	273–1028	Lit.
K, 25°C	1.739×10^6	1.760×10^6	(**22, 23**)

N_2O_3, Nitrogen trioxide (**78**)

NH_3, Ammonia; *cf. also* (**7, 14, 41, 46, 76, 82**)

$$\log_{10} K = \frac{0.05223\text{A}}{T} + \text{B}$$

From 0 to 10°C, A = −9376, B = 4.987.
From 14 to 28°C, A = −10746, B = 5.238.
At t = 12°C, K = 1863 (**72**).
Up to C = 1.6 moles NH_3 per liter of solution, p_{NH_3} (mm) = 12.9C (1 + 0.046C) at 25°C (**94**).

t = 0°C (**64**)

p_{NH_3}, mm	Ratio NH_3/H_2O g/g	Ratio NH_3/H_2O cm³/cm³	d^0_4	p_{NH_3}, mm	Ratio NH_3/H_2O g/g	Ratio NH_3/H_2O cm³/cm³	d^0_4
900	0.997	1312	0.844	1500	1.588	2090	0.812
1000	1.094	1440	0.839	1600	1.688	2221	0.807
1100	1.192	1569	0.833	1700	1.778	2340	0.802
1200	1.288	1695	0.828	1800	1.847	2431	0.798
1300	1.388	1827	0.822	1865	1.887	2483	0.795
1400	1.488	1958	0.817				

t = 20°C (**64**)

p_{NH_3}, mm	g/g	cm³/cm³	d^0_4	p_{NH_3}, mm	g/g	cm³/cm³	d^0_4
700	0.497	652.9	0.883	2100	0.984	1292.6	0.833
800	0.544	714.6	0.878	2200	1.007	1322.8	0.831
900	0.588	772.4	0.873	2300	1.029	1351.7	0.829
1000	0.629	826.2	0.868	2400	1.052	1381.8	0.828
1100	0.669	878.8	0.863	2500	1.074	1410.8	0.826
1200	0.707	928.8	0.858	2600	1.096	1439.6	0.824
1300	0.745	978.7	0.854	2700	1.117	1467.3	0.823
1400	0.781	1025.9	0.851	2800	1.140	1497.4	0.822
1500	0.815	1070.6	0.848	2900	1.162	1526.4	0.820
1600	0.847	1112.6	0.845	3000	1.185	1556.6	0.819
1700	0.877	1152.1	0.842	3100	1.207	1585.5	0.817
1800	0.906	1190.1	0.840	3200	1.230	1615.7	0.816
1900	0.934	1226.9	0.838	3277	1.249	1640.7	0.815
2000	0.959	1259.7	0.836				

t = 40°C (**64**)

p_{NH_3}, mm	g/g	cm³/cm³	d^0_4	p_{NH_3}, mm	g/g	cm³/cm³	d^0_4
750	0.315	411.3	0.9019	2200	0.611	797.8	0.8556
800	0.329	429.6	0.8994	2400	0.644	840.9	0.8518
1000	0.386	504.0	0.8896	2600	0.676	882.7	0.8480
1200	0.433	565.4	0.8811	2800	0.706	921.7	0.8444
1400	0.472	616.3	0.8740	3000	0.732	955.8	0.8407
1600	0.508	663.3	0.8685	3200	0.758	989.8	0.8367
1800	0.543	709.0	0.8638	3400	0.784	1023.7	0.8327
2000	0.577	753.4	0.8596	3640	0.816	1065.5	0.8280

P,* mm	Ratio NH_3/H_2O g/g	Ratio NH_3/H_2O cm³/cm³	P,* mm	Ratio NH_3/H_2O g/g	Ratio NH_3/H_2O cm³/cm³
t = 10°C (**29**)			t = 20°C (**29**)		
300	0.414	544.6	300	0.2945	386.9
500	0.541	711.7	500	0.4124	541.7
700	0.6584	866.2	700	0.5083	667.7
900	0.7637	1004.7	900	0.5911	776.5
1100	0.8709	1145.7	1100	0.6694	879.3
1300	0.9782	1286.9	1300	0.7422	974.9
1500	1.0855	1428.0	1500	0.8149	1070.4

P,* mm	Ratio NH_3/H_2O g/g	Ratio NH_3/H_2O cm³/cm³
t = 30°C (**29**)		
300	0.2121	277.9
500	0.3080	403.5
700	0.3879	508.2
900	0.4556	596.9
1100	0.5186	679.5
1300	0.5773	756.4
1500	0.6313	827.1

* Total pressure, $NH_3 + H_2O$ = approx. p_{NH_3}.

PH_3, Phosphine; *cf. also* (**46**). At 17°C, $K = 3.63 \times 10^6$ (**86**)

AsH_3, Arsine (**83**)

SbH_3, Stibine (**87**)

CO, Carbon monoxide; *cf. also* (**46**)

t, °C	20	25	Lit.
K	3.916×10^7	4.281×10^7	(**39**)

CO.—(*Continued*)

t, °C (100, 104)	$10^{-7}\times K$	t, °C	$10^{-7}\times K$	t, °C	$10^{-7}\times K$	t, °C	$10^{-7}\times K$
0	2.673	10	3.357	20	4.070	30	4.711
1	2.736	11	3.428	21	4.137	35	5.007
2	2.801	12	3.499	22	4.185	40	5.285
3	2.868	13	3.571	23	4.272	45	5.540
4	2.934	14	3.643	24	4.337	50	5.784
5	3.002	15	3.715	25	4.401	60	6.247
6	3.072	16	3.787	26	4.467	70	6.420
7	3.142	17	3.858	27	4.530	80	6.425
8	3.213	18	3.931	28	4.592	90	6.43
9	3.284	19	3.997	29	4.652	100	6.43

p_{CO}, mm	$10^3\alpha$ (15)		p_{CO}, mm	$10^3\alpha$ (15)	
	17.7°C	19°C		17.7°C	19°C
900	26.18	25.41	4500	25.97	25.09
1000	26.17	25.40	5000	25.93	25.04
1500	26.15	25.37	5500	25.88	24.98
2000	26.13	25.33	6000	25.83	24.91
2500	26.11	25.28	6500	25.77	24.82
3000	26.08	25.23	7000	25.70	24.71
3500	26.05	25.19	7500	25.61	24.58
4000	26.01	25.14	8000	25.50	24.45

CO_2, Carbon dioxide; *cf. also* (11, 46, 68). At 25°C, $K = 1.247 \times 10^6$ (39)

p_{CO_2}, mm.................	743–1351	270–988
K, 25°C.................	1.254×10^6	1.256×10^6
Lit......................	(22, 25)	(24, 26)

t(9)	$10^{-6}\times K$	t	$10^{-6}\times K$	t	$10^{-6}\times K$	t	$10^{-6}\times K$
0	0.5526	9	0.7642	18	1.018	27	1.309
1	0.5751	10	0.7915	19	1.049	28	1.342
2	0.5976	11	0.8197	20	1.079	29	1.379
3	0.6199	12	0.8455	21	1.111	30	1.414
4	0.6426	13	0.8732	22	1.144	35	1.588
5	0.6663	14	0.9018	23	1.177	40	1.771
6	0.6893	15	0.9297	24	1.209	45	1.954
7	0.7132	16	0.9581	25	1.243	50	2.153
8	0.7381	17	0.9877	26	1.278	60	2.590

t, °C (45)...............	20	22	24	26
$10^{-6}\times K$*.............	1.127	1.174	1.229	1.290
t, °C (45)...............	28	30	32	34
$10^{-6}\times K$*.............	1.358	1.434	1.518	1.613

* In the original the volume of dissolved gas (in cm³ at t,°C under atmospheric pressure) per 1 cm³ of solvent is given. Since the gas was saturated with the solvent the volume of dissolved gas is independent of the pressure (assuming Henry's Law). *See* Manchot (57).

P = total pressure in atm. cm³ = cm³ of CO_2 (reduced to 0°C and 1 atm.) dissolved by 1 cm³ of the solution at P and t (77).

t = 20°C

P	cm³
25	16.33
30	18.21
35	20.11
40	22.02
45	23.93
50	25.79
53	26.87

t = 35°C

P	cm³	
30	9.98	11.2
35	11.68	13.1

t = 35°C.—(*Continued*)

P	cm³	
40	13.38	15.1
45	15.11	17.1
50	16.83	19.1
55	18.59	21.0
60	20.39	23.0
65	22.28	24.9
68	23.43	
70		26.9
75		28.8
77		29.6

t = 60°C

P	cm³	
40	8.5	8.5
45	9.2	9.4
50	10.0	10.4
55	10.9	11.4
60	11.8	12.4
65	12.8	13.5
70	13.8	14.5
75	14.9	15.5
80	16.0	16.6
85	17.2	17.8
90	18.5	19.1
95	19.7	20.4
100	21.0	21.8
105	22.5	23.3
110	23.9	24.7
115	25.3	26.3
116	25.6	26.6

t = 100°C

P	cm³	
58	6.35	
60	6.49	
65	6.84	

t = 100°C.—(*Continued*)

P	cm³	
70	7.22	5.31
75	7.63	6.05
80	8.05	6.76
85	8.56	7.43
90	9.07	8.05
95	9.57	8.68
100	10.06	9.30
105	10.57	9.93
110	11.09	10.51
115	11.59	11.05
120	12.09	11.54
125	12.60	11.94
130	13.10	12.28
135	13.61	12.53
140	14.10	12.72
145	14.61	12.87
150	15.12	
155	15.55	
160	15.91	
165	16.15	

CH_4, Methane (104); *cf. also* (28, 46, 56)

t, °C	$10^{-6}\times K$	t, °C	$10^{-6}\times K$	t, °C	$10^{-6}\times K$	t, °C	$10^{-6}\times K$
0	16.994	10	22.575	20	28.531	30	34.08
1	17.504	11	23.210	21	29.069	35	36.95
2	18.029	12	23.814	22	29.665	40	39.46
3	18.564	13	24.403	23	30.239	45	41.83
4	19.116	14	25.001	24	30.804	50	43.85
5	19.689	15	25.600	25	31.36	60	47.57
6	20.249	16	26.192	26	31.93	70	50.62
7	20.828	17	26.769	27	32.48	80	51.84
8	21.422	18	27.383	28	33.03	90	52.60
9	22.024	19	27.961	29	33.56	100	53.3

C_2H_2, Acetylene (108); *cf. also* (46)

t, °C	$10^{-6}\times K$	t, °C	$10^{-6}\times K$	t, °C	$10^{-6}\times K$	t, °C	$10^{-6}\times K$
0	0.547	8	0.690	16	0.841	24	0.993
1	0.564	9	0.708	17	0.858	25	1.01
2	0.581	10	0.727	18	0.878	26	1.03
3	0.599	11	0.746	19	0.897	27	1.05
4	0.619	12	0.765	20	0.917	28	1.07
5	0.635	13	0.783	21	0.935	29	1.09
6	0.653	14	0.803	22	0.955	30	1.11
7	0.671	15	0.822	23	0.974		

C_2H_4, Ethylene (108); *cf. also* (46)

t, °C	$10^{-6}\times K$	t, °C	$10^{-6}\times K$	t, °C	$10^{-6}\times K$	t, °C	$10^{-6}\times K$
0	4.19	8	5.48	16	6.97	24	8.48
1	4.33	9	5.66	17	7.16	25	8.67
2	4.48	10	5.84	18	7.36	26	8.86
3	4.64	11	6.03	19	7.55	27	9.03
4	4.80	12	6.22	20	7.74	28	9.24
5	4.96	13	6.41	21	7.93	29	9.42
6	5.14	14	6.59	22	8.12	30	9.62
7	5.30	15	6.80	23	8.31		

C_2H_6, Ethane, *v.* p. 261

C_3H_6, Propylene (89); *cf. also* (46)

t, °C	$10^{-6}\times K$	t, °C	$10^{-6}\times K$	t, °C	$10^{-6}\times K$
2	2.305	8	3.162	14	3.845
4	2.632	10	3.390	16	4.080
6	2.916	12	3.620	18	4.322

C_3H_8, Propane (47)

C_4H_{10}, Butane (12, 34, 48, 93)

90% CH_4 + 10% C_2H_6, Pittsburgh natural gas; K, at 25°C = 2.95×10^7 (61)

C_2H_6, Ethane (104); *cf. also* (46)

t, °C	$10^{-6} \times K$	*t*, °C	$10^{-6} \times K$	*t*, °C	$10^{-6} \times K$	*t*, °C	$10^{-6} \times K$
0	9.547	10	14.386	20	19.978	30	25.976
1	9.972	11	14.936	21	20.562	35	29.097
2	10.400	12	15.477	22	21.157	40	32.18
3	10.838	13	16.032	23	21.757	45	35.15
4	11.294	14	16.593	24	22.360	50	37.94
5	11.772	15	17.163	25	22.970	60	42.89
6	12.264	16	17.734	26	23.579	70	47.38
7	12.776	17	18.308	27	24.162	80	50.23
8	13.304	18	18.872	28	24.765	90	52.2
9	13.849	19	19.432	29	25.388	100	52.6

$(C_6H_{14})_x$, Casing-head gasoline; 81° Bé

K, at 25°C = 7.9×10^7 (61)

$(C_7H_{16})_x$, Motor gasoline; 66° Bé

K, at 25°C = 5.5×10^7 (61)

CH_2O, Formaldehyde (33)

CHF_3, Fluoroform (58)

$C_2H_2F_2$, Acetylene difluoride (88)

C_2H_5F, Fluoroethane (62)

C_3H_5F, Fluoropropylene (58)

C_3H_7F, Propyl fluoride (58)

CH_3Cl, Methyl chloride; *cf. also* (46)

$$\log_{10} K = \frac{0.05223}{T} \times (-26382) + 10.224;\ \text{range, 20 to 60°C}$$

K, at 70°C = 1.52×10^6; *K*, at 80°C = 1.77×10^6 (70)

P, atm	1	2	3	4	5	Lit.
α, 18°C	3.2	5.0	6.5	7.9	9.3	(70)

COS, Carbonyl sulfide (106); *cf. also* (46)

t, °C	0	5	10	15	20	25	30
$10^{-6} \times K$	0.7020	0.8911	1.121	1.380	1.662	1.967	2.314

$S(CH_2.CH_2Cl)_2$, Mustard gas; 0.684 g/l at 25°C (95)

CH_3PH_2, Methylphosphine (37)

HCN, Hydrogen cyanide; for 18°C, *v. p.* 365

K, at 25°C = 4.81×10^3 (49)

CH_3NH_2, Methylamine; *cf. also* (46)

K, at 12.5°C = 1575, *K*, at 25°C = 1730 (109); other amines (19)

Base	$10^{-6} \times K$	Base	$10^{-6} \times K$
NH_3	0.739	$C_2H_5NH_2$	0.765
CH_3NH_2	0.692	$(C_2H_5)_2NH$	0.877
$(CH_3)_2NH$	0.805	$C_3H_7NH_2$	0.804

LITERATURE

(For a key to the periodicals see end of volume)

(1) Antropoff, *9*, **25**: 269; 19. (2) Arkadiev, *53*, **50**: 205; 18. (3) Bakhuis Roozeboom, *70*, **3**: 59; 84. (4) Bakhuis Roozeboom, *70*, **3**: 84; 84. (5) Bakhuis Roozeboom, *70*, **4**: 102; 85. (6) Bates and Kirschman, *1*, **41**: 1991; 19. (7) Baume and Tykociner, *42*, **12**: 270; 14. (8) Berthelot, *27*, **19**: 351; 73. (9) Bohr, *8*, **68**: 500; 99.

(10) Boyle, *Bull. Macdonald Physics Bldg.*, **1**: 52; 10. *199*, **7**: 200; 10. (11) Buch, *138*, **2**: No. 16; 25. (12) Bunsen *13*, **93**: 1; 55. *B72*. (13) Cady, Elsey and Berger, *1*, **44**: 1456; 22. (14) Calingaert and Huggins, *1*, **45**: 915; 23. (15) Cassuto, *63*, **5**: 233; 04. (16) Coste, *50*, **31**: 81; 27. (17) Dancer, *4*, **15**: 477; 62. (18) Dietze, *487*, **43**: 290; 98. (19) Doijer, *7*, **6**: 481; 90.

(20) Drucker and Moles, *7*, **75**: 405; 11. (21) Estreicher, *7*, **31**: 176; 99. (22) Findlay and Creighton, *4*, **97**: 536; 10. (23) Findlay and Howell, *4*, **105**: 291; 14. (24) Findlay and Howell, *4*, **107**: 282; 15. (25) Findlay and Shen, *4*, **101**: 1459; 12. (26) Findlay and Williams, *4*, **103**: 636; 13. (27) Fischer and Tropsch, *25*, **50**: 765; 17. (28) Fischer and Zerbe, *416*, **4**: 17; 23. (29) Foote, *1*, **43**: 1031; 21.

(30) Fox, *83*, **5**: 68; 09. (31) Freese, *136*, **44**: 294; 20. (32) Geffcken, *7*, **49**: 257; 04. (33) Hantzsch and Vagt, *7*, **38**: 705; 01. (34) Henrich, *7*, **9**: 435; 92. (35) Herz and Kurger, *9*, **16**: 240, 869; 10. (36) Hevesy, *63*, **12**: 1214; 11. *50*, **16**: 429; 12. (37) Hofmann, *25*, **4**: 605; 71. (38) Hudson, *4*, **127**: 1332; 25. (39) Just, *7*, **37**: 342; 01.

(40) Kendall and Andrews, *1*, **43**: 1545; 21. (41) Klarmann, *93*, **132**: 289; 24. (42) Klaus, *63*, **6**: 820; 05. (43) Knopp, *7*, **48**: 97; 04. (44) Kofler, *63*, **9**: 6; 08. (45) Kunerth, *2*, **19**: 512; 22. (46) Landolt-Börnstein, *B3*; 774. (47) Lebeau, *34*, **140**: 1454, 1572; 05. *27*, **33**: 1137; 05. (48) Lebeau, *28*, **1908**: 300. (49) Lewis and Keyes, *1*, **40**: 472; 18.

(50) Lindner, *57*, **33**: 613; 12. (51) Lunge, *25*, **18**: 1391; 85. (52) Lurié, *Diss.*, Grenoble, 1910. *10*, **2**: 401; 11. (53) McAmis and Felsing, *1*, **47**: 2633; 25. (54) McCrae and Wilson, *93*, **35**: 11; 03. (55) Mailfert, *34*, **119**: 951; 94. (56) Malisoff and Egloff, *50*, **22**: 529; 19. (57) Manchot, *93*, **141**: 38; 24. (58) Meslans, *6*, **1**: 346; 94. (59) Metzner, *34*, **119**: 682; 94.

(60) Meyer, *75*, **122 IIA**: 1281; 13. (61) Milligan, *50*, **28**: 494; 24. (62) Moissan, *6*, **19**: 266; 90. (63) Naumann, *9*, **16**: 772; 10. (64) Neuhausen and Patrick, *50*, **25**: 693; 21. (65) Öman, *485*, *Uppl. D.*, **54**: 81; 24. (66) Oliveri-Mandalà, *36*, **50 I**: 273; 20. **50 II**: 98; 20. (67) Perman, *4*, **83**: 1168; 03. (68) Piazza, *7*, **93**: 183; 18. (69) Pickering, *3*, **36**: 111; 93.

(70) Plank, *Magyar Chem. Folyóirat*, **27**: 1; 21. (71) Ramsay, Collie and Travers, *4*, **67**: 684; 95. (72) Raoult, *6*, **1**: 262; 74. (73) Rex, *7*, **55**: 355; 06. (74) Roscoe and Dittmar, *13*, **112**: 327; 59. (75) Rothmund, *B13*, 391; 12. (76) Rupert, *1*, **32**: 748; 10. (77) Sander, *7*, **78**: 513; 12. (78) Sapožnikov, *53*, **32**: 375; 00. (79) Scheffer, *64P*, **13**: 829; 11. **14**: 195; 11.

(80) Schulze, *7*, **95**: 257; 20. (81) Smith, *50*, **25**: 204, 605, 721; 21. (82) Smits and Postma, *64P*, **17**: 182; 14. (83) Soubeiran, *6*, **43**: 407; 1830. (84) Speller, *143*, **193**: 515; 22. (85) Stegmüller, *9*, **16**: 85; 10. (86) Stock, Böttcher and Lenger, *25*, **42**: 2853; 09. (87) Stock and Guttmann, *25*, **37**: 885; 04. (88) Swarts, *28*, **1901**: 383. (88.5) Szeparowicz, *75*, **129**: 437; 20. (89) Than, *13*, **123**: 187; 62.

(90) Thomas, *34*, **123**: 943; 96. (91) Timofeev, *7*, **6**: 141; 90. (92) Valentiner, *Preuss. Bergakad. Clausthal. Festschrift*, **1925**: 414. (93) Wiedemann, *8*, **17**: 349; 82. (94) de Wijs, *Thesis*, Delft, 1923. (95) Wilson, Fuller and Schur, *1*, **44**: 2867; 22. (96) Winkler, *25*, **22**: 1764; 89. (97) Winkler, *25*, **24**: 89; 91. (98) Winkler, *25*, **24**: 3602; 91. (99) Winkler, *Math. Naturw. Ber. aus Ungarn*, **9**: 195; 92.

(100) Winkler, *7*, **9**: 171; 92. (101) Winkler, *Kisérleti Chemia*, **1**: 854; 97. (102) Winkler, *Magyar Chem. Folyóirat*, **4**, 33; 98. (103) Winkler, *136*, **23**: 687; 99. (104) Winkler, *25*, **34**: 1408; 01. (105) Winkler, *7*, **55**: 344; 06. (106) Winkler, *144*, **25**: 86; 07. (107) Winkler, *in* Lunge, *Chemisch-technische Untersuchungsmethoden*, Berlin, Springer. **I**: 822; 04. **I**: 573; 21. (108) Winkler, *in B3*. (109) Würtz, *6*, **30**: 443; 50.

(110) Yannakis, *27*, **37**: 389; 25. (111) Valentiner, *96*, **42**: 253; 27.

SOLUBILITIES OF GASES IN NON-AQUEOUS PURE LIQUIDS

A. G. Loomis

CONTENTS

A-TABLE, ELEMENTARY SUBSTANCES AND ATMOSPHERIC AIR

An, Actinon (Ac. Em.). Concd. H_2SO_4 and organic solvents (52).

Br_2. CCl_4, CH_3CO_2H and $C_6H_5NO_2$ (60, 61).

Cl_2. CCl_4; $\alpha_{19} = 30.2$ (118); $\alpha_{15} = 49.0$ (60); α_{13} (101).

For p_{Cl_2} = 1 atm.; g/g = g Cl_2 per g solvent

t, °C	0	10	20	30	40	Lit.
g/g	0.196	0.140	0.103	0.081	0.064	(129)

Solvent	*t*, °C	g/g	Lit.
Heptane	0	0.266	(129)
Silicon tetrachloride	0	0.169	
Ethylene dibromide	20	0.090	
	40	0.060	

Acetic anhydride, $\alpha_{15} = 37.16$ (60); $(CHCl_2)_2$ and C_2HCl_5 (26); CrO_2Cl_2 (5); SO_2Cl_2 (115).

H_2

Solvent	*t*, °C	$10^3\alpha_t$	Lit.
H_2SO_4 (95.6%)	20	10.20	(21)
Liquid air			(29)
NH_3	−70		(112)

H_2.—(*Continued*)

Solvent	t, °C	$10^3\alpha_t$	Lit.
CS_2, Carbon disulfide	20	31.3	(63)
	25	34.4	
$CHCl_3$, Chloroform			(1)
CH_4O, Methyl alcohol	20	84.0	(63); *cf.*
	25	86.6	(1)
$C_2H_4O_2$, Acetic acid	20	57.5	(63); *cf.*
	25	58.0	(140)
C_2H_6O, Ethyl alcohol (98.8%)	20	80.3	(63); *cf.* (1, 18)
	25	81.9	(20, 48, 131)
C_3H_6O, Acetone	20	65.5	(63)
	25	70.0	
$C_4H_8O_2$, Ethyl acetate	20	73.4	(63)
	25	78.1	
$C_4H_{10}O$, Isobutyl alcohol	20	86.6	(63)
	25	89.4	
$C_4H_{10}O$, Ethyl ether	0	111.5	(22); *cf.*
	5	112.9	(1)
	10	115.3	
	15	119.2	
	For p up to 1200 atm., *v.* (24)		
$C_5H_{12}O$, Amyl alcohol	20	32.9	(63); *cf.*
	25	27.6	(40)
$C_6H_5NO_2$, Nitrobenzene	20	32.9	(63); *cf.*
	25	34.0	(1)
C_6H_6, Benzene	20	65.9	(63); *cf.*
	25	69.3	(1, 30, 140)
C_6H_7N, Aniline	20	28.2	(63)
	25	26.1	
C_7H_8, Toluene	20	78.1	(63)
	25	80.1	
$C_7H_{14}O_2$, Amyl acetate	20	69.2	(63)
	25	70.9	
C_8H_{10}, Xylene	20	73.0	(63)
	25	75.0	
Other organic solvents			(35)
Transformer oil*	25	51	(86)
	80	69	
Russian petroleum	10	65.2	(43)
	20	58.2	
Kerosene			(95)
Cottonseed oil			(135)
Train oil (blubber)			(135)

He. C_2H_5OH and C_6H_6 (104); HCO_2H, $CHBr_3$, CH_3CO_2H, $C_6H_5NO_2$ and cyclohexane (41).

N_2

Solvent	t, °C	$10^3\alpha_t$	Lit.
O_2, liquid			(34); *cf.* (123)
H_2SO_4 (95.6%)	20	15.55	(21)
CS_2, Carbon disulfide	20	49.29	(63)
	25	53.69	
$CHCl_3$, Chloroform	20	119.5	(63)
	25	123.5	

* A mineral oil of Pennsylvania base, 96% saturated hydrocarbons and distilling between 300 and 400°C. Commercially known as "Wemco A." $d_4^{25} = 0.840$; $d_4^{80} = 0.800$.

N_2.—(*Continued*)

Solvent	t, °C	$10^3\alpha_t$	Lit.
CH_4O, Methyl alcohol	20	125.6	(63); *cf.*
	25	129.6	(72)
$C_2H_4O_2$, Acetic acid	20	109.2	(63)
	25	109.0	
C_2H_6O, Ethyl alcohol (99.8%)	20	130.4	(63); *cf.*
	25	131.2	(18, 20, 48)
C_3H_6O, Acetone	20	128.9	(63)
	25	133.8	
	p_{N_2}, mm	$\alpha_{25\cdot05}$	
$C_4H_8O_2$, Isobutyric acid	300	1498	(32)
	400	1503	
	500	1508	
	600	1512	
	700	1517	
	800	1521	
	900	1527	
	t, °C	$10^3\alpha_t$	
$C_4H_8O_2$, Ethyl acetate	20	156.3	(63)
	25	158.2	
$C_4H_{10}O$, Ethyl ether	0	258.0	(22)
	10	247.1	
$C_5H_{12}O$, Amyl alcohol	20	112.6	(63)
	25	112.2	
$C_6H_5NO_2$, Nitrobenzene	20	56.67	(63)
	25	57.30	
C_6H_6, Benzene	20	103.8	(63)
	25	106.2	
C_6H_7N, Aniline	20	27.88	(63)
	25	28.16	
$C_6H_{12}O_2$, Isobutyl acetate	20	158.5	(63)
	25	158.9	
C_7H_8, Toluene	20	110.5	(63)
	25	113.1	
$C_7H_{14}O_2$, Amyl acetate	20	140.9	(63)
	25	141.3	
C_8H_{10}, Xylene	20	110.4	(63)
	25	111.5	
Various organic solvents			(35)
Transformer oil*	25	84.8	(86)
	80	91.6	
Russian petroleum	10	135	(43)
	20	117	
Kerosene			(95)

O_2

Solvent	t, °C	$10^3\alpha_t$	Lit.
Liquid air			(6)
H_2SO_4 (95.6%)	20	29.45	(21)
CCl_4, Carbon tetrachloride	25	225	(88)
	17.8	230	(36)
$CHCl_3$, Chloroform	16.3	205	(36)
CH_4O, Methyl alcohol	18.8	175	(36)
$\lambda = 0.31864 - 0.002572t - 0.0_42866t^2$; range, 5 to 30°C			(72)
$C_2H_2Cl_4$, 1, 1, 2, 2-Tetrachloroethane	18.3	100	(36)
C_2H_6O, Ethyl alcohol (96%)	19.8	143	(36)
$\alpha = 0.23370 - 0.0_374688t + 0.0_53288t^2$ (99.7% alcohol); range, 0 to 24°C			(131)

* *See* note to H_2.

O_2.—(*Continued*)

Solvent	t, °C	$10^3\alpha_t$	Lit.
C_3H_6O, Acetone	19.3	207	(36)
$\lambda = 0.2997 - 0.00318t - 0.0_412t^2$; range, 5 to 25°C			(72)
$C_4H_8O_2$, Ethyl acetate	20	163	(36)
$C_4H_{10}O$, Ethyl ether	20.3	415	(36)
	0	423.5	(22)
	10	406.6	(22)
C_5H_5N, Pyridine	18.5	99	(36)
$C_5H_{12}O$, Isoamyl alcohol	17.3	163	(36)
$C_6H_5NO_2$, Nitrobenzene	18.5	70	(36)
C_6H_6, Benzene	19	163	(36)
C_7H_8, Toluene	18	168	(36)
C_8H_{10}, Xylene	16	169	(36)
$C_{10}H_{12}$, Tetralin	17.3	94	(36)
Other organic solvents			(35)
Petroleum ether, fraction to 65°C.	18.5	409	(36)
	d = 0.668		
Benzine, fraction 65 to 100°C	18	292	(36)
	d = 0.709		
Paraffin oil	18	114	(36)
	d = 0.881		
Transformer oil*	25	156.2	(86)
	80	148.5	
Russian petroleum	10	229	(43)
	20	202	
Kerosene (commercial)	18	159	(36); *cf.*
	d = 0.809		(95)

* *See* note to H_2, p. 262.

O_3. CCl_4, $P = 760$ mm, $t = 15$°C, 0.0064 g O_3 per l of solution (37).

Rn, Radon

H_2SO_4 (16)

t, °C	α
CS_2 (116)	
−18	53.85
−15	49.52
−10	43.08
− 5	37.69
0	33.30
+ 5	29.46
10	26.24
15	23.13
20	21.43
25	19.61
30	18.11
40	15.79
$CHCl_3$ (116)	
−20	32.05
−15	28.04
−10	24.70
− 5	22.00
0	19.70
+ 5	17.77
10	16.11
15	14.79
20	13.60
25	12.64
30	11.71
35	10.99
40	10.38
45	9.87
50	9.47

CH_2O_2, Formic acid (53)

t, °C	α
19.8	4.04

CH_4O, Methyl alcohol (53)

3.8	7.33
16.2	5.39

$C_2H_4O_2$, Acetic acid (53)

12.6	4.62 (?)
17.5	4.71
21.0	4.62
25.8	4.31
27.1	4.12

C_2H_6O, Ethyl alcohol (116)

−18	12.20
−15	11.32
−10	10.07
− 5	9.07
0	8.24
+10	6.69
20	5.62
30	4.78
40	4.12
50	3.60
(17)	
14	6.98

t, °C	α
(53)	
2.0	9.41
15.5	6.84
29.2	5.34
37.8	4.85

v. also (16)

C_3H_6O, Acetone (116)

−20	11.98
−15	10.79
−10	9.65
− 5	8.66
0	7.90
+ 5	7.27
10	6.66
15	6.16
20	5.68
25	5.41
30	5.04
40	4.54

$C_3H_6O_2$, Propionic acid (53)

20.7	6.79
29.7	6.15

C_3H_8O, *n*-Propyl alcohol (53)

13.6	8.69

C_3H_8O, Isopropyl alcohol (53)

t, °C	α
14.3	6.91
27.2	5.60

$C_3H_8O_3$, Glycerol (81)

3	2.9
10	2.1
20	1.4
30	0.9
50	0.1

$C_4H_8O_2$, *n*-Butyric acid (53)

19.8	7.86
19.9	8.18

$C_4H_8O_2$, Isobutyric acid (53)

19.8	8.44
19.9	8.56

$C_4H_8O_2$, Ethyl acetate (116)

−18	14.56
−15	13.12
−10	11.83
− 5	10.49
0	9.43
+ 5	8.53
10	7.74
15	7.09
20	6.50
25	6.00
30	5.60
35	5.23
40	4.92
50	4.41
60	4.02

$C_4H_{10}O$, Ethyl ether (116)

−18	31.15
−10	25.12
− 5	22.31
0	19.90
+ 5	17.97
10	16.30
15	14.88
20	13.79
25	12.83
30	11.98

$C_4H_{10}O$, *n*-Butyl alcohol (53)

11.2	9.40

$C_4H_{10}O$, Isobutyl alcohol (53)

3.4	10.29
16.3	7.94

$C_4H_{10}O$, *sec.*-Butyl alcohol (53)

16.7	7.14

$C_5H_{12}O$, Amyl alcohol (17)

t, °C	α
14	8.86

$C_5H_{12}O$, Isoamyl alcohol (53)

0.1	11.33
6.9	9.78
15.0	8.55
25.1	7.20

C_6H_6, Benzene (128)

6	20.020
8	17.650
10	15.730
12	14.180
14	12.835
16	11.750
18	10.810
20	9.845
22	8.975
24	8.275
26	7.643
28	7.045
30	6.516
35	5.387
40	4.468
45	3.796
50	3.360
55	3.072
60	2.868
65	2.716
70	2.590
73	2.523

C_6H_{14}, *n* (?)- Hexane (116)

−18	37.68
−15	34.18
−10	29.58
− 5	26.18
0	23.40
+ 5	21.02
10	18.91
15	16.97
20	15.19
25	13.56
30	11.98

C_7H_8, Toluene (55, 116)

−18	28.91
−10	23.36
− 5	20.78
0	18.50
+ 5	16.49
10	14.76
15	13.18
20	11.83
25	10.63
30	9.55
35	8.62
40	7.81
50	6.42
60	5.26
(17)	
14	13.0

$C_7H_{14}O_2$, Amyl acetate (81)

t, °C	α
−20	39.5
0	21.2
+20	14.2
50	7.8
70	4.3

C_8H_{10}, Xylene (81)

−20	27.5
0	19.6
+20	13.6
50	7.7
70	4.9

Other organic solvents, *v.* (89, 105, 133).

Colza oil (81)

− 3	51.2
0	46.9
+10	33.9
20	26.1
30	22.2
40	19.2
50	16.6
75	10.9
100	6.2
200	3.3

Olive oil (81)

0	45.9
15	29.5
30	22.1
40	18.3
60	11.4

Poppy oil (81)

− 5	50.5
0	44.2
+10	34.3
20	27.8
30	22.9
40	19.1
50	16.0
60	13.4
70	11.5
80	9.9
90	8.4

Turpentine (81)

−21	45.5
0	23.1
+20	15.9
50	7.5
65	4.1

Petroleum ether (16)

Vaseline (81)

−10	23.9
0	15.2
+15	10.7
25	8.9
35	7.7
50	6.6

Kerosene (55)

Tn, Thoron (Th. Em.)

H_2SO_4, C_2H_5OH and petroleum ether (16); H_2SO_4 and organic solvents (52); kerosene (64)

Xe

C_6H_7N, Aniline (2)

t, °C	10	20	30	40	50
α	0.669	0.500	0.453	0.428	0.406

Air

Liquid chlorine: $\alpha_{-30} = 0.30$; $\alpha_{-2} = 0.32$, $\alpha_{30} = 0.37$, for p_A between 1 and 7 atm. (108); 95.6% H_2SO_4; $\alpha_{20} = 0.01703$ (21); *cf.* (132).

$CHCl_3$, $C_6H_5NO_2$, C_6H_6, CH_3OH, C_2H_5OH, $(C_2H_5)_2O$, *v.* (1); C_6H_6, *v.* (30); C_2H_5OH, C_6H_6, kerosene, oil of lavender, and turpentine, *v.* (107.5).

Solubility of air in liq. C_2H_5Cl at 11° is about 3 times its solubility in H_2O at 11° (59.5).

$C_4H_{10}O$, Ethyl ether (22); *cf.* (1)

t, °C	α
0	0.290
10	0.277
15	0.271

𝔅-TABLE

HCl

$CHCl_3$ at 10°C (139)

t, °C	g HCl/g soln.; P = 760 mm		
	CH_3OH (75)	C_2H_5OH (75)	$(C_2H_5)_2O$ (117); *cf.* (62)
−10	0.546		0.375
− 5			0.370
0	0.519	0.454	0.356
+ 5		0.445	0.331
10	0.492	0.434	0.304
15		0.423	0.276
20	0.464	0.410	0.249
25		0.398	0.222
30	0.435	0.386	0.195
32		0.381	

SO_2 (74)

t, °C	cm³ SO_2 (S. T. P.) per cm³ sat. soln.; P = 756–760 mm					
	C_6H_6	$C_6H_5NO_2$	C_7H_8	$C_7H_7NO_2$*	t, °C	$(CH_3CO)_2O$†
15		108.94		101.73	−5	68.6
20		93.54	76.08	82.56	0	52.2
25		79.73	56.00	67.24	+5	46.8
30	44.60	66.47	43.52	56.22	10	43.0
40	30.02	46.18	32.74	41.45	15	39.9
50	19.95	34.53	25.70	31.05	20	37.2
60	11.89	27.50	19.75	23.05	25	34.6
					30	31.9

* *o*-Nitrotoluene. † Acetic anhydride.

$CHCl_3$, Chloroform (73)

p_{SO_2}, mm Hg	g SO_2/l soln.		p_{SO_2}, mm Hg	g SO_2/l soln.	
	0°	25°		0°	25°
2.5	0.73		100.0	34.6	14.28
5.0	1.52	0.69	150.0	53.8	21.73
10.0	3.08	1.25	200.0	74.0	29.51
15.0		1.93	219	82.17	
25.0	7.97	3.34	300.0		45.9
50.0	16.60	6.98	400.0		62.9
			488.8		78.39

Alcohols (75); *cf.* (18, 20). Wt. % SO_2 in solution, P = 760–770 mm Hg

t, °C	0	5	10	15	20	25
CH_3OH	71.1	63.5	55.8	48.3	40.8	33.2
C_2H_5OH	53.5	47.8	42.2	36.6	31.0	25.5

H_2SO_4 (33); SO_2Cl_2, formic and acetic acids and acetone (115).

H_2S

Liquid S (100); C_2H_5OH (18, 20, 48); $(C_2H_5)_2O$ (97); pyridine at 22° (113); other organic solvents (42).

H_2Se

Liquid Se (99).

N_2O

Values of α* (69)

t, °C	$CHCl_3$	$C_2H_2Br_2$	CH_3OH	CH_3-CO_2H	C_2H_5OH	$(CH_3)_2$-CO
18	5.35	2.69	3.17	4.69	2.88	5.91
20	5.22	2.61	3.10	4.52	2.79	5.63
22	5.07	2.54	3.03	4.35	2.70	5.35
24	4.87	2.47	2.96	4.18	2.61	5.06
26	4.63	2.40	2.88	4.01	2.52	4.73
28	4.38	2.34	2.79	3.85	2.44	4.39
30	4.12	2.27	2.69	3.70	2.35	4.02
32	3.84	2.21	2.58	3.56	2.27	3.64
34	3.58	2.15		3.41	2.19	3.25
36	3.27	2.09		3.31		2.85

* As computed by Manchot (84.7), assuming Henry's and Dalton's laws.

t, °C	$C_5H_{12}O$, Isoamyl alcohol	C_5H_5N, Pyridine	C_6H_7N, Aniline	C_7H_6O, Benzaldehyde	$C_7H_{14}O_2$, *n*-Amyl acetate
18	2.36		1.41	3.03	4.92
20	2.30	3.34	1.38	2.94	4.79
22	2.24	3.24	1.34	2.85	4.66
24	2.18	3.14	1.31	2.76	4.53
26	2.12	3.05	1.28	2.67	4.40
28	2.07	2.95	1.24	2.58	4.27
30	2.01	2.86	1.21	2.50	4.14
32	1.96	2.77	1.18	2.43	4.02
34	1.92	2.69	1.16	2.36	3.90
36	1.87	2.60	1.13	2.29	3.80

Russian petroleum; $\alpha_{10} = 2.49$; $\alpha_{20} = 2.11$ (43); C_2H_5OH (9, 18, 20, 48); olive oil and sesame oil (90, 138); kerosene (95); various organic solvents (35, 42); general discussion (14).

NO

H_2SO_4 (79, 80, 84.5, 106, 132); C_2H_5OH (18, 20, 48); alcoholic $FeCl_2$ solution (85); general discussion (14).

N_2O_4

HNO_3; P = 762.5 mm Hg (98) (*See also* p. 304)

t, °C	$\frac{g\ N_2O_4}{g\ HNO_3}$	t, °C	$\frac{g\ N_2O_4}{g\ HNO_3}$
22	∞	55	0.121
22.8	2 layers	60	0.085
33	0.370	65	0.055
35	0.340	70	0.032
40	0.274	75	0.017
45	0.216	87	0
50	0.165		

NH_3

Alcohols: P = 760 mm Hg; Wt. % NH_3 in the CH_3OH solution; g NH_3 per 100 cm³ of the C_2H_5OH solution (28, 75)

t, °C	0	5	10	15	20	25	30
CH_3OH	29.3	26.7	24.2	21.7	19.2	16.5	14.0
C_2H_5OH	13.05	12.00	10.75	9.24	7.55	5.78	4.0

$(C_2H_5)_2O$; $\alpha_0 = 17.13$; $\alpha_{10} = 11.91$; $\alpha_{15} = 9\ 74$ (22).

$CHCl_3$ (8); C_2H_5OH (4, 93); C_6H_6 (126); $C_6H_5CH_3$ (46); ethyl, propyl and isobutyl alcohols (96); quinoline (102).

SbH_3 in organic liquids (124)

C-TABLE. THE C-ARRANGEMENT

Solubilities of organic compounds

CO, Carbon monoxide

Solvent	t, °C	$10^3\alpha$	Lit.
H_2SO_4 (95.6%)	20	21.64	(21)
CS_2, Carbon disulfide	20	75.58	(63)
	25	76.17	(63)
	25	87.9	(119)
$CHCl_3$, Chloroform	20	176.8	(63)
	25	179.0	(63)
	25	189	(119)
CH_4O, Methyl alcohol	20	170.5	(63)
	25	179.1	(63)
	25	180	(119)
$C_2H_4Cl_2$, Ethylene chloride	20	135	(119)
$C_2H_4O_2$, Acetic acid	20	157.4	(63)
	25	157.0	(63)
	25	158	(119)
C_2H_6O, Ethyl alcohol; *cf.* (18, 20)	20	177.1	(63)
	25	176.0	(63)
	25	176	(119)
C_3H_6O, Acetone	20	198.3	(63)
	25	203.8	(63)
	25	218	(119)
$C_3H_8O_3$, Glycerol	25	Very small	(119)
$C_4H_8O_2$, Ethyl acetate	20	225.4	(63)
	25	230.5	(63)
$C_4H_{10}O$, Ethyl ether	0	361.8	(22)
	10	370.6	
For *P* up to 1200 atm			(24)
$C_5H_{12}O$, Amyl alcohol	20	159.0	(63)
	25	157.0	(63)
$C_6H_5NO_2$, Nitrobenzene	20	84.84	(63)
	25	85.81	(63)
	25	85	(119)
C_6H_6, Benzene	20	153.3	(63)
	25	156.4	(63)
	25	159	(119)
C_6H_7N, Aniline; *cf.* (77)	25	49	(119)
	20	47.10	(63)
	25	49.09	(63)
$C_6H_{12}O_2$, Isobutyl acetate	20	215.6	(63)
	25	216.7	(63)
C_7H_8, Toluene	20	162.3	(63)
	25	165.6	(63)
	25	167	(119)
$C_7H_{14}O_2$, Amyl acetate	20	196.4	(63)
	25	196.1	(63)
C_8H_{10}, Xylene	20	162.5	(63)
	25	163.2	(63)
Various organic solvents, *v.* (35, 107)			
Russian petroleum	10	134	(43)
	20	123	
Transformer oil "Wemco A"*	25	186	(86)
	80	153	

* *See* note to H_2, p. 262.

CO_2

95.6% H_2SO_4 (21); *cf.* (84)

t, °C	α
20	0.9230

CCl_4 (63)

t, °C	α
15	2.467
20	2.331
25	2.102

CS_2 (63); *cf.* (136)

t, °C	α
15	0.8954
20	0.8282
25	0.7969

$CHCl_3$; *cf.* (1, 30, 68, 136.5)

(63)

t, °C	α
15	3.750
20	3.430
25	3.142

(69)

t, °C	α
18	3.59
20	3.47
22	3.34
24	3.22
26	3.09
28	2.96
30	2.81
32	2.66
34	2.50
36	2.37

CH_4O, Methyl alcohol (63)

t, °C	α
15	4.366
20	3.918
25	3.515

(69)

t, °C	α
18	3.41
20	3.33
22	3.25
24	3.16
26	3.07
28	2.97
30	2.87
32	2.76
34 *cf.* (1)	2.64

$t = -78°C$; $d_4^{-78} = 0.884$ (109, 122)

p_{CO_2}, mm	α
100	167.4
200	168.1
300	169.4
400	171.1
500	172.7
600	174.8
700	177
740	177.5

$t = -59°C$; $d_4^{-59} = 0.866$

p_{CO_2}, mm	α
100	54.2
200	54.5
300	54.7
400	54.9
500	55.1
600	55.2
700	55.3

$C_2H_4Br_2$, Ethylene bromide

(63)

t, °C	α
15	2.298
20	2.137
25	1.976

(69)

t, °C	α
18	2.18
20	2.12
22	2.06
24	2.00
26	1.94
28	1.85
30	1.82
32	1.76
34	1.71
36	1.65

$C_2H_4Cl_2$, Ethylene chloride

(63)

t, °C	α
15	3.850
20	3.536
25	3.229

$C_2H_4O_2$, Acetic acid (glacial)

(63)

t, °C	α
15	5.322
20	4.779
25	4.287

(69)

t, °C	α
18	5.07
20	4.87
22	4.69
24	4.51
26	4.32
28	4.15
30	3.97
32	3.80
34	3.66
36	3.53

C_2H_6O, Ethyl alcohol (97%)

(63)

t, °C	α
15	2.967
20	2.724
25	2.479

(69)

t, °C	α
18	2.77
20	2.67
22	2.59
24	2.50
26	2.41
28	2.32
30	2.23
32	2.15
34	2.07

(99%) (15)

t, °C	α
−65.3	39.38
−25	8.86
−20	7.67
−10	5.75
0	4.44
+10	3.57
20	3.00
30	2.59

C_2H_6O.—(*Cont'd.*)

t, °C	α
40	2.23
50	1.89

$t = -78°C$; $d_4^{-78} = 0.872$ (109, 122)

p_{CO_2}, mm	α
100	95.75
200	97.15
300	98.65
400	100.1
500	101.6
600	103.1
700	104.6

$t = -59°C$; $d_4^{-59} = 0.856$

p_{CO_2}, mm	α
100	34.7
200	34.8
300	35.1
400	35.27
500	35.45
600	35.63
700	35.78
740	35.84

(110)

p_{CO_2}, atm.	β′*
$t = 20°C$	
30	98.9
35	119.0
40	140.2
45	158.7
50	176.1
$t = 35°C$	
30	69.98
35	85.4
40	100.9
45	114.9
50	127.9
55	140.2
60	153.8
65	169.4
70	189.5
$t = 60°C$	
40	61.3
45	71.3
50	81.2
55	91.0
60	101.1
65	110.6
70	119.2
75	127.1
80	134.2
85	140.7
90	146.9
95	153.1
100	159.2
$t = 100°C$	
50	32.9
55	44.6
60	50.2
65	58.6
70	66.9
75	75.1
80	82.3
85	88.8
90	95.0

CO_2.—(*Continued*)

C_2H_6O.—(*Continued*)

$t = 100°C$.—(*Continued*)

p_{CO_2}, atm.	β'*
95	100.9
100	106.1
105	111.3
110	116.5
115	121.5
120	125.5
125	128.4
130	130.7
135	132

See further (1, 9, 13, 18, 20, 48, 92).

$C_3H_6Br_2$, Propylene bromide (63)

t, °C	α
15	2.451
20	2.286
25	2.108

$C_3H_6Cl_2O$, Dichlorohydrin (63)

15	1.928
20	1.786
25	1.658

C_3H_6O, Acetone

(63)

20	6.449
25	5.767

(69)

20	6.50
22	6.26
24	5.98
26	5.68
28	5.33
30	4.95
32	4.55
34	4.14

$t = -78°C$, $d_4^{-78} = 0.900$ (109, 122)

p_{CO_2}, mm	α
50	275.2
100	277.3
200	281.9
300	286.8
400	291.6
500	296.2
600	300.9
650	303.5

$t = -59°C$; $d_4^{-59} = 0.879$

100	85.7
200	86.7
300	88.3
400	89.3
500	90.6
600	93.0
700	92.9

* β' = cm³ gas (S.T.P.) at t and p.

$C_3H_6O_2$, Propionic acid (63)

t, °C	α
15	4.538
20	4.106
25	3.736

$C_3H_6O_2$, Methyl acetate (109, 122)

$t = -78°C$; $d_4^{-78} = 1.056$

p_{CO_2}, mm	α
50	313.8
100	313.9
200	314.1
300	314.6
400	315.8
500	318.2
600	321.7
650	323.6

$t = -59°C$; $d_4^{-59} = 1.032$

100	97.5
200	98.1
300	98.5
400	99.0
500	99.6
600	100.1
700	100.8

(63)

t, °C	α
25	5.949

C_3H_8O, Propyl alcohol (63)

25	2.289

(110)

p_{CO_2}, atm.	β'*
$t = 20°C$	
19	51.11
20	52.46
25	66.43
30	81.09
35	96.76
40	115.21
45	139.11
50	166.0
$t = 35°C$	
19	33.55
20	35.68
25	47.1
30	58.3
35	70.5
40	83.6
45	97.3
50	111.9
55	129.1
60	148.5
65	170.1
70	194.1
75	220.3
80	246
$t = 60°C$	
19	19.00
20	20.58
25	29.07
30	37.8

C_3H_8O.—(*Continued*)

p_{CO_2}, atm.	β'*
35	46.5
40	55.1
45	64.2
50	73.3
55	82.6
60	92.2
65	102.2
70	111.8
75	121.5
80	131.3
85	141.6
90	152.7
95	165.1
100	178
$t = 100°C$	
38	17.16
40	21.74
45	32.28
50	40.85
55	48.64
60	55.74
65	62.7
70	69.5
75	76.1
80	82.3
85	88.5
90	94.7
95	100.8
100	106.8
105	112.7
110	118.5
115	124.4
116	125.5

$C_3H_8O_3$, Glycerol (63)

t, °C	α
25	0.0277

$C_4H_6O_3$, Acetic anhydride (63)

15	5.894
20	5.330
25	4.769

$C_4H_8O_2$, *n*-Butyric acid (63)

t, °C	α
15	3.871
20	3.510
25	3.186

$C_4H_8O_2$, Ethyl acetate (109, 122)

p_{CO_2}, mm	α
$t = -78°C$; $d_4^{-78} = 1.017$	
50	247.9
100	248.6
200	250.6
300	253.3
400	256.6
500	260.5
600	265.1
650	267.6

* β' = cm³ gas (S. T. P.) at t and p.

$C_4H_8O_2$.—(*Cont'd.*)

p_{CO_2}, mm	α
$t = -59°C$; $d_4^{-59} = 0.994$	
100	83.3
200	83.9
300	84.2
400	85.1
500	86.2
600	87.5
700	88.9

(110)

p_{CO_2}, atm.	β'*
$t = 20°C$	
24	141.8
25	147.9
30	174.1
35	193.7
40	209.2
$t = 35°C$	
29	124.5
30	128.5
35	148.6
40	165.1
45	177.7
50	185.0
55	187.7
60	189.1
$t = 60°C$	
29	85.6
30	88.5
35	102.6
40	114.3
45	124.6
50	133.9
55	142.8
60	151.0
65	158.5
70	165.5
75	172.6
78	176.6
$t = 100°C$	
39	57.79
40	60.0
45	71.2
50	80.9
55	89.2
60	96.4
65	102.7
70	108.3
75	113.7
80	118.6
85	123.3
90	127.9
95	132.5
97	134.2

C_4H_9Cl, Isobutyl chloride (63)

t, °C	α
15	3.468
20	3.157
25	2.845

$C_4H_{10}O$, Isobutyl alcohol (63)

15	1.979
20	1.830
25	1.694

$C_4H_{10}O$, Ethyl ether (22)

t, °C	α
0	7.330
10	5.831
15	5.180

(130)

t, °C	$\frac{g\ CO_2}{g\ Ether}$
−78.6	0.551
−70	0.320
−60	0.192
−50	0.125
−40	0.083
−30	0.057
−20	0.039
−10	0.026
0	0.019
+10	0.017
15.2 *cf.*(1)	0.016

(110)

p_{CO_2}, atm.	β'*
$t = 35°C$	
43	175.2
45	179.2
50	189.8
55	200.4
58	207.1
$t = 60°C$	
48	135.4
50	139.5
55	149.8
60	157.6
65	163.6
70	168.9
75	174.1
80	179.4
85	184.6
90	189.9
95	195.2
97	197.4
$t = 100°C$	
58	71.4
60	76.2
65	86.8
70	95.1
75	101.9
80	108.1
85	113.7
90	119.2
95	124.7
97	127

C_5H_5N, Pyridine (63)

t, °C	α
15	4.068
20	3.598
25	3.349

(69)

18	3.71
20	3.59
22	3.47
24	3.34
26	3.22

C_5H_5N.—(*Cont'd.*)

t, °C	α
28	3.11
30	3.00
32	2.89
34	2.78
36	2.68

$C_5H_{11}Br$, Amyl bromide (63)

15	2.657
20	2.458
25	2.249

$C_5H_{11}Cl$, Amyl chloride (63)

15	3.188
20	2.914
25	2.666

$C_5H_{12}O$, Amyl alcohol (63)

15	1.951
20	1.809
25	1.677

(69)

20	1.78
22	1.74
24	1.70
26	1.65
28	1.60
30	1.56
32	1.51
34	1.46

$C_6H_3Cl_3$, Trichlorobenzene (63)

25	1.505

C_6H_5Br, Bromobenzene (63)

15	1.983
20	1.830
25	1.688

(110)

p_{CO_2}, atm.	β'*
$t = 20°C$	
19	44.82
20	47.57
25	61.59
30	77.48
35	95.41
40	113.58
45	131.33
50	150.2
$t = 35°C$	
19	36.65
20	38.25
25	46.9
30	56.2
35	67.2
40	79.5
45	92.2
50	104.7
55	117.4
60	131.1
65	147.7
70	166.6
75	188.4
78	203.4

* β' = cm³ gas (S. T. P.) at t and p.

C_6H_5Br.—(*Cont'd.*)

p_{CO_2}, atm.	β′*
t = 60°C	
19	23.78
20	25.03
25	31.44
30	37.84
35	44.3
40	50.9
45	57.7
50	64.6
55	71.5
60	78.3
65	85.0
70	91.8
75	98.9
80	106.3
85	113.9
90	122.0
95	130.4
100	139.5
105	149.6
107	153.9
t = 100°C	
29	22.8
30	23.7
35	28.3
40	32.9
45	37.8
50	42.5
55	47.1
60	51.6
65	56.1
70	60.5
75	64.9
80	69.1
85	73.4
90	77.6
95	81.7
100	85.7
105	89.9
110	94.2
115	98.6
116	99.4

C_6H_5Cl, Chlorobenzene (110)

p_{CO_2}, atm.	β′*
t = 20°C	
19	55.37
20	58.19
25	72.91
30	89.03
35	107.9
40	129.2
45	151.8
50	177.0
t = 35°C	
19	39.22
20	41.33
25	52.46
30	64.62
35	77.13
40	90.9
45	106.8
50	122.1
55	135.5
60	149.9
65	166.4
68	177.2

*β′ = cm³ gas (S.T.P.) at *t* and *p*.

C_6H_5Cl.—(*Continued*)

p_{CO_2}, atm.	β′*
t = 60°C	
19	27.9
20	29.3
25	36.6
30	44.8
35	53.5
40	62.1
45	71.0
50	80.0
55	88.8
60	96.5
65	103.2
70	109.5
75	115.6
80	121.5
85	128.1
90	135.4
95	143.2
100	151.4
105	159.8
107	168.1
t = 100°C	
30	24.9
35	30.6
40	36.0
45	41.4
50	46.6
55	51.8
60	56.7
65	61.8
70	66.5
75	70.9
80	74.9
85	78.8
90	82.3
95	85.9
100	89.3
105	92.6
110	95.7
115	98.6
120	101.2
125	103.6
126	104.5

(63)

t, °C	α
15	2.447
20	2.255
25	2.075

C_6H_5I, Iodobenzene (63)

t, °C	α
15	1.365
20	1.277
25	1.192

$C_6H_5NO_2$, Nitrobenzene (63)

t, °C	α
15	2.697
20	2.474
25	2.250

(110)

p_{CO_2}, atm.	β′*
t = 20°C	
15	38.85
20	53.20
25	67.8
30	83.1

*β′ = cm³ gas (S.T.P.) at *t* and *p*.

$C_6H_5NO_2$.—(*Continued*)

p_{CO_2}, atm.	β′*
35	97.8
40	112.6
45	128.9
48	139.1
50	146.1
t = 35°C	
20	39.40
25	49.66
30	60.5
35	71.7
40	82.1
45	92.2
50	102.8
55	116.0
60	129.9
65	145.4
70	161.7
75	183.8
78	197.1
t = 60°C	
20	24.5
25	28.9
30	33.3
35	37.9
40	42.6
45	47.5
50	52.1
55	56.7
60	60.8
65	63.9
70	65.9
75	67.1
78	67.6
t = 100°C	
20	18.2
25	23.6
30	28.9
35	34.1
40	38.6
45	42.6
50	46.0
55	49.0
60	51.9
65	54
70	57
75	60
78 *cf.* (1)	61

C_6H_6, Benzene (110)

p_{CO_2}, atm.	β′*
t = 20°C	
15	44.40
20	67.09
25	91.9
30	118.5
35	148.9
40	182.3
45	214.2
48	238.3
50	250.6
t = 35°C	
15	32.4
20	48.9
25	66.1
30	84.7
35	104.6
40	124.0

*β′ = cm³ gas (S.T.P.) at *t* and *p*.

C_6H_6.—(*Continued*)

p_{CO_2}, atm.	β′*
45	144.8
50	166.1
55	186.7
60	207
65	225
67	229
t = 60°C	
19	20
20	23
25	37
30	51
35	63.6
40	76.4
45	89.7
50	103.1
55	116.3
60	129.0
65	141.2
70	153.1
75	165.1
80	177.5
85	189.9
90	202.0
95	214.3
96	216.8
t = 100°C	
38	29.1
40	32.1
45	39.8
50	48.5
55	58.3
60	68.1
65	78.6
70	90.0
75	102.5
80	114.0
85	125.1
90	136.3
95	147.2
100	156.6
105	165.9
110	174.3
115	181.4
116	182.7

(63)

t, °C	α
15	2.569
20	2.367
25 *cf.* (1, 30)	2.222

C_6H_7N, Aniline (63)

t, °C	α
15	1.451
20	1.336
25	1.213
(69)	
20	1.48
22	1.27
24	1.21
26	1.17
28	1.13
30	1.10
32	1.08
34	1.06
36 *cf.* (76)	1.04

*β′ = cm³ gas (S.T.P.) at *t* and *p*.

$C_6H_{12}O_2$, *n*-Amyl formate (63)

t, °C	α
15	4.404
20	4.034
25	3.688

$C_6H_{12}O_2$, Isobutyl acetate (63)

t, °C	α
20	4.629
25	4.298

C_7H_6O, Benzaldehyde (63)

t, °C	α
15	3.132
20	2.848
25	2.603
(69)	
18	2.88
20	2.78
22	2.67
24	2.58
26	2.49
28	2.41
30	2.33
32	2.26
34	2.19
36	2.11

C_7H_7Cl, Benzyl chloride (63)

t, °C	α
15	2.066
20	1.931
25	1.775

C_7H_8, Toluene (63)

t, °C	α
15	2.424
20	2.260
25	2.112

(110)

p_{CO_2}, atm.	β′*
t = 20°C	
20	54.99
25	75.43
30	97.5
35	120.4
40	148.4
45	185.7
50	224.4
t = 35°C	
20	44.32
25	58.41
30	72.1
35	85.9
40	101.3
45	119.1
50	137.8
55	155.1
60	170.7
65	185.5
68	194.5
t = 60°C	
30	45.22
35	55.34
40	65.5
45	75.9
50	86.0
55	95.8

*β′ = cm³ gas (S.T.P.) at *t* and *p*

C_7H_8.—(*Continued*)

p_{CO_2}, atm.	β′*
60	105.0
65	114.1
70	123.2
75	132.2
80	140.7
85	148.7
90	156.3
95	163.9
97	166.9
t = 100°C	
30	21.89
35	29.43
40	36.7
45	43.5
50	50.3
55	57.1
60	63.2
65	68.9
70	74.7
75	80.4
80	86.2
85	91.9
90	97.6
95	103.3
100	108.6
105	113.4
110	117.5
115	121.0
120	123.8
125	126.2
130 *cf.* (46)	128.4

C_7H_9N, Toluidine (63)

t, °C	α
Ortho	
15	1.459
20	1.372
25	1.265
Meta	
15	1.640
20	1.473
25	1.316

$C_7H_{14}O_2$, Amyl acetate (63)

t, °C	α
15	4.587
20	4.110
25	3.774
(69)	
18	4.49
20	4.34
22	4.20
24	4.08
26	3.96
28	3.85
30	3.75
32	3.66
34	3.57

C_8H_{10}, *m*-Xylene (63)

t, °C	α
15	2.224
20	2.065
25	1.915

*β′ = cm³ gas (S.T.P.) at *t* and *p*.

CO_2.—(*Continued*)

C_9H_{12}, Cumene (63)

t, °C	α
15	1.875
20	1.751
25	1.633

$C_{10}H_{12}O_2$, Eugenol (63)

t, °C	α
15	1.670
20	1.540
25	1.410

$C_{10}H_{14}O$, Carvol (63)

t, °C	α
15	2.762
20	2.506
25	2.289

$C_{10}H_{16}$, *d*-Limonene (63)

t, °C	α
15	1.924
20	1.790
25	1.651

$C_{16}H_{18}N_2O_3$, *p*-Azoxyphenetole (56)

For various organic solvents, *v.* (20.5, 42).

Russian petroleum (43); *cf.* (95)

t, °C	α
10	1.31
20	1.17

Transformer oil* (86)

t, °C	α
25	0.99
50	0.77
80	0.57

* *See* note to H_2, p. 262.

For general discussion, *v.* (14).

$COCl_2$, Phosgene

Atmospheric pressure; 20–21°C (7)

Solvent	g $COCl_2$ / g sol.
CCl_4	0.28
$CHCl_3$	0.59
$C_2H_4O_2$ (glacial)	0.621
$CH_3CO_2C_2H_5$	0.985
C_6H_6	0.993
C_7H_8	0.666
Paraffin oil	0.0
Russian mineral oil	0.359
Gasolene	0.81
"Chlorocosane" (Chlorinated paraffin)	0.310

$C_2H_2Cl_4$, 1, 1, 2, 2-Tetrachloroethane (3)

t, °C	g $COCl_2$ / 100 g sol.
16.8	149.7
25.1	89.4
29.9	74.9

C_6H_5Cl, Chlorobenzene (3)

t, °C	g $COCl_2$ / 100 g sol.
12.3	422.1
17	190.8
20	129.2
25	96.7
29.7	81.9

$C_6H_5NO_2$, Nitrobenzene (3)

t, °C	g $COCl_2$ / 100 g sol.
16.8	106.4

C_7H_8, Toluene (3)

t, °C	g $COCl_2$ / 100 g sol.
17	244.7
20	169.1
25	110.9
30	81.4
32	72.8

C_8H_{10}, Xylene (from tar) (37)

t, °C	g $COCl_2$ / 100 g sol.
12.3	457.3
15	309.0
20	136.9
25	96.1
29.8	71.24

$C_{10}H_7Cl$, α-Chloronaphthalene (3)

t, °C	g $COCl_2$ / 100 g sol.
17.0	104.5

Kerosene B. P., 180–280° (3)

t, °C	g $COCl_2$ / 100 g sol.
12.3	263.8
14	213.2
16	159.1
18	117.9
20	95.8
22	81.5
24	70.6
26	62.0
28	54.9
30	48.7

Heavy lubricating oil (3)

t, °C	g $COCl_2$ / 100 g sol.
15.6	79.7
23.5	39.3
31.0	24.5

Creosote (3)

t, °C	g $COCl_2$ / 100 g sol.
16.2	77.42

COS

Toluene (125, 137); pyridine (47); nitrobenzene (47); alcohol (125).

CHF_3 (87)

CH_3Br, Methyl bromide

Olive oil and sesame oil at 17 and 37°C (90).

CH_3Cl, Methyl chloride

Values of α (65)

t, °C	CCl_4	$(CHCl)_2$	CCl_3CHCl_2	CH_3Cl
−5	117.5	243.8	171.2	281.9
0	87.6	174.8	125.2	208.6
+5	67.8	128.4	96.4	153.8
10	53.8	96.8	76.2	115.3
15	43.5	73.1	61.7	88.7
20	35.4	54.6	50.4	67.9

Ethyl alcohol and acetic acid (11); olive oil and sesame oil at 17 and 37°C (90).

CH_3PH_2

C_2H_5OH and $(C_2H_5)_2O$ at 0° (54).

CH_4

Solvent: for general discussion *v.* (14)	*t*, °C	cm³ per g solvent at 1 atm.	Lit.
H_2SO_4 (95.6%); α = 0.03072	20		(21)
CS_2	20	0.36	(38)
$CHCl_3$	20	0.32	(38)
CH_4O, Methyl alcohol	20	0.46	(38)
$\lambda = 0.5644 - 0.0046t - 0.0_44t^2$; range, 5 to 25°C; *v. also infra*			(72)
C_2H_6O, Ethyl alcohol; *cf.* (18, 20, 48); *v. also infra*	21	0.60	(38)
C_3H_6O, Acetone	20	0.61	(38)
$\lambda = 0.5906 - 0.00613t - 0.0_46t^2$; range, 5 to 25°C			(72)
C_3H_8O, Propyl alcohol; *v. infra*			
$C_4H_8O_2$, Ethyl acetate	20	0.45	(38)
$C_4H_{10}O$, Isobutyl alcohol; *v.* (141)			
$C_4H_{10}O$, Ether	20	0.91	(38)
α = 1.066	0		(22)
α = 0.922	10		(22)
$C_5H_{12}O$, Amyl alcohol; *cf.* (40)	20	0.44	(38)
$C_6H_5NO_2$, Nitrobenzene	20	0.16	(38)
C_6H_6, Benzene; *v. also infra*	23	0.51	(38)
C_6H_7N, Aniline	20	0.16	(38)
C_6H_{14}, Hexane; C_7H_8, Toluene; C_7H_{16}, Heptane } *v. infra*			
C_8H_{10}, Xylene; *v. infra*	23	0.53	(38)
$C_{10}H_{16}$, α-Pinene; *v. infra*			
Various organic solvents, *v.* (35)			
Petroleum ether; B. P. 65°	22	1.34	(38)
65–100°	20	0.84	(38)
100–150°	20	0.66	(38)
Paraffin oil	20	0.44	(38)
Kerosene	20	0.55	(38)
Russian petroleum; α = 0.144	10		(43)
α = 0.131	20		
Transformer oil ("Wemco" A*) α = 0.381	25		(86)
α = 0.164	80		
Hydrocarbons from low-temp. (primary) tar	20	0.40	(38)
Phenols from low-temp. (primary) tar	20	0.27	(38)
Fraction from low-temp. (primary) tar.	21	0.36	(38)
Heavy (machine) oil from brown coal.	21	0.39	(38)
Creosote from brown coal	21	0.22	(38)
Phenol from bituminous coal	22	0.32	(38)

* *See* note to H_2, p. 262.

Values of α (83)

t, °C	CH_3OH (99%)	C_2H_5OH (99.8%)	C_3H_7OH, Isopropyl	C_6H_6
21			0.4287	
22	0.4106	0.4288		0.4605
25	0.4032	0.4196	0.4193	0.4466
30	0.3891	0.4054	0.4078	0.4224
35	0.3711	0.3910	0.3956	0.3967
40	0.3436	0.3771	0.3837	0.3684
45	0.2962		0.3724	0.3387
50	0.2247		0.3630	0.3074
55			0.3549	
60			0.3482	

CH_4: Values of α (83).—*(Continued)*

t, °C	C_6H_{14}, *n*-Hexane	C_7H_8, Toluene	C_7H_{16}, *n*-Heptane	C_8H_{10}, *m*-Xylene	$C_{10}H_{16}$, *dl*-α-Pinene
20					0.4565
21				0.4780	
22	0.5597		0.6733		
25		0.4450			
30	0.5139	0.4300	0.6225	0.4540	0.4168
35		0.4171	0.5999		0.4011
40	0.4647	0.4081	0.5820	0.4337	0.3898
45		0.4034			0.3811
50	0.4373	0.4015		0.4203	
55.2					0.308
60	0.407	0.369		0.399	

C_2N_2, Cyanogen

Acetic acid and aniline (57, 76).

C_2H_2, Acetylene

Solvent (59)	B. P., °C	P (average) mm Hg	β,*; $t = -10$°C
Acetal		742	28.8
Acetaldehyde	20.8	744	60.2
Ethyl acetate	77.0	742	44.5
Ethyl formate	54.5	738	42.2
Isoamyl acetate	139.0	738.5	29.3
Isoamyl formate	123.0	739	17.5
Methyl acetate	57.5	736.5	52.3
Methylal	45.5	735	54.3
Methyl formate	32.3	740	48.4

Acetone, at −80°C (23); at 0 and 25°C (67); H_2SO_4, C_2H_5OH and acetone (134); paraffin oil (94); olive oil (138); various solvents (12, 25, 42).

Solvent (41)	p_{mm}	°C	g C_2H_2/100 g solvent
Aniline	?	4.2	0.800
Benzene	755	4	0.744
Cyclohexane	535	3	0.3107
Dimethylaniline	751	0.3	0.737
Nitrobenzene	735	3.8	0.5537

* At the barometric pressure given.

$C_2H_2F_2$ and C_2H_3F, Chloroform, alcohol and acetone (127)

C_2H_3FO, Acetyl fluoride (87)

C_2H_4, Ethylene

Solvent	t	α	Lit.
H_2SO_4			(134)
CH_3OH	$\lambda = 3.3924 - 0.05083t + 0.00001t^2$; range, 5 to 25°C		(72)
C_2H_5OH			(18, 20, 134)
$(CH_3)_2CO$	$\lambda = 4.0652 - 0.06949t + 0.000126t^2$; range, 5 to 25°C		(72)
	20.0	2.2900	(83)
	35.0	2.0460	
C_6H_6	22.0	2.7865	(83)
	35.0	2.3530	
	50.0	2.1000	
C_6H_{14}, Hexane	22.0	2.8141	(83)
	35.0	2.5050	
	45.0	2.2190	
C_7H_{16}, Heptane	22.4	3.2071	(83)
	35.0	2.8245	
	39.0	2.7215	
Russian petroleum	10	0.164	(43)
	20	0.142	

See also (10, 14, 18, 20, 48, 134).

C_2H_4O; olive oil and sesame oil at 17 and 37°C (90)

C_2H_5Cl; olive oil and sesame oil at 17 and 37°C (90)

C_2H_5F (91)

C_2H_6, Ethane

Values of α (83)

t, °C	CH_3OH (99%)	t, °C	C_2H_5OH (99.8%)	t, °C	$C_4H_8O_2$, Ethyl acetate
23	1.8587	22	2.1616	22	2.8521
30	1.6973	25	2.0981	25	2.8179
35	1.6124	30	1.9951	30	2.7575
40	1.5457	35	1.8968	35	2.6902
45	1.4874	40	1.8020	40	2.6178
		45	1.6958		
		50	1.5651		

t, °C	C_6H_{14}, Hexane	t, °C	C_7H_{16}, Heptane	t, °C	Amyl acetate
22.1	3.1035	25	4.1220	22.0	3.3085
30.0	2.8685	30	3.9820	30.0	3.0518
55.0	2.4008	35	3.8498	50.0	2.4433
		40	3.7182		

Amyl alcohol (40).

Ethyl alcohol (114).

C_2H_6O, Methyl ether; olive and sesame oil at 17 and 37°C (90)

C_3H_4, Allylene

Vols. C_3H_4 dissolved by 1 vol. of $(C_2H_5)_2O$ at 1 atm. = 100; at 1°C; = 30 at 16°C (70).

C_3H_5F (87)

C_3H_6 (10)

C_3H_7F (87)

C_3H_8; amyl alcohol (40); other solvents (71)

C_3H_9N, Trimethylamine (44)

Solvent		α_{25}
Formula	Name	
$CHCl_3$	Chloroform	548
CH_3NO_2	Nitromethane	51.8
CH_4O	Methyl alcohol	651
C_2H_3N	Acetonitrile	58.4
C_2H_6O	Ethyl alcohol	431
C_3H_6O	Acetone	70.3
C_3H_8O	Propyl alcohol	432
$C_4H_8O_2$	Ethyl acetate	77.4
$C_4H_{10}O$	Ethyl ether	48.8
$C_5H_{12}O$	Amyl alcohol	353
$C_6H_5NO_2$	Nitrobenzene	48.6
C_6H_6	Benzene	99.9
C_6H_{14}	Hexane	68.7
$C_7H_7NO_2$	*o*-Nitrotoluene	50.1
C_7H_8O	Benzyl alcohol	1198
C_8H_8O	Acetophenone	53.0
$C_9H_{10}O_2$	Ethyl benzoate	69.8
$C_{10}H_7Br$	α-Bromonaphthalene	43.1

C_4H_8, Pseudobutylene; absolute ethyl alcohol: $\alpha_{19} = 47$ (121)

C_4H_8, Isobutylene; absolute ethyl alcohol: $\alpha_{19} = 42$ (121)

C_4H_{10}, Butane; C_2H_5OH (39); amyl alcohol (40); ethyl alcohol, ether and chloroform (71)

$C_6H_{15}N$, Triethylamine

Solvent (44)	α_{25}
CH_3NO_2, Nitromethane	366
C_6H_{14}, Hexane	1979

For solubilities of various gases in cyclohexanol, *v.* Cauquil, *42*, **24**: 53; 27.

LITERATURE

(For a key to the periodicals see end of volume)

(1) Ångström, *8*, **33**: 223; 88. (2) Antropoff, *9*, **25**: 269; 19. (3) Atkinson, Heycock and Pope, *4*, **117**: 1410; 20. (4) Baeyer and Villiger, *25*, **36**: 2774; 03. (5) Bakhuis Roozeboom, *70*, **4**: 379; 85. (6) Baly, *3*, **49**: 517; 00. (7) Baskerville and Cohen, *45*, **13**: 333; 21. (8) Bell and Field, *1*, **33**: 940; 11. (9) Bellati and Lussana, *24*, **7**: 1169; 89.

(10) Berthelot, *6*, **43**: 276; 55. (11) Berthelot, *6*, **52**: 97; 58. (12) Berthelot, *6*, **9**: 421; 66. (13) Blümcke, *8*, **23**: 404; 84. **30**: 243; 87. (14) Bohr, *8*, **62**: 644; 97. (15) Bohr, *8*, **1**: 244; 00. (16) Boyle, *Bull. MacDonald Phys. Bldg.*, **1**: 52; 10. *199*, **7**: 200; 10. (17) Boyle, *3*, **22**: 840; 11. (18) Bunsen, *B72*. (19) Butler, *54*, **40**: 25T; 21.

(20) Carius, *13*, **94**: 129; 55. *6*, **47**: 418; 56. (20.5) Christoff, *7*, **53**: 321; 05. (21) Christoff, *7*, **55**: 622; 06. (22) Christoff, *7*, **79**: 456; 12. (23) Claude, *34*, **128**: 303; 99. (24) Claude, *34*, **172**: 974; 21. (25) Claude and Hess, *34*, **124**: 626; 97. (26) Consortium für elektrochemische Industrie, *136*, **31**: 1095; 07. (27) Dawson and McCrae, *182*, **17**: 5; 01. (28) Delépine, *49*, **25**: 496; 92. (29) Dewar, *182*, **13**: 186; 97.

(30) Dolezalek, *7*, **71**: 191; 10. (31) Drucker, *7*, **49**: 563; 04. (32) Drucker and Moles, *7*, **15**: 405; 10. (33) Dunn, *135*, **45**: 270; 82. (34) Erdmann and Bedford, *25*, **37**: 1184, 2545; 04. (35) Falciola, *22*, **17 II**: 324; 08. *36*, **39 I**: 398; 09. (36) Fischer and Pfleiderer, *93*, **124**: 61; 22. (37) Fischer and Tropsch, *25*, **50**: 765; 17. (38) Fischer and Zerbe, *416*, **4**: 17; 23. (39) Frankland, *13*, **71**: 171; 49.

(40) Friedel and Gorgeu, *34*, **127**: 590; 08. (41) Garelli, *22*, **2**: 120; 25. (42) Garelli and Falciola, *22*, **13**: 110; 04. *36*, **34 II**: 1; 04. (43) Gniewoszy and Walfisz, *7*, **1**: 70; 87. (44) Halban, *7*, **84**: 129; 13. (45) Hantzsch and Sebalt, *7*, **30**: 258; 99. (46) Hantzsch and Vagt, *7*, **38**: 705; 01. (47) Hempel *92*, **14**: 865; 01. (48) Henrich, *7*, **9**: 453; 92. (49) Herz, *B13*, p. 190.

(50) Herz and Fischer, *25*, **37**: 4746; 04. (51) Herz and Kurzer, *9*, **16**: 240, 869; 10. (52) Hevesy, *63*, **12**: 1214; 11. *50*, **16**: 429; 12. (53) Hofbauer, *75*, **123 IIa**: 2001; 14. (54) Hofmann, *25*, **4**: 605; 71. (55) Hofmann, *63*, **6**: 337; 05. (56) Homfray, *4*, **97**: 1669; 10. (57) Jacquemin, *34*, **100**: 1005; 85. (58) Jakovkin, *7*, **29**: 613; 99. (59) James, *45*, **5**: 115; 13. (59.5) Jenkins and Shorthose, *B67*.

(60) Jones, *4*, **99**: 392; 11. (61) Joseph, *4*, **107**: 1; 15. (62) Jüttner, *7*, **38**: 56; 01. (63) Just, *7*, **37**: 342; 01. (64) Klaus, *63*, **6**: 820; 05. (65) Kling, *165*, **1915 A**: 1. (66) Kofler, *63*, **9**: 6; 08. (67) Kremann and Hönel, *57*, **34**: 1089; 13. (68) Kuenen, *68*, **23**: 312; 00. (69) Kunerth, *2*, **19**: 512; 22.

(70) Lagermark, *53*, **12**: 287; 80. (71) Lebeau, *34*, **140**: 1454, 1572; 05. (72) Levi, *36*, **31 II**: 513; 01. (73) Linder, *57*, **33**: 613; 12. (74) Lloyd, *50*, **22**: 300; 18. (75) Lobry de Bruyn, *7*, **10**: 782; 92. *70*, **11**: 112; 92. (76) Loeb, *4*, **53**: 812; 88. (77) Loeb, *4*, **53**: 805; 88. (78) Löfmann, *93*, **107**: 241; 19. (79) Lubarsch, *Diss.*, Halle, 1886. *427*, **42 I**: 547; 86.

(80) Lunge, *25*, **18**: 1391; 85. (81) Lurié, *Thesis*, Grenoble, 1910. *10*, **2**: 401; 11. (82) MacCrae and Wilson, *93*, **35**: 11; 03. (83) McDaniel, *50*, **15**: 587; 11. (84) Mai, *25*, **41**: 3897; 08. (84.5) Manchot, *92*, **23**: 2113; 10. (84.7) Manchot, *93*, **141**: 38; 24. (85) Manchot and Zechentmayer, *13*, **350**: 368; 06. (86) Maude, Westinghouse Electric and Mfg. Co., Pittsburgh, *0*. (87) Meslans, *6*, **1**: 346; 94. (88) Metschl, *50*, **28**: 417; 24. (89) Meyer, *75*, **122 IIa**: 1281; 13.

(90) Meyer and Gottlieb-Billroth, *202*, **112**: 55; 21. (91) Moissan, *6*, **19**: 266; 90. (92) Müller, *8*, **37**: 24; 89. (93) Müller, *Diss.*, Erlangen, 1891. (94) Müller, *52*, **58**: 1; 98. (95) Ostrejko, *Trudy bak. otd. imp. russk. techn. obschtsch*, **10**: No. 6; 96. *373*, **20**: 196; 96. (96) Pagliani and Emo, *23*, **18**: 67; 82. (97) Parsons, *1*, **47**: 1820; 25. (98) Pascal and Garnier, *27*, **25**: 309; 19. (99) Pélabon, *34*, **116**: 1292; 93.

(100) Pélabon, *34*, **124**: 35; 97. (101) Perkin, *4*, **65**: 20; 94. (102) Perman, *4*, **67**: 868, 983; 95. (103) Pieroni and Angeli, *22*, **2**: 120; 25. (104) Ramsay, Collie and Travers, *4*, **67**: 684; 95. (105) Ramstedt, *199*, **8**: 253; 11. (106) Raschig, *92*, **18**: 1281; 05. (107) Ritzel, *7*, **60**: 319; 07. (107.5) Robinet, *34*, **58**: 608; 64. (108) Roessler and Hasslacher Chemical Co., Perth Amboy, N. J., *0*. (109) Sackur, *9*, **18**: 641; 12.

(110) Sander, *7*, **78**: 513; 12. (111) Sapožnikov, *53*, **32**: 375; 00. (112) Schlubach and Ballauf, *25*, **54**: 2825; 21. (113) Schneider, *25*, **49**: 1638; 16. (114) Schorlemmer, *13*, **132**: 234; 64. *4*, **2**: 262; 64. (115) Schulze, *52*, **24**: 168; 81. (116) Schulze, *7*, **95**: 257; 20. (117) Schuncke, *7*, **14**: 331; 94. (118) Schwab and Hanke, *7*, **114**: 251; 24. (119) Skirrow, *7*, **41**: 139; 02.

(120) Smith, *50*, **25**: 204, 605, 721; 21. (121) Sporry, *Thesis*, Zürich, 1922. (122) Stern, *7*, **81**: 441; 12. (123) Stock, *25*, **37**: 1432; 04. (124) Stock and Guttmann, *25*, **37**: 885; 04. (125) Stock and Kuss, *25*, **50**: 159; 17. (126) Stock and Somieski, *25*, **54**: 740; 21. (127) Swarts, *186*, **1901**: 383. (128) Szeparowicz, *75*, **129 IIa**: 437; 20. (129) Taylor and Hildebrand, *1*, **45**: 682; 23.

(130) Thiel and Schulte, *7*, **96**: 312; 20. (131) Timofeev, *7*, **6**: 141; 90. (132) Tower, *93*, **50**: 382; 06. (133) Traubenberg, *63*, **5**: 130; 04. (134) Tucker and Moody, *1*, **23**: 671; 01. (135) Ubbelohde and Svanoe, *92*, **32**: 257; 19. (136) Vukolov, *34*, **108**: 674; 89. (136.5) Vukolov, *34*, **109**: 61; 89. (137) Weigert, *25*, **36**: 1007; 03. (138) Wieland, *277*, **92**: 96; 22. (139) Williams, *135*, **122**: 62; 21.

(140) Willstätter and Waldschmidt-Leitz, *25*, **54**: 133; 21. (141) Winkler, *92*, **29**: 218; 16.

THE SOLUBILITY OF GASES IN MOLTEN METALS AND ALLOYS

DAVID F. SMITH

Symbols and Abbreviations

v The volume of gas in cm^3 (reduced to S. T. P.) dissolved at the temperature t, by 10 g of solvent when the partial pressure of the gas is 760 mm.

p partial pressure of the gas in mm Hg.

M. P. Melting point.

Ag

O_2 (2)

t, °C	$\sqrt{p}/v$	p, range
1020	1.35	751–753
1075	1.40	39–1203

Al

H_2 (3)

t, °C	v
695	0.203
730	0.426
824	1.10
873	1.44
922	1.82
(1)	
670	0.187

N_2 (3)

t, °C	v
690	1.19
760	1.245
850	1.66
930	2.01

Cu

H_2 (5)

t, °C	v
(1084 M. P.)	0.600
1150	0.725
1250	0.910
1350	1.094
1450	1.278
1550	1.38
(3)	
1118	1.27
1199	1.39
1285	1.56

According to (7) $\sqrt{p}/v$ = 44.4 from p = 281 to 1046 mm at 1123°C.

d_4^t = *ca.* 8.9

N_2 (3)

t, °C	v
1110	0.287
1168	.460
1255	.570
1320	.908

SO_2 (6); *cf.* (8)

t, °C	v
1100	14.5
1150	16.7
1200	18.9
1250	21.1
1300	23.3
1350	25.5

According to (7) $\sqrt{p}/v$ = const. from p = 20 to 1000 mm.

CO (3)

t, °C	v
1105	2.65
1173	2.36
1256	2.06

CO_2 (3)

t, °C	v
1105	1.88
1179	1.86
1268	1.72

Fe

H_2 (5)

t, °C	v
(1530 M. P.)	2.72*
1550	2.79
1650	3.10

At 1550°, $\sqrt{p}/v$ = const.

*Given in the original as 2.66 at M. P. = 1510°.

N_2 (4)

At 1530°, (Wt. % N_2)/$\sqrt{p}$ = 0.021 for p in atm., between 3 and 200 atm.

O_2 (9)

0.21 Wt. % O_2 at 1530°

Ni

H_2 (5)

t, °C	v
(1450 M. P.)	3.87
1500	4.03
1600	4.33

At 1500° $\sqrt{p}/v$ = const.

Sn

H_2 (3)

t, °C	v
400	0.044
553	.058
704	.071
798	.094
900	.141
1005	.147
(1)	
800	0.042

Solubility of SO_2 in Liquid Cu Alloys (6)

x_{Cu} = mole fraction of Cu in alloy

x_{Cu}	t, °C	v
With Ag		
0.6292	1220	5.53
With Au		
0.9654	1220	14.13
0.8786	1220	6.23
With Cu_2O		
0.9575	1220	3.46
0.9575	1330	5.81
0.9842	1170	12.87
0.955	1270	3.60
0.970	1270	9.72

x_{Cu}	t, °C	v
0.990	1270	17.95
With Cu_2S*		
0.975	1270	13.75
0.985	1270	13.78
0.992	1270	15.29
0.995	1270	17.49
With Pt		
0.8775	1330	4.44

* $\sqrt{p}/v$ = const.

LITERATURE

(For a key to the periodicals see end of volume)

(1) Bircumshaw, *3*, **1**: 510; 26. (2) Donnan and Shaw, *54*, **29**: 987; 10. (3) Iwasé, *159*, **15**: 531; 26. (4) Sawyer, *80*, **69**: 798; 23. (5) Sieverts, *7*, **77**: 591; 11. (6) Sieverts and Bergner, *7*, **82**: 257; 13. (7) Sieverts and Krumbhaar, *7*, **74**: 277; 10. (8) Stubbs, *4*, **103**: 1445; 13. (9) Tritton and Hanson, *140*, **110**: 90; 24.

THE SOLUBILITY OF GASES IN SOLUTIONS

DAVID F. SMITH

Introduction

Arrangement.—The A-component is the dissolving gas. The B-component is the major and the C-component the minor constituent of the solution in which the gas is dissolved. Standard arrangement by A-components.

Abbreviations.—α and λ, *v.* p. 254.

d the density (or sp. gr.) of the solution, before saturation with the gas except as otherwise noted.

M_C Moles of C per 1000 g B.

N_C Gram-equivalents of C per l of (B + C).

N'_C Moles of C per l of (B + C).

x_C Mole fraction of C in the solution, (B + C).

Introduction

Arrangement.—Le constituant A est le gaz dissout. Le constituant B et le constituant C sont respectivement le constituant le plus important et le constituant moins important de la solution dans laquelle le gaz est dissout. Arrangement type suivant les constituants A.

Abréviations.—α et λ, *v.* p. 254.

d La densité (ou le p. sp.) de la solution, avant saturation par le gaz, à moins d'une autre indication.

M_C Molécules de C pour 1000 g de B.

N_C Equivalent-grammes de C par litre de (B + C).

N'_C Molécules de C par litre de (B + C).

x_C Fraction moléculaire de C dans la solution (B + C).

Einleitung

Anordnung.—Die A-Komponente ist das gelöste Gas. Die B-Komponente ist der Hauptbestandteil, die C-Komponente der kleinste Bestandteil der Stoffe welche die Lösung zusammensetzen in welchen das Gas gelöst ist. Die Standard-Anordnung richtet sich nach der A-Komponente.

Abkürzungen.—α und λ *siehe* S. 254.

d Dichte der Lösung vor der Gassättigung, ausser es ist etwas anderes angegeben.

M_C Mole C auf 1000 g B.

N_C Grammäquivalente von C pro l von (B + C).

N'_C Mole von C pro l von (B + C).

x_C Molenbruch von C in der Lösung (B + C).

Introduzione

Convenzioni.—Il componente A è il gas disciolto. Nella soluzione in cui il gas è disciolto, B è il costituente in proporzione maggiore e C quello in proporzione minore. La disposizione è quella Standard per i componenti A.

Abbreviazioni.—α e λ, *vedi* pag. 254.

d Densità (o p. sp.) della soluzione, prima della saturazione col gas, salvo indicazioni contrarie.

M_C Grammi-molecole di C per 1000 g di B.

N_C Grammi-equivalenti di C per l di (B + C).

N'_C Grammi-molecole di C per l di (B + C).

x_C Frazione di grammi-molecole di C nella soluzione (B + C).

The data on solubilities in colloidal solutions (p. 281) are not as nearly complete as are the data on true solutions. Since these solubilities usually refer to a specifically prepared solute, typical examples only are presented.

Rn, Radon

Solution (94)	t, °C	α
10% by wt. damar gum in oil of turpentine	18.0	16.7
5% by wt. rosin in amyl alcohol	20.0	11.2
20% by wt. rosin in amyl alcohol	20.0	11.1
v. also Vol. I, p. 364.		

O_2

B = H_2O

AQUEOUS SOLUTIONS OF ELECTROLYTES

For pure H_2O, $10^3\alpha_{15}$ = 34.41; $10^3\alpha_{25}$ = 28.22

C \ N_C	$10^3\alpha_{15}$ (45) 0.5	1.0	2.0	$10^3\alpha_{25}$ (45) 0.5	1.0	2.0
HCl	32.6	31.0	28.3	27.1	26.3	24.5
½H_2SO_4	32.0	30.2		26.4	25.2	23.0

C \ N_C	$10^3\alpha_{25}$ (45) 0.5	1.0	2.0	$10^3\alpha_{25}$ (45) 0.5	1.0	2.0
HNO_3	33.0	31.9	29.9	27.7	27.0	26.0
NaOH	27.3	21.9	14.4	22.9	18.7	12.2
NaCl	29.2	24.6	17.3	24.0	20.4	14.5
KOH	27.6	22.2		23.1	18.9	
½K_2SO_4	27.9	22.5		23.2	19.0	

C \ N_C	3.0	4.0	5.0	3.0	4.0	5.0	Lit.
½H_2SO_4	24.3	22.1	20.2	21.0	19.1	17.8	(45)

C	N_C	$10^3\alpha_0$	$10^3\alpha_{10}$	$10^3\alpha_{20}$	$10^3\alpha_{30}$	Lit.
	0.0	48.72	37.93	30.91	26.12	(67)
NaCl	0.1	44.31	34.59	28.47	24.49	
NaBr	1.0	29.85	23.42	19.75	17.84	
NaI	1.0	31.51	25.75	21.96	19.77	
KCl	1.0	31.08	24.98	21.20	18.67	
KBr	1.0	30.94	21.11	19.88	18.18	
KI	1.0	31.87	25.31	21.26	18.96	

O_2: B = H_2O.—(*Continued*)

C = **NaCl**; (for sea water *v. infra*)

Values of $10^3\alpha_t$ (150)

°C \ N_C	0.0	1	2	3	5.431
0	48.95	31.2	22.5	15.1	6.1
5	42.9	27.9	20.4	13.65	5.9
10	38.1	25.3	18.6	12.5	5.6
15	34.2	23.1	17.0	11.7	5.4
20	31.1	21.4	15.75	11.0	5.2
25	28.5	20.0	14.7	10.45	5.0
30	26.2	18.7	14.05	10.0	4.8

C = **KCN** (98)

M_C	0.2	2.0	4.0	7.0	15.0
$10^3\alpha_{20}$	28.6	16.8	11.5	7.5	3.1

Aqueous Solutions of Organic Compounds

C = C_2H_6O, Ethyl alcohol (91)

M_C*	α_{20}	M_C*	α_{20}	M_C*	α_{20}
0.0	2.84	6.0	2.45	20.0	3.24
2.0	2.70	8.0	2.35	40.0	4.65
4.0	2.55	10.0	2.42	87.0	5.57

* Original results, which were given as volume % O_2 dissolved at 20°C and 760 mm, were first corrected for the partial pressures of alcohol and water interpolated from data of Konovalov (79.5).

C = $C_2H_3Cl_3O_2$, Chloral hydrate (111)

M_C	1.8	3.0	5.0	6.3	8.5	14.0	25.5
d_{20}^{20}	1.113	1.173	1.244	1.280	1.334	1.426	1.521
$10^3\alpha_{15}$	29.6	26.1	23.8	23.4	24.1	27.0	32.7

M_C	1.2	2.8	6.8	9.5	15.1	21.4
d_{20}^{20}	1.076	1.161	1.294	1.354	1.441	1.46
$10^3\alpha_{20}$	28.03	25.01	23.26	24.11	27.31	32.77

C = $C_3H_8O_3$, Glycerol (111)

M_C	2.8	3.6	6.5	8.9	11.8	27.2	83.6
$10^3\alpha_{15}$	27.43	25.28	20.17	17.44	15.69	9.53	8.86

C = $C_6H_{12}O_6$, Glucose (111)

M_C	0.7	1.5	3.0	6.0	8.0
$10^3\alpha_{20}$	26.76	22.25	17.82	13.88	12.45

C = $C_{12}H_{22}O_{11}$, Sucrose (111)

M_C	0.4	0.9	1.2	2.2	2.9
$10^3\alpha_{15}$	29.75	24.30	21.60	16.01	13.63

Air

B = H_2O; C = H_2SO_4

M_C	500.0	92.0	40.0	25.0	15.0	10.0	Lit.
$10^3\alpha_{18}$	16.2	10.0	6.44	5.26	5.55	7.20	(138)

Values of cm³ of N_2 and O_2 at S.T.P. dissolved by 1 l of soln. in equilibrium with the normal dry atmosphere (11)

N_C	t, °C	N_2	O_2
0.0	20.9	15.6	31.0
4.9	20.9	9.1	19.5
8.9	20.9	7.2	15.5
10.7	21.2	6.6	14.3
20.3	21.1	4.9	11.9
24.8	21.5	4.8	10.3
29.6	20.8	5.1	11.7
34.3	20.9	10.0	20.1
35.8	21.1	12.9	27.5

O_2 and N_2 in Sea Water (43)

In equilibrium with the dry atmosphere at 760 mm the number (S) of cm³ of gas (S.T.P.) dissolved in 1 l of sea water is

$$S_{O_2} = 10.291 - 0.2809t + 0.006009t^2 + 0.0000632t^3 - \pi_{Cl}(0.1161 - 0.003922t + 0.0000631t^2)$$

$$S_{N_2} = 18.639 - 0.4304t + 0.007453t^2 - 0.0000549t^3 - \pi_{Cl}(0.2172 - 0.007187t + 0.0000952t^2)$$

where π_{Cl} is parts per 1000 of Cl in the sea water.

Range: t, 0 to 28°; π_{Cl}, 0 to 20.

O_3

B = H_2O

C = H_2SO_4 (125)

N_C	0.0	0.100
$10^3\alpha_0$	494 (extrap.)	487

H_2

B = H_2O

Aqueous Salt Solutions

Values of $10^3\alpha_{15}$ for various salts; for pure H_2O, $10^3\alpha_{15}$ = 18.83 (134)

C \ N_C	1	2	3	4	5	6
½$ZnSO_4$	14.46	11.13	8.52	6.67	5.10	
⅓$AlCl_3$	15.11	12.21	9.93	8.10	6.67	5.50
½$MgSO_4$	14.51	11.20	8.56	6.59	4.99	
½$CaCl_2$	14.93	11.95	9.58	7.80	6.35	5.10
LiCl	15.74	13.25	11.21	9.49		
NaCl*	14.78	11.44	8.80	6.99	5.73	
½Na_2SO_4	13.70	9.91	7.10			
$NaNO_3$*	14.96	12.01	9.84	8.08	6.67	5.42
½Na_2CO_3	13.40	6.99				
KCl*	15.02	12.17	9.96	8.20		
KNO_3*	15.24	12.76	10.76			
½K_2CO_3	13.38	9.67	7.00	5.08	3.72	2.73†

* *See* special tables below.

† 2.06 for N_C = 7; 1.58 for N_C = 9.

C = NH_4NO_3 (75)

M_C	d	$10^3\alpha_{20}$	M_C	d	$10^3\alpha_{20}$
0.0	0.9983	18.83	0.9	1.02602	17.55
0.2	1.00485	18.6	1.2	1.03445	17.05
0.5	1.01411	18.2	1.7	1.04846	16.25

C = **$BaCl_2$**

Values of $10^3\alpha$ (14)

M_C \ °C	5	10	15	20	25
0.0	23.7	22.1	20.6	19.1	17.5
0.1	21.95	20.6	19.2	17.85	16.33
0.2	20.68	19.48	18.2	16.85	15.43
0.3	19.81	18.75	17.5	16.25	14.85
0.35	19.47	18.43	17.23	15.99	14.63

C = **NaCl**

Values of $10^3\alpha$ (14)

M_C \ °C	5	10	15	20	25	M_C	15°C
0.2	22.0	20.65	19.3	17.78	16.3	3.0	9.21
0.4	20.8	19.7	18.4	17.0	15.5	5.0	6.29
0.6	19.96	18.96	17.75	16.4	14.9		
0.8	19.3	18.34	17.2	15.9	14.4		
1.1	18.37	17.48	16.38	15.29	13.8		

C = $NaNO_3$
Values of $10^3\alpha$

t = 15°C (48)		t = 20°C (75)		
N_C	$10^3\alpha$	N_C	d	$10^3\alpha$
0.7	15.96	0.1	1.0039	18.5
1.5	13.45	0.2	1.0094	18.0
2.5	10.87	0.3	1.0150	17.6
4.0	8.0	0.5	1.0259	16.7
5.7	5.59	0.9	1.0469	15.1
		1.75	1.0873	13.0

C = **KCl** (75)

M_C	d	$10^3\alpha_{20}$	M_C	d	$10^3\alpha_{20}$
0.1	1.0030	18.43	0.9	1.0388	15.35
0.3	1.01222	17.6	1.2	1.0516	14.41
0.6	1.0257	16.45	2.1	1.0867	12.59

C = KNO_3 (75)

M_C	d	$10^3\alpha_{20}$	M_C	d	$10^3\alpha_{20}$
0.1	1.0043	18.6	0.9	1.0516	16.5
0.3	1.0169	18.1	1.2	1.0676	15.5
0.5	1.0287	17.6	1.6	1.0896	14.2
0.7	1.0404	17.1			

AQUEOUS SOLUTIONS OF ACIDS AND BASES

C = H_2SO_4 (19)

M_C	0.0	5.69	16.37	221.5
$10^3\alpha_{20}$	19.4	8.89	6.60	10.2

Values of $10^3\alpha_{25}$ ($10^3\alpha_{25}$ for pure H_2O = 17.65) (45)

C \ N_C	0.5	1.0	2.0	3.0	4.0
HCl	17.0	16.4	15.4	14.6	
$\frac{1}{2}H_2SO_4$	16.9	16.2	14.9	13.7	12.9
HNO_3	17.2	16.8	15.9	15.3	14.7
CH_3COOH	17.6	17.5	17.2	17.0	17.0
$CH_2ClCOOH$	17.3	17.0	16.5		
NaOH	15.1	12.7	8.9	6.6	5.0
KOH	15.3	13.0			

AQUEOUS SOLUTIONS OF ORGANIC COMPOUNDS

C = C_2H_6O, Ethyl alcohol (91)

M_C	0.0	2.0	4.0	6.0	8.5	11.0	22.0	44.0
α_{20}	1.84	1.38	1.225	1.14	1.01	1.14	1.97	2.51

C = $C_3H_8O_3$, Glycerol

M_C	1.9	3.2	6.6	10.0	23.0	106.0	Lit.
$10^3\alpha_{15}$	16.5	15.1	12.2	10.5	8.1	8.7	(111)

M_C	$10^3\alpha_{14}$	$10^3\alpha_{21}$	M_C	$10^3\alpha_{14}$	$10^3\alpha_{21}$
0.0	19.28	18.38	1.4	18.00	17.08
0.2	19.03	18.17	1.6	17.86	16.90
0.4	18.80	17.97	1.8	17.74	16.72
0.6	18.60	17.78	2.0	17.63	16.5
0.8	18.43	17.60	2.2		16.3
1.0	18.28	17.43	2.4		16.1
1.2	18.14	17.26	Lit.	(57)	

M_C	$10^3\alpha_{25}$	M_C	$10^3\alpha_{25}$	M_C	$10^3\alpha_{25}$
0.0	17.98	7.0	10.7	95.0	3.7
0.5	17.12	10.0	9.2	205.0	3.2
1.5	15.7	20.0	6.6	Lit.	(28)
3.0	13.9	40.0	4.9		

C = $C_2H_3Cl_3O_2$, Chloral hydrate (111)

M_C	0.6	3.5	6.0	9.5	14.5	23.0
d_{15}^{15}	1.040	1.193	1.276	1.356	1.433	1.504
$10^3\alpha_{15}$	17.7	14.8	13.2	12.3	12.8	13.2

M_C	1.0	2.5	5.0	7.0	10.0	13.0	22.0
d_{20}^{20}	1.066	1.145	1.243	1.300	1.368	1.411	1.500
$10^3\alpha_{20}$	17.2	15.5	13.6	12.8	12.4	12.7	13.8

Values of $10^3\alpha$ for N_C' = 1 mole/l (64)

C	Urea	Acetamide	Alanine	Glycocoll
°C	20.17	20.11	20.08	20.16
$10^3\alpha$	17.0	18.0	15.6	15.8

C = $C_3H_6O_2$, Propionic acid
Values of $10^3\alpha_t$ (14)

M_C \ °C	5	10	15	20	25
0.4	22.3	21.3	20.0	18.8	17.2
0.8	21.9	21.1	19.6	18.4	17.0
1.2	21.6	20.7	19.2	18.05	16.5
1.5	21.3	20.3	18.9	17.8	16.0

C = $C_6H_{12}O_6$, Glucose (111)

M_C	0.8	1.5	2.5	4.5	8.0
$10^3\alpha_{20}$	15.90	14.42	12.76	10.34	7.79
N_C', mole/l	0.0	0.230	0.485	0.966	Lit.
°C	20.11	20.00	20.25	20.28	(64)
$10^3\alpha$	18.1	17.6	16.6	15.2	

C = $C_{12}H_{22}O_{11}$, Sucrose (111)

M_C	0.2	0.5	0.7	1.3	1.9	2.2
$10^3\alpha_{15}$	16.9	15.5	14.7	12.2	10.4	9.4

M_C	1	2	Lit.
$10^3\alpha_{15}$	12.80	7.31	(134)

Cl_2

B = H_2O

C = HCl (104); *cf.* (112)

N_C	0.0	0.1	0.3	1.0	3.0	4.0	6.0	9.0
α_{21}	2.117	1.48	1.405	1.61	2.16	2.415	2.904	3.65

C = $C_2H_4O_2$, Glacial acetic acid (71)

Vol. % C	99.84	90.00	75.00	65.00
°C	16	15	15	15
α_t	34.7	24.0	15.57	12.73

C = **NaCl** (82)

$\alpha = 2.23 - 0.05505t + 0.000025t^2$ for 9.97 Wt. % NaCl; and

$\alpha = 2.19 - 0.1128t + 0.00328t^2 - 0.0000422t^3$ for 16.01 Wt. % NaCl; and

$\alpha = 1.74 - 0.0672t + 0.00117t^2 - 0.0000097t^3$ for 19.66 Wt. % NaCl; range, 0 to 25°C.

26.39 Wt. % NaCl; d = 1.205 at 15°C (78)

t, °C	85	70	60	30	15	Lit.
α_t*	0.048	0.099	0.133	0.28	0.38	(112)

* Contrary to the statement of Kumpf (82) the authors observed no precipitation of NaCl from concentrated solutions upon passing chlorine through them. They found, however, an increase in solubility after long continued passage of Cl_2 through the solution which they attributed to the formation of oxygenated chlorine compounds.

HCl

B = H_2O

C = H_2SO_4 (23)

x_B	α_{25}	x_B	α_{25}
0.0	4.505	0.35	1.028
0.07	2.208	0.40	1.022
0.15	1.486	0.50	1.23
0.20	1.27	0.55	1.56
0.30	1.06	0.63	3.96

HCl: B = H_2O.—*(Continued)*

C = C_2H_5OH, Ethyl alcohol (72)

The following equation reproduces the results within the experimental error which is about 2.5% for p > 2.50 mm. The percentage error for $p < 2.50$ mm is usually considerably greater than this.

$$\log_{10} p_A = a \log_{10} N_A + bN_A + dN_A^2 + f$$
p_A = partial pressure of HCl in mm Hg
N_A = moles HCl per liter of solution
$$a = 1.3171 + 1.0306N_B + 0.3907N_B^2$$
$$100b = 3.847 - 12.11N_B - 3.851N_B^2$$
$$100d = 1.2633 + 0.398N_B + 0.10798N_B^2$$
$$f = -0.2437 - 0.2175N_B - 0.1107N_B^2$$
N_B = moles H_2O per liter of solution
Range, N_A = 0.3 to 3.0 and N_B = 0 to 2.5.

SO_2

B = H_2O

Aqueous Solutions of Acids

C = H_2SO_4 (106)

N_C	α_{20}	N_C	α_{20}	N_C	α_{20}
16.0	26.1	26.0	20.3	34.0	19.8
18.0	25.8	28.0	19.0	35.0	21.2
20.0	25.1	30.0	18.0	35.5	23.0
22.0	23.7	31.3	17.5	36.0	24.5
24.0	22.0	32.0	17.9	37.0	26.1

C = H_2SO_4; d_4^{20} = 1.836; N_C = 36.3 at 20°C (29)

t, °C	d_4^t*	α_t	t, °C	d_4^t*	α_t
0		53.0	50	1.8186	9.5
10	1.8232	35.0	60	1.8165	7.0
20	1.8225	25.0	70	1.8140	5.5
25	1.8221	21.0	80	1.8112	4.5
30	1.8216	18.0	90	1.8080	4.0
40	1.8205	13.0			

* *d* of satd. soln.

Aqueous Salt Solutions

Values of α_{25} (41)

C \ N_C	0.5	1.0	1.5	2.0	2.5	3.0
NH_4NO_3	31.11	32.13	33.24	34.14	34.82	35.86
NH_4Cl	31.68	33.32	34.87	36.43	37.90	39.19
NH_4Br	33.21	36.15	39.19	42.20	45.05	47.87
$(NH_4)_2SO_4$	30.55	30.98	31.45	32.02	32.50	32.94
NH_4CNS	34.61	39.16	43.30	47.88	52.23	56.31
$CdCl_2$	29.00	27.99	26.99	25.80	24.82	23.87
$CdBr_2$	29.23	28.41	27.64	26.82	25.79	25.16
CdI_2	30.48	30.93	31.30	31.83	32.05	32.77
$CdSO_4$	28.50	27.22	25.87	24.35	23.03	21.77
NaCl	29.74	29.55	29.28	29.10	28.87	28.73
NaBr	30.93	31.64	32.31	33.22	33.75	34.58
Na_2SO_4	29.28	28.53	27.90	27.04	26.26	26.06
NaCNS	32.47	35.03	37.36	39.73	42.01	44.29
KCl	31.53	33.03	34.59	36.02	37.53	38.73
KBr	32.93	35.83	38.85	41.49	44.71	47.88
KI	35.42	41.01	46.34	51.99	57.38	62.63
K_2SO_4	30.42	30.79				
KNO_3	30.97	31.87	32.77	33.59	34.42	35.29
KCNS	34.42	38.83	43.08	47.47	51.18	56.12

Values of α_{35} (41)

C \ N_C	0.5	1.0	1.5	2.0	2.5	3.0
NH_4NO_3	20.70	21.48	21.96	22.67	23.63	24.31
$(NH_4)_2SO_4$	20.31	20.51	20.82	21.21	21.48	21.81
$CdCl_2$	19.26	18.82	18.22	17.75	17.05	16.56
$CdBr_2$	19.39	19.02	18.45	18.26	17.46	16.99
CdI_2	20.17	20.44	20.71	21.02	21.26	21.54
$CdSO_4$	19.01	18.11	17.21	16.23	15.43	14.40
Na_2SO_4*	19.39	18.92	18.45	17.91	17.51	17.08
KCl*	21.04	22.29	23.53	24.77	25.64	26.61
KBr	22.01	24.37	26.27	28.30	30.24	32.03
KI	23.31	26.81	30.70	33.72	37.11	40.27
KNO_3	20.63	21.30	21.97	22.80	23.53	24.23
KCNS	22.72	25.52	28.39	31.07	33.80	38.06

* *See* special tables below.

C = Na_2SO_4

Values of moles SO_2 per 1000 g H_2O* (62)

M_C \ °C	20	30	40	50	M_C \ °C	20	30	40	50
0.0	1.661	1.188	0.872	0.644	0.5	1.626	1.208	0.925	
0.1	1.664	1.199	0.895	0.680	0.6	1.605	1.201	0.924	
0.2	1.663	1.209	0.910	0.709	0.7	1.583	1.192	0.921	0.742
0.3	1.657	1.214	0.919	0.725	1.0	1.519		0.907	0.738
0.4	1.644	1.213	0.924	0.733	1.1	1.499		0.901	0.736
					1.4	1.433	1.096	0.880	0.726

* The partial pressure of SO_2 was in all except three cases within 10 mm of 760 mm. Thus the values given above are in general subject to an error of about 1 %. It will be noted that the values here given for pure water are somewhat different from those determined by the author in connection with his measurements on KCl solutions.

C = **KCl** (62)

$M_A = M_{0_A} + 10^{-3}aM_C$, for p_A = 760 mm Hg; M_A (resp. M_{0_A}) = solubility of SO_2 in moles per 1000 g H_2O in the solution (resp. in pure water). M_C = moles of KCl per 1000 g H_2O; range, M_C = 0 to 5.

°C	M_{0_A}	a	°C	M_{0_A}	a
10	2.374	387.3	50	0.6528	57.0
15	1.976	294.9	60	0.5099	34.99
20	1.650	227.9	70	0.4082	23.96
30	1.179	141.7	80	0.3343	15.06
40	0.8674	88.03	90	0.2799	10.93

H_2S

B = H_2O

C = HCl (74)

N_C	α_{25}	N_C	α_{25}	N_C	α_{25}	N_C	α_{25}
0.0	2.266	0.6	2.250	2.0	2.272	3.5	2.308
0.1	2.256	1.0	2.256	2.5	2.280	4.5	2.384
0.3	2.247	1.5	2.264	3.0	2.290	4.8	2.422

C = **HI**

Total pressure = 760 mm; t = 25°C (116)

N_C	0.0	1.0	2.0	3.0	4.0	5.0	6.0	9.0
N'_A	0.100	0.111	0.124	0.140	0.155	0.169	0.187	0.26

C = **Various electrolytes** (97)

C	N_C	α_{25}	C	N_C	α_{25}
Nil		2.292	NaCl	1.0	1.941
HCl	0.5	2.235	NaCl	0.5	2.132
H_2SO_4	0.5	2.074	NaBr	1.0	2.143
NH_4NO_3	1.0	2.269	Na_2SO_4	0.5	1.673
NH_4Cl	1.0	2.200	Na_2SO_4	0.25	1.960
NH_4Br	1.0	2.292	$NaNO_3$	1.0	2.047
$(NH_4)_2SO_4$	0.5	1.879	KCl	1.0	1.955
$(NH_4)_2SO_4$	0.25	2.086	KBr	1.0	2.166
$CO(NH_2)_2$	1.0	2.338	KI	1.0	2.246
$NH_4C_2H_3O_2$	1.0	2.498	K_2SO_4	0.5	1.788
$C_4H_6O_6$, Tartaric acid	1.0	2.164	K_2SO_4	0.25	2.040
$C_4H_6O_6$, Tartaric acid	3.0	1.967	KNO_3	1.0	2.093

C = **NaCl** (67)

N_C	α_0	α_{10}	α_{20}	α_{30}
0.1	4.230	3.062	2.330	1.853
1.0	3.296	2.552	2.070	1.738
3.0	2.383	1.753	1.354	1.138

C = **NaHS** (46)

N'_C	α_{15}	α_{25}	α_{35}	α_{45}
0.05			1.84	1.43
0.10	2.96	2.33	1.84	
0.20	2.89	2.32		

N_2

B = H_2O

AQUEOUS SOLUTIONS OF ACIDS

C = H_2SO_4 (11)

N_C	0.0	5.0	10.0	20.0	25.0	34.0	36.0
$10^3\alpha_{21}$	15.6	9.2	6.5	4.7	5.0	9.7	13.4

C = $C_3H_6O_2$, Propionic acid

Values of $10^3\alpha_t$ (14)

M_C \ °C	5	10	15	20	25
0.6	21.0	19.1	16.8	15.3	13.7
1.0	20.8	18.6	16.5	14.8	13.5
1.4	20.3	18.2	16.2	14.7	13.2
1.7	19.6	17.8	16.0	14.6	13.1

C = $C_4H_8O_2$, Isobutyric acid

For $M_C = 6.81$, $\alpha_{23.02} = 0.0364$; $\alpha_{29.02} = 0.0346$ between 231 and 720 mm Hg (28).

AQUEOUS SALT SOLUTIONS

C = $BaCl_2$

Values of $10^3\alpha_t$ (14)

°C \ M_C	0.18	0.36	0.65	0.77
5	18.1	16.0	13.5	12.8
10	16.7	14.66	12.5	11.74
15	14.9	13.2	11.3	10.6
20	13.35	11.78	9.80	9.20
25	11.6	10.3	8.5	7.9

C = NaCl; for sea water, *v.* p. 272

Values of $10^3\alpha_t$ (14)

°C \ M_C	0.1	0.4	0.8	1.2	1.6	2.3
5	21.4	17.7	15.5	13.7	12.3	10.3
10	18.65	16.2	14.2	12.47	11.05	9.26
15	16.5	14.54	12.7	11.2	9.85	8.02
20	14.9	12.9	11.1	9.7	8.45	6.6
25	13.1	11.1	9.4	8.0	6.9	5.2

AQUEOUS SOLUTIONS OF ORGANIC COMPOUNDS

C (64)	N'_C	°C	$10^3\alpha_t$
Glucose	1.0	20.18	12.15
Glucose	0.5	20.21	13.80
Glucose	0.25	20.2	14.80
Alanine	1.0	20.19	12.13
Glycocoll	1.0	20.16	12.12
Arabinose	1.0	20.21	12.03
Levulose	1.0	20.25	12.21
Erythritol	1.0	20.25	13.21
Urea	1.0	20.18	14.77
Acetamide	1.0	20.22	14.75

C = C_2H_6O, Ethyl alcohol

Vol. % C	0.0	20.0	50.0	100.0	Lit.
$10^3\alpha_{25}$	14.97	14.07	13.58	13.12	(73)

C = $C_2H_3Cl_3O_2$, Chloral hydrate

M_C	$10^3\alpha_{25}$	M_C	$10^3\alpha_{15}$	M_C	d^{20}_{20}	$10^3\alpha_{15}$
0.0	16.45	0.0	17.02	1.0	1.067	16.0
1.0	14.77	0.5	16.20	2.5	1.148	14.1
2.0	13.41	1.0	15.38	3.5	1.191	13.3
4.0	11.71	2.0	13.86	5.0	1.243	12.5
6.0	11.04	4.0	12.12	8.0	1.327	12.6
10.0	11.06	6.0	11.52	15.0	1.440	14.1
15.0	12.75	9.0	11.46	22.5	1.504	15.0
23.0	15.15	14.0	12.78	Lit	(111)	
Lit.	(53)	24.0	15.83			
		Lit.	(53)			

C = $C_3H_8O_3$, Glycerol

M_C	$10^3\alpha_{15}$	M_C	$10^3\alpha_{25}$	M_C	$10^3\alpha_{15}$*	M_C	$10^3\alpha_{25}$*
3.6	12.68	0.0	14.3	0.0	17.1	25.0	5.8
8.0	9.60	2.0	9.5	1.0	15.4	45.0	5.1
12.0	7.43	4.5	6.4	3.0	12.9	60.0	5.0
15.0	7.03	10.0	4.5	4.0	11.8	95.0	5.0
45.0	7.3	30.0	2.7	7.0	9.5	205.0	5.0
95.0	7.8	60.0	2.0	10.0	8.2	∞	5.0
205.0	9.1	Lit.	(28)	15.0	6.9	(pure glyc.)	
Lit.	(111)						

* Argon-free N_2 (53).

C = $C_{12}H_{22}O_{11}$, Sucrose

M_C	0.4	0.8	1.2	2.7	Lit.
$10^3\alpha_{15}$	14.7	12.5	10.9	7.5	(111)

B = CH_4O, Methyl alcohol

C = **KI** (84)

M_C	d^5_4	$10^3\alpha_5$	d^{15}_4	$10^3\alpha_{15}$	d^{25}_4	$10^3\alpha_{25}$
0.0	0.8080	212	0.7980	184	0.7937	151
0.1324	0.8171	199	0.8070	173	0.8019	140
0.1897	0.8249	193	0.8150	168	0.8101	134
0.7398	0.8930	165	0.8841	140	0.8801	115

C = CH_4N_2O, Urea (84)

M_C	d^5_4	$10^3\alpha_5$	d^{15}_4	$10^3\alpha_{15}$	d^{25}_4	$10^3\alpha_{25}$
0.0	0.8080	212	0.7980	184	0.7937	151
0.4688	0.8148	199	0.8050	175	0.7997	143
0.847	0.8231	192	0.8122	168	0.8080	137
1.326	0.8350	184	0.8241	162	0.8193	132

NH_3

B = H_2O

According to Konovalov (80) the solubility of NH_3 in aqueous solutions of C = $AgNO_3$, $Cd(NO_3)_2$, $Zn(NO_3)_2$, $NiCl_2$, $Cu(NO_3)_2$, $CuCl_2$, $CuSO_4$ or $Cu(C_2H_3O_2)_2$ is given by

$$p_{NH_3} = k(N_{NH_3} - 2N_C)$$

For p in mm Hg, $k = 56.58$ for C = $AgNO_3$.

C = **Various salts**

Values of moles NH_3 per l of saturated solution for $N_C = 1$, at $t = 60$°C and $p_A = 61.1$ mm (80.5).

C		C	
$\frac{1}{2}CaCl_2$	1.171	HCOONa	0.905
$\frac{1}{2}SrCl_2$	1.071	CH_3COONa	0.879
$\frac{1}{2}BaCl_2$	0.998	KOH	0.787
$\frac{1}{2}(HCOO)_2Ba$	0.856	KCl	0.917
$\frac{1}{2}(CH_3COO)_2Ba$	0.777	$\frac{1}{2}K_2CO_3$	0.807
NaOH	0.826	CH_3COOK	0.836
NaCl	0.963	$\frac{1}{2}(COOK)_2$	0.842
$\frac{1}{2}Na_2CO_3$	0.841		

C = NH_4NO_3

Up to $N_A = 0.8$, p_A/N_A at 25°C is the same as in pure water, for $N_C = 0.15$ (146).

NH_3 : B = H_2O.—(*Continued*)

Values of moles NH_3 per l of saturated solution, at 25°C; p_A = 13.45 mm Hg (1, 121)

C \ N_C	0.5	1.0	1.5
LiOH	0.863	0.808	0.768
LiCl	0.980	1.008	1.045
LiBr	1.001	1.040	1.090
LiI	1.030	1.094	1.190
NaOH	0.876	0.789	0.716
NaCl	0.938	0.889	0.843
NaBr	0.965	0.916	0.890
NaI	0.995	0.992	0.985
Na_2S	0.887	0.795	0.726
KOH	0.852	0.716	0.607
KF	0.839	0.722	0.626
KCl	0.930	0.866	0.809
$KClO_3$	0.927*		
KBr	0.950	0.904	0.857
$KBrO_3$	0.940*		
KI	0.970	0.942	0.900
KIO_3	0.951*		
K_2SO_4	0.875	0.772	0.678
KNO_2	0.920	0.855	0.798
KNO_3	0.923	0.862	0.804
K_2HPO_4	0.860	0.749	0.664
K_2CO_3	0.778	0.650	0.554
$K_2C_2O_4$	0.866	0.771	0.675
HCOOK	0.868	0.760	0.678
CH_3COOK	0.866	0.765	0.685
KCN	0.926	0.858	0.802
KCNS	0.932	0.868	0.814
K_2CrO_4	0.866	0.771	0.675
KBO_2	0.814	0.677	0.560

* N_C = 0.25.

t = 35°C, p = 22.1 mm, N_C = 0.5

C		C	
NaOH	0.896	KCl	0.923
NaCl	0.966	½K_2CO_3	0.914*
½Na_2CO_3	0.932*	½$(COOK)_2$	0.902
KOH	0.870	CH_3COOK	0.902

* N_C = 0.426.

C = **C_6H_6O,** Phenol

t = 25°C (15)

N'_A	N'_C	p_A(mm)	N'_A	N'_C	p_A(mm)
1.008	0.000	13.56	0.900	1.33	6.49
0.988	0.245	11.47	0.493	0.260	4.99
0.969	0.492	9.91	0.480	0.516	4.08
0.929	0.980	7.90	0.246	0.260	2.08
0.925	1.03	7.76	0.917	1.024	5.01*
0.917	1.024	7.35			

* t = 18°C.

NO

B = H_2O

C = H_2SO_4 (138)

M_C	10.0	15.0	25.0	40.0	91.8
d_{15}^{15}	1.394	1.498	1.6275	1.729	1.820
$10^3\alpha_{18}$	11.2	11.0	10.6	10.95	18.1

N_2O

B = H_2O

AQUEOUS SOLUTIONS OF ACIDS

Values of $10^3\alpha_{25}$ (102)

C	M_C	d_4^{25}	$10^3\alpha_{25}$	C	M_C	d_4^{25}	$10^3\alpha_{25}$
HNO_3	1.139	1.0351	541	HIO_4	2.616	1.4066	238
HNO_3	2.428	1.0731	551	H_2SO_4	1.181	1.0680	442
HNO_3	4.091	1.1191	562	H_2SO_4	3.079	1.1630	387
HCl	1.105	1.0168	512	H_2SO_4	5.684	1.2687	382
HCl	2.217	1.0335	501	H_2SO_4	8.02	1.3363	399
HCl	5.049	1.0741	499	H_3PO_4	1.239	1.0593	464
HCl	7.49	1.1050	521	H_3PO_4	2.088	1.0964	438
HIO_4	1.097	1.1740	387	H_3PO_4	6.640	1.2557	353

C = **HCl** (45)

N_C	0.500	1.000	2.000
$10^3\alpha_{15}$	716	700	679
$10^3\alpha_{25}$	529	520	510

C = **H_2SO_4** (45)

N_C	0.500	1.000	2.000	3.000	4.000
$10^3\alpha_{15}$	696	663	611	571	533
$10^3\alpha_{25}$	519	497	466	442	424

C = **HNO_3** (45)

N_C	0.580	1.000	2.001
$10^3\alpha_{15}$	737	737	735
$10^3\alpha_{25}$	547	552	560

C = **H_3PO_4**

Values of $10^3\alpha_t$ (124)

°C \ M_C	0.357	0.505	0.989	1.119	1.571
5	1057	1036	988	964	917
10	883	866	830	810	771
15	739	726	698	683	650
20	625	615	593	581	556
25	543	533	514	505	486

C = **$C_2H_2O_4$,** Oxalic acid

Values of $10^3\alpha_t$ (124)

°C	5	10	15	20	25
M_C = 0.0909	1145	953	794	669	578
M_C = 0.427	1109	926	774	654	564

C = **$C_3H_6O_2$,** Propionic acid (75)

N_C	0.2046	0.816	2.139	2.385	4.646
$10^3\alpha_{20}$	632	637	650	653	722

AQUEOUS SOLUTIONS OF BASES

C = **NaOH** (143)

N_C	0.0	1.018	2.544	5.088	10.18
$10^3\alpha_0$	1140	823	434.5	185.0	115.7
$10^3\alpha_{10}$	868	600	302.9	103.8	62.8
$10^3\alpha_{20}$	641	438.0	253.3	78.2	78.2

C = **KOH** (143)

N_C	0.0	0.713	1.782	3.565	7.130
$10^3\alpha_0$	1140	921	666	348.5	157.2
$10^3\alpha_{10}$	868	694	531	274.7	120.1
$10^3\alpha_{20}$	641	538	419	251.6	251.6

AQUEOUS SALT SOLUTIONS
Values of $10^3\alpha_{25}$ (102)

C	M_C	d_4^{25}	$10^3\alpha_{25}$
NH_4NO_3	0.933	1.0249	498
NH_4NO_3	2.045	1.0527	464
NH_4NO_3	4.463	1.1040	409
NH_4NO_3	11.95	1.2116	308
NH_4Cl	1.118	1.0146	466
NH_4Cl	2.470	1.0312	411
NH_4Cl	5.185	1.0594	347
NH_4Br	1.093	1.0535	474
NH_4Br	2.341	1.1088	423
NH_4Br	5.161	1.2122	358
$(NH_4)_2SO_4$	1.476	1.0896	271
$(NH_4)_2SO_4$	2.561	1.1393	175
$ZnSO_4$	0.963	1.1403	299
$ZnSO_4$	1.891	1.2699	169
$Zn(NO_3)_2$	0.872	1.1223	397
$Zn(NO_3)_2$	1.816	1.2433	291
$Cd(NO_3)_2$	0.8145	1.1435	350
$Cd(NO_3)_2$	1.701	1.2874	270
$Cu(NO_3)_2$	0.709	1.1028	356
$Cu(NO_3)_2$	1.459	1.2049	278
$MnSO_4$	0.9585	1.1226	306
$MnSO_4$	2.022	1.2460	170
$FeSO_4$	0.726	1.1017	340
$FeSO_4$	1.463	1.2011	216
$Fe_2(SO_4)_3$	0.687	1.2240	259
$Fe_2(SO_4)_3$	1.460	1.4319	131
$CoSO_4$	0.795	1.1131	275
$CoSO_4$	1.612	1.2218	171
$NiSO_4$	0.946	1.1355	246
$NiSO_4$	1.924	1.2642	138
$Cr_2(SO_4)_3$	0.605	1.1657	318
$Cr_2(SO_4)_3$	1.294	1.3280	182
$Al_2(SO_4)_3$	0.528	1.1558	224
$Al_2(SO_4)_3$	0.849	1.2381	134
$Al(NO_3)_3$	0.495	1.0703	361
$Al(NO_3)_3$	1.0235	1.1414	293
$MgSO_4$	0.908	1.0992	295
$MgSO_4$	1.820	1.1925	159
$Mg(NO_3)_2$	1.0215	1.0935	392
$Mg(NO_3)_2$	2.1485	1.1846	285
$CaCl_2$	0.9535	1.0786	339
$CaCl_2$	2.104	1.1665	202
$Ca(NO_3)_2$	1.474	1.1503	322
$Ca(NO_3)_2$	3.232	1.2927	194
$BaCl_2$	0.633	1.1090	374
$BaCl_2$	1.374	1.2290	261
NaCl	1.178	1.0438	390
NaCl	2.426	1.0874	285
NaCl	4.761	1.1600	172
NaBr	1.161	1.0849	401
NaBr	2.306	1.1645	309
NaBr	5.098	1.3338	178
Na_2SO_4	0.470	1.0550	365
Na_2SO_4	1.002	1.1141	248
$NaNO_3$	1.120	1.0560	423
$NaNO_3$	1.370	1.0677	403
$NaNO_3$	2.334	1.1141	335
$NaNO_3$	3.350	1.1543	277
$NaNO_3$	4 894	1.2152	216
Na_3PO_4	0.220	1.0348	407
Na_2HPO_4	0.402	1.0470	376
KCl	0.800	1.0334	453
KCl	1.301	1.0540	410
KCl	2.112	1.0850	355
KCl	3.570	1.1385	281
KCl	4.632	1.1734	240
KBr	1.160	1.0891	430
KBr	2.339	1.1752	351
KBr	4.992	1.3380	247
KIO_4	0.0164	1.0008	521
K_2SO_4	0.6165	1.0762	355
KNO_3	1.0675	1.0586	448
KNO_3	2.374	1.1231	383

Values of $10^3\alpha_t$ (48)

C	N_C \ °C	5	10	15	20
$MgSO_4$	1.042	766	664	561	471
$MgSO_4$	1.374	708	586	488	414
$MgSO_4$	1.994	569	491	417	346
$CaCl_2$	1.094	819	697	591	500
$CaCl_2$	1.928	668	586	509	435
$CaCl_2$	2.832	510	441	380	328
$SrCl_2$	0.430	928	788	671	578
$SrCl_2$	0.760	848	709	610	550
$SrCl_2$	1.978	644	547	463	390
LiCl	0.319	986	831	700	594
LiCl	0.928	878	743	629	536
LiCl	2.883	606	512	437	382
Li_2SO_4	0.438	934	792	670	569
Li_2SO_4	1.042	795	665	557	474
Li_2SO_4	1.672	646	555	477	415
NaCl	1.107	800	682	585	509
NaCl	1.614	713	603	510	434
NaCl	2.391	634	532	449	386
Na_2SO_4	0.854	808	677	584	495
Na_2SO_4	1.292	692	574	482	416
Na_2SO_4	1.948	559	486	417	354
KCl	0.676	879	751	643	555
KCl	1.037	799	693	591	494
KCl	2.147	654	574	500	430
KCl	3.414	544	459	390	339
K_2SO_4	0.308	986	831	701	605
K_2SO_4	0.570	918	763	637	542

Values of $10^3\alpha_t$ (45)

C	N_C \ °C	15	25	C	N_C \ °C	15	25
NH_4Cl	0.5	692	510	KBr	0.5	661	491
NH_4Cl	1.0	655	485	KBr	1.0	594	444
LiCl	0.5	661	490	KI	0.5	665	496
LiCl	1.0	591	442	KI	1.0	600	451
KOH	0.5	633	471	RbCl	0.5	659	488
KOH	1.0	530	399	RbCl	1.0	592	442
KCl	0.5	650	483	CsCl	0.5	673	498
KCl	1.0	584	435				

C = **NaCl**
Values of $10^3\alpha_t$ (124)

M_C \ °C	5	10	15	20	25
0.1694	1061	881	734	619	536
0.3093	1003	838	703	596	519
0.665	913	770	650	552	478
1.003	843	709	598	509	442

C = $NaNO_3$

N_C	0.1336	0.3052	0.629	1.120	Lit.
$10^3\alpha_{20}$	609	588	546	493	(75)

N_2O : B = H_2O.—(*Continued*)
C = KNO_3

N_C	0.1061	0.2764	0.563	1.168	Lit.
$10^3\alpha_{20}$	617	600	571	520	(75)

Aqueous Solutions of Organic Compounds

C = $C_3H_8O_3$, Glycerol
Values of $10^3\alpha_t$ (124)

°C \ M_C	0.389	0.784	1.498	2.106
5	1097	1055	999	959
10	917	887	841	810
15	767	745	710	686
20	647	630	605	585
25	556	542	527	508

Values of $10^3\alpha_t$ (57)

M_C	$10^3\alpha_{15}$	M_C	$10^3\alpha_{20}$	M_C	$10^3\alpha_{20}$
0.0	733	0.0	630	1.6	549
0.2	722	0.2	619	1.8	541
0.4	711	0.4	608	2.0	533
0.6	700	0.6	598	2.2	527
0.8	690	0.8	588	2.4	522
1.0	680	1.0	577	2.6	517
1.2	669	1.2	567	2.8	512
1.4	659	1.4	558	3.0	508
1.6	649				
1.8	640				
2.0	632				
2.2	625				

C = CH_4N_2O, Urea
Values of $10^3\alpha_t$ (124)

°C \ M_C	0.570	0.871	1.133	1.312	1.844
5	1104	1096	1088	1101	1069
10	921	920	909	921	901
15	771	773	761	772	761
20	653	656	644	655	651
25	569	567	559	570	569

M_C	1.0155	2.139	4.955	7.995	Lit.
d_4^{25}	1.0134	1.0287	1.0619	1.0905	(102)
$10^3\alpha_{25}$	510	492	463	445	

CO

B = H_2O
C = H_2SO_4 (19)

x_C	0.0	0.1	0.25	0.6	0.8
$10^3\alpha_{20}$	23.13	10.23	9.22	16.1	20.92

C = **Cuprous ammonium carbonate and formate**

Moles per liter: Cu, 0.84; HCOOH, 3.04; NH_3, 6.52. Values of p_{CO} (mm Hg) and of v = volumes of CO at S. T. P. dissolved by 1 vol. of solution (83)

p_{CO}, 0°	v, 0°	p_{CO}, 20°	v, 20°	p_{CO}, 40°	v, 40°
12	4.59	62	3.85	64	1.17
33	8.29	141	6.67	128	1.91
73	11.56	239	9.08	p_{CO}, 60°	v, 60°
166	14.20	369	11.10	185	0.90
				331	1.49

The authors state that the results of this experiment are typical of all the experiments. For details of the solubilities in solutions of other compositions, the original paper must be consulted. In general the solubility is proportional to the cuprous copper concentration, increases with increase in free NH_3 and is not greatly dependent on total carbonate or formate. At the higher temperatures the solubility approaches simple solution and approximates to Henry's Law.

B = **$CHCl_3$**, Chloroform
C = **CH_4O**, Methyl alcohol

x_C	0.0	0.4	1.0	Lit.
$10^3\alpha_{25}$	190	184.8	180	(131)

B = CS_2, Carbon disulfide
C = $C_2H_4Cl_2$, Ethylene chloride

x_C	0.0	0.2	0.5	0.8	1.0	Lit.
$10^3\alpha_{25}$	76	129.7	146.9	142.6	135	(131)

B = **CH_4O**, Methyl alcohol
C = $C_3H_8O_3$, Glycerol

x_C	0.0	0.3	0.5	0.7	1.0	Lit.
$10^3\alpha_{25}$	196	88.7	48.5	21.8	Very small	(131)

B = **$C_2H_4O_2$**, Acetic acid (131)
C = **$CHCl_3$**, Chloroform

x_B	0.7	0.0
$10^3\alpha_{25}$	180.8	189

C = **$C_6H_5NO_2$**, Nitrobenzene

x_B	0.9	0.7	0.0
$10^3\alpha_{25}$	145.3	122.3	85

C = **C_6H_6**, Benzene

x_B	0.75	0.40	0.20	0.00
$10^3\alpha_{25}$	181.3	181.1	172.2	159

C = **C_6H_7N**, Aniline

x_B	1.0	0.9	0.7	0.3	0.0
$10^3\alpha_{25}$	158	98	68	53	49

C = **C_7H_8**, Toluene

x_B	0.85	0.65	0.30	0.00
$10^3\alpha_{25}$	173	179.2	174.3	167

B = **C_3H_6O**, Acetone (131)
C = **$CHCl_3$**, Chloroform

x_B	0.8	0.4	0.0
$10^3\alpha_{25}$	206.7	193.5	190

C = **CS_2**, Carbon disulfide

x_B	0.85	0.60	0.30	0.20	0.00
$10^3\alpha_{25}$	215.8	209.5	166	137.3	76

C = **$C_6H_5NO_2$**, Nitrobenzene

x_B	0.9	0.7	0.6	0.0
$10^3\alpha_{25}$	193.6	151.8	136.2	85

C = **C_6H_7N**, Aniline

x_B	1.0	0.9	0.8	0.6	0.0
$10^3\alpha_{25}$	218	177.7	145.6	105.5	49

C = **$C_{10}H_8$**, Naphthalene

x_B	0.95	0.85
$10^3\alpha_{25}$	186	170

C = **$C_{10}H_8O$**, β-Naphthol

x_B	0.95	0.90	0.85
$10^3\alpha_{25}$	178.7	161.8	149.5

C = **$C_{14}H_{10}$**, Phenanthrene

x_B	0.95	0.90
$10^3\alpha_{25}$	185.8	166.2

B = C_6H_6 (131)

C = C_2H_6O, Ethyl alcohol

x_B	0.4	0.3	0.0
$10^3\alpha_{25}$	165	167.3	176

C = $C_6H_5NO_2$, Nitrobenzene

x_B	0.8	0.6	0.5	0.0
$10^3\alpha_{25}$	138.5	119.7	111.7	85

C = C_6H_7N, Aniline

x_B	0.9	0.8	0.7	0.5	0.2	0.0
$10^3\alpha_{25}$	143	127	113	88	60	49

C = $C_{10}H_8$, Naphthalene

x_C	1.0	0.9	0.8	0.7
$10^3\alpha_{25}$	174	146.6	134	121.3

C = $C_{10}H_8O$, α-Naphthol

x_B	0.98	0.93
$10^3\alpha_{25}$	136.5	126.8

C = $C_{10}H_8O$, β-Naphthol

x_B	0.99	0.97
$10^3\alpha_{25}$	147	133

C = $C_{14}H_{10}$, Phenanthrene

x_B	0.95	0.85
$10^3\alpha_{25}$	131.8	115

B = C_7H_8, Toluene (131)

C = $C_6H_5NO_2$, Nitrobenzene

x_B	1.00	0.85	0.60	0.30	0.00
$10^3\alpha_{25}$	167	146	121	99.6	85

C = C_6H_7N, Aniline

x_B	1.0	0.9	0.8	0.6	0.4	0.2	0.0
$10^3\alpha_{25}$	167	145	134	112	91	70	49

C = $C_{10}H_8$, Naphthalene

x_B	1.0	0.95	0.90	0.85	0.80
$10^3\alpha_{25}$	167	158	150	142	134

C = $C_{10}H_8O$, α-Naphthol

x_B	1.0	0.97	0.94
$10^3\alpha_{25}$	167	156.5	147

C = $C_{14}H_{10}$, Phenanthrene

x_B	1.00	0.97	0.94	0.87
$10^3\alpha_{25}$	167	156	147.5	134

CO_2

B = H_2O

Aqueous Solutions of Electrolytes

For pure H_2O α_{15} = 1.014, α_{25} = 0.7563

C \ N_C	0.5	1.0	2.0	0.5	1.0	2.0
	$10^3\alpha_{15}$ (45)			$10^3\alpha_{25}$ (45)		
HCl	989	974	948	738	732	728
½H_2SO_4	965	927	869	727	705	669
HNO_3	1022	1029	1043	770	781	803
KCl	925	850		695	641	
KBr	935	866		704	653	
KI	940	875		710	666	
KNO_3	953	897		718	684	
RbCl	938	873		705	658	
CsCl	954			716		

C \ N_C	$10^3\alpha_{15}$ 3.0	$10^3\alpha_{15}$ 4.0	$10^3\alpha_{25}$ 3.0	$10^3\alpha_{25}$ 4.0	Lit.
½H_2SO_4	825	785	639	611	(45)

C = H_2SO_4

x_C	0.0	0.093	0.2	0.3	0.6	0.8	Lit.
$10^3\alpha_{20}$	901	608	656	701	835	923	(19)

N_C	0.0	35.8	Lit.
$10^3\alpha_{20.2}$	873	926	(11)

C = NH_4Cl

N_C	0.0	0.5	1.0	1.5	2.0	3.2	Lit.
d		1.006	1.014	1.021	1.029	1.045	(36)
$10^3\alpha_{25}$	756	720	692	668	648	609	

C = $Fe(NH_4)_2(SO_4)_2$

N'_C	d	$10^3\alpha_{25}$
0.3	1.047	604
0.4	1.062	560
0.8	1.125	419
Lit.	(36)	

C = $BaCl_2$ (36)

N_C	d	$10^3\alpha_{25}$
0.2	1.013	732
0.6	1.043	678
0.8	1.058	646
1.0	1.073	612

C = NaCl

Values of $10^3\alpha_t$ (10)

°C \ M_C	1.195	3.659	°C \ M_C	1.195	3.659
0	1234	678	35	462	288
5	1024	577	40	415	263
10	875	503	45	378	239
15	755	442	50	350	221
20	664	393	55	328	204
25	583	352	60	310	190
30	517	319			

C = KCl

N_C	0.0	0.3	0.5	0.8	1.0	Lit.
d		1.011	1.021	1.035	1.044	(36)
$10^3\alpha_{25}$	756	719	695	662	642	

Aqueous Solutions of Organic Compounds

Values of $10^3\alpha_{20}$ for N_C = 0.5 (142)

C	d_{20}^{20}	$10^3\alpha_{20}$	C	d_{20}^{20}	$10^3\alpha_{20}$
Dextrose	1.0328	792	Urethane	1.0037	869
Mannitol	1.03031	782	Urea	1.00715	864
Glycocoll	1.01413	843	Thiourea	1.00917	859
Pyrogallol	1.01718	853	Antipyrine	1.01339	859
Hydroquinol	1.00946	887	Acetamide	1.0005	879
Resorcinol	1.00958	901	Acetic acid	1.0026	868
Pyrocatechol	1.0107	868	n-Propyl alcohol	0.9939	869

C = C_2H_6O, Ethyl alcohol

x_C	d_4^{20} (112.5)	α_{20} (109)	x_C	d_4^{20} (112.5)	α_{20} (109)
0.00	0.998	0.88	0.50	0.8635	1.50
0.05	0.982	0.84	0.70	0.829	1.99
0.10	0.966	0.808	0.99	0.791	2.71
0.14	0.9545	0.793	N'_C	d_{15}^{25}	α_{20} (35)
0.20	0.937	0.843	0.7	0.9926	0.7435
0.25	0.923	0.935	1.9	0.98355	0.7202
0.30	0.910	1.044			

C = $C_3H_8O_3$, Glycerol (53)

M_C	0.0	1.0	2.5	4.5	7.0	10.0
$10^3\alpha_{15}$	1008	934	847	758	676	608
M_C	16.0	25.0	42.0	98.0	205.0	∞ (pure glyc.)
$10^3\alpha_{15}$	528	467	426	414	413	411

CO_2: B = H_2O.—(*Continued*)

C = $C_2H_3Cl_3O_2$, Chloral hydrate(53)

M_C	$10^3\alpha_{15}$	M_C	$10^3\alpha_{15}$	M_C	$10^3\alpha_{15}$
0.0	100_8	4.0	77_6	12.0	78_9
1.0	90_4	7.0	76_5	14.0	80_4
2.0	84_1	8.0	76_8	24.0	90_8
3.0	79_7	9.0	77_3		

N'_C	d	$10^3\alpha_{25}$	Lit.
0.3	1.018_5	$747._5$	(36)
0.6	1.040_1	$728._7$	

C = C_6H_7N, Aniline

N'_C	0.02	0.04	0.06	0.08	Lit.
$10^3\alpha_{25}$	783	818	849	864	(31)

C = $C_{12}H_{22}O_{11}$, Sucrose

N'_C	d_{20}^{20}	$10^3\alpha_{20}$	N'_C	d	$10^3\alpha_{25}$ (36)
0.1250	1.0151_8	846	0.0		$756._3$
0.2500	1.0312_5	815	0.05	1.005_7	749
0.500	1.0637_2	756	0.10	1.011_7	741
1.000	1.1280_9	649	0.15	1.017_9	732
Lit.	(142)		0.25	1.032_6	711
			0.30	1.040_9	$698._6$
			0.35	1.049_3	685

CH_4

B = H_2O

C = H_2SO_4 (19)

M_C	0.0	5.70	16.40	221.0
$10^3\alpha_{20}$	35.0_0	16.9_0	13.1_2	30.7_6

C_2H_2(102)

B = H_2O

C	M_C	d_4^{25}	$10^3\alpha_{25}$
NH_4Cl	1.137	1.0141	827
NH_4Cl	2.381	1.0294	747
NH_4Cl	5.254	1.0600	643
NH_4Br	1.125	1.0540	844
NH_4Br	2.372	1.1100	788
NH_4Br	5.323	1.2215	686
$(NH_4)_2SO_4$	1.511	1.0911	524
$(NH_4)_2SO_4$	2.727	1.1501	363
$ZnSO_4$	0.926	1.1359	549
$ZnSO_4$	1.884	1.2666	319
$Zn(NO_3)_2$	0.860	1.1210	745
$Zn(NO_3)_2$	1.789	1.2406	597
$MnSO_4$	1.000	1.1283	548
$MnSO_4$	2.053	1.2507	314
$FeCl_3$	0.855	1.1030	630
$FeCl_3$	1.402	1.1638	516
$FeSO_4$	0.726	1.1017	616
$FeSO_4$	1.463	1.2011	411
$Fe_2(SO_4)_3$	0.687	1.2240	458
$Fe_2(SO_4)_3$	1.460	1.4319	227
$CoSO_4$	0.805	1.1139	588
$CoSO_4$	1.632	1.2238	371
$NiSO_4$	0.741	1.1096	599
$NiSO_4$	1.495	1.2156	380
$Cr_2(SO_4)_3$	0.605	1.1657	567
$Cr_2(SO_4)_3$	1.294	1.3280	324
$AlCl_3$	0.633	1.0672	623
$AlCl_3$	1.107	1.1150	471
$Al_2(SO_4)_3$	0.528	1.1558	416
$Al_2(SO_4)_3$	0.849	1.2381	254
$Al(NO_3)_3$	0.577	1.0822	755
$Al(NO_3)_3$	1.095_5	1.1502	629
$MgCl_2$	1.132	1.0802	584
$MgCl_2$	2.246	1.1501	397
$MgSO_4$	0.904	1.0999	548
$MgSO_4$	1.832	1.1944	311
$Mg(NO_3)_2$	0.999	1.0916	743
$Mg(NO_3)_2$	2.110_5	1.1821	598
$CaCl_2$	0.979	1.0806	606
$CaCl_2$	2.170_5	1.1675	391
$Ca(NO_3)_2$	1.474	1.1503	648
$Ca(NO_3)_2$	3.232	1.2927	441
$BaCl_2$	0.645	1.1085	675
$BaCl_2$	1.376	1.2266	491
NaCl	1.147	1.0420	706
NaCl	2.372	1.0850	541
NaCl	5.012	1.1660	320
NaBr	1.157_5	1.0829	727
NaBr	2.392_5	1.1668	579
NaBr	5.152	1.3307	361
Na_2SO_4	0.4734	1.0538	670
Na_2SO_4	0.992_5	1.1111	476
$NaNO_3$	1.120_5	1.0556	785
$NaNO_3$	2.330	1.1106	667
$NaNO_3$	5.072	1.2189	490
KCl	1.956	1.0807	653
KCl	4.176	1.1588	481
KBr	1.139	1.0866	779
KBr	2.381	1.1750	655
KBr	5.272	1.3459	478
K_2SO_4	0.611	1.0753	649
KNO_3	1.129	1.0618	824
KNO_3	2.376	1.1232	737

Values of α_{15} (= 1.186 for pure H_2O) (7)

C \ N_C	0.01	0.025	0.05	0.10	0.15
$\frac{1}{2}H_2SO_4$				1.128	
NH_4OH	1.153			1.155	
$\frac{1}{2}Ca(OH)_2$	1.166				
$\frac{1}{2}Ba(OH)_2$		1.155		1.166	1.175
NaOH	1.147		1.138	1.119	
$\frac{1}{2}Na_2SO_4$				1.109	
KOH	1.149			1.123	

C \ N_C	0.25	0.50	1.00	2.00	3.00
$\frac{1}{2}H_2SO_4$		1.062	0.986	0.853	0.739
NH_4OH	1.156	1.161	1.166	1.171	1.175
NaOH	1.069	0.986	0.839	0.569	0.351
$\frac{1}{2}Na_2SO_4$	1.012	0.891	0.683	0.322	
KOH	1.071	1.001	0.865	0.626	0.436

C_2H_4

B = H_2O

Values of $10^3\alpha_{15}$ (= 151 for pure H_2O) (7)

C \ N_C	0.1	0.25	0.50	0.75	1.0
NH_4OH		149	148	147	146
$\frac{1}{2}Na_2SO_4$	145	135	120	103	88
NaOH	145	137	121	108	96
KOH	146	137	123	112	100

CH_3Cl

Methyl chloride
B = H_2O
C = HCl
Values of α_t (115)

°C \ N_C	0.0	1.0	2.0	6.0	12.0
20	2.86	2.44	2.60	2.44	2.39
30	1.95	1.68	1.97	1.87	1.17
40	1.40	1.26	1.55	1.40	0.19*
50	1.05	0.96	1.20	1.00	
60	0.76	0.75	0.94	0.72	
70	0.61	0.61	0.78	0.53	
80	0.52	0.56	0.67	0.43	

* 38.5°C.

SOLUBILITY OF GASES IN COLLOIDAL SOLUTIONS IN WATER

Some typical examples: B = H_2O in all cases

Rn, Radon

C = SiO_2-hydrosol (30)

At N'_C = 0.29, α_{17} = 0.242 to 0.280.

H_2

C = Gelatin* (36)

g C/l	0.0	10.0	30.0	50.0	60.0
d_4^{25}		1.000	1.006	1.012	1.016
$10^3\alpha_{25}$	18.0	17.77	17.3	16.8	16.56

* The average deviation from Henry's law is about 0.8 % from p = 750 to 1400 mm.

C = Starch* (36)

g C/l	0.0	20.0	50.0	90.0
d_4^{25}		1.005	1.017	1.031
$10^3\alpha_{25}$	18.0	17.7	17.2	16.6

C = Dextrin* (36)

g C/l	0.0	40.0	60.0	80.0	190.0
d_4^{25}		1.012	1.0205	1.0276	1.065
$10^3\alpha_{25}$	18.0	17.7	17.5	17.3	15.93

* Henry's law holds from p = 700 to 1400 mm.

CO_2

C = Gelatin

26.0 g C/l; d = 1.006 (37)

p(mm)	250	400	500	650	750
λ_{25}	0.857	0.843	0.836	0.831	0.833

49.0 g C/l; d = 1.012 (37)

p(mm)	250	450	650	750
λ_{25}	0.871	0.848	0.839	0.838

10.6 g C/l; d = 0.999 (31)

λ_{25} = 0.815 between p = 740 and 1370 mm

16.8 g C/l; d = 1.000 (31)

$_{25}$ = 0.817 ± 0.001 between p = 740 and 1325 mm.

33.6 g C/l; d = 1.003 (31)

λ_{25} = 0.826 at p = 740; λ = 0.819 ± 0.001 between p = 825 and 1390 mm.

60.9 g C/l; d = 1.008 (31)

p(mm)	750	850	950	1050	1200	1400
λ_{25}	0.8345	0.8265	0.824	0.8242	0.825	0.826

C = Starch

46.0 g C/l; d = 1.018 (37)*

λ_{25} = 0.787 ± 0.002 between p = 260 and 735 mm.

51.0 g C/l; d = 1.021 (37)*

λ_{25} = 0.783 between p = 265 and 738 mm

91.3 g C/l; d = 1.035 (37)*

p(mm)	250	400	500	650	750
λ_{25}	0.751	0.754	0.756	0.759	0.761

* The authors state that the solubility is not affected by changes in the method of preparation of the starch; v. (34).

25.0 g C/l; d = 1.009 (31)

p(mm)	750	850	950	1050	1200	1350
λ_{25}	0.796	0.7975	0.799	0.801	0.804	0.8065

50.0 g C/l; d = 1.016 (31)

p(mm)	750	850	1000	1200	1300
λ_{25}	0.778	0.7803	0.7837	0.788	0.7903

75.0 g C/l; d = 1.023 (31)

p(mm)	750	850	1000	1100	1200	1350
λ_{25}	0.762	0.764	0.7673	0.7694	0.7715	0.7747

100 g C/l; d = 1.030 (31)

p(mm)	760	900	1000	1100	1200	1350
λ_{25}	0.750	0.753	0.755	0.757	0.759	0.762

C = Dextrin

50.0 g C/l; d = 1.018 (37)

p(mm)	250	400	500	600	700	750
λ_{25}	0.816	0.807	0.803	0.801	0.800	0.799

194.0 g C/l; d = 1.065 (37)

p(mm)	250	400	500	700	750
λ_{25}	0.743	0.730	0.726	0.721	0.722

35.0 g C/l; d = 1.008 (31)

λ_{25} = 0.800 ± 0.001 between p = 750 and 1260 mm.

56.0 g C/l; d = 1.015 (31)

p(mm)	750	850	1000	1100	1250
λ_{25}	0.785	0.785	0.786	0.7876	0.791

95.0 g C/l; d = 1.034 (31)

p(mm)	750	850	950	1100	1300
λ_{25}	0.761	0.758	0.759	0.762	0.7685

130.0 g C/l; d = 1.040 (31)

p(mm)	750	800	900	1000	1150	1250
λ_{25}	0.744	0.741	0.743	0.746	0.749	0.751

189.0 g C/l; d=1.064 (31)

p(mm)	750	850	950	1050	1200	1350
λ_{25}	0.7146	0.710	0.7134	0.7163	0.7207	0.7252

206.0 g C/l; d = 1.069 (31)

p(mm)	750	850	900	1000	1150	1350
λ_{25}	0.7017	0.6972	0.6979	0.699	0.701	0.704

C = Egg Albumen (37)

1.05 g C/l; d = 0.992

p(mm)	268	389	484	770
λ_{25}	0.826	0.816	0.819	0.819

2.1 g C/l; d = 0.995

p(mm)	269	387	483	664	772
λ_{25}	0.844	0.827	0.823	0.826	0.824

C = Serum Albumin (31)

4.4 g C/l; d = 0.998

p(mm)	750	850	950	1100	1250	1400
λ_{25}	0.804	0.801	0.802	0.8045	0.806	0.806

12.9 g C/l; d = 1.000

p(mm)	750	850	950	1050	1250	1430
λ_{25}	0.7786	0.7746	0.779	0.783	0.789	0.792

CO_2.—(*Continued*)

C = **Glycogen** (31)

3.4 g C/l; d = 0.998

p(mm)	750	850	950	1150	1400
λ_{25}	0.820	0.806	0.810	0.810	0.810

6.8 g C/l; d = 1.000

p(mm)	750	850	950	1100	1400
λ_{25}	0.817	0.804_5	0.807	0.807	0.807

C = **Peptone** (36)*

g C/l	0.0	10.0	20.0	30.0
d		0.999_7	1.003	1.006_8
α_{25}	0.756	0.78_7	0.81_0	0.83_1

* The average deviation from Henry's law from p = 750 to 1360 mm is about 1 %.

C = **Propeptone** (36)*

g C/l	0.0	3.0	8.0
d		0.998	1.000
α_{25}	0.756	0.76_4	0.77_3

* The average deviation from Henry's law from p = 740 to 1360 mm is about 0.4 %.

C = **Hemoglobin** (36)*

g C/l	0.0	2.0	5.0	8.0
d		0.998	0.999_1	1.000_1
α_{25}	0.756	0.76_2	0.78_0	0.80_6

* The average deviation from Henry's law from p = 730 to 1340 mm is about 0.8 %.

C = As_2S_3 (31)

3.92 g C/l; d = 0.997

p(mm)	750	950	1050	1150	1250
λ_{25}	0.816	0.814	0.816	0.817_7	0.819_8

14.10 g C/l; d = 1.003

λ_{25} = 0.811 ± 0.001 between p = 750 and 1280 mm.

22.89 g C/l; d = 1.007

λ_{25} = 0.806 between p = 750 and 1210 mm.

C = **Bone Charcoal** (31)

2.36 g C/l; d = 1.000

p(mm)	750	800	900	1050	1150	1250	1372
λ_{25}	0.815_6	0.821	0.842	0.885	0.914	0.940	(0.950)

C = **Silicic acid**

2.53 g SiO_2/l; d = 1.000* (31)

p(mm)	750	850	950	1050	1200	1300	1400
λ_{25}	0.814	0.815_5	0.817	0.819	0.821_4	0.823	0.824_7

* Suspension of SiO_2 in water. According to Findlay and Williams (37) suspensions of SiO_2 give same values as pure water.

4.5 g SiO_2/l; d = 0.996 (37)

λ_{25} = 0.816 ± 0.001 between p = 267 and 762 mm

9.5 g SiO_2/l; d = 0.999 (37)

p(mm)	260	400	500	650	750
λ_{25}	0.83_7	0.82_4	0.82_0	0.81_6	0.82_2

12.5 g SiO_2/l; d = 1.000 (37)

p(mm)	265	400	500	650	750
λ_{25}	0.84_2	0.82_7	0.82_3	0.82_1	0.82_3

14.0 g SiO_2/l; d = 1.000 (31)

p(mm)	730	830	940	1355
λ_{25}	0.822	0.819	0.816	0.816

22.0 g SiO_2/l; d = 1.002 (31)

p(mm)	730	830	940	1335
λ_{25}	0.828	0.822	0.820	0.820

28.0 g SiO_2/l; d = 1.003 (31)

p(mm)	730	870	950	1330
λ_{25}	0.831	0.825	0.824	0.824

C = **$Fe(OH)_3$**

5.69 g C/l; d = 1.000 (31)

p(mm)	750	850	950	1050	1350
λ_{25}	0.848	0.843	0.841	0.842	0.845

6.3 g C/l; d = 1.003 (37)

p(mm)	250	350	450	600	750
λ_{25}	1.044	0.986	0.953	0.922	0.903

8.54 g C/l; d = 1.003 (31)

p(mm)	750	850	950	1050	1250	1350
λ_{25}	0.862	0.858	0.856	0.857	0.860	0.861_5

12.6 g C/l; d = 1.006 (37)

p(mm)	240	300	400	600	750
λ_{25}	1.272	1.188	1.119	1.024	0.987

12.77 g C/l; d = 1.005 (31)

p(mm)	750	850	1000	1100	1250
λ_{25}	0.886	0.881	0.87_7	0.878	0.886

16.61 g C/l; d = 1.009 (31)

p(mm)	750	850	1000	1150	1300
λ_{25}	0.904	0.901	0.900	0.900_5	0.903

C = **Methyl Orange** (36)*

g C/l	0.0	3.0	6.0	9.0
d		0.998	1.002	1.004
α_{25}	0.756	0.77_0	0.80_3	0.85_9

* The average deviation from Henry's law in these solutions is about 1.5 % from p = 730 to 1340 mm.

N_2O

NOTE.—The following solutions were freed from air by boiling under reduced pressure and where necessary were purified by dialysis. The maximum deviation in the values obtained from two series of experiments was usually ±0.002, although graphs of the results sometimes indicate a maximum error somewhat greater than this. The results confirm earlier data at higher pressures by Findlay and Creighton (31).

C = **Gelatin** (33)

14.5 g C/l; d = 1.000

p(mm)	260	370	550	600	750	1000
λ_{25}	0.583	0.580	0.576	0.575_6	0.576	0.581

31.2 g C/l; d = 1.004

p(mm)	250	350	550	650	750	1000
λ_{25}	0.577	0.573	0.568	0.569	0.571	0.576

61.0 g C/l; d = 1.008

p(mm)	260	350	550	650	750	1000
λ_{25}	0.557	0.554	0.548	0.547	0.548	0.556

C = **Soluble Starch** (33)

67.0 g C/l; d = 1.023

p(mm)	260	400	500	650	750	1000
λ_{25}	0.560_1	0.563	0.560_5	0.557	0.554_7	0.548_7

94.0 g C/l; d = 1.029

p(mm)	290	400	550	650	750	1000
λ_{25}	0.552	0.550	0.548	0.545	0.542_5	0.537

136.0 g C/l; d = 1.039

p(mm)	260	350	500	650	750	1000
λ_{25}	0.541_5	0.538_2	0.536	0.532_5	0.530_2	0.524_5

C = **Dextrin** (33)

68.2 g C/l; d = 1.019

p(mm)	280	400	600	700	800	1000
λ_{25}	0.557	0.550	0.541_8	0.542_3	0.545	0.555

124.1 g C/l; d = 1.037

p(mm)	280	400	600	700	800	1000
λ_{25}	0.537_3	0.532_1	0.526	0.525	0.526_2	0.535

192.4 g C/l; d = 1.060

p(mm)	280	400	600	700	800	1000
λ_{25}	0.515_9	0.510_2	0.503_6	0.501_0	0.500	0.506_2

C = **Egg Albumen** (33)

3.8 g C/l; d = 0.998

From p = 250 to 1000 mm, λ_{25} = 0.572 ± 0.0005

6.1 g C/l; d = 1.000

From p = 250 to 1000 mm, λ_{25} = 0.568 ± 0.001

C = **Carbon** (33)

30.0 g C/l

p(mm)	250	400	550	560	750	1000
λ_{25}	0.583	0.581	0.584	0.588	0.593	0.610

C = SiO_2 (33)

16.2 g C/l; d = 1.000

p(mm)	250	400	550	700	750	1030
λ_{25}	0.599	0.596	0.594	0.593	0.594	0.598

35.0 g C/l; d = 1.004

p(mm)	250	400	550	700	750	1030
λ_{25}	0.594	0.591	0.589	0.588	0.588	0.591

C = $Fe(OH)_3$ (33)

4.3 g C/l; d = 1.001

p(mm)	250	400	600	800	1000
λ_{25}	0.595	0.593	0.589_7	0.585_5	0.580

9.2 g C/l; d = 1.003

p(mm)	250	400	600	800	1000
λ_{25}	0.590	0.587	0.583_5	0.579_6	0.575

38.2 g C/l; d = 1.027

p(mm)	250	400	600	800	1000
λ_{25}	0.583	0.580_7	0.577_2	0.573	0.567

LITERATURE

(For a key to the periodicals see end of volume)

(1) Abegg and Riesenfeld, *7*, **40**: 84; 02. (2) Adeney and Becker, *3*, **38**: 317; 19. **39**: 385; 20. (3) Appell, *Chaleur et Industrie*, **2**: 345; 21. (4) Baly, *3*, **49**: 517; 00. (5) Berthelot, *34*, **91**: 191; 80. (6) Berthelot, *6*, **43**: 276; 55. (7) Billitzer, *7*, **40**: 535; 02. (8) Bohr, *Beitr. Physiol.* (Ludwig Festschrift), **1887**: 164. (9) Bohr, *8*, **62**: 644; 97.

(10) Bohr, *8*, **68**: 500; 99. (11) Bohr, *7*, **71**: 47; 10. (12) Boyle, *Bull. Macdonald Physics Bldg.*, **1**: 52; 10. *51*, **7**: 200; 10. (13) Boyle, *3*, **22**: 840; 11. (14) Braun, *7*, **33**: 721; 00. (15) Buch, *7*, **70**: 66; 10. (16) Buchanan, *5*, **22**: 192, 483; 74. (17) Chlopin, *Arch. Hygiene*, **27**: 18; 96. (18) Christoff, *7*, **53**: 321; 05. (19) Christoff, *7*, **55**: 622; 06.

(20) Clowes and Biggs, *54*, **23**: 358; 04. (21) Coppadoro, *36*, **39 II**: 616; 09. (22) Coste and Andrews, *50*, **28**: 285; 24. (23) Cupr, *70*, **44**: 476; 25. (24) Cupr, *Spisy Vydávané Přírodovedeckou Fakultou Masarykovy Univ.*, No. **68**: 5; 26. (25) Dawson and MacCrae, *4*, **77**: 1239; 00. **79**: 493; 01. (26) Delépine, *49*, **25**: 496; 92. (27) Dittmar, *B81*, **1**: 172; 84. (28) Drucker and Moles, *7*, **75**: 405; 10. (29) Dunn, *135*, **45**: 270; 82.

(30) Ebler and Fellner, *93*, **73**: 1; 12. (31) Findlay and Creighton, *4*, **97**: 536; 10. (32) Findlay and Harby, *55*, **3**: 169; 08. (33) Findlay and Howell, *4*, **105**: 291; 14. (34) Findlay and Howell, *4*, **107**: 282; 15. (35) Findlay and Shen, *4*, **99**: 1313; 11. (36) Findlay and Shen, *4*, **101**: 1459; 12. (37) Findlay and Williams, *4*, **103**: 636; 13. (38) Foerster, Burchardt and Friche, *92*, **33**: 113, 122, 129; 20. (39) Fonda, *Diss.*, Karlsruhe, 1910.

(40) Foote, *1*, **43**: 1031; 21. (41) Fox, *7*, **41**: 458; 02. (42) Fox, *Intern. hydrograph. Ges., Publications de circonstance*, 41; 07. (43) Fox, *83*, **5**: 68; 09. (44) Gaus, *93*, **25**: 236; 00. (45) Geffcken, *7*, **49**: 257; 04. (46) Goldschmidt and Larsen, *7*, **71**: 437; 10. (47) Goodwin, *25*, **15**: 3039; 82. (48) Gordon, *7*, **18**: 1; 95. (49) Gréhaut, *34*, **118**: 594; 94.

(50) Hainsworth and Titus, *1*, **43**: 1; 21. (51) Hamberg, *Stockh., Ak. Handl. Bihang*, **10**: No. 13: 85. *52*, **33**: 433; 86. (52) Hamburger, *278*, **143**: 186; 11. (53) Hammel, *Diss.*, Münster, 1914. *7*, **90**: 121; 15. (54) Hantzsch and Sebaldt, *7*, **30**: 258; 99. (55) Hantzsch and Vagt, *7*, **38**: 705; 01. (56) Hempel, *92*, **14**: 865; 01. (57) Henkel, *Diss.*, Berlin, 1905. (58) Herz, *B13*: 190; 12. (59) Herz and Kurzer, *9*, **16**: 240, 869; 10.

(60) Hevesy, *63*, **12**: 1214; 11. *50*, **16**: 429; 12. (61) Hooker, *33*, **23**: 961; 20. (62) Hudson, *4*, **127**: 1332; 25. (63) Hüfner, *203*, **1895**: 209. (64) Hüfner, *7*, **57**: 611; 07. (65) Hüfner, *7*, **59**: 416; 07. (66) Hüfner and Külz, *52*, **28**: 256; 83. (67) Irk, *Magyar Chem. Folyóirat*, **13**: 92; 12. (68) Jakobsen, *Medd. Komm. Havundersög Ser. Hydrogr.*, **1**: 8; 05. (69) Jakovkin, *7*, **29**: 613; 99.

(70) Jolin, *203*, **1889**: 265. (71) Jones, *4*, **99**: 392; 11. (72) Jones, Lapworth and Lingford, *4*, **103**: 252; 13. (73) Just, *7*, **37**: 342; 01. (74) Kendall and Andrews, *1*, **43**: 1545; 21. (75) Knopp, *7*, **48**: 97; 04. (76) Kofler, *63*, **9**: 6; 08. (77) Kofler, *75*, **122 IIa**: 1473; 13. (78) Kohn and O'Brien, *54*, **17**: 1100; 98. (79) Kolb, *Bull. soc. ind. Mulhouse*, **42**: 209; 72. (79.5) Konovalov, *8*, **14**: 34; 81.

(80) Konovalov, *53*, **30**: 367; 98. (80.5) Konovalov, *53*, **31**: 910, 985; 99. (81) Kremann and Hönel, *57*, **34**: 1089; 13. (82) Kumpf, *Diss.*, Graz, 1881. (83) Larson and Teitsworth, *1*, **44**: 2878; 22. (84) Levi, *36*, **31 II**: 513; 01. (85) Lévy and Marboutin, *34*, **124**: 959; 97. (86) Lévy and Marboutin, *27*, **19**: 149; 98. (87) Lobry de Bruyn, *70*, **11**: 18; 92. (88) Lobry de Bruyn, *7*, **10**: 782; 92. *70*, **11**: 112; 92. (89) Locke and Forssall, *11*, **31**: 268; 04.

(90) Lubarsch, *Diss.*, Halle, 1886. (91) Lubarsch, *8*, **37**: 524; 89. (92) Lunge, *25*, **14**: 2188; 81. (93) Lunge, *25*, **18**: 1391; 85. (94) Lurié, *Diss.*, Grenoble, 1910. *10*, **2**: 401; 11. (95) MacArthur, *50*, **20**: 495; 16. (96) Mackenzie, *8*, **1**: 438; 77. (97) McLauchlan, *7*, **44**: 600; 03. (98) Maclaurin, *4*, **63**: 724; 93. (99) Mai, *25*, **41**: 3897; 08.

(100) Mailfert, *34*, **119**: 951; 94. (101) Manchot, *92*, **23**: 2113; 10. (102) Manchot, Jahrstorfer and Zepter, *93*, **141**: 45; 24. (103) Manchot and Zechentmayer, *13*, **350**: 368; 06. (104) Mellor, *4*, **79**: 216; 01. (105) Meslans, *6*, **1**: 346; 94. (106) Miles and Fenton, *4*, **117**: 59; 20. (107) Mitchell, *4*, **123**: 1887; 23. (108) Moissan, *6*, **19**: 266; 90. (109) Müller, *8*, **37**: 24; 89.

(110) Müller, *52*, **58**: 1; 98. (111) Müller, *7*, **81**: 483; 12. (112) Oliveri-Mandalà and Angenica, *36*, **50 I**: 273; 20. **50 II**: 89, 98; 20. (112.5) Osborne, McKelvy and Bearce, *31A*, **9**: 327; 13. (113) Pascal and Garnier, *27*, **25**: 309; 19. (114) Philip, *4*, **91**: 711; 07. *182*, **23**: 85; 07. (115) Plank, *Magyar Chem. Folyóirat*, **27**: 7; 21. (116) Pollitzer, *93*, **64**: 121; 09. (117) Porter, *J. Roy. Tech. Coll. Glasgow*, **2**: 19; 25. (118) Raoult, *6*, **1**: 262; 74. *34*, **77**: 1078; 73. (119) Raschig, *92*, **18**: 1281; 05.

(120) Rideal, *45*, **12**: 531; 20. (121) Riesenfeld, *7*, **45**: 461; 03. (122) Ritzel, *7*, **60**: 319; 07. (123) Roscoe, *13*, **95**: 357; 55. *4*, **8**: 14; 56. (124) Roth, *7*, **24**: 114; 97. (125) Rothmund, *B12*: 391; 12. (126) Ruppin, *92*, **38**: 117; 04. (127) Secenov, *278*, **8**: 1; 74. *7*, **4**: 117; 89. *Mém. Acad. Sci. St. Petersburg*, **22**: No. 6; 76. **26**: No. 13; 79. **34**: No. 3; 86. **35**: No. 7; 87. *Nouveaux Mém. Soc. Imp. Natur. Moscou*, **15**: 201; 98. (128) Secenov, *6*, **25**: 226; 92. (129) Siebeck, *Skand. Arch. Physiol.*, **21**: 368; 09.

(130) Sieverts and Bergner, *7*, **82**: 257; 13. (131) Skirrow, *7*, **41**: 139; 02. (132) Smith and Parkhurst, *1*, **44**: 1918; 22. (133) Stegmüller, *9*, **16**: 85; 10. (134) Steiner, *8*, **52**: 275; 94. (135) Stock, Böttcher and Lenger, *25*, **42**: 2853; 09. (135.5) Tammann, *93*, **158**: 25; 26. (136) Thomas, *34*, **123**: 943; 96. (137) Tornöe, *52*, **19**: 401; 79. **20**: 44; 79. *Den. Norske Nordhaus Expedition*, (1876–78) *Chemie*, 1880. (138) Tower, *93*, **50**: 382; 06. (139) Traubenberg, *63*, **5**: 130; 04.

(140) Tucker and Moody, *1*, **23**: 671; 01. (141) Usher, *7*, **62**: 622; 08. (142) Usher, *4*, **97**: 66; 10. (143) Viollier, *Thesis*, Geneva, 1913. (144) Weigert, *25*, **43**: 164; 10. (145) Whipple and Whipple, *1*, **33**: 362; 11. (146) de Wijs, *Thesis*, Delft, 1923. (147) Winkler, *136*, **23**: 454, 541; 99. **25**: 586; 01. (148) Winkler, *91*, **40**: 523; 01. (149) Winkler, *91*, **40**: 772; 01. **42**: 735; 03.

(150) Winkler, *92*, **24**: 341, 831; 11. (150.5) Winkler, *92*, **26**: 134; 13. (151) Winkler, *92*, **28**: 366; 15. (152) Wroblewski, *8*, **4**: 268; 78. **7**: 11; 79. **17**: 103; 82. **18**: 290; 83.

PARTIAL VAPOR PRESSURES FROM ALLOYS, AMALGAMS AND SOLUTIONS OF METALS IN LIQUID AMMONIA

J. Johnston

Hg

Fractional vapor pressure of mercury (p/p_o where p is pressure over the amalgam with the metal M, p_o the vapor pressure of Hg at the same temperature) in equilibrium with amalgams containing mercury at the mole fraction x.

M	°C	x (mole fraction Hg)									Lit.
		0.9	0.8	0.7	0.6	0.5	0.4	0.3	0.2	0.1	
Bi	320–2	0.931	0.872	0.796	0.710	0.614	0.509	0.394	0.271	0.140	(3)
Cd	322	.890	.765	.630	.487	.340	.213	.150	.085	.012	(8)
K	*ca.* 0	$.1_5$									(14)
Na	*ca.* 0	$.6_5$	$.1_5$	.02	10^{-3}	10^{-5}					(14)
Pb	324	.937	.895	.850	.780	.695	.587	.470	.327	.170	(8)
Sn	324	.944	.905	.856	.778	.688	.575	.448	.312	.162	(8)
Tl	324	.883	.764	.644	.535	.437	.341	.250	.165	.082	(7)
Zn	300	.913	.828	.750	.667	.577	.484				(6)

M	x (mole fraction Hg) t = *ca.* 357°C							Lit.
	0.99	0.98	0.97	0.96	0.94	0.92	0.90	
Ag	0.990	0.980	0.972	0.965	0.951			(1, 15)
Al	.993	.985						(15)
Au	.991	.983	.975	.969				(1, 15)
Ba	.982							(15)
Bi	.992	.984	.976	.969	.954	0.941	0.931	(1, 3, 15)
Ca	.988	.973	.955	.931	.865	0.70 for x = 0.86 (satd. soln.)		(1, 2, 15)
Cd	.990	.979	.968	.958	.936	.914	.890	(1, 8, 15)
Ga	.990	.980						(15)
K	.987	.969	.950					(1, 15)
Li	.990	.980						(15)
Mg	.988	.976	.964	.952	.928	0.39 for x = 0.64 (satd. soln.)		(1, 2, 15)
Mn	.987							(15)
Na	.989	.977	.962	.945	.907			(1, 15)
Pb	.991	.983	.976	.969	.957	.947	.937	(1, 8, 15)
Sb	.992	.984						(15)
Sn	.991	.983	.976	.970	.960	.951	.944	(1, 8, 15)
Tl	.990	.979	.969	.958	.935	.911	.883	(1, 7, 15)
Zn	.991	.981	.971	.962	.945	.928	.913	(1, 6, 15)

Zn

Fractional vapor pressure of zinc (p/p_o, where p is the pressure over the alloy, p_o that of pure zinc at the same temperature) in equilibrium with brasses containing zinc at the mole fraction x (4, 5, 10).

Temperature range	100x (mole % Zn)							
	45	40	35	30	25	20	15	10
900–1350°	0.32	0.27	0.21	0.15	0.10	0.06	0.03	0.02

NH_3

Relative vapor pressure of NH_3, p/p_o (where p is its vapor pressure over the solution designated, p_o that of pure liquid NH_3 at the same temperature) over solutions of metals in liquid NH_3. Solutions saturated with the metal M (*i.e.*, solid phase is pure M).

t, °C	30	20	10	±0	−10	−20	−30	Lit.
	$10^3\ p/p_o$ for saturated solutions							
Ca*	1.68	1.27	0.95	0.70	0.52	0.38	0.26	(11)
Li	1.94	1.53	1.25	1.03	0.89	0.78	0.70	(11)
Na	540	534	530	527	524	521	519	(9)

* In presence of the solid phase [$Ca(NH_3)_6$], the vapor pressure of NH_3, p, is 471.8 mm at −32.5° and 192.8 mm at −50°.

Unsaturated solutions of Li, of mole fraction x with respect to NH_3, at −39.4° (12)

x =	1.00	0.98	0.96	0.94	0.92	0.90	0.86	0.82	0.783 (satd.)
p/p_o =	1.00	0.973	0.973	0.963	0.942	0.908	0.757	0.418	0.0065

Solutions of the complex telluride, Na_2Te_n; temp. 18–20° (13)

x =	1.00	0.998	0.996	0.994	0.992	0.990
p/p_o =	1.000	0.9990	0.9979	0.9968	0.9957	0.9946

LITERATURE

(For a key to the periodicals see end of volume)

(1) Beckmann and Liesche, *93*, **89**: 171; 14. (2) Cambi and Speroni, *22*, **24 I**: 734; 15. (3) Eastman and Hildebrand, *1*, **36**: 2020; 14. (4) Gillett, *29*, No. **73**; 14. (5) Guillet and Ballay, *34*, **175**: 1057; 22. (6) Hildebrand, *78*, **22**: 319; 13. *172*, (8th), **XXII**: 147; 12. (7) Hildebrand and Eastman, *1*, **37**: 2452; 15. (8) Hildebrand, Foster and Beebe, *1*, **42**: 545; 20. (9) Joannis, *34*, **110**: 238; 90.
(10) Johnston, *40*, **12**: 15; 18. (11) Kraus, *1*, **30**: 653; 08. (12) Kraus and Johnson, *1*, **47**: 725; 25. (13) Kraus and Zeitfuchs, *1*, **44**: 2714; 22. (14) Poindexter, *2*, **28**: 208; 26. (15) Ramsay, *4*, **55**: 521; 89.

TWO-PHASE LIQUID—VAPOR SYSTEMS AT CONSTANT TEMPERATURE, TWO COMPONENTS VOLATILE, PARTIAL AND TOTAL VAPOR PRESSURES*

Alfons Klemenc

CONTENTS

P, p, total, resp. partial vapor pressure.

x, mole fraction.

"Ideal," Each partial pressure is (within the accuracy of the data) given by the expression $p_A = p_0 x_A$ where p_0 is p_A for $x_A = 1$.

Values of the vapor pressures of the pure liquids recorded in the following tables are those given by the observer. They usually differ more or less from the "best" values, *q.v.* p. 201, 202, 213.

I. TWO-COMPONENT SYSTEMS

(*a*) Non-Aqueous Systems

1. One Component a Non-Metallic Element

**See also* "Vapor-Pressure Lowering," p. 292, "Solubility of Gases," p. 254 and "*P-T-X* Relations," p. 351.

A

Argon

B = O_2, *v.* p. 351

B = N_2 (47); *cf.* p. 309, 351

−188.0°

Vol % B	P in mm
0.0	602.8
10.0	747.8
31.5	1005
65.3	1379
82.6	1562
100.0	1743

Let $x_A/x_B = r$ (in liquid), and $x_A/x_B = r'$ (in gas) then $\log_{10} r = 1.11$; $\log_{10} r' - 0.466$.

O_2

B = N_2, *v.* p. 309, 351

Cl_2

B = $COCl_2$, *v.* p. 353

Br_2

B = I_2, *v.* p. 354

B = CCl_4 (70)

At 25°, p_A(mm) = 410.7x_A, in region x_A = 0 to 0.025.

2. Both Components Chemical Compounds

𝔅-Table, standard arrangement, *v.* p. viii

HCl

B = N_2O (56.5) *P* in mm

$100x_B$	−100°	−95°	−90°	$100x_B$	−100°	−95°	−90°
0	293	411	561	30	339	472	644
10	308	432	589	40	353	491	671
20	323	453	617	50	366	507	696

B = C_2H_6O (33, 61)
Methyl ether

SO_2

B = CO_2 (10)
P in atm. (± 2 to 13 %)
See also p. 354

Wt. % B / t°	5	10	15	20	25	30
−17	2.6	4.3	6.8			
0	4.0	6.3	8.3$_0$	10.3$_0$	12.5	(14.7)
+10	5	8.3	10.9	13.0	15.6	(18.6)
30	9.$_2$	13.5	16.6	20.2	24.0	
35	10.$_3$	15.0	18.6	22.3	26.3	(31.5)

B = C_2H_6O (11)
Methyl ether
P at 56.1°, 77.1°, 108.7°
Not very accurate

NO_2

B = N_2O_3 (7)
P in mm

Wt. % B / t°	0	20	40	60	80	100 (Extrapolated)
−24		110	170	268	460	865
−16		168	260	409	685	1250
− 8	172	262	398	623	1018	1785
0	266	400	600	925	1475	2480
+ 8	396	590	882	1331	2072	3360
16	598	860	1270	1857	2825	4430
20	684	1040	1520	2130	3260	5000

N_2O

B = $C_{10}H_{14}N_2$ Nicotine at 59.6°
Slightly > 1st crit. soln. temp.

Wt. % B	*P* in mm	Lit.
17.22	137.5 ± 0.3	(104)
82.10	132.1 ± 0.7	

N_2O_3

B = N_2O_4, *v.* p. 355

$SnCl_4$

B = C_6H_6 (108)
P at 100°, 125°

For systems composed of two carbon compounds, *v.* Part 3.

NaCl

B = **KCl** (38); *P* in mm

Wt. % A / t°	0	20	50	70	100
870	2.6	2.0	1.2	0.8	0.4$_5$
890	3.5	2.8	1.8$_6$	1.3	0.6$_7$
910	4.6	3.8	2.7	2.1	1.1
920	5.2	4.4	3.2	2.5	1.5
930	5.7	(4.9)	3.7	2.9	1.9

t°	Wt. % A	p_B(mm)	p_A(mm)
900	15	3.3$_6$	0.1
920	43	2.6	0.9
940	69	1.5	2.0
950	82	0.8$_4$	2.6$_6$

Na_2CO_3

B = **NaCN** (49); *P* in mm

t°	1000 ± 1	1100 ± 1
P	12.8x_B	35.2x_B

3. Both Components Carbon Compounds with Key-Formulae Beginning with 16

ℭ-Table. The ℭ-arrangement in order of the components ("A") having the lowest C-formulae (*v.* p. viii)

CCl_4

B = CS_2 (12, 13, 14, 91, 102)
P at 0, 10, 20, 30, 60, 80°

B = C_2H_5I Ethyl iodide (142); *cf.* (93, 94)
49.99°, *p* in mm (±1.5)

$100x_B$	p_A	p_B
0	306	0
3.64	296	15
8.84	282	37
19.66	250	79
28.50	227	111
40.26	193	154
49.33	167	184
100	0	354

B = C_2H_6O Ethyl alcohol, *v.* p. 358

B = $C_4H_8O_2$ Ethyl acetate (142); *cf.* (93, 94)
49.99°, *p* in mm (±0.8)

$100x_B$	p_A	p_B
0	306.0	0
9.65	276.8	34.4
11.97	272.0	42.6
19.78	249.5	67.0
21.49	245.5	72.3
32.65	214.1	103.0
32.57	214.8	103.9
42.50	189.6	126.5
59.84	136.5	175.0
68.38	110.4	196.5
74.81	90.1	213.3
80.64	70.7	228.4
84.88	56.2	239.7
100	0	280.5

B = $C_6H_5NO_2$ Nitrobenzene (71); *cf.* (57, 67, 141)
P and *p*

B = C_6H_6 (102, 106, 107.5); *P* in mm

$100x_A$	P_0	P_{10}	P_{20}	P_{30}	P_{40}	P_{50}*	P_{80}†	P_{85}	P_{95}
0	26.9	44.6	74.0	115.8	177.3	270.9		912	1184
15.78						281.0			
20	29.6	50.0	80.2	123.9	187.8			926	1191
25							793		
30.44						290.0			
40	31.4	54.3	84.5	130.2	199.0			941	1206
50	32.3	56.4	86.3	132.6	196.3		816	948	1206
60	33.0	58.2	88.0	134.7	201.8			956	1213
61.31						302.3			
75.8							831		
80	34.5	61.3	90.0	137.6	205.5			964	1221
100	35.6	64.2	89.9	138.1	206.6	310.2		971	1235

* *P* in mm (± 0.1 %) (67, 68).
† (141).

B = C_6H_6.—(*Continued*)
P and *p* at 34.8° (71); *cf.* (57, 67, 141).
49.99°, *p* in mm (±1.5) (142); *cf.* (93, 94)

$100x_A$	p_A	p_B
0	0	268.0
5.07	18.9	253.3
11.70	40.5	237.1
17.72	59.9	221.8
25.25	83.4	201.8
29.47	97.0	191.3
39.59	128.9	165.0
56.00	176.2	124.5
67.74	212.2	92.8
76.58	238.9	68.0
100	308.0	0

B = C_7H_8 Toluene (102)
P in mm, also values at 10, 30, 40, 50, 60, 70, 75°

B = C_7H_8.—(*Continued*)

$100x_A$	P_0	P_{20}	P_{50}*
0	9.9	26.5	93.0
3.99			99.0
10	12.8	33.$_5$	
20	16.$_0$	40.$_3$	
24.01			140.8
40	24.$_0$	51.$_9$	
50	27.$_3$	58.$_3$	
51.42			197.7
60	29.$_0$	66.$_1$	
73.98			248.5
80	35.$_1$	79.$_8$	
90	38.$_6$	86.$_2$	
90.99			288.8
100	41.2	93.2	310.2

* *P* in mm (±0.1%) (67, 68).

B = C_7H_8O, Cresol
P at 0 and 20° (9)

B = C_7H_8O Anisole
P at 15° (135); at 0 and 20° (9)

CCl_4.—(*Continued*)

B = $C_{10}H_{11}Cl$
1-Chlorotetrahydronaphthalene; *P* at 20° (123)

B = $C_{10}H_{12}$
Tetrahydronaphthalene (tetralin); *P* at 20° (137)

CO_2 (40)

B = CH_3Cl Methyl chloride
At 9.5°, *P* (atm.) = $3.45x_B + 44.3x_A$

$100x_A$ in vapor	*P* (atm.)
100	3.45
80	4.75
60	6.1
50	7.2
40	9.2
30	12.8
20	19.2
10	30.0
0.0	44.3

B = C_3H_6O Acetone
Some approx. values of *P* at "freezing mixture" temperatures (40); at 6.8, 15.5, 25.5° (11).

CS_2

B = $CHCl_3$ Chloroform
P at 0, 10, 20, 30, 40, 60, 80° (101, 102); at 13.8, 16.0° (37)

B = CH_4O, *v.* p. 359

B = C_2H_6O Ethyl alcohol (12, 13, 14)

B = C_3H_6O Acetone
P at 0, 10, 20, 30, 35° (102).

$100x_A$	p_A	p_B
24.78°, *p* in mm (±0.5) (75)		
0	0	231.6
18.6	176.0	197.0
30.8	240.0	175.5
50.1	289.0	159.0
80.2	327.5	125.2
100	358.5	0
35.17°, *p** in mm (±1.1) (142); *cf.* (93, 94)		
0	0	343.8
6.24	110.7	331.0
7.11	123.1	328.7
12.12	191.7	313.5
19.91	271.9	290.6
27.61	323.3	275.2
35.02	358.3	263.9
44.74	390.4	250.2
49.74	404.1	242.1
61.24	426.9	227.0
67.13	438.0	217.0
71.97	447.5	207.1
82.80	464.9	180.2
93.50	491.9	109.4
96.20	500.8	73.4
100	512.3	0

*For application of Duhem-Margules equation, *v.* (142); *cf.* (93, 94).

B = $C_3H_8O_2$ Methylal

$100x_A$	p_A	p_B
16.53°, *p* in mm (±0.5) (75)		
0	0	265.5
22.5	107.3	210.5
48.0	173.0	168.0
79.5	225.0	101.0
100	263.1	0
35.17°, *p* in mm (±1.1) (142); *cf.* (93, 94)		
0	0	587.7
4.89	54.5	558.3
10.30	109.3	529.1
16.40	159.5	500.4
27.10	234.8	451.2
34.70	277.6	419.0
39.01	297.8	402.7
45.36	324.8	378.0
49.46	340.2	360.8
53.93	357.2	342.2
60.71	381.9	313.3
68.27	407.0	277.8
73.77	424.3	250.1
79.50	442.6	217.4
84.45	458.1	184.9
91.08	481.8	124.2
95.54	501.0	65.1
100	514.5	0

B = $C_4H_8O_2$ *n*-Butyric acid
P at 20° (123)

B = $C_4H_{10}O$ Ethyl ether
20.0°, *p* in mm (±0.5) (36); *cf.* (75)

$100x_B$	p_A	p_B
0	298	0
5.1	284	41
15	265	101
25	243	150
40	208	213
50	182	250
65	144	299
80	88	357
90	45	401
100	0	441

B = $C_6H_5NO_2$ Nitrobenzene
P at 20° (124)

B = C_6H_6
p in mm (±1) (100); *cf.* (12, 13, 14, 19, 36)

$100x_B$	p_A	p_B
20°		
0	297.4	0
11.35	263.8	13.4
24.82	228.1	25.4
37.47	198.4	34.0
46.24	175.8	39.9
62.51	131.6	50.3
87.80	42.5	68.2
100	0	75.2

B = C_6H_6.—(*Continued*)

$100x_B$	p_A	p_B
25°		
0	361.1	0
2.11	352.7	3.5
4.68	344.1	7.1
11.53	321.4	16.0
18.24	299.1	24.0
30.02	263.6	35.1
49.86	197.4	53.7
63.02	156.6	63.5
76.63	102.5	75.3
87.14	60.2	83.8
94.19	27.9	89.5
100	0	94.9
30°		
0	434.6	0
8.00	398.4	14.7
22.86	343.1	35.8
37.23	287.5	53.3
65.16	177.5	81.6
88.45	62.2	107.3
100	0	119.3

P at 0, 10, 20, 30, 40, 60, 80° (102).

B = C_7H_8 Toluene (101, 102)
P at 0, 10, 20, 30, 40, 60, 80, 90, 100°

B = C_7H_8O *m*-Cresol (136)
P at 15°

B = C_7H_8O Anisole (135)
P at 15°

$CHBr_3$

Bromoform

B = C_3H_6O Acetone (125)
P at 20°

B = $C_3H_6O_2$ Methyl acetate (125)
P at 20°

B = $C_4H_{10}O$ Ethyl ether
P at 20° (125); at 25.0, 75° (25)

$CHCl_3$

Chloroform

B = C_3H_6O Acetone

$100x_A$	p_A	p_B
35.17°, *p* in mm (±0.8) (142); *cf.* (93, 94)		
0	0	344.5
5.88	9.2	323.2
12.32	20.4	299.3
18.53	31.9	275.4
26.57	50.7	240.9
29.70	55.4	230.3
36.64	74.3	197.9
42.32	88.9	174.3
49.39	111.8	143.6
51.43	117.8	135.0
58.72	139.9	108.5
66.35	170.2	79.0
79.97	224.4	37.5
91.75	267.1	13.0
100	293.1	0

B = C_3H_6O.—(*Continued*)

$100x_B$	p_A	p_B
55.10°, *p* in mm (±0.5) (8)		
0	632.8	0
11.8	548.1	54.9
23.4	469.4	110.1
36.0	359.7	202.4
50.8	257.7	322.7
58.2	193.6	405.9
64.5	161.2	454.1
72.1	120.7	521.1
90	39.0	658.2
100	0	741.8

For 40.4 and 28.15°, *v.* (8).
P at 0, 10, 20, 30, 40, 50, 55°, *v.* (101, 102).

B = $C_4H_8O_2$ *n*-Butyric acid
P at 20° (123)

B = $C_4H_{10}O$ Ethyl ether
P in mm (102)*

$100x_B$	P_0	P_{20}	$P_{33.25}$†
0	61	163	
5.0			276
8.0			276
10	70	178	
20	79	196	
20.3			282
29.5			294
40	100	240	
50	109	268	355
58.8			412
60	122	299	
69.5			500
80	151	364	
89.8			657
90	168	404	
95.5			697
100	187	443	731

$100x_A$	p_A	p_B
17° (36)		
0	0	397
10	6	354
20	13	304
30	22	251
40	34	196
50	50	143
60	71	95
70	91	60
80	111	32
90	129	14
100	143	0

* Also values at 10 and 30°.
† *P* in mm (±2) (8).

B = $C_6H_5NO_2$ Nitrobenzene
P at 20° (124)

B = C_6H_6 *P* in mm (101, 102)

$100x_A$	P_0	P_{20}	P_{40}	P_{60}
0	26.9	77	185	394
10	30.9	87	201	425
20	33.4	96	216	459
30	36.8	104	232	493
40	40.8	112	249	533
50	44.2	120	266	567
60	47.4	128	289	602
70	51.2	137	307	638

B = C_6H_6.—(*Continued*)

$100x_A$	P_0	P_{20}	P_{40}	P_{60}
80	54.6	145	330	677
90	57.9	155	353	738
100	61.2	165	372	754

P at 80, 100° (101); at 10, 20, 30, 40, 50, 60° (102); at 34.8° (71); *cf.* (57, 67, 141); *P* and *p* at 20 and 90° (107.5).

B = C_6H_7N Aniline
P at 20° (132)

B = $C_6H_{10}O$ Cyclohexanone
P at 20° (123, 133)

B = $C_6H_{12}O$ Hexahydrophenol
P at 20° (127)

B = C_7H_8 Toluene
P and *p* at 34.8° (71); *cf.* (57, 67, 141)

B = C_7H_8O *m*-Cresol
P at 15° (136)

B = $C_7H_{14}O$ Hexahydrocresols
P at 15° (136)

B = $C_8H_{11}N$ Dimethylaniline
P at 20° (125, 132)

B = $C_{10}H_{11}Cl$ 1-Chlorotetrahydronaphthalene
P at 20° (123)

B = $C_{10}H_{12}$ Tetrahydronaphthalene (tetralin)
P at 20° (125, 133)

CH_2O_2
Formic acid

B = C_3H_9N Trimethylamine (5)

B = C_5H_5N Pyridine (2, 3, 34)

B = C_6H_7N Picoline (34)

CH_3NO_2
Nitromethane

B = C_2H_5I Ethyl iodide (39)
*P** in mm

$100x_B$	P_{60}	P_{65}
0	179	(222)
8.06	312	367
16.2	386	453
24.2	433	508
37.2	470	557
73.0	524	620
87.6	537	632
92.6	531	625
100	513	607

* Calc'd. values for p_A and p_B at 65° also given.

CH_4O
Methyl alcohol

B = C_2H_6O Ethyl alcohol (101)
At *t*°C, *P* (in mm) = zx_A + constant

t°	z	const.
20	50	44
40	119	135
60	244	357
80	450	813
100	763	1701

P at 0, 10, 20, 30, 40, 50, 60, 80, 100°, *v.* (102).

B = C_3H_8O *n*-Propyl alcohol
P in mm ± 1 (102)

$100x_A$	P_0	P_{20}
0	3.5	15.1
10	5.6	24.4
20	8.2	37.9
30	11.6	40.5
40	14.9	48.7
50	18.2	56.0
60	20.7	63.8
70	22.8	72.0
80	25.3	80.0
90	28.0	88.0
100	31.9	96.3

Values also given at 10, 30, 40, 50, 60°.

B = $C_6H_5NO_2$ Nitrobenzene
P at 20° (124)

B = C_6H_6, *v. infra*

B = C_6H_7N Aniline
P at 20° (132)

B = $C_6H_{12}O$ Hexahydrophenol
P at 20° (127, 128)

B = C_6H_{14}, *v. infra*

B = C_7H_6O Benzaldehyde
P at 20° (130)

B = C_7H_8O *m*-Cresol
P at 15° (136)

B = $C_7H_{14}O$ Hexahydrocresols
P at 20° (130)

B = $C_8H_{11}N$ Dimethylaniline
P at 20° (132)

C_2HCl_3
Trichloroethylene

B = $C_6H_{10}O$ Cyclohexanone
P at 20° (131)

B = $C_{10}H_{12}$ Tetrahydronaphthalene (tetralin)
P at 20° (137)

A = CH_4O; B = C_6H_{14} Hexane; *P* in mm (±1.5) (104)

$100x_B$	0	6.84	9.21	14.37	42.3	51.0	64.0	100
$P_{43.8}$*	306	509	529	539	556	547	550	309

* Slightly above critical soln. temp.

A = CH_4O; B = C_6H_6; *P** in mm (101, 102)

$100x_A$	P_0	P_{20}	P_{40}	P_{60}	P_{80}	P_{100}
0	26.9	77	186	394	755	1344
10	36.4	107	266	622	1208	2150
20	44.1	128	329	742	1472	2658
30	48.5	140	356	802	1581	2845
40	48.8	144	362	811	1611	2875
50	49.1	146	365	816	1627	2889
60	49.2	145	367	827	1631	2894
70	48.6	145	363	824	1622	2884
80	48.3	142	348	782	1581	2837
90	44.2	123	309	718	1490	2723
100	31.9	94	254	601	1263	2464

P at 10, 20, 30, 40, 60, 80, 100°, *v.* (102).
* Error: 20, 40°, ±2%; 60°, −4 to 1.7%; 80, 100°, 0 to −6%.

C_2HCl_5
Pentachloroethane

B = C_3H_6O Acetone
P at 20° (134)

B = $C_3H_6O_2$ Methyl acetate
P at 20° (134)

B = $C_4H_8O_2$ Ethyl acetate
P at 20° (134)

B = $C_4H_{10}O$ Ethyl ether
P at 20° (134)

B = C_6H_6; *P* at 20° (134)

C_2H_3N
Methyl cyanide

B = C_2H_6O Ethyl alcohol (116)

C_2H_4
Ethylene

B = C_2H_6O Methyl ether (11)
P at 33, 40, 54.5, 76° (approx.)

$C_2H_4Br_2$
Ethylene bromide

B = $C_3H_6Br_2$ 1, 2-Dibromopropane (142); *cf.* (93, 94)
85.05°, *p* in mm (±1.5)

$100x_B$	p_A	p_B
0	172.6	0
2.02	167.8	3.2
14.75	145.1	19.9
30.48	120.8	38.1
41.80	100.5	52.9
62.03	64.0	79.3
80.05	34.3	102.5
91.48	13.8	117.1
96.41	4.6	123.8
100	0	127.2

$C_2H_4Cl_2$
Ethylene chloride

B = C_6H_6 (108, 142); *cf.* (93, 94)
Ideal over 9 to 95°

$C_2H_4Cl_2$
1, 1-Dichloroethane

B = $C_{10}H_{12}$ Tetrahydronaphthalene (tetralin)
P at 20° (137)

C_2H_4O
Acetaldehyde

B = C_2H_6O Ethyl alcohol
P in mm (109)*

$100x_A$	*t*°	*P*
15.5	25	34
54.5	25	398
82	25	699
30	40	398
48	40	699
16.5	60	699
2.5	60	398

* *q. v.* for additional data.

$C_2H_4O_2$
Acetic acid

B = C_3H_9N Trimethylamine (5)

B = $C_4H_8O_2$ Butyric acid (55, 56)
P of equimol. mixtures, 13–52°

B = C_5H_5N Pyridine (2, 3, 34, 142); *cf.* (93, 94)
P and *p* at 80.05°

B = C_6H_6 (142); *cf.* (93, 94)*
49.99°, *p* in mm(±*ca.* 1.0)

$100x_A$	p_A	p_B
1.60	3.63	262.9
4.39	7.25	257.2
8.35	11.51	249.6
11.38	14.2	244.8
17.14	18.4	231.8
29.79	24.8	211.2
36.96	28.7	195.6
58.34	36.3	153.2
66.04	40.2	135.1
84.35	50.7	75.3
99.31	54.7	3.5

For *P* at 10, 20, 30, 40, 50, 60, 70°, *v.* (102). For *P* and *p* at 20, 35°, *v.* (71); *cf.* (57, 67, 141).

* *q. v.*, for x_A in gas phase; for application of Duhem-Margules equation.

B = $C_6H_{15}N$ Triethylamine (34)

$C_2H_4O_2$.—(*Continued*)

B = C_7H_8 Toluene (142); *cf.* (93, 94)*

69.94°, *p* in mm (±*ca.* 1.0)

$100x_A$	p_A	p_B
4.35	17.2	193.5
9.42	30.5	186.1
17.11	46.5	176.2
24.03	57.8	167.3
23.80	69.3	155.7
40.88	78.2	154.2
46.51	83.7	137.6
51.40	88.2	130.7
59.81	95.7	117.8
68.79	103.0	101.9
76.90	110.8	84.8
87.50	120.5	54.8

At 35° (71); *cf.* (57, 67, 141).

* *q. v.* for x_A in gas phase.

C_2H_5Br

Ethyl bromide

B = C_2H_5I Ethyl iodide (37, 140)

P at 16.7° approx. linear function of *x*

C_2H_5I

Ethyl iodide

B = $C_4H_8O_2$ Ethyl acetate (142); *cf.* (93, 94)

49.99°, *p* in mm (±0.8)

$100x_A$	p_A	p_B
0	0	280.4
5.79	28.0	266.1
10.95	52.7	252.3
19.18	87.7	231.4
23.53	105.4	220.8
37.18	155.4	187.9
54.78	213.3	144.2
63.49	239.1	122.9
82.53	296.9	66.6
90.93	322.5	38.2
100	353.4	0

B = C_6H_{14} *n*-Hexane (39)

*P** in mm

$100x_A$	P_{60}	P_{65}
0	(571)	670
4.75		693
23.6	629	741
38.2	640	749
48.1	638	749
66.6	623	733
72.7	613	721
84.2	582	684
94.1	541	636
100	513	607

* p_A and p_B at 65°, calc'd. from Duhem-Margules equation also given.

C_2H_6O

Ethyl alcohol

B = C_3H_8O *n*-Propyl alcohol (29)

Ideal (±0.5mm) at 25°

B = $C_3H_8O_3$ Glycerol

v. p. 360

B = $C_4H_{10}O$ Ethyl ether

P in mm (80)* *v. also* p. 361

Wt. % B	19°	18°	10°	0°	−18°
10	115			54	
20	160			74	28
40		238	171	104	
60				132	50
80		347		157	63

* Composition of gas phase (very inaccurate) also given.

B = $C_6H_5NO_2$ Nitrobenzene (88)

P at 20, 30, 40, 50, 60°

B = C_6H_6, *v.* p. 360

B = $C_6H_{10}O$ Cyclohexanone

P at 20° (133)

B = $C_7H_6O_2$ *o*-Salicylaldehyde

P at 20° (122)

B = C_7H_8 Toluene (67, 68)

$100x_A$	*P* in mm (±0.1%)
0	93.0
4.20	141.2
17.75	214.8
30.89	233.1
46.13	242.1
57.65	244.2
66.80	249.2
76.27	248.2
83.69	244.4
88.02	243.0
95.99	230.9
100	219.5

B = C_7H_8O Cresol (9); *cf.* (126, 128)

p in mm (techn. B. P. 196 to 201°)

Wt. % A	p_A	Wt. % A	p_A
0°C		20°C	
11.1	0.62	1.45	0.21
14.7	1.03	6.08	1.23
22.5	1.59	13.95	3.30
31.9	2.40	24.8	6.92
		31.7	9.15

B = C_7H_8O Anisole (9)

p at 0, 20°

B = $C_{10}H_{11}Cl$ 1-Chlorotetrahydronaphthalene

P at 20° (123)

B = $C_{10}H_{12}$ Tetrahydronaphthalene (tetralin)

P at 20° (133)

B = $C_{10}H_{12}O$ *ar*-Tetrahydro-*β*-naphthol

P at 15° (133)

$C_3H_5N_3O_9$

Trinitroglycerol

B = C_3H_6O Acetone (74)

v. also p. 300

18°, *p* in mm

Wt. % B	p_B	10^6p_A
0	0	
10	30	135
20	54	89
30	76	
40	95	35
50	112	20
60	129	
70	142	6
80	150	
90	157	
100	162	0

C_3H_6O

Acetone

B = C_3H_8O Isopropyl alcohol (145)

B = C_4H_8O Ethyl methyl ketone

P in mm (88, 89)

$100x_A$	P_{20}	P_{30}	P_{40}	P_{50}
0	77	121	188	300
20	116	168	246	358
30	126	184	269	390
40	138	201	294	421
60	158	234	338	485
70	163	247	359	517
80	168	257	381	553
100	186	285	425	621

B = $C_4H_8O_2$ *n*-Butyric acid

P at 20° (123)

B = $C_4H_{10}O$ Ethyl ether

P in mm 0.0° (22)

$100x_A$ Liq.	$100x_A$ Vap.	*P*
0	0	70
15.6	44.6	119
19.2	43.6	117
36.4	61.7	142
51	67	150
61.7	72.8	167
83.5	86.1	181
100	100	185

p in mm (±1) (100); *cf.* (106, 107.5)

$100x_A$	p_A	p_B
	20.00°	
0	0	444
5.20	20	422
12.71	42	394
24.90	70	350
45.7	105	282
61.2	127	224
66.6	135	199
84.2	160	111
93.6	175	46
97.9	181	15
99.6	184	2
100	185	0

B = $C_4H_{10}O$.—(*Continued*)

$100x_A$	p_A	p_B
	30.00°	
0	0	646
3.87	22	632
13.27	66	571
25.1	107	510
34.5	132	464
49.6	167	390
65.1	214	266
83.8	243	166
93.4	267	71
95.3	271	55
98.0	276	21
100	283	0

B = $C_6H_5NO_2$ Nitrobenzene

P at 20° (124)

B = C_6H_7N Aniline

P at 20° (125, 132)

B = $C_6H_{10}O$ Cyclohexanone

P at 20° (133)

B = $C_6H_{12}O$ Hexahydrophenol

P at 20° (127, 128)

B = $C_7H_6O_2$ *o*-Salicylaldehyde

P at 20° (122)

B = C_7H_8 Toluene (92, 93)

Comp. of vapor phase

B = C_7H_8O Cresol (9); *cf.* (126, 129)

Techn. B. P. 196–201°

Wt. % A	p_A in mm 0°	p_A in mm 20°
6.7	0.76	2.39
8.3	1.20	3.31
14.8	2.71	7.56
22.4	5.30	15.45

B = C_7H_8O Anisole

p at 0, 20° (9)

B = $C_8H_{11}N$ Dimethylaniline

p at 15° (135); *P* at 20° (132)

B = $C_{10}H_{11}Cl$ 1-Chlorotetrahydronaphthalene

P at 20° (123)

B = $C_{10}H_{12}$ Tetrahydronaphthalene (tetralin)

P at 20° (133)

B = $C_{10}H_{12}O$ *ar*-Tetrahydro-*β*-naphthol

P at 15° (133)

$C_3H_6O_2$

Propionic acid

B = C_5H_5N Pyridine (2, 3, 34)

$C_3H_6O_2$

Methyl acetate

B = $C_4H_8O_2$ *n*-Butyric acid

P at 20° (123)

B = $C_4H_8O_2$ Ethyl acetate

P in mm (±1) (102)

$100x_B$	P_0	P_{20}
0	25.2	83.3
10	28.8	92.5
20	32.7	103.1

B = $C_4H_8O_2$.—(*Continued*)

$100x_B$	P_0	P_{20}
30	37.9	112.5
40	41.1	122.8
50	44.2	132
60	47.9	141
70	51.8	150
80	56.0	159
90	60.8	166
100	65.0	172.5

Values also given for *P* at 10, 30, 40, 50, 60, 80, 100°.

B = C_6H_6, *P* in mm (101)

$100x_A$	P_0	P_{20}	P_{40}	P_{60}
0	26.9	77	185	394
10	32.3	94	228	473
20	40.2	107	262	542
30	46.8	122	290	606
40	50.4	134	312	662
50	54.1	144	335	713
60	57.2	154	356	752
70	58.2	162	375	787
80	60.5	166	388	814
90	61.9	168	400	840
100	64.1	171	407	854

P at 10, 20, 30, 40, 50, 60, 70, 80, 90, 100° (101, 102).

B = C_6H_7N Aniline
P at 20° (132)

B = $C_8H_{11}N$ Dimethylaniline
P at 20° (132)

B = $C_{10}H_{11}Cl$ 1-Chlorotetrahydronaphthalene
P at 20° (123)

C_3H_8O

Propyl alcohol

B = C_6H_6 (102) *P* at 0, 10, 20, 30, 40, 50, 60, 70°

$C_4H_8O_2$

n-Butyric acid

B = C_6H_6, *P* at 20° (123)

$C_4H_8O_2$

Ethyl acetate

B = $C_4H_{10}O$ Ethyl ether (102)

P at 10, 30, 40, 50°; P_0 and P_{20} (±1 mm); almost linear

B = $C_6H_5NO_2$ Nitrobenzene
P at 20° (124)

B = C_6H_6, *P* in mm ± 1 (102)

$100x_A$	P_0	P_{20}
0	26.9	76.9
10	26.9	86.3
20	27.0	95.8
30	27.0	103.4
40	27.1	106.5
50	27.2	107.3
60	27.1	104.6
70	26.9	101.3
80	26.5	94.3
90	26.0	83.4
100	24.6	73.8

Also values at 10, 30, 40, 50, 60°.

B = $C_6H_{10}O$ Cyclohexanone
P at 20° (130)

B = $C_6H_{12}O$ Hexahydrophenol
P at 20° (127, 128)

B = $C_6H_{12}O_2$ Propyl propionate (141)

$100x_B$	p_{85} (mm)
0	968
25	857
50	733
74.6	610
100	480

B = C_7H_8O *m*-Cresol
P at 15° (136)

B = $C_7H_{14}O$ Hexahydrocresols
P at 15° (136)

B = $C_7H_{14}O_2$ Amyl acetate
P in mm ± 1 mm (102)

$100x_A$	P_0	P_{20}
0	1.0	6.5
10	5.1	14.0
20	8.2	20.8
30	10.9	29.0
40	12.6	36.3
50	14.8	43.7
60	18.1	50.2
70	20.2	57.1
80	22.0	63.5
90	25.1	69.9
100	27.2	76.5

Also values at 10, 20, 30, 40, 50, 60, 70°.

B = $C_{10}H_{12}$ Tetrahydronaphthalene (tetralin)
P at 20° (137)

C_4H_{10}

Butane

B = C_5H_{12} Pentane (16)
P and *p* at 25°

B = C_6H_6; *P* and *p* at 25° (16)

B = C_7H_{16} *n*-Heptane (16)
P and *p* at 25°

$C_4H_{10}O$

Ethyl ether

B = $C_6H_5NO_2$ Nitrobenzene
P at 16° (90); *cf.* (71); at 20° (124)

B = C_6H_6 (101)
At *t*°C, *P* (in mm) = zx_B + constant

t°	z	const.
20	358	76.5
40	726.5	185.5
60	1326	395
70	1758	551.5

B = $C_7H_6O_2$ Salicylaldehyde
P at 20° (122)

B = C_7H_8O Cresol
p in mm (9); *cf.* (126, 129)
Techn. B. P. 196–201°

Wt. % A (0°)	p_A (0°)	Wt. % A (20°)	p_A (20°)
2.31	0.61	0.53	0.37
5.86	1.62	5.52	4.18
10.8	3.33	7.00	6.08
14.5	5.22	9.9	10.4
		11.4	13.3

B = C_7H_8O Anisole (9)
p at 0, 20°

B = $C_8H_8O_3$ Methyl salicylate
16° (90); *cf.* (71)

B = $C_9H_{10}O_2$ Ethyl benzoate
P at 16° (90); *cf.* (71)

B = $C_{10}H_{12}$ Tetrahydronaphthalene (tetralin)
P at 20° (133)

B = $C_{10}H_{16}$ Turpentine
16° (90); *cf.* (71)

C_5H_{12}

Pentane

B = C_7H_{16} *n*-Heptane (16)
P and *p* at 25°

C_6H_5Br

Bromobenzene

B = C_6H_5Cl Chlorobenzene
Ideal at 140° (140)

B = C_6H_6 (71); *cf.* (57, 67, 141)
P and *p* at 34.8°

$C_6H_5NO_2$

Nitrobenzene

B = C_6H_6; *P* at 20° (124)

C_6H_6

B = C_6H_7N Aniline (132)
P at 20°

B = $C_6H_{10}O$ Cyclohexanone
P at 20° (133)

B = $C_6H_{12}O$ Hexahydrophenol
P at 20° (127)

B = $C_7H_6O_2$ Salicylaldehyde
P at 20° (122)

B = C_7H_8 Toluene (101); *cf.* (73, 102)

$100x_A$	P_0	P_{20}	P_{40}
0	9.7	24	64
10	10.4	30	78
20	12.2	36	94
30	14.0	42	109
40	15.6	47	122
50	17.7	51	136
60	19.6	56	148
70	21.8	62	158
80	23.7	68	168
90	25.8	74	178
100	26.9	76	186

60–120°, ideal.

B = C_7H_8O Cresol
p in mm (9); *cf.* (126)
Techn. B. P. 196–201°

Wt. % A (0°)	p_A (0°)	Wt. % A (20°)	p_A (20°)
1.15	0.85	1.70	3.82
6.40	4.75	3.00	6.93
9.20	7.00	3.58	8.05
12.4	9.84	4.60	10.30
		7.30	15.20

B = C_7H_8O Anisole
P at 0 and 20° (9)

B = $C_7H_{14}O$ Hexahydrocresols
P at 20° (127, 128)

B = $C_8H_{11}N$ Dimethylaniline
P at 20° (132)

B = $C_{10}H_{12}$ Tetrahydronaphthalene (tetralin)
P at 20° (133)

C_6H_6O

Phenol

B = C_7H_8O Cresol, ideal (23)

C_6H_{12}

Cyclohexane

B = $C_{11}H_{20}$ 1-Methyldecahydronaphthalene
P at 20° (123)

B = $C_{11}H_{20}$ 2-Methyldecahydronaphthalene
P at 20° (123)

B = $C_{12}H_{22}$ 1, 6-Dimethyldecahydronaphthalene
P at 20° (123)

B = $C_{12}H_{22}$ 2, 6-Dimethyldecahydronaphthalene
P at 20° (123)

C_6H_{14}

Hexane

B = C_8H_{18} Octane (141)

$100x_B$	P_{80} (mm)
0	1062
23	861
50	618
75	330
100	174.8

B = $C_{10}H_{12}$ Tetrahydronaphthalene (tetralin)
P at 20° (133)

C_7H_8

Toluene

B = C_7H_8O *m*-Cresol
P at 15° (136)

B = C_8H_{10} Ethylbenzene (141)

$100x_B$	P_{118} (mm)
0	965
25	813
50	692
75	565
100	456.6

C_7H_{12}

Methylcyclohexene (Mix.)

B = $C_{11}H_{20}$ 1-Methyldecahydronaphthalene
P at 20° (123)

B = $C_{11}H_{20}$ 2-Methyldecahydronaphthalene
P at 20° (123)

B = $C_{12}H_{22}$ 1, 6-Dimethyldecahydronaphthalene
P at 20° (123)

B = $C_{12}H_{22}$ 2, 6-Dimethyldecahydronaphthalene
P at 20° (123)

C_7H_{14}

Methylcyclohexane

B = $C_{11}H_{20}$ 1-Methyldecahydronaphthalene
P at 20° (123)

B = $C_{11}H_{20}$ 2-Methyldecahydronaphthalene
P at 20° (123)

B = $C_{12}H_{22}$ 1, 6-Dimethyldecahydronaphthalene
P at 20° (123)

B = $C_{12}H_{22}$ 2, 6-Dimethyldecahydronaphthalene
P at 20° (123)

C_8H_{16}

1, 3-Dimethylcyclohexane

B = $C_{11}H_{20}$ 2-Methyldecahydronaphthalene
P at 20° (123)

B = $C_{11}H_{20}$ 1-Methyldecahydronaphthalene
P at 20° (123)

B = $C_{12}H_{22}$ 1, 6-Dimethyldecahydronaphthalene
P at 20° (123)

B = $C_{12}H_{22}$ 2, 6-Dimethyldecahydronaphthalene
P at 20° (123)

(*b*) Aqueous Systems

B = **HCl,** *v.* p. 258, 293, 301, 361
B = **HBr,** *v.* p. 258, 306, 361
B = **HI,** *v.* p. 258, 306
B = SO_2, *v.* p. 258, 302, 361
B = H_2SO_4, *v.* p. 293, 302

B = NH_3 (138); *cf.* (144)

The total vapor pressure for any composition and for any temperature between 0 and 90°C may be computed with the aid of the empirical equations

$$\theta = \frac{T}{1 + 0.703_6(1 - x_B^z)}$$

and

$$z = (x_B + 0.05)^{1/4}\,(1.34_7 - 2.9x_B + 1.77x_B^2)$$

in which *T* is the absolute temperature of the solution of composition $100x_B$ mole % NH_3, and θ is the absolute temperature at which pure liquid NH_3 (*q. v.*) has the same vapor pressure as the solution.

The partial vapor pressure of H_2O (0–90°) may be computed from the empirical relations:

$p_A = (1 - \alpha)x_Ap_0$

$\alpha = 0.1x_B$ for $x_B < 0.53$

$\alpha = 0.055x_B$ for $x_B > 0.53$

p_0 = the vapor pressure of pure H_2O at the same temperature. *v. also* p. 259 and 362.

B = HNO_3, *v.* p. 304 and 309
B = H_3PO_4, *v.* p. 293
B = **HCN,** *v.* p. 261 and 365

B = CH_2O Formaldehyde (64)
p_B in mm

t° \ Wt. %B	1	5	10	15	20	25	30	35
0		(0.037)	0.070	0.098	0.120	0.141	0.162	
20		(0.18)	0.351	0.487	0.600	0.714	(0.83)	
35	(0.13)	0.605	1.150	1.58	1.96	2.28	2.575	2.85
45		(1.20)	2.21	3.11	3.89	4.56	5.14	5.72

B = CH_2O_2 Formic acid, *v.* p. 364

B = CH_4O Methyl alcohol (119)
p in mm (±*ca.* 0.9)

$100x_B$	p_A	p_B
	39.9°	
0	54.7	0
14.99	39.2	66.1
17.85	38.5	75.5
21.07	37.2	85.2
27.31	35.8	100.6
31.06	34.9	108.8
40.1	32.8	127.7

B = CH_4O.—(*Continued*)

$100x_B$	p_A	p_B
47.0	31.5	141.6
55.8	27.3	158.4
68.9	20.7	186.8
86.0	10.1	225.2
100	0	260.7
	59.4°	
0	145.4	0
22.17	106.9	210.1
27.40	102.2	240.2
33.24	96.6	272.1
39.80	91.7	301.9

B = CH_4O.—(*Continued*)

$100x_B$	p_A	p_B
47.08	84.8	335.6
55.5	76.9	373.7
69.2	57.8	439.4
78.5	43.8	486.6
85.9	30.1	526.9
100	0	609.3

B = $C_2H_4O_2$ Acetic acid
v. p. 306

B = C_2H_6O Ethyl alcohol (23, 31, 119, 139); *cf.* (57, 60)

Log p_A or log p_B for any given composition is a linear function of $\frac{1}{t + 273.1}$ between any two values in the following table.

Wt. % B	p_A	p_B
	20°	
0	17.5	0.0
10	16.8	(6.7)
20	15.9	(12.6)
30	15.1	(17.1)
40	14.7	20.7
50	14.5	23.5
60	14.1	25.6
70	13.1	28.0
80	11.3	31.2
90	7.5	35.8
98	1.9	42.3
100	0.0	43.6
	40°	
0	54.3	0.0
10	51.6	26.9
20	47.6	43.5
30	46.2	54.7
40	45.5	62.5
50	44.6	68.2
60	42.9	74.8
70	40.5	82.8
80	35.9	91.8
90	24.7	106.4
98	6.5	123.0
100	0.0	134
	55°	
0	117	0.0
10	110.7	59.3
20	104.0	94.4
30	100.5	114.8
40	98.8	130.8
50	97.3	142.6
60	94.4	155.6
70	89.1	172.6
80	77.6	192.8
90	52.5	223.9
98	14.3	262.4
100	0.0	283
	75°	
0	287	0
10	276	144.0
20	261	218.8
30	254	269.2
40	245	305
50	241	336
60	235	365
70	224	405

B = C_2H_6O.—(*Continued*)

Wt. % B	p_A	p_B
80	191.4	454
90	130.3	527
98	34.7	625
100	0.0	667

B = C_3H_6O Acetone (110); *cf.* (103)
p in mm (±4)

$100x_B$	25°	30°	45°	60°
		p_A*		
0.0	23	31	71	149
3.33	27	34	76	149
7.20	27	34	70	143
11.7	25	30	66	134
17.1	24	34	71	145
23.6	22	29	62	129
31.8	28	35	67	126
42.0	23	29	59	116
55.4	16	20	47	102
73.7	17	21	45	97
100	0	0	0	0
		p_B*		
0.0	0	0	0	0
3.33	38	47	101	190
7.20	77	96	192	342
11.7	105	134	253	443
17.1	125	157	293	495
23.6	146	182	329	553
31.8	152	189	346	588
42.0	164	205	369	624
55.4	182	225	400	672
73.7	192	236	423	711
100	229	281	505	860

* For data at 35, 40, 50, 55°, *v.* (110).

B = $C_3H_6O_2$ Propionic acid
P in mm (±2) (60)

$100x_B$	7.48	19.1	43.2
P_{20}	18	17	16
P_{40}	52	51	47
P_{60}	147	143	130
P_{80}	353	355	315
P_{100}	765	750	687

For additional data, *see* (60).

B = $C_3H_6O_2$ Methyl acetate
56.9°, *p* in mm (74); *cf.* (143)
v. also p. 364, 365

$100x_B$	p_A	p_B
65*	121	633
75	111	654
85	96	678
90	78	698
100	0	760

* Saturated solution.

B = C_3H_8O *n*-Propyl alcohol (119); *cf.* (57, 60)
v. also p. 365
p in mm (±1)

$100x_B$	p_A	p_B
	30.3°	
0	32.2	0
8.66	29.3	16.3
15.77	29.8	17.2
39.02	28.5	18.5

B = C_3H_8O.—(*Continued*)

$100x_B$	p_A	p_B
	30.3°.—(*Continued*)	
55.5	27.2	19.8
100	0	28.5
	49.9°	
0	92.0	0
9.04	87.2	49.2
15.97	87.0	51.7
30.47	84.5	54.6
41.14	83.0	57.4
55.5	78.2	60.2
73.9	60.9	68.4
82.0	49.2	72.1
100	0	90.0
	65.9°	
0	195.6	0
8.87	187.2	105.5
15.81	187.6	108.5
30.28	180.1	119.1
47.82	171.3	128.7
55.5	162.3	135.1
73.9	124.7	153.1
82.0	99.0	162.2
100	0	198.8
	79.8°	
0	352.6	0
8.56	342.3	187.7
15.58	339.7	199.9
30.12	324.9	222.1
47.82	306.9	238.8
55.5	290.3	251.4
73.9	218.4	288.2
82.0	171.2	308.0
100	0	374.6

B = $C_3H_8O_3$ Glycerol

P in mm, at 25° (27); at 100° (35); *v. also* p. 310

Wt. % B	P_{25}	Wt. % B	P_{100}
0	23.7	0	760
15.5	23.0	10	740
25	22.0	25	704
35	20.2	40	657
50	17.4	65	553
60	14.8	75	450
75	10.5	80	396
83	8.0	85	326
92	4.0	90	247
98	0.4	98	107
		100	64

B = C_4H_8O Methyl ethyl ketone

73.6°, p in mm (74)

$100x_B$	p_A	p_B
58.72*	263	495
65	259	501
70	252	508
80	216	532
90	146	568
100	0	619

* Saturated solution.

B = $C_4H_8O_2$ *n*-Butyric acid

P in mm (30)

$100x_B$	P_0	$P_{18.2}$	$P_{58.7}$
0	4.57	15.67	140.6
9.6	4.18	14.10	140.9
23.4	3.79	12.42	134.9
38.0	2.96	10.24	123.2
52.6	2.26	9.2	
100	(0.12)	0.7	(9.5)

P in mm (±2) (60)

$100x_B$	6.67	17.3	32.9
P_{20}	18	19	17
P_{40}	49	55	46
P_{60}	155	150	145
P_{80}	360	356	346
P_{100}	775	762	741

For additional data, *v.* (60).

37.5 Wt. % soln.	$t°$	P (mm)
Isobutyric acid (27)	23.02	21.6
	29.02	30.6

B = $C_4H_{10}O$ Isobutyl alcohol *v.* p. 365

B = C_5H_5N Pyridine (142); *cf.* (93, 94)

80.05°, p in mm

$100x_A$	p_A	p_B
0	0	239
10	109	201
25	201	163
58	308	124
78	333	107
89	335	103
95	336	93
100	355	0

B = $C_5H_8O_2$ Acetylacetone *v.* p. 365

B = $C_6H_5NO_2$ Nitrobenzene (18)

$t°$	Wt. % A	Wt. % A (vap.)	10^4 Wt. A/cm³ (vap.)	10^4 Wt. B/cm³ (vap.)
175.1	5.60	57.87	44.54	32.43
188.6	6.95*	58.64	54.31	38.31
212.0	10.10	60.05	88.65	58.98
228.1	16.00	65.37	117.7	62.35
233.2	82.30	77.90	146.4	41.71
224.8	87.00	81.70	133.2	29.66
172.7	96.2	89.70	66.11	73.00

* P = 11.43 atm. (calc'd.).

B = C_6H_6O Phenol

P in mm (±1) (104); *v. also* p. 365

$100x_B$	0	2.51	4.70	7.74	14.97	31.65	44.8	85.6
P_{69}*	223.8	233.7	224.2	224	222	224	211.3	175

* Slightly > crit. soln. temp.

P in mm (65)

$100x_B$	P_{75}	P_{77}	P_{79}	P_{81}	P_{83}	P_{85}
0	289	314	340	369	400	433
1	293	318	344	373	403	436
2	294	319	345	374	405	438
4	294	319	345	374	405	438
17	294	319	345	374	404	438
39	268	289	310	336	364	397
50	201	223	245	267	290	311

B = $C_7H_7NO_2$ *o*-Nitrotoluene (18)

$t°$	Wt. % A	Wt. % A (vap.)	10^4 Wt. A/cm³ (vap.)	10^4 Wt. B/cm³ (vap.)
183.9	5.20	62.97	56.07	32.97
237.0	15.5	66.59	143.8	72.15
252.2	83.0	78.71	200.0	54.09
230.0	92.1	79.06	147.7	38.69
194.3	96.2	88.26	80.08	10.61

II. THREE-COMPONENT SYSTEMS

H_2O

B = CH_4O (60); *cf.* (57) Methyl alcohol

C = various salts

B = C_2H_6O Ethyl alcohol

20° (139)

C = $C_3H_8O_3$ Glycerol

5 g-mol C/1000g (A + B)

$100x_B$	p_A	p_B
0	15.5	0
16.3	13.5	18.1
27.7	12.6	23.0
42.5	10.9	26.8
70.0	7.2	31.5
90.4	3.5	35.9
98.0		38.3

Wt. % A = 62, Wt. % B = 38

C Mol/l.......	0	0.263
p_A(mm).......	17.2	16.3
p_B(mm).......	20.2	21.1

C = $C_4H_{10}O$ Ethyl ether, *v.* p. 377

C = (*a*) $C_7H_6O_2$ Benzoic acid (*b*) $C_7H_6O_3$ Salicylic acid

1 g-mol C/1000g equimol. mixture (A + B), p in mm (±5%)

C	None	$C_7H_6O_2$	$C_7H_6O_3$
p_A	13.7	13.9	14.4
p_B	27.9	25.6	26.0

C = C_7H_8O Benzyl alcohol

Mol C/1000g equimol. mixture (A + B), p in mm (±5 %)

Mol C	p_A	p_B
0	13.6	27.9
1	14.0	25.8
3	14.3	22.2
6	14.1	19.7
10	14.1	17.8

C = C_7H_8O.—(*Continued*)

1 g-mol C/1000g equimol. mixture (A + B)

Mol C	None	1 g-mol
p_A	13.7	14.0
p_B	27.9	25.8

Mol C/1000g (A + 20 Mol % B)

Mol C	p_A	p_B
0	16.9	20.0
0.5	15.9	18.1
1	15.3	17.0
2	16.3	15.4
3	16.9	13.8

Wt. % A = 62, Wt. % B = 38, p in mm

Mol/l C	0	0.048
p_A	17.2	14.0
p_B	20.2	16.6

C = (*a*) C_7H_9N *p*-Toluidine
(*b*) $C_8H_8O_2$ Phenylacetic acid
(*c*) C_8H_9NO Acetanilide
(*d*) $C_8H_{10}O$ Phenylethyl alcohol
(*e*) $C_{12}H_{16}O_2$ Amyl benzoate

1 g-mol C/1000g equimol. mixture (A + B) p in mm (±5%)

C	p_A	p_B
None	13.7	27.9
(*a*)	14.2	25.0
(*b*)	13.9	26.0
(*c*)	14.0	25.3
(*d*)	13.9	25.9
(*e*)	14.5	26.5

B = C_2H_6O.—(*Continued*)
C = $C_{12}H_{22}O_{11}$ Sucrose
Wt. % A = 62, Wt. % B = 38,
p in mm

Mol/l C	0	0.072
p_A	17.2	14.6
p_B	20.2	21.3

B = $C_3H_6O_2$ Methyl acetate
C = $C_{12}H_{22}O_{11}$ Sucrose (143)

B = C_6H_6O Phenol
C = C_6H_7N Aniline, *v.* p. 379

CCl_4

B = $C_2H_4Br_2$ Compn. of the vapor phase
C = C_7H_8 Toluene (97)

B = C_2H_6O Ethyl alcohol
C = C_6H_6 Benzene, *v.* p. 375

CS_2

B = C_3H_6O Acetone (75)
C = $C_6H_3N_3O_7$ Picric acid
v. p. 375

C = C_8H_9NO Acetanilide (75)
v. p. 375

B = $C_3H_8O_2$ Methylal (75)
C = $C_6H_3N_3O_7$ Picric acid
v. p. 375

C = $C_{10}H_8$ Naphthalene (75)
v. p. 375

B = $C_4H_{10}O$ Ethyl ether
C = $C_6H_3N_3O_7$ Picric acid
v. p. 375

C = $C_{10}H_8$ Naphthalene
v. p. 375

C = $C_{10}H_{16}O$ Camphor
v. p. 375

$CHCl_3$

Chloroform

B = $C_4H_{10}O$ Ethyl ether
C = $C_6H_3N_3O_7$ Picric acid
v. p. 375

C = C_8H_9NO Acetanilide
v. p. 375

C = $C_{10}H_8$ Naphthalene
v. p. 375

$C_2H_4O_2$ (55, 56)

Acetic acid

B = $C_4H_8O_2$ Butyric acid
C = $C_5H_{10}O_2$ Valeric acid

C = $C_{10}H_{20}O_2$ Capric acid

LITERATURE

(For a key to the periodicals see end of volume)

(1) Alluard, *6*, **1:** 243; 64. (2) André, *34*, **125:** 1187; 97. (3) André, *34*, **126:** 1105; 98. (4) Atkins, *4*, **117:** 218; 20. (5) Bachmann, *93*, **100:** 1; 17. (6) Baly, *3*, **49:** 517; 00. (7) Baume and Robert, *34*, **169:** 968; 19. (8) Beckmann and Faust, *7*, **89:** 235; 14. (9) Berl and Schwebel, *92*, **35:** 189; 22.

(10) Blümcke, *8*, **34:** 10; 88. (11) Briner and Cardoso, *34*, **144:** 911; 07. *42*, **6:** 641; 08. (12) Brown, *4*, **35:** 547; 79. (13) Brown, *4*, **39:** 304; 81. (14) Brown, *4*, **39:** 517; 81. (15) Büchner, *64V*, **26:** 388; 17. (16) Calingaert and Hitchcock, *1*, **49:** 750; 27. (17) Campbell, *83*, **11:** 91; 15. (18) Campetti and Del Grosso, *59*, **6:** 379; 13. (19) Carveth, *50*, **3:** 193; 99.

(20) Chavanne, *27*, **27:** 205; 13. (21) Chavanne, *34*, **158:** 1698; 14. (22) Cunaeus, *7*, **36:** 232; 01. (23) Dobson, *4*, **127:** 2866; 25. (24) Dolezalek and Schulze, *7*, **83:** 45; 13. (25) Dolezalek and Schulze, *7*, **98:** 395; 21. (26) Doroshevskii and Polanskii, *7*, **73:** 192; 10. *53*, **42:** 109, 1448; 10. (27) Drucker and Moles, *7*, **75:** 405; 10. (28) Ebersole, *50*, **5:** 239; 01. (29) Evans, *45*, **8:** 260; 16.

(30) Faucon, *6*, **19:** 70; 10. (31) Foote and Scholes, *1*, **33:** 1309; 11. (32) Fox and Barker, *54*, **36:** 842; 17. (33) Friedel, *27*, **24:** 160, 241; 75. (34) Gardner, *25*, **23:** 1587; 90. (35) Gerlach, *91*, **24:** 110; 85. (36) Guglielmo, *22*, **1 I:** 294; 92. **1 II:** 239; 92. (37) Guthrie, *3*, **18:** 495; 84. (38) Hackspill and Grandadam, *14*, **5:** 218; 26. (39) Halban, *7*, **84:** 128; 13.

(40) Hartmann, *64V*, **7:** 106; 98. *168*, No. **43.** (41) Haywood, *1*, **21:** 994; 99. (42) Haywood, *50*, **3:** 317; 99. (43) Hill, *4*, **101:** 2467; 12. (44) Holley, *1*, **24:** 448; 02. (45) Holley and Weaver, *1*, **27:** 1049; 05. (46) Hollmann, *7*, **43:** 129; 03. (47) Holst and Hamburger, *7*, **91:** 513; 16. (48) Inglis, *67*, **20:** 152; 06. (49) Ingold, *4*, **123:** 885; 23.

(50) Innes, *4*, **81:** 682; 02. **113:** 410; 18. (51) Jackson and Young, *4*, **73:** 922; 98. (52) Jana and Gupta, *1*, **36:** 115; 14. (53) Jones, *54*, **38:** 362T; 19. (54) Kablukow, Solomonow and Galine, *7*, **46:** 399; 03. (55) Kahlbaum, *149*, **31:** 133; 94. (56) Kahlbaum, *7*, **13:** 14; 94. (56.6) Klemenc and Kohl, University of Vienna, *0*. (57) Kohnstamm, *7*, **36:** 41; 01. (58) Kohnstamm and van Dalfsen, *64V*, **10:** 167; 02. (59) Kohnstamm and Timmermans, *64P*, **13:** 865; 11.

(60) Konowalow, *8*, **14:** 34; 81. (61) Kuenen, *7*, **37:** 485; 01. (62) Le Bel, *34*, **88:** 912; 79. (63) Lebo, *1*, **43:** 1005; 21. (64) Ledbury and Blair, *4*, **127:** 2832; 25. (65) van der Lee, *7*, **33:** 622; 00. (66) de Leeuw, *7*, **77:** 284; 11. (67) Lehfeldt, *3*, **46:** 42; 98. (68) Lehfeldt, *7*, **29:** 498; 99. (69) Lewis, *54*, **41:** 97T; 22.

(70) Lewis and Storch, *1*, **39:** 2544; 17. (71) Linebarger, *1*, **17:** 690; 95. (72) Magnus, *8*, **38:** 481; 36. (73) Mangold, *75*, **102 IIa:** 1071; 93. (74) Marshall, *4*, **89:** 1350; 06. (75) Michaud, *Thesis*, Paris, 1916. *16*, **6:** 223; 16. (76) Michels, *64V*, **31:** 53; 23. (77) Miller, *50*, **1:** 633; 97. (78) Narbutt, *7*, **53:** 697; 05. (79) Noyes and Warfel, *1*, **23:** 463; 01.

(80) Olmer, *27*, **29:** 382, 385; 21. (81) Parks and Schwenck, *50*, **28:** 720; 24. (82) Pascal, Dupuy, Ero and Garnier, *27*, **29:** 9; 21. (83) Perman and Price, *83*, **8:** 68; 12. (84) Pettit, *50*, **3:** 349; 99. (85) Pound, *4*, **99:** 698; 11. (86) Pratolongo, *22*, **30 II:** 320; 21. (87) Pratolongo, *22*, **30 II:** 419; 21. (88) Price, *4*, **107:** 188; 15. (89) Price, *4*, **115:** 1116; 19.

(90) Raoult, *7*, **2:** 353; 88. (91) Regnault, *151*, **26:** 724; 62. (92) Rosanoff and Bacon, *1*, **37:** 301; 15. (93) Rosanoff, Bacon and Schulze, *1*, **36:** 1993; 14. (94) Rosanoff, Bacon and White, *1*, **36:** 1803; 14. (95) Rosanoff and Easley, *1*, **31:** 953; 09. (96) Rosanoff and Easley, *7*, **68:** 641; 10. (97) Rosanoff, Schulze and Dunphy, *1*, **36:** 2480; 14. (98) Roscoe, *13*, **125:** 319; 63. (99) Ryland, *11*, **22:** 384; 99.

(100) Sameshima, *1*, **40:** 1482, 1503; 18. (101) Schmidt, *7*, **99:** 71; 21. (102) Schmidt, *7*, **121:** 221; 26. (103) Schreinemakers, *7*, **39:** 485; 02. (104) Schükarew, *7*, **71:** 90; 10. (105) Schulze, *1*, **36:** 498; 14. (106) Schulze, *7*, **86:** 309; 14. (107) Schulze, *8*, **59:** 73; 19. (107.5) Schulze, *7*, **97:** 388; 21. (108) Schulze and Hock, *7*, **86:** 445; 14. (109) Smits and de Leeuw, *64V*, **19:** 283; 10.

(110) Taylor, *50*, **4:** 290, 355, 675; 00. (111) Thayer, *50*, **2:** 382; 98. (112) Thayer, *50*, **3:** 36; 99. (113) Thiel and Caspar, *7*, **86:** 257; 14. (114) Thomas, *54*, **41:** 33; 22. (115) Tyrer, *4*, **101:** 81, 1104; 12. (116) Vincent and Delachanal, *6*, **20:** 207; 80. (117) Vrevskii, *53*, **32:** 593; 00. (118) Vrevskii, *53*, **43:** 1446; 11. (119) Vrevskii, *7*, **81:** 1; 12.

(120) Waentig and Pescheck, *7*, **93:** 529; 19. (121) Wanklyn, *5*, **12:** 534; 63. (122) Weissenberger, Henke and Bregmann, *57*, **46:** 471; 26. (123) Weissenberger, Henke and Katschinka, *93*, **153:** 33, 41; 26. (124) Weissenberger, Henke and Kawenoki, *52*, **113:** 171; 26. (125) Weissenberger, Henke and Schuster, *93*, **152:** 325; 26. (126) Weissenberger and Piatti, *57*, **45:** 187, 281; 25. (127) Weissenberger and Schuster, *57*, **45:** 413; 25. (128) Weissenberger and Schuster, *57*, **45:** 437; 25. (129) Weissenberger and Schuster, *57*, **46:** 157; 25.

(130) Weissenberger, Schuster and Henke, *57*, **46:** 47; 25. (131) Weissenberger, Schuster and Henke, *57*, **46:** 57; 25. (132) Weissenberger, Schuster and Lielacher, *57*, **46:** 301; 26. (133) Weissenberger, Schuster and Mayer, *57*, **45:** 449; 25. (134) Weissenberger, Schuster and Pamer, *57*, **46:** 281, 291; 26. (135) Weissenberger, Schuster and Schuler, *57*, **45:** 425; 25. (136) Weissenberger, Schuster and Wojnoff, *57*, **46:** 1; 25. (137) Weissenberger, Schuster and Zack, *92*, **39:** 270; 26. (138) Wilson, *86*, No. **146:** 25. (139) Wright, *4*, **121:** 2251; 22. **123:** 2493; 23.

(140) Young, *4*, **81:** 768; 02. (141) Young and Fortey, *4*, **83:** 45; 03. (142) Zawidsky, *7*, **35:** 129; 00. (143) McKeown and Stowell, *4*, **1927:** 97. (144) Mittasch, Kuss and Schlueter, *93*, **159:** 1; 26. (145) Parks and Chaffee, *50*, **31:** 439; 27.

TWO-PHASE LIQUID—VAPOR ISOTHERMAL SYSTEMS, VAPOR-PRESSURE LOWERING*

J. C. W. Frazer, R. K. Taylor and A. Grollman

CONTENTS

p = partial vapor pressure of the solvent from the solution.

p_0 = its vapor pressure in the pure state at the same temperature.

For values of p_0 consult the section on vapor pressures of pure liquids, p. 201, 202, 213.

* *See also* "Partial Vapor Pressures" p. 284, and "*P-T-X* Relations" p. 351.

AQUEOUS SOLUTIONS

(Standard arrangement, *v.* p. viii)

The quantities appearing in the tables are M, the number of gram-formula weights of solute per 1000 g H_2O, and $100R = \frac{100(p_0 - p)}{Mp_0}$. Within the accuracy of the data, the relation between M and $100R$ is linear between values marked with an arrow, thus $\begin{matrix}0.1\\2.2\end{matrix}\Big\downarrow$.

Two-Component Systems

HCl

M	$100R$
24.95° (24)	
0.05	2.80
0.10	3.00
0.20	3.20
0.4	3.42
0.6	3.56
1.5 ↓	4.13
3.6 ↓	5.63

H_2SO_4

M	$100R$
25° (19)	
0.1	3.47
0.2	3.49
0.3	3.52
0.5	3.58
0.7	3.64
0.9	3.73
1.1	3.82
1.3	3.93
1.7	4.20
1.8	4.27

NH_4NO_3

v. also p. 362

M	$100R$
40° (37)	
11.5	1.51
19.0	1.54
60° (37)	
11.5	1.75
19.0	1.47
80° (37)	
11.5	1.99
19.0	1.40
100° (48)	
0.6	3.10
0.7	2.88
1.5	2.79
2.5	2.76
4.0	2.72
5.0	2.69
6.5 ↓	2.61
12 ↓	2.27
15 ↓	2.10
24 ↓	1.77

NH_4Cl

v. also p. 362

M	$100R$
30–95° (47, 48)	
1.0	2.70
3.0	3.01
4.0	3.06
5.0	3.03
9.5 ↓	2.81
100°	
2.0	3.06
4.0	3.12
5.0	3.12
7.5	2.95
11.5	2.77

NH_4OCl

Hydroxylamine hydrochloride

(continued)

M	$100R$
100° (48)	
1.5	3.00
3.0	2.98
6.0	2.92

NH_4Br

v. also p. 363

M	$100R$
40–95° (47, 48)	
2.0	3.14
3.0	3.22
5.0	3.22
100°	
1.2	3.10
2.5	3.275
3.0	3.27
4.0	3.25
6.0 ↓	3.21
12 ↓	2.91

NH_4I

M	$100R$
100° (48)	
0.8	3.29
1.8	3.27
3.0	3.39
4.0	3.45
4.5	3.45
6.5	3.40
10.5	3.19
14.5	2.95

NH_4HSO_4

M	$100R$
100° (48)	
1.0	3.04
2.5	3.09
3.5	3.12
5.0	3.11
9.0	2.95
12.0	2.78

$(NH_4)_2SO_4$ (47, 48)

v. also p. 363

M	$100R$
50°	
1.2	3.33
2.3	3.29
3.0	3.32
60°	
2.3	3.27
3.0	3.29
65°	
2.3	3.26
3.0	3.275
70°	
1.2	3.24
2.3	3.245
3.0	3.24
75°	
2.3	3.21
3.0	3.22
80°	
1.2	3.20
3.0	3.21
85°	
1.2	3.17
2.3	3.17
3.0	3.18
90°	
1.2	3.15
2.3	3.14
3.0	3.15
95°	
1.2	3.10
2.3	3.11
3.0	3.10
100°	
0.4	2.88
0.8	3.11
1.5	3.11
2.5	3.05
3.3	3.03
4.5	3.07
5.0	3.09
5.5	3.11
6.0	3.10

$(NH_4)_2S_2O_6$

M	$100R$
100° (48)	
0.5	3.566
1.5	3.77
2.0	3.84
3.0	3.93
4.0	3.98

H_3PO_4

M	$100R$
0° (12, 13, 14, 15)	
0.1	1.80
0.2	1.88
0.3	1.95
0.5	2.07
1.0	2.26

H_3AsO_4

M	$100R$
100° (48)	
1.0	1.93
2.0	1.98
3.0	2.02
4.5	2.05

$(NH_4)_2SiF_6$

M	$100R$
100° (48)	
0.5	3.05
2.5 ↓	2.82

HCO_2H

v. p. 364

$C_3H_8O_3$

Glycerol (12, 13, 14, 15, 36)

M	$100R$
0°	
0.5	1.78
1.0	1.77
2.0	1.79
6.0	1.95
10.0	1.89
20.0	1.64
40.0	1.27
70°	
1.5	1.61
6.0	1.62
10.0	1.61
20.0	1.46
40.0	1.19
80.0	0.82

$C_4H_6O_4$

Succinic acid

M	$100R$
100° (48)	
1.2	1.61
2.8	1.616
4.0	1.595
4.7	1.562
8.0	1.546

$C_4H_6O_6$

d-Tartaric Acid

M	$100R$
100° (48)	
2.0	1.97
3.0	2.08
4.0	2.22
5.3	2.29
6.5	2.24
10.0	2.20

dl-Tartaric acid

M	$100R$
100° (48)	
0.7	2.17
3.0	2.14
5.0	2.24
7.0	2.37
8.0	2.49

$C_6H_6O_2$

Resorcinol

M	$100R$
23° (6)	
2.4	1.08
4.0	0.89
6.0	0.96
8.8	0.87

$C_6H_6O_3$

Pyrogallol

M	$100R$
23° (6)	
2.4	1.24
4.0	1.31
5.0	1.28

$C_6H_8O_7$

Citric acid

M	$100R$
100° (48)	
1.0	1.90
6.0 ↓	2.48

$C_6H_{12}O_6$

Dextrose

M	$100R$
0° (12, 13, 14, 15)	
0.2	1.66
1.0 ↓	1.72

$C_6H_{14}O_6$

Mannitol

M	$100R$
20° (17)	
0.1	1.775
1.0 ↓	1.785

$C_7H_{14}O_6$ (5)

α-Methylglucoside

M	$100R$
0°	
2.0	2.13
2.5	2.18
3.0	2.23
3.5	2.27
4.0	2.29
4.5	2.31
5.5	2.34
30°	
2.0	1.97
2.5	2.01
3.0	2.04
3.5	2.06
4.0	2.08
4.5	2.09
5.5	2.12

$C_{12}H_{22}O_{11}$

Sucrose

M	$100R$
0° (5, 43, 44, 45)	
0.2	1.86
0.5	1.89
1.0	1.97
3.5	2.39
4.5	2.50
5.0	2.55
6.0	2.59
7.0	2.63
30° (5)	
1.0	1.94
1.7	2.05
3.0	2.25
4.0	2.36
5.0	2.46
6.5	2.55
20–25° (3, 35; *cf.* 52)	
0.1	1.76
0.4	1.80
1.0	1.91
2.0	2.09
3.0	2.23
4.0	2.35
5.0	2.45
100° (46)	
0.3	1.82
0.6	1.85
0.8	1.88
1.2	1.91
1.5	1.94

$C_{18}H_{32}O_{16}$

Raffinose

70° (36)

CH_4N_2O

Urea

M	$100R$
0° (12, 13, 14, 15)	
1.0	1.52
2.0	1.49
4.0	1.46
6.0	1.45
10.0	1.43
70° (36)	
3.0	1.15
18.0 ↓	1.16
90° (36)	
2.0	1.30
4.0	1.26
7.0	1.23
18.0 ↓	1.20
60° (36)	

$C_2H_5NO_2$

Aminoacetic acid

M	$100R$
100° (48)	
1.6	1.58
3.7	1.505
7.5	1.527

$(CH_3)_4NCl$

M	$100R$
100° (48)	
1.5	3.10
3.0	3.32
4.0	3.45
6.0	3.62
10.5	3.62

$(CH_3)_2NH_2Cl$

M	$100R$
100° (48)	
1.5	2.82
3.0	2.70
3.5	3.00
6.5	3.12
11.0	3.02

CH_3NH_3Cl

M	$100R$
100° (48)	
1.0	2.63
2.0	2.85
3.5	3.06
7.0	3.03
10.0	2.87
14.5	2.62

$(CH_3)_3NHCl$

M	$100R$
100° (48)	
1.3	2.21
7.5	3.02
10.0	2.99

$C_6H_7N.HCl$

M	$100R$
100° (48)	
1.0	2.70
2.0	2.60
3.0	2.50
4.0	2.42
5.0	2.34
12.0	1.89

$(C_2H_5)_3NHCl$

M	$100R$
100° (48)	
1.0	1.96
1.5	2.20
3.0	2.83
4.5	3.04
6.5	3.13
7.5	3.04

NH_4CNS

M	$100R$
100° (48)	
1.0	2.88
1.5	2.99
3.5	3.01
4.5	3.10
21.0 ↓	2.27

Gelatin

% gel.	$100R$
25.2° (18)	
76	17.5
90 ↓	76
92.5	86
95	94
97	98
99	100

$Pb(NO_3)_2$

M	100R
100° (48)	
0.6	3.23
1.2	3.15
2.1	2.96
2.4	2.88
3.4	2.69

$Pb(C_2H_3O_2)_2$

M	100R
100° (48)	
1.0	1.87
1.5	1.64
2.0	1.54
5.0	1.32
6.0 ↓	1.30

$ZnCl_2$

M	100R
14.6° (29)	
11.0	5.90
13.5	5.89
17.0	5.22
24.6°	
11.0	5.93
13.5	5.78
17.0	5.14
29.6°	
11.0	5.93
13.5	5.72
17.0	5.09
100° (29, 48)	
1.3	2.70
2.7	3.20
5.0	4.03
7.0	4.64
9.0	5.04

$ZnSO_4$

M	100R
0° (11)	
0.5	1.19
1.0	1.34
1.5	1.57
2.0	1.84
2.5	2.24
50° (47)	
1.9	2.15
2.8	3.60
65° (47)	
1.9	2.02
2.8	3.36
80° (47)	
1.9	1.82
2.8	2.98
95° (47)	
1.9	1.61
2.8	2.68
100° (48)	
1.0	1.35
1.5	1.23
2.2	1.50
2.7	1.70
4.8	2.38

$Zn(NO_3)_2$

M	100R
0° (11)	
0.5	4.22
3.0 ↓	7.20
3.7	7.90
100° (48)	
0.5	4.36
1.1	5.24
1.7	5.96
2.2	6.40
3.1	6.98
4.1	7.38

$CdCl_2$

M	100R
0° (11)	
1.0	2.05
1.5	2.02
2.0	2.06
3.0	2.03
4.0	2.05
100° (48)	
1.0	2.48
2.0	2.39
3.0	2.45
3.5	2.51
3.8	2.54
5.4 ↓	2.65
5.6	2.66

$Cd(ClO_3)_2$

M	100R
100° (48)	
0.5	4.58
1.0	5.30
1.5	5.68
2.0	6.15
3.0	6.80
5.4	7.48

$CdBr_2$

M	100R
100° (48)	
1.0	2.31
2.0	2.37
3.0	2.43
4.0	2.64

CdI_2

M	100R
100° (48)	
1.0	1.98
2.0	2.21
3.0	2.37

$Cd(NO_3)_2$

M	100R
0° (11)	
0.5	4.13
1.0	4.62
1.5	5.06
2.0	5.44
4.0 ↓	6.50
100° (48)	
0.3	4.02
0.8	4.47
1.0	4.62
2.0	5.09
4.0 ↓	5.76

$CdSO_4$

M	100R
0° (11)	
0.5	1.02
1.0	1.42
1.5	1.69
2.2	2.14
2.5	2.35
3.2	3.16
100° (48)	
0.8	1.18
1.2	1.14
1.5	1.13
2.0	1.20
2.4	1.27

$Hg(CN)_2$

M	100R
100° (48)	
0.5	1.72
0.8	1.64
1.0	1.61
1.2	1.63

$CuCl_2$

M	100R
23° (6)	
1.5	2.22
2.0	2.29
4.0	2.50
5.5	2.59
8.5	2.65

$CuSO_4$ (47, 48)

M	100R
50°	
1.2	1.87
1.9	2.44
60°	
1.2	1.79
1.9	2.31
70°	
1.2	1.65
1.9	2.10
80°	
1.2	1.55
1.9	1.98
90°	
1.2	1.49
1.9	1.90
100°	
0.7	1.61
1.5	1.67
2.5	1.91
3.5	2.21

$MnCl_2$

M	100R
100° (48)	
0.7	4.10
1.5	4.74
2.5	5.18
3.5	5.44
4.0	5.51
5.3	5.48

$MnSO_4$ (47, 48)

M	100R
40°	
2.0	1.82
3.3	3.20
50°	
2.0	1.79
3.3	3.06
60°	
2.0	1.76
3.3	2.93
65°	
2.0	1.70
3.3	2.82
70°	
2.0	1.66
3.3	2.70
75°	
2.0	1.61
3.3	2.58
80°	
2.0	1.54
3.3	2.42
85°	
2.0	1.50
3.3	2.30
90°	
2.0	1.44
3.3	2.15
95°	
2.0	1.38
3.3	1.98
100°	
0.3	1.70
1.0	1.46
1.6	1.32
1.8	1.35
2.0	1.39
2.7	1.56

$AgNO_3$

M	100R
23 ± 1° (6)	
1.0	1.63
2.0	1.60
5.0	1.53
8.0	1.50

$FeCl_2$

M	100R
100° (48)	
0.3	4.23
1.5 ↓	5.11
2.0	5.47
3.5	6.23
4.0	6.40
6.0	6.56
7.0	6.34

$FeSO_4$ (47, 48)

M	100R
50°	
1.7	2.06
3.0	2.56
60°	
1.7	2.01
3.0	2.42
65°	
1.7	1.99
3.0	2.35
70°	
1.7	1.96
3.0	2.24
75°	
1.7	1.94
3.0	2.17
80°	
1.7	1.91
3.0	2.11
85°	
1.7	1.88
3.0	2.06
90°	
1.7	1.84
3.0	2.02
95°	
1.7	1.82
3.0	1.95
100°	
0.5	1.53
1.0	1.38
1.5	1.37
2.0	1.56
3.0	1.84
3.5	1.87

$CoCl_2$

M	100R
100° (48)	
0.5	3.94
1.0	4.67
2.0	5.44
2.2	5.57
3.2	6.02
4.5 ↓	6.17

$CoCl_3$

t, °C	100R
M = 2.85 (10)	
20	21.4
30	22.1
40	23.1
50	24.6
60	25.6
70	26.0
80	26.0
90	26.3

$CoSO_4$

t, °C	100R
M = 2.901 (47, 48)	
30	2.70
50	2.67
60	2.63
70	2.53
80	2.40
90	2.24
100	1.79
M = 1.612 (47, 48)	
30	1.75
40	1.79
50	1.81
60	1.78
70	1.72
100 ↓	1.39

$Co(NO_3)_2$

M	100R
100° (48)	
1.0	5.04
3.0 ↓	6.72
4.0	7.25
5.0	7.40
7.0	7.02

$NiCl_2$

M	100R
0° (11)	
1.0	5.60
2.0	7.15
2.6	9.00
100° (48)	
0.5	4.25
2.5 ↓	6.05
3.0	6.45
3.5	6.75
4.0	7.00
5.0	7.25

$NiSO_4$

M	100R
0° (11)	
0.5	1.22
1.0	1.27
1.5	1.39
30° (47)	
1.7	1.98
2.9	2.70
40°	
1.7	1.94
2.9	2.62
50°	
1.7	1.90
2.9	2.58
60°	
1.7	1.85
2.9	2.51
65°	
1.7	1.82
2.9	2.48
70°	
1.7	1.79
2.9	2.44
75°	
1.7	1.74
2.9	2.35
80°	
1.7	1.68
2.9	2.28
85°	
1.7	1.65
2.9	2.25
90°	
1.7	1.60
2.9	2.17
95°	
1.7	1.53
2.9	2.10
100°	
0.7	1.33
1.3	1.33
1.7	1.34
2.2	1.47
2.5	1.67

$Ni(NO_3)_2$

M	100R
0° (11)	
1.0	4.70
3.0 ↓	7.20
3.6	8.10
100° (48)	
0.5	4.40
2.5 ↓	6.45
3.5	7.30
4.0	7.60
4.5	7.70

$UO_2(NO_3)_2$

M	100R
100° (48)	
0.4	4.72
1.2 ↓	5.54

H_3BO_3

M	100R
100° (48)	
0.8	1.58
2.0	1.65
3.5	1.67
4.5	1.67

$AlCl_3$

M	100R
100° (48)	
0.5	5.90
0.7	6.55
1.2	8.50
1.5	9.85
1.8	10.90
2.3	12.65
2.8 ↓	13.57
3.4	14.05

$Al_2(SO_4)_3$ (47, 48)

M	100R
40°	
0.3	2.60
0.6	3.14
0.9	5.54
1.15	6.99
50°	
0.3	2.52
0.6	3.10
0.9	5.48
1.15	6.83
60°	
0.3	2.45
0.6	3.04
0.9	5.38
1.15	6.70
65°	
0.3	2.40
0.6	3.00
0.9	5.30
1.15	6.60
70°	
0.3	2.33
0.6	2.93
0.9	5.21
1.15	6.51
75°	
0.3	2.27
0.6	2.88
0.9	5.13
1.15	6.39
80°	
0.3	2.22
0.6	2.83
0.9	5.05
1.15	6.28
90°	
0.3	2.12
0.6	2.67
0.9	4.71
1.15	5.84
95°	
0.3	2.06
0.6	2.58
0.9	4.53
1.15	5.63
100°	
0.3	3.23
0.4	3.10
0.7	3.80
1.05	4.90
1.17	5.77

$AlNH_4(SO_4)_2$

M	100R
100° (48)	
0.5	3.10
1.0	3.13
1.5	3.39
2.0	3.80
3.0	4.50

$CeCl_3$

M	100R
100° (48)	
0.3	5.10
2.0 ↓	9.00
2.5	9.52
4.0	10.50

$BeCl_2$

M	100R
100° (48)	
0.4	4.35
0.8	5.17
1.2	5.87
1.8	6.90
2.2	7.55
2.5	7.95
3.0	8.55
3.8	9.37
4.4	9.67
5.0	9.70

$BeBr_2$

M	100R
100° (48)	
0.7	5.20
0.9	6.00
1.5	7.30
2.0	8.15
2.5	9.00
3.2	10.15
4.2	10.90
4.6	11.50

$BeSO_4$ (47)

M	100R
30°	
1.5	1.86
3.0	2.96
4.3	3.83
40°	
1.5	1.81
3.0	2.89
4.3	3.78
50°	
1.5	1.76
3.0	2.75
4.3	3.62
60°	
1.5	1.66
3.0	2.60
4.4	3.48
65°	
1.5	1.61
3.0	2.52
4.4	3.37
70°	
1.5	1.54
3.0	2.41
4.4	3.22
75°	
1.5	1.50
3.0	2.35
4.4	3.14
80°	
1.5	1.46
3.0	2.28
4.4	3.03
85°	
1.5	1.42
3.0	2.21
4.4	2.95
95°	
1.5	1.35
3.0	2.10
4.4	2.81
100° (48)	
1.0	1.55
2.0	1.80
3.6	2.56
6.0	3.55

$Be(NO_3)_2$

M	100R
100° (48)	
0.3	3.86
0.9	5.28

$MgCl_2$ (47, 48)
v. also p. 367

M	100R
30°	
2.1	7.48
3.7	9.60
40°	
2.1	7.38
3.7	9.53
50°	
1.3	5.90
2.0	7.19
3.7	9.48
60°	
1.0	5.27
2.0	7.08
3.7	9.35
65°	
2.2	7.30
3.7	9.22
70°	
1.0	5.16
2.0	6.93
3.7	9.15
75°	
1.5	6.00
2.0	6.83
3.7	9.03
90°	
1.1	5.12
2.0	6.63
3.7	8.76
95°	
1.1	5.00
2.0	6.53
3.7	8.67
100°	
0.7	4.70
1.0	5.10
2.0	6.72
4.0	9.20
4.5	9.64
5.0	10.01
5.5	10.22
6.2	10.12

$MgBr_2$ (47, 48)

M	100R
30°	
1.0	6.48
1.5	7.33
3.0	10.05
40°	
1.0	6.28
1.5	7.18
3.0	9.80
50°	
1.0	6.13
1.5	7.00
3.0	9.68
65°	
1.0	5.90
1.5	6.78
3.0	9.38
80°	
1.0	5.73
1.5	6.57
3.0	9.13
100°	
0.4	4.55
1.0	5.60
2.5	8.27
3.5	9.55
4.0	10.02
5.0	10.65

$MgSO_4$ (47, 48)

M	100R
50°	
1.0	1.86
1.5	2.01
2.0	2.24
60°	
1.0	1.81
1.5	1.95
2.0	2.15
65°	
1.0	1.75
1.5	1.87
2.0	2.06
70°	
1.0	1.71
1.5	1.80
2.0	1.98
75°	
1.0	1.65
1.5	1.76
2.0	1.93
80°	
1.0	1.61
1.5	1.70
2.0	1.87
85°	
1.0	1.55
1.5	1.66
2.0	1.79
90°	
1.0	1.51
1.5	1.61
2.0	1.73
95°	
1.0	1.48
1.5	1.58
2.0	1.68
100°	
1.0	1.59
1.5	1.51
2.0	1.63
2.5	1.83
4.3 ↓	2.62

$Mg(HSO_4)_2$

M	100R
100° (48)	
0.3	4.69
0.5	5.00
0.8	5.53
1.2	6.28
1.6	7.04
2.2	7.99

$Mg(NO_3)_2$

M	100R
100° (48)	
0.3	4.39
1.0	5.43
1.5	6.05
2.0	6.53
2.5	7.20
3.4	7.88

$CaCl_2$ (2, 11, 12, 13, 14, 15, 34, 36, 39, 48)

M	100R
0°	
2.5	8.23
3.5	9.17
4.0	9.53
5.0	10.15
6.0	10.62
7.0	10.56
11.0	8.10
40°	
1.0	5.75
2.0	7.37
3.0	8.35
4.0	9.15
5.0	9.70
6.0	9.76
7.0	9.49
8.0	9.02
12.0 ↓	7.14
70°	
1.0	5.37
3.0	7.72
6.0	9.12
12.0 ↓	6.78
90°	
1.0	5.07
3.0	7.42
6.0	8.60
9.0	7.59
14.0 ↓	5.88
100°	
0.5	4.38
1.0	5.00
3.0	7.28
6.0	8.40
9.0	7.40
14.0 ↓	5.71
110°	
6.0	8.17
9.0	7.21
11.5	6.43
14.0	5.63
120°	
6.0	7.98
9.0	7.03
11.5	6.30
14.0	5.57
130°	
8.0	7.10
12.5 ↓	5.92
14.0	5.51
140°	
11.0	6.15
13.0	5.71
14.0	5.44

$CaBr_2$ (47, 48)

M	100R
50°	
1.0	5.84
3.0	8.48
4.0	9.60
70°	
1.0	5.77
3.0	8.33
4.0	9.42
85°	
1.0	5.71
3.0	8.12
4.0	9.27
95°	
1.0	5.64
3.0	7.98
4.0	9.00
100°	
0.5	4.71
1.0	5.46
2.0	7.00
3.0	8.40
4.0	9.40
4.5	9.70
5.5	9.94

CaI_2 (12, 13, 14, 15)

M	100R
0°	
1.0	4.49
2.0	5.36
5.0	7.21
7.0	7.39

CaS_2O_3 (48)

M	100R
100°	
0.6	2.68
1.5	3.14
2.0	3.17
3.0	4.47
3.3	4.81

$Ca(NO_3)_2$ (48)

M	100R
100°	
0.5	4.23
1.5	4.77
4.0 ↓	5.37
4.5	5.40
5.0	5.43
10.0	5.20

$Ca_2Fe(CN)_6$ (4)

M	100R
0°	
1.0	3.00
1.3	3.80
1.5	4.61
1.7 ↓	5.64

$SrCl_2$ (47, 48)

M	100R
30°	
0.7	5.10
1.3	6.03
1.8	6.82
50°	
0.7	4.93
1.3	5.88
1.8	6.59
70°	
0.7	4.73
1.3	5.64
1.8	6.29
90°	
0.7	4.60
1.3	5.47
1.8	6.06
100°	
0.5	4.31
1.5	5.52
2.0	6.03
2.5	6.49
3.0	6.86
4.0	7.38
4.5	7.49
5.4	7.38

$SrBr_2$ (47, 48)

M	100R
50°	
0.8	5.60
3.2 ↓	9.10
70°	
0.8	5.45
1.6	6.62
2.4	7.75
3.2	8.80
90°	
0.8	5.30
1.6	6.45
2.4	7.55
3.2	8.50
100°	
0.4	4.55
0.6	4.80
2.0 ↓	6.70
2.5	7.35
2.8	7.70
3.4	8.35
3.9	8.75
4.6	9.10

SrS_2O_6 (48)

M	100R
100°	
0.6	2.00
1.0	2.27
1.8	2.86
2.0	3.14
2.4	3.44

$Sr(NO_3)_2$ (48)

M	100R
100°	
0.3	4.23
0.6	4.10
0.9	4.09
3.0 ↓	4.34
3.7	4.37

$Ba(OH)_2$ (48)

M	100R
100°	
0.5	3.25
0.8	3.12
1.1	2.95
1.9	2.63

$BaCl_2$ (47)

M	100R
50–95°	
0.5	4.36
1.4	5.07
1.9	5.03
100°	
0.5	4.33
1.0	4.85
1.7	5.10
2.5 ↓	5.30

$Ba(ClO_3)_2$ (48)

M	100R
100°	
0.3	4.09
0.7	4.27
1.1	4.41
1.5	4.53
2.5	4.77
2.7	4.81
2.8	4.79

$BaBr_2$ (47)

M	100R
40°	
1.0	5.33
1.7	6.14
2.5	6.79
3.4	7.28
50°	
1.0	5.27
1.7	6.08
2.5	6.73
3.4	7.22
60°	
1.0	5.24
1.7	6.03
2.5	6.68
3.4	7.15
65°	
1.0	5.20
1.7	5.98
2.5	6.62
3.4	7.08
70°	
1.0	5.15
1.7	5.92
2.5	6.57
3.4	7.02
75°	
1.0	5.12
1.7	5.89
2.5	6.52
3.4	6.98
80°	
1.0	5.09
1.7	5.85
2.5	6.48
3.4	6.94
85°	
1.0	5.05
1.7	5.80
2.5	6.45
3.4	6.89
90°	
1.0	5.02
1.7	5.76
2.5	6.41
3.4	6.86
95°	
1.0	4.98
1.7	5.72
2.5	6.37
3.4	6.82
100° (48)	
0.4	4.34
0.6	4.58
1.2	5.25
1.8	5.81
2.7	6.47
3.0	6.60
3.5	6.74
4.2	6.80
4.4	6.76

BaS_2O_6

M	100R
100° (48)	
1.0	1.97
1.5	2.25
1.7	2.27
1.8	2.26

$Ba(NO_3)_2$

M	100R
100° (48)	
0.5	3.55
0.7	3.54
0.9	3.51
1.0	3.48_8
1.2	3.45_4

$Ba(C_2H_3O_2)_2$

M	100R
100° (48)	
0.8	3.76
1.6	3.73
2.2	3.53
2.8	3.38

$Ba(BF_4)_2$

M	100R
100° (48)	
0.5	5.33
1.0	5.59
1.8	5.93
2.6	6.12
3.2	6.19

LiOH (48)

M	100R
100°	
0.5	4.21
1.0	4.81
2.0	5.13
2.5	5.15
2.8	5.13

LiCl

M	100R
0° (50)	
3.5	4.55
5.0	5.07
10.0	5.49
20° (25)	
0.1	3.29
0.8 ↓	3.50
1.0	3.57
40° (47)	
2.0	3.86
5.0	4.95
6.0	5.20
60° (47)	
3.0	4.13
5.0	4.85
6.0	5.10
80° (47)	
2.0	3.75
3.0	4.09
5.0	4.70
6.0	4.92
100° (48)	
1.0	3.38
4.0 ↓	4.35
6.0	4.82
8.0	5.14
9.0	5.24
10.0	5.21
12.0	5.02
15.0	4.69
23.0 ↓	3.67

LiBr (47, 48)

v. also p. 369

M	100R
30°	
1.5	5.07
7.0 ↓	6.63
50°	
2.0	4.65
3.5	5.13
5.0	5.53
7.0	5.96
70–95°	
2.0	3.97
3.5	4.60
5.0	5.15
7.0	5.66
100°	
0.5	3.19
1.5	3.65
2.5	4.08
3.5	4.47
5.5	5.13
6.5	5.39
8.0	5.65
10.0	5.69
12.0	5.62
15.5	5.27

LiI (47, 48)

v. also p. 369

M	100R
40°	
0.8	4.13
3.8	5.17
50°	
0.8	3.93
3.8	5.44
60°	
0.8	3.80
3.8	5.32
65°	
0.8	3.73
3.8	5.23
70°	
1.0	3.78
3.8	5.13
75°	
1.0	3.75
3.8	5.10
80°	
1.5	3.96
3.8	5.07
85°	
1.5	3.95
3.8	5.04
95°	
0.8	3.61
3.8	5.01
100°	
0.8	3.68
1.3	3.84
2.6	4.44
4.5	5.29
6.5	6.00
10.0	6.47
11.0	6.44
12.5	6.28

Li_2SO_4 (47, 48)

M	100R
65°	
0.5	3.87
1.0	4.14
1.4	4.48
70°	
0.5	3.68
1.0	3.94
1.4	4.23
75°	
0.5	3.52
1.4 ↓	4.10
80°	
0.5	3.41
1.4 ↓	3.97
90°	
0.5	3.34
1.4 ↓	3.91
100°	
0.5	3.50
1.0	3.71
2.8	3.88

$Li_2S_2O_6$

M	100R
100° (48)	
0.5	4.06
1.0	4.87
1.5	5.47
2.5	6.45
3.0	6.90
4.5	7.60

$LiHSO_4$

M	100R
100° (48)	
0.8	3.44
1.5	3.61
2.0	3.79
3.5	4.19
5.5	4.48

$LiNO_3$ (47, 48)

M	100R
30–40°	
2.0	4.91
5.0	4.88
9.0	5.50
12.5	5.24
55°	
2.0	4.77
5.0	4.79
9.0	5.42
12.5	5.16
70°	
2.0	4.73
5.0	4.72
9.0	5.34
12.5	5.07
80°	
2.0	4.68
5.0	4.68
9.0	5.29
12.5	5.02
90°	
2.0	4.64
5.0	4.64
9.0	5.25
12.5	4.97
100°	
0.5	3.02
1.0	3.31
2.0	3.63
3.0	3.85
5.0	4.08
6.0	4.13
8.0	4.15
11.0	4.03
12.0	3.96
18.5	3.57

Li_2SiF_6

M	100R
100° (48)	
0.5	4.16
1.2	4.13
3.0	4.64

Li_2CrO_4

M	100R
100° (48)	
1.0	4.2_0
3.5 ↓	5.48
4.5	5.92

NaOH

v. also p. 369, 370

M	100R
0° (12, 13, 14, 15)	
1.0	3.00
3.0	3.55
4.0	3.90
5.0	4.31
7.0	4.87
9.0	5.27
10.0	5.42
12.0	5.52
15.0	5.24

M	100R
25° (34)	
4.0	3.64
5.0	4.08
6.0	4.40
7.0	4.69
8.0	4.92
9.0	5.09
10.0	5.21
11.0	5.23
12.5	5.20
20.0	4.33
28.0	3.31
100° (48)	
0.5	3.05
2.0	3.20
3.5	3.46
5.5	3.73
8.0	4.00
10.0	4.16
12.0	4.17
15.0	4.09
19.0	3.80

t, °C	100R
M = 25.0 (30)	
225	1.58
245	1.75
260	1.80
270	1.77
280	1.70
290	1.66
300	1.66
320	1.70
335	1.75
350	1.80
M = 58.3 (30)	
225	1.02
255	1.11
275	1.15
300	1.18
320	1.19
340	1.19

NaF

v. p. 369

NaCl

v. also p. 369, 370

M	100R
0° (12, 13, 14, 15)	
4.0	3.76
5.0	3.92
5.8	3.99
20–25° (31, 33)	
0.1	3.29
0.2	3.28
0.4	3.27
0.6	3.27
0.8	3.28
1.0	3.30
2.0	3.42
2.8 ↓	3.53
5.0 ↓	3.87
6.0	3.99
80° (47)	
4.0	3.65
5.0	3.79
6.0	3.91

M	100R
100° (7, 48)	
2.5	3.47
3.5	3.57
4.0	3.62
5.0	3.76
6.3	3.91
6.7	3.89

$NaClO_3$

v. also p. 369, 370

40 to 95° (47)	
2.5	3.28
5.0	3.26
12.5	2.81
100° (7, 48)	
1	3.08
2.5	3.21
4.5	3.25
5.5	3.24
8.0	3.13
11.5	2.80
15.0	2.54
19.0	2.39

NaBr (7, 47, 48)

v. also p. 371

40°	
2.0	3.49
3.0	3.73
4.0	3.93
5.8	4.15
50°	
2.0	3.52
3.0	3.77
4.0	3.97
5.8	4.20
60°	
2.0	3.56
3.0	3.80
4.0	4.00
5.8	4.25
65°	
2.0	3.58
3.0	3.82
4.0	4.02
5.8	4.27
70–95°	
2.0	3.61
3.0	3.86
4.0	4.06
5.8	4.30
100°	
1.0	3.35
2.0	3.63
3.0	3.86
4.0	4.05
5.0	4.20
6.0	4.33
7.0	4.39
8.5	4.41
12.0	4.18

$NaBrO_3$

100° (48)	
0.6	3.20
2.5	3.57
3.7	3.61
5.5	3.54

NaI (47, 48)

v. also p. 371

M	100R
30–95°	
1.0	3.63
6.0	4.77
100°	
0.7	3.25
1.5	3.62
4.0	4.46
5.0	4.67
6.0	4.82
7.0	4.91
9.0	5.00
11.0 ↓	4.89
17.0 ↓	4.25
20.0	3.85

Na_2SO_4 (7, 47, 48)

v. also p. 371

40°	
2.5	3.52_5
3.5	3.54
50°	
2.5	3.48_5
3.5	3.50_5
60°	
3.0	3.47_5
3.5	3.48_5
65°	
2.8	3.46_5
3.5	3.47
70°	
2.0	3.44_5
3.5	3.45_5
75°	
1.5 ↓	3.44
3.5 ↓	3.44
80°	
1.5 ↓	3.39_5
3.5 ↓	3.41
85°	
1.5	3.37
2.8	3.38
3.5	3.39
90°	
1.5	3.36
2.8	3.37
3.5	3.38
95°	
1.0	3.33_5
3.0	3.34
3.5	3.34_5
100°	
0.5	3.32
1.0	3.28
1.5	3.25
2.0	3.23
2.5	3.24
3.0	3.28

$Na_2S_2O_3$ (47)

v. also p. 372

30°	
1.5	4.06
3.0	4.31
3.5	4.46
4.7	5.36

M	100R
50°	
1.5	4.02
3.0	4.28
3.5	4.38
4.7	5.20
70°	
1.5	4.00
3.0	4.25
3.5	4.36
4.7	4.95
90°	
1.5	3.96
3.0	4.22
3.5	4.33
4.7	4.80
100°	
1.0 ↓	3.86
4.5 ↓	4.60
5.5	4.74
6.5	4.73
7.0	4.70
11.5	4.14

$Na_2S_2O_6$

100° (48)	
0.8	3.7_2
1.6 ↓	4.06
3.0 ↓	4.41

$NaHSO_4$

100° (48)	
1.5	3.00
2.0	3.14
3.0	3.30
5.0	3.33
7.5	3.15
10.0	3.06

$NaNO_2$

100° (48)	
1.0	3.12
2.0	3.20
4.0	3.26
6.0	3.22
8.0	3.11
10.0	2.98
15.0	2.65
16.0	2.59

$NaNO_3$

v. also p. 372

0° (12, 13, 14, 15, 43, 44, 45)	
1.0	2.88
2.0	2.73
4.0	2.55
8.0	2.35
85° (32, 47)	
1.0	3.40
3.0	3.10
5.0	2.93
7.0	2.79
10.0	2.60
14.0	2.40
100° (7, 48)	
5.0	2.79
7.0	2.82

M	100R
14.0	2.43
21.0	2.15

Na_3PO_4

100° (48)	
0.6	4.41
1.0	4.05
1.5	3.71
2.1	3.45
2.8	3.32

$(NaPO_3)_3$

100° (48)	
0.4	4.54
0.7	4.64
1.0	4.76

$Na_4P_2O_7$

100° (48)	
0.5	3.48
0.7	3.23
0.9	3.02
1.0	2.95
1.1	2.90
1.2	2.91
1.3	2.97

NaH_2PO_4

100° (48)	
1.0	2.65
2.0	2.40
3.0	2.28
4.0	2.20
5.0	2.15
7.0	2.11
11.0	2.07

Na_2HPO_4

100° (48)	
0.5	3.18
1.0	3.10
1.5	2.99
2.0	2.83
2.5	2.63
3.0	2.56
4.0	2.58
5.5	2.61
6.0	2.69

NaH_2AsO_4

100° (48)	
0.6	2.95
1.5	2.59
2.5	2.52
3.5	2.48
4.5	2.45
6.0	2.43

Na_2HAsO_4

100° (48)	
0.5	3.79
1.0	3.55
1.5	3.38
2.0	3.3_2
2.5	3.30
3.7	3.33

Na_2CO_3 (47, 48)

v. also p. 372

M	100R
30°	
1.9	4.16
2.8	4.32
40°	
1.0	3.85
1.9	4.12
2.8	4.28
50°	
1.0	3.80
1.9	4.01
2.8	4.16
60°	
1.9	3.94
2.8	4.07
65°	
1.0	3.72
2.8	3.99
70°	
1.0	3.69
1.9	3.86
2.8	3.93
75°	
1.0	3.67_5
1.9	3.83
2.8	3.87
80°	
1.0	3.67
1.9	3.80
2.8	3.81
85°	
1.0	3.66
1.9	3.78_5
2.8	3.76
90°	
1.0	3.64
1.9	3.77
2.8	3.72
95°	
1.0	3.63
1.9	3.75
2.8	3.68
100°	
0.7	3.78
1.0	3.67
1.9	3.48
2.2	3.49
3.0	3.53
3.9	3.61

$NaCHO_2$

Formate

v. p. 372

$NaC_2H_3O_2$

Acetate

100° (48)	
1.0	3.19
2.0	3.45
3.0	3.61
4.0	3.73
5.0	3.79
6.0	3.80
8.0	3.73
9.5	3.61

$Na_2C_4H_4O_4$ Succinate

M	100R
100° (48)	
0.6	4.42
1.5	4.87
2.0	5.06
3.0 ↓	5.35
4.3	5.47

$Na_2C_4H_4O_6$ Tartrate

M	100R
100° (48)	
1.0	3.83
2.0	3.76
3.0	3.67
4.0	3.55
5.0	3.40
7.5	2.87

$Na_3C_6H_5O_7$ Citrate

M	100R
100° (48)	
0.5	4.41
1.2	4.63
2.0	4.96
2.5	5.09
3.0	5.19
3.5	5.27

NaCNS

M	100R
100° (48)	
0.5	3.07
1.5	3.42
5.0	4.13
6.5	4.30
9.0	4.20
11.0	4.08
12.0	4.02
13.0	3.94

Na_2CrO_4

M	100R
100° (48)	
0.5	3.78
3.0 ↓	4.65
3.5	4.74
4.5	4.68

Na_2MoO_4

M	100R
100° (48)	
0.7	4.38
1.3	4.42
2.0	4.69
3.0 ↓	5.19
3.3	5.33
4.0	5.59

Na_2WO_4

M	100R
100° (48)	
0.3	3.64
0.7	4.12
1.0	4.32
1.5	4.57
3.5 ↓	5.29

$Na_2W_4O_{13}$

M	100R
100° (48)	
0.2	3.50
0.5	2.94
1.0	2.77
2.2	3.72
3.3	5.08

$Na_2B_4O_7$

M	100R
100° (48)	
0.3	6.11
0.6	5.15
0.7	4.93
1.0	4.40
1.3	3.98
2.0	3.48
2.5	3.33

KOH

v. also p. 373

M	100R
0° (43, 44, 45)	
0.5	3.32
1.0	3.54
2.5	4.05
0° (12, 13, 14, 15)	
1.0	2.88
2.0	2.98
5.0	3.29
7.0	3.48
12.0	3.71
19.0	3.52
31.0	2.80
25° (34)	
3.5	4.14
6.0	5.20
8.0	5.53
10.0	5.62
13.0	5.45
16.0	5.10
20.0	4.51
24.0	3.83
100° (48)	
0.5	3.92
1.0	4.00
2.0	4.17
3.0	4.37
5.0	4.77
8.0	5.14
9.0	5.18
11.0	5.06
13.5	4.81

KF (7, 47, 48)

M	100R
30°	
3.0	3.94
8.5	4.78
12.0	4.88
40°	
3.0	3.65
8.5	4.47
12.0	4.58
50°	
3.0	3.46
8.5	4.31
12.0	4.42
60°	
3.5	3.44
8.5	4.18
12.0	4.30
70°	
2.0	3.19
3.5	3.41
8.5	4.06
12.0	4.19
80°	
2.0	3.16
3.5	3.38
8.5	3.96
12.0	4.07
90°	
2.0	3.14
3.5	3.36
8.5	3.86
12.0	3.97
100°	
1.0	2.95
2.0	3.22
3.0	3.36
6.0	3.67
7.0	3.73
10.0	3.84
12.5	3.83
26.0 ↓	2.97

KCl

20° (26)
30° (20)
70–95° (32)
100° (7, 48)

v. also p. 373

(No apparent change with temp.)

M	100R
0.05	3.36
0.10	3.28
0.20	3.22
0.50	3.17_5
1.0	3.16
1.5	3.16
2.0	3.16_8
2.5	3.18
7.0	3.34_5
7.5	3.36

$KClO_3$ (47)

M	100R
65°	
0.7	1.45
1.3 ↓	1.09
70°	
0.8	1.74
1.2 ↓	1.26
75°	
0.8	1.88
1.2 ↓	1.39
80°	
0.8	1.97
1.2 ↓	1.53
85°	
0.8	2.41
1.2 ↓	1.98
90°	
0.8	2.48
1.2 ↓	2.23
95°	
0.8	2.56
1.2 ↓	2.15
100° (7, 48)	
0.5	2.87
1.0	2.85
1.5	2.82
2.5	2.74
3.0	2.71
4.0	2.64
4.7	2.55

$KClO_4$

M	100R
100° (48)	
0.4	2.86
0.8	2.96
1.0	2.89

KBr

M	100R
0° (12, 13, 14, 15)	
1.0	3.15
4.0 ↓	3.18
65° (47)	
2.2	2.99
3.0	3.13
3.8	3.24
5.8	3.08
70° (47)	
2.2	3.03
3.0	3.18
3.8	3.29
5.8	3.14
75° (47)	
2.2	3.05
3.0	3.19
3.8	3.32
5.8	3.15
80° (47)	
2.2	3.11
3.0	3.24
3.8	3.36
5.8	3.20
85° (47)	
2.2	3.15
3.0	3.28
3.8	3.40
5.8	3.23
90° (47)	
2.2	3.17
3.0	3.30
3.8	3.43
5.8	3.24
95° (47)	
2.2	3.19
3.0	3.32
3.8	3.44
5.8	3.27
100° (7, 48)	
1.0	3.15
2.0	3.28
3.0	3.38
4.0	3.45
5.0	3.49
6.0	3.50
7.5	3.49
9.0	3.46

$KBrO_3$

M	100R
100° (48)	
0.5	2.85
2.5 ↓	3.02

KI (47)

M	100R
30°	
2.0	2.64
4.0	2.90
5.7	3.02
40°	
1.0	2.54
2.0	2.82
4.0	3.10
5.7	3.22
50°	
1.0	2.72
2.0	2.99
4.0	3.30
5.7	3.39
60°	
1.0	2.85
2.0	3.12
4.0	3.43
5.7	3.53
70°	
1.0	2.94
2.0	3.22
4.0	3.51
5.7	3.60
80°	
1.0	3.00
2.0	3.28
4.0	3.55
5.7	3.65
90°	
1.0	3.05
2.0	3.33
4.0	3.60
5.7	3.69
100°	
1.5	3.30
2.5	3.54
3.5	3.67
4.5	3.73
6.0	3.78
8.0	3.76
10.0	3.67
12.0	3.52
23° (6)	
1.0	2.77
2.0	3.03
4.0	3.47
6.5	3.56
9.5	3.31

K_2SO_4

v. also p. 373

M	100R
30° (20)	
0.1	3.54
0.8 ↓	3.43
100° (7, 48)	
0.4	3.62
1.4 ↓	3.42

$K_2S_2O_3$

M	100R
100° (48)	
0.3	3.65
0.5	3.56
1.0	3.50
2.0	3.50
3.0	3.63
4.0	3.75
5.0	3.83
7.5	3.89
10.5	3.65

$K_2S_2O_6$

M	100R
100° (48)	
0.5	3.21
1.0	3.17
1.5	3.15
1.7	3.12
2.0	3.05

$KHSO_4$

M	100R
100° (48)	
1.0	2.89
2.0	2.90
4.0	2.88
5.0	2.87
6.0	2.85
8.0	2.80
9.0	2.77

KNO_2

M	100R
100° (48)	
2.0	2.96
3.0	2.97
4.0	2.95
6.0	2.87
8.0	2.75
10.0	2.63
21.0 ↓	2.03
27.0	1.80

KNO_3

M	100R
19.94° (49)	
0.2	3.09
0.5	2.90
1.5	2.45
2.0	2.29
2.5	2.16
3.0	2.03
70° (32, 47)	
1.1	2.88
2.2	2.57
3.0	2.42
5.0	2.16
10.0	1.80
15.0	1.57
80° (32, 47)	
1.1	2.94
2.2	2.65
3.0	2.49
5.0	2.24
10.0	1.87
15.0	1.63
90° (32, 47)	
1.0	3.02
2.2	2.72
3.0	2.57

M	100R
5.0	2.30
10.0	1.92
15.0	1.67
100° (7, 48)	
0.5	3.23
1.0	3.05
2.5	2.71
3.0	2.62
5.0	2.34
10.0	1.96
15.0	1.70
20.0	1.54
24.0	1.44

KH_2PO_4

100° (48)

1.0	2.55
2.0	2.24
3.0	2.10
4.0	2.01
5.0	1.92
7.0	1.84

KH_2AsO_4

100° (48)

0.8	2.80
1.5	2.55
2.5	2.41
3.5	2.32
4.5	2.27

K_2CO_3 (47, 48)

30°	
1.5	4.58
3.5	5.40
6.0	6.40
8.0	6.80
40°	
1.5	4.52
3.5	5.36
6.0	6.30
8.0	6.72
50°	
1.5	4.44
3.5	5.30
6.0	6.21
8.0	6.64
60°	
1.5	4.38
3.5	5.22
6.0	6.12
8.0	6.54
70°	
1.5	4.26
3.5	5.10
6.0	5.98
8.0	6.34
80°	
1.5	4.13
3.5	4.92
6.0	5.78
8.0	6.14

M	100R
90°	
1.5	4.04
3.5	4.82
6.0	5.64
8.0	6.03
100°	
1.5	4.16
3.5	4.78
6.0	5.59
8.0	5.76
10.6	5.2

$K_2C_2O_4$

Oxalate

100° (48)

0.5	3.67
1.0	3.74
1.5	3.84
2.0	3.96
4.5 ↓	4.40

$KCHO_2$

Formate

100° (48)

1.0	3.10
2.0	3.28
3.0	3.38
4.0	3.45
5.0	3.49
6.0	3.50
8.0 ↓	3.50
12.0	3.28
16.0	2.96
21.0	2.65

$KC_2H_3O_2$

Acetate

100° (48)

1.0	3.32
2.0	3.56
3.0	3.75
4.0	3.90
5.0	4.01
7.0	4.13
9.0	4.10
10.0	4.04
11.0	3.96
20.0 ↓	3.16
28.0	2.60

$K_2C_3H_2O_4$

Malonate

100° (48)

0.75	3.77
1.5	4.48

$KC_3H_5O_2$

Propionate

100° (48)

1.0	3.25
2.0	3.50
6.0	4.00
8.0	3.91
10.0	3.78
13.0	3.57

$KC_4H_7O_2$

Butyrate

M	100R
100° (48)	
1.2	3.34
2.0	3.57
4.2	3.74
6.0	3.70
7.0	3.67
11.5	3.44

Isobutyrate

100° (48)

2.0	3.42
3.5	3.65
5.5	3.68
7.5	3.61
10.0	3.50
15.0	3.20

$KC_5H_9O_2$

Valerate

100° (48)

1.5	3.15
2.2	3.26
3.9	3.27
4.2	3.26
9.0	3.09
17.0	2.77

$KC_7H_5O_2$

Benzoate

100° (48)

1.5	3.21
3.0	3.19
4.0	3.17
5.7	3.13

$K_2C_4H_4O_4$

Succinate

100° (48)

0.8	4.60
1.6	5.07
2.5	5.51
3.5	5.92
5.0	6.17
5.5	6.10

$K_2C_4H_4O_6$

Tartrate

100° (48)

1.0	3.90
3.0 ↓	4.05
4.5	4.22
9.5 ↓	3.86

$K_3C_6H_5O_7$

Citrate

100° (48)

0.6	4.60
2.0 ↓	5.99
2.8	6.39
4.6	6.73
5.0	6.77

KCNS (47)

M	100R
40°	
2.0	2.62
5.0	2.95
8.0	2.85
50°	
2.0	2.77
5.0	3.09
8.0	2.98
60°	
2.0	2.92
5.0	3.18
8.0	3.08
70°	
2.0	3.03
5.0	3.22
8.0	3.13
80°	
2.0	3.15
5.0	3.29
8.0	3.19
90°	
2.0	3.25
5.0	3.34
8.0	3.25
100° (48)	
0.8	2.93
1.5	3.21
3.0	3.34
5.0	3.39
8.0	3.32
16.5 ↓	2.78
27.0	2.20

$KSbOC_4H_4O_6$

Antimonyl tartrate

100° (48)

0.4	1.83
0.7	1.83
1.4	1.62

$K_4Fe(CN)_6$

100° (48)

0.2	4.05
0.5	4.33
0.8	4.63
1.2	4.90
1.5	5.13

K_2CrO_4 (47)

M	100R
40–50°	
1.3	3.94
2.0	4.19
2.6	4.36
3.6	4.56
60°	
1.3	3.92
2.0	4.18
2.6	4.32
3.6	4.51
70°	
1.3	3.86
2.0	4.11
2.6	4.26
3.6	4.45
80°	
1.3	3.79
2.0	4.03
2.6	4.18
3.6	4.38
90°	
1.3	3.70
2.0	3.94
2.6	4.10
3.6	4.28
100° (48)	
0.6	4.18
0.8	4.02
1.0	3.93
1.4	3.84
1.8	3.82
2.5	4.00
2.8	4.07

K_2MoO_4

100° (48)

0.8	3.91
1.6	4.40
2.3	4.75
3.7	5.34
4.7	5.56

K_2WO_4

100° (48)

0.6	3.80
1.5	4.52
2.0	4.85
2.5	5.13
3.0	5.36
4.0	5.72
5.0	5.94

RbCl (47, 48)

v. also p. 374

50°	
1.5	3.13
3.0	3.33
6.0	3.56
70°	
1.5	3.07
3.0	3.29
6.0	3.54
90°	
1.5	3.03
3.0	3.26
6.0	3.51
100°	
1.5	3.27
3.0	3.35
4.0	3.39
5.0	3.40
10.0	3.26

Rb_2SO_4

100° (48)

0.4	3.86
0.7	3.80
1.2	3.69
1.6	3.70
2.4	3.81

$RbHSO_4$

100° (48)

0.5	2.87
1.1	2.89
1.7	2.88
2.4	2.85
5.2	2.73

$RbNO_3$

M	100R
100° (48)	
0.7	2.86
1.4	2.84
2.2	2.75
3.2	2.50
5.8	2.25

CsCl

t, °C	100R
M = 1.783 (47)	
30	4.05
40	3.95
75 ↓	3.47
80	3.42
90	3.37
100	3.36

Three-Component Systems

$C_{12}H_{22}O_{11}$

Sucrose

B = **NaCl**

C = **H_2O**

25° (41)

ΣM	100R
Mole ratio A/B = 0.0636	
2.2	2.72
2.8	3.22
5.0	3.48
Mole ratio A/B = 0.187	
5.4	3.01
7.0	2.98
Mole ratio A/B = 0.487	
5.4	2.43
6.4	2.56
8.0	2.60
Mole ratio A/B = 0.588	
3.2	2.06
4.4	2.46
6.2	2.25
Mole ratio A/B = 0.918	
2.7	2.04
4.0	2.00
7.9	2.28
Mole ratio A/B = 1.760	
3.0	1.60
4.3	2.21
6.6	2.11
Mole ratio A/B = 3.400	
2.7	2.24
3.8	1.96
5.4	2.42
6.8	2.51

NON-AQUEOUS SOLUTIONS

The quantities appearing in the tables are: 100 x_1, the mole per cent of the solute; and $k_R = \frac{p_0 - p}{x_1 p_0}$. Within the accuracy of the data the relation between x_1 and k_R is linear between values marked with an arrow, thus 13, 16 ↓.

Solvent = Br_2 (53)

BrI

$100x_1$	$100k_R$
2.55	99

S_2

$100x_1$	$100k_R$
4	143
7	105

$SnBr_4$

$100x_1$	$100k_R$
8.3	94
8.6	87

$SbBr_3$

$100x_1$	$100k_R$
8.7	75
8.9	83

$CHBr_3$

$100x_1$	$100k_R$
10.0	97
10.2	103

Solvent = Hg

v. also p. 284

Bi 320–322° (16)

$100x_1$	$100k_R$
5	77
10	67
20	63.5
35	68.5
50	77
60	82.5
100 ↓	100

Sn 305–358° (42)

$100x_1$	$100k_R$
95	95
97	97

Tl 325° (21, 22)

$100x_1$	$100k_R$
5	105
10	116
20	121
35	118
50	113
70	107
80	104

Zn (22)

$100x_1$	$100k_R$
10	93
30	84
40	82
50	83
60	87

Ag 313–320° (16)

$100x_1$	$100k_R$
0.25	101

Au 313–320° (16)

$100x_1$	$100k_R$
5	55
10	51
20	35

Solvent = NH_3

NH_4N_3 −33° (8)

	$100x_1$	$100k_R$
	13	181
	16 ↓	246
Supersat.	17	262
Supersat.	18	275
Supersat.	19	285
Supersat.	20	291

0° (8)

$100x_1$	$100k_R$
19	231
22 ↓	248

Solvent = C_6H_6

$C_{10}H_8$ Naphthalene (38)

$100x_1$	$100k_R$
0.5	101.9
3 ↓	97.5
4	96.4
5	96.0
6	95.9
7	95.9
8	96.1
9	97.1

$C_{14}H_{10}$ Anthracene (40)

Solvent = CH_3OH

$C_3H_8O_3$ Glycerol 40° (9)

$100x_1$	$100k_R$
6	82.0
22	63.0
37	61.9
50	69.4
60	76.3
80	86.2
85	89.3

$C_{14}H_{10}O_2$ Benzil 15° (51)

$100x_1$	$100k_R$
0.2	84
0.4	85
0.6	86

$C_4H_{12}IN$ Tetramethyl-ammonium iodide

$100x_1$	$100k_R$
0.0461	64.3
0.0616	87.6

LiCl

$100x_1$	$100k_R$
0.5	170
1	173
1.5	176
2	182
2.5	188
3	193
4	198

KI

$100x_1$	$100k_R$
1.0	164
1.5	165
2.0	167
2.5	169

Solvent = C_2H_5OH

$C_3H_8O_3$ Glycerol 15° (1)

$100x_1$	$100k_R$
20	44.0
30	45.0
40	46.3
50	48.0
60	51.0
70	56.5
80	66.8
90	80.0

$C_7H_6O_2$ Benzoic acid 19.5° (54)

$100x_1$	$100k_R$
2.676	95.1

$C_{14}H_{10}O_2$ Benzil 15° (51)

$100x_1$	$100k_R$
0.1	98.9
0.2	106.3
0.3	109.6
0.6	100.7

$CO(NH_2)_2$ Urea 19.0° (54)

$100x_1$	$100k_R$
2.788	107.1

CH_3CONH_2 Acetamide 17.0° (54)

$100x_1$	$100k_R$
2.811	100.8

LiCl 15° (51)

$100x_1$	$100k_R$
1.5	118
1.8	127
2.2	162
3.8	144
4.0	139

KI 15° (51)

$100x_1$	$100k_R$
0.17	115.0
0.27	127.5
0.46	127.8

Solvent = $(CH_3)_2CO$ Acetone

$C_{18}H_{34}O_2$ Oleic acid 30° (9)

$100x_1$	$100k_R$
40	82
60	87
90	95

$C_3H_5N_3O_9$ Nitroglycerine 18° (28)

$100x_1$	$100k_R$
10	130
20	154
30	148
40	140
50	131
60	124
70	117
80	111
90	105

v. also p. 288

Solvent = $(C_2H_5)_2O$ Ethyl ether

H_2SO_4 30° (9)

$100x_1$	$100k_R$
2	71
19	76
37 ↓	175
39	182
52	184

For aqueous H_2SO_4, *v.* (55)

$C_{18}H_{34}O_2$ Oleic acid 30° (9)

$100x_1$	$100k_R$
14	120
100 ↓	100

C_6H_7N Aniline 20° (9)

$100x_1$	$100k_R$
12	125
18	96
50	87
60	86
70	87
90	93

Solvent = CCl_4

$C_{10}H_8$ Naphthalene 15.5° (54)

$100x_1$	$100k_R$
1.92	107.8

$C_{14}H_{10}$ Phenanthrene 19.0° (54)

$100x_1$	$100k_R$
1.85	105.0

Solvent = CS_2

$C_{18}H_{34}O_2$ Oleic acid 30° (9)

$100x_1$	$100k_R$
18	87.5
44 ↓	105.0
60	104.8
90	101.2

Solvent = Na_2CO_3

NaCN

v. p. 285

LITERATURE

(For a key to the periodicals see end of volume)

(1) Anderson, *7*, **88**: 191; 14. (2) Baker and Waite, *33*, **25**: 1174; 21. (3) Beard, *Diss.*, Johns Hopkins Univ., 1922. (4) Berkeley, Hartley and Burton, *62*, **209**: 177; 09. (5) Berkeley, Hartley and Burton, *62*, **218**: 295; 19. (6) Boswell and Cantelo, *324*, **6**: 109; 22. (7) Brönsted, *7*, **82**: 621; 13. (8) Brown and Houlehan, *1*, **35**: 649; 13. (9) Campbell, *83*: **11**: 91; 15.

(10) Charpy, *34*, **113**: 794; 91. (11) Dieterici, *8*, **70**: 617; 23. (12) Dieterici, *8*, **42**: 513; 91. (13) Dieterici, *8*, **50**: 47; 93. (14) Dieterici, *8*, **62**: 616; 97. (15) Dieterici, *8*, **67**: 859; 99. (16) Eastman and Hildebrand, *1*, **36**: 2020; 14. (17) Frazer, Lovelace and Rogers, *1*, **42**: 1793; 20. (18) Gerike, *55*, **17**: 78; 15. (19) Grollman and Frazer, *1*, **47**: 712; 25.

(20) Hartung, *83*, **15 III**: 150; 20. (21) Hildebrand, *Comm. 8th Int. Cong. Appl. Chem.*, **22**: 147; 12. (22) Hildebrand, *78*, **22**: 335; 13. (23)Hildebr and and Eastman, *1*, **37**: 2452; 15. (24) Holland, *Diss.*, Johns Hopkins Univ., 1924. (25) Lovelace, Bahlke and Frazer, *1*, **45**: 2930; 23. (26) Lovelace, Frazer and Sease, *1*, **43**: 102; 21. (27) Marshall, *182*, **29**: 157; 15. (28) Marshall and Peace, *4*, **109**: 298; 16. (29) Menzies and Boving, *Comm. 8th Int. Cong. Appl. Chem.*, **22**: 219; 12.

(30) Muralt, *Diss.*, Zurich Tech. Hoch., 1919. (31) Negus, *Diss.*, Johns Hopkins Univ., 1923. (32) Nicol, *3*, **22**: 502; 86. (33) Norris, *Diss.*, Johns Hopkins Univ., 1922. (34) Paranjpé, *318*, **2**: 59; 18. (35) Parker, *Diss.*, Johns Hopkins Univ., 1921. (36) Perman and Price, *83*, **8**: 68; 12. (37) Prideaux and Caven, *54*, **38**: 353; 19. (38) Raoult, *271*, **14**: 225; 00. (39) Roozeboom, *7*, **4**: 31; 89.

(40) Rosanoff and Dunphy, *1*, **36**: 1411; 14. (41) Schoorl, *70*, **42**: 790; 23. (42) Sieverts and Oehme, *25*, **46**: 1238; 13. (43) Smits, *18*, **1**: 97; 98. (44) Smits, *7*, **39**: 385; 02. (45) Smits, *7*, **51**: 33; 05. (46) Swietoslawski, *27*, **37**: 263; 25. (47) Tammann, *8*, **24**: 523; 85. (48) Tammann, *St. Pétersb. Ac. Sci. Mém.* **35**: No. 9; 87. (49) Taylor, *Diss.*, Johns Hopkins Univ., 1923.

(50) Tower, *1*, **30**: 1219; 08. (51) Tower and Germann, *1*, **36**: 2449; 14. (52) Washburn and Heuse, *1*, **37**: 309; 15. (53) Wright, *4*, **109**: 1134; 16. (54) Wright, *4*, **115**: 1165; 19. (55) Pound, *4*, **99**: 698; 11.

THE VAPOR PRESSURES OF AQUEOUS SOLUTIONS OF COMMERCIAL ACIDS

FRED C. ZEISBERG, W. B. VAN ARSDEL, FRANK C. BLAKE, C. H. GREENEWALT AND G. B. TAYLOR

PARTIAL VAPOR PRESSURES OF AQUEOUS SOLUTIONS OF HCl

FRED C. ZEISBERG

$\log_{10} p_{mm} = A - B/T$, which, however agrees only approximately with the table. The table is more nearly correct.

Partial Pressure of H_2O, mm Hg, °C

% HCl	A	B	0°	5°	10°	15°	20°	25°	30°	35°	40°	45°	50°	60	70°	80°	90°	100°	110°
6	8.99156	2282	4.18	6.04	8.45	11.7	15.9	21.8	29.1	39.4	50.6	66.2	86.0	139	220	333	492	715	
10	8.99864	2295	3.84	5.52	7.70	10.7	14.6	20.0	26.8	35.5	47.0	61.5	80.0	130	204	310	463	677	960
14	8.97075	2300	3.39	4.91	6.95	9.65	13.1	18.0	24.1	31.9	42.1	55.3	72.0	116	185	273	425	625	892
18	8.98014	2323	2.87	4.21	5.92	8.26	11.3	15.4	20.6	27.5	36.4	47.9	62.5	102	162	248	374	550	783
20	8.97877	2334	2.62	3.83	5.40	7.50	10.3	14.1	19.0	25.1	33.3	43.6	57.0	93.5	150	230	345	510	729
22	9.02708	2363	2.33	3.40	4.82	6.75	9.30	12.6	17.1	22.8	30.2	39.8	52.0	85.6	138	211	317	467	670
24	8.96022	2356	2.05	3.04	4.31	6.03	8.30	11.4	15.4	20.4	27.1	35.7	46.7	77.0	124	194	290	426	611
26	9.01511	2390	1.76	2.60	3.71	5.21	7.21	9.95	13.5	18.0	24.0	31.7	41.5	69.0	112	173	261	388	554
28	8.97611	2395	1.50	2.24	3.21	4.54	6.32	8.75	11.8	15.8	21.1	27.9	36.5	60.7	99.0	154	234	349	499
30	9.00117	2422	1.26	1.90	2.73	3.88	5.41	7.52	10.2	13.7	18.4	24.3	32.0	53.5	87.5	136	207	310	444
32	9.03317	2453	1.04	1.57	2.27	3.25	4.55	6.37	8.70	11.7	15.7	21.0	27.7	46.5	76.5	120	184	275	396
34	9.07143	2487	0.85	1.29	1.87	2.70	3.81	5.35	7.32	9.95	13.5	18.1	24.0	40.5	66.5	104	161	243	355
36	9.11815	2526	0.68	1.03	1.50	2.19	3.10	4.41	6.08	8.33	11.4	15.4	20.4	34.8	57.0	90.0	140	212	311
38	9.20783	2579	0.53	0.81	1.20	1.75	2.51	3.60	5.03	6.92	9.52	13.0	17.4	29.6	49.1	77.5	120	182	266
40	9.33923	2647	0.41	0.63	0.94	1.37	2.00	2.88	4.09	5.68	7.85	10.7	14.5	25.0	42.1	67.3	105	158	230
42	9.44953	2709	0.31	0.48	0.72	1.06	1.56	2.30	3.28	4.60	6.45	8.90	12.1	21.2	35.8	57.2	89.2	135	195

Partial Pressure of HCl, mm Hg, °C

% HCl	A	B	0°	5°	10°	15°	20°	25°	30°	35°	40°	45°	50°	60°	70°	80°	90°	100°	110°
2	11.8037	4736			0.0000117	0.000023	0.000044	0.000084	0.000151	0.000275	0.00047	0.00083	0.00140	0.00380	0.0100	0.0245	0.058	0.132	0.28
4	11.6400	4471	0.000018	0.000036	0.000069	0.000131	0.00024	0.00044	0.00077	0.00134	0.0023	0.00385	0.0064	0.0165	0.0405	0.095	0.21	0.46	0.93
6	11.2144	4202	0.000066	0.000125	0.000234	0.000425	0.00076	0.00131	0.00225	0.0038	0.0062	0.0102	0.0163	0.040	0.094	0.206	0.44	0.92	1.78
8	11.0406	4042	0.000118	0.000323	0.000583	0.00104	0.00178	0.0031	0.00515	0.0085	0.0136	0.022	0.0344	0.081	0.183	0.39	0.82	1.64	3.10
10	10.9311	3908	0.00042	0.00075	0.00134	0.00232	0.00395	0.0067	0.0111	0.0178	0.0282	0.045	0.069	0.157	0.35	0.73	1.48	2.9	5.4
12	10.7900	3765	0.00099	0.00175	0.00305	0.0052	0.0088	0.0145	0.0234	0.037	0.058	0.091	0.136	0.305	0.66	1.34	2.65	5.1	9.3
14	10.6954	3636	0.0024	0.00415	0.0071	0.0118	0.0196	0.0316	0.050	0.078	0.121	0.185	0.275	0.60	1.25	2.50	4.8	9.0	16.0
16	10.6261	3516	0.0056	0.0095	0.016	0.0265	0.0428	0.0685	0.106	0.163	0.247	0.375	0.55	1.17	2.40	4.66	8.8	16.1	28
18	10.4957	3376	0.0135	0.0225	0.037	0.060	0.095	0.148	0.228	0.345	0.515	0.77	1.11	2.3	4.55	8.6	15.7	28	48
20	10.3833	3245	0.0316	0.052	0.084	0.132	0.205	0.32	0.48	0.72	1.06	1.55	2.21	4.4	8.5	15.6	28.1	49	83
22	10.3172	3125	0.0734	0.119	0.187	0.294	0.45	0.68	1.02	1.50	2.18	3.14	4.42	8.6	16.3	29.3	52	90	146
24	10.2185	2995	0.175	0.277	0.43	0.66	1.00	1.49	2.17	3.14	4.5	6.4	8.9	16.9	31.0	54.5	94	157	253
26	10.1303	2870	0.41	0.64	0.98	1.47	2.17	3.20	4.56	6.50	9.2	12.7	17.5	32.5	58.5	100	169	276	436
28	10.0115	2732	1.0	1.52	2.27	3.36	4.90	7.05	9.90	13.8	19.1	26.4	35.7	64	112	188	309	493	760
30	9.8763	2593	2.4	3.57	5.23	7.60	10.6	15.1	21.0	28.6	39.4	53	71	124	208	340	542	845	
32	9.7523	2457	5.7	8.3	11.8	16.8	23.5	32.5	44.5	60.0	81	107	141	238	390	623	970		
34	9.6061	2316	13.1	18.8	26.4	36.8	50.5	68.5	92	122	161	211	273	450	720				
36	9.6262	2229	29.0	41.0	56.4	78	105.5	142	188	246	322	416	535	860					
38	9.4670	2094	63.0	87.0	117	158	210	277	360	465	598	758	955						
40	9.2156	1939	130	176	233	307	399	515	627	830									
42	8.9925	1800	253	332	430	560	709	900											
44	8.8621	1681	510	655	840														
46			940																

Accuracy, *ca.* 2 % for solutions of 15 to 30 % HCl between 0 and 100°; for solutions of >30 % HCl the accuracy is *ca.* 5 % at the lower temperatures and *ca.* 15 % at the higher temperatures. Below 15 % HCl, the accuracy is *ca.* 5 % at the lower temperatures and higher strengths to *ca.* 15–20 % at the lower strengths and perhaps 15–20 % at the higher temperatures and lower strengths. The above table is practically based upon the data of (2, 6, 9, 10, 13, 15), the data of other observers being discordant. The new data by Klemenc and Nagel (11) at 12.5°C were not available for consideration at the time the table was prepared.

LITERATURE

(For a key to the periodicals see end of volume)

(1) Allan, *50*, **2**: 120; 98. (2) Bates and Kirschman, *1*, **41**: 1991; 19. (3) Bineau, *6*, **7**: 257; 43. (4) Dobson and Masson, *4*, **125**: 668; 24. (5) Dolezalek, *7*, **26**: 321; 98. (6) Dunn and Rideal, *4*, **125**: 676; 24. (7) Foulk and Hollingsworth, *1*, **45**: 1220; 23. (8) Gahl, *7*, **33**: 178; 00. (9) Harned, *1*, **44**: 252; 22. (10) Hulett and Bonner, *1*, **31**: 390; 09. (11) Klemenc and Nagel, *93*, **155**: 257; 26. (12) Roscoe, *13*, **116**: 203; 60. (13) Roscoe and Dittmar, *13*, **112**: 327; 59. (14) Vrevskii, *53*, **42**: 1349; 10. (15) Vrevskii, Zavarickii, and Sharlov, *53*, **54**: 360; 23. (16) Yannakis, *34*, **177**: 174; 23.

PARTIAL VAPOR PRESSURES OF AQUEOUS SOLUTIONS OF SULFUR DIOXIDE

W. B. Van Arsdel

Partial Pressures of H_2O and SO_2, mm Hg, °C

v. also p. 258

Grams SO_2 per 100 g water	10°C		20°C		30°C		40°C		50°C		60°C		70°C	
	H_2O	SO_2	H_2O	SO_2	H_2O	SO_2	H_2O	SO_2	H_2O	SO_2	H_2O	SO_2	H_2O	SO_2
0.0	9.2		17.5		31.8		55.3		92.5		149.5		234	
0.5	9.2	21	17.5	29	31.7	42	55.2	60	92.3	83	149.2	111	234	144
1.0	9.2	42	17.4	59	31.7	85	55.1	120	92.2	164	149.0	217	233	281
1.5	9.2	64	17.4	90	31.6	129	55.0	181	92.0	247	148.8	328	233	426
2.0	9.1	86	17.4	123	31.6	176	55.0	245	91.9	333	148.6	444	233	581
2.5	9.1	108	17.4	157	31.5	224	54.9	311	91.8	421	148.3	562	232	739
3.0	9.1	130	17.3	191	31.5	273	54.7	378	91.6	511	148.1	682	232	897
3.5	9.1	153	17.3	227	31.5	324	54.7	447	91.5	603	147.9	804		
4.0	9.1	176	17.3	264	31.4	376	54.6	518	91.4	698				
4.5	9.1	199	17.3	300	31.4	428	54.5	588	91.2	793				
5.0	9.1	223	17.2	338	31.3	482	54.4	661						
5.5	9.0	247	17.2	375	31.3	536	54.4	733						
6.0	9.0	271	17.2	411	31.2	588	54.3	804						
6.5	9.0	295	17.2	448	31.2	642								
7.0	9.0	320	17.1	486	31.1	698								
7.5	9.0	345	17.1	524	31.1	752								
8.0	9.0	370	17.1	562	31.0	806								
8.5	9.0	395	17.0	600										
9.0	9.0	421	17.0	638										
9.5	8.9	447	17.0	676										
10.0	8.9	473	17.0	714										
10.5	8.9	499	17.0	751										
11.0	8.9	526	16.9	789										
11.5	8.9	553												
12.0	8.9	580												
12.5	8.9	608												
13.0	8.8	635												
13.5	8.8	662												
14.0	8.8	689												
14.5	8.8	716												
15.0	8.8	743												
15.5	8.8	771												
16.0	8.8	799												

Grams SO_2 per 100 g water	80°C		90°C		100°C		110°C		120°C		130°C	
	H_2O	SO_2	H_2O	SO_2	H_2O	SO_2	H_2O	SO_2	H_2O	SO_2	H_2O	SO_2
0.0	355		526		760		1074		1488		2026	
0.5	354	182	525	225	758	274	1072	326	1486	377	2024	420
1.0	354	356	524	445	757	548	1071	661	1484	775	2022	879
1.5	353	543	523	684	756	850	1070	1032				
2.0	353	746	523	940								
2.5	352	956										

The above table is based upon the data of the following observers, the weight assigned to each being indicated: Schoenfeld, 0; Sims, 3; Smith-Parkhurst, 4; Freese, 0; Öman, 3; Enckell, 3; Hudson, 5; Taylor, 2; and Taylor and Chase, 4. The partial pressure of water was calculated using Fulda's values for the ionization constant of H_2SO_3.

LITERATURE

(For a key to the periodicals see end of volume)

(1) Enckell, *Papp. träv. tids. Finland*, No. **4:** 93; 25. *472*, **23:** 633; 25. (2) Freese, *491*, **51:** 861; 20. (3) Fulda, *291*, **30:** 81; 09. (4) Hudson, *4*, **127:** 1332; 25. (5) Öman, *485*, **54:** 81; 24. (6) Scheel and Heuse, *8*, **31** 715; 10. (7) Schönfeld, *13*, **95:** 1; 55. (8) Sims, *4*, **14:** 1; 62. (9) Smith and Parkhurst, *1*, **44:** 1918; 22.
(10) Taylor, Research Dept., The Brown Co., Berlin, New Hampshire, *0*. (11) Taylor and Thing, Research Dept., The Brown Co., Berlin, New Hampshire, *0*. (12) Taylor and Chase, The Brown Co., Berlin, N. H., *0*.

VAPOR PRESSURES, NORMAL BOILING POINTS, AND LATENT HEATS OF VAPORIZATION FOR AQUEOUS SOLUTIONS OF H_2SO_4

Frank C. Blake and C. H. Greenewalt

% = Wt. % H_2SO_4 in the solution.
A and B are constants in the equation $\log_{10} p_{mm} = A - B/T$
l = total heat of vaporization in g-cal_{15} per g of water evaporated.
B. P. = normal boiling point, °C.
For bibliography and discussion of data, *v.* Greenewalt, *45*, **17:** 522; 25.

% =	95	90	85	80	75	70	65	60	55	50	45	40	35	30	25	20	10
A =	9.790	9.255	9.239	9.293	9.034	9.032	8.853	8.841	8.827	8.832	8.809	8.844	8.873	8.864		8.922	8.925
B =	3888	3390	3175	3040	2810	2688	2533	2458	2400	2357	2322	2299	2286	2271		2268	2259
l =	987	861	806	772	713	682	643	624	609	598	590	584	580	577		576	574
B. P. =	290	255	225	202	182	165	151	140	130	123	118	114	110	108	106	104	102
°C	Total vapor pressure, mm Hg																
0			0.00418	0.0144	0.0550	0.154	0.377	0.686	1.08	1.55	2.07	2.55	3.06	3.43	3.72	4.02	4.38
5		0.00118	0.00680	0.0230	0.0867	0.235	0.558	1.03	1.60	2.26	2.99	3.69	4.40	4.94	5.33	5.87	6.30
10		0.00196	0.0108	0.0358	0.128	0.342	0.800	1.46	2.26	3.19	4.19	5.22	6.23	6.91	7.46	8.05	8.80
15		0.00318	0.0169	0.0555	0.195	0.506	1.15	2.05	3.19	4.50	5.85	7.27	8.65	9.65	10.5	11.3	12.3
20		0.00497	0.0257	0.0835	0.284	0.723	1.61	2.87	4.43	6.20	8.10	9.95	11.8	13.2	14.3	15.4	16.6
25		0.00765	0.0390	0.124	0.408	1.03	2.24	3.97	6.15	8.45	10.9	13.5	15.8	17.8	19.4	20.8	22.4
30		0.0117	0.0585	0.183	0.580	1.44	3.09	5.41	8.29	11.3	14.7	18.0	21.2	23.8	26.0	27.8	30.0
35	0.00150	0.0179	0.0860	0.265	0.822	2.00	4.23	7.39	11.2	15.4	19.7	24.3	28.6	31.9	35.0	37.2	40.1
40	0.00235	0.0265	0.125	0.381	1.14	2.75	5.66	9.85	14.8	20.3	26.0	31.8	37.3	41.7	45.6	48.6	52.9
45	0.00370	0.0395	0.181	0.540	1.57	3.73	7.60	13.0	19.5	26.7	33.0	41.0	48.6	54.7	59.0	63.3	68.1
50	0.00580	0.0580	0.260	0.770	2.20	5.17	10.2	17.5	26.0	35.2	44.7	53.9	63.0	71.3	76.7	82.2	88.5
55	0.00877	0.0840	0.367	1.06	2.95	6.89	13.4	22.7	33.7	45.5	57.5	69.0	80.2	91.0	98.2	106	113
60	0.0133	0.120	0.411	1.47	3.98	9.12	18.6	29.3	43.0	58.0	73.0	87.3	102	116	124	133	143
65	0.0196	0.169	0.707	2.00	5.30	10.2	22.7	37.7	55.1	73.7	92.3	110	127	145	156	167	178
70	0.0288	0.236	0.960	2.68	7.02	15.6	29.0	48.0	69.6	92.5	116	138	159	180	195	207	223
75	0.0415	0.327	1.31	3.60	9.26	20.3	37.0	60.2	87.0	115	144	171	198	222	240	256	274
80	0.0606	0.450	1.77	4.77	12.0	26.0	47.0	75.3	108	143	179	211	244	273	295	314	337
85	0.0879	0.618	2.37	6.35	15.6	33.4	59.7	94.3	136	178	211	261	300	333	360	385	413
90	0.123	0.823	3.14	8.30	20.0	42.5	74.6	117	167	217	271	319	369	404	437	468	498
95	0.172	1.12	4.18	10.8	25.7	53.9	92.7	144	205	268	335	390	450	493	531	580	608
100	0.237	1.49	5.39	13.9	32.0	67.0	114	178	253	326	405	474	540	590	637	678	720
105	0.321	1.93	6.95	17.6	40.0	82.3	140	213	302	393	484	568	642	702	758	812	
110	0.437	2.52	9.00	22.5	50.0	103	172	260	367	471	580	679	768				
115	0.590	3.23	11.4	28.3	62.0	126	207	313	435	562	684	800					
120	0.788	4.19	14.5	35.6	76.5	153	251	377	522	670	812						
125	1.07	5.43	18.3	44.7	94.5	188	304	452	625	797							
130	1.42	6.97	23.2	56.0	117	230	370	544	744								
135	1.87	8.85	29.1	69.0	142	277	440	647									
140	2.40	11.2	36.3	85.5	173	332	525	760									
145	3.11	13.9	44.3	104	208	397	622										
150	4.02	17.5	54.6	127	248	471	730										
155	5.13	21.9	68.2	157	299	564											
160	6.47	27.7	82.0	188	354	665											
165	8.39	33.2	99.5	226	422	790											
170	10.3	39.8	119	267	496												
175	12.9	48.4	143	319	585												
180	15.9	59.0	169	378	685												
185	20.2	71.2	206	450	810												
190	24.8	85.0	245	535													
195	30.7	102	291	637													
200	36.7	120	340	735													
205	45.3	143	402														
210	55.0	170	472														
215	66.9	203	557														
220	79.8	240	647														
225	95.5	279	750														
230	115	326															
235	137	380															

°C	95 %	90 %
240	164	450
245	193	520
250	229	604
255	268	700
260	314	800
265	363	
270	430	
275	500	
280	580	
285	682	
290	790	

The Partial Pressure of SO_3 above Fuming Sulfuric Acid, mm Hg, °C

Total H_2SO_4	% SO_3	20°	25°	30°	35°	40°	45°	50°	55°	60°	65°	70°	75°	80°	85°	90°
102%	83.265				0.4	0.6	1.0	1.6	2.5	3.8	5.7	8.5	12.5	18.2	26.3	37.5
103.0	84.081				0.5	0.9	1.3	2.1	3.2	4.8	6.8	10.5	15.3	22.0	31.4	44.4
104.0	84.897	0.2	0.3	0.5	0.8	1.3	2.0	3.0	4.5	6.7	9.8	14.2	20.4	29.0	40.8	56.8
104.5	85.305	0.3	0.4	0.7	1.1	1.7	2.6	4.0	6.0	8.9	12.9	18.8	26.7	37.9	53.5	73.9
105.0	85.714	0.4	0.7	1.1	1.7	2.6	4.0	6.0	9.0	13.1	19.0	27.2	38.6	54.1	75.2	103.7
105.5	86.122	0.8	1.2	1.9	2.9	4.4	6.6	9.8	14.3	20.7	29.5	42.1	58.1	81.5	112.6	153.1
106.0	86.530	1.4	2.1	3.2	4.9	7.3	10.8	15.7	22.6	32.1	45.2	63.0	87.0	119.0	161.5	217.2
106.5	86.938	2.4	3.6	5.5	8.2	12.0	17.4	25.0	35.4	49.8	69.0	95.5	129.3	171.2	230.1	311.9
107.0	87.346	4.0	6.0	8.9	13.0	18.8	26.9	38.1	53.4	74.0	101.6	138.2	186.4	249.2	330.5	434.9
107.5	87.754	6.9	10.0	14.6	20.7	29.2	40.7	56.4	77.1	104.6	140.2	167.3	246.5	323.7	422.2	547.7
108.0	88.163		15.9	22.4	31.4	43.4	59.4	80.6	108.3	144.2	190.4	249.4	324.2			
108.5	88.571			35.1	47.8	64.8	86.9	115.7	152.3	199.4	257.9	333.6	425.1			
109.0	88.979				64.5	86.6	115.3	152.1	199.0	258.3	332.5	425.0	539.5			
110.0	89.795				100.5	133.7	176.1	230.1	298.2	383.5	489.5					
111.0	90.612			105.2	140.5	185.7	243.4	316.3	407.9							
112.0	91.428	76.1	103.2	138.5	184.0	242.4	316.5	409.9	526.6							
113.0	92.244	96.9	130.9	175.1	232.1	304.9	397.1	512.9	657.4							
114.0	93.060	119.1	160.7	214.9	284.5	373.3	485.8	626.9	802.8							
115.0	93.877	144.2	194.3	259.2	342.6	448.8	583.0	751.2	960.4							

Unpublished determinations from the Eastern Laboratory of E. I. du Pont de Nemours & Company.

The Partial Pressures of H_2SO_4 and H_2O over Sulfuric Acid Solutions

t, °C	$p_{H_2SO_4}$	p_{H_2O}
89.25% H_2SO_4		
183.0	0.5	78.8
197.5	1.3	116.9
216.5	2.1	233.1
230.0	3.6	306.3
241.5	5.3	414.8
91.26% H_2SO_4		
191.0	0.6	50.7
205.0	1.9	84.7
222.0	4.5	158.5
242.5	6.4	271.6
252.5	11.3	385.3
258.0	13.6	448.7
262.5	16.3	411.1

t, °C	$p_{H_2SO_4}$	p_{H_2O}
95.06% H_2SO_4		
180.0	2.1	10.1
200.0	4.8	21.2
215.5	8.5	46.5
232.0	13.4	91.9
244.5	19.9	120.1
252.0	20.0	156.5
261.0	27.9	180.7
270.0	39.9	254.9
280.5	52.0	310.0
282.0	52.6	350.2

t, °C	$p_{H_2SO_4}$	p_{H_2O}
98.06% H_2SO_4		
204.0	5.9	0.0
218.5	9.8	1.5
234.5	14.7	3.2
249.0	28.5	2.6
261.0	38.8	5.0
273.0	61.9	5.3
285.0	91.6	11.8
295.0	132.3	14.7

t, °C	$p_{H_2SO_4}$	p_{H_2O}
99.23% H_2SO_4		
211.0	33.2	<0.1
225.0	49.9	
227.0	55.4	
244.0	84.1	
261.0	163.8	
270.0	229.8	
281.0	272.3	
290.0	381.5	

Measurements by Thomas and Barker, *4*, **127**: 2824; 25. *p* in mm Hg. Accuracy, 5 to 15%.

PARTIAL VAPOR PRESSURES OF AQUEOUS SOLUTIONS OF HNO_3, MM HG

G. B. Taylor

Based chiefly upon the data of Creighton and Githens, Carpenter and Babor, Burdick and Freed, Sproesser and Taylor, Pascal, and Klemenc

Percentages are Wt. % HNO_3 in solution

°C	20%		25%		30%		35%	
	HNO_3	H_2O	HNO_3	H_2O	HNO_3	H_2O	HNO_3	H_2O
0		4.1		3.8		3.6		3.3
5		5.7		5.4		5.0		4.6
10		8.0		7.6		7.1		6.5
15		10.9		10.3		9.7		8.9
20		15.2		14.2		13.2		12.0
25		20.6		19.2		17.8		16.2
30		27.6		25.7		23.8	0.09	21.7
35		36.5		33.8		31.1	0.13	28.3
40		47.5		44	0.11	41	0.20	37.7
45		62	0.09	57.5	0.17	53	0.28	48
50		80	0.13	75	0.25	69	0.42	63
55	0.09	100	0.18	94	0.35	87	0.59	79

°C	20%		25%		30%		35%	
	HNO_3	H_2O	HNO_3	H_2O	HNO_3	H_2O	HNO_3	H_2O
60	0.13	128	0.28	121	0.51	113	0.85	102
65	0.19	162	0.40	151	0.71	140	1.18	127
70	0.27	200	0.54	187	1.00	174	1.63	159
75	0.38	250	0.77	234	1.38	217	2.26	198
80	0.53	307	1.05	287	1.87	267	3.07	243
85	0.74	378	1.44	352	2.53	325	4.15	297
90	1.01	458	1.95	426	3.38	393	5.50	359
95	1.37	555	2.62	517	4.53	478	7.32	436
100	1.87	675	3.50	628	6.05	580	9.7	530
105	2.50	800	4.65	745	7.90	690	12.7	631
110							16.5	755

°C	40%		45%		50%		55%		60%	
	HNO_3	H_2O	HNO_3	H_2O	HNO_3	H_2O	HNO_3	H_2O	HNO_3	H_2O
0		3.0		2.6		2.1		1.8	0.19	1.5
5		4.2		3.6		3.0	0.14	2.5	0.28	2.1
10		5.8		5.0	0.12	4.2	0.21	3.5	0.41	3.0
15		8.0	0.10	6.9	0.18	5.8	0.31	4.9	0.59	4.1
20		10.8	0.15	9.4	0.27	7.9	0.45	6.7	0.84	5.6
25	0.12	14.6	0.23	12.7	0.39	10.7	0.66	9.1	1.21	7.7
30	0.17	19.5	0.33	16.9	0.56	14.4	0.93	12.2	1.66	10.3
35	0.25	25.5	0.48	22.3	0.80	19.0	1.30	16.1	2.28	13.6
40	0.36	33.5	0.68	29.3	1.13	25.0	1.82	21.3	3.10	18.1
45	0.52	43	0.96	38.0	1.57	32.5	2.50	28	4.20	23.7
50	0.75	56	1.35	49.5	2.18	42.5	3.41	36.3	5.68	31.0
55	1.04	71	1.83	62.5	2.95	54	4.54	46.0	7.45	39
60	1.48	90	2.54	80	4.05	70	6.15	60	9.9	51
65	2.05	114	3.47	100	5.46	88	8.18	76	13.0	64
70	2.80	143	4.65	126	7.25	110	10.7	95	16.8	81
75	3.80	178	6.20	158	9.6	138	13.9	120	21.8	102
80	5.10	218	8.15	195	12.5	170	18.0	148	27.5	126
85	6.83	268	10.7	240	16.3	211	23.0	182	34.8	156
90	9.0	325	13.7	292	20.9	258	29.4	223	43.7	192
95	11.7	394	17.8	355	26.8	315	37.3	272	55.0	233
100	15.5	480	23.0	430	34.2	383	47	331	69.5	285
105	20.0	573	29.2	520	43.0	463	58.5	400	84.5	345
110	25.7	688	37.0	625	54.5	560	73	485	103	417
115	32.5	810	46	740	67	665	90	575	126	495
120					84	785	110	685	156	590
125									187	700

°C	65%		70%		80%		90%		100%
	HNO_3	H_2O	HNO_3	H_2O	HNO_3	H_2O	HNO_3	H_2O	HNO_3
0	0.41	1.3	0.79	1.1	2		5.5		11
5	0.60	1.8	1.12	1.6	3		8		15
10	0.86	2.6	1.58	2.2	4	1.2	11		22
15	1.21	3.5	2.18	3.0	6	1.7	15		30
20	1.68	4.9	3.00	4.1	8	2.4	20		42
25	2.32	6.6	4.10	5.5	10.5	3.2	27	1	57
30	3.17	8.8	5.50	7.4	14	4	36	1.3	77
35	4.26	11.6	7.30	9.8	18.5	5.5	47	1.8	102
40	5.70	15.5	9.65	12.8	24.5	7	62	2.4	133
45	7.55	20.0	12.6	16.7	32	9.5	80	3	170
50	10.0	26.0	16.5	21.8	41	12	103	4	215
55	12.8	33.0	21.0	27.3	52	15	127	5	262
60	16.8	43.0	27.1	35.3	67	20	157	6.5	320
65	21.7	54.5	34.5	44.5	85	25	192	8	385
70	27.5	68	43.3	56	106	31	232	10	460
75	35.0	86	54.5	70	130	38	282	13	540
80	43.5	106	67.5	86	158	48	338	16	625
85	54.5	131	83	107	192	60	405	20	720
90	67.5	160	103	130	230	73	480	24	820
95	83.5	195	125	158	278	89	570	29	
100	103	238	152	192	330	108	675	35	
105	124	288	183	231	392	129	790	42	
110	152	345	221	270	465	155			
115	181	410	262	330	545	185			
120	218	490	312	393	640	219			
125	260	580	372	469					

LITERATURE

(For a key to the periodicals see end of volume)

(1) Berl and Samtleben, *92*, **35**: 201; 22. (2) Burdick and Freed, *1*, **43**: 518; 21. (3) Carpenter and Babor, *79*, **16 I**: 111; 25. (4) Creighton and Githens, *143*, **179**: 161; 15. (5) Klemenc and Nagel, *93*, **155**: 257; 26. (6) Pascal, *315*, **20**: 40; 23. (7) Roscoe, *4*, **13**: 146; 61. (8) Sapozhnikov, *7*, **53**: 225; 05. (9) Sproesser and Taylor, *1*, **43**: 1782; 21.

THE VAPOR PRESSURES OF AQUEOUS SOLUTIONS OF CH_3COOH, HBr AND HI

C. H. Greenewalt

Total Vapor Pressure of Acetic Acid—Water Mixtures (mm Hg)

% = Wt. % acetic acid in the solution. Based upon the data of Kahlbaum (2) and Konowalow (3)

C° \ %	25	50	75
20	16.3	15.7	15.3
25	22.1	21.4	20.8
30	29.6	28.8	27.8
35	39.4	38.3	36.6
40	51.7	50.2	48.1
45	67.0	65.0	62.0
50	87.2	85.0	80.1
55	110	107	102
60	141	138	130
65	178	172	162
70	223	216	203
75	277	269	251
80	342	331	310
85	419	407	376
90	510	497	458
95	618	602	550
100	743	725	666

Aqueous Solutions of HBr, p_{mm} at 25°C (1)

% HBr	p_{HBr}	% HBr	p_{HBr}	% HBr	p_{HBr}
32	0.0016	38	0.0061	44	.048
34	.0022	40	.011	46	.10
36	.0033	42	.023		

Partial Pressures of H_2O and HBr (mm Hg) (4)

% HBr	20°C		25°C		50°C		55°C	
	HBr	H_2O	HBr	H_2O	HBr	H_2O	HBr	H_2O
48	0.09	6.2	0.13	8.2	1.3	30.2	2.0	38
50	0.23	4.5	0.37	6.1	3.2	24.3	4.6	31
52	0.71	3.3	1.1	4.5	7.2	19.3	10.2	25
54	2.2	2.4	3.2	3.3	17	16.0	23.0	21
56	6.8	1.7	9.3	2.4	40	13.3	51	18
58	21	1.3	27	1.9	91	10.4	115	14
60							260	11.4

Partial Pressure of HI over Aqueous Solutions of HI, 25°C (mm Hg) (1)

% HI..........	44	46	48	50	52	54	56
p_{HI}.............	0.00064	0.0010	0.0022	0.0050	0.013	0.035	0.10

LITERATURE

(For a key to the periodicals see end of volume)

(1) Bates and Kirschman, *1*, **41**: 1991; 19. (2) Kahlbaum, *7*, **13**: 14; 94. (3) Konowalow, *8*, **14**: 34; 81. (4) Vrevskii, Zavarickii and Sharlov, *53*, **54**: 360; 23.

VAPOR PRESSURES, BOILING POINTS AND VAPOR COMPOSITIONS FOR THE SYSTEM $H_2O—H_2SO_4—HNO_3$

F. C. Zeisberg

The available information is summarized and presented below in graphical form. The small circles on the left-hand sides of Figs. 2 and 3 are the critical values for the system $H_2O—HNO_3$ as given above (p. 304). They show that the best available data for the ternary svstem are inconsistent with the best data for the binary system.

LITERATURE

(For a key to the periodicals see end of volume)

(1) Berl and Samtleben, *92*, **35**: 206; 22. (2) Carpenter and Babor, *79*, **16 I**: 111; 25. (3) Creighton and Smith, *143*, **180**: 703; 15. (4) Pascal and Garnier, *14*, **15**: 253; 21. (5) Sapozhnikov, *7*, **49**: 697; 04. **51**: 609; 05. **53**: 225; 05. (6) Sapozhnikov, *245*, **4**: 441, 462; 09.

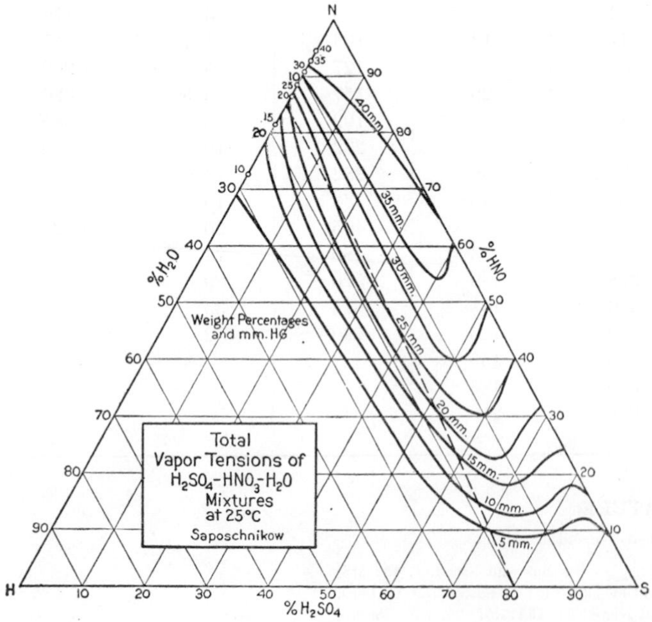

Fig. 2.

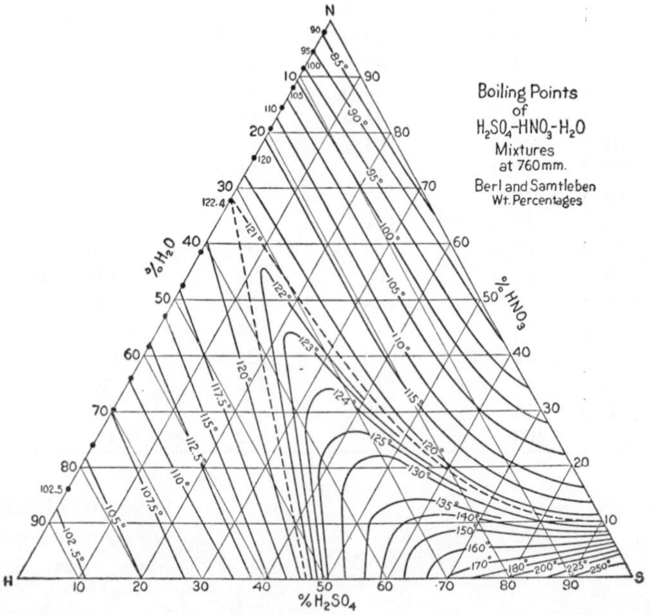

Fig. 3.

Fig. 1.

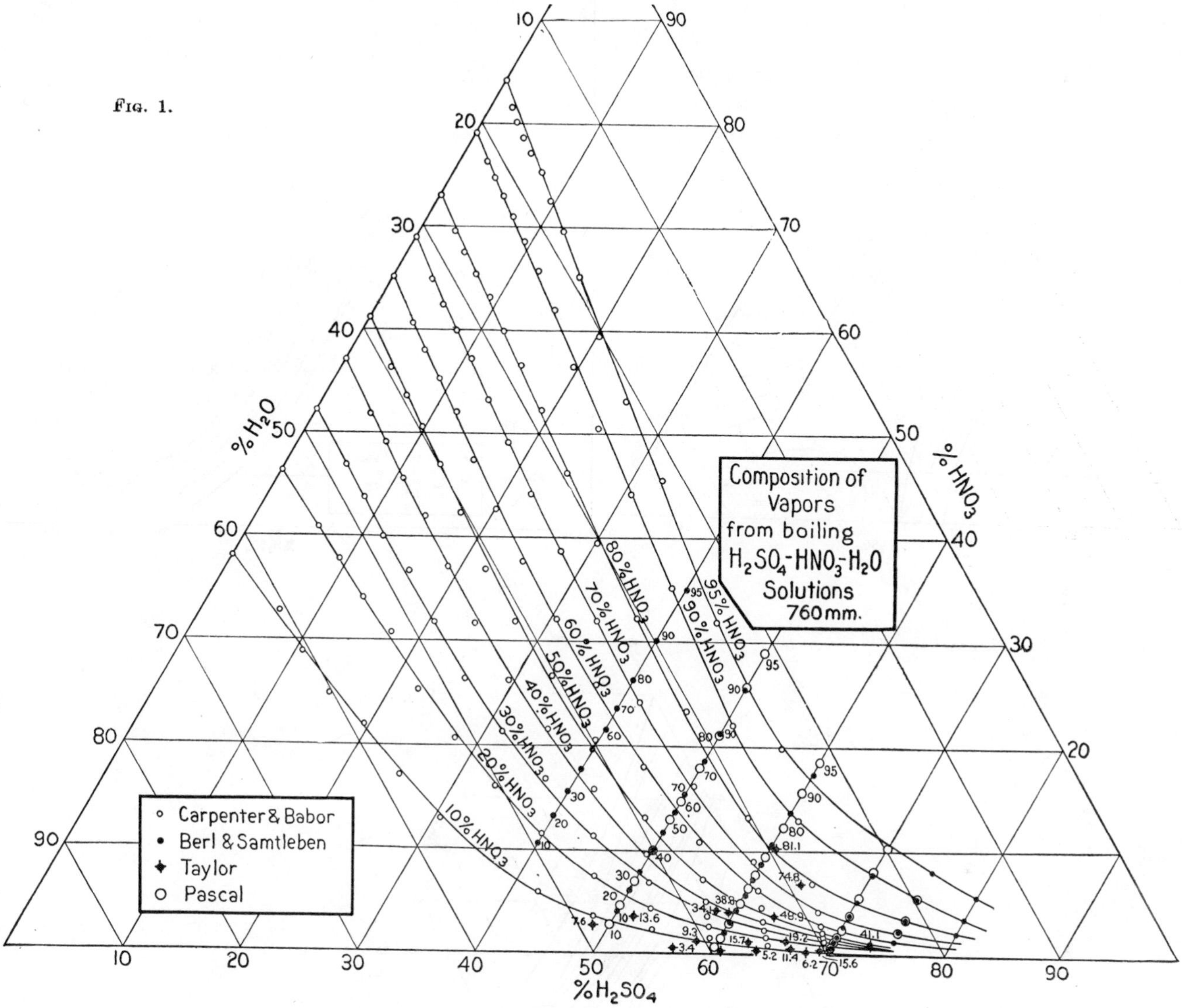

Fig. 4.

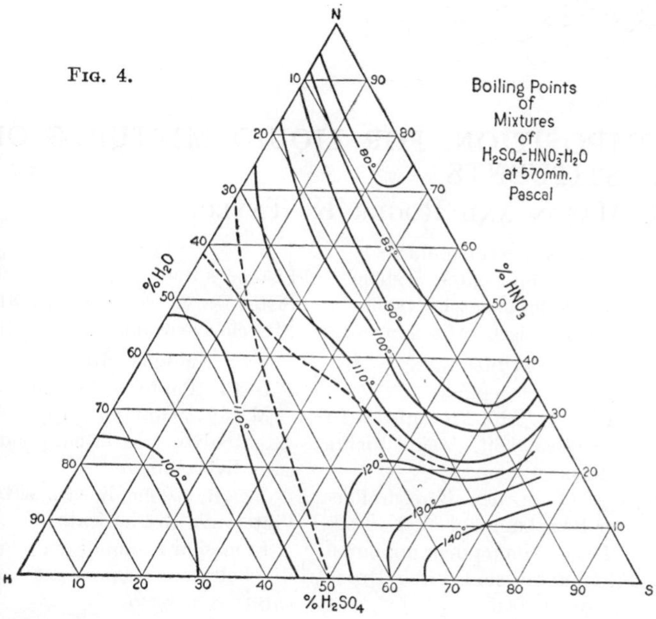

Fig. 5.

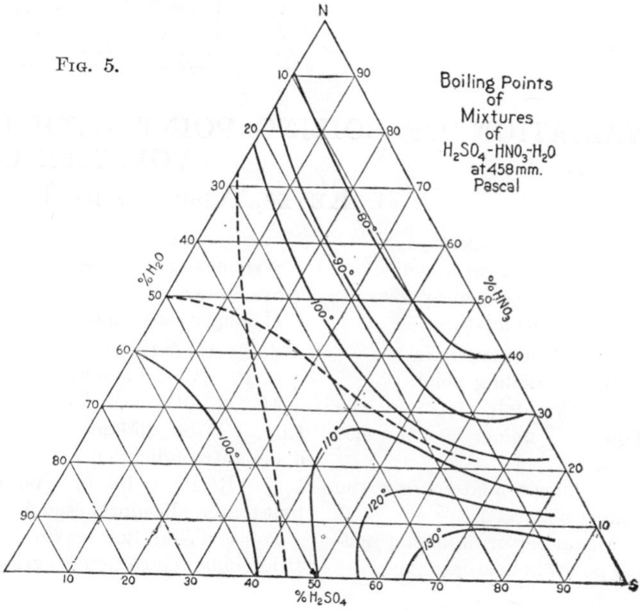

FIG. 6.

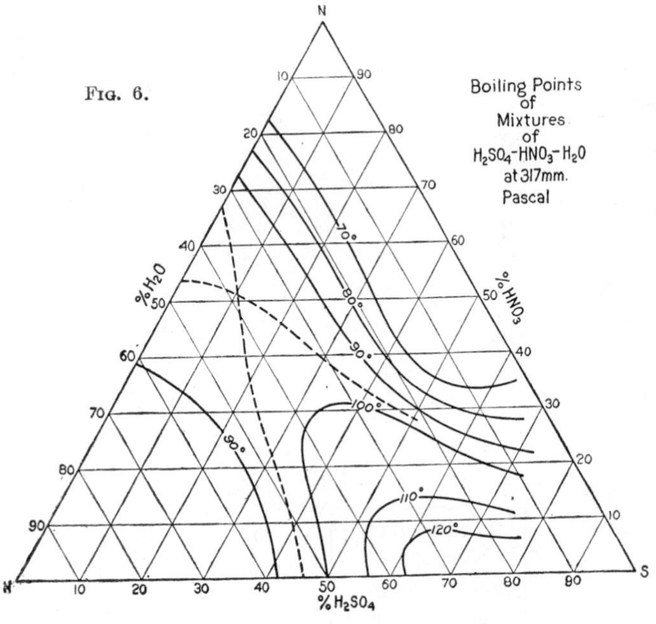

FIG. 7.

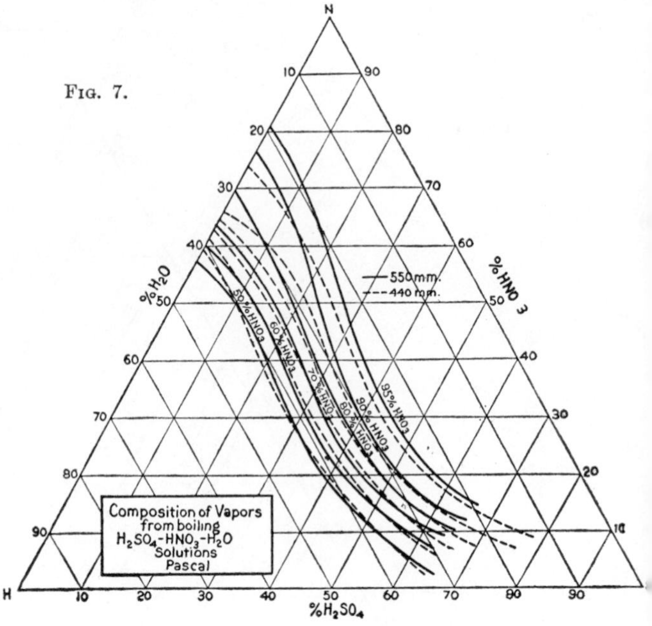

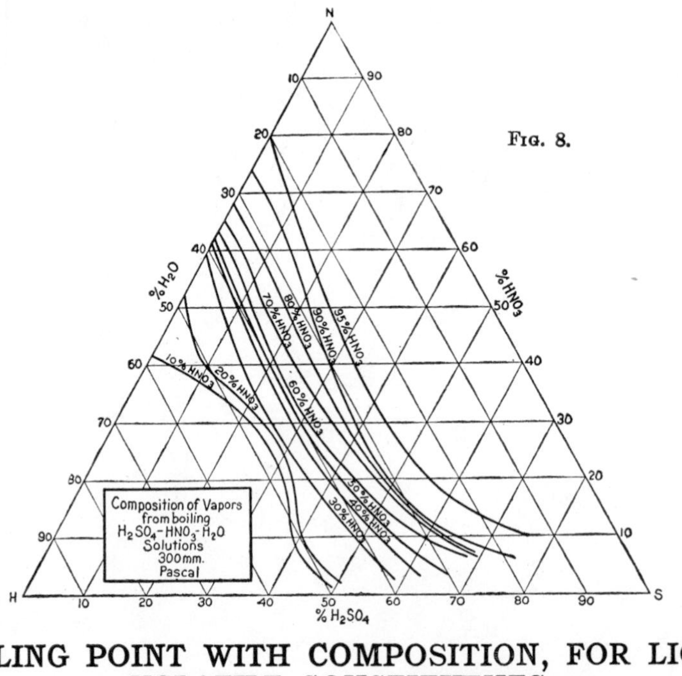

FIG. 8.

VARIATION OF BOILING POINT WITH COMPOSITION, FOR LIQUID MIXTURES OF VOLATILE CONSTITUENTS

D. B. KEYES, ASSISTED BY D. B. MASON AND ROGER K. TAYLOR

CONTENTS

ABBREVIATIONS

B. P. Boiling point.

M % Mole %. (In the liquid unless otherwise indicated.)

↓ Linear relation over the range so marked.

Maximum or minimum boiling points in bold-face type.

MATIÈRES

ABRÉVIATIONS

B. P. Point d'ébullition.

M % Pourcent moléculaire. (Dans le liquide à moins d'une autre indication.)

↓ Relation linéaire pour tout l'intervalle ainsi désigné.

Points d'ébullition maximum et minimum en caractères gras.

INHALTSVERZEICHNIS

ABKÜRZUNGEN

B. P. Siedepunkt.

M % Mol-Prozente. (In der Flüssigkeit, wenn nichts anderes angegeben.)

↓ Gibt den Bereich linearer Beziehung an.

Die maximum oder minimum Siedepunkte sind durch Druck hervorgehoben.

INDICE PAGE

ABBREVIAZIONI

B. P. Punto di ebollizione.

M % Grammi molecole %. (Salvo i casi in cui è indicato diversamente.)

↓ Relazione lineare entro l'intervallo così indicato.

I massimi e minimi nei punti di ebollizione sono segnati in carattere neretto.

TWO-COMPONENT SYSTEMS

A-B-Table

Standard arrangement (*v.* p. viii)

Argon

B = **N_2** (20)

B. P., °K	M % A Liq.	M % A Vap.
1500 mm		
83.55	0	0
84.9	20	9.5
86.4	40	21.5
89.5	70	49.0
92.3	90	77.5
94.18	100	100
1000 mm		
79.70	0	0
80.9	20	8.7
82.4	40	20.4
85.2	70	45.5
87.95	90	75.0
89.93	100	100
760 mm		
77.30	0	0
78.48	20	8.6
79.8	40	19.0
82.6	70	43.6
85.25	90	73.5
87.25	100	100
500 mm		
73.90	0	0
74.97	20	7.8
76.22	40	17.7
78.8	70	41.0
81.42	90	70.4
83.45	100	100

O_2

B = **N_2** (1)

B. P., °K	M % A Liq.	M % A Vap.
760 mm		
77.3	0	0
78.0	8.10	2.2
79.0	21.60	6.8
80.0	33.4	12.0
81.0	43.4	17.7
82.0	52.2	23.6
83.0	59.5	29.9
84.0	66.2	36.9
85.0	72.3	44.3
86.0	77.8	52.2
87.0	82.9	60.3
88.0	88.5	69.6
89.0	93.8	79.8
89.5	96.5	87.0
90.1	100	100

H_2O

Aqueous Mixtures

B = **HCl** (7)

v. also p. 301

B. P., °C	M % B
100	0.0
101.8	2.0
103.3	4.0
105.3	6.0
108.0	8.0
109.7	10.5
109.0	12.0
105.2	14.0
92.0	17.0
82.7	18.5
19.0	26.3

B = **Br_2**, *v.* (52)

B = **HBr** (8)

v. also p. 306

B. P., °C	M % B Vap.
760 mm	
100.0	0
114.7	2
122.4	6
126.0	15
124.3	25
104.3	70
92.0	80
36	90
26	95

B = **HNO_3** (10)

v. also p. 304

B. P., °C	M % B
760 mm	
100.0	0
106.0	10
114.6	20
120.4	30
121.9	37
120.4	45
114.9	55
103.4	70
95.2	86
360 mm	
80.5	0
86.5	10
92.3	20
98.2	30
100.2	39
96.6	50
89.6 ↓	60
63 5 ↓	99

p, mm Hg	B. P., °C	M % B (37) Liq.	M % B (37) Vap.
190	65.5	8.20*	0.404*
237	72	8.28	0.495
465	93	8.54	0.522
566	100	8.28	0.638
760	106.5	8.36	0.627
870	115.5	8.78	0.462
40	40.2	13.9†	1.54‡
116	59.0	12.4	1.48
318	87.5	12.4	1.47
458	97.5	12.8	1.51
570	104.0	12.3	1.57
680	108.5	12.3	1.42
760	112	12.3	1.76
40	45.8	22.90§	7.14‖
116	66.5	22.2	6.66
317	95.0	21.7	6.08
458	105.5	22.5	7.14
570	111.0	22.1	5.16
760	118.5	22.1	6.60
870	124.2	22.3	4.87
40	52	30.8¶	22.2**
116	70.2	30.5	17.1
317	98.5	30.8	18.9
353	104	31.0	22.4
463	109.5	30.8	22.5
517	112.5	30.7	22.6
553	113.5	31.0	22.9
622	115.5	31.0	22.3
670	117.5	30.8	22.2
725	120.5	30.8	19.0
763	121.6	30.8	16.6
40	52.6	34.6††	34.6‡‡
116	72.0	35.8	35.6
116	72.1	36.0	36.1
324	102	33.6	22.3
458	109	37.4	36.7
465	110.1	35.3	34.7
574	113.9	38.1	38.0
760.2	121.9	38.3	38.3
870	126.0	34.2	29.1
870	126.3	36.3	34.8
1010	130.6	34.9	34.8
40	52.0	40.3‡‡	62.0‡‡
116	71.5	40.1	64.3
325	98.5	40.3	52.2
398	104	40.0	53.8
458	108	39.5	53.5
570	113.5	40.0	49.3
754	121	40.2	60.2
40	47.6	46.0§§	84.3‖‖
116	67.0	45.7	74.2
325	93.0	46.0	71.5
408	103.0	45.8	65.2
540	110.0	45.1	83.8
760	118.0	46.5	75.9
40	43	53.2¶¶	92.5¶¶
116	56	56.2	91.8
458	91	56.2	93.1
570	98	54.9	88.8
760	112	53.0	89.1
870	120.5	54.2	86.0
40	38	61.2***	95.3†††
116	52.5	63.0	96.8
345	78	61.2	95.4
458	84	61.5	95.9
570	92	61.5	94.2
760	99	61.5	92.1

*† 0.05 M % NO_2 present.
‡ 0.04 M % NO_2 present.
§ 0.14 M % NO_2 present.
‖ 0.11 M % NO_2 present.
¶ 0.16 M % NO_2 present.
** 0.14 M % NO_2 present.
†† 0.18 M % NO_2 present.
‡‡ 0.23 M % NO_2 present.
§§ 0.3 M % NO_2 present.
‖‖ 0.4 M % NO_2 present.
¶¶ 0.2 M % NO_2 present.
*** 0.4 M % NO_2 present.
††† 0.2–0.7 M % NO_2 present.

p, mm Hg	B. P., °C	M % B Liq.	M % B Vap.
40	32.5	71.5‡‡‡	99.5§§§
116	47.5	72.7	98.6
315	63	74.6	98.9
458	75	73.7	99.2
570	80.3	73.9	99.2
760	90.5	71.6	98.4
870	100.0	76.3	95.4
40	29	83.7‖‖‖	98.9¶¶¶
116	43.5	84.7	99.3
458	69	84.0	99.1
760	85.5	86.2	99.1
870	90.5	85.4	99.4
40	27.5	92.6****	98.8****
116	41.5	92.3	98.6
315	59.0	92.9	99.1

‡‡‡ 0.4–0.6 M % NO_2 present.
§§§ 0.1–0.7 M % NO_2 present.
‖‖‖ 0.3–0.6 M % NO_2 present.
¶¶¶ 0.2–0.5 M % NO_2 present.
**** 0.4 M % NO_2 present.

B = **CH_2O_2**

Formic acid, *v.* p. 364

B = **CH_4O** (12)

Methyl alcohol

B. P., °C	M % B
800 mm	
101.4	0
93.0	6
87.9	12
83.4	20
79.6	30
76.9	40
73.8	55
68.4 ↓	85
65.9	100
760 mm	
100.0	0
91.6	6
86.5	12
82.0	20
78.2	30
75.6	40
72.4	55
67.1 ↓	85
64.6	100
700 mm	
97.7	0
89.3	6
84.3	12
79.8	20
76.1	30
73.5	40
70.3	55
65.1 ↓	85
62.6	100

B = **C_2HBr_3O** (13)

Bromal

B. P., °C	M % B
760.4 mm	
100.0	0
100.2	4
100.3	10.8
100.2	24.2
99.8	35.6

B = C_2HBr_3O.—(*Continued*)

B. P., °C	M % B
759.8 mm	
99.3	42.7
100.1	50.0
758.7 mm	
100.2	89.3
100.4	95.8
100.6	98.4

B = C_2H_4O (35)

Acetaldehyde

B. P., °C	M % B Liq.*	M % B Vap.†
100	0	0
93.5	0.5	25
82	1	50
63	4	75
43	10	89
33	20	93
29	30	
25.3	50	
24.6	60	
23.8	75	

* 760 mm ± 5.
† 761 mm.

B = $C_2H_4O_2$ (38)

Acetic acid

v. also p. 306

B. P., °C	M % B Liq.	M % B Vap.
760 mm		
100.00	0	0
100.50	10	6.3
101.18	20	12.2
102.05	30	18.5
103.15	40	26.0
104.33	50	34.0
105.78	60	43.0
108.95	75	60.0
111.85	85	73.8
118.10	100	100
763 mm (average) (35)		
100	0	0
101.1	20	15
102.5	40	28.5
105.3	60	45
110.4	85	70
118.0	100	100

B = C_2H_6O

Ethyl alcohol

v. also p. 290

M % B	B. P., °C 800 mm (12)	B. P., °C 760 mm (12)
0	101.4	100.0
2	96.7	95.1
5	92.0	90.5
7	90.0	88.6
10	87.9	86.5
20	84.6	83.2
30	83.0	81.7
40	82.1	80.8
50	81.3	80.0
60	80.7	79.4
75	80.0	78.7
90	79.5	78.2
100	79.7	78.4

B = C_2H_6O.—(*Continued*)

M % B	B. P., °C 700 mm (12, 39)	B. P., °C 640 mm (39)
0	97.7	95.2
2	92.8	90.3
5	88.3	85.8
7	86.4	83.9
10	84.3	81.9
20	81.1	78.9
30	79.6	77.5
40	78.7	76.6
50	77.9	75.9
60	77.3	75.3
75	76.6	74.6
90	76.2	74.3
100	76.3	74.3

B. P., °C	M % B (14) Liq.	M % B (14) Vap.
760 mm		
100.0	0	0
93.9	2	24.0
89.2	5	40.8
87.2	7	47.3
85.3	10	52.4
82.2	20	59.8
81.0	30	63.0
80.3	40	65.2
79.6	50	68.6
78.9	60	72.0
78.3	70	78
78.2	80	80

B. P., °C	M % B (33)
760 mm	
95.3	2
90.4	5
86.1	10
83.5	20
81.9	30
79.8	50
78.6	70
78.3	80
78.2	85
78.2	90
78.3	100

B = C_3H_6O (19)

Acetone

v. also p. 290

B. P., °C	M % A
56.9	0
59.0	30
61.6 ↓	60
62.6	70
64.5	80
69.6	90
77.9	95
100.0	100

B = C_3H_8O (12)

n-Propyl alcohol

B. P., °C	M % B
800 mm	
92.8	3.2
89.9	10
89.4	20
89.1	40
89.2	50
90.9	75
98.5	100
760 mm	
91.7	3
88.5	10
88.1	20
87.75	40
87.9	55
89.7	75
97.26	100
700 mm	
89.0	3.2
86.3	10
85.9	20
85.6	40
85.8	55
87.5	75
95.0	100

B = C_3H_8O (12)

Isopropyl alcohol

B. P., °C	M % B
800 mm	
101.45	0
90.5	3
85.0	10
83.6	20
83.1	30
82.6	40
81.9	55
81.7	67
81.8	75
83.7	100
760 mm	
100	0
89.8	3
83.6	10
82.0	25
80.5 ↓	56
80.4	67
80.5	75
82.4	100
700 mm	
97.7	0
87.5	3
81.5	10
80.2	20
79.1	40
78.5	56
78.3	70
80.3	100

B = C_3H_8O.—(*Continued*)

B. P., °C	M % B Liq.	M % B Vap.
760 mm (24)		
100	0	0
95	1	19
90	2	34
86.7	3	43
83.5	6	50.5
81.5	15	56
81.0	30	58
80.7	50	63
80.5	70	70
81.0	80	77
82.3	90	83

B = $C_3H_8O_3$ (6)

Glycerol

v. also p. 291

M % B	*p*, mm Hg	B. P., °C
81.11	189.1	125.11
	268.6	136.72
	363.5	147.48
	538.7	161.99
63.02	120.6	86.00
	187.8	97.49
	244.0	104.45
	367.3	116.07
	451.6	122.39
	549.6	128.55
55.04	114.9	78.35
	330.8	105.80
	461.7	115.50
	580.4	122.50
38.04	115.5	68.22
	185.5	79.24
	262.5	87.84
	389.2	98.32
	525.5	106.81
20.90	194.0	77.85
	312.7	89.57
	415.0	96.95
	541.5	104.33
20.46	145.3	66.64
	246.5	78.88
	370.0	89.05
	515.5	97.72
12.61	190.3	69.34
	393.9	87.09
	499.9	93.34
	612.1	98.85
7.22	127.8	58.77
	223.4	71.23
	331.2	80.71
	468.3	89.53
	631.2	97.61
4.68	180.8	65.32
	293.3	77.08
	525.0	91.42
	640.9	96.84
2.01	190.7	65.87
	341.3	79.58
	502.3	89.41
	672.8	97.37

B = $C_3H_8O_3$.—(*Continued*)

B. P., °C	M % B
760 mm (16, 27, 29)	
100	0
103.5	10
107.5	20
113.0	30
118.0	40
125.0	50
133.5	60
145.5	70
162	80
174	85
193	90
223	95
249	98
290	100

M % B	B. P., °C (29)	
	700 mm	650 mm
0	98	96
10	101.5	99
20	105.5	103
30	110.5	108
45	119	117
65	137	134
100	287	284.5
	600 mm	550 mm
0	93.5	91
10	97	94.5
20	101	98.5
30	105.5	103.5
45	114.5	112
65	131.5	129
100	282	279
	500 mm	450 mm
0	89	86
10	92	89
20	96	93
30	100.5	97.5
45	109.5	106.5
65	126	122.5
100	276	272
	400 mm	350 mm
0	83	79.5
10	86	82.5
20	89.5	86
30	94.5	91
45	103	99.5
65	119	115
100	268	264
	300 mm	250 mm
0	76	71.5
10	79	74.5
20	82.5	78
30	87	82.5
45	95	90.5
65	110.5	105
100	259	253.5
	200 mm	150 mm
0	66.5	60
10	69	62.5
20	72.5	66
30	77	70
45	85	78
65	99	91.5
100	247	238.5

B = $C_3H_8O_3$.—(*Continued*)

M % B	B. P., °C (29)	
	100 mm	40 mm
0	52	34
10	54	36
20	57	38.5
30	61	42.5
45	69	49.5
65	81.5	60
100	227.5	210*

* At 50 mm.

B = $C_4H_{10}O$ (12)
Trimethylcarbinol

B. P., °C	M % B
800 mm	
101.45	0
85.7	3
82.5	10
82.0	30
81.6	50
81.3	69
83.85	100
760 mm	
100.00	0
85.0	3
81.1	10
80.7	30
80.3	50
80.0	69
82.55	100
700 mm	
97.70	0
82.0	3
79.1	10
78.6	30
78.2	50
77.9	69
80.45	100

B = $C_5H_4O_2$ (28)
Furfural

B. P., °C	M % B	
	Liq.	Vap.
760 mm		
100.00	0	0
98.56	1	5.5
98.07	2	8.0
97.90	4	9.2
97.90	9.2	9.2
97.90	50	9.2
98.7	70	9.5
100.6	80	11
109.5	90	19
122.5	92	32
146.0	94	64
154.8	96	81
158.8	98	90
161.7	100	100

B = $C_6H_8N_2$ (4)
Phenylhydrazine

B. P., °C	M % B
104	15
106	30
114	65
168	86
243	100

Non-Aqueous Mixtures

HCl

B = C_6H_7N (26)
Aniline

B. P., °C	M % A
755 mm	
183	0
186	20
190	30
205	40
244	48
245	49
220	50
206	50.2

SO_3

B = H_2SO_4
v. p. 304

H_2SO_4

B = NH_3 (22)

B. P., °C	M % B
490	50
474	52
431	54
410	55
394	56
381	57
371	58
361	59

$S_2O_5Cl_2$

B = $ClSO_2OH$ (44)

N_2O_4

B = HNO_3 (36)

B. P., °C	M % A	
	Liq.	Vap.
87.0	0	0
65.0	3.5	58.0
55.0	7.8	77.0
33.0	20.3	99.9
22.0	100	100

NH_4Cl

B = $ZnCl_2$ (17)

B. P., °C	M % B
342	40
343	49
345	58
350	70
358	75
385	87
730	100

B = $CdCl_2$ (17)

B. P., °C	M % B
338	0
340	28
342	40
363	50
399	60
442	70

B = $CdCl_2$.—(*Continued*)

B. P., °C	M % B
492	80
550	90
964	100

B = CuCl (17)

B. P., °C	M % B
338	32
340	41
346	54
360	66
382	80
415	91
954	100

B = LiCl (17)

B. P., °C*	M % B
332	35
338	45
344	54
351	64

* Liq. phase, only between 35 and 64 M % B.

$SnBr_4$

B = SnI_4 (40)

B. P., °C	M % B
206.8	0
209.6	10
215.0	20
221.7	30
230.0	40
240.7	50
253.5	60
268.2	70
288.2	80
312.1	90
346.0	100

NaCl

B = KCl (18)

B. P., °C	M % A	
	Liq.	Vap.
3.49 mm		
890	0	0
894	20	
903		20
914	40	
927		40
928	60	
937		60
946	80	
950		80
965	100	100

B. P., °C		M % A
2.44 mm	1.08 mm	Liq.
870	830	0
873	834	20
891	851	40
906	869	60
924	890	80
945	920	100

C-Compounds

C-TABLE, the C-Arrangement

CO

$B = C_4H_{10}O$ (47)
Ethyl ether

B. P., °C	M % A Liq.	M % A Vap.
	750 mm	
34.2	0	0
+15.0	1.4	55.0
0	2.3	76.2
−24.0	6.8	94.0
−64.0	27.4	99.8
−78.6	47.4	100.0

CCl_4

$B = CS_2$ (42)

B. P., °C	M % A
46.4	0
48.7	15
51.5	30
56.1	50
60.5	65
64.0	75
68.3	85
70.9	90
76.7	100

$B = CHCl_3$ (19)

B. P., °C	M % A
61.50	0
63.1	20
65.0	40
66.3	50
67.7	60
69.3	70
71.3	80
73.8	90
76.75	100

$B = C_2H_4Br_2$ (45)
Ethylene bromide

B. P., °C	M % A
	749 mm
130.2	0
112.5	15
104.1	25
98.0	35
93.1	45
89.4	55
86.3	65
80.6	85
76.8	100

$B = C_2H_6O$ (48)
Ethyl alcohol

B. P., °C	M % A Liq.	M % A Vap.
	745 mm	
77.9	0	0
72.8	6.4	25
70.3	11.4	35
68.0	17.6	45
65.0	33.6	55
63.8	60	60
(63.6)	(63)	(63)
64.3	72.8	67
75.9	100	100

$B = C_4H_8O_2$ (48)
Ethyl acetate

B. P., °C	M % A Liq.	M % A Vap.
	745 mm	
76.5		0
75.8	9.5	10
75.2	17.9	20
74.7	28.4	30
74.3	37.3	40
74.1	44.0	50
74.1	58.0	60
74.3	68.2	70
74.9	83.9	85
75.9	100	100

$B = C_4H_{10}O$ (48)
Ethyl ether

B. P., °C	M % A Liq.	M % A Vap.
34.75	0	0
44.7	10	2
50.6	20	5
56.8	32	10
60.5	40	15
65.6	53	25
70.2	67	40
72.4	76	50
77.7	100	100

$B = C_6H_6$ (42)

B. P., °C	M % B
76.69	0
77.03	25
77.32	40
77.60	50
77.97	60
78.47	70
79.30	85
80.23	100

$B = C_7H_8$ (45)
Toluene

B. P., °C	M % A
	749 mm
110.1	0
105.2	10
101.2	20
97.2	30
93.2	40
90.0	50
87.0	60
84.2	70
80.3	85
76.8	100

CS_2

$B = C_3H_6O_2$ (42)
Methyl acetate

B. P., °C	M % B
56.2	0
51.3	5
48.3	10
43.8	20
41.2	30
40.1	40
39.5	50
39.1	65
39.6	80
41.0	90
42.5	95
46.3	100

$B = C_6H_6$ (9)

B. P., °C	M % B
45.75	0
47.6	20
48.7	30
51.3	50
52.9	60
55.3	70
59.5	80
65.7	90
79.55	100

$CHCl_3$

$B = CH_4O$ (48)
Methyl alcohol

B. P., °C	M % A Liq.	M % A Vap.
	757 mm	
64.9	0	0
63.7	3.6	10
60.8	10	23.4
59.5	13.7	30
57.7	20	39.8
55.6	30.4	50
54.4	40	54.4
53.7	50	58.4
53.4	(63)	(63)
53.6		68
53.7	71	
61.4	100	100

$B = C_2H_6O$ (46)
Ethyl alcohol

B. P., °C	M % B
60.95	0
59.1	7
59.6	15
61.4	30
63.3	40
65.7	50
68.4	60
71.0	70
73.6	80
75.8	90
77.9	100

$B = C_3H_6O$ (48)
Acetone

B. P., °C	M % A Liq.	M % A Vap.
	750 mm	
56.0	0	0
58.6 ↓	16	10
60.5	29	20
61.8	39	30
62.8	47	40
63.5	54	50
63.9	65	70
63.0	82	90
61.2	100	100

$B = C_3H_6O$.—(*Continued*)

B. P., °C	M % A
	750 mm (42)
56.20	0
59.40 ↓	20
62.76	40
63.88	50
64.59	65
64.25	75
63.24	85
61.32	100

$B = C_6H_6$ (48)

B. P., °C	M % A Liq.	M % A Vap.
80.6	0	0
79.8	8	10
79.0	15	20
78.2	22	30
77.3	29	40
76.4	36	50
75.3	44	60
74.0	54	70
71.9	66	80
68.9	79	90
61.4	100	100

$B = C_7H_8$ (41)
Toluene

B. P., °C	M % B
61.4	0
66.0	15
71.5	30
80.3	50
85.3	60
90.8	70
96.3	80
102.2	90
108.9	100

CH_4O

Methyl alcohol
$B = C_2H_6O$ (19)
Ethyl alcohol

B. P., °C	M % B
65.10	0
66.38	15
67.32	25
68.90	40
70.10	50
71.48	60
73.90	75
75.73	85
78.75	100

$B = C_3H_6O$ (19)
Acetone

B. P., °C	M % A
56.65	0
55.84	16
55.90	25
56.08	35
56.54	50
57.48	60
58.68	70
60.27	80
62.48	90
65.20	100

$C_2H_4Cl_2$

Ethylene chloride

B = C_6H_6 (42)

B. P., °C	M % A
80.24	0
80.51	10
80.78	20
81.08	30
81.39	40
82.35 ↓	70
82.74	80
83.20	90
83.66	100

$C_2H_4Br_2$

Ethylene bromide

B = C_7H_8 (45)

Toluene

B. P., °C	M % A
749 mm	
110.1	0
111.5	10
113.0	20
114.6	30
116.3	40
118.0	50
120.8	65
124.5	85
130.2	100

C_2H_4O

Acetaldehyde

B = C_2H_6O (25)

Ethyl alcohol

B. P., °C	M % B Liq.	M % B Vap.
699 mm		
20.1	0	0
25.7	20	
29.5	30	
33.7	40	
41.5	55	4.1
47.4	65	12.3
58.1	80	31.8
65.8	90	50.5
76.2	100	100
398 mm		
5.8	0	0
11.5	20	
21.2	40	
30.5	55	6.4
36.8	65	16.7
43.5	75	29.0
51.3	85	49.2
62.8	100	100
77 mm		
−23.9	0	0
−15.2	35	
0	50	
+ 4.6	60	9.2
17.0	70	22.4
22.7	80	33.0
28.0	90	50.0
31.2	95	78.8
34.3	100	100

B = $C_2H_4O_2$ (35)

Acetic acid

B. P., °C	M % B Liq.	M % B Vap.
768 mm		
42.0	3.5	58.2
55.5	10	73.7
69.3	20	82.5
83.7	36	90.8

$C_2H_4O_2$

Acetic acid

B = C_6H_6 (42)

B. P., °C	M % A
80.2	0
84.6	35
88.8	55
92.0	65
94.0	70
98.8	80
105.8	90
109.5	93.5
79.576 (3)	0.0
79.451	1.0
79.420	2.6
79.448	4.0
79.480	5.0
79.596	8.0
79.667	9.4

C_2H_5Br

B = C_6H_6 (48)

B. P., °C	M % A Liq.	M % A Vap.
760 mm		
80.2	0	0
79.4	1	10
78.5	2	20
77.4	4	30
76.1	6	40
74.7	8	50
72.8	10	60
70.5	14	70
66.8	21	80
59.8	34	90
49.2	61	97
38.4	100	100

C_2H_6O

Ethyl alcohol

B = C_2H_5I (21)

B. P., °C	M % B
70.9	26
68.5	35
66.2	45
64.4	55
62.4	70
61.6	80
61.3	87
61.4	90
62.2	95
72.3	100

B = C_3H_6O (46)

Acetone

B. P., °C	M % A
55.6	0
56.7	10
58.0	20
59.3	30
60.8	40
62.5	50
64.4	60
66.8	70
69.8	80
73.4	90
77.7	100

B = C_3H_8O (34)

n-Propyl alcohol

B. P., °C	M % B Vap.
761 mm	
78.4	0
81.0	10
83.5	20
86.1	30
87.8	40
89.3	50
93.1	75
97.2	100

B = $C_4H_{10}O$ (19)

Ethyl ether

B. P., °C	M % A
35.0	0
43.5 ↓	40
46.0	50
58.5	75
70.0	90
79.0	100

B = C_6H_6 (46)

B. P., °C	M % A
72.1	16
70.2	25
68.4	35
67.4	46
66.9	65
67.1	75
67.6	85
70.5	95
79.5	100

B. P., °C	M % B Liq.	M % B Vap.
750 mm (48)		
78.1	0	0
74.4	6	20
72.4	11	30
70.1	20	40
68.3	39	50
67.8	57?	56
68.3	72	60
70.8	89	70
75.2	96	85
79.7	100	100

C_3H_6O

Acetone

B = $C_4H_{10}O$ (19)

Ethyl ether

B. P., °C	M % A
35.0	0
35.9	20
36.7	30
37.8	40
39.2	50
41.0	60
43.4	70
46.5	80
49.8	90
56.8	100

B = C_7H_8 (41)

Toluene

B. P., °C	M % B
56.5	0
58.7	10
60.9	20
64.7	35
69.2	50
74.8	65
88.2	85
109.4	100

$C_4H_{10}O$

Ethyl ether

B = C_6H_6 (19)

B. P., °C	M % B
34.7	0
38.3	15
42.4	30
45.8	40
49.4	50
53.8	60
62.0	75
68.9	85
80.3	100

C_5H_{12}

Isopentane

B = $C_6H_5NO_2$ (23)

Nitrobenzene

B. P., °C	M % B
28	0
29	1
30	10
30.5	20
33	60
210.8	100

$C_6H_4Br_2$

Dibromobenzene

Binary mixtures of *o*-, *m*-, and *p*-derivs. Compn. of vap. phase given (32)

$C_6H_5NO_2$

B = C_6H_{14} (5)
n-Hexane

B. P., °C	M % A
69.0	0
71.7	10
72.9	20
73.8	30
74.6	40
75.4	50
77.7	60
85.0	70
103.4	80
143.4	90
210	100

C_6H_6

B = C_7H_8 (50)
Toluene

B. P., °C	M % B
81.0	3.8
84.5	20
86.9	30
89.5	40
92.4	50
95.5	60
98.8	70
102.3	80
106.3	90
110.0	98.6

C_6H_6O

Phenol
B = C_7H_8O (15)
o-Cresol

B. P., °C	M % A
191.0	0
189.9	10
185.9 ↓	60
185.1	70
184.1	80
183.1	90
182.2	100

B = C_7H_8O (15)
m-Cresol

B. P., °C	M % A
202.3	0
199.9	10
196.8	20
194.3	30
192.1	40
190.3	50
189.1	60
187.6	70
186.0	80
184.2	90
182.4	100

B = C_7H_8O (15)
p-Cresol

B. P., °C	M % A
201.7	0
198.8	10
195.9	20
193.6	30
191.5	40
189.6	50
188.0	60
186.5	70
182.3 ↓	100

B = C_7H_8O (15)
Cresol*

B. P., °C	M % A
197.8	0
192.1	30
188.9 ↓	50
187.3	60
185.8	70
183.4 ↓	90
182.2	100

* 32.0 Wt. % *o*-, 43.4 % *m*-, 24.6 % *p*-.

$C_6H_5NH_2$

Aniline
B = C_6H_{12} (23)
Cyclohexane

B. P., °C	M % A
80.8	0
81.2	2
86.0	35
96.0	70
184.4	100

B = C_6H_{14} (23)
n-Hexane

B. P., °C	M % A
68.9	0
70.8	10
72.2	20
73.0	30
73.4	40
73.4 ↓	60
74.1	70
78.9	80
83.4	85
184.4	100

C_7H_8O

o-Cresol
B = C_7H_8O (15)
m-Cresol

B. P., °C	M % A
202.3	0
197.3 ↓	40
196.2	50
192.3 ↓	90
191.2	100

THREE-COMPONENT SYSTEMS

Standard Arrangement
A = H_2O, B = H_2SO_4, C = HNO_3 (37)

p, mm Hg	B. P., °C	M % in liq.*		M % in vap.*	
		C	B	C	A
300	87	9.08	2.50	1.77	98.3
440	95	9.80	2.57	1.25	98.7
570	102	9.79	2.46	1.19	98.8
760	110	9.79	2.48	1.21	98.8
300	92	16.2	2.77	6.35	93.7
440	103	18.2	2.97	6.70	93.3
550	107.5	17.8	2.89	5.26	94.8
760	117	18.2	2.88	4.98	95.0
760	121	23.0	3.39	13.8	86.2
760	121.2	23.8	3.19	15.2	84.8
300	97.0	21.2	2.79	15.2	84.8
440	104.5	24.5	3.30	20.9	79.1
570	112.5	25.5	3.31	22.6	77.4
760	121.5	25.7	3.36	22.3	77.6
300	96.0	27.2	3.36	27.5	72.5
400	103	26.3	3.38	22.4	77.6
440	104	26.3	3.38	22.4	77.6
760	121	26.1	3.34	26.7	73.3
300	95	31.9	3.60	51.8	48.2
400	102.5	31.1	3.55	47.5	52.5
440	103.5	31.1	3.55	47.6	52.4
550	110	31.9	3.63	46.6	53.4
760	120.5	33.3	3.98	46.2	53.8
300	89	41.7	5.36	85.0	15.0
440	102	35.3	3.36	77.9	22.1
550	97.5	46.5	4.32	77.1	22.9
760	117.5	36.1	3.07	86.2	13.8
300	78.5	51.8	4.78	96.5	3.5
440	89.0	49.9	4.53	93.9	6.09
550	92.5	53.4	4.87	90.8	9.19
760	102	52.8	5.16	88.8	11.2
300	85.0	8.27	5.36	0.94	99.0
440	97.5	8.42	5.53	.94	99.0
550	93.0	8.52	5.71	.96	99.0
760	113.0	8.43	5.76	.90	99.0
300	93.5	14.1	6.36	3.0	97.0
440	103.0	14.9	6.49	3.0	97.0
550	110.0	13.9	5.98	3.0	97.0
760	119.5	13.8	5.90	3.0	97.0
300	96.0	16.8	6.30	10.9	89.1
440	106.0	17.3	6.40	10.8	89.2
550	112.0	17.4	6.68	10.4	89.6
760	122.0	17.1	6.30	10.3	89.7
300	97.0	21.7	6.78	37.8	62.2
440	106.0	20.5	6.99	37.3	62.7
550	112.0	20.9	6.85	35.7	64.3
760	122.0	21.6	6.76	33.9	66.1
300	94.0	30.3	8.03	58.2	41.8
440	104.5	30.6	7.98	56.6	43.4
550	110.0	30.0	7.68	57.9	42.1
760	120.0	30.4	7.82	54.2	45.8
300	71.5	49.0	9.83	90.9	9.13
440	84.5	48.4	9.70	88.8	11.2
550	91.5	48.4	9.70	88.8	11.2
760	120.5	48.8	9.92	87.8	12.2
300	89.0	4.88	9.00	1.2	98.8
440	100.0	4.79	8.98	0.88	99.1
550	107.5	4.70	8.58	.70	99.3
760	116.0	4.90	8.92	.59	99.4

* M % A = 100 − M % (B + C), *v. also* p. 306.

p, mm Hg	B. P., °C	M % in liq.*		M % in vap.*	
		C	B	C	A
300	94.5	10.25	10.05	0.40	99.6
440	104.5	9.58	9.53	.42	99.6
550	111.5	10.14	9.56	3.8	96.2
760	121.5	9.05	9.80	3.0	97.0
300	98.0	18.1	11.6	37.4	62.6
440	108.0	17.3	11.5	34.7	65.3
550	114.5	17.2	11.4	31.8	68.2
760	124.0	17.7	11.0	32.8	67.2
300	97.6	24.2	12.3	78.4	21.6
440	102.5	24.6	12.4	77.9	22.1
550	110.0	25.0	13.1	76.7	23.3
760	120.0	25.3	13.0	75.5	24.5
300	71.0	47.4	17.2	99.3	0.69
440	82.5	46.0	17.2	98.5	1.5
550	83.0	44.6	16.3	98.3	1.7
760	99.0	43.9	15.4	97.1	2.9
300	98.0	4.8	12.2	8.0	92.0
440	106.0	6.2	13.8	8.3	91.6
550	114.0	4.9	12.8	7.5	92.4
760	124.0	4.9	13.2	7.2	92.8
300	102.0	8.4	14.7	12.9	87.1
440	111.0	8.5	14.7	13.4	86.6
550	117.5	8.7	14.3	13.4	86.6
760	127.0	7.7	13.1	13.6	86.4
300	105.0	11.1	14.6	43.9	56.1
440	112.0	11.0	14.4	43.8	56.2
550	118.0	11.0	15.3	41.2	58.8
760	128.0	10.5	17.3	41.0	59.0
300	100.0	18.5	15.9	76.7	23.3
440	105.5	18.6	16.0	76.3	23.7
550	110.0	18.9	16.1	74.7	25.3
760	119.5	20.5	17.2	73.2	26.8
300	71.5	23.5	18.3	97.4	2.6
440	82.0	24.0	17.8	94.5	5.5
550	102.5	24.0	17.7	87.3	12.7
760	110.0	23.6	18.0	95.0	5.0
300	104.0	6.0	16.4	12.4	87.6
440	114.5	5.4	16.3	12.1	87.9
550	120.5	5.5	16.6	12.1	87.9
760	130.0	5.5	17.6	17.2	82.8
300	106.5	9.0	19.8	31.4	68.6
440	116.0	9.0	19.0	31.4	68.6
550	122.5	8.9	18.4	30.0	70.0
760	133.5	8.9	19.0	30.0	70.0
300	106.0	12.3	21.0	75.9	24.1
440	116.0	12.7	22.0	75.7	24.3
550	122.0	12.8	21.9	74.3	25.7
760	130.0	12.8	22.0	72.0	28.0
300	80.0	23.5	25.7	93.3	6.7
440	89.0	22.3	25.0	93.4	6.6
550	100.0	23.2	25.4	90.5	9.5
760	110.0	23.1	24.5	91.8	8.2
300	66.5	40.6	32.5	99.0	1.0
440	80.0	38.1	30.5	99.3	0.7
550	86.5	37.5	30.0	98.6	1.4
760	97.5	40.3	31.2	97.2	2.8
300	116.0	3.8	24.4	23.0	76.9
440	127.5	3.1	23.3	23.0	77.0
550	135.0	3.0	23.2	21.7	78.3
760	145.0	3.1	23.5	20.9	79.1

p, mm Hg	B. P., °C	M % in liq.*		M % in vap.*	
		C	B	C	A
300	116.5	6.5	25.1	38.3	61.7
440	127.5	6.7	25.1	37.9	62.1
550	135.0	6.7	25.3	37.5	62.5
760	145.0	6.5	25.3	36.7	63.3
440	103.0	16.7	30.6	99.8	0.2
550	110.0	15.6	30.2	96.5	3.5
760	120.0	15.8	30.9	95.9	4.1
300	71.00	33.3	40.8	99.8	0.2
440	82.50	32.8	39.2	99.8	0.2
550	89.00	33.9	39.4	96.6	3.4
760	99.00	31.5	37.4	99.7	0.3
300	105.0	14.6	29.4	94.2	5.8
440	116.0	13.7	29.1	93.3	6.7
550	124.0	14.0	30.1	93.6	6.4
760	134.0	13.6	29.1	91.8	8.2
300	121	7.2	30.2	72.5	27.5
440	132.0	7.7	32.3	71.4	28.6
550	137.5	8.3	31.8	69.8	30.2
760	147.0	7.3	30.2	71.0	29.0
300	95.0	14.1	27.8	98.6	1.4
440	106.0	17.9	36.2	98.6	1.4
550	112.5	17.7	37.4	98.6	1.4
760	118.0	17.6	36.5	97.1	2.9

p, mm Hg	B. P., °C	M % liq.			M % vap.		
		C	B	NO_2	C	NO_2	A
300	66.0	65.9	27.6	1.1	86.6	5.1	8.3
440	79.0	63.2	28.4	1.1	85.2	5.7	9.1
550	87.0	62.8	28.3	1.5	85.1	5.1	9.8
760	91	63.2	28.5	1.1	84.3	5.2	10.5
300	54	76.3	15.3	1.7	87.6	5.0	7.3
440	73	73.8	14.6	1.7	87.4	5.1	7.5
760	87.5	76.0	15.7	1.6	85.3	5.2	9.5
300	75	37.5	52.4	1.1	90.5	1.7	7.9
440	86	37.3	52.8	1.1	85.4	2.7	12.0
550	95	39.1	54.0	1.1	83.4	3.9	12.7
760	104	24.5	37.2	0.7	78.7	4.9	16.4
300	67	31.8	23.2	0.7	93.8	1.5	4.8
440	79.5	31.8	22.9	0.7	93.5	1.5	5.0
550	87	31.4	22.9	0.9	93.2	1.6	5.2
760	97	31.8	23.2	0.7	93.2	1.6	5.2
300	73	28.0	24.2	0.7	94.0	1.3	4.7
440	85	27.5	24.0	0.8	93.8	1.3	4.8
550	90	27.9	24.1	0.6	93.5	1.4	5.1
760	100	27.6	24.7	0.7	93.7	1.3	5.0
300	66	39.3	35.2	0.3	94.8	1.3	3.8
440	78	38.0	34.8	0.4	94.2	1.5	4.3
550	88	37.9	34.5	0.4	94.2	1.6	4.2
760	98	44.5	43.7	1.4	93.8	1.6	4.5
300	66	46.7	28.9	0.6	94.5	1.3	4.1
440	78	47.8	28.8	0.4	93.4	1.6	4.9
550	84	48.3	28.9	0.3	93.4	1.4	5.1
760	94	47.0	28.3	0.8	92.0	1.7	6.3
760	88.5	63.6	16.5	0.8	90.2	2.3	7.6
760	84	83.5	5.5	0.2	88.3	2.8	8.8
760	92	53.9	21.4	1.0	91.3	1.9	6.7

* M % A = 100 − M % (B + C), *v. also* p. 306.

A = H_2O, B = H_2SO_4, C = CH_3CO_2H (35)

B. P., °C	p, mm Hg	Liq.* M % C	Liq.* M % B	Vap.† M % C
298	761	14.74	80.33	23.08
250	761	28.17	67.54	58.88
200	761	39.63	55.84	61.71
170	761	49.92	44.88	74.82
160	761	60.54	36.20	78.01
140	761	74.38	24.11	80.44
128	761	85.03	12.46	91.54
121	761	90.74	5.05	93.33
105	763	7.15	4.37	7.02
105	760	16.60	4.36	18.57
105	761	26.57	3.24	23.08
110	761	9.82	8.97	11.30
113	761	30.65	9.89	43.23
110	761	43.48	5.60	54.71
115	759	75.07	4.32	72.98
115	762	37.46	9.85	54.86
115	762	25.26	11.60	41.53
120	760	11.33	13.87	23.15
130	760	47.04	18.13	72.98
130	760	17.93	17.89	41.42
136	762	27.22	21.42	63.15
148	762	21.14	27.37	54.86
150	762	16.29	29.91	41.18
150	762	5.48	26.01	11.40
170	762	20.22	42.71	39.01
160	762	9.34	30.98	23.22
200	760	10.84	53.06	24.68
250	761	8.44	83.45	22.23

* M % A = 100 − M % (B + C). † M % A = 100 − M % C.

A = H_2O, B = HNO_3, C = $KHSO_4 + H_2SO_4$ (11)
B. P. at 200, 360 and 760 mm Hg

A = H_2O, B = CH_3CHO, C = CH_3CO_2H (35)

B. P., °C	p, mm Hg	Liq.* M % B	Liq.* M % C	Vap.* M % B	Vap.* M % C
70	756	7.53	22.51	65.76	5.52
77	756	5.83	23.07	63.22	6.45
85	756	4.02	21.88	52.45	8.04
90	756	2.80	24.35	35.77	10.09
70	756	9.82	39.37	72.71	4.79
77	756	7.53	40.52	69.46	9.89
85	756	5.08	41.80	53.87	13.63
90	756	3.87	43.22	39.88	17.24
26.3	766	58.60	3.83		
27	766	55.76	3.87		
30	766	41.43	5.44		
32	766	35.90	7.39		
30	766	57.10	16.87		
32	766	51.89	20.32		
33	766	47.39	22.86		
35	763	26.45	8.55	96.91	0.79
39.5	763	20.67	9.38	89.78	0.76
45	763	15.06	10.07	90.26	0.59
50	763	12.26	10.62	87.07	0.80
55	763	9.37	11.06	87.04	0.89
60	763	8.00	11.02	83.83	1.73
35	764	40.26	22.63	88.74	5.92
39.5	764	36.45	27.96	85.17	11.18
45	764	27.07	29.98	80.69	12.01
50	764	22.76	33.16	78.73	13.94
55	764	17.65	34.58	70.66	19.75
60	764	16.52	37.27		

* M % A = 100 − M % (B + C).

A = H_2O, B = C_2H_5OH, C = C_6H_6 (2); *cf.* (51)

The following diagram shows the boiling point relations for this system at 760 mm Hg. The lines shown are isotherms. The heavy line separates the region of homogeneous solutions (above) from that of heterogeneous (below). The small cross on this line denotes the composition of a constant boiling mixture which is, however, neither a maximum nor a minimum. The mixture with a minimum boiling point consists of two liquid layers having the compositions of the ends of the 64.85° tie-line.

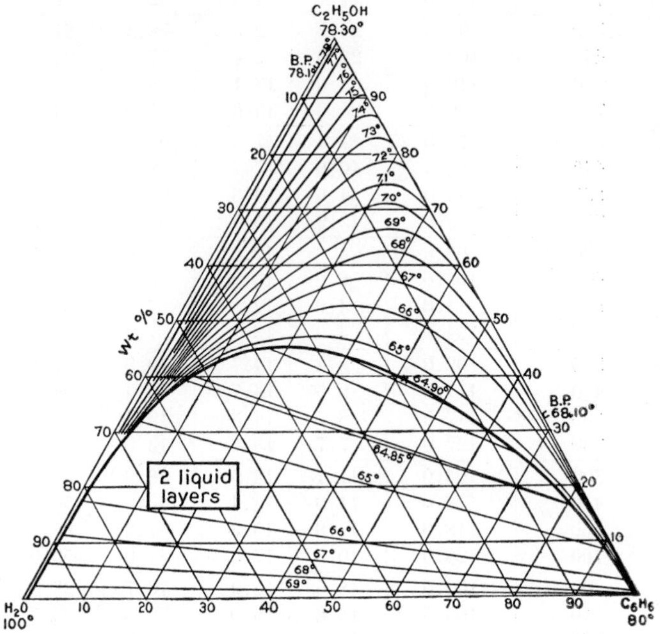

Fig. 1.

A = H_2O, B = $C_3H_8O_3$ Glycerol, C = NaCl (6)

M % B in (A + B)	g C per 1 soln.	p, mm Hg	B. P., °C
81.10	245	228.5	134.48
		327.4	146.95
		451.9	158.98
55.04	225	143.3	90.43
		159.5	93.22
		302.9	110.79
		397.0	118.87
		594.9	131.58
38.08	205	121.2	74.75
		265.8	94.23
		404.9	105.77
		519.7	113.16
31.24	184	129.9	73.37
		295.4	93.67
		429.2	104.04
		540.6	110.81
22.76	162	135.7	71.27
		150.4	73.63
		215.5	82.28
		268.9	87.80
		389.0	97.60
		480.9	103.51
16.80	143	159.4	73.12
		186.6	76.69
		270.5	85.83
		411.4	96.90
		574.0	106.23

A = H_2O, B = $C_3H_8O_3$ Glycerol, C = NaCl (6).—(*Continued*)

M % B in (A + B)	g C per 1 soln.	p, mm Hg	B. P., °C
11.60	122	148.1	69.85
		264.6	83.66
		398.3	94.28
		542.7	102.85
		605.1	105.97
7.89	111	141.8	67.85
		422.9	94.49
		541.2	101.47
4.75	94	150.6	67.82
		264.2	81.15
		463.7	95.72
		565.9	101.40
2.23	81	147.5	66.43
		281.6	82.00
		513.8	97.74
		622.3	103.31

A = H_2O, B = C_6H_6 Benzene, C = C_7H_8 Toluene (25)

A = CCl_4, B = $C_2H_4Br_2$ Ethylene bromide, C = C_7H_8 Toluene (43)

B. P., °C	M % in liq.*		M % in vap.*	
	C	B	C	B
83	25.50	0	11.6	0
83	22.02	3.31	10.1	1.5
83	13.97	10.79	6.2	3.6
83	10.20	14.44	4.3	4.9
83	6.65	17.74	3.0	5.6
83	3.25	20.94	1.3	7.0
83	0	23.88	0	7.7
91	53.32	0	31.3	0
91	52.22	0.91	30.8	0.4
91	35.03	16.05	20.0	6.2
91	20.85	29.24	11.8	11.0
91	14.77	35.11	8.5	12.9
91	9.35	40.30	5.1	14.5
91	0	49.21	0	17.2
99	75.30	0	55.0	0
99	65.56	8.27	48.2	4.0
99	48.05	23.19	34.3	10.4
99	33.80	35.85	23.9	16.2
99	22.55	45.95	16.4	20.0
99	9.53	58.12	6.9	24.6
99	0	67.21	0	28.2
107	93.83	0	86.0	0
107	71.81	17.45	65.4	10.2
107	54.25	31.83	49.1	18.4
107	40.15	43.83	36.0	24.1
107	20.59	60.93	19.0	31.9
107	8.38	71.55	8.1	36.3
107	0	74.20	0	39.6
115	67.46	32.54	77.6	22.4
115	51.25	45.34	58.6	31.1
115	38.78	55.42	43.3	37.4
115	29.59	62.82	34.9	40.4
115	16.28	73.97	19.2	47.2
115	7.92	81.00	9.9	51.0
115	0	88.05	0	55.1

* M % A = 100 − M % (B + C).

A = CCl_4, B = $C_2H_4Br_2$, C = C_7H_8 Toluene (45)
B. P., °C (749 mm) of A = 76.87; of B = 130.23; of C = 110.11

B. P., °C 749 mm	M %		
	A	C	B
110.8	0	94.8	5.2
107.44	6.3	88.8	4.8
104.07	13.5	82.1	4.5
100.75	21.2	74.7	4.1
97.21	29.6	66.8	3.6
93.92	38.7	58.2	3.2
90.49	48.6	48.7	2.7
87.12	59.4	38.5	2.1
83.21	71.5	27.0	1.5
80.19	85.2	14.8	0.8
111.61	0	89.2	10.8
107.69	7.4	82.6	10.1
104.17	14.4	76.8	9.3
100.72	22.1	69.4	8.5
96.9	31.1	61.3	7.5
93.49	40.4	53.1	6.5
90.03	50.4	44.2	5.4
86.71	61.2	34.7	4.2
83.49	72.7	24.5	3.0
80.08	85.7	12.6	1.6
113.80	0	75.4	24.6
109.37	7.5	69.8	22.8
104.79	15.7	63.5	20.7
100.64	24.3	57.0	18.6
96.52	33.4	50.1	16.4
93.00	42.8	43.1	14.0
89.47	53.0	35.5	11.6
86.14	63.7	27.3	8.9
82.99	74.9	18.9	6.2
79.79	86.6	10.1	3.3
112.63	0	82.6	17.4
108.44	7.3	76.5	16.3
104.50	15.0	70.2	14.8
100.41	23.7	63.0	13.4
96.69	31.9	56.3	11.8
93.18	41.7	48.1	10.1
89.84	51.3	40.3	8.5
86.60	62.2	31.3	6.6
83.21	73.8	21.6	4.5
79.99	85.8	11.8	2.5
115.05	0	67.2	32.8
109.87	8.1	61.7	30.2
104.60	17.0	55.6	27.3
100.63	25.5	50.0	24.6
96.33	34.7	43.8	21.5
92.51	46.6	37.2	18.2
88.68	54.6	30.5	15.0
85.62	65.2	23.4	11.5
82.61	76.2	16.0	7.8
79.70	88.0	8.1	4.0
116.68	0	57.7	42.3
110.71	8.6	52.8	38.8
105.12	17.7	47.4	34.8
100.27	26.9	42.2	31.0
95.91	36.5	36.6	26.9
92.46	46.2	30.9	22.8
88.68	56.2	25.2	18.5
85.37	66.7	19.2	14.1
82.42	77.4	13.0	9.6
79.48	88.7	6.5	4.8

A = CCl_4, B = $C_2H_4Br_2$, C = C_7H_8 Toluene (45).—(*Continued*)

B. P., °C 749 mm	M %		
	A	C	B
121.04	0	33.7	66.3
112.51	10.0	30.4	59.5
105.33	20.2	26.9	52.8
99.55	30.7	23.4	45.9
94.79	40.4	20.1	39.5
90.95	50.2	16.8	32.9
87.69	60.1	13.5	26.4
84.51	70.2	10.1	19.7
81.61	80.2	6.6	13.0
79.33	90.0	3.4	6.7
118.54	0	46.6	53.4
111.39	9.5	42.3	48.3
105.32	18.7	37.9	43.4
100.01	28.3	33.5	38.3
95.42	38.3	28.8	32.8
92.00	48.2	24.1	27.6
88.03	58.4	19.4	22.2
84.99	68.5	14.7	16.8
82.12	78.7	9.9	11.3
79.49	88.7	5.2	5.96
124.33	0	18.5	84.2
113.49	11.2	16.4	72.3
105.04	21.9	14.4	63.7
98.98	32.1	12.5	55.3
94.31	42.4	10.7	46.8
90.23	52.6	8.8	38.6
87.05	62.6	6.9	30.5
84.21	72.2	5.2	22.8
81.49	81.7	3.4	14.9
79.17	90.8	1.7	7.5

CONSTANT-BOILING (AZEOTROPIC) MIXTURES

The data in the following tables are based largely on Lecat, *La tension de vapeur des mélanges de liquides. L'azéotropisme,* Brussels, 1918, *q. v.* for literature and for further details.

Only those systems are included for which both the composition and the boiling point are known. In a few cases, the system is composed of two liquid phases. Such cases are marked "2-phase."

The pressure is 760 mm unless otherwise stated. "L. No." = Lecat's number.

CONTENTS

Two-Component Mixtures with Minimum Boiling Point

B-TABLE

B-Constituent (the C-Arrangement)	Min. B. P., °C	Mole % A	L. No.
H_2O			
C_2H_6O Ethyl alcohol (*v. also* p. 310, 322)	78.15	10.57	524
C_3H_6O Allyl alcohol	88.2	54.5	527
$C_3H_6O_2$ Propionic acid	99.98	94.7	105
C_3H_8O *n*-Propyl alcohol	87.72	56.83	528
C_3H_8O Isopropyl alcohol	80.37	31.46	525
C_4H_8O Methyl ethyl ketone	73.45	33	1060
$C_4H_8O_2$ Isobutyric acid	99.3	94.5	106
$C_4H_8O_2$ Ethyl acetate (*v. also* p. 322)	70.4	24	1690
$C_4H_{10}O$ Ethyl ether	34.15	5	1708
$C_4H_{10}O$ *n*-Butyl alcohol (2-phase)	92.25	71	532
$C_4H_{10}O$ Isobutyl alcohol	89.92	67.14	531
$C_4H_{10}O$ *sec.*-Butyl alcohol	88.5	66	529
$C_4H_{10}O$ *tert.*-Butyl alcohol	79.91	35.41	526
$C_5H_{12}O$ Isoamyl alcohol (2-phase)	95.15	82.79	533
$C_5H_{12}O$ *tert.*-Amyl alcohol	87	65	530
C_6H_6 Benzene (2-phase)	69.25	29.6	1700
C_7H_8 Toluene (2-phase)	84.1	44.4	1704
$SnCl_4$			
C_7H_8 Toluene	109.15	28	1981

C-TABLE

The C-Arrangement by A-Constituent (*v.* p. viii)

B-Constituent (the C-Arrangement)	B. P., °C	Mole % A	L. No.
CCl_3NO_2 Chloropicrin			
C_3H_6O Allyl alcohol	92	40	475
CCl_4 Carbon tetrachloride			
CH_4O Methyl alcohol	55.70	44.5	319
C_2H_6O Ethyl alcohol	64.95	61.3	353
C_3H_6O Allyl alcohol	72.32	73	394
C_3H_8O *n*-Propyl alcohol	72.8	75	408
C_3H_8O Isopropyl alcohol	67	64	379
C_4H_8O Methyl ethyl ketone	73.8	53.4	1012
$C_4H_8O_2$ Ethyl acetate	74.75	43	1301
$C_4H_8O_2$ Methyl propionate	75.5	46	1302
$C_4H_{10}O$ Isobutyl alcohol	75.8	89	432
$C_4H_{10}O$ *tert.*-Butyl alcohol	69.5	71	388
CS_2 Carbon disulfide			
CH_4O Methyl alcohol	37.65	72	514
$C_2H_4Br_2$ Ethylene bromide	37.85	41.3	1239
$C_2H_4O_2$ Methyl formate	24.75	27	1637
C_2H_6O Ethyl alcohol	42.4	86	515
C_3H_6O Acetone	39.25	61	1047
$C_3H_6O_2$ Ethyl formate	39.35	62.5	1638
$C_3H_6O_2$ Methyl acetate	40.15	69.5	1639
C_3H_8O Isopropyl alcohol	44.6	90	516
$C_3H_8O_2$ Methylal	37.25	46	1682
C_4H_8O Methyl ethyl ketone	45.85	84.1	1048
$C_4H_{10}O$ *tert.*-Butyl alcohol	45.3	94	517
$C_4H_{10}O$ Ethyl ether	34.5	1	1680
$CHBrCl_2$ Dichlorobromomethane			
C_2H_6O Ethyl alcohol	75.5	42	356
C_3H_6O Allyl alcohol	85.85	62	397
C_3H_8O *n*-Propyl alcohol	86.4	60	411
C_3H_8O Isopropyl alcohol	78	49	381
$C_4H_{10}O$ Isobutyl alcohol	89.3	78	435
$CHBr_3$ Bromoform			
$C_4H_8O_2$ Butyric acid	146	82	71
$CHCl_3$ Chloroform			
CH_4O Methyl alcohol	53.5	65	312
C_2H_6O Ethyl alcohol	59.3	84	346
C_3H_8O Isopropyl alcohol	60.8	92	374
CH_2O_2 Formic acid			
C_3H_7Br Propyl bromide	64	40	21
C_4H_9Cl Isobutyl chloride (B. P., 68°)	62.95	32	20

B-Constituent (the ℭ-Arrangement)	B. P., °C	Mole % A	L. No.
CH_3I Methyl iodide			
CH_4O Methyl alcohol	39	74.4	305
$C_2H_4O_2$ Methyl formate	31	8	1275
C_2H_6O Ethyl alcohol	41.5	89	337
C_3H_8O Isopropyl alcohol	42.3	93	372
$C_3H_8O_2$ Methylal	39.35	42	1501
CH_3NO_2 Nitromethane			
C_3H_6O Allyl alcohol	89	39	500
C_3H_8O *n*-Propyl alcohol	89.15	44	501
$C_4H_{10}O$ Isobutyl alcohol	94.7	70	503
$C_5H_{10}O$ Diethyl ketone	99.1	64	1038
$C_5H_{10}O$ Methyl propyl ketone	99.15	65	1039
CH_4O Methyl alcohol			
C_2HCl_3 Trichloroethylene	60.2	70	321
C_2H_3N Acetonitrile	63.45	84.5	764
$C_2H_4Cl_2$ Ethylene chloride	59.5	62	320
$C_2H_4Cl_2$ 1, 1-Dichloroethane	49.05	28.5	309
C_2H_5Br Ethyl bromide	34.95	14	303
C_2H_5ClO Chloromethyl methyl ether	56	57.5	482
C_2H_5I Ethyl iodide	54.7	52.5	317
C_3H_6O Acetone	55.7	20	269
$C_3H_6O_2$ Ethyl formate	50.95	30.5	541
$C_3H_6O_2$ Methyl acetate	54.0	35	542
C_3H_7Br *n*-Propyl bromide	54.1	49	316
C_3H_7I *n*-Propyl iodide	63.5	88	325
$C_3H_8O_2$ Methylal	41.82	34.5	778
$(CH_3)_3BO_3$ Trimethyl borate	59	87	543
$C_4H_8O_2$ Ethyl acetate	62.3	91.7	544
$C_4H_8O_2$ *n*-Propyl formate	63.7	97	546
C_4H_9Cl Isobutyl chloride	53.05	46.4	314
C_5H_{10} 2-Methyl-2-butene	31.75	13.5	638
C_5H_{12} *n*-Pentane	31	13	635
C_5H_{12} Isopentane	24.5	9	632
C_6H_6 Benzene	58.34	61.4	658
C_6H_8 1, 3-Cyclohexadiene	56.38	61.4	680
C_6H_{10} Cyclohexene	55.9	63.0	689
C_6H_{10} 1, 5-Hexadiene	47.05	43.5	644
C_6H_{12} Cyclohexane	54.2	61	670
C_6H_{14} *n*-Hexane	50.6	51	647
C_7H_{14} Methylcyclohexane	60	88	703
C_7H_{16} *n*-Heptane	60.5	83	698
$C_{10}H_{16}$ α-Pinene	64.5	98.5	731
C_2Cl_4 Tetrachloroethylene			
C_2H_6O Ethyl alcohol	77.95	6	367
C_3H_5ClO α-Epichlorohydrin	110.12	36.5	1210
C_3H_6O Allyl alcohol	94.0	27	399
$C_3H_6O_2$ Propionic acid	118.95	81	49
C_3H_8O *n*-Propyl alcohol	94	24	417
C_3H_8O Isopropyl alcohol	81.7	8	384
$C_4H_{10}O$ *n*-Butyl alcohol	110	47	449
$C_4H_{10}O$ Isobutyl alcohol	103.05	40	443
$C_5H_{10}O_3$ Diethyl carbonate	118.55	67	1330
$C_5H_{12}O$ Isoamyl alcohol	116.0	69	457
$C_6H_{12}O_2$ Isobutyl acetate	116.6	35.5	1327
$C_6H_{12}O_3$ Paraldehyde	118.75	63	863
C_2Cl_6 Hexachloroethane			
$C_2H_2Cl_2O_2$ Dichloroacetic acid	181	80	214
C_2HCl_3 Trichloroethylene			
C_3H_6O Allyl alcohol	80.95	70	396
C_3H_8O *n*-Propyl alcohol	81.75	69	410
C_3H_8O Isopropyl alcohol	74	54	380

B-Constituent (the ℭ-Arrangement)	B. P., °C	Mole % A	L. No.
C_2HCl_3 Trichloroethylene.—(*Continued*)			
$C_4H_{10}O$ Isobutyl alcohol	85.4	86	434
$C_4H_{10}O$ *tert.*-Butyl alcohol	75	74	389
$C_5H_{12}O$ *tert.*-Amyl alcohol	84	83	426
C_2HCl_5 Pentachloroethane			
$C_4H_6O_4$ Dimethyl oxalate	157.55	55.4	1361
$C_5H_{10}O_2$ Isovaleric acid (B. P., 176.5°)	160.0	82	82
C_6H_6O Phenol	160.85	81.5	1526
$C_6H_{12}O$ Cyclohexanol	157.9	47	462
$C_8H_{16}O_2$ Isoamyl propionate	158.7	41.7	1360
$C_2H_2Cl_2$ *cis*-1, 2-Acetylene dichloride			
C_2H_6O Ethyl alcohol	57.7	81.4	345
$C_2H_2Cl_2$ *trans*-1, 2-Acetylene dichloride			
C_2H_6O Ethyl alcohol	46.5	88.2	339
$C_2H_2Cl_2$ Dichloroethylene			
C_3H_6O Allyl alcohol	79.6	76	395
C_3H_8O *n*-Propyl alcohol	80	77	409
$C_2H_2Cl_4$ Tetrachloroethane			
$C_2H_4O_2$ Acetic acid	107.35	36.5	42
$C_4H_8O_3$ Methyl lactate	143.3	36	1343
C_2H_3BrO *cis*-Acetyl bromide			
C_2H_6O Ethyl alcohol	77.7	10.5	363
C_2H_3BrO *trans*-Acetyl bromide			
C_2H_6O Ethyl alcohol	75.7	30.5	361
$C_2H_3ClO_2$ Chloroacetic acid			
C_7H_7Br *o*-Bromotoluene	172.95	46	206
C_7H_7Br *p*-Bromotoluene	174	62	208
C_7H_7Cl Benzyl chloride	172	34	205
$C_{10}H_{14}O$ Carvol	167.8	43	219
$C_2H_3Cl_3$ 1, 1, 2-Trichloroethane			
C_2H_6O Ethyl alcohol	77.3	16	364
$C_2H_3Cl_3O_2$ Chloral hydrate			
C_6H_{12} Cyclohexane	76	13	834
C_2H_3N Acetonitrile			
C_2H_6O Ethyl alcohol	72.5	47	765
C_3H_8O *n*-Propyl alcohol	81.2	79	767
C_3H_8O Isopropyl alcohol	75	55	766
C_2H_4BrCl 1-Bromo-2-chloroethane			
C_3H_5ClO α-Epichlorohydrin	103.5	76	1207
$C_2H_4Br_2$ 1, 1-Dibromoethane			
C_2H_6O Ethyl alcohol	77	18	362
$C_2H_4Br_2$ Ethylene bromide			
$C_2H_4O_2$ Acetic acid	114.35	20.7	43
$C_3H_6O_2$ Propionic acid	127.75	65	50
$C_4H_{10}O$ Isobutyl alcohol	106.2	22	444
$C_5H_{12}O$ Isoamyl alcohol	123.2	52	458
C_8H_{10} Ethylbenzene	131.1	83.5	1457
$C_2H_4Cl_2$ 1, 1-Dichloroethane			
C_2H_6O Ethyl alcohol	54.5	84	342
$C_2H_4O_2$ Acetic acid			
C_6H_5Cl Chlorobenzene	114.65	72.5	44
C_6H_6 Benzene	80.05	97.5	127
C_7H_8 Toluene	105.4	62.7	132
C_8H_{10} *m*-Xylene	115.38	40	136

B-Constituent (the ℭ-Arrangement)	B. P., °C	Mole % A	L. No.
$C_2H_4O_2$ Methyl formate			
C_2H_5Br Ethyl bromide	29.85	76.5	1270
$C_4H_{10}O$ Ethyl ether	28.25	61.5	1842
C_5H_{12} Isopentane	17.05	51.5	1752
C_2H_5Br Ethyl bromide			
C_2H_6O Ethyl alcohol	37.6	93	336
C_2H_5ClO Chloromethyl methyl ether			
C_2H_6O Ethyl alcohol	58.4	75	483
C_2H_5I Ethyl iodide			
C_2H_6O Ethyl alcohol	63	66.3	351
C_3H_8O *n*-Propyl alcohol	70.1	81.7	406
$C_4H_8O_2$ Ethyl acetate	70.5	63	1295
C_6H_{14} *n*-Hexane	68	63	1426
$C_2H_5NO_2$ Nitroethane			
$C_4H_{10}O$ Isobutyl alcohol	102.5	36	505
C_2H_6O Ethyl alcohol			
C_3H_5Br *α-cis*-Bromopropylene	57.7	18.6	343
C_3H_5I 3-Iodopropylene	75.6	71	358
$C_3H_6O_3$ Dimethyl carbonate	75.7	91	553
C_3H_7Br *n*-Propyl bromide	63	35	350
C_3H_7Cl *n*-Propyl chloride	44.9	10.5	338
C_4H_8O Methyl ethyl ketone	74.8	45	274
$C_4H_8O_2$ Ethyl acetate (*v. also* p. 323)	71.8	46	550
$C_4H_8O_2$ Methyl propionate	73.2	67.5	551
$C_4H_8O_2$ *n*-Propyl formate	73.5	72	552
C_4H_9Br *tert.*-Butyl bromide	63.8	34	352
C_4H_9Cl Isobutyl chloride	61.45	28	348
C_4H_9I Isobutyl iodide	77.65	90.5	365
$C_5H_{11}Br$ Isoamyl bromide (B. P., 120°)	77.6	88	366
C_6H_6 Benzene	68.24	44.8	659
C_6H_8 1, 3-Cyclohexadiene	66.7	47.3	681
C_6H_{10} Cyclohexene	66.7	49.5	690
C_6H_{10} 1, 5-Hexadiene	53.5	21	645
C_6H_{12} Cyclohexane	64.9	44.5	671
C_6H_{14} *n*-Hexane	58.68	33.2	648
C_7H_8 Toluene	76.65	81	707
C_7H_{14} Methylcyclohexane	73	70	704
C_7H_{16} *n*-Heptane	72	67	699
$C_2H_6O_2$ Glycol			
$C_8H_8O_2$ Phenyl acetate	191	48.4	615
$C_9H_{18}O_3$ Diisobutyl carbonate	187	41	613
$C_{10}H_{16}$ Carvene (2-phase)	163	28	753
C_3H_5ClO *α*-Epichlorohydrin			
C_3H_6O Allyl alcohol	95.8	15.3	487
C_3H_8O *n*-Propyl alcohol	96.0	16.3	488
$C_4H_{10}O$ *n*-Butyl alcohol	112.0	51.5	491
$C_4H_{10}O$ Isobutyl alcohol	105.0	34.3	490
$C_5H_{12}O$ Isoamyl alcohol	115.35	80.2	492
$C_5H_{12}O$ *tert.*-Amyl alcohol	100.1	29	489
C_7H_8 Toluene	108.25	26	1596
$C_3H_5Cl_3$ 1, 2, 3-Trichloropropane (B. P., 158°)			
$C_4H_8O_2$ Isobutyric acid	150	58	64
$C_6H_{12}O$ Cyclohexanol	155	55	460
$C_{10}H_{16}$ *α*-Pinene	154.5	48	1479
C_3H_5I 3-Iodopropylene			
C_3H_8O *n*-Propyl alcohol	90.0	46.7	413
$C_4H_{10}O$ Isobutyl alcohol	96	68	437
$C_5H_{10}O$ Diethyl ketone	100.8	50	1020
$C_5H_{10}O$ Methyl propyl ketone	100.9	50	1024

B-Constituent (the ℭ-Arrangement)	B. P., °C	Mole % A	L. No.
$C_3H_6Br_2$ *cis*-Dibromopropane			
C_3H_8O *n*-Propyl alcohol	97.05	1.05	421
$C_3H_6Br_2$ *trans*-Dibromopropane			
C_3H_8O *n*-Propyl alcohol	95.75	17.75	418
$C_3H_6Br_2$ 1, 2-Dibromopropane			
C_8H_{10} Ethylbenzene	135.95	2.7	1465
$C_3H_6Cl_2$ 2, 2-Dichloropropane			
$C_6H_{12}O$ Cyclohexanol	155.6	79	495
$C_3H_6Cl_2O$ 1, 1′-Dichloroisopropyl alcohol			
$C_4H_6O_4$ Methyl oxalate	162	13	831
$C_{10}H_{14}$ Cymene	165	53	838
$C_{10}H_{16}$ Camphene	154	81	837
$C_{10}H_{16}$ Carvene	165.75	58	839
$C_{10}H_{16}$ *α*-Pinene	152	86	836
$C_3H_6Cl_2O$ 2, 3-Dichloropropyl alcohol			
C_7H_7Br *o*-Bromotoluene	171.6	51	825
C_7H_7Cl Benzyl chloride	171	40	824
$C_{10}H_{16}$ Carvene	169.3	41	841
C_3H_6O Allyl alcohol			
C_4H_9Br Isobutyl bromide	83.9	35	398
C_4H_9Cl Isobutyl chloride	67	11	393
$C_5H_{10}O_2$ Ethyl propionate	93.2	67	564
$C_5H_{10}O_2$ Isobutyl formate	93	65	563
C_6H_6 Benzene	76.75	22.2	662
C_6H_8 1, 3-Cyclohexadiene	75.9	26.5	684
C_6H_{10} Cyclohexene	76.3	28.2	693
C_6H_{12} Cyclohexane	74	26.6	674
C_6H_{14} *n*-Hexane	65.5	6.5	651
C_7H_8 Toluene	92.4	61.5	709
C_3H_6O Acetone			
$C_3H_6O_2$ Methyl acetate	56.1	61	1069
C_4H_9Cl Isobutyl chloride	55.8	81	1001
$C_4H_{11}N$ Diethylamine	51.5	43.5	909
$C_3H_6O_2$ Propionic acid			
$C_5H_{11}I$ Isoamyl iodide (B. P., 147.5°)	136.5	68.5	53
C_8H_{10} *o*-Xylene	134.5	71	145
C_8H_{10} *p*-Xylene	132.0	72	143
C_9H_{12} Mesitylene	139.3	32.5	149
$C_{10}H_{16}$ *α*-Pinene	136.15	56.5	146
$C_3H_6O_3$ Dimethyl carbonate			
C_3H_8O *n*-Propyl alcohol	88.2	70	567
C_4H_9Br Isobutyl bromide	87.7	60.4	1309
C_3H_7Br *n*-Propyl bromide			
C_3H_8O *n*-Propyl alcohol	69.2	82.5	405
C_3H_8O Isopropyl alcohol	65.2	72	376
C_3H_7Cl *n*-Propyl chloride			
C_3H_8O Isopropyl alcohol	45.8	95	373
C_3H_7I *n*-Propyl iodide			
C_3H_8O *n*-Propyl alcohol	90.2	50	414
$C_4H_{10}O$ Isobutyl alcohol	96	67	438
$C_5H_{10}O$ Diethyl ketone	100.9	48.4	1021
C_3H_8O *n*-Propyl alcohol			
C_4H_9Cl Isobutyl chloride	67.2	10	404
$C_5H_{10}O_2$ Ethyl propionate	93.4	64	570
$C_5H_{10}O_2$ Methyl butyrate	94.2	80.7	572
$C_5H_{10}O_2$ Methyl isobutyrate	89.5	36	568
$C_5H_{10}O_2$ *n*-Propyl acetate	94	74	571
$C_5H_{11}Br$ Isoamyl bromide	94.5	80	416

B-Constituent (the ℭ-Arrangement)	B. P., °C	Mole % A	L. No.
C_3H_8O *n*-Propyl alcohol.—(*Continued*)			
C_6H_5Cl Chlorobenzene	96.5	87	420
C_6H_6 Benzene	77.12	20.9	663
C_6H_8 1, 3-Cyclohexadiene	76.1	26.2	685
C_6H_{10} Cyclohexene	76.6	27.8	694
C_6H_{12} Cyclohexane	74.3	26	675
C_6H_{14} *n*-Hexane	65.65	6	652
C_7H_8 Toluene	92.6	60	710
C_8H_{18} *n*-Octane	95	84	718
C_3H_8O Isopropyl alcohol			
$C_4H_8O_2$ Ethyl acetate	74.8	30.5	556
$C_4H_8O_2$ Methyl propionate	77	36.5	557
C_4H_9Br Isobutyl bromide	75.5	53	382
C_4H_9Cl Isobutyl chloride	63.8	24	375
C_4H_9I Isobutyl iodide	81.8	91	383
C_6H_6 Benzene	71.92	39.3	660
C_6H_8 1, 3-Cyclohexadiene	70.4	42.9	682
C_6H_{10} Cyclohexene	71	43.5	691
C_6H_{12} Cyclohexane	68.6	40.8	672
C_6H_{14} *n*-Hexane	61	29	649
C_7H_8 Toluene	80.6	77	708
$C_4H_6O_4$ Dimethyl oxalate			
$C_6H_{12}O$ Cyclohexanol	155.6	37.3	605
C_7H_7Cl *p*-Chlorotoluene	157.0	41.7	1357
C_9H_{12} Mesitylene	154.8	50.2	1817
$C_{10}H_{16}$ α-Pinene	144.1	37.5	1814
$C_{10}H_{16}$ β-Pinene	147.1	44	1816
C_4H_8O Methyl ethyl ketone			
C_6H_6 Benzene	78.35	39.4	1101
$C_4H_8O_2$ Butyric acid			
C_7H_7Cl *o*-Chlorotoluene	153	26.5	73
C_8H_{10} *m*-Xylene	138.1	94.5	166
C_8H_{10} *p*-Xylene	137.5	95.5	165
C_9H_{12} Mesitylene	158.5	73.5	170
$C_{10}H_{16}$ Carvene	151.0	30.5	161
$C_4H_8O_2$ Isobutyric acid			
C_6H_5Br Bromobenzene	148.6	49	63
C_7H_7Cl *p*-Chlorotoluene	152.2	53	65
C_8H_{10} Ethylbenzene	131.9	84.7	154
$C_{10}H_{22}$ 2, 7-Dimethyloctane	147.6	66.4	158
$C_4H_8O_2$ Ethyl acetate			
C_4H_9Br *tert.*-Butyl bromide	71.5	40	1298
$C_4H_{10}O$ *tert.*-Butyl alcohol	75.2	71.6	559
$C_4H_8O_2$ *n*-Propyl formate			
C_6H_6 Benzene	72	45	1778
C_4H_9Br *n*-Butyl bromide			
$C_4H_{10}O$ Isobutyl alcohol	89	80	436
C_4H_9Cl Isobutyl chloride			
$C_4H_{10}O$ *tert.*-Butyl alcohol	65	83	387
C_4H_9I Isobutyl iodide			
$C_5H_{12}O$ Isoamyl alcohol	116	67	455
$C_6H_{12}O_2$ Isoamyl formate	117.5	59.4	1321
$C_6H_{12}O_2$ Isobutyl acetate	116.6	35.8	1319
$C_4H_{10}O$ *n*-Butyl alcohol			
C_6H_{12} Cyclohexane	79.8	11	679
$C_6H_{12}O_2$ *n*-Butyl acetate	113.5	56	593
$C_6H_{12}O_2$ Ethyl isobutyrate	108.5	28	591
$C_6H_{12}O_2$ Methyl isovalerate	113	43	592
C_7H_8 Toluene	105.5	37	713

B-Constituent (the ℭ-Arrangement)	B. P., °C	Mole % A	L. No.
$C_4H_{10}O$ Isobutyl alcohol			
$C_5H_{11}Br$ Isoamyl bromide	103.8	60	442
C_6H_5Cl Chlorobenzene	107.2	74	445
C_6H_6 Benzene	79.84	10	666
C_6H_8 1, 3-Cyclohexadiene	79.35	12.7	687
C_6H_{10} Cyclohexene	80.5	15.6	696
C_6H_{12} Cyclohexane	78.1	15.7	678
C_6H_{14} *n*-Hexane	68.1	1	655
C_7H_8 Toluene	101.15	50	712
$C_{10}H_{16}$ α-Pinene	107.9	96.5	734
$C_4H_{10}O$ *sec.*-Butyl alcohol			
$C_5H_{10}O_2$ Ethyl propionate	85.5	63	575
$C_5H_{10}O_2$ *n*-Propyl acetate	96.5	60	576
$C_4H_{10}O$ *tert.*-Butyl alcohol			
$C_5H_{10}O_2$ Methyl butyrate	101	25	584
$C_5H_{10}O_2$ *n*-Propyl acetate	100.8	12	583
C_6H_6 Benzene	73.95	37.7	661
C_6H_8 1, 3-Cyclohexadiene	73.4	40.5	683
C_6H_{10} Cyclohexene	73.7	40.5	692
C_6H_{12} Cyclohexane	71.8	40	673
$C_6H_{12}O_2$ Ethyl isobutyrate	105.5	63	585
$C_6H_{12}O_2$ Methyl isovalerate	107.5	93	586
C_6H_{14} *n*-Hexane	63.7	28	650
$C_5H_8O_3$ Methyl acetoacetate			
$C_{10}H_{16}$ α-Pinene	150.5	40	1149
$C_{10}H_{18}$ Menthene	160	56	1151
$C_5H_8O_4$ Dimethyl malonate			
$C_{10}H_{18}O$ Cineole	173.5	30	1861
$C_5H_{10}O$ Diethyl ketone			
$C_5H_{12}O$ *tert.*-Amyl alcohol	98.5	50.5	283
$C_5H_{10}O$ Methyl propyl ketone			
$C_5H_{10}O_2$ *n*-Propyl acetate	101.35	42	1081
C_7H_{14} Methylcyclohexane	100.6	43.5	1110
$C_5H_{10}O_2$ Isovaleric acid			
C_7H_7Br *o*-Bromotoluene	172.1	52.3	85
$C_{10}H_{16}$ Camphene	163.8	80	180
$C_{10}H_{16}$ Carvene	168.9	66	182
$C_5H_{10}O_2$ Ethyl propionate			
$C_5H_{12}O$ *tert.*-Amyl alcohol	96.5	67	577
$C_5H_{10}O_2$ Methyl butyrate			
$C_5H_{12}O$ *tert.*-Amyl alcohol	99	53	579
$C_5H_{10}O_2$ *n*-Propyl acetate			
$C_5H_{12}O$ *tert.*-Amyl alcohol	98.5	63.5	578
$C_5H_{10}O_3$ Ethyl lactate			
C_7H_8O Anisole	150.0	54	1851
$C_5H_{11}Br$ Isoamyl bromide			
$C_5H_{12}O$ Isoamyl alcohol	116.4	70	456
$C_6H_{12}O_3$ Paraldehyde	118.5	74	862
$C_5H_{12}O$ *n*-Amyl alcohol			
$C_7H_{14}O_2$ Isoamyl acetate	131.3	96.4	599
$C_7H_{14}O_2$ Isobutyl propionate	130.5	85	598
$C_5H_{12}O$ Isoamyl alcohol			
C_6H_5Cl Chlorobenzene	124.3	42	459
C_8H_8 Styrene	128.5	69	730
C_8H_{10} Ethylbenzene	125.9	54	722
C_8H_{10} *o*-Xylene	128	64	729
C_8H_{10} *m*-Xylene	127.0	58	727
C_8H_{10} *p*-Xylene	126.8	56	723
$C_{10}H_{16}$ α-Pinene	130	85	735

B-Constituent (the ℭ-Arrangement)	B. P., °C	Mole % A	L. No.
$C_6H_3Cl_3$ 1, 3, 5-Trichlorobenzene			
$C_8H_{11}N$ Ethylaniline	203	56	944
C_6H_5Br Bromobenzene			
$C_6H_{12}O$ Cyclohexanol	153.6	55	459a
$C_6H_{14}O_2$ Pinacone	152	82	466
$C_8H_{16}O_2$ *n*-Propyl isovalerate	154	50	1350
$C_{10}H_{16}$ α-Pinene	153.4	46.3	1475
C_6H_5ClO *p*-Chlorophenol			
$C_{10}H_8$ Naphthalene	215.9	36.5	1606
C_6H_5I Iodobenzene			
C_6H_6O Phenol	177.7	34.2	1532
$C_6H_5NO_2$ Nitrobenzene			
C_7H_8O Benzyl alcohol	204.3	39	508
$C_{10}H_{18}O$ Borneol	207.75	60	509
$C_{10}H_{20}O$ Menthol	207.9	60	510
C_6H_6O Phenol			
C_7H_7Br *p*-Bromotoluene	176.2	58	1531
$C_{10}H_{16}$ Carvene	169.0	49.5	1965
$C_{10}H_{16}$ α-Pinene	152.75	25	1957
C_6H_7N Aniline			
$C_{10}H_{16}$ Carvene	171.35	48	974
$C_6H_{10}O_3$ Ethyl acetoacetate			
C_8H_8 Styrene	145.2	3	1153
$C_{10}H_{16}$ Carvene	169.05	44	1160
$C_{10}H_{16}$ α-Pinene	153.35	23	1154
$C_{10}H_{16}$ δ-1, 5-Terpinene	171	50	1161
$C_6H_{10}O_4$ Diethyl oxalate			
C_7H_7Br *o*-Bromotoluene	177.35	43.8	1373
C_7H_7Br *p*-Bromotoluene	180.4	56.6	1375
$C_6H_{12}O$ Cyclohexanol			
C_8H_{10} *m*-Xylene	138.9	5.5	728
$C_8H_{16}O_2$ Isoamyl propionate	157.7	77	604
$C_8H_{16}O_2$ Isobutyl butyrate	155	26.5	603
C_9H_{12} Pseudocumene	158	64.5	745
C_9H_{12} Mesitylene	156.3	54.5	742
$C_{10}H_{14}$ Cymene	159	76	748
$C_{10}H_{16}$ Camphene	153	42	740
$C_{10}H_{16}$ Carvene	159.25	78.5	751
$C_{10}H_{16}$ α-Pinene	149.9	43	736
$C_{10}H_{18}$ Menthene	157.5	69	746
$C_6H_{12}O_2$ Isoamyl formate			
$C_6H_{12}O_3$ Paraldehyde	122.5	57	882
$C_6H_{12}O_3$ *n*-Propyl lactate			
$C_6H_{14}O_2$ Pinacone	168	35	607
$C_{10}H_{16}$ Carvene	166.35	64	1826
$C_6H_{14}O_2$ Pinacone			
$C_8H_{10}O$ Phenetole	169	48	798
$C_7H_6Cl_2$ Benzal chloride			
$C_8H_{16}O_3$ Isoamyl lactate	201.3	45	1387
C_7H_6O Benzaldehyde			
C_7H_7Cl Benzyl chloride	177.9	54	866
$C_{10}H_{14}$ *m*-Cymene	171	33	897
$C_{10}H_{16}$ Carvene	171.2	49	898
C_7H_7Br *o*-Bromotoluene			
C_7H_8O *o*-Cresol	180.3	77	1539
$C_7H_{14}O_3$ Isobutyl lactate	180	52	1372

B-Constituent (the ℭ-Arrangement)	B. P., °C	Mole % A	L. No.
C_7H_7Br *p*-Bromotoluene			
C_7H_8O *o*-Cresol	181.7	68	1541
C_7H_7Cl Benzyl chloride			
$C_9H_{18}O_2$ Isoamyl butyrate	177.1	55	1365
$C_7H_7NO_2$ Nitrotoluene			
$C_{10}H_{18}O$ Geraniol	227.5	67	512
C_7H_8O Benzyl alcohol			
$C_7H_8O_2$ Guaiacol	204.4	38	807
$C_8H_{18}O_2$ Isoamylmethylal	198.7	63	803
$C_{10}H_8$ Naphthalene	204.3	64	760
$C_{10}H_{16}$ Carvene	176.25	13	755
$C_{12}H_{18}$ 1, 3, 5-Triethylbenzene	200.2	67	757
C_7H_8O *o*-Cresol			
$C_{10}H_{16}$ Carvene	175.35	30	1972
C_7H_8O Anisole			
$C_8H_{16}O_2$ Isobutyl butyrate	151	73	1852
$C_{10}H_{16}$ α-Pinene	150.45	62	1945
C_7H_9N Methylaniline			
$C_{10}H_{16}$ Carvene	174.5	16	978
$C_7H_{14}O_2$ Isoamyl acetate			
C_8H_{10} *m*-Xylene	136	45	1802
$C_7H_{14}O_2$ Isobutyl propionate			
C_8H_{10} Ethylbenzene	133	43	1800
$C_7H_{14}O_3$ Isobutyl lactate			
$C_{10}H_{16}$ Carvene	172.5	38	1832
$C_8H_{11}N$ Dimethylaniline			
$C_{10}H_{16}$ Carvene	174	29	977
$C_8H_{18}O$ *sec.*-Octyl alcohol			
$C_{10}H_{16}$ Carvene	174.4	42	752
$C_9H_{10}O_2$ Ethyl benzoate			
$C_{10}H_{18}O$ Borneol	211	69	622
$C_9H_{18}O_2$ Isoamyl butyrate			
$C_{10}H_{16}$ Carvene	174	43	1828
$C_{10}H_{12}O_2$ Propyl benzoate			
$C_{10}H_{18}O$ Geraniol	228	43	624
$C_{10}H_{18}O$ Borneol			
$C_{12}H_{18}$ 1, 3, 5-Triethylbenzene	211	59	758

Effect of Pressure upon Azeotropic Mixtures

A = H_2O, B = C_2H_5OH (30, 31, 49)

p, mm Hg	B. P., °C	M % B	*p*, mm Hg	B. P., °C	M % B
100	34.2	99.6	760	78.1	90.0
150	42.0	96.2	1100	87.8	89.3
200	47.8	93.8	1450	95.3	89.0
400	62.8	91.4			

A = H_2O, B = $C_4H_8O_2$ Ethyl acetate (30, 31, 49)

p, mm Hg	B. P., °C	M % A	*p*, mm Hg	B. P., °C	M % A
25	− 1.9	14.7	600	64.0	28.9
50	+10.0	16.2	760	70.4	30.5
100	23.0	18.8	900	75.1	31.6
150	31.4	20.7	1050	79.6	32.6
200	37.6	22.2	1200	83.5	33.3
300	46.8	24.5	1350	87.1	34.1
400	53.7	26.1	1500	90.3	34.8
500	59.4	27.6			

A = C_2H_5OH, B = $C_4H_8O_2$ Ethyl acetate (30, 31, 49)

p, mm Hg	B. P., °C	M % A	p, mm Hg	B. P., °C	M % A
25	− 1.4	22.1	600	65.4	43.6
50	+10.6	24.6	760	71.8	46.4
100	23.8	28.2	900	76.5	48.5
150	32.3	31.1	1050	81.1	50.4
200	38.4	33.4	1200	85.0	52.2
300	47.8	37.0	1350	88.7	53.9
400	54.9	39.6	1500	91.8	55.4
500	60.8	41.8			

Two-Component Mixtures with Maximum Boiling Point

𝔅-Table

B-Constituent (standard arrangement)	Max. B. P., °C	Mole % A	L. No.
H_2O			
HF	120	65.4	2034
HCl	110	88.9	2035
$HClO_4$	203	32	2041
HBr	126	83.1	2036
HI	127	84.3	2037
HNO_3 (735 mm)	120.5	62.2	2039
CH_2O_2 Formic acid	107.1	43.3	2040
HCl			
C_2H_6O Dimethyl ether	−1.5	65	2042

ℭ-Table

B-Constituent (standard arrangement)	Max. B. P., °C	Mole % A	L. No.
$CHCl_3$			
C_3H_6O Acetone	64.5	65.5	2107
CH_2O_2 Formic acid			
$C_5H_{10}O$ Diethyl ketone	105.4	48	2021
$C_5H_{10}O$ Methyl propyl ketone	105.3	47	2022
C_6H_6O Phenol			
$C_6H_{12}O$ Cyclohexanol	182.45	90	2061
C_7H_6O Benzaldehyde	185.6	54	2089
C_7H_8O Benzyl alcohol	206	8	2066
$C_8H_{18}O$ *sec.*-Octyl alcohol	184.65	58	2063
$C_9H_{18}O_3$ Diisobutyl carbonate	192.5	39.3	2162
$C_6H_{10}O_4$ Diethyl oxalate			
C_7H_8O *o*-Cresol	193.9	27	2169
C_7H_8O *o*-Cresol			
C_8H_8O Acetophenone	203.7	24	2126
$C_8H_8O_2$ Phenyl acetate	198.6	42.5	2171
$C_8H_{16}O$ Methyl hexyl ketone	191.5	97	2125
$C_9H_{18}O_2$ Isoamyl butyrate	192.0	80	2167
C_7H_8O *m*-Cresol			
C_8H_8O Acetophenone	209	54	2133
$C_8H_{16}O_3$ Isoamyl lactate	207.6	60	2190
C_7H_8O *p*-Cresol			
C_7H_8O Benzyl alcohol	207.0	38	2079
C_7H_9N *o*-Toluidine	204.5	53	2105
C_7H_9N *p*-Toluidine	204.35	57	2104
C_8H_8O Acetophenone	208.45	52	2129
$C_{10}H_{16}O$ Camphor	213.15	38	2131

Three-Component Mixtures

𝔅-Table

A = H_2O

Constituents (the ℭ-Arrangement)	Mole %	B. P., °C	L. No.
CCl_4	57.6	61.8	2249
C_2H_5OH	23.0	2-phase	
CCl_4	53.8	65.15	2259
C_3H_6O Allyl alcohol	18.7	2-phase	
CCl_4	54.4	65.4	2264
C_3H_8O *n*-Propyl alcohol	18.0	2-phase	
C_2Cl_2 *cis*-Dichloroacetylene	37.8	53.8	2243
C_2H_5OH	56.2		
C_2Cl_2 *trans*-Dichloroacetylene	86.2	44.4	2240
C_2H_5OH	8.4		
C_2HCl_3 Trichloroethylene	38.4	67.25	2251
C_2H_5OH	41.2	2-phase	
C_2HCl_3 Trichloroethylene	49.2	71.4	2260
C_3H_6O Allyl alcohol	17.3	2-phase	
C_2HCl_3 Trichloroethylene	51.1	71.55	2266
C_3H_8O *n*-Propyl alcohol	16.6	2-phase	
$C_2H_4Cl_2$ Ethylene chloride	54.9	66.7	2250
C_2H_5OH	25.7	2-phase	
C_2H_5I	53.9	61	2248
C_2H_5OH	19.1	2-phase	
C_2H_5OH	21.5	60	2247
C_3H_7Br *n*-Propyl bromide	55.6	2-phase	
C_2H_5OH	12.4	70.3	2304
$C_4H_8O_2$ Ethyl acetate	60.1		
C_2H_5OH	37.1	69.5	2253
C_4H_9Br Isobutyl bromide	32.5	2-phase	
C_2H_5OH	19.8	58.62	2246
C_4H_9Cl Isobutyl chloride	62.6	2-phase	
C_2H_5OH	22.8	64.86	2314
C_6H_6 Benzene	53.9		
C_2H_5OH	25.0	63.6	2316
C_6H_8 1, 3-Cyclohexadiene	52.6		
C_2H_5OH	25.3	64.05	2317
C_6H_{10} Cyclohexene	51.9	2-phase	
C_2H_5OH	22.2	62.1	2315
C_6H_{12} Cyclohexane	54.3		
C_3H_5I 3-Iodopropylene	35.5	78.15	2268
C_3H_8O *n*-Propyl alcohol	27.6	2-phase	
C_3H_6O Allyl alcohol	9.5	68.3	2333
C_6H_6 Benzene	62.2		
C_3H_6O Allyl alcohol	9.3	68.21	2334
C_6H_6 Benzene	62.5		
C_3H_6O Allyl alcohol	11.5	67.95	2337
C_6H_{10} Cyclohexene	59.7		
C_3H_6O Allyl alcohol	11.8	66.18	2335
C_6H_{12} Cyclohexane	60.3		
C_3H_6O Allyl alcohol	6.1	59.7	2332
C_6H_{14} *n*-Hexane	74.1		
C_3H_8O *n*-Propyl alcohol	15.4	81.2	2222
$C_5H_{10}O$ Diethyl ketone	32.6	2-phase	
C_3H_8O *n*-Propyl alcohol	8.9	68.48	2340
C_6H_6 Benzene	62.8		
C_3H_8O *n*-Propyl alcohol	11.9	67.75	2342
C_6H_8 1, 3-Cyclohexadiene	58.4		
C_3H_8O *n*-Propyl alcohol	11.5	68.2	2343
C_6H_{10} Cyclohexene	58.3		
C_3H_8O *n*-Propyl alcohol	10.3	66.55	2341
C_6H_{12} Cyclohexane	60.3		
C_3H_8O Isopropyl alcohol	18.6	66.51	2322
C_6H_6 Benzene	56.5		
C_3H_8O Isopropyl alcohol	21.8	66.1	2325
C_6H_{10} Cyclohexene	52.7		

Constituents (the ℭ-Arrangement)	Mole %	B. P., °C	L. No.
C_3H_8O Isopropyl alcohol	19.2	64.3	2323
C_6H_{12} Cyclohexane	54.8		
$C_4H_{10}O$ *tert.*-Butyl alcohol	17.5	67.30	2328
C_6H_6 Benzene	55.0		
$C_4H_{10}O$ *tert.*-Butyl alcohol	18.0	65	2329
C_6H_{12} Cyclohexane	53.7		

ℭ-Table

The ℭ-Arrangement

Constituents	Mole%	B. P., °C	L. No.
A = CS_2			
CH_3OH	24.1	33.92	2236
C_2H_5Br Ethyl bromide	35.4		
A = $C_2H_4O_2$ Methyl formate			
C_2H_5Br Ethyl bromide	23.8	16.95	2417
C_5H_{12} Isopentane	31.0		
$C_4H_{10}O$ Ethyl ether	7.2	20.4	2443
C_5H_{12} *n*-Pentane	48.2		
A = $C_6H_{12}O_3$ *n*-Propyl lactate			
$C_8H_{10}O$ Phenetole	35.2	163.0	2445
$C_{10}H_{18}$ Menthene	34.1		

LITERATURE

(For a key to the periodicals see end of volume)

(1) Baly, University of Liverpool, *0*. (2) Barbaudy, *34*, **180**: 1924; 25. (3) Beckmann, Liesche and Gabel, *7*, **92**: 421; 17. (4) Blanksma, *176*, **7**: 417; 10. (5) Büchner, *64P*, **20**: 322; 17. (6) Carr, Townsend and Badger, *45*, **17**: 643; 25. (7) Carrière and Armand, *34*, **179**: 1265; 24. (8) Carrière and Cerveau, *34*, **177**: 46; 23. (9) Carveth, *50*, **3**: 193; 99.

(10) Creighton and Githens, *143*, **179**: 161; 15. (11) Creighton and Smith, *143*, **180**: 703; 15. (12) Doroshevskii and Polianskii, *7*, **73**: 192; 10. (13) Efremov, *53*, **50**: 351; 18. *10*, **5**: 295; 25. (14) Evans, *45*, **8**: 260; 16. (15) Fox and Barker, *54*, **36**: 842; 17. (16) Grün and Wirth, *92*, **32**: 61; 19. (17) Hachmeister, *93*, **109**: 145; 19. (18) Hackspill and Grandadam, *34*, **179**: 464; 24. (19) Haywood, *50*, **3**: 317; 99.

(20) Holst and Hamburger, *64P*, **18**: 872; 16. (21) Jana and Gupta, *1*, **36**: 115; 14. (22) Jänecke, *92*, **33**: 278; 20. (23) Kohnstamm and Timmermans, *64P*, **13**: 865; 11. *64V*, **19**: 1022; 11. (24) Lebo, *1*, **43**: 1005; 21. (25) de Leeuw, *7*, **77**: 284; 11. (26) Leopold, *7*, **71**: 59; 10. (27) Lewis, *54*, **41**: 97; 22. (28) Mains, *33*, **26**: 779, 841; 22. (29) Mayer-Bugström, *465*, **44**: 417; 24.

(30) Merriman, *4*, **103**: 1790; 13. (31) Merriman, *4*, **103**: 628; 13. (32) Narbutt, *7*, **53**: 697; 05. (33) Noyes and Warfel, *1*, **23**: 463; 01. (34) Parks and Schwenck, *50*, **28**: 720; 24. (35) Pascal, Duprey and Garnier, *27*, **29**: 9; 21. (36) Pascal and Garnier, *27*, **25**: 309; 19. (37) Pascal and Garnier, *315*, **20**: 39; 23. (38) Povarnin and Markov, *53*, **55**: 381; 24. (39) Pratolongo, *22*, **30**: 323; 21.

(40) Räder, *93*, **130**: 325; 23. (41) Rosanoff, Bacon and White, *1*, **36**: 1803; 14. (42) Rosanoff and Easley, *1*, **31**: 953; 09. (43) Rosanoff, Schulze and Dunphy, *1*, **36**: 2480; 14. (44) Sanger and Reigel, *65*, **47**: 673; 12. (45) Schulze, *1*, **36**: 498; 14. (46) Thayer, *50*, **2**: 382; 98. (47) Thiel and Schulte, *7*, **96**: 312; 20. (48) Tyrer, *4*, **101**: 81, 1104; 12. (49) Wade and Merriman, *4*, **99**: 997; 11.

(50) Young, *4*, **83**: 68; 03. (51) Barbaudy, *42*, **24**: 1; 27. (52) Rhodes and Bascom, *45*, **19**: 480; 27.

BOILING-POINT ELEVATIONS, NON-VOLATILE SOLUTES

Blair Saxton

With James B. Austin, Harold G. Dietrich, Florence Fenwick, Arthur Fleischer, George L. Frear, Elliott J. Roberts, Rodney P. Smith, Myer Solomon and Harold M. Spurlin

CONTENTS

INTRODUCTION

This section includes systems in which one component only, the solvent, is appreciably volatile or in which the necessary correction has been made for the small vapor pressure of the solute or solutes. The data represent elevations of the boiling point at temperatures at which the vapor pressure of the solvent is equal to the constant external pressure; whenever possible the elevations have been corrected to normal atmospheric pressure. (For method, *v.* (234).)

In the following tables:

Δt_B = boiling-point elevation for normal atmospheric pressure.

T_B = normal boiling point of solvent, absolute scale.

i = the mole number, or the total number of ions and molecules per formula weight of solute in a binary system, or the corresponding number in a system of more than two components.

x_1 = mole fraction of solute.

N = formality of solute or the gram-formula-weights per kg of solvent.

† = saturated solution.

For binary systems:

$$k_B = \lim._{x_1=0} \frac{i\Delta t_B}{x_1}$$

For systems of more than two components:

$$k_B = \lim._{x=0} \frac{i\Delta t_B}{\Sigma x}$$

The latent heat of vaporization of the pure solvent, per gram-formula-weight may be computed from the relation

$$L_v = \frac{RT_B^2}{k_B} = 8.315\frac{T_B^2}{k_B}, \text{ in joules } = 1.9869\frac{T_B^2}{k_B}, \text{ in cal}_{15}.$$

TWO-COMPONENT SYSTEMS

The solvent is an elementary substance

The systems are arranged in order of the solvent following the 𝔄-arrangement. Under each solvent the solutes follow the Standard, resp., ℭ-arrangement; *v.* p. viii.

Br_2

T_B = 331.9

k_B = 33.0

S_2 (32)

N	$\frac{\Delta t_B}{x_1}$
0.05	31.2
0.1	30.9
0.15	30.8

Se (32)

$AsBr_3$ (24)

N	$\frac{\Delta t_B}{x_1}$
0.05	32.5
0.1	32.6
0.15	32.8
0.2	33.1

$SbBr_5$ (24)

N	$\frac{\Delta t_B}{x_1}$
0.05	32.4
0.1	32.2
0.15	32.0

$SnBr_4$ (24)

N	$\frac{\Delta t_B}{x_1}$
0.05	33.1
0.1	33.3
0.15	33.5
0.2	33.6

CBr_4 (24)

N	$\frac{\Delta t_B}{x_1}$
0.05	32.4
0.08	32.1

$C_7H_5BrO_2$ (24)

m-Bromobenzoic acid

N	$\frac{\Delta t_B}{x_1}$
0.04	21.9

Al_2Br_6 (24)

N	$\frac{\Delta t_B}{x_1}$
0.05	33.3
0.1	32.3
0.15	31.3
0.2	30.4

Cl_2

T_B = 238.5

k_B = 23.3

S (27, 126)

SCl_2 (27, 41)

N	$\frac{\Delta t_B}{x_1}$
0.1	22.6
0.2	22.9
0.3	23.3
0.5	23.9

S_2Cl_2 (27, 41)

N	$\Delta t_B/x_1$
0.1	24.8
0.2	23.3
0.25	22.2

CCl_4 (27)

N	$\Delta t_B/x_1$
0.15	23.8
0.2	23.8
0.25	23.9
0.3	24.0

C_2Cl_6 (27, 126)

N	$\Delta t_B/x_1$
0.05	23.2
0.1	23.4
0.2	23.8
0.25	24.0

I_2

$T_B = 457.5$

$k_B = 43$

S (37)

Se (37)

N	$\Delta t_B/x_1$
0.05	28.4
0.1	26.3
0.2	24.9
0.3	24.1

Te (37)

N	$\Delta t_B/x_1$
0.06	30.7
0.08	29.7
0.1	28.7
0.12	27.9

P (red) (37)

N	$\Delta t_B/x_1$
0.05	39.2
0.1	40.1
0.12	40.5

SbI_5 (36)

N	$\Delta t_B/x_1$
0.01	42.5
0.04	40.9
0.05	40.3

BiI_3 (36)

N	$\Delta t_B/x_1$
0.01	43
0.02	41

SnI_4 (36)

N	$\Delta t_B/x_1$
0.02	39.1
0.05	39.4
0.1	39.9
0.12	40.0

Fe_3I_6 (36)

N	$\Delta t_B/x_1$
0.015	41.4
0.02	41.3
0.025	41.1

Al_2I_6 (36)

N	$\Delta t_B/x_1$
0.05	38.8
0.1	36.2
0.15	33.7

KI (36)

N	$\Delta t_B/x_1$
0.02	33.0
0.04	32.3
0.05	32.0
0.06	31.7

RbI (36)

N	$\Delta t_B/x_1$
0.02	35.5
0.04	32.3
0.05	31.0
0.06	30.2
0.08	29.3

CsI (36)

N	$\Delta t_B/x_1$
0.01	42.9
0.02	40.0
0.03	37.4
0.04	35.4
0.05	33.6
0.06	32.3

O_2

$T_B = 90.1$

$k_B = 8.2$

C_2H_4, Ethylene (104)

C_2H_6, Ethane (104)

N	$\Delta t_B/x_1$
2.17	9.0
3.71	9.6

S_8

(partially dissociated)

$T_B = 717.7$

$k_B = 60$

Se (42)

N	$\Delta t_B/x_1$
0.1	26.0
0.2	26.6
0.3	27.3
0.5	28.7

Te (42)

N	$\Delta t_B/x_1$
0.1	47.9
0.2	48.9
0.3	49.9

As (42)

N	$\Delta t_B/x_1$
0.06	65
0.1	64
0.2	62

As_2S_3 (42)

Sb_2S_3 (42)

The solvent is a chemical compound

The systems are arranged in order of the solvent following the Standard arrangement. Under each solvent, the solutes follow the Standard, resp., ℭ-arrangement; *v.* p. viii.

AQUEOUS SOLUTIONS

H_2O

$T_B = 373.1$

$k_B = 28.9$

HIO_3 (12, 182)

N	$\Delta t_B/x_1$
0.2	39.7
0.5	34.1
1.7	26

H_2SO_4 (70)

x_1	$\Delta t_B/x_1$
0.06	87.7
0.1	108.4
0.2	160.5
0.3	212.7

NH_4NO_3 (90)

N	$\Delta t_B/x_1$
0.1	48
0.2	51
0.3	54
0.4	57
0.5	61
0.6	66
0.7	74
0.8	86
0.84	94

NH_4Cl (90, 108)

N	$\Delta t_B/x_1$
0.6	51.6
1.0	51.7
1.5	52.2
2.0	53.2
5.0	56
10.0	62
16.3	65†

NH_4Br (108, 110, 111)

N	$\Delta t_B/x_1$
1.0	52.9
1.5	54.0
2.0	55.0
5.0	56.6
10.0	59.2
15.0	61.8
18.0	63.3

NH_4I (108, 110)

N	$\Delta t_B/x_1$
0.6	52.6
1.0	53.7
1.5	55.0
2.0	56.3
5.0	62.7
9.0	69

$(NH_4)_2SO_4$ (68, 90, 110)

N	$\Delta t_B/x_1$
0.6	47
1.0	48
2.0	49
3.0	52
4.0	54
6.0	58
8.3	62†

H_3PO_3 (183)

N	$\Delta t_B/x_1$
0.3	35.4
0.5	32.4
1.0	29.5

H_3AsO_3 (55)

N	$\Delta t_B/x_1$
0.1	28.4
0.15	27.8
0.2	27.3

For C-compounds belonging here, *v.* ℭ-Table, p. 326.

$SnCl_2$ (53)

N	$\Delta t_B/x_1$
0.18	50.5

$Pb(NO_3)_2$ (68, 199)

N	$\Delta t_B/x_1$
0.5	55.4
1.0	52.7
2.0	49.9
3.0	49.1
3.5	48.8

$Pb(C_2H_3O_2)_2$ (90)

x_1	$\Delta t_B/x_1$
0.1	23
0.3	26
0.5	29
0.7	32
0.9	33

TlCl (54)

N	$\Delta t_B/x_1$
0.1	53.6†

Tl_2SO_4 (54)

N	$\Delta t_B/x_1$
0.365	48.4†

$TlNO_3$ (54)

$ZnCl_2$ (53)

N	$\Delta t_B/x_1$
0.17	49.5

$ZnSO_4$ (90, 122)

N	$\Delta t_B/x_1$
0.5	23.1
1.0	23.5
1.5	25.1
2.5	32.9
4.0	48
5.3	57†

$CdCl_2$ (110)

N	$\Delta t_B/x_1$
0.8	35
2.0	33
3.0	31

CdI_2 (18, 110)

N	$\Delta t_B/x_1$
0.3	30.4
0.5	30.4
1.0	32.1
1.5	34.6

$CdSO_4$ (122)

N	$\Delta t_B/x_1$
0.5	23.0
1.0	20.4
1.2	18.4
1.6	21.9
2.0	24.0
2.6	26.5

$HgCl_2$ (122)

N	$\Delta t_B/x_1$
0.5	24.7
1.0	22.9
1.5	21.1
1.9	19.4

$Hg(CN)_2$ (63)

N	$\Delta t_B/x_1$
0.5	28.8
1.0	29.2
1.5	29.2
1.9	29.2

$CuCl_2$ (107)

N	$\Delta t_B/x_1$
0.2	69.2
0.25	67.9
0.3	69.7
0.4	72.1

$CuSO_4$ (122)

N	$\Delta t_B/x_1$
0.5	21.7
1.0	21.2
2.0	24.6
3.0	32.2
4.0	42.6
4.5	47.9

$Cu(C_2H_3O_2)_2$ (92)

N	$\Delta t_B/x_1$
1.1	57.7†

Ag_2SO_4 (250)

$AgNO_3$ (122, 199)

N	$\Delta t_B/x_1$
0.1	51.3
0.5	48.4
1.0	45.6
2.0	42.8
3.0	40.7
5.0	37.6
8.0	35.1

$MnCl_2$ (189)

N	$\Delta t_B/x_1$
0.3	74.2
0.6	75.5
1.0	78.8

$MnSO_4$ (90, 122)

N	$\Delta t_B/x_1$
0.3	25.4
0.7	22.8
1.0	22.2
1.5	23.9
3.0	29
4.5	32

$FeSO_4$ (122)

N	$\Delta t_B/x_1$
0.5	22.9
1.0	22.6
1.5	22.6
2.0	25.1
2.3	27.3

$CoCl_2$ (53)

N	$\Delta t_B/x_1$
0.2	67.8
0.4	70.9
0.7	73.6

$CoBr_2$ (107)

N	$\Delta t_B/x_1$
0.1	74.6
0.2	75.1
0.3	76.5

$CoSO_4$ (122)

N	$\Delta t_B/x_1$
0.6	23.8
1.0	23.4
1.5	25.3
2.0	28.7

$NiCl_2$ (189)

N	$\Delta t_B/x_1$
0.2	74.5
0.5	80.3
0.75	87.2

$NiSO_4$ (122)

N	$\Delta t_B/x_1$
0.2	29.9
0.5	27.2
1.0	26.0
1.5	28.3
2.0	34.0
2.4	40.7

CrO_3 (130)

N	$\Delta t_B/x_1$
5.0	74
10.0	85
15.0	89
25.0	88

H_3BO_3 (108, 122)

N	$\Delta t_B/x_1$
0.4	29.4
0.8	29.7
1.0	29.8
2.0	30.2
4.0	31.0
5.0	31.3
5.9	31.5

$AlCl_3$ (53, 90)

N	$\Delta t_B/x_1$
0.5	91
1.0	98
2.0	114
4.7	167

$Al_2(SO_4)_3$ (10, 77)

N	$\Delta t_B/x_1$
1.0	95
3.0	140

$(NH_4)_2SO_4$.-$Al_2(SO_4)_3$ (161)

N	$\Delta t_B/x_1$
4.38	145†

$MgCl_2$ (90, 122, 198)

N	$\Delta t_B/x_1$
0.1	67.4
0.2	66.4
0.5	72.6
1.0	90.4
2.0	125
4.0	193
6.0	262

$MgSO_4$ (122)

N	$\Delta t_B/x_1$
0.5	21.7
1.0	18.4
2.0	14.0
4.0	25.5
6.0	36.6

$CaCl_2$ (11, 90, 111, 198)

N	$\Delta t_B/x_1$
0.1	66.8
0.2	65.6
0.5	71.9
1.0	87.8
5.0	183
7.0	208
10.0	220
27.5	236†

$CaBr_2$ (111)

N	$\Delta t_B/x_1$
0.5	46.3
1.0	49.5
2.0	59.0
3.0	70.3
5.0	94
14.0	220

$Ca(NO_3)_2$ (13, 141)

N	$\Delta t_B/x_1$
2.0	80
5.0	115
10.0	150
15.0	170
20.0	170
22.9	175†

$CaC_{10}H_4N_2O_8S$ (127) Naphthol yellow S

$SrCl_2$ (12, 90, 141)

N	$\Delta t_B/x_1$
0.3	68.8
0.5	72.2
1.0	82
3.0	111
5.0	140
7.0	150
7.41	152†

$SrBr_2$ (111)

N	$\Delta t_B/x_1$
1.0	74
2.0	98
3.0	122
10.0	170

H_2O.—(*Cont'd*)

$Sr(NO_3)_2$ (54, 68, 199)

N	$\Delta t_B / x_1$
0.5	66.8
1.0	68.9
2.0	72.9
3.0	77
4.0	81
4.8	86†

$Ba(OH)_2$ (15)

7.0	26
8.0	36
9.0	46
10.0	50
11.0	51

$BaCl_2$ (122)

0.5	70.5
1.0	76.7
1.5	83.2
2.0	89.6
2.5	96

$Ba(ClO_3)_2$ (207)

3.66	86†

$BaBr_2$ (111)

1.0	85.3
2.0	117
3.0	129.3
4.0	135
5.0	139

$Ba(BrO_3)_2$ (207)

$Ba(IO_3)_2$ (207)

BaS_2O_6 (241)

$Ba(NO_3)_2$ (68, 199)

0.1	66.7
0.3	62.9
0.5	60.7
0.9	57.7
1.33	54.8

LiCl (57, 90, 110, 111)

0.5	58.3
1.0	56.2
2.0	56
5.0	80
10.0	120
15.0	150
20.0	170
30.0	170
35.0	170

LiBr (110, 111)

0.5	60.2
1.0	59.1
2.0	65.3
5.0	95
10.0	158
15.0	184
17.0	191

LiI (111)

0.5	48.3
1.0	48.9
2.0	53.0
5.0	65
9.0	81

Li_2SO_4 (111)

N	$\Delta t_B / x_1$
1.0	50.2
2.0	51.3
3.0	52.6
4.0	50.4

$LiNO_3$ (110)

0.5	40.5
1.0	40.6
2.0	42.6
5.0	49.8
7.0	54.0
9.0	58

Li_2CO_3 (250)

$LiC_7H_5O_3$ (192)
Salicylate

0.3	52.3
0.5	50.5
1.0	49.6
1.2	49.2

NaOH (90, 148)

x_1	$\Delta t_B / x_1$
0.01	54.2
0.1	79
0.2	112
0.3	136
0.4	148
0.5	157
0.6	164
0.7	170
0.8	180
0.9	195

NaCl (54, 57, 90, 108, 199)

N	$\Delta t_B / x_1$
0.5	53.3
1.0	54.7
2.0	58.7
3.0	63
4.0	67
5.0	72
6.78	79.6†

$NaClO_3$ (72)

10.0	58
15.0	59
20.0	62
26.86	67†

NaBr (108, 111)

0.5	56.0
1.0	56.5
2.0	57.5
10.0	76

NaI (108, 111, 192)

0.2	53.2
0.5	55.5
1.0	59.1
2.0	66.4
5.0	87.4
10.0	120.8

$NaIO_4$ (182)

0.5	49

Na_2SO_4 (115)

0.1	58.4
0.5	59.2
1.0	60.3

Na_2SO_4.—(*Cont'd*)

N	$\Delta t_B / x_1$
1.5	61.3
2.0	59.8
2.96	56.8†

$Na_2S_2O_3$ (90)

1.0	64
3.0	74
5.0	87
10.0	101
15.0	101
22.0	92†

$NaNO_3$ (54, 90, 141, 199)

0.1	52.1
0.5	50.1
1.0	50.1
5.0	54
10.0	57
15.0	59
24.86	65.3†

Na_2HPO_4 (90)

0.1	47
0.3	48
0.5	50
0.8	53

Na_2CO_3 (115, 141)

0.1	73.3
0.5	60.1
1.0	53.4
2.0	50.1
3.0	48
4.0	55

$NaC_2H_3O_2$
Acetate
(18, 90, 192)

0.2	51.1
0.5	50.1
1.0	53.1
2.0	57.5
5.0	70
10.0	82
15.0	83
25.2	80†

$NaC_3H_5O_2$ (134)
Propionate

0.5	53.6
1.0	56.0
2.0	61.8

$Na_2C_4H_4O_6$ (90)
Tartrate

1.0	63
2.0	64
4.0	67
6.0	69
7.5	70†

$NaC_7H_5O_3$ (192)
Salicylate

0.1	49.1
0.5	50.3
0.8	51.3

$Na_2O + SiO_2$ (71)

0.5	51
1.0	43

Na_2SiF_6 (262)

$Na_2B_4O_7$ (90)

N	$\Delta t_B / x_1$
0.5	65
1.0	66
2.0	62
3.0	58
5.0	52

KOH (90)

x_1	$\Delta t_B / x_1$
0.1	100
0.2	154
0.3	225
0.4	283
0.5	319
0.6	343
0.66	358

KCl (54, 90, 108)

N	$\Delta t_B / x_1$
0.1	57.8
0.3	52.3
0.5	52.3
1.0	54.1
2.0	55.0
5.0	63
7.82	69.6†

$KClO_3$ (122, 141)

0.5	59.6
1.0	55.0
2.0	51.2
3.0	50.0
4.0	51.4
5.0	51

KBr (108, 122)

0.5	52.7
1.0	54.1
1.5	55.7
2.0	57.9
3.0	61.6
4.0	65.4
4.3	66.7

KI (90, 108, 122)

0.2	51.6
0.5	53.0
1.0	55.4
2.0	60.4
5.0	74.5
10.0	87
13.3	96†

KIO_3 (182)

0.3	46.7
0.5	45.5
1.0	42.5

$KH(IO_3)_2$ (182)

0.2	98
0.6	96

K_2SO_4 (12, 54)

0.2	63.7
0.5	59.4
1.0	57.4
1.39	56.9†

KNO_2 (172)

55.6	60†

KNO_3 (54, 90, 122, 199)

0.5	50.0
1.0	48.5

KNO_3.—(*Cont'd*)

N	$\Delta t_B / x_1$
2.0	47.1
5.0	44.2
10.0	40
25.0	39
36.7	39.0

K_2CO_3 (90, 115, 141)

0.1	56.7
0.4	52.8
1.0	61.0
2.0	77.0
5.0	102
10.0	145
15.0	164

$K_2C_2O_4$ (128, 131)
Oxalate

0.3	65.8
4.77	79†

$KC_2H_3O_2$ (141)
Acetate

x_1	$\Delta t_B / x_1$
0.02	53
0.05	60
0.1	78
0.2	100
0.3	108
0.5	113
0.6	116

$KH_3(C_2O_4)_2$ (131)
Trihydrogen dioxalate

N	$\Delta t_B / x_1$
3.31	61†

$K_2C_4H_4O_6$ (90)
Tartrate

1.0	75
2.0	77
4.0	81
6.0	85
8.0	88
10.0	90
10.9	90†

KHC_2O_4 (131)
Hydrogen oxalate

$KHC_4H_4O_6$ (1)
Hydrogen tartrate

$K_2C_{28}H_{22}N_4O_8S_2$
Chrysophenine
(127)

$K_2C_{34}H_{26}N_6S_2O_6$
Benzopurpurin 4B
(127)

$KSbOC_4H_4O_6$ (14)
Antimonyl tartrate

0.03	28
0.06	30
0.12	31

KCN (92)

$K_3Fe(CN)_6$ (232)

2.5	103

K_2CrO_4 (12, 130)

0.3	63.3
0.5	63.4
1.0	64.1
1.5	65.3
4.57	76†

$K_2Cr_2O_7$ (12, 130)

N	$\Delta t_B / x_1$
0.2	72.0
0.3	70.6
0.4	70.9
3.65	78†

$K_2SO_4.CuSO_4$ (92)

$K_2SO_4.Al_2(SO_4)_3$ (90)

0.5	92
1.0	113
1.5	135
2.0	157
2.2	164

$KNaC_4H_4O_6$
(90, 128)

0.5	64.0
1.0	63.4
2.0	62.1
3.0	60.8
10.0	79
30.0	82
50.0	83

RbCl (54, 57)

0.1	52.3
0.3	50.8
0.5	50.7
1.0	51.6
2.0	52
5.0	62
12.17	75.1†

Rb_2SO_4 (54)

3.11	66.2†

$RbNO_3$ (54)

43.34	44.3†

CsCl (54, 68)

0.5	53.4
1.0	50.7
2.0	52.3
3.0	55.8
4.0	59.5
5.0	63.1
17.2	84.2†

Cs_2SO_4 (54)

6.3	98.2†

$CsNO_3$
(54, 110)

0.5	50.5
1.0	47.2
11.5	42.2†

$Cs_2SO_4.Al_2(SO_4)_3$
(54)

0.325	68.9†

C-Table, the C-Arrangement

CH_4N_2O
Urea
(139, 152, 201, 231)

N	$\Delta t_B / x_1$
0.5	26.9
1.0	27.4
1.5	27.8
2.5	28.6

CH_6ClN (133)
Methylammonium chloride

N	$\Delta t_B/x_1$
0.1	54.2
0.3	54.7
0.5	55.7
0.8	57.8
1.0	60.0
1.1	60.9

$C_2H_2O_4$
Oxalic acid
(12, 131, 175)

0.5	35.9
1.0	34.7
2.0	35.8
5.0	39.2
10.0	46.7
15.0	54.6

$C_2H_3ClO_2$ (206)
Chloroacetic acid

$C_2H_3Cl_2NO$ (152)
Dichloroacetamide

0.5	23.9
0.6	24.3
0.75	25.7

C_2H_4ClNO (152)
Chloroacetamide

0.8	25.2
1.0	26.3
1.2	27.0
1.4	27.5
1.6	27.8

$(NH_4)_2C_2O_4$ (92)
Oxalate

3.3	60†

C_2H_5NO (152)
Acetamide

1.5	28.3
2.0	29.5

$C_2H_5NO_2$ (154)
Glycolamide

0.5	26.6
0.7	27.2
0.9	28.3

$C_3H_4Cl_3NO_2$ (152)
Trichlorolactamide

0.6	26.2
0.7	25.6
0.8	25.4

$C_3H_6N_2O_2$ (152)
Malonamide

1.0	28.0
1.3	30.6

C_3H_7NO (154)
Propionamide

0.8	15.2
1.0	15.4
1.4	15.4
1.6	15.3

$C_3H_7NO_2$ (154)
Lactamide

N	$\Delta t_B/x_1$
0.75	27.5
1.0	27.4
1.5	27.2

$C_3H_7NO_2$ (201)
Urethane

0.2	14.0
0.3	14.4
0.5	14.7
0.7	14.6

$C_3H_8O_3$ (89)
Glycerol

x_1	$\Delta t_B/x_1$
0.02	43
0.05	38
0.1	35
0.2	39
0.3	43
0.4	47
0.5	51
0.6	58
0.7	69

$C_4H_5NO_2$ (201)
Succinimide

N	$\Delta t_B/x_1$
0.2	26.8
0.5	27.5
0.7	27.9
1.0	28.1
1.3	27.2

$C_4H_6O_4$ (12, 175)
Succinic acid

0.5	28.0
1.0	27.5
2.0	27.3
2.5	27.2

$C_4H_6O_6$
(12, 90, 110, 120)
Tartaric acid

0.5	30.8
1.0	31.7
3.0	35.7
5.0	39.4
20.0	61
50.0	73
100.0	75
200.0	74

C_4H_9NO (154)
n-Butyramide

0.5	25.5
0.6	25.0
0.7	24.4
0.8	23.9

C_4H_9NO (154)
Isobutyramide

0.55	24.1
0.65	23.7
0.75	23.6

$C_4H_{12}ClN$ (214)
Isobutylammonium chloride

0.3	55.3
0.5	51.0
0.8	49.4

$C_4H_{12}ClN$.—*(Cont'd)*

N	$\Delta t_B/x_1$
1.0	48.7
1.2	47.9

$C_4H_{12}ClN$ (214)
Diethylammonium chloride

$C_5H_{11}NO$ (154)
Valeramide

0.5	23.5
0.6	23.0
0.7	22.5
0.8	22.0
0.9	21.5

$C_6H_3N_3O_7$ (128)
Picric acid

0.1	52

$C_6H_5NO_3$ (175)
p-Nitrophenol

0.16	25.2
0.2	23.6
0.3	21.3
0.4	20.2

C_6H_6O (84)
Phenol

0.2	32
0.3	32

$C_6H_6N_2O_2$* (175)
m-Nitroaniline

1.2	22.1
1.4	22.3
1.6	22.6

$C_6H_6O_2$ (175, 185)
Catechol

0.3	24.9
0.4	24.8
0.5	24.7
1.0	22
1.5	20
2.0	17

$C_6H_6O_2$ (175, 185)
Hydroquinol

0.4	27
0.6	25
0.8	25
1.0	24
1.5	22
2.0	21

$C_6H_6O_2$
Resorcinol
(175, 185, 201)

0.4	26.6
0.5	26.1
0.7	25.0
1.0	24
1.5	22
2.0	21

$C_6H_6O_3$ (185)
Hydroxyhydroquinol

0.5	27
1.0	26
1.5	25
1.9	24

$C_6H_6O_3$ (175)
Phloroglucinol

N	$\Delta t_B/x_1$
0.4	21.7
0.6	23.2
0.8	23.2

$C_6H_6O_3$ (175, 185)
Pyrogallol

0.5	26.7
0.7	26.3
1.0	25.6
1.5	24
2.0	22

$C_6H_8O_7$ (12, 90, 120)
Citric acid

0.5	31.8
1.0	32.6
2.0	34.9
5.0	42.5
10.0	55
20.0	63
50.0	65
70.0	65

$C_6H_{12}O_6$ (120)
d-Glucose

0.2	30.0
0.5	30.0
1.0	30.0
2.0	30.0
3.0	30.0

$C_6H_{12}O_6$ (120)
Fructose

0.5	30.3
1.0	30.2
2.0	30.2
2.5	30.5
3.0	31.3

$C_6H_{13}NO$ (154)
Isobutylacetamide

0.55	19.7
0.65	18.3

$C_6H_{14}O_6$
Mannitol
(18, 139, 201)

0.2	27.9
0.5	28.1
1.0	28.6
1.2	29.1

$C_6H_{16}BrN$ (214)
Triethylammonium bromide

$C_6H_{16}ClN$ (214)
Triethylammonium chloride

$C_6H_{16}IN$ (214)
Triethylammonium iodide

0.25	55
0.5	48

$C_7H_5ClO_2$ (196)
m-Chlorobenzoic acid

$C_7H_5NO_4$ (196)
o-Nitrobenzoic acid

77.2	29.2†

$C_7H_6O_2$ (175)
Benzoic acid

N	$\Delta t_B/x_1$
0.5	14.8
0.6	13.4

$C_7H_6O_3$ (175)
m-Hydroxybenzoic acid

0.35	25.1
0.45	24.0
0.55	22.9

$C_7H_6O_3$ (175, 196)
p-Hydroxybenzoic acid

0.3	28.1
0.4	26.5
0.5	25.0
2.43	22†

$C_7H_6O_3$ (175)
Salicylic acid

0.3	22.2
0.4	19.8
0.55	16.4

$C_7H_6O_4$ (175)
3,4-Dihydroxybenzoic acid

0.3	23.5
0.7	22.9

$C_7H_6O_5$ (128)
Gallic acid

0.2	28.0
0.4	26.1
0.6	25.4

C_7H_7NO (152)
Benzamide

0.75	20.8
1.0	19.8
1.25	19.2

C_7H_7NO (154)
Formanilide

0.4	21.2
0.6	19.5
0.75	17.9

$C_7H_7NO_2$ (152)
Salicylamide

0.7	18.1
1.0	15.8

$C_7H_8N_2O$ (154)
Phenylurea

0.2	27.4
0.3	25.8
0.4	24.3

C_7H_9N (84)
Benzylamine

0.1	26.3
0.2	28.0
0.3	30.7
0.35	32.3

$C_8H_6O_4$ (175)
Phthalic acid

0.35	36.8
0.55	34.9

$C_8H_8O_2$ (175)
Phenylacetic acid

0.4	20.8
0.7	16.9

$C_8H_8O_2$ (196)
o-Toluic acid

N	$\Delta t_B/x_1$
0.24	24.8†

$C_8H_8O_3$ (196)
2-Hydroxytoluene-4-carboxylic acid

0.35	27.5†

$C_8H_8O_3$ (175)
Mandelic acid‡

0.3	27.8
0.45	27.6

C_8H_9NO (152)
Acetanilide

0.3	19.0
0.4	17.9
0.45	17.3

C_8H_9NO (154)
Phenylacetamide

0.4	24.6
0.5	22.8
0.7	20.2
0.9	18.7

$C_8H_9NO_2$ (154)
Glycolanilide

0.3	24.7
0.4	23.2
0.5	22.2

$C_8H_{12}ClN$ (214)
Ethylphenylammonium chloride

$C_8H_{20}BrN$ (214)
Tetraethylammonium bromide

0.13	51.7

$C_8H_{20}ClN$ (214)
Tetraethylammonium chloride

$C_8H_{20}IN$ (214)
Tetraethylammonium iodide

0.25	44.4
0.3	42.9
0.35	43.9

$C_9H_{11}NO$ (154)
Methylacetanilide

$C_9H_{11}NO_2$ (154)
Lactanilide

0.4	23.7
0.5	22.3
0.65	20.7

$C_{10}H_6N_2O_8S$ (127)
2, 4-Dinitro-1-naphthol-7-sulfonic acid naphthol yellow S)

$C_{11}H_{12}IN$ (214)
N-Ethylquinoline iodide

* Uncorrected for partial pressure of solute.
‡ The isomer used is not given.

H_2O.—(*Cont'd*)

$C_{12}H_{22}O_{11}$ (120, 122)
Sucrose

N	$\Delta t_B / x_1$
0.5	29.9
1.0	31.3
2.0	34.0
3.0	38.3
4.0	43.0
5.0	46.2
6.0	49.0
7.0	50.9
8.5	54.0

$C_{12}H_{28}IN$ (214)
Tetrapropylammonium iodide

$C_{12}H_{28}N_2O_3$ (214)
Tetrapropylammonium nitrate

$C_{23}H_{28}N_2O_7$ (150)
d-Cinchonine hydrogen tartrate

N	$\Delta t_B / x_1$
0.2	40.0

$C_{23}H_{28}N_2O_7$ (150)
l-Cinchonine hydrogen tartrate

N	$\Delta t_B / x_1$
0.1	42.0
0.2	40.2

$C_{37}H_{29}N_3O_9S_3$ (127)
Triphenylpararosaniline trisulfonic acid (soluble blue)

NON-AQUEOUS SOLUTIONS

The solvent is an inorganic compound

Standard arrangement. Under each solvent, the solutes are in the Standard, resp., $\mathfrak{C}$-arrangement; *v.* p. viii.

HCl

T_B = 188.1
k_B = 18

$C_4H_{10}O$ (149)
Ethyl ether

N	$\Delta t_B / x_1$
0.5	14
1.0	22.4
1.5	33.0
2.0	43.6
2.5	58

C_7H_8 (50)
Toluene

0.276	18

HBr

T_B = 206.1
k_B = 24

C_3H_6O (149)
Acetone

0.5	14.0
0.75	17.7
1.0	23.4
1.25	30.7

$C_4H_{10}O$ (149)
Ethyl ether

0.5	24.9
0.75	29.3
1.0	36.0
1.25	44.6

C_7H_8 (50, 149)
Toluene

0.075	23
0.15	21
0.5	27.4
0.75	27.5

HI

T_B = 237.4
k_B = 26

C_7H_8 (50)
Toluene

0.05	26
0.08	26

SO_2

T_B = 263.1
k_B = 22.9

SCl_2 (40)

0.1	10.4
0.2	10.4

SCl_2.—(*Cont'd*)

N	$\Delta t_B / x_1$
0.3	10.5
0.4	10.7

S_2Cl_2 (40)

0.2	21.7
0.3	21.4
0.4	22.1

NH_4I (219)

0.2	14.3
0.3	13.1
0.4	12.0
0.5	11.1
0.6	10.5
0.7	10.0

NH_4CNS (229)

0.5	8.4
1.0	6.8
2.0	7.5
3.0	12.6
4.0	23.0

CH_6ClN (229)
Methylammonium chloride

0.2	10.8
0.3	9.6
0.4	8.7

$C_2H_4O_2$ (40)
Acetic acid

0.1	16
0.2	16
0.4	16

C_2H_8ClN (229)
Dimethylammonium chloride

0.15	18.7
0.3	19.2
0.5	19.8

C_2H_8ClN (229)
Ethylammonium chloride

0.4	11.6
0.5	11.1
0.6	10.7
0.7	10.6
1.0	10.4

C_3H_9IS (40, 219)
Trimethylsulfonium iodide

C_3H_9IS.—(*Cont'd*)

N	$\Delta t_B / x_1$
0.5	25
1.0	38
1.3	46.5

$C_3H_{10}ClN$ (229)
Trimethylammonium chloride

0.2	23.0
0.3	24.0
0.4	24.8
0.5	25.8

$C_4H_6O_3$ (40)
Acetic anhydride

0.1	25.1
0.2	25.0
0.3	24.9

$C_4H_{12}BrN$ (229)
Tetramethylammonium bromide

0.05	21.8
0.1	22.5
0.2	24.1
0.3	25.7
0.4	27.3

$C_4H_{12}ClN$ (229)
Diethylammonium chloride

0.2	16.8
0.3	16.8
0.4	16.8
0.5	16.9

$C_4H_{12}ClN$ (229)
Tetramethylammonium chloride

0.1	24.1
0.2	25.0
0.3	25.8
0.4	26.7
0.5	27.5

$C_4H_{12}IN$ (229)
Tetramethylammonium iodide

0.1	28.4
0.2	28.8
0.3	29.3
0.4	29.7

$C_6H_4Cl_2$ (40)
p-Dichlorobenzene

N	$\Delta t_B / x_1$
0.2	23.1
0.3	22.9
0.4	22.8
0.5	22.9

$C_6H_{16}ClN$ (229)
Triethylammonium chloride

0.1	24.1
0.2	24.2
0.3	24.4
0.5	24.7

$C_7H_6O_2$ (40)
Benzoic acid

0.1	13.1
0.2	13.0
0.3	12.9
0.4	12.8
0.5	12.7
0.6	12.5

C_7H_8 (219)
Toluene

0.5	24.7
1.0	26.5
1.5	28.7

$C_7H_{10}ClN$ (229)
Benzylammonium chloride

0.3	12.4
0.4	11.9
0.5	11.5
0.6	11.3

C_8H_9NO (219)
Acetanilide

0.05	23.6
0.07	24.5

$C_8H_{20}IN$ (229)
Tetraethylammonium iodide

0.05	26.9
0.1	28.2
0.15	29.6
0.2	30.8
0.25	32.1

$C_{10}H_8$ (219)
Naphthalene

0.3	23.8
0.5	23.9

$C_{12}H_{22}O_6$ (229)
Isobutyl tartrate

0.1	24
0.2	24
0.3	30

$C_{14}H_{10}O_3$ (40)
Benzoic anhydride

0.05	22.5
0.1	23.6
0.15	24.7

$C_{16}H_{11}N_3O_8$ (229)
β-Naphthol picrate

0.035	48.5
0.065	48.3

$C_{19}H_{16}$ (229)
Triphenylmethane

N	$\Delta t_B / x_1$
0.2	22
0.4	22
0.6	22.4

NaI (219)

0.27	13.5

KI (40, 219, 229)

0.1	16.0
0.5	12.1
0.8	12.0
1.0	12.6
1.4	14.7
1.7	19.6
2.0	26.1

KCNS (40, 219)

0.1	16.5
0.3	12.7
0.5	11.4
1.0	10.9
2.0	15.5
3.0	28.5

RbI (229)

0.3	14.9
0.5	13.3
0.7	12.6

SO_3

T_B = 317.7
k_B = 14.0

H_2SO_4 (38)

0.05	18.3
0.1	17.0
0.2	14.8
0.5	11.4
1.0	9.8
1.5	10.4
2.0	12.1
2.2	13.3

$C_7H_{16}O_4S_2$ (38)
Sulfonal

0.05	15.2
0.1	16.5
0.2	19

$C_8H_{18}O_4S_2$ (38)
Trional

0.05	15.6
0.1	17.2
0.15	18.8

H_2S

T_B = 213.5
k_B = 23

C_7H_8 (50, 149)
Toluene

0.3	22.5
0.5	22.0
1.0	22.6
1.5	19.3
2.0	17.8

$C_6H_{16}ClN$ (149)
Triethylammonium chloride

0.25	27.9
0.5	32.5

H_2SO_4*

T_B = 604
k_B = 60

As_4O_6 (25)
Mo_2O_6 (25)

N	$\Delta t_B / x_1$
0.05	62
0.1	59
0.15	55

B_4O_6 (25)

0.05	56
0.1	54
0.15	52
0.2	50

Na_2SO_4 (25)

0.08	65
0.1	66
0.15	70
0.19	73

$Na_2S_2O_7$ (25)

0.08	55
0.1	58
0.13	63

K_2SO_4 (25)

0.1	70
0.18	74

$K_2S_2O_7$ (25)

0.1	64
0.15	66
0.2	68

$KHSO_4$ (25)

0.2	30
0.3	31
0.4	33

* Constant boiling *Ca.* 98.3 % H_2SO_4 by weight. Partially dissociated.

S_2Cl_2

T_B = 411
k_B = 36.3

S (27)

0.4	34.4
0.6	24.7
1.0	21.9
2.0	19.0
2.5	18.3
5.5	20.6

Se (27)

0.2	45.6
0.3	44.8

$C_{14}H_{10}$ (27)
Anthracene

0.15	37.8
0.25	38.8

SO_2Cl_2

T_B = 342.2
k_B = 34.5

I_2 (97)

0.05	29
0.1	28

Al_2Cl_6 (38)

0.05	49.6
0.1	49.1
0.13	49.2

$C_7H_{16}O_4S_2$ (38)
Sulfonal

N	$\Delta t_B/x_1$
0.05	34.5
0.1	34.5
0.15	34.4
0.2	34.1

$C_8H_{18}O_4S_2$ (38)
Trional

N	$\Delta t_B/x_1$
0.05	36.3
0.1	36.3
0.2	36.3

$C_{10}H_{16}O$ (38)
Camphor

N	$\Delta t_B/x_1$
0.05	35.9
0.1	34.2
0.15	34.0
0.2	34.0
0.25	34.0

N_2O_4

$T_B = 294.4$
$k_B = 14.2$

$C_2HBr_3O_2$ (86)
Tribromoacetic acid

N	$\Delta t_B/x_1$
0.1	7.6

$C_2H_2Br_4$ (86)
1, 1, 2, 2-Tetrabromoethane

N	$\Delta t_B/x_1$
0.2	16.3
0.3	16.2
0.4	16.1
0.5	15.9

$C_2H_4Br_2$ (86)
Ethylene bromide

N	$\Delta t_B/x_1$
0.2	16.4
0.4	16.7
0.6	16.6
0.8	16.6
1.0	16.5
1.2	16.5
1.6	16.4

$C_2H_4O_2$ (86)
Acetic acid

N	$\Delta t_B/x_1$
0.46	7.7

$C_4H_5Cl_3O_2$ (86)
Trichlorobutyric acid

N	$\Delta t_B/x_1$
0.1	11.3
0.2	11.0
0.3	10.8

$C_6H_3N_3O_7$ (86)
Picric acid

N	$\Delta t_B/x_1$
0.1	15.7
0.2	15.1
0.3	14.6
0.4	14.1

$C_6H_4N_2O_4$ (86)
m-Dinitrobenzene

N	$\Delta t_B/x_1$
0.1	14.5
0.2	14.6
0.3	14.7
0.4	14.8
0.5	14.9
0.7	15.2

$C_6H_4N_2O_5$ (86)
2, 4-Dinitrophenol

N	$\Delta t_B/x_1$
0.05	15.3
0.1	15.5

$C_6H_4O_2$ (86)
Quinone

N	$\Delta t_B/x_1$
0.2	15.0
0.3	15.5

$C_6H_5NO_2$ (86)
Nitrobenzene

N	$\Delta t_B/x_1$
0.2	14.3
0.4	14.6
0.8	15.3
1.0	15.6
1.5	16.4
1.8	17.0

$C_7H_6O_2$ (86)
Benzoic acid

N	$\Delta t_B/x_1$
0.4	8.2
0.6	8.4
0.8	8.5

C_7H_7Cl (86)
Benzyl chloride

N	$\Delta t_B/x_1$
0.2	16.1
0.4	16.3
0.6	16.4
0.8	16.5
1.0	16.7
1.2	16.8
1.4	16.9

$C_7H_7NO_2$ (86)
p-Nitrotoluene

N	$\Delta t_B/x_1$
0.1	14.3
0.2	14.6
0.3	14.9
0.4	15.1
0.5	15.4
0.7	16.0

C_7H_8 (86)
Toluene

N	$\Delta t_B/x_1$
0.2	15.3
0.4	15.9
0.6	16.2
0.8	16.4
1.0	16.5
1.2	16.6

C_8H_8O (86)
Acetophenone

N	$\Delta t_B/x_1$
0.3	15.2
0.4	15.5
0.5	15.7
0.6	15.9
0.8	16.3

$C_8H_8O_2$ (86)
o-Toluic acid

N	$\Delta t_B/x_1$
0.2	8.9
0.4	8.8
0.6	8.8

$C_8H_8O_2$ (86)
m-Toluic acid

N	$\Delta t_B/x_1$
0.1	9.1
0.2	9.0

$C_8H_8O_2$ (86)
p-Toluic acid

N	$\Delta t_B/x_1$
0.1	10.5

NH_3

$T_B = 239.7$
$k_B = 20.2$

H_2O (87)

N	$\Delta t_B/x_1$
0.5	20.6
1.0	20.7
2.0	20.9
3.0	21.1
5.0	21.5
7.0	22.3
10.0	25

NH_4NO_3 (87)

N	$\Delta t_B/x_1$
0.5	21.0
1.0	21.9
2.0	24.3
3.0	28.2
4.0	32.8

CH_4N_2O (87)
Urea

N	$\Delta t_B/x_1$
0.5	19.4
1.0	18.9
2.0	17.8
3.0	16.7
4.0	15.6

C_2H_6O (87)
Ethyl alcohol

N	$\Delta t_B/x_1$
0.5	19.8
1.0	20.1
2.0	20.4
3.0	20.8
5.0	21.5
7.0	22.2
9.0	22.6

C_3H_8O (87)
Propyl alcohol

N	$\Delta t_B/x_1$
0.5	20.2
1.0	19.9
2.0	19.4
3.0	19.0
5.0	18.6
7.0	18.7
9.0	18.8

C_5H_5N (87)
Pyridine

N	$\Delta t_B/x_1$
0.5	18.9
1.0	18.2
2.0	17.1
3.0	16.3
5.0	15.0
8.0	13.8

$C_6H_5NO_3$ (87)
o-Nitrophenol

N	$\Delta t_B/x_1$
0.5	20.1
1.0	20.0
1.5	19.8

C_6H_6 (87)
Benzene

N	$\Delta t_B/x_1$
0.6	15
0.8	15
1.0	14.8
1.3	14.5

C_6H_6O (87)
Phenol

N	$\Delta t_B/x_1$
0.5	19.6
1.0	19.1

C_6H_6O.—(*Cont'd*)

N	$\Delta t_B/x_1$
2.0	18.1
3.0	17.4

$C_6H_6O_2$ (87)
Catechol

N	$\Delta t_B/x_1$
0.5	19.3
1.0	19.3
2.0	19.3
2.5	19.3

$C_6H_6O_2$ (87)
Hydroquinol

N	$\Delta t_B/x_1$
0.5	22
1.0	23
1.5	23
2.0	25

$C_6H_6O_2$ (87)
Resorcinol

N	$\Delta t_B/x_1$
0.5	21.1
1.0	21.1
1.5	21.1
2.0	21.1

C_6H_7N (87)
Aniline

N	$\Delta t_B/x_1$
0.5	20.1
1.0	19.9
2.0	19.7
3.0	19.5
3.5	19.4

$C_{12}H_{22}O_{11}$ (87)
Sucrose

N	$\Delta t_B/x_1$
0.5	21
1.0	23
1.5	26
2.0	28

Li (87)

N	$\Delta t_B/x_1$
2.0	9.1
3.0	7.7
3.5	7.5
4.0	7.7
4.5	8.4

Na (87)

N	$\Delta t_B/x_1$
0.5	14
1.0	13
2.0	10.0
2.5	8.7

$NaNO_3$ (87)

N	$\Delta t_B/x_1$
0.5	17.7
1.0	19.8
2.0	22.6
3.0	25.0
4.0	29.2

$NaC_2H_3O_2$ (87)
Acetate

N	$\Delta t_B/x_1$
0.1	22
0.3	16
0.4	13

K (109)

KI (87)

N	$\Delta t_B/x_1$
0.5	21.4
1.0	23.8
2.0	28.6
3.0	34.0
3.5	36.5

PCl_3

$T_B = 346.6$
$k_B = 33.9$

AsI_3 (27)

SbI_3 (27)

$C_{14}H_{10}$ (27)
Anthracene

N	$\Delta t_B/x_1$
0.025	34.2
0.05	34.5

SnI_4 (27)

$AsCl_3$

$T_B = 395$
$k_B = 40.1$

S_8 (rhombic) (27)

N	$\Delta t_B/x_1$
0.08	38.5
0.1	38.6
0.15	39.0

S_8 (monoclinic) (27)

N	$\Delta t_B/x_1$
0.05	43
0.1	42.1
0.14	41.2

As_2O_3 (27)

AsI_3 (27)

SbI_3 (27)

$C_{14}H_{10}$ (27)
Anthracene

N	$\Delta t_B/x_1$
0.03	40.2
0.06	40.4
0.09	41.0

SnI_4 (27)

$BiCl_3$

$T_B = 720$
$k_B = 54.7$

$BiPO_4$ (186)

$PbCl_2$ (186)

N	$\Delta t_B/x_1$
0.04	55.3
0.07	55.0

$ZnCl_2$ (186)

N	$\Delta t_B/x_1$
0.05	54.7
0.07	54.4

$CdCl_2$ (186)

N	$\Delta t_B/x_1$
0.05	56.0
0.1	55.0

CuCl (186)

N	$\Delta t_B/x_1$
0.04	52.0
0.1	54.0
0.16	56.0

$CuCl_2$ (186)

N	$\Delta t_B/x_1$
0.05	60.0
0.07	60.4

AgCl (186)

N	$\Delta t_B/x_1$
0.07	56.7
0.1	57.3
0.15	57.6

$PtCl_2$ (186)

N	$\Delta t_B/x_1$
0.02	55.0
0.05	56.0

$PdCl_2$ (186)

N	$\Delta t_B/x_1$
0.02	57.0
0.05	56.0

$MnCl_2$ (186)

N	$\Delta t_B/x_1$
0.03	54.0
0.07	57.0

$FeCl_2$ (186)

N	$\Delta t_B/x_1$
0.05	56.0
0.1	57.0

$CoCl_2$ (186)

N	$\Delta t_B/x_1$
0.05	59.0

$CaCl_2$ (186)

N	$\Delta t_B/x_1$
0.02	51.5
0.03	51.3

$SrCl_2$ (186)

N	$\Delta t_B/x_1$
0.03	53.7
0.05	54.1

$BaCl_2$ (186)

N	$\Delta t_B/x_1$
0.04	55.3
0.05	55.5
0.07	55.9
0.1	56.8

LiCl (186)

N	$\Delta t_B/x_1$
0.07	53.0
0.13	56.0

NaCl (186)

N	$\Delta t_B/x_1$
0.05	53.0
0.1	54.0

KCl (186)

N	$\Delta t_B/x_1$
0.07	58.0
0.16	60.0

RbCl (186)

N	$\Delta t_B/x_1$
0.07	60.1
0.1	60.3

CsCl (186)

N	$\Delta t_B/x_1$
0.05	56.0
0.1	55.5

$SnCl_4$

$T_B = 387.2$
$k_B = 36.1$

S_8 (rhombic) (27)

N	$\Delta t_B/x_1$
0.025	39.0
0.05	37.8
0.075	36.8
0.1	36.5
0.125	36.4

S_8 (plastic) (27)

N	$\Delta t_B/x_1$
0.05	40.0
0.075	39.1
0.1	38.0

AsI_3 (27)

SbI_3 (27)

$C_{14}H_{10}$ (27)
Anthracene

N	$\Delta t_B/x_1$
0.03	36.5
0.05	36.7
0.06	36.8

SnI_4 (27)

CrO_2Cl_2

$T_B = 449$
$k_B = 35$

CrO_3 (38)

N	$\Delta t_B/x_1$
0.05	35.4
0.1	35.9
0.15	36.5
0.2	37.1

The solvent is an organic compound

The ℭ-arrangement. Under each solvent, the solutes are in the Standard, resp., ℭ-arrangement.

CCl_2O

Phosgene

$T_B = 281.4$

$k_B = 29$

I_2 (40)

ICl_3 (40)

N	$\Delta t_B / x_1$
0.02	32
0.03	31
0.035	30

SCl_2 (40)

N	$\Delta t_B / x_1$
0.05	24
0.1	23.4
0.2	23.4
0.3	23.4
0.35	23.4

S_2Cl_2 (40)

N	$\Delta t_B / x_1$
0.1	30
0.15	29.8
0.2	29.8

$AsCl_3$ (40)

N	$\Delta t_B / x_1$
0.2	28.6
0.5	28.9
0.7	29.1

$SbCl_3$ (40)

N	$\Delta t_B / x_1$
0.02	27.6
0.06	27.2
0.1	26.8
0.14	26.5

$SbCl_5$ (40)

N	$\Delta t_B / x_1$
0.02	27.8
0.05	28.0
0.1	28.2
0.12	28.3

C_2Cl_6 (40) Hexachloroethane

N	$\Delta t_B / x_1$
0.05	30.5
0.1	30.7
0.2	31.1
0.25	31.3

$C_2H_4O_2$ (40) Acetic acid

N	$\Delta t_B / x_1$
0.08	14.7
0.1	14.6
0.2	14.4
0.25	14.3

$C_4H_6O_3$ (40) Acetic anhydride

N	$\Delta t_B / x_1$
0.05	29
0.08	28
0.1	28
0.15	27

$C_6H_4Cl_2$ (40) *p*-Dichlorobenzene

N	$\Delta t_B / x_1$
0.05	27.5
0.1	27.8
0.2	28.2
0.3	28.6

$C_6H_4Br_2$ (40) *p*-Dibromobenzene

N	$\Delta t_B / x_1$
0.05	32.1
0.1	32.0
0.2	31.8
0.3	31.5

$C_7H_6O_2$ (40) Benzoic acid

N	$\Delta t_B / x_1$
0.05	14.7
0.1	14.1
0.13	13.7

$C_{10}H_8$ (40) Naphthalene

N	$\Delta t_B / x_1$
0.05	31
0.1	31
0.15	30.6
0.2	30.5

$C_{12}H_{10}$ (40) Diphenyl

N	$\Delta t_B / x_1$
0.05	28.5
0.08	28.6
0.1	28.7
0.15	28.8

$C_{14}H_{10}O_3$ (40) Benzoic anhydride

N	$\Delta t_B / x_1$
0.02	32.0
0.05	30.6
0.1	28.6

$C_{14}H_{14}$ (40) Dibenzyl

N	$\Delta t_B / x_1$
0.05	27.8
0.08	27.8
0.12	27.9
0.18	28.1

CCl_4

$T_B = 349.9$

$k_B = 31.4$

I_2 (30, 217)

N	$\Delta t_B / x_1$
0.05	32.4
0.1	32.4
0.2	32.5
0.46	30†

S_8 (168)

N	$\Delta t_B / x_1$
0.05	35.0
0.1	34.2
0.15	33.3

S_2Cl_2 (164, 167)

N	$\Delta t_B / x_1$
0.1	31.4
0.2	31.4
0.3	31.5
0.4	31.5

N_4S_4 (2)

N	$\Delta t_B / x_1$
0.05	33

$POCl_3$ (164)

N	$\Delta t_B / x_1$
0.1	27.7
0.2	24.6
0.3	22

$POBr_3$ (167)

N	$\Delta t_B / x_1$
0.1	34
0.15	33

PCl_5 (158)

N	$\Delta t_B / x_1$
0.1	33.0
0.2	33.7
0.3	34.1

$SbCl_5$ (159)

N	$\Delta t_B / x_1$
0.05	36.7
0.07	35.9
0.1	34.7

$C_2H_3BrO_2$ (224) Bromoacetic acid

N	$\Delta t_B / x_1$
0.1	18.4
0.2	18.0
0.5	17.0

$C_5H_{10}O_2$ (224) Isovaleric acid

N	$\Delta t_B / x_1$
0.2	17.8
0.3	17.8
0.5	17.8

C_6H_6O (46) Phenol

N	$\Delta t_B / x_1$
0.05	28
0.1	27
0.2	25
0.4	22

C_7H_9N (224) *p*-Toluidine

N	$\Delta t_B / x_1$
0.03	34.0
0.05	33.8
0.1	33.3

C_9H_7N (81) Quinoline

N	$\Delta t_B / x_1$
0.1	31
0.3	31.6
0.5	32.2
0.7	32.8

$C_9H_{10}O_2$ (158) Ethyl benzoate

N	$\Delta t_B / x_1$
0.05	31.7
0.1	31.8
0.2	32.1
0.3	32.4

$C_9H_{12}ClNO_2$ (224) *p*-Toluidine chloroacetate

N	$\Delta t_B / x_1$
0.05	33
0.1	31

$C_{10}H_8$ (61) Naphthalene

N	$\Delta t_B / x_1$
0.05	31.6
0.1	31.7
0.2	31.9

$C_{10}H_{10}O_2$ (81) Safrole

N	$\Delta t_B / x_1$
0.2	33.6
0.3	35.4
0.4	36.9
0.5	38.1

$C_{10}H_{16}O$ (158) Camphor

N	$\Delta t_B / x_1$
0.15	31.7
0.25	32.1

$C_{12}H_{24}O_2$ (281) Lauric acid

N	$\Delta t_B / x_1$
0.1	19

$C_{13}H_{10}O_2$ (49) Phenyl benzoate

N	$\Delta t_B / x_1$
0.1	32.0
0.2	32.1
0.3	32.2

$C_{13}H_{11}N_3O_9$ (224, 228) Dimethylpyrone picrate

N	$\Delta t_B / x_1$
0.01	56.8
0.02	51.2

$C_{13}H_{13}NO_3$ (224, 228) Aniline salicylate

N	$\Delta t_B / x_1$
0.1	41.7
0.2	39.2
0.3	36.8

$C_{14}H_{10}O_2$ (30) Benzil

N	$\Delta t_B / x_1$
0.05	32.3
0.1	32.4
0.2	32.5
0.3	32.6

$C_{14}H_{15}NO_3$ (224, 228) *p*-Toluidine salicylate

N	$\Delta t_B / x_1$
0.05	45.8
0.1	42.2
0.2	36.6

$C_{16}H_{16}$ (203) α, γ-Diphenyl-α, β-butene

N	$\Delta t_B / x_1$
0.05	32.5
0.1	32.4
0.15	32.2

$C_{16}H_{16}$ (203) α, δ-Diphenyl-α, β-butene

N	$\Delta t_B / x_1$
0.05	32.8
0.1	32.8

$C_{16}H_{32}O_2$ (218) Palmitic acid

N	$\Delta t_B / x_1$
0.03	21
0.05	21

$C_{17}H_{12}O_2$ (166) β-Naphthyl benzoate

N	$\Delta t_B / x_1$
0.05	31

$C_{17}H_{19}NO_3$ (81) Piperine

N	$\Delta t_B / x_1$
0.1	29.2
0.2	27.0

$C_{21}H_{36}N_4O_7$ (224) Triamylammonium picrate

N	$\Delta t_B / x_1$
0.05	13
0.1	11.4

$ZrC_{20}H_{28}O_8$ (60) Acetylacetonate

N	$\Delta t_B / x_1$
0.03	35.1
0.05	35.3

CrO_2Cl_2 (160)

N	$\Delta t_B / x_1$
0.1	28.9
0.2	29.3
0.3	29.7

CS_2

$T_B = 319.4$

$k_B = 31$

I_2 (18, 136, 165, 168, 188, 217)

N	$\Delta t_B / x_1$
0.2	31
0.5	31
1.0	31
1.84	30†

S_8 (rhombic) (4)

N	$\Delta t_B / x_1$
0.1	30.2
0.2	30.0
0.5	29.2
0.8	28.5
1.0	28.0

S_6 (E) (7)

N	$\Delta t_B / x_1$
0.1	31.6
0.15	31.0
0.2	30.5

P_4 (yellow) (18, 98)

N	$\Delta t_B / x_1$
0.1	31.0
0.2	30.4
0.5	28.8
1.0	26.7
1.5	25.4

$POCl_3$ (165, 167)

N	$\Delta t_B / x_1$
0.25	29.8
0.35	30.6

P_4S_3 (98)

N	$\Delta t_B / x_1$
0.05	30.1
0.1	29.7
0.3	28.0
0.5	27.2

AsI_3 (210)

N	$\Delta t_B / x_1$
0.1	32.5
0.2	31.0

SbI_3 (210)

N	$\Delta t_B / x_1$
0.05	31.5
0.07	31.5

$C_4H_7Cl_3O_2$ (65) Chloral alcoholate

N	$\Delta t_B / x_1$
0.3	14.0

$C_6H_5ClO_2S$ (129) Benzenesulfone chloride

N	$\Delta t_B / x_1$
0.34	31.8

C_7H_5NS (18) Phenyl isothiocyanate

N	$\Delta t_B / x_1$
0.1	31.2

$C_7H_6O_2$ Benzoic acid (18, 139, 180)

N	$\Delta t_B / x_1$
0.1	16.1
0.2	16.0
0.5	15.5
0.7	15.2

$C_8H_{12}O_6$ (221) Dimethyl acetylmalate

N	$\Delta t_B / x_1$
0.1	20.3
0.2	19.3
0.5	16.7
0.8	14.2

$C_8H_{18}O_4S_2$ (83) Trional

N	$\Delta t_B / x_1$
0.05	32.0
0.1	32.3

$C_{10}H_8$ Naphthalene (18, 139, 169, 224)

N	$\Delta t_B / x_1$
0.1	31.8
0.3	31.8
0.5	31.9
1.0	32.0

$C_{10}H_{16}O$ (39) Camphor

N	$\Delta t_B / x_1$
0.1	30.0
0.2	30.0
0.5	30.0

$C_{12}H_{10}N_2$ Azobenzene (76, 139, 180)

N	$\Delta t_B / x_1$
0.1	30.2
0.2	30.6
0.25	30.8

$C_{12}H_{11}N$ (76, 139) Diphenylamine

N	$\Delta t_B / x_1$
0.1	29.8
0.2	30.2
0.3	30.7

$C_{13}H_{10}O$ (18) Benzophenone

N	$\Delta t_B / x_1$
0.1	31.4
0.15	31.0

$C_{13}H_{10}O_2$ (18, 83) Phenyl benzoate

N	$\Delta t_B / x_1$
0.05	32.1
0.1	31.4
0.2	30.1
0.3	28.8

$C_{13}H_{10}O_3$ (83) Phenyl salicylate

N	$\Delta t_B / x_1$
0.05	32.4
0.1	32.5
0.2	32.8

$C_{13}H_{13}NO_3$ (228) Aniline salicylate

N	$\Delta t_B / x_1$
0.03	58.4
0.05	54.6

$C_{14}H_{10}$ (18) Anthracene

N	$\Delta t_B / x_1$
0.1	32.2
0.2	32.2
0.5	32.2
1.0	32.4
2.0	32.6

$C_{14}H_{10}$ (83) Phenanthrene

N	$\Delta t_B / x_1$
0.05	31.7
0.1	33.0
0.15	34.4

$C_{14}H_{10}O_2$ (39)
Benzil

N	$\Delta t_B/x_1$
0.1	30
0.2	29

$C_{14}H_{12}O_2$ (83)
Benzyl benzoate

N	$\Delta t_B/x_1$
0.3	31.5
0.5	32.6
0.7	33.8

$C_{15}H_{12}O_4$ (83)
Phenyl acetylsalicylate

N	$\Delta t_B/x_1$
0.05	29.8
0.07	30.8
0.08	31.2

$ThC_{20}H_{28}O_8$ (58)
Acetylacetonate

N	$\Delta t_B/x_1$
0.1	29.8
0.2	29.3

CrO_2Cl_2 (160)

N	$\Delta t_B/x_1$
0.1	30.1
0.2	29.5
0.3	28.9
0.4	28.3

Al_2Br_6 (129)

N	$\Delta t_B/x_1$
0.05	30.9
0.1	31.0
0.2	31.2

Al_2I_6 (129)

N	$\Delta t_B/x_1$
0.05	31.3
0.1	31.1
0.15	30.9

$Al_2Br_6.2C_6H_5ClO_2S$ (129)
Aluminium bromide benzenesulfone chloride

N	$\Delta t_B/x_1$
0.05	31.2
0.1	31.2

$Al_2Br_6.2C_6H_5NO_2$ (129)
Aluminium bromide nitrobenzene

N	$\Delta t_B/x_1$
0.05	30.9
0.1	30.9

$AlC_{15}H_{21}O_6$ (129)
Acetylacetonate

N	$\Delta t_B/x_1$
0.1	31.1
0.15	31.1

$AlC_{18}H_{27}O_9$ (129)
Ethyl acetoacetate

N	$\Delta t_B/x_1$
0.1	31.3
0.15	31.3

$ScC_{15}H_{21}O_6$ (59)
Acetylacetonate

N	$\Delta t_B/x_1$
0.1	30.7
0.15	30.0

$PrC_{15}H_{21}O_6$ (58)
Acetylacetonate

$SaC_{15}H_{21}O_6$ (58)
Acetylacetonate

$BeC_{10}H_{14}O_4$ (59)
Acetylacetonate

$BeC_{10}H_{14}O_4$.—(*Cont'd*)

N	$\Delta t_B/x_1$
0.1	28.0
0.15	27.7

$CHCl_3$
Chloroform

$T_B = 334.3$

$k_B = 32.0$

I_2 (30, 217)

N	$\Delta t_B/x_1$
0.05	30.5
0.1	30.5
0.2	30.8
0.43	34†

S_6 (204)

N	$\Delta t_B/x_1$
0.4	30.7
0.5	30.8
0.7	31.0
0.9	31.3

$SOCl_2$ (164, 167)

N	$\Delta t_B/x_1$
0.1	33
0.2	28
0.3	22

$POCl_3$ (164, 167)

N	$\Delta t_B/x_1$
0.1	30.6
0.2	30.7
0.3	30.8
0.5	31

$SbCl_3$ (210)

N	$\Delta t_B/x_1$
0.3	29.2
0.4	28.4
0.5	27.7

$SbCl_5$ (159)

N	$\Delta t_B/x_1$
0.05	46.8
0.1	40.2
0.15	35.7

$SbBr_3$ (210)

N	$\Delta t_B/x_1$
0.15	30.8
0.2	30.0
0.3	28.7

$C_2HCl_3O_2$ (243)
Trichloroacetic acid

N	$\Delta t_B/x_1$
0.1	21.9
0.15	20.5

$C_2H_2Cl_3NO$ (152)
Trichloroacetamide

N	$\Delta t_B/x_1$
0.25	26.3
0.3	25.9
0.4	25.0

$C_2H_3Cl_2NO$ (152)
Dichloroacetamide

N	$\Delta t_B/x_1$
0.25	25.5
0.35	24.0

$C_2H_3BrO_2$ (225)
Bromoacetic acid

N	$\Delta t_B/x_1$
0.1	30.9
0.2	27.0
0.3	24.8
0.4	23.4
0.5	22.5

C_2H_4ClNO (152)
Chloroacetamide

N	$\Delta t_B/x_1$
0.1	27.3
0.2	25.8

C_2H_5NO (152)
Acetamide

C_9H_5NO.—(*Cont'd*)

N	$\Delta t_B/x_1$
0.2	25.0
0.3	22.8
0.5	20.3
0.8	18

$C_2H_7NO_4S$ (225)
Dimethylsulfoxide nitrate

N	$\Delta t_B/x_1$
0.2	43
0.3	37
0.4	30

C_2H_8ClN (225)
Dimethylammonium chloride

N	$\Delta t_B/x_1$
0.2	7.5
0.3	7.5
0.5	7.5

$C_3H_4Cl_3NO_2$ (152)
Trichlorolactamide

N	$\Delta t_B/x_1$
0.1	27.6
0.2	23.2
0.25	21.1

C_3H_7I (225)
n-Propyl iodide

N	$\Delta t_B/x_1$
0.1	33
0.3	33
0.5	33
0.8	34

C_3H_7NO (153)
Propionamide

N	$\Delta t_B/x_1$
0.2	24.5
0.3	23.9
0.4	22.8

$C_3H_7NO_2$ (153, 201)
Urethane

N	$\Delta t_B/x_1$
0.1	29.2
0.2	28.4
0.5	26.7
0.7	24.6

$C_3H_{10}ClN$ (210)
n-Propylammonium chloride

N	$\Delta t_B/x_1$
0.1	7
0.15	6

$C_4H_4N_2$ (222)
Succinonitrile

N	$\Delta t_B/x_1$
0.1	28
0.2	25
0.3	23
0.5	19
0.8	16

C_4H_9I (225)
tert.-Butyl iodide

N	$\Delta t_B/x_1$
0.1	24.8
0.2	24.4
0.3	24.1
0.4	23.7

C_4H_9NO (153)
n-Butyramide

N	$\Delta t_B/x_1$
0.3	26.8
0.4	25.9

C_4H_9NO (153)
Isobutyramide

N	$\Delta t_B/x_1$
0.2	27.7
0.3	26.7
0.4	25.6

$C_4H_{10}O_2S$ (225)
Diethylsulfone

N	$\Delta t_B/x_1$
0.2	22.0
0.4	25.6
0.7	30

$C_4H_{12}ClN$ (210)
Diethylammonium chloride

N	$\Delta t_B/x_1$
0.1	14.1
0.2	13.3
0.3	12.5
0.4	11.7
0.5	10.8

$C_4H_{12}ClN$ (210)
Isobutylammonium chloride

N	$\Delta t_B/x_1$
0.3	7.2
0.4	7.2
0.5	7.1

$C_4H_{12}IN$ (210)
Isobutylammonium iodide

N	$\Delta t_B/x_1$
0.3	6.0
0.4	5.4
0.5	4.8

$C_5H_{10}O_2$ (225)
Isovaleric acid

N	$\Delta t_B/x_1$
0.5	19.0
0.7	19.7
0.9	20.3

$C_5H_{11}NO$ (153)
Valeramide

N	$\Delta t_B/x_1$
0.2	25.9
0.3	25.2
0.4	24.5

$C_5H_{14}ClN$ (225)
Amylammonium chloride

N	$\Delta t_B/x_1$
0.2	9.4
0.3	8.5
0.4	7.8

$C_6H_3N_3O_7$ (136)
Picric acid

N	$\Delta t_B/x_1$
0.05	31.6
0.1	31.0
0.3	28.7

$C_6H_{10}O_5$ (221)
Dimethyl malate

N	$\Delta t_B/x_1$
0.2	29.3
0.3	29.7
0.5	30.3
0.7	30.9
1.0	31.8

$C_6H_{10}O_6$ (221)
Dimethyl tartrate

N	$\Delta t_B/x_1$
0.2	22.3
0.3	23.1
0.4	23.3
0.5	22.9

$C_6H_{13}NO$ (153)
Isobutylacetamide

N	$\Delta t_B/x_1$
0.1	27.2
0.2	25.4
0.3	23.8

$C_6H_{15}BrS$ (210)
Triethylsulfonium bromide

N	$\Delta t_B/x_1$
0.2	7.2
0.3	6.2
0.4	5.3

$C_6H_{15}ClS$ (210)
Triethylsulfonium chloride

N	$\Delta t_B/x_1$
0.2	8.5
0.3	8.0
0.35	7.5

$C_6H_{15}IS$ (210)
Triethylsulfonium iodide

N	$\Delta t_B/x_1$
0.25	4.4
0.3	4.2
0.4	3.5
0.5	2.8

$C_6H_{16}BrN$ (210)
Triethylammonium bromide

N	$\Delta t_B/x_1$
0.2	19.6
0.3	18.0
0.4	16.8
0.5	15.8

$C_6H_{16}ClN$ (210)
Dipropylammonium chloride

N	$\Delta t_B/x_1$
0.2	15.9
0.3	15.6
0.5	14.8

$C_6H_{16}ClN$ (225)
Triethylammonium chloride

N	$\Delta t_B/x_1$
0.2	24.5
0.3	24.3
0.4	24

$C_6H_{16}IN$ (210)
Triethylammonium iodide

N	$\Delta t_B/x_1$
0.1	18
0.2	14.7
0.3	12.1
0.35	11.2

$C_7H_6O_2$
Benzoic acid (18, 139, 231)

N	$\Delta t_B/x_1$
0.1	19
0.3	18
0.5	18

$C_7H_6O_3$ (18)
Salicylic acid

N	$\Delta t_B/x_1$
0.1	19.6
0.2	18.3
0.3	17.7

C_7H_7NO (152)
Benzamide

N	$\Delta t_B/x_1$
0.25	25.9
0.3	25.5
0.35	24.8

C_7H_7NO (153)
Formanilide

N	$\Delta t_B/x_1$
0.2	26
0.3	25

$C_7H_7NO_2$ (152)
Salicylamide

N	$\Delta t_B/x_1$
0.1	28.1

$C_7H_9BrO_2$ (225)
Dimethylpyrone hydrobromide

N	$\Delta t_B/x_1$
0.2	21
0.3	18.7
0.4	17.2

C_7H_9N (201, 225)
p-Toluidine

N	$\Delta t_B/x_1$
0.1	33.5
0.2	33.5
0.3	33.6
0.4	33.6
0.5	33.7

$C_7H_{10}BrN$ (225)
Methylaniline hydrobromide

N	$\Delta t_B/x_1$
0.1	9.6
0.2	10.0
0.3	10.3
0.5	11.0

$C_7H_{10}ClN$ (210)
Methylaniline hydrochloride

N	$\Delta t_B/x_1$
0.2	15.4
0.3	14.7
0.4	13.8

C_8H_7NO (139)
Phthalimidine

N	$\Delta t_B/x_1$
0.1	30.8

C_8H_9NO (201)
Acetanilide

N	$\Delta t_B/x_1$
0.1	28.3
0.2	24.8
0.5	21.7

C_8H_9NO (153)
Phenylacetamide

N	$\Delta t_B/x_1$
0.15	28.1
0.2	28.1

$C_8H_9NO_2$ (153)
Glycolanilide

N	$\Delta t_B/x_1$
0.2	19.6
0.25	17.1

$C_8H_{10}O$ (171)
p-Methoxymethylbenzene

N	$\Delta t_B/x_1$
0.1	34.7
0.15	34.6

$C_8H_{11}N$ (93)
Dimethylaniline

N	$\Delta t_B/x_1$
0.1	31.9

$C_8H_{12}BrN$ (225)
Dimethylaniline hydrobromide

N	$\Delta t_B/x_1$
0.1	11.2
0.2	12.4
0.3	13.3
0.45	13.0

$CHCl_3$.—(*Cont'd*)

$C_8H_{12}ClN$ (210)
Ethylaniline hydrochloride

N	$\frac{\Delta t_B}{x_1}$
0.15	15.1
0.2	15.2
0.3	15.2

$C_8H_{12}IN$ (210)
Ethylaniline hydroiodide

N	$\frac{\Delta t_B}{x_1}$
0.15	16.4
0.2	15.8
0.3	14.8

$C_8H_{12}O_6$ (221)
Dimethyl acetylmalate

N	$\frac{\Delta t_B}{x_1}$
0.1	29.7
0.2	31.8
0.3	33.4
0.5	36.3
0.7	38.8
0.9	41.4

$C_8H_{13}ClN_2$ (210)
Ethylphenylhydrazine hydrochloride

N	$\frac{\Delta t_B}{x_1}$
0.2	13
0.3	12.6
0.4	12.0
0.5	11.1

$C_8H_{14}O_5$ (221)
Diethyl malate

N	$\frac{\Delta t_B}{x_1}$
0.2	28.6
0.3	29.5
0.4	30.6
0.5	31.6

$C_8H_{14}O_6$ (221)
Diethyl tartrate

N	$\frac{\Delta t_B}{x_1}$
0.1	27.1
0.2	27.4
0.3	27.8
0.4	28.3
0.5	28.6

$C_8H_{20}BrN$ (225)
Tetraethylammonium bromide

N	$\frac{\Delta t_B}{x_1}$
0.1	6.9
0.2	7.4
0.3	7.9

$C_8H_{20}ClN$ (225)
Tetraethylammonium chloride

N	$\frac{\Delta t_B}{x_1}$
0.1	14
0.2	13.4
0.3	12.9

$C_8H_{20}N_2O_3$ (225)
Tetraethylammonium nitrate

N	$\frac{\Delta t_B}{x_1}$
0.2	7
0.3	7
0.4	7

C_9H_8BrN (210)
Quinoline hydrobromide

C_9H_8BrN.—(*Cont'd*)

N	$\frac{\Delta t_B}{x_1}$
0.3	12.8
0.4	11.9
0.5	11.1

C_9H_8ClN (210)
Quinoline hydrochloride

N	$\frac{\Delta t_B}{x_1}$
0.2	15.8
0.5	14.4
0.7	13.5

C_9H_8IN (210)
Quinoline hydroiodide

N	$\frac{\Delta t_B}{x_1}$
0.03	28.3
0.05	21.2

$C_9H_{10}O_2$ (18)
Ethyl benzoate

N	$\frac{\Delta t_B}{x_1}$
0.2	31.3
0.5	34.4
0.8	39.4

$C_9H_{11}NO$ (83)
o-Acetotoluide

N	$\frac{\Delta t_B}{x_1}$
0.1	30.7

$C_9H_{11}NO$ (209)
Methylacetanilide

N	$\frac{\Delta t_B}{x_1}$
0.1	34
0.2	34

$C_9H_{11}NO_2$ (153)
Lactanilide

N	$\frac{\Delta t_B}{x_1}$
0.15	24.8
0.2	22.8

$C_9H_{11}NO_2$ (153)
Phenylurethane

N	$\frac{\Delta t_B}{x_1}$
0.2	31.6

$C_9H_{12}ClNO_2$ (225)
p-Toluidine chloroacetate

N	$\frac{\Delta t_B}{x_1}$
0.05	73.6
0.1	61.6
0.2	41.6
0.25	33.5

$C_9H_{21}N$ (225)
Tripropylamine

N	$\frac{\Delta t_B}{x_1}$
0.2	28.9
0.5	31.8
0.7	32.7

$C_{10}H_8$ (31, 201, 225)
Naphthalene

N	$\frac{\Delta t_B}{x_1}$
0.05	32.7
0.1	32.7
0.2	32.8
0.3	32.8

$C_{10}H_9N$ (142)
α-Naphthylamine

N	$\frac{\Delta t_B}{x_1}$
0.05	32

$C_{10}H_{12}O$ (171)
Metanethole (liq.)

N	$\frac{\Delta t_B}{x_1}$
0.02	26.8
0.05	27.3
0.07	27.5
0.1	27.9
0.12	28.1

$C_{10}H_{13}NO$ (153)
Ethylacetanilide

$C_{10}H_{13}NO$.—(*Cont'd*)

N	$\frac{\Delta t_B}{x_1}$
0.15	39.8
0.2	35.7

$C_{10}H_{16}ClN$ (210)
Diethylaniline hydrochloride

N	$\frac{\Delta t_B}{x_1}$
0.2	24.0
0.3	22.9
0.4	21.8

$C_{10}H_{16}IN$ (210)
Diethylaniline hydroiodide

N	$\frac{\Delta t_B}{x_1}$
0.2	17.4
0.3	16.2
0.4	15.0

$C_{10}H_{16}O$
Camphor
(31, 39, 43, 75)

N	$\frac{\Delta t_B}{x_1}$
0.05	32.7
0.1	33.1
0.15	33.3
0.2	33.4
0.25	33.5

$C_{10}H_{24}ClN$ (225)
Diisoamylammonium chloride

N	$\frac{\Delta t_B}{x_1}$
0.1	19.2
0.2	20.0
0.3	20.7

$C_{11}H_{12}IN$ (210)
Quinoline ethiodide

$C_{11}H_{14}N_4O_7$ (225)
Piperidine picrate

N	$\frac{\Delta t_B}{x_1}$
0.02	29.5

$C_{12}H_{10}$ (201)
Acenaphthene

N	$\frac{\Delta t_B}{x_1}$
0.1	33.2
0.15	33.4
0.2	33.5
0.25	33.5

$C_{12}H_{10}$ (209)
Diphenyl

N	$\frac{\Delta t_B}{x_1}$
0.1	32.1
0.15	32.8
0.2	33.4

$C_{12}H_{10}N_2$ (125)
Azobenzene

N	$\frac{\Delta t_B}{x_1}$
0.05	29

$C_{12}H_{11}N$ (139, 209)
Diphenylamine

N	$\frac{\Delta t_B}{x_1}$
0.1	33
0.2	32

$C_{12}H_{28}BrN$ (210)
Tetrapropylammonium bromide

N	$\frac{\Delta t_B}{x_1}$
0.2	8.8
0.3	9.1
0.4	9.4

$C_{12}H_{28}ClN$ (210)
Tetrapropylammonium chloride

N	$\frac{\Delta t_B}{x_1}$
0.2	12
0.3	12.3
0.4	13.0
0.5	13.6

$C_{12}H_{28}IN$ (210)
Tetrapropylammonium iodide

N	$\frac{\Delta t_B}{x_1}$
0.1	7.8
0.3	7.8
0.4	7.7

$C_{12}H_{28}N_2O_3$ (225)
Tetrapropylammonium nitrate

N	$\frac{\Delta t_B}{x_1}$
0.1	12.9
0.2	12.8
0.3	12.8

$C_{13}H_{11}NO$ (152)
Benzanilide

N	$\frac{\Delta t_B}{x_1}$
0.2	29.8
0.25	30.3

$C_{13}H_{11}N_3O_9$
Dimethylpyrone picrate
(225, 228)

N	$\frac{\Delta t_B}{x_1}$
0.05	53.3
0.1	51.9

$C_{13}H_{13}NO_3$
Aniline salicylate
(225, 228)

N	$\frac{\Delta t_B}{x_1}$
0.05	60.0
0.1	54.6
0.15	51.9

$C_{13}H_{20}IN$ (235)
Allylethylmethyltolylammonium iodide

N	$\frac{\Delta t_B}{x_1}$
0.04	52.0
0.08	47.6

$C_{14}H_{10}$ (209)
Anthracene

N	$\frac{\Delta t_B}{x_1}$
0.1	34
0.15	34

$C_{14}H_{10}O_2$ (31)
Benzil

N	$\frac{\Delta t_B}{x_1}$
0.05	32
0.1	32
0.2	32
0.3	33

$C_{14}H_{14}OS$ (225)
Dibenzyl sulfoxide

N	$\frac{\Delta t_B}{x_1}$
0.1	28.8
0.2	31.9
0.25	33.5

$C_{14}H_{16}ClN$ (210)
Dibenzylammonium chloride

N	$\frac{\Delta t_B}{x_1}$
0.3	16.0

$C_{16}H_{11}N_3O_7$ (136)
Naphthalene picrate

N	$\frac{\Delta t_B}{x_1}$
0.05	65
0.1	61

$C_{17}H_{20}IN$ (93)
Allylbenzylmethylphenylammonium iodide

N	$\frac{\Delta t_B}{x_1}$
0.1	60

$C_{18}H_{31}N_4O_7$ (225)
Tetrapropylammonium picrate

N	$\frac{\Delta t_B}{x_1}$
0.05	12
0.1	11.7
0.15	11.5
0.2	11.3

$C_{19}H_{13}N$ (95)
Phenylacridine

N	$\frac{\Delta t_B}{x_1}$
0.1	33.3

$C_{19}H_{14}ClN$ (95)
Phenylacridinium chloride

N	$\frac{\Delta t_B}{x_1}$
0.02	25.5
0.04	25.2

$C_{19}H_{14}IN$ (95)
Phenylacridinium iodide

N	$\frac{\Delta t_B}{x_1}$
0.03	23
0.06	24

$C_{19}H_{16}$ (31)
Triphenylmethane

N	$\frac{\Delta t_B}{x_1}$
0.04	26.0
0.06	28.3
0.08	29.8

$C_{20}H_{16}BrN$ (95)
N-Methylphenylacridinium bromide

N	$\frac{\Delta t_B}{x_1}$
0.07	15

$C_{20}H_{16}ClN$ (95)
N-Methylphenylacridinium chloride

N	$\frac{\Delta t_B}{x_1}$
0.03	16.7
0.05	16.0
0.08	15.0

$C_{20}H_{16}IN$ (95)
N-Methylphenylacridinium iodide

N	$\frac{\Delta t_B}{x_1}$
0.05	6.5
0.1	6.5
0.25	6.4

$C_{20}H_{24}O_2$ (171)
Isoanethole

N	$\frac{\Delta t_B}{x_1}$
0.01	30.9
0.02	29.7
0.03	28.6
0.05	26.7

$C_{20}H_{44}IN$ (210)
Tetraisoamylammonium iodide

N	$\frac{\Delta t_B}{x_1}$
0.05	28.8
0.1	24.1
0.15	19.3

$C_{21}H_{22}ClN$ (210)
Tribenzylammonium chloride

N	$\frac{\Delta t_B}{x_1}$
0.1	27.2
0.15	26.9

$C_{21}H_{36}N_4O_7$ (225)
Triisoamylammonium picrate

N	$\frac{\Delta t_B}{x_1}$
0.05	26.8
0.1	29.9
0.13	31

$C_{51}H_{98}O_6$ (222)
Tripalmitin

N	$\frac{\Delta t_B}{x_1}$
0.03	33
0.05	33
0.07	34.7

$C_{57}H_{110}O_6$ (222)
Tristearin

N	$\frac{\Delta t_B}{x_1}$
0.04	30.4
0.05	30.6
0.06	30.8
0.07	31.0

$ThC_{20}H_{28}O_8$ (58)
Acetylacetonate

N	$\frac{\Delta t_B}{x_1}$
0.05	34.2
0.1	36.8
0.15	39.3

$FeCl_3$ (264)

N	$\frac{\Delta t_B}{x_1}$
0.036	32.4

$NiC_{36}H_{66}O_6$ (225)
Ricinoleate

N	$\frac{\Delta t_B}{x_1}$
0.15	6.0
0.2	7.4
0.25	9.3

CH_2Cl_2

Dichloromethane

$T_B = 313.1$

$k_B = 31$

$C_2H_3BrO_2$ (227)
Bromoacetic acid

N	$\frac{\Delta t_B}{x_1}$
0.2	18.3
0.4	18.1
0.6	17.6
0.8	17.2
1.0	16.9

$C_4H_{12}BrN$ (227)
Diethylammonium bromide

N	$\frac{\Delta t_B}{x_1}$
0.1	10.7
0.2	9.3
0.3	8.0

$C_4H_{12}ClN$ (227)
Diethylammonium chloride

N	$\frac{\Delta t_B}{x_1}$
0.1	13.1
0.2	12.2
0.4	11.6
0.6	11.3

$C_4H_{12}N_2O_3$ (227)
Diethylammonium nitrate

N	$\frac{\Delta t_B}{x_1}$
0.15	8.1
0.2	7.2
0.3	6.7
0.4	6.5
0.5	6.3

$C_6H_3N_3O_7$ (227)
Picric acid

N	$\frac{\Delta t_B}{x_1}$
0.05	28.0
0.1	27.3
0.2	26.3
0.25	25.9

$C_6H_{16}BrN$ (227)
Triethylammonium bromide

N	$\Delta t_B / x_1$
0.1	22.5
0.2	23.1

$C_6H_{16}ClN$ (227)
Triethylammonium chloride

N	$\Delta t_B / x_1$
0.1	27.7
0.2	26.2
0.3	25.7
0.4	25.4

$C_6H_{16}N_2O_3$ (227)
Triethylammonium nitrate

N	$\Delta t_B / x_1$
0.1	22.1
0.2	21.1
0.3	20.2
0.4	19.5
0.5	19.1

$C_7H_6O_3$ (227)
Salicylic acid

N	$\Delta t_B / x_1$
0.1	25.3
0.2	18.2
0.25	15.8

$C_7H_8O_2$ (227)
Dimethylpyrone

N	$\Delta t_B / x_1$
0.2	30.6
0.3	31.3

C_7H_9N (227)
p-Toluidine

N	$\Delta t_B / x_1$
0.1	30.5
0.2	31.4

$C_8H_{20}BrN$ (227)
Tetraethylammonium bromide

N	$\Delta t_B / x_1$
0.15	13.9
0.2	12.6
0.3	11.5
0.35	11.3

$C_8H_{20}ClN$ (227)
Tetraethylammonium chloride

N	$\Delta t_B / x_1$
0.05	17.7
0.1	15.5
0.2	14.0
0.3	13.5
0.4	13.3

$C_8H_{20}N_2O_3$ (227)
Tetraethylammonium nitrate

N	$\Delta t_B / x_1$
0.2	9.6
0.3	10.1
0.4	10.4
0.45	10.6

$C_9H_{12}ClNO_2$ (227)
p-Toluidine chloroacetate

N	$\Delta t_B / x_1$
0.05	49.2
0.1	38.0
0.2	26.8

$C_{10}H_8$ (227)
Naphthalene

$C_{10}H_8$.—(*Cont'd*)

N	$\Delta t_B / x_1$
0.05	33.3
0.1	32.5
0.2	31.0
0.25	30.2

$C_{11}H_{26}IN$ (227)
Ethyltripropylammonium iodide

N	$\Delta t_B / x_1$
1.0	15.7
1.5	16.5
2.0	17.0

$C_{12}H_{28}IN$ (227)
Tetrapropylammonium iodide

N	$\Delta t_B / x_1$
0.1	12.3
0.2	14.7
0.3	16.0
0.4	17.1

$C_{12}H_{28}N_2O_3$ (227)
Tetrapropylammonium nitrate

N	$\Delta t_B / x_1$
0.05	25.8
0.1	21.9
0.15	20.7

$C_{13}H_{11}N_3O_9$ (227, 228)
Dimethylpyrone picrate

N	$\Delta t_B / x_1$
0.025	52.8
0.05	49.4
0.1	43.3
0.15	37.2

$C_{14}H_{15}NO_3$ (227, 228)
p-Toluidine salicylate

N	$\Delta t_B / x_1$
0.05	50.2
0.1	46.5
0.15	43.8

$C_{20}H_{44}IN$ (227)
Tetraamylammonium iodide

N	$\Delta t_B / x_1$
0.05	14.0
0.1	17.1
0.2	19.4
0.25	20.5

$C_{21}H_{36}N_4O_7$ (227)
Triamylammonium picrate

N	$\Delta t_B / x_1$
0.05	29.3
0.1	28.8
0.2	28.7

CH_2O_2

Formic acid*
$T_B = 373.6$
$k_B = 53.0$

$C_6H_3N_3O_6$ (66)
1, 3, 5-Trinitrobenzene

$C_7H_5N_3O_7$ (66)
2, 4, 6-Trinitroanisole

$C_7H_6O_2$ (66)
Benzoic acid

* Not anhydrous.

$C_9H_8O_2$ (29)
Cinnamic acid

N	$\Delta t_B / x_1$
0.1	51.6
0.2	50.0
0.3	48.4
0.4	46.5

$C_9H_9N_3O_6$ (66)
Trinitromesitylene

$C_9H_{10}N_2O_4$ (66)
Dinitromesitylene

$C_{10}H_8O$ (66)
β-Naphthol

$C_{13}H_{11}NO$ (29)
Benzanilide

N	$\Delta t_B / x_1$
0.1	52.0
0.2	50.5
0.3	49.1
0.4	47.6

$C_{14}H_{10}O_2$ (29)
Benzil

N	$\Delta t_B / x_1$
0.1	49.7
0.2	47.8
0.3	46.0
0.4	44.1
0.5	42.2

$NaCHO_2$ (29)
Formate

N	$\Delta t_B / x_1$
0.3	92.0
0.4	93.4
0.5	94.9
0.6	96.4

K_2SO_4 (29)

N	$\Delta t_B / x_1$
0.15	149.8
0.2	147.7
0.3	143.4
0.35	141.1

$KCHO_2$ (29)
Formate

N	$\Delta t_B / x_1$
0.2	95.4
0.3	96.7
0.4	98.1
0.5	99.5
0.6	100.8

CH_3I

Methyl iodide
$T_B = 315.7$
$k_B = 29.6$

$C_4H_7Cl_3O_2$ (65)
Chloral alcoholate

N	$\Delta t_B / x_1$
0.1	23.2
0.2	24.2
0.3	25.2

$C_6H_4Br_2$* (65)
Dibromobenzene

N	$\Delta t_B / x_1$
0.05	28.8
0.1	30.5
0.15	32.2

$C_7H_6O_2$ (34)
Benzoic acid

N	$\Delta t_B / x_1$
0.1	16.2
0.2	15.8
0.3	15.5

* The isomer used is not given.

$C_{10}H_{16}O$ (34)
Camphor

N	$\Delta t_B / x_1$
0.1	29.6
0.2	30.2
0.3	30.7
0.5	31.9
0.6	32.5

$C_{12}H_{11}N$ (34)
Diphenylamine

N	$\Delta t_B / x_1$
0.1	29.7
0.2	29.9
0.3	30.2
0.5	30.5

$C_{14}H_{10}O_2$ (34)
Benzil

N	$\Delta t_B / x_1$
0.1	29.0
0.2	29.1
0.3	29.2
0.4	29.3

CH_3NO_2

Nitromethane
$T_B = 375$
$k_B = 33.7$

C_2H_5NO (220)
Acetamide

N	$\Delta t_B / x_1$
0.1	30.0
0.2	29.6
0.3	29.3
0.4	28.9
0.5	28.5

$C_6H_4N_2O_4$ (220)
m-Dinitrobenzene

N	$\Delta t_B / x_1$
0.1	33.0
0.2	33.0
0.3	33.1
0.4	33.1

C_8H_7N (220)
Benzyl cyanide

N	$\Delta t_B / x_1$
0.1	30.5
0.2	30.9
0.3	31.3

$C_8H_{20}IN$ (220)
Tetraethylammonium iodide

N	$\Delta t_B / x_1$
0.05	53
0.1	51
0.15	49
0.2	48

$C_{12}H_{11}N$ (220)
Diphenylamine

N	$\Delta t_B / x_1$
0.1	33.7
0.2	33.7
0.3	33.7
0.4	33.7

$C_{14}H_{10}O_2$ (220)
Benzil

N	$\Delta t_B / x_1$
0.1	30.6
0.2	31.5

$C_{19}H_{16}$ (220)
Triphenylmethane

N	$\Delta t_B / x_1$
0.1	32.8
0.2	33

CH_4

Methane
$T_B = 111.7$
$k_B = 17$

C_2H_4 (104)
Ethylene

N	$\Delta t_B / x_1$
1.0	16
4.0	13
6.0	12

C_2H_6 (104)
Ethane

N	$\Delta t_B / x_1$
5.0	18
10.0	15

CH_4O

Methyl alcohol
$T_B = 337.6$
$k_B = 26.8$

I_2 (49)

N	$\Delta t_B / x_1$
0.2	25.7
0.5	24.3

NH_4ClO (124)
Hydroxylamine hydrochloride

N	$\Delta t_B / x_1$
0.5	36
1.0	36
1.5	37

NH_4Br (113)

N	$\Delta t_B / x_1$
0.2	39.1
0.3	39.1

NH_4I (113)

N	$\Delta t_B / x_1$
0.1	40.0
0.2	38.6

NH_4NO_3 (124)

N	$\Delta t_B / x_1$
0.1	31
0.2	32
0.4	34
0.6	34
0.8	33

NH_4CNS (124)

N	$\Delta t_B / x_1$
0.1	36
0.2	36
0.5	38
1.0	41
1.5	43

CH_4N_2O (265, 267)
Urea

N	$\Delta t_B / x_1$
0.5	24.9
1.0	23.9
2.0	22.9
3.0	22.0
4.0	21.3
5.0	20.6

C_2H_5NO (113, 267)
Acetamide

N	$\Delta t_B / x_1$
0.5	26.0
1.0	26.1
2.0	26.3
3.0	26.5
4.0	26.7
4.5	26.8

$C_3H_7NO_2$ (201, 267)
Urethane

N	$\Delta t_B / x_1$
0.2	26.7
0.5	26.6
1.0	26.5

$C_3H_7NO_2$.—(*Cont'd*)

N	$\Delta t_B / x_1$
1.5	26.4
2.0	26.3
3.0	25.7
3.5	25.7

$C_6H_2ClN_3O_6$ (67)
Picryl chloride

N	$\Delta t_B / x_1$
0.1	46.8
0.2	45.7

$C_6H_3Cl_3$ (67)
1, 3, 5-Trichlorobenzene

N	$\Delta t_B / x_1$
0.1	30
0.2	30
0.3	31
0.4	32

$C_6H_3N_3O_7$ (265)
Picric acid

N	$\Delta t_B / x_1$
0.2	25.3
0.5	24.1
1.0	22.1

C_6H_8ClN (124)
Aniline hydrochloride

N	$\Delta t_B / x_1$
0.3	29
0.5	30
1.0	32
1.5	32

$C_6H_9ClN_2$ (124)
Phenylhydrazine hydrochloride

N	$\Delta t_B / x_1$
0.1	31
0.2	33
0.5	36

$C_6H_{10}O_5$ (221)
Dimethyl malate

N	$\Delta t_B / x_1$
0.1	20.3
0.3	21.6
0.5	22.6
0.8	23.5
1.0	24.0
1.5	24.5

$C_6H_{10}O_6$ (221)
Dimethyl tartrate

N	$\Delta t_B / x_1$
0.3	24.6
0.5	25.3
0.7	26.0

$C_6H_{15}IS$ (73)
Triethylsulfonium iodide

N	$\Delta t_B / x_1$
0.1	35.0
0.2	34.1
0.3	33.2
0.4	32.2

$C_7H_6O_2$ (267)
Benzoic acid

N	$\Delta t_B / x_1$
0.5	26.3
1.0	26.3
2.0	26.4
2.5	26.4

$C_7H_6O_3$ (267)
Salicylic acid

N	$\Delta t_B / x_1$
0.5	26
1.0	26.5
2.0	28

CH_4O.—(*Cont'd*)

$C_8H_7N_3O_6$ (67) Trinitro-*p*-xylene

C_8H_9NO (113, 267) Acetanilide

N	$\Delta t_B / x_1$
0.5	25.6
1.0	25.2
2.0	24.3

$C_8H_{12}O_6$ (221) Dimethyl acetylmalate

0.2	19.4
0.5	22.1
1.0	22.7

$C_8H_{14}O_5$ (221) Diethyl malate

0.1	23.8
0.3	24.5
0.5	25.2
0.8	26.2

$C_8H_{14}O_6$ (221) Diethyl tartrate

0.3	24.2
0.5	25.1
0.8	26.5

$C_8H_{20}IN$ (220) Tetraethylammonium iodide

0.1	36.6
0.2	34.7
0.3	32.9

$C_9H_{10}N_2O_4$ (67) Dinitromesitylene

$C_{10}H_8$ (201, 265, 267) Naphthalene

0.1	26.2
0.3	24.9
0.5	23.8
0.8	22.2
1.0	21.4
2.0	19.5
3.0	17.6
4.0	15.7

$C_{10}H_{15}BrO$* (267) Bromocamphor

0.5	24.8
1.0	23.4

$C_{10}H_{16}O$ (267) Camphor

0.5	25.4
1.0	24.4

$C_{11}H_{16}O_3$ (64) Camphocarboxylic acid

0.2	27.1
0.5	27.0
0.6	26.9

$C_{12}H_{10}$ (201) Acenaphthene

0.1	24.8
0.2	24.5
0.5	23.7
0.6	23.5

* The isomer used is not given.

$C_{12}H_{11}N$ (113) Diphenylamine

N	$\Delta t_B / x_1$
0.2	26.4

$C_{12}H_{13}NO_3S$ (124) Aniline benzenesulfonate

0.1	29
0.2	30
0.3	30
0.4	31

$C_{14}H_{10}O_2$ (125, 267) Benzil

0.2	23.3
0.5	22.2
1.0	20.3
1.5	18.4

$C_{19}H_{16}$ (113) Triphenylmethane

0.1	26.3
0.2	25.1

$HgCl_2$ (189)

0.05	40.0
0.1	35.8
0.2	31.6
0.4	30.5
0.8	31.7

$CuCl_2$ (189)

0.1	35
0.2	35
0.3	34

$MnCl_2$ (189)

0.1	42
0.3	43
0.5	43
1.0	44

$CoCl_2$ (189)

0.1	40.6
0.2	36.2
0.3	31.7

$NiCl_2$ (189)

0.1	53
0.2	47
0.3	41
0.5	42
0.8	45

$NiSO_4.6H_2O$ (251)

$NiSO_4.7H_2O$ (251)

$CrCl_3.6H_2O$ (green) (177, 248)

$CrCl_3.6H_2O$ (violet) (248)

$MoO(OH)_2Cl_2$ (215)

0.3	55
0.5	55
0.8	56

$CaCl_2$ (124)

0.2	26
0.5	32
1.0	41
1.5	51

$Ca(NO_3)_2$ (239)

N	$\Delta t_B / x_1$
0.1	36.9
0.2	35.2
0.3	33.8
0.5	32.3
0.8	32.3
1.0	32.9
1.1	33.5

$BaBr_2$ (124)

0.1	48
0.2	51
0.3	53

$LiCl$ (118, 239)

0.1	41.7
0.2	41.0
0.3	41.4
0.5	42.8
0.8	45.2
1.0	47.2
1.5	53.0
1.7	55.5

$LiBr$ (118)

0.1	43.5
0.2	42.2
0.3	42.0
0.5	43.0
0.8	46.3
1.0	49.2
1.2	52.4

$LiNO_3$ (118)

0.1	36.8
0.2	37.8
0.5	40.6
0.8	43.3
1.0	45.2

$NaBr$ (113, 124)

0.1	40.0
0.2	41.5
0.5	46.4
0.7	50

NaI (239)

0.1	47.1
0.2	44.5
0.3	43.6
0.5	44.3
0.8	47.0
1.0	49.2
1.5	55.5
1.8	59.7

$NaCH_3O$ (269) Methylate

$NaC_2H_3O_2$ (239) Acetate

0.1	39
0.2	36
0.3	34.2
0.5	34.5
0.8	35.4
1.0	35.7
1.5	35.5

KBr (113)

0.1	39.3

KI (239)

N	$\Delta t_B / x_1$
0.1	42
0.2	40
0.3	39.8
0.5	40.0
0.8	41.5

$KC_2H_3O_2$ (113, 239) Acetate

0.1	37.2
0.2	35.3
0.3	34.7
0.5	35.2
0.8	37.1
1.0	37.8
1.5	39.2
1.7	39.5

$C_2H_2Cl_2$

1, 2-Dichloroethylene*

$T_B = 328.6$

$k_B = 30.7$

$C_{10}H_8$ (157) Naphthalene

0.4	31.7
0.6	32.2

$C_{13}H_{10}O$ (157) Benzophenone

0.4	32.0

$C_{18}H_{16}O_3$ (157) γ-Ketopropionyldibenzoylmethane

0.1	27.9
0.2	28.2
0.3	28.3

* A mixture of the *cis* and *trans* forms.

$C_2H_3Cl_3O_2$

Chloral hydrate

$T_B = 371$*

$k_B = 14.5$

$C_6H_4Br_2$‡ (65) Dibromobenzene

0.1	14
0.2	12.6

$C_6H_6O_2$ (47) Hydroquinol

0.1	11.8
0.2	12.3
0.3	12.9

$C_6H_{12}O_6$ (47) *d*-Glucose

0.1	14

$C_{10}H_8$ (47, 65) Naphthalene

0.1	14.5
0.2	14.3
0.3	13.9
0.4	13.1

$C_{10}H_{14}O$ (47) Thymol

0.1	16.1
0.2	16.0
0.3	15.9

* With dissociation.

‡ The isomer used is not given.

C_2H_3N

Acetonitrile

$T_B = 355$

$k_B = 30$

C_2H_5NO (220) Acetamide

N	$\Delta t_B / x_1$
0.1	35.0
0.25	33.8
0.35	33.4
0.45	33.1

$C_4H_5NO_2$ (220) Methyl cyanoacetate

0.2	32.2
0.3	31.7

$C_4H_{12}ClN$ (214) Diethylammonium chloride

0.85	17.3

$C_4H_{12}ClN$ (214) Isobutylammonium chloride

$C_6H_2ClN_3O_6$ (67) Picryl chloride

0.05	65.0
0.1	59.7
0.2	53.4

$C_6H_3Cl_3$ (67) 1, 3, 5-Trichlorobenzene

0.2	41.5
0.3	41.9

$C_6H_3N_3O_7$ (67) Picric acid

0.1	49.6
0.15	46.4

$C_6H_{10}O_6$ (221) Dimethyl tartrate

0.1	27.2
0.4	29.0
0.6	30.2

C_7H_5N (220) Benzonitrile

0.5	31.5
0.7	32.0

$C_7H_5N_3O_6$ (67) 2, 4, 6-Trinitrotoluene

0.1	56.1
0.2	53

$C_7H_8O_2$ (220) Dimethylpyrone

0.1	31.2
0.2	32.4
0.3	33.5
0.4	34.0
0.6	33.9

C_8H_7N (220) Benzyl cyanide

0.15	29.8
0.25	31.1
0.35	31.5
0.45	32.0

$C_8H_7N_3O_6$ (67) Trinitro-*p*-xylene

N	$\Delta t_B / x_1$
0.04	60.0
0.09	58.5

$C_8H_{20}IN$ (220) Tetraethylammonium iodide

0.1	46
0.2	46

$C_9H_9BrN_2O_4$ (67) Bromodinitromesitylene

0.1	42.1
0.15	42.7

$C_9H_{10}N_2O_4$ (67) Dinitromesitylene

$C_{10}H_8$ (123) Naphthalene

0.2	31.4
0.5	31.9
0.7	32.2

$C_{12}H_{10}$ (123) Diphenyl

0.2	32.1
0.3	33.0
0.5	34.8

$C_{12}H_{11}N$ (220) Diphenylamine

0.2	32.0
0.3	31.6
0.4	31.2
0.5	30.8

$C_{12}H_{28}IN$ (214) Tetrapropylammonium iodide

$C_{12}H_{28}N_2O_3$ (214) Tetrapropylammonium nitrate

$C_{14}H_{10}$ (220) Anthracene

0.1	28.4

$C_{14}H_{14}$ (67) Dibenzyl

0.1	44.0
0.2	43.1

$C_{19}H_{16}$ (220) Triphenylmethane

0.1	28.3
0.2	27.9
0.3	27.4

$C_{19}H_{16}O$ (220) Triphenylcarbinol

0.2	28.1
0.35	28.6

$AgNO_3$ (123)

0.1	44.7
0.3	43.6
0.5	42.5

C_2H_3NS

Methyl thiocyanate

$T_B = 406$

$k_B = 36.3$

$C_6H_{10}O_6$ (220) Dimethyl tartrate

N	$\Delta t_B / x_1$
0.05	33
0.1	32.7
0.2	32.9
0.25	33.0

$C_{12}H_{11}N$ (220) Diphenylamine

N	$\Delta t_B / x_1$
0.1	36.4
0.2	36.7
0.3	36.9
0.4	37.1

$C_{14}H_{10}$ (220) Phenanthrene

N	$\Delta t_B / x_1$
0.1	35.9
0.2	36.8
0.3	37.7

$C_{14}H_{10}O_2$ (220) Benzil

N	$\Delta t_B / x_1$
0.05	36.2
0.1	36.3
0.15	36.4

$C_{19}H_{16}$ (220) Triphenylmethane

N	$\Delta t_B / x_1$
0.05	35.8
0.1	35.3
0.15	34.6

$C_2H_4Br_2$

1, 2-Dibromoethane

$T_B = 404.8$

$k_B = 34.3$

$C_8H_8O_3$ (18) Phenoxyacetic acid

N	$\Delta t_B / x_1$
0.1	28
0.2	26.4
0.3	26.0

$C_{10}H_{16}O$ (34) Camphor

N	$\Delta t_B / x_1$
0.1	32.0
0.2	32.4
0.3	32.8
0.5	33.6
0.7	34.4

$C_{12}H_{10}NO$ (237) 1-Benzoylpyridinium

$C_{12}H_{11}N$ (34) Diphenylamine

N	$\Delta t_B / x_1$
0.1	34
0.2	35.0
0.3	35.8
0.4	36.6

$C_{13}H_{10}O_2$ (34) Phenyl benzoate

N	$\Delta t_B / x_1$
0.1	36.3
0.2	36.6
0.3	36.9
0.4	37.2
0.5	37.8

$C_{14}H_{10}$ (169) Anthracene

N	$\Delta t_B / x_1$
0.01	33.3
0.02	34.0
0.03	34.3

$C_{14}H_{10}O_2$ (34) Benzil

N	$\Delta t_B / x_1$
0.1	36.6
0.2	36.9
0.3	37.1
0.5	37.5
0.7	38.0

$C_{19}H_{16}$ (169) Triphenylmethane

N	$\Delta t_B / x_1$
0.01	35
0.02	35
0.03	36

$C_{21}H_{23}NO_6$* (240) Colchiceine

N	$\Delta t_B / x_1$
0.02	35
0.03	35.6
0.04	36.0

$C_{22}H_{25}NO_6$ (240) Colchicine

N	$\Delta t_B / x_1$
0.03	36

$C_{30}H_{20}O_2S_2$ (20) Desaurin

N	$\Delta t_B / x_1$
0.03	33.5

$C_2H_4Cl_2$

1, 1-Dichloroethane

$T_B = 330.4$

$k_B = 31.3$

$C_2HBr_3O_2$* (270) Tribromoacetic acid

$C_5H_{10}O_2$* (270) Isovaleric acid

$C_7H_6O_2$ (34) Benzoic acid

N	$\Delta t_B / x_1$
0.1	18.4
0.3	17.7
0.5	17.4
0.9	17.2
1.1	17.0

$C_8H_{20}BrN$* (270) Tetraethylammonium bromide

$C_{10}H_{16}O$ (34) Camphor

N	$\Delta t_B / x_1$
0.2	31.9
0.4	32.7
0.6	33.4
0.8	34.1
1.0	34.8

$C_{12}H_{11}N$ (34) Diphenylamine

N	$\Delta t_B / x_1$
0.1	31.1
0.3	30.9
0.5	30.8
0.7	30.8

$C_{12}H_{28}IN$* (270) Tetrapropylammonium iodide

$C_{14}H_{10}O_2$ (34) Benzil

N	$\Delta t_B / x_1$
0.1	31.9
0.2	33.2
0.5	37.0

* Associated.

$C_2H_4Cl_2$

1, 2-Dichloroethane

$T_B = 356.8$

$k_B = 31.5$

I_2 (49)

N	$\Delta t_B / x_1$
0.1	42
0.2	42

$C_7H_6O_2$ (34) Benzoic acid

N	$\Delta t_B / x_1$
0.2	21.4
0.5	20.2
0.7	19.8

$C_8H_8O_3$ (34) Anisic acid

N	$\Delta t_B / x_1$
0.2	19.0
0.3	18.9

C_8H_9NO (34) Acetanilide

N	$\Delta t_B / x_1$
0.1	31.2
0.2	29.6
0.3	28.2
0.5	25.7
0.8	23.5

$C_{10}H_{16}O$ (34) Camphor

N	$\Delta t_B / x_1$
0.1	33.2
0.2	33.5
0.5	34.3
0.7	35.0
1.0	35.8
1.2	36.4

$C_{12}H_{11}N$ (34) Diphenylamine

N	$\Delta t_B / x_1$
0.1	30.8
0.2	31.4
0.5	32.9
0.8	33.7

$C_{14}H_{10}O_2$ (34) Benzil

N	$\Delta t_B / x_1$
0.1	33.3
0.2	33.4
0.3	33.5
0.4	33.7

C_2H_4O

Acetaldehyde

$T_B = 293.3$

$k_B = 27$

C_2H_7NO (5) Acetaldehyde ammonia

N	$\Delta t_B / x_1$
0.15	45.6
0.3	49.8
0.4	52.1
0.55	53.6

$C_{10}H_{18}O$ (5) *l*-Borneol

N	$\Delta t_B / x_1$
0.005	26.1
0.01	26.0
0.02	27.9
0.025	28.1

$C_{13}H_{10}O$ (5) Benzophenone

N	$\Delta t_B / x_1$
0.15	27.7
0.35	27.5

$C_2H_4O_2$*

Acetic acid

$T_B = 391.2$

$k_B = 51.8$

$BiC_6H_9O_6$ (29) Acetate

N	$\Delta t_B / x_1$
0.05	52
0.1	52
0.2	52

$C_6H_3N_3O_7$ (29) Picric acid

N	$\Delta t_B / x_1$
0.1	51.8
0.2	51.0
0.25	50.4

$C_6H_5NO_3$ (156) *p*-Nitrophenol

N	$\Delta t_B / x_1$
0.4	42.7

$C_6H_{16}BrN$ (214) Triethylammonium bromide

$C_6H_{16}IN$ (214) Triethylammonium iodide

$C_7H_5BrO_2$ (29) *p*-Bromobenzoic acid

N	$\Delta t_B / x_1$
0.1	47.1
0.3	46.1
0.5	45.4

$C_7H_6O_2$ (18) Benzoic acid

N	$\Delta t_B / x_1$
0.06	40.4
0.15	42.9
0.25	43.0
0.45	43.1
0.65	43.3
1.0	45.0

C_8H_9NO (29) Acetanilide

N	$\Delta t_B / x_1$
0.1	53.3
0.2	53.1
0.3	52.2

$C_8H_{20}BrN$ (214) Tetraethylammonium bromide

$C_{10}H_{10}N_2O_2$ (156) *o*-Phenylenesuccinamide

N	$\Delta t_B / x_1$
0.1	42.3

$C_{12}H_{10}N_2$ (29) Azobenzene

N	$\Delta t_B / x_1$
0.1	47.9
0.2	48.1

$C_{12}H_{11}N$ (33) Diphenylamine

N	$\Delta t_B / x_1$
0.05	51.4
0.1	51.2
0.2	50.9
0.3	50.5

$C_{13}H_{11}NO$ (29) Benzanilide

N	$\Delta t_B / x_1$
0.05	50.7
0.1	49.2
0.15	48.4
0.2	47.9

$C_{14}H_{10}$‡ (18) Anthracene

N	$\Delta t_B / x_1$
0.05	42.3
0.1	43.1
0.2	44.3

$C_{14}H_{10}O_2$ (29, 97) Benzil

N	$\Delta t_B / x_1$
0.1	51.4
0.15	50.6
0.25	49.8

$C_{14}H_{12}O_2$ (29) Benzoin

N	$\Delta t_B / x_1$
0.05	50
0.1	51
0.2	51
0.25	51

$C_{19}H_{21}NO_5$ (240) Trimethylcolchicinic acid

N	$\Delta t_B / x_1$
0.02	33.6
0.05	33.8
0.09	34.1

$C_{20}H_{12}O_3$ (156) Fluoran

N	$\Delta t_B / x_1$
0.15	42.4
0.2	42.7

$C_{21}H_{23}NO_6$ (240) Colchiceine

N	$\Delta t_B / x_1$
0.02	51.4
0.03	52.5
0.05	53.1
0.07	53.3

$C_{22}H_{25}NO_6$ (240) Colchicine

N	$\Delta t_B / x_1$
0.01	47.0
0.03	45.6
0.05	44.0

$PbC_4H_6O_4$ (29) Acetate

N	$\Delta t_B / x_1$
0.05	55
0.1	54
0.2	52

$PbC_8H_{12}O_8$ (247) Tetraacetate

N	$\Delta t_B / x_1$
0.05	54
0.1	53
0.2	53

$CuC_9H_{21}ClN_3O_3S_3$ Cuprous trixanthamidechloride (257)

N	$\Delta t_B / x_1$
0.02	149
0.05	136
0.08	132

$CaC_4H_6O_4$ (29) Acetate

N	$\Delta t_B / x_1$
0.04	46.5
0.1	42.2
0.15	39.4

$SrC_4H_6O_4$ (29) Acetate

N	$\Delta t_B / x_1$
0.05	51.3
0.1	48.0
0.2	42.3

$BaC_4H_6O_4$ (29) Acetate

N	$\Delta t_B / x_1$
0.04	48.7
0.1	49.9
0.15	50.5
0.2	50.5
0.25	50.9

$LiC_2H_3O_2$ (29) Acetate

N	$\Delta t_B / x_1$
0.1	54
0.2	53
0.3	51.8
0.4	50.9
0.55	49.7

$NaC_2H_3O_2$ (18, 29) Acetate

N	$\Delta t_B / x_1$
0.1	49.2
0.3	50.0
0.5	50.2
0.8	51.0

$KC_2H_3O_2$ (29) Acetate

N	$\Delta t_B / x_1$
0.1	50.8
0.2	52.1
0.3	53.0
0.4	53.6
0.55	54.3

* Partially associated at T_B.

‡ Acid not anhydrous.

$C_2H_4O_2$

Methyl formate

$T_B = 304.9$

$k_B = 25.1$

$C_{14}H_{10}O_2$ (34) Benzil

N	$\Delta t_B / x_1$
0.1	25.3
0.2	25.4
0.3	25.6

C_2H_5Br

Ethyl bromide

$T_B = 311.1$

$k_B = 29.4$

$C_4H_7Cl_3O_2$ (65) Chloral alcoholate

N	$\Delta t_B / x_1$
0.1	28.5
0.2	28.6
0.3	28.7

$C_6H_4Br_2$* (65) Dibromobenzene

N	$\Delta t_B / x_1$
0.1	32
0.18	34.6

$C_7H_6O_2$ (266) Benzoic acid

N	$\Delta t_B / x_1$
0.1	15.3
0.5	16.0
1.0	16.9

C_8H_9NO (34) Acetanilide

N	$\Delta t_B / x_1$
0.2	27
0.3	24
0.5	17

C_2H_5Br.—(*Cont'd*)

$C_{10}H_8$ (267)
Naphthalene

N	$\Delta t_B / x_1$
0.2	28.4
0.5	29.0
0.7	29.5

$C_{10}H_{15}BrO$* (267)
Bromocamphor

N	$\Delta t_B / x_1$
0.1	28.6
0.3	29.5
0.5	30.3

$C_{10}H_{16}O$ (34)
Camphor

N	$\Delta t_B / x_1$
0.1	30.8
0.3	31.6
0.5	32.4
0.7	33.2
0.9	34.0

$C_{12}H_{11}N$ (34)
Diphenylamine

N	$\Delta t_B / x_1$
0.1	29.9
0.3	30.0
0.5	30.1
0.7	30.2

$C_{14}H_{10}O_2$ (34)
Benzil

N	$\Delta t_B / x_1$
0.1	29.7
0.3	29.9
0.5	30.1

$AlBr_3$ (249)

N	$\Delta t_B / x_1$
0.48	25.1

* The isomer used is not given.

C_2H_5Cl

Ethyl chloride
$T_B = 285.3$
$k_B = 30$

I_2 (40)

N	$\Delta t_B / x_1$
0.05	29.6
0.1	30.8
0.15	32.0

SCl_2 (40, 121)

N	$\Delta t_B / x_1$
0.1	26.6
0.2	26.7
0.25	26.8

S_2Cl_2 (40)

N	$\Delta t_B / x_1$
0.1	32.0
0.3	31.6
0.5	31.2

$C_6H_4Br_2$ (40)
p-Dibromobenzene

N	$\Delta t_B / x_1$
0.1	30.7
0.15	31.0
0.2	31.3

$C_6H_4Cl_2$ (40)
p-Dichlorobenzene

N	$\Delta t_B / x_1$
0.1	29.0
0.2	29.5
0.25	29.7

$C_{10}H_8$ (40)
Naphthalene

N	$\Delta t_B / x_1$
0.1	30.2
0.2	30.0
0.3	29.7

$C_{12}H_{10}$ (40)
Diphenyl

N	$\Delta t_B / x_1$
0.1	32.0
0.2	32.1
0.25	32.1

C_2H_5I

Ethyl iodide
$T_B = 345.3$
$k_B = 32.4$

C_8H_9NO (34)
Acetanilide

N	$\Delta t_B / x_1$
0.1	25.5
0.2	18.9
0.3	18.1
0.4	17.7

$C_{10}H_{16}O$ (34)
Camphor

N	$\Delta t_B / x_1$
0.1	33.0
0.2	33.3
0.4	33.9
0.6	34.5

$C_{12}H_{11}N$ (34)
Diphenylamine

N	$\Delta t_B / x_1$
0.1	32.5
0.2	32.7
0.4	33.1
0.6	33.5

$C_{14}H_{10}O_2$ (34)
Benzil

N	$\Delta t_B / x_1$
0.1	32.3
0.2	32.2
0.3	32.1
0.5	31.9

$C_2H_5NO_2$

Nitroethane
$T_B = 387.9$
$k_B = 37$

$C_7H_6O_2$ (34)
Benzoic acid

N	$\Delta t_B / x_1$
0.1	34.0
0.2	31.5
0.3	30.1

$C_{14}H_{10}O_2$ (34)
Benzil

N	$\Delta t_B / x_1$
0.1	35.6
0.2	34.3

C_2H_6O

Ethyl alcohol
$T_B = 351.6$
$k_B = 26$

I_2 (49)

N	$\Delta t_B / x_1$
0.1	26.2
0.3	27.3
0.4	27.5
0.5	27.3

SeO_2 (178)

N	$\Delta t_B / x_1$
0.1	24.7
0.2	24.8
0.5	25.0
1.0	25.5
2.0	26.4
3.0	27.2
4.0	28.1
5.0	29.3
6.0	32.2

NH_4ClO (124)
Hydroxylamine hydrochloride

N	$\Delta t_B / x_1$
0.3	19.1
0.5	19.6
1.0	20.8
1.5	22.1

NH_4Br (113)

N	$\Delta t_B / x_1$
0.15	30.5
0.2	30.4
0.25	30.4

NH_4I (116)

N	$\Delta t_B / x_1$
0.05	35.1
0.1	33.7
0.15	32.2
0.2	33.0
0.3	34.9

NH_4NO_3 (124)

N	$\Delta t_B / x_1$
0.1	23.2
0.2	24.8
0.4	25.7
0.6	25.3

NH_4CNS (124)

N	$\Delta t_B / x_1$
0.2	24.0
0.3	25.7
0.5	28.2
0.7	30.0
1.0	31.8
1.2	32.9
1.6	35.3

CH_4N_2O (152, 201)
Urea

N	$\Delta t_B / x_1$
0.4	24.9
0.5	24.7
1.0	23.8
1.5	22.9

$C_2H_2Cl_3NO$ (152)
Trichloroacetamide

N	$\Delta t_B / x_1$
0.4	27.3
0.5	27.4
0.6	27.5

$C_2H_3Cl_2NO$ (152)
Dichloroacetamide

N	$\Delta t_B / x_1$
0.6	27.8
0.8	28.0
1.0	28.2

C_2H_4ClNO (152)
Chloroacetamide

N	$\Delta t_B / x_1$
0.7	25.9
1.0	25.9
1.1	25.9

C_2H_5NO (103, 152)
Acetamide

C_2H_5NO.—(*Cont'd*)

N	$\Delta t_B / x_1$
0.1	24.7
0.2	24.7
0.4	24.7
0.6	25.3
0.8	26.2
1.0	27.0
1.2	27.4

$C_2H_5NO_2$ (153)
Glycolamide

N	$\Delta t_B / x_1$
0.4	24.6
0.5	24.7
0.7	24.9
0.9	25.1

$C_3H_4Cl_3NO_2$ (152)
Trichlorolactamide

N	$\Delta t_B / x_1$
0.3	27.7
0.4	27.9
0.5	28.1
0.6	28.3

$C_3H_6N_2O_2$ (152)
Malonamide

N	$\Delta t_B / x_1$
0.15	25.3
0.2	23.4
0.25	21.6

C_3H_7NO (153)
Propionamide

N	$\Delta t_B / x_1$
0.5	23.2
0.7	23.4
1.0	23.6
1.1	23.7

$C_3H_7NO_2$ (153)
Lactamide

N	$\Delta t_B / x_1$
0.4	25.7
0.5	25.4
0.7	24.9

$C_3H_7NO_2$ (153, 201)
Urethane

N	$\Delta t_B / x_1$
0.3	24.6
0.5	24.7
0.7	24.9
1.0	25.1
1.2	25.3

$C_4H_5NO_2$ (201)
Succinimide

N	$\Delta t_B / x_1$
0.3	24.7
0.5	24.1
1.0	22.7
1.2	22.1

$C_4H_6O_4$ (18)
Succinic acid

N	$\Delta t_B / x_1$
0.2	24.3
0.3	25.1
0.5	26.8

$C_4H_6O_6$ (18)
d-Tartaric acid

N	$\Delta t_B / x_1$
0.1	24.4
0.2	24.6
0.5	25.4
1.0	26.7
1.4	27.2

$C_4H_6O_6$ (18)
dl-Tartaric acid

$C_4H_6O_6$.—(*Cont'd*)

N	$\Delta t_B / x_1$
0.1	26.7
0.2	26.1
0.4	25.0

C_4H_9NO (153)
n-Butyramide

N	$\Delta t_B / x_1$
0.4	25.9
0.6	26.5
0.8	27.1

C_4H_9NO (153)
Isobutyramide

N	$\Delta t_B / x_1$
0.4	25.8
0.5	26.0
0.7	26.5
0.9	26.9

$C_4H_{12}ClN$ (214)
Diethylammonium chloride

$C_4H_{12}ClN$ (214)
Isobutylammonium chloride

$C_5H_{11}NO$ (153)
Isovaleramide

N	$\Delta t_B / x_1$
0.4	26.8
0.5	27.4
0.7	28.1
1.0	28.4

$C_5H_{12}ClN$ (200)
Piperidinium chloride

$C_5H_{12}N_2O_3$ (200)
Piperidinium nitrate

$C_6H_2ClN_3O_6$ (67)
Picryl chloride

N	$\Delta t_B / x_1$
0.1	26.2
0.2	24.8

$C_6H_3N_3O_7$ (265)
Picric acid

N	$\Delta t_B / x_1$
0.1	25.0
0.5	23.1
1.0	20.7
1.2	19.8

$C_6H_4N_2O_4$ (175)
m-Dinitrobenzene

N	$\Delta t_B / x_1$
0.3	24.3
0.5	22.8
0.7	21.3

$C_6H_6O_2$ (26, 139, 201)
Resorcinol

N	$\Delta t_B / x_1$
0.2	25.6
0.3	26.4
0.5	28.0
0.7	28.9
1.0	30.2

$C_6H_6O_3$ (213)
Pyrogallol

N	$\Delta t_B / x_1$
0.3	25.2
0.5	25.8
0.6	26.1

C_6H_7N (146)
Aniline

N	$\Delta t_B / x_1$
0.7	24.9
0.8	24.9
1.0	24.9

C_6H_8ClN (124)
Aniline hydrochloride

N	$\Delta t_B / x_1$
0.2	14.2
0.4	16.4
0.5	16.6
0.7	16.9
0.9	17.2

$C_6H_9ClN_2$ (124)
Phenylhydrazine hydrochloride

N	$\Delta t_B / x_1$
0.15	24.2
0.2	25.1

$C_6H_{13}NO$ (153)
Isobutylacetamide

N	$\Delta t_B / x_1$
0.3	25.5
0.5	26.8
0.7	28.1

$C_6H_{15}IS$ (73)
Triethylsulfonium iodide

N	$\Delta t_B / x_1$
0.1	22.6

$C_6H_{16}BrN$ (214)
Triethylammonium bromide

$C_6H_{16}ClN$ (214)
Triethylammonium chloride

$C_6H_{16}IN$ (214)
Triethylammonium iodide

$C_7H_6O_2$ (18, 103, 139)
Benzoic acid

N	$\Delta t_B / x_1$
0.1	25.1
0.2	25.2
0.5	25.4
0.7	25.5
1.0	25.7
1.1	25.7

$C_7H_6O_3$ (22, 139, 188, 267)
Salicylic acid

N	$\Delta t_B / x_1$
0.2	24.6
0.3	25.5
0.4	26.0
0.5	26.3
0.7	26.6
1.0	26.9
1.5	28.0

$C_7H_6O_6S$ (200)
Salicylsulfonic acid

C_7H_7NO (152, 201)
Benzamide

N	$\Delta t_B / x_1$
0.2	26.1
0.5	25.6
0.7	25.2
1.0	24.8
1.3	24.4

C_7H_7NO (153) Formanilide

N	$\Delta t_B/x_1$
0.4	26.9
0.5	26.9
0.9	26.9

$C_7H_7NO_2$ (152) Salicylamide

N	$\Delta t_B/x_1$
0.3	25.8
0.4	26.1
0.5	26.4

$C_7H_8N_2O$ (153) Phenylurea

N	$\Delta t_B/x_1$
0.5	22.9
0.7	22.6
1.0	22.1

C_7H_9N (201) *p*-Toluidine

N	$\Delta t_B/x_1$
0.1	26.0
0.3	25.6
0.5	25.2
0.7	24.9
0.9	24.5

$C_7H_{12}O_4$ (269) Diethyl malonate

N	$\Delta t_B/x_1$
0.1	25.3
0.2	24.2
0.3	23.0

$C_8H_4O_3$ (231) Phthalic anhydride

N	$\Delta t_B/x_1$
0.5	24.2
1.0	24.9
1.5	25.7

C_8H_9NO Acetanilide (18, 103, 139, 152, 188, 200, 201)

N	$\Delta t_B/x_1$
0.1	26.1
0.2	26.0
0.4	25.7
0.6	25.5
0.8	25.2
1.0	24.9

C_8H_9NO (18) Acetophenone oxime

N	$\Delta t_B/x_1$
0.1	26.1
0.2	25.3
0.3	24.6
0.5	23.4
0.7	22.4
0.9	22.0

C_8H_9NO (153) Phenylacetamide

N	$\Delta t_B/x_1$
0.3	25.9
0.5	26.4
0.8	26.8

$C_8H_9NO_2$ (153) Glycolanilide

N	$\Delta t_B/x_1$
0.3	27.1
0.4	26.5
0.5	26.0
0.6	25.8

$C_8H_{11}N$ (166) Dimethylaniline

$C_8H_{11}N$.—(*Cont'd*)

N	$\Delta t_B/x_1$
0.3	23.2
0.4	22.2

$C_8H_{12}ClN$ (214) Ethylphenylammonium chloride

$C_8H_{20}BrN$ (214) Tetraethylammonium bromide

N	$\Delta t_B/x_1$
0.2	30.4
0.4	28.3
0.5	27.9
0.6	28.5
0.8	29.5

$C_8H_{20}ClN$ (214) Tetraethylammonium chloride

$C_8H_{20}IN$ (214, 220) Tetraethylammonium iodide

N	$\Delta t_B/x_1$
0.1	28.3
0.3	26
0.5	24
0.6	22

$C_9H_{10}O_2$ (18) Ethyl benzoate

N	$\Delta t_B/x_1$
0.1	22.1
0.4	20.9
0.5	20.7
0.7	20.4
1.0	20.0
1.3	19.6

$C_9H_{11}NO$ (153) Methylacetanilide

N	$\Delta t_B/x_1$
0.4	26.5
0.5	26.5
0.8	26.6
1.0	26.6

$C_9H_{11}NO_2$ (153) Lactanilide

N	$\Delta t_B/x_1$
0.4	26.6
0.5	26.5
0.7	26.3

$C_9H_{11}NO_2$ (153) Phenylurethane

N	$\Delta t_B/x_1$
0.4	26.4
0.5	26.3
0.7	25.9

$C_{10}H_8$ (201) Naphthalene

N	$\Delta t_B/x_1$
0.2	23.8
0.3	23.4
0.5	22.7
0.7	21.9
1.0	21.2
1.1	21.0

$C_{10}H_{10}IN$ (205) *N*-Methylquinolinium iodide

N	$\Delta t_B/x_1$
0.33	25.3

$C_{10}H_{10}IN$ (94) *N*-Methylisoquinolinium iodide

N	$\Delta t_B/x_1$
0.17	26.7

$C_{10}H_{13}NO$ (153) Ethylacetanilide

N	$\Delta t_B/x_1$
0.3	27.3
0.5	27.1
0.7	26.9

$C_{10}H_{16}O$ (43, 75) Camphor

N	$\Delta t_B/x_1$
0.1	24.2
0.2	24.2
0.3	24.2
0.5	24.2

$C_{10}H_{18}O$ (18) Borneol

N	$\Delta t_B/x_1$
0.1	24.5
0.2	24.2
0.5	23.5
0.7	23.1
1.0	22.3

$C_{11}H_{12}IN$ (214) *N*-Ethylquinolinium iodide

N	$\Delta t_B/x_1$
0.1	33.2
0.2	26.6
0.3	24.2
0.5	21.4

$C_{12}H_{10}$ (201) Acenaphthene

N	$\Delta t_B/x_1$
0.2	24.8
0.4	23.8
0.6	22.8
0.8	21.8
1.0	20.8

$C_{12}H_{10}N_2$ (146) Azobenzene

N	$\Delta t_B/x_1$
0.4	26.3

$C_{12}H_{10}O_2S$ (48) Phenylsulfone

N	$\Delta t_B/x_1$
0.1	24.8
0.2	23.8
0.5	20.9

$C_{12}H_{11}N$ (175) Diphenylamine

N	$\Delta t_B/x_1$
0.5	22.7
0.6	23.0
0.8	23.6

$C_{12}H_{11}N_3O_2$ (233) *o*-Nitrobenzidine

N	$\Delta t_B/x_1$
0.1	26.4

$C_{12}H_{12}ClN_2OP$ Chlorophosphoxydianilide (163)

N	$\Delta t_B/x_1$
0.08	31.3
0.1	33.2
0.14	36.8

$C_{12}H_{13}NO_3S$ (124) Aniline benzenesulfonate

N	$\Delta t_B/x_1$
0.1	22.2
0.2	23.7
0.3	24.3
0.4	24.6

$C_{12}H_{28}IN$ (214) Tetrapropylammonium iodide

$C_{12}H_{28}IN$.—(*Cont'd*)

N	$\Delta t_B/x_1$
0.2	27.7
0.4	25.9
0.6	25.3

$C_{12}H_{28}N_2O_3$ (214) Tetrapropylammonium nitrate

$C_{13}H_{10}O$ (146) Benzophenone

N	$\Delta t_B/x_1$
0.5	27.6
0.6	26.6
0.7	25.5

$C_{13}H_{10}O_2$ (18) Phenyl benzoate

N	$\Delta t_B/x_1$
0.2	23.2
0.3	22.7
0.5	21.7

$C_{13}H_{11}NO$ (152) Benzanilide

N	$\Delta t_B/x_1$
0.2	27.0
0.3	27.5

$C_{13}H_{12}N_2O$ (153) Diphenylurea

N	$\Delta t_B/x_1$
0.1	26.9

$C_{14}H_{10}$ (201) Phenanthrene

N	$\Delta t_B/x_1$
0.1	25.2
0.2	24.5
0.5	22.4
0.8	20.3

$C_{14}H_{10}O_2$ (18, 139, 175) Benzil

N	$\Delta t_B/x_1$
0.1	24.3
0.3	22.8
0.5	21.4
0.6	20.7

$C_{18}H_{34}O_2$ (138) Oleic acid

N	$\Delta t_B/x_1$
0.1	25
0.5	25
1.0	25
1.8	25

$C_{19}H_{16}$ (31) Triphenylmethane

N	$\Delta t_B/x_1$
0.1	28
0.2	27
0.3	26

$C_{20}H_{13}N_3O_7$ (52) Phenanthrene picrate

N	$\Delta t_B/x_1$
0.05	48.1
0.1	46.0
0.2	41.9
0.25	39.8

$C_{20}H_{16}BrN$ (94) *N*-Methylphenylacridinium bromide

N	$\Delta t_B/x_1$
0.15	25.8

$C_{20}H_{16}ClN$ (94) *N*-Methylphenylacridinium chloride

N	$\Delta t_B/x_1$
0.1	29.2

$C_{20}H_{16}IN$ (94) *N*-Methylphenylacridinium iodide

N	$\Delta t_B/x_1$
0.15	27.6

$C_{20}H_{30}O_2$ (216) Pinabietic acid

N	$\Delta t_B/x_1$
0.05	26.8
0.1	25.5

$C_{21}H_{32}O_2$ (216) Methyl pinabietate

N	$\Delta t_B/x_1$
0.05	25.8
0.1	25.7

$TlC_5H_7O_2$ (250.5) Acetylacetonate

$ZnC_{10}H_{14}O_4$ (263.5) Acetylacetonate

$ZnCl_2$ (56)

N	$\Delta t_B/x_1$
0.1	24.6
0.2	26.2
0.3	27.5

CdI_2 (116, 135)

N	$\Delta t_B/x_1$
0.1	27.3
0.2	27.7
0.3	28.1
0.5	28.8
1.0	30.8
1.5	32.7
1.8	33.2

$HgCl_2$ (18, 188)

N	$\Delta t_B/x_1$
0.1	25.8
0.2	25.9
0.5	26.2
1.0	26.3

HgI_2 (246)

N	$\Delta t_B/x_1$
0.04	27.9

$CuCl_2$ (145)

N	$\Delta t_B/x_1$
0.05	25.8
0.1	25.7
0.2	25.4
0.25	25.3

$AgNO_3$ (239)

N	$\Delta t_B/x_1$
0.06	38.5
0.1	35.6
0.15	32.6
0.2	29.6

$FeCl_3$ (24)

N	$\Delta t_B/x_1$
0.1	20.9
0.3	22.5
0.5	24.1
0.7	25.6

$CoCl_2$ (74)

$Co(CNS)_2$ (96)

N	$\Delta t_B/x_1$
0.08	25.2
0.27	25.4

$CrCl_3 \cdot 6H_2O$* (green) (177, 271)

N	$\Delta t_B/x_1$
0.05	30.5
0.1	28.9
0.25	24.0

Mo_3Cl_6 (253)

N	$\Delta t_B/x_1$
0.02	23.9
0.04	24.6

$MoO(OH)_2Cl_2$ (215)

N	$\Delta t_B/x_1$
0.1	32.1
0.2	32.5
0.5	33.5
1.0	35.2
1.1	35.5

$LaCl_3$ (58)

N	$\Delta t_B/x_1$
0.1	24.6
0.2	23.4
0.3	22.1

$CeCl_3$ (162)

N	$\Delta t_B/x_1$
0.05	30.3
0.2	30.2

$PrCl_3$ (242)

$Pr(NO_3)_3$ (140)

N	$\Delta t_B/x_1$
0.1	25.6
0.2	25.6
0.3	25.7

$NdCl_3$ (252)

N	$\Delta t_B/x_1$
0.1	26
0.4	27.6

$MgCl_2$ (197)

N	$\Delta t_B/x_1$
0.5	22
1.0	33.6
1.5	45.0
1.7	49.5

$MgC_{10}H_{14}O_4$ (263.5) Acetylacetonate

$CaCl_2$ (124, 197, 239)

N	$\Delta t_B/x_1$
0.1	28
0.3	24
0.5	25.2
1.0	28.4
1.5	31.6
2.0	36.1
2.5	40.7
3.0	45.3

$Ca(NO_3)_2$ (113, 117, 118, 239)

N	$\Delta t_B/x_1$
0.06	29.0
0.1	27.4
0.2	25.7
0.3	24.9
0.5	24.3
0.7	24.2
0.9	24.2

$LiCl$ (117, 118, 139, 197, 211)

N	$\Delta t_B/x_1$
0.1	29.4
0.3	31.4
0.5	33.5
1.0	38.7
1.5	47.2
2.0	56.6
4.5	69

$LiBr$ (118)

N	$\Delta t_B/x_1$
0.1	27.7
0.2	29.3
0.5	34.1
1.0	42.1
1.2	45.4

C_2H_6O.—(*Cont'd*)

LiI (211)

N	$\Delta t_B/x_1$
0.5	35.6
0.8	35.7

$LiNO_3$ (117, 118)

N	$\Delta t_B/x_1$
0.1	28.1
0.2	28.7
0.5	30.7
1.0	34.1
1.5	37.4
1.7	38.8

$NaClO_4$ (179)

N	$\Delta t_B/x_1$
0.6	25.7
0.8	26.9
1.0	28.1

NaBr (113)

N	$\Delta t_B/x_1$
0.05	32.1
0.1	31.0
0.2	28.9
0.3	26.8

NaI (113, 116, 135)

N	$\Delta t_B/x_1$
0.1	33.3
0.3	32.2
0.5	33.4
1.0	38.4
1.5	44.3

$NaC_2HCl_2O_2$ (200)
Dichloroacetate

$NaC_2H_3O_2$ (113, 239)
Acetate

N	$\Delta t_B/x_1$
0.05	32.6
0.1	28.2

NaC_2H_5O (48)
Ethylate

N	$\Delta t_B/x_1$
0.2	29.6
0.5	31.6
0.7	33.0
1.0	35.0

$NaC_6H_9O_3$ (48)
Ethyl acetoacetate

N	$\Delta t_B/x_1$
0.1	27.6
0.2	25.9
0.3	24.2

$NaC_7H_{11}O_4$ (48)
Diethylmalonate

N	$\Delta t_B/x_1$
0.1	26.1
0.2	24.7
0.3	23.3

$NaC_{12}H_{23}O_2$ (132)
Laurate

N	$\Delta t_B/x_1$
0.14	23.5

$NaC_{14}H_{27}O_2$ (132)
Myristate

N	$\Delta t_B/x_1$
0.1	24.8

$NaC_{16}H_{31}O_2$ (132)
Palmitate

N	$\Delta t_B/x_1$
0.07	24.7

$NaC_{18}H_{33}O_2$ (174)
Oleate

N	$\Delta t_B/x_1$
0.05	31.0
0.1	28.6
0.15	27.2
0.2	25.8

KI (113, 116)

N	$\Delta t_B/x_1$
0.05	32.0
0.1	32.0
0.2	31.9
0.3	31.3
0.35	31.3

$KCHO_2$ (132)
Formate

N	$\Delta t_B/x_1$
0.42	24.4

$KC_2H_3O_2$ (18, 113, 239)
Acetate

N	$\Delta t_B/x_1$
0.1	29.8
0.3	26.9
0.5	26.2
0.7	25.8
1.0	25.3
1.1	25.1

KC_2H_5O (48)
Ethylate

N	$\Delta t_B/x_1$
0.1	28.2
0.2	29.0
0.5	31.4
0.6	32.2

$KC_7H_5O_3$ (244)
Salicylate

N	$\Delta t_B/x_1$
0.15	26.8
0.25	26.9

$KC_7H_{13}O_2$ (132)
Heptylate

N	$\Delta t_B/x_1$
0.4	25.0
0.5	25.1
0.7	25.2
1.0	25.4

$KC_{14}H_{11}O_6$ (244)
Hydrogen *p*-hydroxybenzoate

N	$\Delta t_B/x_1$
0.1	47.9
0.2	46.1
0.25	45.3

$KC_{18}H_{33}O_2$ (138)
Oleate

N	$\Delta t_B/x_1$
0.1	26.4
0.2	26.5
0.5	26.8
0.7	27.0
1.0	27.2
1.1	27.3

* Uncorrected for partial vapor pressure of solute.

C_2H_6S

Methyl sulfide

$T_B = 309.3$

$k_B = 30.4$

$C_{12}H_{11}N$ (238)
Diphenylamine

N	$\Delta t_B/x_1$
0.05	30.4
0.1	30.4
0.3	30.4
0.5	30.4

$ZnCl_2$ (238)

N	$\Delta t_B/x_1$
0.1	32.1
0.2	31.9
0.3	31.8

$ZnBr_2$ (238)

N	$\Delta t_B/x_1$
0.1	30.9
0.2	32.2

ZnI_2 (238)

N	$\Delta t_B/x_1$
0.1	30.6
0.2	30.5

CdI_2 (238)

N	$\Delta t_B/x_1$
0.05	28.7
0.1	29.7
0.2	31.6

$HgCl_2$ (238)

N	$\Delta t_B/x_1$
0.05	32
0.1	33
0.15	33

HgI_2 (238)

N	$\Delta t_B/x_1$
0.1	29.4
0.2	29.7
0.3	29.9

$HgCH_3Cl$ (238)

N	$\Delta t_B/x_1$
0.1	29
0.2	31

$HgCH_3I$ (238)

N	$\Delta t_B/x_1$
0.1	30.1
0.2	32.5

CuCl (238)

N	$\Delta t_B/x_1$
0.1	23
0.2	24
0.4	24

$CuCl_2$ (238)

N	$\Delta t_B/x_1$
0.2	34.7
0.4	31.5

CuBr (238)

N	$\Delta t_B/x_1$
0.1	29.2
0.2	30.7
0.3	32.1
0.35	32.9

C_2H_6S (56)

Ethyl hydrogen sulfide

$T_B = 307.8$

$k_B = 30.6$*

* No experimental data given.

C_3H_5N

Propionitrile

$T_B = 370.2$

$k_B = 34.4$

C_2H_5NO (220)
Acetamide

N	$\Delta t_B/x_1$
0.2	34.4
0.3	34.2
0.4	34.1
0.45	34.1

$C_4H_5NO_2$ (220)
Methylcyanoacetate

N	$\Delta t_B/x_1$
0.1	31.3
0.2	31.6
0.3	31.8
0.35	31.9

$C_7H_6O_2$ (34)
Benzoic acid

$C_7H_6O_2$.—(*Cont'd*)

N	$\Delta t_B/x_1$
0.25	47
0.4	44
0.5	42

$C_7H_8O_2$ (220)
Dimethylpyrone

N	$\Delta t_B/x_1$
0.15	34.6
0.25	34.8
0.35	35.1
0.5	35.5
0.6	35.9

C_8H_7N (220)
Benzyl cyanide

N	$\Delta t_B/x_1$
0.15	33.2
0.2	33.8
0.25	34.4

$C_8H_{20}IN$ (220)
Tetraethylammonium iodide

N	$\Delta t_B/x_1$
0.05	51.4
0.08	49.2
0.1	48.2
0.12	47.4
0.15	46.5

$C_{10}H_8$ (220)
Naphthalene

N	$\Delta t_B/x_1$
0.1	34
0.2	34.6
0.3	34.8
0.4	35.2
0.5	35.4
0.6	35.5
0.7	35.7

$C_{12}H_{11}N$ (220)
Diphenylamine

N	$\Delta t_B/x_1$
0.1	34.0
0.2	34.5
0.3	34.9
0.4	35.4
0.5	35.8
0.6	36.3

$C_{14}H_{10}O_2$ (34)
Benzil

N	$\Delta t_B/x_1$
0.1	42
0.2	42

C_3H_6O

Acetone

$T_B = 329.2$

$k_B = 29.8$

I_2 (49)

N	$\Delta t_B/x_1$
0.1	34.0
0.2	34.9
0.3	35.6
0.4	36.3

NH_4CNS (114)

N	$\Delta t_B/x_1$
0.2	26.5
0.4	25.0
0.6	23.5

CH_4N_2O (152)
Urea

N	$\Delta t_B/x_1$
0.15	28

$C_2H_2Br_4$ (222)
1, 1, 2, 2-Tetrabromoethane

$C_2H_2Br_4$.—(*Cont'd*)

N	$\Delta t_B/x_1$
0.2	29.4
0.4	29.9
0.6	30.4

$C_2H_2Cl_3NO$ (152)
Trichloroacetamide

N	$\Delta t_B/x_1$
0.7	35.5
0.8	36.1
0.9	36.6
1.0	36.6

$C_2H_3ClO_2$* (206)
Chloroacetic acid

N	$\Delta t_B/x_1$
0.2	26.0
0.4	28.3
0.6	29.2

$C_2H_3Cl_3O_2$ (65)
Chloral hydrate

N	$\Delta t_B/x_1$
0.2	30.6
0.4	31.0
0.6	31.3

$C_2H_3Cl_2NO$ (152)
Dichloroacetamide

N	$\Delta t_B/x_1$
0.4	32.6
0.6	33.9
0.8	35.2

C_2H_4ClNO (152)
Chloroacetamide

N	$\Delta t_B/x_1$
0.8	30.7
1.0	30.5
1.2	30.1

C_2H_5NO (153)
Acetamide

N	$\Delta t_B/x_1$
0.4	28.5
0.6	27.3
0.8	26.2
1.0	24.9

$C_2H_5NO_2$ (153)
Glycolamide

N	$\Delta t_B/x_1$
0.15	30.5
0.2	29.9

$C_3H_4Br_2O_2$* (206)
1, 2-Dibromopropionic acid

N	$\Delta t_B/x_1$
0.1	33.4
0.2	30.5
0.3	27.5

$C_3H_4Cl_3NO_2$ (152)
Trichlorolactamide

N	$\Delta t_B/x_1$
0.4	31.3
0.6	32.7
0.8	33.2
0.9	33.0

C_3H_7NO (153)
Propionamide

N	$\Delta t_B/x_1$
0.4	28.5
0.6	27.5
0.8	26.5
1.0	25.5

$C_3H_7NO_2$ (153)
Lactamide

N	$\Delta t_B/x_1$
0.4	26.9
0.5	25.3
0.6	24.5

$C_3H_7NO_2$ (153)
Urethane

$C_3H_7NO_2$.—(*Cont'd*)

N	$\Delta t_B/x_1$
0.3	27.3
0.5	29.3
0.7	29.1

$C_4H_7Cl_3O_2$ (65)
Chloral alcoholate

N	$\Delta t_B/x_1$
0.1	28.4
0.2	28.6
0.3	28.7

C_4H_9NO (153)
n-Butyramide

N	$\Delta t_B/x_1$
0.4	28.7
0.6	28.1
0.8	27.5

C_4H_9NO (153)
Isobutyramide

N	$\Delta t_B/x_1$
0.4	29.0
0.6	28.6
0.8	28.2
1.0	27.8

$C_5H_{11}NO$ (153)
Valeramide

N	$\Delta t_B/x_1$
0.4	30.3
0.6	29.3
0.7	28.8

$C_6H_2ClN_3O_6$ (67)
Picryl chloride

N	$\Delta t_B/x_1$
0.15	32.2
0.2	32.7

$C_6H_6O_2$ (139, 231)
Resorcinol

N	$\Delta t_B/x_1$
0.5	33

$C_6H_{10}O_5$ (221)
Dimethyl malate

N	$\Delta t_B/x_1$
0.2	23.1
0.4	26.4
0.6	27.9
0.8	28.7
1.0	29.2
1.2	29.6

$C_6H_{10}O_6$ (221)
Dimethyl tartrate

N	$\Delta t_B/x_1$
0.2	22.6
0.4	25.6
0.6	27.1
0.7	27.5

$C_6H_{13}NO$ (153)
Isobutylacetamide

N	$\Delta t_B/x_1$
0.4	39.8
0.6	29.3
0.8	28.7

$C_6H_{15}IS$ (73)
Triethylsulfonium iodide

N	$\Delta t_B/x_1$
0.1	30.5
0.2	25.5

$C_7H_6O_2$ (18)
Benzoic acid

N	$\Delta t_B/x_1$
0.2	30.4
0.4	30.2
0.6	30.1
0.8	30.2
1.0	30.4
1.5	30.9

$C_7H_6O_3$ (81)
Salicylic acid

N	$\Delta t_B / x_1$
0.4	31.6
0.6	32.9
0.8	34.2
1.0	35.0
1.4	38.2

C_7H_7NO (152)
Benzamide

N	$\Delta t_B / x_1$
0.4	30.3
0.6	30.1
0.8	29.9
1.0	29.6
1.3	29.3

C_7H_7NO (153)
Formanilide

N	$\Delta t_B / x_1$
0.2	32.1
0.4	30.4
0.6	30.5

$C_7H_7NO_2$ (152)
Salicylamide

N	$\Delta t_B / x_1$
0.4	33.6
0.6	35.1
0.8	36.6

$C_7H_8N_2O$ (153)
Phenylurea

N	$\Delta t_B / x_1$
0.2	28.6
0.4	26.2
0.6	23.8

$C_8H_8O_3$ (176)
l-Mandelic acid

N	$\Delta t_B / x_1$
0.2	29.5

$C_8H_8O_3$ (176)
dl-Mandelic acid

N	$\Delta t_B / x_1$
0.15	22.8
0.2	30.8

C_8H_9NO (152)
Acetanilide

N	$\Delta t_B / x_1$
0.4	32.1
0.6	33.3
0.8	34.1

C_8H_9NO (153)
Phenylacetamide

N	$\Delta t_B / x_1$
0.4	28.3
0.6	27.6
0.7	27.3

$C_8H_9NO_2$ (153)
Glycolanilide

N	$\Delta t_B / x_1$
0.3	29.4
0.4	29.5
0.6	29.7

$C_8H_{12}O_6$ (221)
Dimethyl acetylmalate

N	$\Delta t_B / x_1$
0.2	25.5
0.4	28.5
0.6	29.8
0.7	30.3

$C_8H_{14}O_5$ (221)
Diethyl malate

N	$\Delta t_B / x_1$
0.2	23.5
0.4	27.4
0.6	28.9

$C_8H_{14}O_5$.—(*Cont'd*)

N	$\Delta t_B / x_1$
0.8	29.8
1.0	30.5

$C_8H_{14}O_6$ (221)
Diethyl tartrate

N	$\Delta t_B / x_1$
0.2	23.5
0.4	27.4
0.6	28.7
0.8	29.5

$C_9H_{11}NO$ (153)
Methylacetanilide

N	$\Delta t_B / x_1$
0.3	30.4
0.4	30.3
0.6	30.0

$C_9H_{11}NO_2$ (153)
Lactanilide

N	$\Delta t_B / x_1$
0.4	30.6
0.5	30.3
0.6	30.1

$C_9H_{11}NO_2$ (153)
Phenylurethane

N	$\Delta t_B / x_1$
0.2	32.3
0.4	31.9
0.6	31.6
0.7	31.4

$C_9H_{22}BrN$ (270)
Tripropylammonium bromide

$C_9H_{22}ClN$ (270)
Tripropylammonium chloride

$C_{10}H_7NO_2$ (142)
1-Nitronaphthalene

N	$\Delta t_B / x_1$
0.15	28.7
0.16	28.2

$C_{10}H_8$ (18)
Naphthalene

N	$\Delta t_B / x_1$
0.4	28.6
0.6	27.7
0.8	27.2
1.0	26.8
1.5	26.2
1.8	26.0

$C_{10}H_{10}O_4$ (81)
Resodiacetophenone

N	$\Delta t_B / x_1$
0.1	31.5
0.3	29

$C_{10}H_{13}NO$ (153)
Ethylacetanilide

N	$\Delta t_B / x_1$
0.2	30.1
0.4	29.8
0.6	31.7

$C_{10}H_{16}N_2O_3$ (100)
Bornylene nitrosite

N	$\Delta t_B / x_1$
0.1	17.4
0.2	18.6

$C_{10}H_{16}O$ (18)
Camphor

N	$\Delta t_B / x_1$
0.2	29.4
0.4	29.2
0.6	28.9
0.8	28.7
1.0	28.4
1.5	27.8

$C_{12}H_{10}$ (81)
Diphenyl

N	$\Delta t_B / x_1$
0.2	29.5
0.4	30.0
0.6	30.4
0.8	30.9
1.0	31.3

$C_{12}H_{10}N_2$ (139, 180)
Azobenzene

N	$\Delta t_B / x_1$
0.14	30.6
0.37	28.9

$C_{12}H_{11}N$ (139)
Diphenylamine

N	$\Delta t_B / x_1$
0.3	28.9
0.5	29.9

$C_{12}H_{28}IN$ (214)
Tetrapropylammonium iodide

N	$\Delta t_B / x_1$
0.1	32.5
0.2	29.3
0.3	26.0

$C_{12}H_{28}N_2O_3$ (214)
Tetrapropylammonium nitrate

N	$\Delta t_B / x_1$
0.2	30.0
0.4	25.0
0.6	23.2
0.8	22.0

$C_{13}H_{11}NO$ (152)
Benzanilide

N	$\Delta t_B / x_1$
0.4	31.9
0.6	31.5

$C_{13}H_{12}N_2O$ (153)
Diphenylurea

N	$\Delta t_B / x_1$
0.15	29.2

$C_{14}H_{10}O_2$ (125)
Benzil

N	$\Delta t_B / x_1$
0.1	26.8
0.2	27.6
0.3	28.4

$C_{15}H_{34}BrN$ (270)
Triamylammonium bromide

$C_{15}H_{34}ClN$ (270)
Triamylammonium chloride

$C_{16}H_{34}N_2S$ (270)
Triamylammonium thiocyanate

$C_{19}H_{21}NO_5$ (240)
Trimethylcolchicinic acid

N	$\Delta t_B / x_1$
0.05	31.2
0.1	31.1

$C_{20}H_{10}Br_4O_4$ (155)
Tetrabromophenolphthalein

$C_{20}H_{44}IN$ (270)
Tetraamylammonium iodide

$C_{22}H_{42}O_3$ (222)
Isobutyl ricinoleate

N	$\Delta t_B / x_1$
0.2	30.0
0.4	29.5

$C_{24}H_{24}N_2$ (236)
Dibenzyltetrahydrodipyridyl

N	$\Delta t_B / x_1$
0.04	30.1
0.06	31.6
0.07	32.4

$C_{51}H_{98}O_6$ (222)
Tripalmitin

N	$\Delta t_B / x_1$
0.02	31
0.04	30
0.06	30
0.08	29
0.1	29
0.15	27

$C_{57}H_{110}O_6$ (222)
Tristearin

N	$\Delta t_B / x_1$
0.02	33
0.04	32
0.06	31
0.08	28

CdI_2 (114)

N	$\Delta t_B / x_1$
0.1	24.0
0.2	22.8
0.3	22.0
0.4	21.4

$HgCl_2$ (114)

N	$\Delta t_B / x_1$
0.2	30.6
0.3	30.5
0.4	30.4

$CuCl_2$ (144)

$FeCl_3$ (264)

N	$\Delta t_B / x_1$
0.07	34.4
0.1	33.7
0.15	30.2

$CrCl_3.6H_2O$ (green) (177)

N	$\Delta t_B / x_1$
0.02	33.0
0.04	30.5
0.06	29.0
0.08	26.5

$MoO(OH)_2Cl_2$ (215)

N	$\Delta t_B / x_1$
0.2	26.4
0.4	28.3

$C_6H_{15}BO_8$ (85)
Mannitoboric acid

N	$\Delta t_B / x_1$
0.26	22.6

$LiCl$ (78)

$LiNO_3$ (119)

N	$\Delta t_B / x_1$
0.1	24.2
0.2	20.6
0.3	18.5
0.4	17.4
0.5	16.4
1.0	14.2

NaI (147)

N	$\Delta t_B / x_1$
0.1	28.7
0.2	29.1
0.4	29.8
0.6	30.6
0.8	31.4

* Stable, high melting form.

$C_3H_6O_2$

Propionic acid
$T_B = 414.2$
$k_B = 47.4$

$C_6H_4N_2O_4$* (29)
Dinitrobenzene

N	$\Delta t_B / x_1$
0.1	57.9
0.2	56.2
0.3	55.2
0.4	54.3

$C_{12}H_{11}N$ (29)
Diphenylamine

N	$\Delta t_B / x_1$
0.1	47
0.2	46
0.3	46
0.4	45
0.5	45

$C_{13}H_{10}O$ (29)
Benzophenone

N	$\Delta t_B / x_1$
0.04	45.0
0.1	44.2
0.2	42.4
0.3	40.2

$C_{13}H_{11}NO$ (29)
Benzanilide

N	$\Delta t_B / x_1$
0.05	47
0.1	46
0.2	45
0.3	44
0.4	44

$C_{14}H_{10}O_2$ (29)
Benzil

N	$\Delta t_B / x_1$
0.05	47.4
0.1	46.2
0.2	44.0
0.3	41.7
0.4	39.4

$NaC_3H_5O_2$ (29)
Propionate

N	$\Delta t_B / x_1$
0.1	50.9
0.2	51.2
0.3	51.6
0.4	52.0

* The isomer used is not given.

$C_3H_6O_2$

Ethyl formate
$T_B = 327.4$
$k_B = 29.9$

$C_7H_6O_2$ (34)
Benzoic acid

N	$\Delta t_B / x_1$
0.2	28.4
0.3	28.9
0.5	29.2
0.9	29.2

$C_{10}H_{16}O$ (34)
Camphor

N	$\Delta t_B / x_1$
0.3	29.6
0.5	28.9
0.7	28.1

$C_{13}H_{10}O_2$ (34)
Phenyl benzoate

N	$\Delta t_B / x_1$
0.1	29.6
0.3	29.2
0.5	28.7
0.7	28.3

$C_{14}H_{10}O_2$ (34)
Benzil

N	$\Delta t_B / x_1$
0.1	29.4
0.2	28.9
0.3	28.5

$C_3H_6O_2$

Methyl acetate
$T_B = 330.2$
$k_B = 27.9$

$BiCl_3$ (195, 202)

N	$\Delta t_B / x_1$
0.05	43.1
0.1	40.0
0.15	37.1

$C_6H_3N_3O_7$ (270)
Picric acid

$C_7H_6O_2$ (34)
Benzoic acid

N	$\Delta t_B / x_1$
0.1	29.6
0.2	29.7
0.3	29.8
0.4	29.8
0.5	29.9
0.6	30.0

$C_{10}H_8$ (202)
Naphthalene

N	$\Delta t_B / x_1$
0.1	27.9
0.2	27.6
0.3	27.5
0.4	27.3
0.5	27.1
0.6	26.9

$C_{10}H_{16}O$ (34, 202)
Camphor

N	$\Delta t_B / x_1$
0.1	27.2
0.3	27.2
0.5	27.1
0.7	27.1
1.0	27.0

$C_{12}H_{11}N$ (34, 202)
Diphenylamine

N	$\Delta t_B / x_1$
0.2	27.8
0.4	27.8
0.6	27.7
0.8	27.7
1.0	27.6
1.2	27.6
1.4	27.5

$C_{13}H_{10}O_2$ (34)
Phenyl benzoate

N	$\Delta t_B / x_1$
0.1	27.8
0.3	27.5
0.5	27.1
0.7	26.8

$C_{14}H_{10}O_2$ (34, 202)
Benzil

N	$\Delta t_B / x_1$
0.05	28.0
0.1	27.9
0.2	27.6
0.3	27.1
0.5	26.3
0.6	25.8

$C_3H_6O_2$.—(*Cont'd*)

$C_{15}H_{34}BrN$* (270) Triamylammonium bromide

$C_{15}H_{34}ClN$* (270) Triamylammonium chloride

$C_{15}H_{34}FN$* (270) Triamylammonium fluoride

$C_{16}H_{34}N_2S$* (270) Triamylammonium thiocyanate

$C_{18}H_{31}N_4O_7$* (270) Tetrapropyl-ammonium picrate

$C_{20}H_{44}IN$* (270) Tetraamyl-ammonium iodide

$SnCl_2$ (195, 202)

N	$\Delta t_B / x_1$
0.05	49.2
0.1	46.2
0.15	43.3
0.2	40.4

$Zn(NO_3)_2$ (195, 202)

N	$\Delta t_B / x_1$
0.05	34.6
0.1	32.6
0.15	30.6
0.2	28.5
0.25	26.5

CdI_2 (195, 202)

N	$\Delta t_B / x_1$
0.01	59.5
0.02	58.0
0.03	56.6
0.04	55.1

$HgCl_2$ (195, 202)

N	$\Delta t_B / x_1$
0.05	31.7
0.1	31.4
0.3	30.7
0.5	30.4
0.7	30.3

$HgBr_2$ (195, 202)

N	$\Delta t_B / x_1$
0.05	34.4
0.1	32.9
0.2	31.6
0.3	31.3
0.4	31.0
0.5	30.8

HgI_2 (195, 202)

$Hg(CN)_2$ (195, 202)

N	$\Delta t_B / x_1$
0.04	28.1
0.05	28.4
0.06	28.7

$CuCl_2$ (195, 202)

$CuBr_2$ (195)

$CoBr_2$ (195, 202)

N	$\Delta t_B / x_1$
0.05	58.3
0.1	53.5
0.15	48.7
0.2	44.0

$Co(NO_3)_2$ (195, 202)

N	$\Delta t_B / x_1$
0.02	50.6
0.05	46.4
0.1	39.1
0.15	31.9

$Ca(NO_3)_2$ (195, 202)

N	$\Delta t_B / x_1$
0.02	48.6
0.05	44.7
0.1	38.0
0.15	31.5
0.2	25.0
0.25	19.6

BaI_2 (195)

N	$\Delta t_B / x_1$
0.02	54.3
0.05	44.5
0.08	34.7
0.1	28.0

LiCl (195)

N	$\Delta t_B / x_1$
0.03	36.9
0.04	31.2

LiBr (195, 202)

N	$\Delta t_B / x_1$
0.1	47.3
0.2	40.3
0.4	32.5
0.6	28.8
0.8	26.7
1.0	25.5

LiI (195, 202)

N	$\Delta t_B / x_1$
0.05	50.2
0.1	44.3
0.15	40.7
0.2	38.3
0.25	36.4

LiCNS (195, 202)

N	$\Delta t_B / x_1$
0.02	56.7
0.05	51.6
0.08	46.4
0.1	42.8

NaCNS (195, 202)

N	$\Delta t_B / x_1$
0.02	50.8
0.05	46.6
0.08	42.3
0.1	39.3
0.12	36.6

KCNS (195, 202)

N	$\Delta t_B / x_1$
0.02	50.6
0.04	48.3
0.05	47.3

* Associated.

C_3H_7Br

n-Propyl bromide

$T_B = 344.0$

$k_B = 29.5$

$C_7H_6O_2$ (266, 267) Benzoic acid

N	$\Delta t_B / x_1$
0.1	19.4
0.5	18.3
1.0	17.0

C_8H_9NO (266, 267) Acetanilide

N	$\Delta t_B / x_1$
0.3	21.4
0.5	19.0
1.0	13.6

$C_{10}H_{15}BrO$* Bromocamphor (266, 267)

N	$\Delta t_B / x_1$
0.1	29.6
0.5	30.3
0.7	30.6

* The isomer used is not given.

C_3H_8O

n-Propyl alcohol

$T_B = 370.9$

$k_B = 27.0$

$C_3H_7NO_2$ (201) Urethane

N	$\Delta t_B / x_1$
0.1	25.2
0.2	25.2
0.4	25.1
0.6	25.0
0.8	24.9
1.0	24.8
1.2	24.7

$C_6H_3N_3O_7$ (265) Picric acid

N	$\Delta t_B / x_1$
0.3	25.1
0.5	24.1
1.0	21.5
1.5	19.0

$C_6H_6N_2O_2$ (34) *p*-Nitroaniline

N	$\Delta t_B / x_1$
0.2	25.1
0.5	25.7
0.8	26.2
1.0	26.5

$C_7H_6O_2$ (34) Benzoic acid

N	$\Delta t_B / x_1$
0.1	25.7
0.2	25.9
0.4	26.3
0.6	26.7
0.8	26.8
1.0	26.9

$C_7H_6O_3$ (192) Salicylic acid

N	$\Delta t_B / x_1$
0.1	29.3
0.2	29.4
0.4	29.6
0.6	29.8
0.8	30.1
1.0	30.5
1.2	30.9

$C_8H_8O_3$ (34) Anisic acid

N	$\Delta t_B / x_1$
0.2	27.7
0.3	27.5
0.6	27.1
0.8	26.9
1.0	26.8

$C_{10}H_8$ (201) Naphthalene

N	$\Delta t_B / x_1$
0.1	24.0
0.2	23.6
0.4	22.9
0.6	22.4
0.8	22.0
1.0	21.6
1.2	21.3

$C_{10}H_{16}O$ (34) Camphor

N	$\Delta t_B / x_1$
0.1	24.4
0.2	24.4
0.4	24.4
0.6	24.4
0.8	24.4
1.0	24.4

$C_{12}H_{10}$ (201) Acenaphthene

N	$\Delta t_B / x_1$
0.1	24.9
0.2	24.5
0.3	24.1
0.4	23.8
0.5	23.5
0.6	23.3
0.7	23.1

$C_{14}H_{10}O_2$ (34) Benzil

N	$\Delta t_B / x_1$
0.05	29.8
0.1	29.1
0.2	27.7
0.3	26.6
0.4	25.7
0.5	25.1
0.7	24.1

LiCl (192)

N	$\Delta t_B / x_1$
0.9	24.8
1.0	26.5
1.1	28.5
1.2	30.8

$LiC_7H_5O_3$ (192) Salicylate

N	$\Delta t_B / x_1$
0.1	15.9
0.2	15.9
0.4	15.8
0.7	15.3
1.0	15

NaI (192)

N	$\Delta t_B / x_1$
0.2	29.4
0.4	29.5
0.7	29.5
1.0	29.6

C_3H_8O (173)

Isopropyl alcohol

$T_B = 355.4$

$k_B = 21.5$*

* Calculated from the average of results obtained by using aniline, benzanilide and dimethylaniline as solutes. No experimental data given.

$C_3H_8O_2$

Methylal

$T_B = 317$

$k_B = 27.4$

I_2 (30)

N	$\Delta t_B / x_1$
0.1	25.8
0.2	26.8
0.3	27.9

$C_7H_6O_2$ (34) Benzoic acid

$C_7H_6O_2$.—(*Cont'd*)

N	$\Delta t_B / x_1$
0.1	26.2
0.2	26.4
0.3	26.6
0.5	27.1
0.8	27.7
1.0	28.2

C_7H_7NO (34) Formanilide

N	$\Delta t_B / x_1$
0.1	24.1
0.2	23.8
0.3	23.4
0.5	22.8
0.8	21.8

$C_{10}H_8$ (34) Naphthalene

N	$\Delta t_B / x_1$
0.1	27.2
0.2	27.2
0.3	27.2
0.5	27.2

$C_{10}H_{16}O$ (34) Camphor

N	$\Delta t_B / x_1$
0.1	27.5
0.2	27.5
0.5	27.5
0.6	27.5

$C_{10}H_{20}O$ (34) Menthol

N	$\Delta t_B / x_1$
0.1	27.3
0.2	27.2
0.3	27.1
0.4	26.9

$C_{14}H_{10}O_2$ (30) Benzil

N	$\Delta t_B / x_1$
0.1	24.7
0.2	25.7
0.3	26.7

$C_4H_6O_3$

Acetic anhydride

$T_B = 412.7$

$k_B = 36$

$C_{14}H_{10}O_2$ (44) Benzil

N	$\Delta t_B / x_1$
0.02	36
0.05	36
0.1	35
0.15	35

$C_4H_8O_2$

n-Butyric acid

$T_B = 436.6$

$k_B = 44.8$

$C_7H_5BrO_2$ (29) *p*-Bromobenzoic acid

N	$\Delta t_B / x_1$
0.1	43.6
0.2	42.8
0.5	40.4
0.8	38.0

$C_{12}H_{11}N$ (29) Diphenylamine

N	$\Delta t_B / x_1$
0.1	44.2
0.2	43.5
0.35	42.4

$C_{13}H_{11}NO$ (29) Benzanilide

$C_{13}H_{11}NO$.—(*Cont'd*)

N	$\Delta t_B / x_1$
0.1	43.1
0.2	41.6
0.3	40.0
0.5	36.9

$C_{14}H_{10}O_2$ (29) Benzil

N	$\Delta t_B / x_1$
0.2	42.0
0.3	40.4
0.5	37.1

$NaC_4H_7O_2$ (29) *n*-Butyrate

N	$\Delta t_B / x_1$
0.1	47.1
0.2	49.3
0.3	49.4

$C_4H_8O_2$

Ethyl acetate

$T_B = 350.2$

$k_B = 31$

I_2 (30)

N	$\Delta t_B / x_1$
0.05	32.4
0.1	32.7
0.2	33.4
0.3	34.1

$C_6H_{10}O_5$ (221) Dimethyl malate

N	$\Delta t_B / x_1$
0.1	25.5
0.2	27.7
0.3	28.7
0.5	29.9
0.7	30.4
1.0	30.5

$C_6H_{10}O_6$ (221) Dimethyl tartrate

N	$\Delta t_B / x_1$
0.1	23.4
0.2	24.6
0.3	25.0
0.4	24.2

$C_7H_6O_2$ (34) Benzoic acid

N	$\Delta t_B / x_1$
0.2	32.1
0.4	31.6
0.6	31.2
0.8	31.1
1.0	31.0
1.3	31.0

$C_8H_{12}O_6$ (221) Dimethyl acetylmalate

N	$\Delta t_B / x_1$
0.2	27.8
0.3	28.4
0.5	29.6
0.7	30.4
1.0	30.8
1.1	30.9

$C_8H_{14}O_5$ (221) Diethyl malate

N	$\Delta t_B / x_1$
0.2	26.8
0.3	28.2
0.5	29.3
0.7	29.9

$C_8H_{14}O_6$ (221) Diethyl tartrate

N	$\Delta t_B / x_1$
0.1	27.0
0.2	28.5
0.3	28.9
0.5	29.3
0.7	29.3

$C_{10}H_8$ (34) Naphthalene

0.2	31.7
0.5	31.5
0.7	31.3
1.0	31.1

$C_{10}H_{16}O$ (34) Camphor

0.1	30.9
0.2	30.7
0.4	30.3
0.6	30.0
0.8	29.6

$C_{10}H_{20}O$ (34) Menthol

0.1	33.4
0.3	32.6
0.5	31.7
0.7	30.8

$C_{14}H_{10}O_2$ (30, 34) Benzil

0.1	30.4
0.2	31.2
0.3	31.8
0.5	31.0
0.7	30.2
0.8	29.8

$HgCl_2$ (254)

$HgBr_2$ (254)

HgI_2 (254)

C_4H_9Br

Isobutyl bromide

$T_B = 364.6$

$k_B = 27.0$

C_8H_8NO (267) Acetanilide

0.2	25.8
0.5	22.1
0.8	18.6

$C_{10}H_8$ (267) Naphthalene

0.1	26.8

$C_{10}H_{15}BrO$* Bromocamphor (266, 267)

0.24	27.6
0.4	29.0
0.6	30.7
0.8	30.9

$C_7H_6O_2$ (267) Benzoic acid

0.24	27.1
0.6	25.0
1.2	23.8

* The isomer used is not given.

$C_4H_{10}O$

Ethyl ether

$T_B = 307.6$

$k_B = 29.2$

I_2 (18, 103, 136)

N	$\Delta t_B / x_1$
0.1	29.0
0.3	29.0
0.5	29.0
1.0	28
1.4	27
1.6	26

$POCl_3$ (167)

0.1	32.1
0.2	31.1

$SbCl_3$ (143)

0.1	28.4
0.3	27.6
0.5	26.9
0.8	25.8

$BiCl_3$ (190)

0.15	23.9
0.2	22.3
0.3	20.1
0.4	18.7
0.5	17.4

CHNS (256) Thiocyanic acid

0.2	26.3
0.5	27

$C_2H_2Cl_3NO$ (152) Trichloroacetamide

0.6	26.7
0.8	26.6
1.0	26.6

$C_2H_3Cl_2NO$ (152) Dichloroacetamide

0.2	24.0
0.3	23.6
0.5	22.6

$C_2H_3ClO_2$ (206) Chloroacetic acid

0.1	30.2
0.2	30.5
0.4	30.9
0.6	31.3

$C_2H_3Cl_3O_2$ (65) Chloral hydrate

0.1	29.2
0.2	29.2
0.4	29.3
0.6	29.4

$C_2H_4Cl_3NO$ (5) Chloral ammonia

0.05	24.0
0.1	23.0
0.15	21.4
0.2	18.3

$C_3H_4Br_2O_2$* (206) 1, 2-Dibromopropionic acid

0.1	33.7
0.2	33.7
0.3	33.7

$C_3H_4Cl_3NO_2$ (152) Trichlorolactamide

N	$\Delta t_B / x_1$
0.4	19.8
0.5	19.2
0.7	17.8
0.9	16.5

$C_3H_4O_4$ (18) Malonic acid

0.2	27.4

C_3H_7NO (153) Propionamide

0.16	28.0
0.18	23.8

$C_3H_7NO_2$ (153) Urethane

0.35	26.8
0.4	26.2
0.45	25.5

$C_4H_7Cl_3O_2$ (65) Chloral alcoholate

0.1	28
0.2	28
0.4	28.7

$C_6H_4Br_2$‡ (65) Dibromobenzene

0.1	30.3
0.3	29.9
0.5	29.5
0.7	29.1

C_6H_6O (16) Phenol

0.5	28.6

$C_6H_6O_2$ (18) Catechol

0.2	29.9

$C_6H_6O_2$ (16) Hydroquinol

0.17	28.1

$C_6H_6O_2$ (21, 23) Resorcinol

0.1	28.7
0.3	28.0
0.5	27.3
0.6	26.3

$C_6H_6O_3$ (16, 18) Pyrogallol

0.15	28.0

C_6H_7N (16) Aniline

0.2	28.6
0.25	28.7

$C_6H_{13}NO$ (153) Isobutylacetamide

0.15	22.7

$C_7H_6O_2$ Benzoic acid (16, 18, 139, 231)

0.1	29.3
0.3	28.8
0.5	28.4
1.0	27.2
1.8	26.5

$C_7H_6O_3$ (17, 18, 139) Salicylic acid

N	$\Delta t_B / x_1$
0.1	29.5
0.2	30.0
0.3	30.4

C_7H_7NO (153) Formanilide

0.25	26.9
0.3	25.4

$C_7H_7NO_2$ (152) Salicylamide

0.15	27.3
0.2	27.4
0.25	27.5

C_7H_9N (231) *p*-Toluidine

0.7	32.4
1.0	32.1
1.5	31.5
1.8	31.2

$C_7H_{11}Cl_3O_2$ (255) Amyl trichloroacetate

0.1	34.1
0.4	30.0

C_8H_9NO (152) Acetanilide

0.15	23.1
0.2	23.1

C_8H_9NO (16) Acetophenone oxime

0.16	28.2

$C_8H_9NO_2$ (153) Glycolanilide

0.12	28

$C_8H_{10}O$ (16) Phenetole

0.4	29.3

$C_8H_{14}O_4$ (19) Tetramethylsuccinic acid

0.05	31.3
0.1	31.8

$C_8H_{14}O_4$ (19) Trimethylglutaric acid

0.08	28.7

C_9H_7N (139) Quinoline

0.2	30.1
0.3	29.8
0.5	29.2
0.7	28.6

$C_9H_{10}O_2$ (16, 139) Ethyl benzoate

0.3	29.1
0.4	29.1

$C_9H_{11}NO$ (153) Methylacetanilide

0.3	29.0
0.4	28.8

$C_9H_{11}NO_2$ (153) Lactanilide

0.35	24.5
0.4	23.5
0.45	22.5

$C_9H_{11}NO_2$ (153) Phenylurethane

N	$\Delta t_B / x_1$
0.4	28.9
0.5	29.4
0.6	29.8

$C_9H_{12}ClNO_2$ (228) *p*-Toluidine chloroacetate

0.07	56.1
0.1	52.3
0.12	49.8

$C_{10}H_8$ (18, 31, 112) Naphthalene

0.1	29.0
0.3	29.5
0.5	29.8
1.0	29
2.0	27

$C_{10}H_{13}NO$ (153) Ethylacetanilide

0.5	28.8
0.6	28.9

$C_{10}H_{14}O$ (18, 139) Thymol

0.1	29.6
0.2	30.4
0.3	31.2

$C_{10}H_{16}O$ (103) Camphor

0.1	28.6
0.2	28.7
0.3	28.8
0.4	28.9

$C_{11}H_{16}O_3$ (64) Camphocarboxylic acid

0.2	23.0
0.5	23.0
0.8	23.0
1.0	21.8

$C_{12}H_{10}N_2$ (139, 180) Azobenzene

0.25	28.2
0.3	29.0

$C_{12}H_{11}N$ (139, 231) Diphenylamine

0.1	30.9
0.3	30.8
0.5	30.7
1.0	30.4
1.3	30.3

$C_{13}H_{10}O$§ (16) α-Benzophenone

0.15	27.6

$C_{14}H_{10}O_2$ (18, 22, 31, 139) Benzil

0.1	29.5
0.3	29.1
0.5	28.7

$C_{16}H_{26}O_3$ (64) Amyl camphocarboxylate

0.32	28.6

$C_{20}H_{30}O_2$ (6, 216) Pinabietic acid

N	$\Delta t_B / x_1$
0.1	29.4
0.2	28.0

$C_{21}H_{36}N_4O_7$ (228) Triamylammonium picrate

0.06	24.2
0.1	17.0

$SnC_4H_{10}I_2$ (238) Diethyl iodide

0.05	26.0
0.1	27.0
0.2	27.2

SnC_6H_{15} (258) Triethyl

0.05	20
0.1	17

$ZnCl_2$ (143)

0.3	16.4
0.5	12.9
1.0	8.4

$HgCl_2$ (143, 263)

0.07	28.6
0.2	22

$FeCl_3$ (24, 143)

0.2	29.2
0.3	29.0
0.5	28.5
0.8	27.9

$MoO(OH)_2Cl_2$ (215)

0.05	29.4
0.1	28.5
0.2	26.9

$UO_2(NO_3)_2.6H_2O$ (143)

* Stable, high melting form.

‡ The isomer used is not given.

§ β-form gives same result.

$C_4H_{10}O$

Isobutyl alcohol

$C_{10}H_{20}O$ (34) Menthol

$T_B = 380.4$

$k_B = 28.3$

0.1	28.1
0.2	28.0
0.5	27.8
0.8	27.5

$C_{14}H_8O_4$ (34) Alizarin

0.047	28.8

$C_{14}H_{10}O_2$ (34) Benzil

0.1	27.8
0.2	27.3
0.3	26.9
0.4	26.5
0.5	26.0

LiCl (211)

0.5	26.9
1.0	29.7
1.3	30.2
1.6	29.0

$C_4H_{10}O$.—(*Cont'd*)

LiBr (211)

N	$\Delta t_B / x_1$
0.1	27
0.4	25.4
0.5	25.7
0.7	26.3

LiI (211)

N	$\Delta t_B / x_1$
0.1	26.5
0.2	25.0
0.3	24.9
0.5	25.7

$LiNO_3$ (211)

N	$\Delta t_B / x_1$
0.1	24.1
0.2	23.7
0.3	23.4
0.5	22.6

$C_4H_{10}O$

tert.-Butyl alcohol

$T_B = 355.9$

$k_B = 18$*

CH_4N_2S (8) Thiourea

N	$\Delta t_B / x_1$
0.1	17.8
0.15	18.7

$C_6H_4Br_2$ (8) *p*-Dibromobenzene

N	$\Delta t_B / x_1$
0.1	19.5
0.2	20.7
0.3	21.9
0.5	24.2

* *See* ternary and four- and five-component systems.

$C_4H_{10}S$

Ethyl sulfide

$T_B = 364.7$

$k_B = 35.8$

$C_{12}H_{11}N$ (238) Diphenylamine

N	$\Delta t_B / x_1$
0.05	36.1
0.1	36.4
0.2	37.0

$SnCl_2$ (238)

N	$\Delta t_B / x_1$
0.1	38.9
0.2	39.3

$SnBr_2$ (238)

N	$\Delta t_B / x_1$
0.05	35.5
0.1	41.0
0.15	43.0

CdI_2 (238)

N	$\Delta t_B / x_1$
0.05	35.5
0.1	35.7
0.2	36.0

$HgCl_2$ (238)

N	$\Delta t_B / x_1$
0.1	35.6
0.2	35.2
0.3	34.7

HgI_2 (238)

N	$\Delta t_B / x_1$
0.05	35.4
0.1	36.1
0.15	36.8

$HgCH_3Cl$ (238)

N	$\Delta t_B / x_1$
0.1	35.8
0.2	36.1
0.25	36.3

$HgCH_3I$ (238)

N	$\Delta t_B / x_1$
0.1	36.1
0.2	36.5
0.3	36.9

CuCl (238)

N	$\Delta t_B / x_1$
0.05	29.3
0.1	28.3
0.2	26.3
0.4	22.4

CuBr (238)

N	$\Delta t_B / x_1$
0.1	23.4
0.2	23.5
0.3	23.6
0.4	23.7

C_5H_5N

Pyridine

$T_B = 388.4$

$k_B = 36$‡

$C_4H_6O_4$ (106) Succinic acid

N	$\Delta t_B / x_1$
0.1	34.7
0.2	35.8
0.4	38.2
0.7	41.6

$C_4H_6O_6$ (105) Tartaric acid

N	$\Delta t_B / x_1$
0.1	34.8
0.4	35.3
0.8	35.9

$C_4H_{12}ClN$ (214) Diethylammonium chloride

N	$\Delta t_B / x_1$
0.1	34.6
0.3	35.1
0.5	35.6
0.6	35.9

$C_6H_3N_3O_7$ (245) Picric acid

N	$\Delta t_B / x_1$
0.15	47.2
0.2	47.3
0.25	47.9
0.3	49.4

$C_6H_6O_2$ (105) Resorcinol

N	$\Delta t_B / x_1$
0.05	36
0.2	37.6
0.4	39.9

$C_6H_{16}ClN$ (214) Triethylammonium chloride

N	$\Delta t_B / x_1$
0.1	34.6
0.2	34.9
0.26	35.0

$C_7H_6O_3$ (105, 191) Salicylic acid

N	$\Delta t_B / x_1$
0.05	37.0
0.1	37.2
0.3	38.0
0.5	38.9
0.9	40.5

C_7H_9N (184) *p*-Toluidine

N	$\Delta t_B / x_1$
0.1	38.9
0.2	39.1
0.5	39.9
0.8	41.0
1.0	41.8

$C_8H_{20}IN$ (230) Tetraethylammonium iodide

N	$\Delta t_B / x_1$
0.025	28.2
0.05	25.8

$C_{10}H_8O$ (105) β-Naphthol

N	$\Delta t_B / x_1$
0.1	36.6
0.2	36.9
0.35	37.5
0.5	38.3
0.7	39.5

$C_{12}H_5N_7O_{12}$ (245) Hexanitrodiphenylamine

N	$\Delta t_B / x_1$
0.05	49.5
0.1	58.2
0.15	63.4

$C_{12}H_{10}$ (184) Diphenyl

N	$\Delta t_B / x_1$
0.2	42
0.3	42.3
0.4	42.5
0.6	42.8
0.8	43.1

$C_{12}H_{11}N$ (230) Diphenylamine

N	$\Delta t_B / x_1$
0.1	37
0.3	37
0.6	37

$C_{13}H_{10}O$ (105) Benzophenone

N	$\Delta t_B / x_1$
0.1	39.9
0.2	39.5
0.3	39.1
0.5	38.6

$C_{14}H_{10}$ (169) Anthracene

N	$\Delta t_B / x_1$
0.01	36
0.02	35.6
0.04	34.4

$C_{14}H_{10}$ (230) Phenanthrene

N	$\Delta t_B / x_1$
0.1	33.7
0.2	34.0
0.3	34.3
0.4	34.6
0.5	35.0

$C_{14}H_{10}O_2$ (191) Benzil

N	$\Delta t_B / x_1$
0.1	33.0
0.2	33.8
0.3	34.3
0.4	34.6
0.5	35.0
0.6	35.2

$C_{18}H_{20}N_2O_4$ (105) Tartaric ditoluide

N	$\Delta t_B / x_1$
0.05	36
0.1	36

$C_{19}H_{16}$ (184) Triphenylmethane

N	$\Delta t_B / x_1$
0.05	39
0.1	39.3
0.2	39.5
0.3	39.8
0.5	40.5

$C_{19}H_{18}O_{11}$ (191) Euxanthic acid

$C_{20}H_{16}IN$ (95) *N*-Methylphenylacridinium iodide

N	$\Delta t_B / x_1$
0.04	36.3
0.08	37.8

$C_{23}H_{24}O_6$ (191) Mangostin

N	$\Delta t_B / x_1$
0.05	32.5
0.1	31.8
0.15	31.3

$SnCl_2$ (238)

N	$\Delta t_B / x_1$
0.05	39
0.1	38
0.2	37

$SnBr_2$ (238)

N	$\Delta t_B / x_1$
0.02	40.2
0.05	40.1
0.08	40.0
0.1	39.8
0.15	38.6

$Pb(NO_3)_2$ (238)

N	$\Delta t_B / x_1$
0.04	36.4
0.08	36
0.12	35

$ZnCl_2$ (238)

N	$\Delta t_B / x_1$
0.05	42.1
0.1	41.0
0.15	39.9
0.2	39.0

$ZnBr_2$ (238)

N	$\Delta t_B / x_1$
0.05	47.0
0.1	47.0
0.15	47.0

CdI_2 (238)

N	$\Delta t_B / x_1$
0.02	35.9
0.05	39.2
0.08	42.5

$HgCl_2$ (194, 230)

N	$\Delta t_B / x_1$
0.05	34.2
0.1	34.6
0.2	35.5
0.5	38.2
0.7	40.0
0.9	41.8

$HgBr_2$ (230)

N	$\Delta t_B / x_1$
0.05	33.2
0.1	33.5
0.2	34.2
0.3	35.0
0.4	35.9
0.5	36.9
0.6	37.9

HgI_2 (230)

N	$\Delta t_B / x_1$
0.1	35.0
0.2	35.7
0.3	36.3
0.4	36.9
0.5	37.6

$Hg(CN)_2$ (230)

N	$\Delta t_B / x_1$
0.05	34.2
0.1	34.8
0.2	36.2
0.4	38.5
0.5	39.6
0.7	41.5

HgC_2H_5Cl (230)

N	$\Delta t_B / x_1$
0.1	34
0.2	34.3
0.4	35.1
0.6	36.0

CuCl (238)

N	$\Delta t_B / x_1$
0.05	31.5
0.1	31.6
0.2	31.7
0.3	30.8

$CuCl_2$* (238)

N	$\Delta t_B / x_1$
0.1	37.9
0.2	37.6
0.3	37.3

CuBr (238)

N	$\Delta t_B / x_1$
0.04	36.8
0.08	36.9
0.15	37.1
0.2	37.2

CuCN (238)

N	$\Delta t_B / x_1$
0.01	19.5
0.03	19.3
0.05	19.1
0.1	18.8
0.15	18.5

$AgNO_3$ (194)

N	$\Delta t_B / x_1$
0.1	30.6
0.25	28.0
0.4	26.9
0.5	26.9
0.7	27.3
0.9	28.3
1.0	29.6

AgCN (194)

N	$\Delta t_B / x_1$
0.05	22.4
0.12	23

AgCNS (194)

N	$\Delta t_B / x_1$
0.02	36.3
0.05	34.9
0.1	32.8

$FeCl_2$* (238)

N	$\Delta t_B / x_1$
0.02	43.0
0.05	45

$FeCl_3$ (77, 238)

N	$\Delta t_B / x_1$
0.05	42.3
0.1	42.0
0.3	40.8
0.5	39.6
0.7	38.4
0.9	37.3

$CoCl_2$ (238)

N	$\Delta t_B / x_1$
0.03	38.4
0.05	39.0
0.08	39.9
0.1	40.4

$CoBr_2$ (238)

N	$\Delta t_B / x_1$
0.02	40.2
0.05	39.7
0.08	39.3
0.1	39.1
0.15	38.7

$AlCl_3$ (238)

N	$\Delta t_B / x_1$
0.05	40.0
0.08	40.1
0.1	40.2
0.2	40.9

$BeCl_2$ (184)

N	$\Delta t_B / x_1$
0.1	37.7
0.2	39.2
0.3	41.0
0.4	43.4

* Schroeder (194) failed to get any rise in boiling point.

‡ Samples of pyridine, unless very carefully purified, show unusually marked anomalies in boiling pt. It is recommended that the constant be determined for the particular sample employed, *cf.* (191). Suitable solutes are anthracene, diphenyl, phenanthrene and triphenylmethane.

C_5H_{10}

Cyclopentane

$T_B = 322.6$

$k_B = 29.5$

$C_{10}H_{10}O$ (81) Benzylideneacetone

N	$\Delta t_B / x_1$
0.3	27.7
0.5	25.4
1.0	21.7

$C_{10}H_{14}O_2$ (81) Resorcinol diethyl ether

N	$\Delta t_B / x_1$
0.5	30.8
1.0	32.0
1.5	33.1

$C_{12}H_{10}$ (81) Diphenyl

N	$\Delta t_B / x_1$
0.3	30.8
0.5	31.5
0.7	32.1
0.9	32.8

C_5H_{10}

β-Amylene

$T_B = 309.5$

$k_B = 27.6$

$C_2HCl_3O_2$ (255) Trichloroacetic acid

N	$\Delta t_B/x_1$
0.1	24.2
0.2	20.4
0.3	18.1
0.45	16.8

$C_2H_2Cl_2O_2$ (255) Dichloroacetic acid

N	$\Delta t_B/x_1$
0.1	8.2
0.2	7.9
0.5	7.3

$C_7H_6O_2$ (255) Benzoic acid

N	$\Delta t_B/x_1$
0.25	13.1
0.3	13.5
0.4	14.2

$C_7H_{11}Cl_3O_2$ (255) Amyl trichloroacetate

N	$\Delta t_B/x_1$
0.05	26.5
0.1	27.6
0.2	28.5
0.6	29.5
0.9	29.5

$C_{10}H_8$ (255) Naphthalene

N	$\Delta t_B/x_1$
0.1	27.8
0.2	28.0
0.3	28.2

$C_5H_{10}O$

Diethyl ketone

$T_B = 374.8$

$k_B = 32$

$C_7H_6O_2$ (268) Benzoic acid

N	$\Delta t_B/x_1$
0.64	31.4

$C_{10}H_8$ (268) Naphthalene

N	$\Delta t_B/x_1$
0.56	32.4

$C_{28}H_{56}O_4$ (268) Polyheptaldehyde

N	$\Delta t_B/x_1$
0.15	67.2
0.3	64.6
0.5	60

$C_5H_{10}O$

Methyl propyl ketone

$T_B = 374.8$

$k_B = 38$

$C_7H_6O_2$ (34) Benzoic acid

N	$\Delta t_B/x_1$
0.1	41.1
0.2	40.3
0.3	39.5
0.4	38.7
0.5	37.9
0.6	37.1

$C_{14}H_{10}O_2$ (34) Benzil

N	$\Delta t_B/x_1$
0.1	37
0.2	37.1
0.3	36.8

$C_5H_{11}N$

Piperidine

$T_B = 378.9$

$k_B = 33.0$

$C_{12}H_{11}N$ (238) Diphenylamine

N	$\Delta t_B/x_1$
0.1	32.8
0.2	33.5
0.4	34.6
0.6	35.5
0.75	35.9

$C_{14}H_{10}$ (238) Anthracene

N	$\Delta t_B/x_1$
0.1	33.8
0.2	34.4
0.3	35.0

$ZnCl_2$ (238)

N	$\Delta t_B/x_1$
0.05	35
0.07	33.8
0.1	31.8
0.2	27.0

$CdBr_2$ (238)

N	$\Delta t_B/x_1$
0.05	33.0
0.1	32.3
0.15	31.7
0.25	30.1
0.35	28.4

CdI_2 (238)

N	$\Delta t_B/x_1$
0.05	36.4
0.1	35.4
0.2	33.6
0.3	32.2
0.35	31.6

$AgCl$ (238)

N	$\Delta t_B/x_1$
0.05	14.7
0.1	14.5
0.17	13.5

$AgBr$ (238)

N	$\Delta t_B/x_1$
0.05	14.4
0.1	14.5
0.2	14.7

AgI (238)

N	$\Delta t_B/x_1$
0.03	17.0
0.09	16.5

$AgNO_3$ (238)

N	$\Delta t_B/x_1$
0.05	33
0.1	27
0.15	22
0.2	20
0.3	16
0.35	15

$CoCl_2$ (238)

N	$\Delta t_B/x_1$
0.04	30.0

$C_5H_{12}O$

Isoamyl alcohol

$T_B = 403.6$

$k_B = 30.5$

$C_4H_{12}ClN$ (214) Diethylammonium chloride

$C_4H_{12}ClN$ (214) Isobutylammonium chloride

$C_6H_6O_3$ (211) Pyrogallol

$C_6H_{16}BrN$ (214) Triethylammonium bromide

$C_6H_{16}ClN$ (214) Triethylammonium chloride

$C_6H_{16}IN$ (214) Triethylammonium iodide

$C_7H_5NO_4$ (208) *o*-Nitrobenzoic acid

N	$\Delta t_B/x_1$
0.1	28.8
0.2	28.8
0.5	28.9

$C_7H_6O_3$ (3, 208) Salicylic acid

N	$\Delta t_B/x_1$
0.1	29.9
0.2	31.0
0.4	33.0
0.6	35.1

$C_7H_{16}O_4S_2$ (208) Sulfonal

N	$\Delta t_B/x_1$
0.1	28.6
0.2	28.5
0.3	28.4

$C_8H_{12}ClN$ (214) Ethylphenylammonium chloride

N	$\Delta t_B/x_1$
0.2	15.0
0.3	18.0
0.4	18.4
0.5	18.5
0.7	18.6

$C_8H_{20}BrN$ (214) Tetraethylammonium bromide

N	$\Delta t_B/x_1$
0.2	20.2
0.3	20.2
0.5	20.2

$C_8H_{20}ClN$ (214) Tetraethylammonium chloride

N	$\Delta t_B/x_1$
0.4	22.6
0.6	25.1
0.8	28.3
1.0	31.4

$C_8H_{20}IN$ (214) Tetraethylammonium iodide

N	$\Delta t_B/x_1$
0.1	22.0
0.2	17.6

$C_9H_8O_2$ (208) Cinnamic acid

N	$\Delta t_B/x_1$
0.1	30.9
0.2	30.3
0.3	29.8
0.4	29.3

$C_{11}H_{12}IN$ (214) *N*-Quinoline ethiodide

$C_{12}H_{11}N$ (208) Diphenylamine

N	$\Delta t_B/x_1$
0.2	28.5
0.3	28.8
0.4	29.0
0.6	29.5

$C_{12}H_{28}IN$ (214) Tetrapropylammonium iodide

$C_{12}H_{28}N_2O_3$ (214) Tetrapropylammonium nitrate

$C_{14}H_{10}O_2$ (34) Benzil

N	$\Delta t_B/x_1$
0.1	30.8
0.2	30.4
0.3	29.6

$C_{14}H_{10}O_9$ (208) Tannin

N	$\Delta t_B/x_1$
0.02	27.2
0.05	27.4
0.1	27.8

$C_{20}H_{24}N_2O_2$ (208) Quinine

N	$\Delta t_B/x_1$
0.1	28.3
0.15	27.8

$(C_{20}H_{24}N_2O_2)_2$-H_2SO_4 (208) Quinine sulfate

N	$\Delta t_B/x_1$
0.01	34.2
0.02	34.9
0.05	36.8
0.07	38.1

$LiCl$ (211)

N	$\Delta t_B/x_1$
0.1	30.5
0.5	30.9
1.3	31.7

$LiBr$ (211)

N	$\Delta t_B/x_1$
0.2	28.8
0.3	28.1
0.5	28.9
0.7	31.1

LiI (211)

N	$\Delta t_B/x_1$
0.1	26.0
0.5	27.3
0.9	28.6

$LiNO_3$ (211)

N	$\Delta t_B/x_1$
0.1	26.7
0.2	26.0
0.5	23.7

$NaC_5H_{11}O$ (208) Isoamylate

N	$\Delta t_B/x_1$
0.2	31
0.4	33
0.6	35

$KC_2H_3O_2$ (208) Acetate

N	$\Delta t_B/x_1$
0.2	31.0
0.3	31.3
0.5	31.7

$C_5H_{12}O$

tert.-Amyl alcohol

$T_B = 374.9$

$k_B = 25.6$

$C_4H_{12}ClN$ (214) Diethylammonium chloride

N	$\Delta t_B/x_1$
0.15	24.8
0.25	22.5
0.35	21.1

$C_{14}H_{10}O_2$ (34) Benzil

N	$\Delta t_B/x_1$
0.15	25.7
0.2	25.9
0.25	26.4

C_6H_5Cl

Chlorobenzene

$T_B = 405.2$

$k_B = 42$

$C_{12}H_{10}NO$ (237) 1-Benzoylpyridinium

N	$\Delta t_B/x_1$
0.023	42.7

$C_{14}H_{10}O_2$ (237) Benzil

N	$\Delta t_B/x_1$
0.027	41.7

$C_6H_5NO_2$

Nitrobenzene

$T_B = 484.0$

$k_B = 42.6$

S_8 (55)

N	$\Delta t_B/x_1$
0.1	42.4
0.2	42.0

As_4O_6 (55)

N	$\Delta t_B/x_1$
0.03	36
0.05	37

$C_6H_6N_2O_2$ (55) *m*-Nitroaniline

N	$\Delta t_B/x_1$
0.1	44.6
0.2	44.5
0.3	44.4

$C_8H_4O_3$ (55) Phthalic anhydride

N	$\Delta t_B/x_1$
0.1	41.4
0.2	41.6
0.5	42.3

C_8H_9NO (55) Acetanilide

N	$\Delta t_B/x_1$
0.1	40.2
0.2	40.2
0.35	40.1

$C_{10}H_{10}O_4$ (55) Dimethyl terephthalate

N	$\Delta t_B/x_1$
0.2	36
0.3	37

$C_{12}H_9N$ (9) Carbazole

N	$\Delta t_B/x_1$
0.1	42.2
0.2	42.2
0.35	42.3
0.5	42.4

$C_{12}H_{11}N$ (55) Diphenylamine

N	$\Delta t_B/x_1$
0.1	41.4

$C_{12}H_{12}N_2$ (9) Benzidine

N	$\Delta t_B/x_1$
0.1	39.6
0.2	40.3
0.35	41.6

$C_{13}H_{10}O_3$ (55) Phenyl salicylate

N	$\Delta t_B/x_1$
0.1	36.6
0.2	36.4

$C_{14}H_8O_2$ (9) Anthraquinone

N	$\Delta t_B/x_1$
0.05	42
0.1	42
0.2	41

$C_{14}H_8O_2$ (55) Phenanthraquinone

N	$\Delta t_B/x_1$
0.1	42.4
0.2	42.3

$C_{14}H_8O_4$ (9, 55) Alizarin

N	$\Delta t_B/x_1$
0.05	39.7
0.1	40.2

$C_{14}H_{10}$ (9) Anthracene

N	$\Delta t_B/x_1$
0.1	40
0.2	40
0.35	40

$C_{14}H_{10}O_2$ (26, 31, 39) Benzil

N	$\Delta t_B/x_1$
0.1	43.3
0.2	43.3
0.35	43.4

$C_{14}H_{10}O_3$ (9) Benzoic anhydride

N	$\Delta t_B/x_1$
0.1	42.3
0.2	42.3
0.35	42.3

$C_{14}H_{12}O_2$ (55) Benzoin

N	$\Delta t_B/x_1$
0.1	38.1
0.2	38.0
0.35	37.7

$C_{19}H_{16}$ (39) Triphenylmethane

N	$\Delta t_B/x_1$
0.04	49.7
0.06	46.4
0.08	45.0
0.1	44.2

$C_{26}H_{22}$ (55) Tetraphenylethane

N	$\Delta t_B/x_1$
0.05	41

$C_{36}H_{18}$ (79) Decacyclene

$C_{48}H_{28}$ (80) Fluorocyclene

C_6H_6

Benzene

$T_B = 353.35$

$k_B = 33.6$

I_2 (30, 136, 217)

N	$\Delta t_B/x_1$
0.05	34
0.1	34
0.2	34
0.3	34
0.5	36
1.0	37
2.0	36
5.07	27†

C_6H_6.—(Cont'd)

S_8 (4, 170)

N	$\Delta t_B / x_1$
0.05	33.6
0.1	32.8
0.3	30.0
0.5	28.2
0.7	27.8
1.0	27.3
1.2	26.9

S_2Cl_2 (164)

N	$\Delta t_B / x_1$
0.1	31.3
0.2	32.5

N_4S_4 (2)

N	$\Delta t_B / x_1$
0.05	34.2
0.1	33.9
0.2	33.3
0.3	32.7

PCl_3 (166)

N	$\Delta t_B / x_1$
0.21	36

$P_4N_4Cl_8$ (103)

N	$\Delta t_B / x_1$
0.06	34.1
0.08	34.3

$POCl_3$ (164, 166, 167)

N	$\Delta t_B / x_1$
0.1	32
0.2	32
0.4	33
0.7	33
1.0	33
1.2	34

$POBr_3$ (164)

N	$\Delta t_B / x_1$
0.05	33.3
0.1	33.1
0.2	32.2
0 3	31.8

$PSCl_3$ (164, 167)

N	$\Delta t_B / x_1$
0.1	25.4
0.2	26.5
0.3	27.6

$P_2O_3Cl_4$ (163)

N	$\Delta t_B / x_1$
0.05	33.1
0.1	32.4

As_2I_4 (259)

N	$\Delta t_B / x_1$
0.03	32.3
0.04	32.2

$C_2H_2Br_4$ (223)
1, 1, 2, 2-Tetrabromoethane

N	$\Delta t_B / x_1$
0.05	33.8
0.1	33.8
0.2	33.8
0.4	33.7

$C_2H_2Cl_3NO$ (152)
Trichloroacetamide

N	$\Delta t_B / x_1$
0.5	26.3
0.6	25.9
0.75	25.4

$C_2H_3ClO_2$* (206)
Chloroacetic acid

N	$\Delta t_B / x_1$
0.1	20.4
0.2	19.9
0.3	19.5
0.4	19.1
0.6	18.2

$C_2H_4Br_2$ (84)
1, 2-Dibromoethane

N	$\Delta t_B / x_1$
0.1	30.6
0.15	30.4

C_2H_4ClNO (152)
Chloroacetamide

N	$\Delta t_B / x_1$
0.1	23.5
0.15	24.3
0.2	25.0

C_2H_5I (166)

N	$\Delta t_B / x_1$
0.17	33

$C_3H_4Br_2O_2$* (206)
1, 2-Dibromopropionic acid

N	$\Delta t_B / x_1$
0.05	32
0.1	30.5
0.15	29.0
0.23	26.2

$C_3H_4Cl_3NO_2$ (152)
Trichlorolactamide

N	$\Delta t_B / x_1$
0.2	25.4
0.25	24.1
0.3	23.0

C_3H_5ClO (166)
Epichlorohydrin

N	$\Delta t_B / x_1$
0.18	30.3
0.23	31.5

C_3H_7I (166)
Isopropyl iodide

N	$\Delta t_B / x_1$
0.19	32.3

C_3H_7NO (153)
Propionamide

N	$\Delta t_B / x_1$
0.2	22.8
0.3	21.5
0.4	20.2
0.5	18.8
0.7	16.2

$C_3H_7NO_2$ (153)
Urethane

N	$\Delta t_B / x_1$
0.4	23.7
0.5	23.3
0.7	22.6

C_4H_9NO (153)
n-Butyramide

N	$\Delta t_B / x_1$
0.3	21.8
0.4	20.3
0.5	19.2
0.6	18.3

C_4H_9NO (153)
Isobutyramide

N	$\Delta t_B / x_1$
0.25	24.0
0.3	23.2
0.35	22.4
0.4	21.7
0.5	20.1
0.6	18.6

$C_5H_{11}NO$ (153)
Valeramide

N	$\Delta t_B / x_1$
0.3	23.8
0.5	21.3
0.7	18.8

$C_6HBr_5O_2$ (51, 155)
Pentabromoresorcinol

N	$\Delta t_B / x_1$
0.04	33
0.07	34
0.1	34
0.12	35

$C_6H_3N_3O_7$ (137)
Picric acid

N	$\Delta t_B / x_1$
0.05	32
0.1	31.5
0.2	31.2
0.3	31.0
0.4	30.7
0.5	30.4

$C_6H_5Cl_2O_2P$ (163)
Dichlorophosphoxyphenolate

N	$\Delta t_B / x_1$
0.09	34.9
0.18	36.2

$C_6H_5NO_3$ (175)
p-Nitrophenol

N	$\Delta t_B / x_1$
0.2	31.5
0.3	29.2
0.4	27.0
0.5	25.2

$C_6H_6Cl_2NOP$ (163)
Dichlorophosphoxymonoanilide

N	$\Delta t_B / x_1$
0.04	33.5
0.1	31.2
0.15	29.5
0.25	26.5

$C_6H_6N_2O_2$ (175)
m-Nitroaniline

N	$\Delta t_B / x_1$
0.2	32.2
0.3	31.2
0.4	30.3
0.5	29.5

C_6H_6O (12)
Phenol

N	$\Delta t_B / x_1$
0.1	30.9
0.2	30.8
0.3	30.7
0.5	30.4

$C_6H_6O_2$ (175)
Catechol

N	$\Delta t_B / x_1$
0.25	31.8
0.3	31.3
0.4	30.3
0.5	29.3
0.6	28.2

$C_6H_6O_2$ (175)
Resorcinol

N	$\Delta t_B / x_1$
0.1	34
0.15	32.8
0.2	31.7
0.25	30.3
0.35	27.3

C_6H_7N (146)
Aniline

N	$\Delta t_B / x_1$
0.3	34.5
0.4	33.1
0.5	31.8
0.6	30.4
0.7	29.0

$C_6H_{10}O_5$ (221)
Dimethyl malate

N	$\Delta t_B / x_1$
0.1	30.4
0.2	27.7
0.3	27.2
0.4	26.7
0.5	26.4
0.6	26.1
0.8	25.7

$C_6H_{10}O_6$ (106, 221)
Dimethyl tartrate

N	$\Delta t_B / x_1$
0.1	29.5
0.2	27.3
0.3	25.5
0.4	24.0
0.6	21.7
1.0	18.3
1.4	16.0

$C_6H_{13}NO$ (153)
Isobutylacetamide

N	$\Delta t_B / x_1$
0.2	27.0
0.3	25.3
0.4	23.5
0.55	20.9

$C_7H_5BrO_2$ (106)
o-Bromobenzoic acid

N	$\Delta t_B / x_1$
0.1	21
0.2	20
0.4	19
0.6	18.6
0.8	18.4
1.0	18.3
1.2	18.2
1.6	18.1

$C_7H_6O_2$ (106)
Benzoic acid

N	$\Delta t_B / x_1$
0.1	21.1
0.3	19.8
0.5	19.0
0.8	18.8
1.0	18.8
1.5	18.7
2.0	18.6

$C_7H_6O_3$ (18)
Salicylic acid

N	$\Delta t_B / x_1$
0.1	24.9
0.2	23.5
0.4	20.8
0.46	20.0

C_7H_7NO (152)
Benzamide

N	$\Delta t_B / x_1$
0.15	26.0
0.2	25.2
0.3	23.5

C_7H_7NO (153)
Formanilide

N	$\Delta t_B / x_1$
0.25	29.2
0.35	27.1
0.5	25.4

$C_7H_7NO_2$ (152)
Salicylamide

$C_7H_7NO_2$.—(Cont'd)

N	$\Delta t_B / x_1$
0.1	29.7
0.15	28.9
0.2	27.9
0.25	26.8
0.3	25.5

$C_7H_{16}O_4S_2$ (187)
Sulfonal

N	$\Delta t_B / x_1$
0.18	33.4

C_8H_8O (81)
Acetophenone

N	$\Delta t_B / x_1$
0.3	32.4
0.4	33.1
0.5	33.5
0.6	33.8
0.7	34.1
0.75	34.2

$C_8H_8O_2$ (175)
Phenylacetic acid

N	$\Delta t_B / x_1$
0.2	22
0.3	21.5
0.5	21.1
0.65	20.6

$C_8H_8O_3$ (176)
d-Mandelic acid

N	$\Delta t_B / x_1$
0.07	21
0.1	21.6
0.12	22.0
0.15	22.6

$C_8H_8O_3$ (176)
l-Mandelic acid

N	$\Delta t_B / x_1$
0.04	20.1
0.045	20.6
0.05	21.2
0.06	22.5

$C_8H_8O_3$ (176)
dl-Mandelic acid

N	$\Delta t_B / x_1$
0.04	21.6
0.07	21.5

C_8H_9NO (18)
Acetanilide

N	$\Delta t_B / x_1$
0.1	29.0
0.2	26.3
0.3	23.7
0.4	21.4
0.5	19.5
0.6	18.0
0.7	16.7

C_8H_9NO (18)
Acetophenone oxime

N	$\Delta t_B / x_1$
0.1	29.4
0.2	27.2
0.3	25.6
0.4	24.6
0.5	23.8
0.6	23.3

$C_8H_9NO_2$ (153)
Glycolanilide

N	$\Delta t_B / x_1$
0.15	27.8
0.2	25.6
0.25	23.7
0.35	20.5

$C_8H_{11}N$ (166)
Dimethylaniline

N	$\Delta t_B / x_1$
0.14	33.5
0.2	34.1

$C_8H_{12}O_6$ (221)
Dimethyl acetylmalate

N	$\Delta t_B / x_1$
0.1	34.3
0.2	32.8
0.3	32.6
0.4	32.6
0.5	32.6

$C_8H_{14}O_5$ (221)
Diethyl malate

N	$\Delta t_B / x_1$
0.3	28.5
0.4	28.1
0.6	27.8
0.7	27.8
0.8	27.8

$C_8H_{14}O_6$ (221)
Diethyl tartrate

N	$\Delta t_B / x_1$
0.2	26.7
0.4	25.2
0.5	24.5
0.7	23.0

$C_9H_{10}O_2$ (18)
Ethyl benzoate

N	$\Delta t_B / x_1$
0.1	31.5
0.2	31.6
0.3	31.7
0.5	31.9
0.8	32.1
1.2	32.4

$C_9H_{11}NO$ (153)
Methylacetanilide

N	$\Delta t_B / x_1$
0.3	33.4
0.4	33.5
0.5	33.6
0.6	33.7

$C_9H_{11}NO_2$ (153)
Lactanilide

N	$\Delta t_B / x_1$
0.15	28.0
0.2	26.5
0.3	23.6
0.4	21.1

$C_9H_{11}NO_2$ (153)
Phenylurethane

N	$\Delta t_B / x_1$
0.3	32.8
0.4	33.1
0.5	33.3
0.6	33.4

$C_9H_{12}ClNO_2$ (223, 228)
p-Toluidine chloroacetate

N	$\Delta t_B / x_1$
0.02	62.3
0.05	55.5
0.08	51.7
0.1	49.6
0.2	40.8
0.3	35.0
0.4	31.0
0.5	27.8

$C_{10}H_7NO_2$ (142)
α-Nitronaphthalene

N	$\Delta t_B / x_1$
0.04	33.6
0.11	34.9

$C_{10}H_8$ (234) Naphthalene

N	$\Delta t_B/x_1$
0.3	35.4
0.5	35.7
1.0	36.2
1.3	36.6
1.6	36.9

$C_{10}H_8O$ (142) β-Naphthol

0.35	35.0

$C_{10}H_{12}O$ (81) Anethole

0.3	34.1
0.4	34.8
0.5	35.4
0.6	36.1
0.7	36.8
0.8	37.5
0.9	38.1

$C_{10}H_{12}O_2$ (81) *o*-Methoxy-*p*-methylacetophenone

0.3	34.9
0.5	35.1
0.7	36.0

$C_{10}H_{13}NO$ (153) Ethylacetanilide

0.2	34
0.4	35.5
0.5	36.1

$C_{10}H_{16}O$ (39, 75) Camphor

0.05	35.6
0.1	35.5
0.2	35.5
0.3	35.4

$C_{10}H_{18}O$ (18) Borneol

0.08	33.3
0.1	32.8
0.2	31.5
0.3	30.8
0.6	30.0

$C_{10}H_{21}Cl_2NO_2$ (223) Diisobutylammonium dichloroacetate

0.05	18.3
0.1	18.0
0.2	17.7
0.3	17.3

$C_{11}H_{14}O$ (146) Propyl benzyl ketone

0.15	34.9

$C_{11}H_{16}O_3$ (64) Camphocarboxylic acid

0.1	21.3
0.2	21.0
0.4	20.4
1.2	18.6

$C_{12}H_{10}$ (234) Diphenyl

N	$\Delta t_B/x_1$
0.5	34.7
1.0	35.4
1.5	36.1
2.0	36.8
3.0	38.2
4.0	39.6
4.5	40.3

$C_{12}H_{11}AsO_2$ (259) Diphenylarsenic acid

0.06	34.8

$C_{12}H_{11}N$ (106) Diphenylamine

0.1	30.6
0.2	31.2
0.5	32.0
0.7	31.8
0.9	31.4

$C_{12}H_{14}O_4$ (81) Ethylresodiacetophenone

0.2	32.8
0.35	33.3
0.5	35.7

$C_{12}H_{18}O_3$ (64) Methyl camphocarboxylate

0.35	32.5
0.4	32.8

$C_{13}H_{10}O$ (106) Benzophenone

0.1	30
0.2	30
0.4	31
0.6	31
0.8	31

$C_{13}H_{10}O_2$ (18) Phenyl benzoate

0.05	33.2
0.1	33.0
0.2	32.7
0.3	32.4
0.5	32.1

$C_{13}H_{10}O_3$ (18) Phenyl salicylate

0.06	30.6
0.1	30.2
0.2	29.8
0.3	29.6
0.4	29.6
0.5	29.6

$C_{13}H_{11}NO$ (152) Benzanilide

0.15	30.8
0.2	30.5
0.25	30.2

$C_{13}H_{11}N_3O_9$ (223, 228) Dimethylpyrone picrate

0.05	58.6
0.1	56.3
0.15	53.7
0.2	50.6
0.26	46.2

$C_{14}H_8O_2$ (155) Anthraquinone

N	$\Delta t_B/x_1$
0.074	34.1

$C_{14}H_{10}$ (18) Anthracene

0.05	33.4
0.1	33.1
0.2	32.4
0.3	31.7

$C_{14}H_{10}$ (52, 106) Phenanthrene

0.05	33.0
0.1	33.1
0.2	33.1
0.7	33.2
1.0	33.3
1.2	33.3

$C_{14}H_{10}O_2$ (30) Benzil

0.1	33.6
0.2	33.6
0.3	33.6

$C_{14}H_{10}O_3$ (18) Benzoic anhydride

0.05	33.2
0.1	32.5
0.2	31.2
0.3	30.2
0.4	29.2

$C_{14}H_{11}NO_2$ (106) β-Benzilmonoxime

0.1	28.3
0.2	27.5
0.3	26.8
0.4	26.1

$C_{14}H_{15}NO_3$ (223, 228) *p*-Toluidine salicylate

0.05	58.0
0.1	52.6
0.15	48.7
0.2	46.9
0.3	44.8

$C_{14}H_{28}O_2$ (223) Myristic acid

0.04	31.6
0.08	29.2
0.11	28.4

$C_{16}H_{11}N_3O_7$ (136) Naphthalene picrate

0.1	68
0.15	66

$C_{16}H_{11}N_3O_8$ (137, 223) β-Naphthol picrate

0.1	64
0.2	64

$C_{16}H_{34}N_2S$ (223) Triamylammonium thiocyanate

N	$\Delta t_B/x_1$
0.15	11.6
0.2	10.8
0.3	9.4
0.4	8.0

$C_{19}H_{13}O$ (259) Phenylxanthyl

0.05	29.8
0.07	29.1

$C_{19}H_{15}$ (259) Triphenylmethyl

0.07	20.6
0.1	20.5

$C_{19}H_{16}$ (31) Triphenylmethane

0.1	33.9
0.2	34.2
0.3	34.6

$C_{19}H_{16}O$ (261) Triphenylcarbinol

$C_{20}H_{13}N_3O_7$ (136) Anthracene picrate

0.05	64.4
0.1	60.4
0.2	53.8
0.3	51.0
0.4	49.2

$C_{21}H_{36}N_4O_7$ (223) Triamylammonium picrate

0.1	21.0
0.2	19.5
0.3	17.5

$C_{24}H_{20}As_2$ (259) Tetraphenylcacodyl

0.035	32.1

$C_{24}H_{24}N_2$ (236) Dibenzyltetrahydrodipyridyl

0.03	46
0.064	37.2

$C_{32}H_{64}O_2$ (81) Cetyl palmitate

0.15	40.0
0.3	47.2
0.5	56.9

$C_{57}H_{110}O_6$ (223) Tristearin

0.05	39.9
0.1	41.0

SnI_4 (223)

0.05	34.0
0.1	33.1
0.15	32.2
0.2	31.3

* Stable, high melting form.

C_6H_6O

Phenol

$T_B = 455$

$k_B = 37.7$

S_8 (170)

N	$\Delta t_B/x_1$
0.03	33.3
0.05	33.3
0.1	33.2
0.2	33.2
0.3	33.1

$C_{14}H_8O_4$ (21) Alizarin

0.06	33.8
0.1	33.6
0.2	33.2
0.3	32.9
0.4	32.7

$C_{14}H_{10}O_2$ (31, 88) Benzil

0.06	37.7
0.1	37.7
0.15	37.7
0.2	37.8
0.3	37.8
0.35	37.9

$C_{16}H_{10}N_2O_2$ (88) Indigotin

$C_{19}H_{16}$ (88) Triphenylmethane

0.05	37.5
0.1	37.4
0.15	37.3
0.2	37.2
0.25	37.1

$C_{21}H_{16}N_2$ (61) Lophine

0.02	33.9
0.05	33.9
0.1	33.9
0.15	40.0

$C_{21}H_{21}N$ (45) Tribenzylamine

0.05	38.1
0.1	38.7
0.16	39.2

C_6H_7N

Aniline

$T_B = 457.5$

$k_B = 38.8$

$C_{12}H_{11}N$ (26) Diphenylamine

0.1	36.6
0.2	36.9
0.3	37.2
0.4	37.5

$C_{12}H_{11}N_3$ (156) Aminoazobenzene

0.25	37.0
0.3	36.7

$C_{13}H_{11}NO$ (21) Benzanilide

0.1	35.7
0.3	36.1

$C_{14}H_8O_2$ (156) Anthraquinone

0.2	38.7

$C_{14}H_{10}O_2$ (31) Benzil

N	$\Delta t_B/x_1$
0.5	38.5
1.0	38.7
1.5	38.8
2.0	38.9
2.5	39.0

$C_{16}H_{10}N_2O_2$ (35) Indigotin

0.044	35.4

$C_{19}H_{16}$ (39) Triphenylmethane

0.05	39.4
0.1	34.4

$C_{21}H_{21}N$ (45) Tribenzylamine

0.04	39.7
0.07	39.9
0.1	40.0

$C_{24}H_{12}S$ (79) Dinaphthalenethiophene

0.05	34.3
0.08	33.4

$C_{36}H_{18}$ (79) Decacyclene

0.03	34.3
0.04	33.6
0.05	32.8

C_6H_{12}

Cyclohexane

$T_B = 354.5$

$k_B = 32.6$

$C_6H_6Cl_6$ (151) Benzene hexachloride

0.05	31
0.1	31.8
0.15	32.2
0.2	32.7

$C_6H_{10}O$ (151) Cyclohexanone

0.1	33.0
0.2	33.3
0.3	33.5
0.4	33.8
0.5	34.0

$C_7H_{12}O$ (151) *o*-Methylcyclohexanone

0.1	30.2
0.2	30.5
0.3	30.8
0.4	31.2
0.5	31.4
0.6	31.5

C_8H_8O (151) Acetophenone

0.1	32.8
0.2	33.2
0.3	33.6
0.4	33.8
0.5	33.9

C_6H_{12}.—(*Cont'd*)

$C_9H_{12}ClNO_2$ (224)
p-Toluidine chloroacetate

N	$\Delta t_B / x_1$
0.1	32.6

$C_{10}H_8$ (151)
Naphthalene

N	$\Delta t_B / x_1$
0.1	33.0
0.2	33.2
0.3	33.3
0.4	33.4
0.5	33.6
0.6	33.7

$C_{10}H_{12}O$ (81)
Anethole

N	$\Delta t_B / x_1$
0.1	32.2
0.3	32.8
0.5	33.4
0.7	34.0
0.9	34.6
1.0	34.9

$C_{10}H_{21}Cl_2NO_2$
Diisobutylammonium dichloroacetate (224)

N	$\Delta t_B / x_1$
0.05	32.8
0.1	33.0
0.2	33.2

$C_{12}H_{10}$ (151)
Diphenyl

N	$\Delta t_B / x_1$
0.1	33.3
0.2	33.9
0.3	34.5

$C_{13}H_{10}O$ (151)
Benzophenone

N	$\Delta t_B / x_1$
0.05	32.9
0.1	33.0
0.2	33.2
0.3	33.5

$C_{13}H_{10}O_2$ (151)
Phenyl benzoate

N	$\Delta t_B / x_1$
0.15	32.3
0.2	32.2
0.25	32.2

$C_{14}H_{10}O_2$ (151)
Benzil

N	$\Delta t_B / x_1$
0.05	34.0
0.1	35.4
0.15	36.8
0.2	38.1
0.25	39.5

$C_{14}H_{12}$ (151)
Stilbene

N	$\Delta t_B / x_1$
0.1	32.3
0.2	32.7
0.3	33.1

$C_{14}H_{15}NO_3$
p-Toluidine salicylate (224, 228)

N	$\Delta t_B / x_1$
0.1	33.0
0.2	33.3
0.3	33.6
0.4	33.9

$C_{19}H_{16}$ (151)
Triphenylmethane

N	$\Delta t_B / x_1$
0.1	33
0.2	33
0.3	33

$C_{32}H_{64}O_2$ (81)
Cetyl palmitate

N	$\Delta t_B / x_1$
0.1	37.0
0.2	41.7
0.3	46.6
0.4	50.1
0.5	56.0

C_6H_{14}

Hexane
$T_B = 342.1$
$k_B = 34$

$C_6H_5NO_2$ (69)
Nitrobenzene

N	$\Delta t_B / x_1$
1.0	28
2.0	23
3.0	20
4.0	18
5.0	17
6.0	15
7.0	15
8.0	14
9.0	14
10.0	14
15.0	13
20.0	17

$C_6H_{15}N$

Di-*n*-propylamine
$T_B = 383.8$
$k_B = 45.5$*

* No experimental data given (56).

C_7H_5N

Benzonitrile
$T_B = 463.8$
$k_B = 33.3$

$C_{12}H_{11}N$ (238)
Diphenylamine

N	$\Delta t_B / x_1$
0.04	34.3
0.05	34.7
0.07	35.3

$HgCl_2$ (238)

N	$\Delta t_B / x_1$
0.05	31.2
0.1	34.0
0.15	39.2

HgI_2 (238)

N	$\Delta t_B / x_1$
0.015	37.3
0.05	31.1

$AgNO_3$ (123, 238)

N	$\Delta t_B / x_1$
0.05	33
0.1	34
0.2	34

C_7H_8

Toluene
$T_B = 383.6$
$k_B = 35$

S_8 (4)

N	$\Delta t_B / x_1$
0.05	38.4
0.1	37.1
0.2	35.2
0.3	33.4
0.4	31.6
0.5	29.8

$C_3H_7NO_2$ (201)
Urethane

N	$\Delta t_B / x_1$
0.2	13.6
0.4	13.7
0.6	13.9
0.8	14.1
1.0	14.3

C_7H_9N (201)
p-Toluidine

N	$\Delta t_B / x_1$
0.1	31.8
0.2	32.0
0.3	32.3
0.4	32.5
0.5	32.7
0.6	32.9
0.7	33.2

$C_{10}H_8$ (61, 169, 201)
Naphthalene

N	$\Delta t_B / x_1$
0.1	35.0
0.2	35.5
0.3	35.9
0.4	36.4
0.5	36.8
0.6	37.3

$C_{10}H_{12}O$ (171)
Methylchavicol

N	$\Delta t_B / x_1$
0.05	33.8
0.1	33.7
0.2	33.5
0.25	33.4

$C_{10}H_{12}O$ (171)
p-Anethole

N	$\Delta t_B / x_1$
0.05	36
0.1	35
0.2	35
0.3	34

$C_{10}H_{14}O$ (171)
p-Methoxypropylbenzene

N	$\Delta t_B / x_1$
0.05	34.2
0.1	33.5
0.15	33.4
0.2	33.6

$C_{10}H_{16}O$ (61)
Camphor

N	$\Delta t_B / x_1$
0.1	32.5
0.2	32.6
0.3	32.7
0.4	32.8
0.5	32.9

$C_{12}H_{10}$ (201)
Acenaphthene

N	$\Delta t_B / x_1$
0.1	37.6
0.2	37.6
0.3	37.7
0.4	37.7
0.5	37.8
0.6	37.9

$C_{14}H_{10}$ (201)
Phenanthrene

N	$\Delta t_B / x_1$
0.1	36.8
0.2	36.4
0.3	36.1
0.4	35.8

$C_{14}H_{10}O_2$ (61)
Benzil

N	$\Delta t_B / x_1$
0.05	33.2
0.1	34.0
0.15	35.0
0.25	34.7

$C_{14}H_{12}$ (4)
Stilbene

N	$\Delta t_B / x_1$
0.05	36.6
0.1	36.5
0.2	36.3
0.3	36.1
0.4	35.8

C_7H_8O

Anisole
$T_B = 428.9$
$k_B = 40$

C_8H_9NO (169)
Acetanilide

N	$\Delta t_B / x_1$
0.1	36.7
0.2	34.5

$C_{14}H_{10}$ (112, 169)
Anthracene

N	$\Delta t_B / x_1$
0.1	37.1

$C_{19}H_{16}$ (169)
Triphenylmethane

N	$\Delta t_B / x_1$
0.05	41.8
0.1	42.1

C_7H_9N

p-Toluidine
$T_B = 473.6$
$k_B = 37.9$

$C_{12}H_{11}N$ (35)
Diphenylamine

N	$\Delta t_B / x_1$
0.05	38.3
0.1	38.7
0.2	39.5
0.3	40.2

$C_{14}H_{10}O_2$ (35)
Benzil

N	$\Delta t_B / x_1$
0.05	38
0.1	38
0.15	39

$C_{16}H_{10}N_2O_2$ (35)
Indigotin

N	$\Delta t_B / x_1$
0.01	37
0.03	38

$C_7H_{14}O_2$

Isoamyl acetate
$T_B = 415.6$
$k_B = 37.2$

$C_7H_6O_2$ (34)
Benzoic acid

N	$\Delta t_B / x_1$
0.2	34.6
0.5	34.2
1.0	33.5

$C_{12}H_{11}N$ (34)
Diphenylamine

N	$\Delta t_B / x_1$
0.1	37.2
0.2	37.2
0.3	37.2
0.5	38
0.8	38

$C_{13}H_{10}O$ (34)
Benzophenone

N	$\Delta t_B / x_1$
0.1	37.0
0.2	36.7
0.4	36.1
0.6	35.5

$C_{14}H_8O_4$ (34)
Alizarin

N	$\Delta t_B / x_1$
0.07	36.0

$C_{14}H_{10}O_2$ (34)
Benzil

N	$\Delta t_B / x_1$
0.1	36.6
0.2	36.1
0.3	35.7
0.5	34.9
0.7	34.2

C_8H_{10}

m-Xylene
$T_B = 412.1$
$k_B = 43$

S_8 (4)

N	$\Delta t_B / x_1$
0.02	42.6
0.05	41.7
0.1	40.3
0.2	37.4
0.27	36.0
0.35	35.0

C_8H_{10}

p-Xylene
$T_B = 410.8$
$k_B = 39.8$

$C_{14}H_{10}O_2$ (61)
Benzil

N	$\Delta t_B / x_1$
0.05	39.5
0.1	39.2
0.2	38.5
0.25	38.2

$C_8H_{10}O$

Phenetole
$T_B = 445$
$k_B = 40.5$

S_8 (170)

N	$\Delta t_B / x_1$
0.02	39.7
0.06	38.3
0.1	37.3
0.14	36.7
0.18	36.3
0.22	35.9

$C_{14}H_{10}$ (169)
Anthracene

N	$\Delta t_B / x_1$
0.03	40.4
0.05	40.9
0.08	41.5

$C_{19}H_{16}$ (169)
Triphenylmethane

$C_{19}H_{16}$.—(*Cont'd*)

N	$\Delta t_B / x_1$
0.03	40.4
0.05	40.4
0.08	40.3
0.1	40.3
0.12	40.2

C_9H_7N

Quinoline
$T_B = 510.8$
$k_B = 43$

$C_{14}H_8O_2$ (193)
Anthraquinone

N	$\Delta t_B / x_1$
0.05	45.6
0.1	45.8
0.2	46.2

$C_{14}H_8O_2$ (193)
Phenanthraquinone

N	$\Delta t_B / x_1$
0.05	43.4
0.1	43.3
0.2	43.6
0.3	43.7

$C_{14}H_9NO_2$ (193)
2-Aminoanthraquinone

N	$\Delta t_B / x_1$
0.05	50
0.1	50
0.16	50

$C_{14}H_{10}N_2O_2$ (193)
1, 5-Diaminoanthraquinone

N	$\Delta t_B / x_1$
0.05	46
0.1	46

$C_{14}H_{10}O_2$ (31, 88)
Benzil

N	$\Delta t_B / x_1$
0.05	42.4
0.1	42.8
0.2	43.5
0.3	44.2

$C_{14}H_{12}O_2$ (88)
Benzoin

N	$\Delta t_B / x_1$
0.05	43.6
0.1	43.9
0.2	44.4
0.3	45.0

$C_{16}H_{10}N_2O_2$ (88)
Indigotin

N	$\Delta t_B / x_1$
0.01	44.5
0.02	44.2
0.03	43.9
0.04	43.6

$C_{18}H_{36}O_2$ (88)
Stearic acid

N	$\Delta t_B / x_1$
0.02	46.1
0.04	45.4
0.06	44.5
0.08	43.8

$C_{19}H_{16}$ (26)
Triphenylmethane

N	$\Delta t_B / x_1$
0.05	41.3
0.1	42.0

$ZnCl_2$ (28)

N	$\Delta t_B / x_1$
0.1	44
0.2	44
0.3	44

$ZnBr_2$ (28)

N	$\Delta t_B / x_1$
0.05	44.8
0.1	44.7
0.15	44.6
0.2	44.5

ZnI_2 (28)

N	$\Delta t_B / x_1$
0.02	43.4
0.04	43.1
0.06	42.9
0.08	42.6

$CdCl_2$ (28)

N	$\Delta t_B / x_1$
0.1	43.1
0.2	43.9
0.3	44.5
0.4	45.0
0.5	45.5
0.7	46.4

$CdBr_2$ (28)

N	$\Delta t_B / x_1$
0.1	43.9
0.2	44.3
0.3	44.8
0.4	45.2

CdI_2 (28)

N	$\Delta t_B / x_1$
0.05	43.4
0.1	44.0
0.2	45.0
0.3	45.8
0.37	46.3

$CuCl$ (28)

N	$\Delta t_B / x_1$
0.05	43.5
0.1	40.6
0.2	36.6
0.3	34.0
0.4	32.3
0.5	31.1
0.6	30.3
0.8	29.7

$CoCl_2$ (28)

N	$\Delta t_B / x_1$
0.03	52.7
0.06	49.1
0.1	46.4
0.2	43.7
0.3	43.0
0.4	42.8

$CoBr_2$ (28)

N	$\Delta t_B / x_1$
0.05	41.2
0.1	41.5
0.2	42.1
0.3	42.6

$NiCl_2$ (28)

N	$\Delta t_B / x_1$
0.05	43.2
0.1	43.2
0.2	43.2
0.3	43.2

$NiBr_2$ (28)

N	$\Delta t_B / x_1$
0.05	41.7
0.1	41.9
0.15	42.0
0.2	42.2

$C_{10}H_8$

Naphthalene

$T_B = 491.0$

$k_B = 46.4$

S_8 (4, 170)

N	$\Delta t_B / x_1$
0.05	46.5
0.1	46.2
0.2	45.5
0.3	44.9

$C_{19}H_{16}$ (169) Triphenylmethane

N	$\Delta t_B / x_1$
0.06	50.4
0.08	49.7
0.1	49.1

$C_{21}H_{16}N_2$ (45) Lophine

N	$\Delta t_B / x_1$
0.02	46.0
0.04	45.7
0.06	45.4
0.08	45.3
0.1	45.3

$C_{10}H_{12}$

1, 2, 3, 4-Tetrahydronaphthalene

$T_B = 480.3$

$k_B = 43.3$

$C_{14}H_{10}$ (102) Anthracene

N	$\Delta t_B / x_1$
0.1	43.5
0.2	43.7
0.3	43.9

$C_{10}H_{14}$

p-Cymene

$T_B = 449$

$k_B = 40.0$

$C_{12}H_{11}N$ (61) Diphenylamine

N	$\Delta t_B / x_1$
0.1	40.0
0.2	40.2

$C_{14}H_{10}O_2$ (34) Benzil

N	$\Delta t_B / x_1$
0.1	40.3
0.2	40.3
0.3	40.3

$C_{10}H_{16}O$

Camphor

$T_B = 482.2$ (48)

$C_{10}H_{16}O$

Fenchone

$T_B = 468$

$k_B = 40.4$

S_8 (181)

N	$\Delta t_B / x_1$
0.02	38.6
0.08	37.7

As_2O_3 (181)

AsI_3 (181)

N	$\Delta t_B / x_1$
0.02	40.4
0.07	39.3

SbI_3 (181)

N	$\Delta t_B / x_1$
0.04	39.4
0.07	39.4
0.09	40.0

BiI_3 (181)

N	$\Delta t_B / x_1$
0.01	39.0
0.02	38.7

$C_{12}H_9N$ (181) Carbazole

$C_{12}H_9N$.—(*Cont'd*)

N	$\Delta t_B / x_1$
0.07	42.9
0.15	42.3
0.2	41.9

$C_{14}H_8O_2$ (181) Anthraquinone

N	$\Delta t_B / x_1$
0.05	40.3
0.1	40.2
0.2	39.5

$C_{14}H_{10}$ (181) Anthracene

N	$\Delta t_B / x_1$
0.07	40.4
0.15	40.4
0.2	40.4

$C_{14}H_{10}O_2$ (181) Benzil

N	$\Delta t_B / x_1$
0.04	40.7
0.07	40.7
0.1	40.7

$HgCl_2$ (181)

N	$\Delta t_B / x_1$
0.07	34.0
0.33	39.5

$HgBr_2$ (181)

N	$\Delta t_B / x_1$
0.03	39.8
0.06	39.8
0.08	39.0
0.18	39.2

HgI_2 (181)

N	$\Delta t_B / x_1$
0.02	39.3
0.06	39.3
0.08	39.4
0.1	39.4

$C_{10}H_{18}$

Decaline

$T_B = 466.4$

$k_B = 41.6$

$C_{14}H_{10}$ (101) Anthracene

N	$\Delta t_B / x_1$
0.2	42.9
0.3	43.5

$C_{10}H_{18}O$

Menthone

$T_B = 480$

$k_B = 40.6$

$C_{12}H_{10}O_2S$ (48) Phenylsulfone

N	$\Delta t_B / x_1$
0.05	41.1
0.1	41.5
0.2	42.4
0.3	43.4

Na_2* (48)

N	$\Delta t_B / x_1$
0.1	45
0.2	44
0.3	44
0.4	43
0.5	43
0.6	42

* Reacts with solvent to give a solute, probably a sodium ketyl, containing 2 atoms of Na per mole.

$C_{10}H_{20}O$

Menthol

$T_B = 485$

$k_B = 41$

$C_{12}H_{10}O_2S$ (48) Phenylsulfone

N	$\Delta t_B / x_1$
0.05	39.5 (Av.)
0.35	

$C_{21}H_{16}N_2$ (48) Lophine

N	$\Delta t_B / x_1$
0.05	41.6 (Av.)
0.25	

Na_2* (48)

N	$\Delta t_B / x_1$
0.1	41
0.2	42
0.3	44
0.4	46

* Reacts with solvent to give a solute containing two atoms of Na per mole.

$C_{12}H_{10}$

Diphenyl

$T_B = 528.0$

$k_B = 44.2$

S_8 (37)

N	$\Delta t_B / x_1$
0.05	37.4
0.1	39.5
0.18	42.7

$C_{14}H_{10}O_2$ (37) Benzol

N	$\Delta t_B / x_1$
0.03	38.9
0.05	38.9
0.1	38.9

$C_{21}H_{16}N_2$ (45) Lophine

N	$\Delta t_B / x_1$
0.02	45.1
0.05	46.3
0.1	48.2

THREE-COMPONENT SYSTEMS

The A-component (the "solvent") is H_2O. (Standard arrangement.)

$T_B = 373.1$; $k_B = 28.9$

B = **NH_4Cl**
C = $(NH_4)_2SO_4$ (68)
C = $CdCl_2$* (62)
C = $Hg(CN)_2$* (63)
C = NaCl (68)

ΣN	$\Delta t_B / \Sigma x$
$N_C/N_B = 1.0$	
5.0	62.6
6.0	65.5
7.0	68.3
8.0	70.4
9.0	72.4
10.0	74.3

B = **$(NH_4)_2SO_4$**
C = K_2SO_4 (68)

ΣN	$\Delta t_B / \Sigma x$
$N_B/N_C = 1.0$	
1.4	53.7
2.0	54.2
2.6	54.7
$N_C/N_B = 1.67$	
4.2	55.8
5.0	58.0
6.0	60.8

B = **$(COOH)_2$** Oxalic acid
C = K_2O* (131)
Data for saturated solutions only

B = **$SnCl_2$**
C = $CoCl_2$* (53)

N_C/N_B	$\Delta t_B / \Sigma x$
$N_B = 0.173$	
$N_C = 0.165$	
0	50.6
0.95	51.2
∞	69.1

B = **$Pb(NO_3)_2$**
C = $Sr(NO_3)_2$ (68)

ΣN	$\Delta t_B / \Sigma x$
$N_B/N_C = 0.5$	
1.5	65.1
1.7	64.2
2.0	64.3
3.0	65.8
4.0	68.2
4.5	69.5
$N_B/N_C = 0.8$	
1.6	62.3
1.8	61.1
2.0	61.2
3.0	61.9
4.0	64.2

C = $Ba(NO_3)_2$ (68)

ΣN	$\Delta t_B / \Sigma x$
$N_C/N_B = 0.333$, 0.5	
1.0	55.8
1.5	53.0
2.0	50.1
2.5	49.1
3.0	48.5

B = **$ZnCl_2$**
C = $CoCl_2$* (53)

N_C/N_B	$\Delta t_B / \Sigma x$
N_B, $N_C = 0.165$	
0	49.5
1.0	54.0
∞	69.1

B = **$CdCl_2$**
C = $CuCl_2$ (53)

N_C/N_B	$\Delta t_B / \Sigma x$
$N_B = 0.167$	
$N_C = 0.215$	
0	33.2
1.29	43.8
∞	49.0

C = $CoCl_2$* (53)

N_C/N_B	$\Delta t_B / \Sigma x$
N_C, $N_B = 0.165$	
0	33.2
1.0	43.4
∞	69.1

C = NaCl* (62)
C = KCl* (62)

B = **$CdSO_4$**
C = NaCl* (91)
C = KCl* (62)

B = **$HgCl_2$**
C = $CuCl_2$* (53)

N_C/N_B	$\Delta t_B / \Sigma x$
$N_B = 0.183$	
$N_C = 0.215$	
0	32.6
1.18	29.2
∞	49.1

C = $CoCl_2$* (53)

N_C/N_B	$\Delta t_B / \Sigma x$
N_B, $N_C = 0.165$	
0	33.3
1.0	37.2
∞	69.1

B = **$Hg(CN)_2$**
C = $MgCl_2$* (63)
C = $BaCl_2$* (63)
C = NaCl* (63)
C = KCl* (63)
C = KBr* (63)
C = KI* (63)

B = **$CuCl_2$**
C = NaCl (53)

N_B/N_C	$\Delta t_B / \Sigma x$
$N_B = 0.215$	
$N_C = 0.339$	
0	49.5
0.63	51.6
∞	49.1

B = **AgI**
C = $AgNO_3$* (99)

B = **$CoCl_2$**
C = $AlCl_3$ (53)

N_C/N_B	$\Delta t_B / \Sigma x$
$N_B = 0.204$	
$N_C = 0.161$	
0	86.2
1.28	78.9
∞	67.8

B = $CoCl_2$.—(Cont'd)

C = $MgCl_2$ (53)

N_B/N_C	$\Delta t_B/\Sigma x$
$N_B = 0.205$, $N_C = 0.240$	
0	74.9
0.85	74.9
∞	67.8

C = $CaCl_2$ (53)

N_B/N_C	$\Delta t_B/\Sigma x$
$N_B = 0.205$, $N_C = 0.176$	
0	43.3
1.17	57.8
∞	67.8

C = $BaCl_2$ (53)

N_B/N_C	$\Delta t_B/\Sigma x$
$N_B = 0.205$, $N_C = 0.100$	
0	57.3
2.05	65.2
∞	67.8

C = NaCl (53)

N_B/N_C	$\Delta t_B/\Sigma x$
$N_B = 0.205$, $N_C = 0.836$	
0	49.5
0.246	57.0
∞	67.8

B = CrO_3

C = K_2O* (130)

Data for saturated solutions only

B = $Sr(NO_3)_2$

C = $Ba(NO_3)_2$ (68)

ΣN	$\Delta t_B/\Sigma x$
$N_C/N_B = 0.264$	
2.0	69.9
2.5	69.2
$N_C/N_B = 0.5$	
1.0	65.0
2.0	65.0

B = $BaCl_2$

C = $Ba(NO_3)_2$ (68)

ΣN	$\Delta t_B/\Sigma x$
$N_C/N_B = 0.25$	
1.0	71.6
2.0	77.9
2.5	81.1
3.0	82.7

C = $Ba(NO_3)_2$.—(Continued)

ΣN	$\Delta t_B/\Sigma x$
$N_C/N_B = 0.4$	
1.5	71.9
2.0	74.8
2.5	77.5
3.0	79.1
3.5	79.8
4.0	80.0

B = $Ba(NO_3)_2$

C = NaCl (68)

ΣN	$\Delta t_B/\Sigma x$
$N_C/N_B = 2.0$	
2.0	58.8
3.0	60.9
4.0	62.9
$N_C/N_B = 4.0$	
4.0	65.5
5.0	68.3
6.0	71.1

B = NaCl

C = KCl (68)

ΣN	$\Delta t_B/\Sigma x$
$N_B/N_C = 0.25, 0.33, 0.5$	
2.5	55.7
3.0	57.3
4.0	60.7
5.0	64.2
6.0	67.3
7.0	70.0
8.0	72.6
9.0	74.8
$N_B/N_C = 0.67, 1.0$	
0.4	54.7
0.6	53.2
0.8	52.4
1.0	52.1
1.5	53.7
2.0	55.6
3.0	59.0
4.0	62.4
5.0	65.8
6.0	69.1
7.0	72.4
8.0	76.0
9.0	79.5

C = KCl.—(Cont'd)

ΣN	$\Delta t_B/\Sigma x$
$N_B/N_C = 1.5, 2.0$	
2.5	57.5
3.0	59.5
4.0	63.4
5.0	67.5
6.0	71.5
7.0	75.3
8.0	77.4
$N_B/N_C = 3.0, 4.0$	
2.5	58.1
3.0	60.3
4.0	64.5
5.0	68.8
6.0	73.0
7.0	76.8
8.0	78.3

B = KCl

C = $KClO_3$ (68)

ΣN	$\Delta t_B/\Sigma x$
$N_B/N_C = 1.0$	
3.0	52.1
4.0	53.3
5.0	54.5
6.0	55.5
$N_B/N_C = 2.0$	
3.0	52.9
4.0	54.7
5.0	56.4
6.0	58.2
7.0	59.4
$N_B/N_C = 3.0$	
4.0	56.7
5.0	58.4
6.0	60.1
7.0	61.8
8.0	63.2
9.0	64.6

C = K_2SO_4 (68)

B = KI

C = CdI_2* (62)

The A-component (the "solvent") is an organic compound. The ℭ-arrangement.

CCl_4

$T_B = 349.9$

$k_B = 31.4$

B = $C_{12}H_{24}O_2$ Lauric acid

C = $C_{16}H_{32}O_2$ (218) Palmitic acid

CS_2

$T_B = 319.4$

$k_B = 31$

B = I_2

C = S_8 (82)

N_B/N_C	$\Delta t_B/\Sigma x$
$N_B = 0.045$	
0	31.9
$N_B = 0.11$	
1.0	32.4
2.0	32.9
2.5	33.2

B = S_4 (7)

C = S_8 (rhombic)

B = S_8

C = P_4 (98)

N_B/N_C	$\Delta t_B/\Sigma x$
$N_C = 0.26$	
0	29.1
0.5	29.6
1.0	29.9
3.0	27.9

N_B/N_C	$\Delta t_B/\Sigma x$
$N_B = 0.099$	
∞	31.9

B = $POCl_3$

C = Al_2Br_6* (129)

N_B/N_C	$\Delta t_B/\Sigma x$
$N_C = 0.063$	
0	30.8
1.75	11.3
2.5	13.5
3.0	15.6

B = $C_6H_4Br_2$ *p*-Dibromobenzene

C = Al_2Br_6 (129)

N_B/N_C	$\Delta t_B/x_1$
$N_C = 0.078$	
0	31.3
1.0	31.4
2.0	31.5
3.0	31.6

B = $C_6H_5ClO_2S$ Benzene sulfone chloride

C = Al_2Br_6* (129)

N_B/N_C	$\Delta t_B/x_1$
$N_C = 0.084$	
0	31.3
1.0	16.4
2.0	12.6
$N_B = 0.34$	
3.0	15.3
5.0	20.7
15.0	28.0
∞	31.8

B = $C_6H_5NO_2$ Nitrobenzene

C = Al_2Cl_6* (129)

B = C_7H_5ClO Benzoyl chloride

C = Al_2Br_6* (129)

N_B/N_C	$\Delta t_B/x_1$
$N_C = 0.084$	
0	31.4
1.0	16.2
2.0	10.7
2.8	14.4

B = $C_{13}H_{10}O$ Benzophenone

C = Al_2Br_6* (129)

N_B/N_C	$\Delta t_B/x_1$
$N_C = 0.051$	
0	30.3
1.0	15.5
2.5	14.6
3.5	18.6

$CHCl_3$

$T_B = 334.3$

$k_B = 32.0$

B = $C_2HCl_3O_2$ Trichloroacetic acid

C = $C_5H_{11}N$* (243) Piperidine

B = $C_4H_{12}ClN$ Diethylammonium chloride

C = $C_{12}H_{28}IN$ Tetrapropylammonium iodide (212)

ΣN	$\Delta t_B/\Sigma x$
$N_B/N_C = 1.0$	
0.3	7.7
0.4	7.3
0.5	7.1
0.6	7.1

B = $C_5H_{11}N$ Piperidine

C = $C_6H_3N_3O_7$ Picric acid* (243)

B = $C_8H_{20}BrN$ Tetraethylammonium bromide

C = $NiC_{36}H_{66}O_6$ Ricinoleate (226)

ΣN	$\Delta t_B/x_1$
$N_C = 0.215$	
0.2	7.9
0.6	11.5

B = $C_8H_{20}ClN$ Tetraethylammonium chloride

C = $NiC_{36}H_{66}O_6$ Ricinoleate (226)

ΣN	$\Delta t_B/x_1$
$N_C = 0.061$	
0.06	6.8
0.2	12.9

B = $C_{10}H_8$ Naphthalene

C = $C_{14}H_{10}O_2$ Benzil (126)

ΣN	$\Delta t_B/x_1$
$N_B = 0.148$	
0.15	33.1
0.2	32.5
0.25	33.0

B = $C_{10}H_{16}ClN$ Diethylaniline hydrochloride

C = $C_{10}H_{16}IN$ Diethylaniline hydriodide (212)

ΣN	$\Delta t_B/x_1$
$N_B/N_C = 2.0$	
0.4	16.6
0.6	17.4

B = $C_{10}H_{16}O$ Camphor

C = $C_{14}H_{10}O_2$ Benzil (126)

ΣN	$\Delta t_B/x_1$
$N_C = 0.11$	
0.1	28.7
0.15	30.5
0.2	32.3

B = $C_{10}H_{24}ClN$ Diamylammonium chloride

C = $CuC_{36}H_{66}O_6$ Ricinoleate (226)

ΣN	$\Delta t_B/x_1$
$N_C = 0.059$	
0.06	12.8
0.2	18.8
0.3	20.2
0.4	21.6

B = $C_{12}H_{28}IN$ Tetrapropylammonium iodide

C = $C_{14}H_{10}$ Anthracene (212)

ΣN	$\Delta t_B/x_1$
$N_C/N_B = 1.0$	
0.2	20.1
0.3	19.2
0.4	18.3

B = $C_{14}H_{10}O_2$ Benzil

C = $C_{19}H_{16}$ Triphenylmethane (126)

ΣN	$\Delta t_B/x_1$
$N_C = 0.083$	
0.08	25.8
0.1	27.1
0.12	28.4

CH_4O

Methyl alcohol

$T_B = 337.6$

$k_B = 26.8$

B = CH_4N_2O Urea

C = $C_7H_6O_2$ (267) Benzoic acid

C = $C_7H_6O_3$ (267) Salicylic acid

C = $C_{10}H_8$ (267) Naphthalene

C = $C_{10}H_{15}BrO$† Bromocamphor (267)

C = $C_{10}H_{16}O$ (267) Camphor

B = C_2H_5NO Acetamide

C = $C_{10}H_8$ (267) Naphthalene

B = $C_3H_7NO_2$ Urethane

C = $C_{10}H_8$ (267) Naphthalene

B = $C_7H_6O_2$ Benzoic acid

C = $C_7H_6O_3$ (267) Salicylic acid

C = $C_{10}H_8$ (267) Naphthalene

C = $C_{10}H_{16}O$ (267) Camphor

B = $C_7H_6O_3$ Salicylic acid

C = $C_{10}H_8$ (267) Naphthalene

C = $C_{10}H_{16}O$ (267) Camphor

B = C_8H_9NO Acetanilide

C = $C_{10}H_8$ (267) Naphthalene

B = $C_{10}H_8$ Naphthalene

C = $C_{10}H_{15}BrO$† Bromocamphor (267)

C = $C_{10}H_{16}O$ (267) Camphor

C = $C_{14}H_{10}O_2$ (267) Benzil

C_2H_5Br
Ethyl bromide
$T_B = 311.1$
$k_B = 29.4$
B = **$C_7H_6O_2$**
Benzoic acid
C = $C_{10}H_{15}BrO$†
Bromocamphor
(267)
C = C_8H_9NO (267)
Acetanilide

B = **C_8H_9NO**
Acetanilide
C = $C_{10}H_{15}BrO$†
Bromocamphor
(267)

B = **$C_{10}H_8$**
Naphthalene
C = $C_{10}H_{15}BrO$†
Bromocamphor
(267)

C_2H_6O
Ethyl alcohol
$T_B = 351.6$
$k_B = 26$
B = **$C_7H_6O_2$**
Benzoic acid
C = $C_{10}H_8$ (267)
Naphthalene

B = **$C_5H_{11}N$**
Piperidine
C = $C_7H_6O_2$* (243)
Benzoic acid
C = $C_6H_3N_3O_7$*
Picric acid
(243)

B = **$C_7H_6O_3$**
Salicylic acid
C = $C_{10}H_8$ (267)
Naphthalene

B = **$HgCl_2$**
C = $CoCl_2$* (74)

N_B/N_C	$\Delta t_B / \Sigma x$
$N_C = 0.035$	
0	22.7
2.5	20.2
3.0	20.2
5.5	20.4
$N_B = 0.195$	
1.0	15.9
2.0	18.3

B = $CoCl_2$
C = $CaCl_2$ (74)
$N_B = 0.067$

ΣN	$\Delta t_B / \Sigma x$
0.05	22.9
0.1	22.9
0.2	23.1

B = **NaC_2H_5O**
Ethylate
C = $NaC_6H_9O_3$
Ethylacetoacetate
(269)
C = $NaC_7H_{11}O_4$
Diethylmalonate
(269)

B = **$KC_7H_5O_3$**
Salicylate
C = C_7H_6O* (244)
Salicylic acid

C_3H_6O
Acetone
$T_B = 329.2$
$k_B = 29.8$
B = **$C_7H_6O_2$**
Benzoic acid
C = $C_{10}H_8$ (267)
Naphthalene

B = $C_{10}H_8$
Naphthalene
C = $C_{28}H_{56}O_4$ (268)
Polyheptaldehyde

C_3H_7Br
n-Propyl bromide
$T_B = 344.0$
$k_B = 29.5$
B = **$C_7H_6O_2$**
Benzoic acid
C = C_8H_8NO (267)
Acetanilide
C = $C_{10}H_{15}BrO$†
Bromocamphor
(267)

B = **C_8H_8NO**
Acetanilide
C = $C_{10}H_{15}BrO$†
Bromocamphor
(267)

C_3H_8O
n-Propyl alcohol
$T_B = 370.9$
$k_B = 27.0$
B = **$C_7H_6O_2$**
Benzoic acid
C = $C_{10}H_8$ (267)
Naphthalene

C_4H_9Br
Isobutyl bromide
$T_B = 364.6$
$k_B = 27.0$
B = **$C_7H_6O_2$**
Benzoic acid
C = C_8H_8NO (267)
Acetanilide
C = $C_{10}H_{15}BrO$†
Bromocamphor
(267)

B = **C_8H_8NO**
Acetanilide
C = $C_{10}H_8$ (267)
Naphthalene

$C_4H_{10}O$
tert.-Butyl alcohol
$T_B = 355.9$
$k_B = 18$
B = **CH_4N_2O**
Urea
C = CH_4N_2S
Thiourea (8)

ΣN	$\Delta t_B / x_1$
$N_C = 0.155$	
0.155	18.8
0.2	20.1
0.3	21.7
0.4	22.4
0.5	22.7

$C_4H_{10}O$
Ethyl ether
$T_B = 307.6$
$k_B = 29.2$
B = **$C_5H_{11}N$**
Piperidine
C = $C_7H_6O_2$* (243)
Benzoic acid

$C_5H_{10}O$
Diethyl ketone
$T_B = 374.8$
$k_B = 32$
B = **$C_{10}H_8$**
Naphthalene
C = $C_{28}H_{56}O_4$ (268)
Polyheptaldehyde

C_6H_6
Benzene
$T_B = 353.35$
$k_B = 33.6$
B = **$C_5H_{11}N$**
Piperidine
C = $C_7H_6O_2$* (243)
Benzoic acid

* Indicates complex or compound formation.
† The isomer used is not given.

FOUR- AND FIVE-COMPONENT SYSTEMS

Solvent CH_4O
Methyl alcohol
$T_B = 337.6$
$k_B = 26.8$
Solutes (267)
$C_7H_6O_2$, Benzoic acid + $C_7H_6O_3$, Salicylic acid + $C_{10}H_8$, Naphthalene

Solvent $C_4H_{10}O$
tert.-Butyl alcohol
$T_B = 355.9$
$k_B = 18$

Solutes (8)
CH_4N_2O, Urea ($N = 0.345$) + CH_4N_2S, Thiourea ($N = 0.155$) + $C_{18}H_{36}O_2$, Stearic acid

ΣN	$\Delta t_B / \Sigma x$
0.155	18.8
0.5	22.0
0.6	22.9

Solutes (8)
CH_4N_2O, Urea ($N = 0.345$) + CH_4N_2S, Thiourea ($N = 0.155$) + $C_{10}H_8$, Naphthalene ($N = 0.146$) + $C_{18}H_{36}O_2$, Stearic acid ($N = 0.108$)

ΣN	$\Delta t_B / x_1$
0.754	21.5

LITERATURE

(For a key to the periodicals see end of volume)

(1) Alluard, *34*, **59**: 500; 64. (2) Andreocci, *93*, **14**: 246; 97. (3) Andrews and Ende, *7*, **17**: 136; 95. (4) Aronstein and Meihuizen, *87*, **6**: No. 3: 99. (5) Aschan, *25*, **48**: 874; 15. (6) Aschan and Ekholm, *13*, **424**: 133; 21. (7) Aten, *7*, **88**: 321; 14. (8) Atkins, *4*, **99**: 10; 11. (9) Bachmann and Dziewónski, *25*, **36**: 971; 03.

(10) Badger and France, *45*, **15**: 364; 23. (11) Baker and Waite, *33*, **25**: 1174; 21. (12) Baroni, *36*, **23 II**: 249; 93. (13) Bassett and Taylor, *4*, **101**: 576; 12. (14) Battelli and Stefanini, *59*, **9**: 5; 99. (15) Bauer, *92*, **16**: 341; 03. (16) Beckmann, *7*, **3**: 603; 89. (17) Beckmann, *7*, **4**: 532; 89. (18) Beckmann, *7*, **6**: 437; 90. (19) Beckmann, *25*, **23**: 301; 90.

(20) Beckmann, *25*, **23**: 1572; 90. (21) Beckmann, *7*, **8**, 223; 91. (22) Beckmann, *7*, **21**: 239; 96. (23) Beckmann, *7*, **40**: 129; 02. (24) Beckmann, *7*, **46**: 853; 03. (25) Beckmann, *7*, **53**: 129; 05. (26) Beckmann, *7*, **53**: 137; 05. (27) Beckmann, *93*, **51**: 96; 06. (28) Beckmann, *93*, **51**: 236; 06. (29) Beckmann, *7*, **57**: 129; 07.

(30) Beckmann, *7*, **58**: 543; 07. (31) Beckmann, *7*, **63**: 177; 08. (32) Beckmann, *7*, **70**: 1; 10. (33) Beckmann, *93*, **74**: 291; 12. (34) Beckmann, Fuchs and Gernhardt, *7*, **18**: 473; 95. (35) Beckmann and Gabel, *25*, **39**: 2611; 06. (36) Beckmann and Hanslian, *93*, **77**: 275; 12. (37) Beckmann and Hanslian, *93*, **80**: 221; 13. (38) Beckmann and Haring, *93*, **77**: 90; 12. (39) Beckmann and Haring, *7*, **79**: 177; 12.

(40) Beckmann and Junker, *93*, **55**: 371; 07. (41) Beckmann and Klopfer, *7*, **65**: 289; 09. (42) Beckmann and Liesche, *93*, **85**: 31; 14. (43) Beckmann and Liesche, *7*, **88**: 23; 14. (44) Beckmann and Liesche, *7*, **88**: 419; 14. (45) Beckmann and Liesche, *7*, **89**: 111; 14. (46) Beckmann and Maxim, *7*, **89**: 411; 14. (47) Beckmann and Maxim, *25*, **47**: 2875; 14. (48) Beckmann and Schliebs, *13*, **289**: 71; 96. (49) Beckmann and Stock, *7*, **17**: 107; 95.

(50) Beckmann and Weber, *93*, **74**: 297; 12. (51) Beckmann and Weber, *7*, **78**: 725; 12. (52) Behrend, *7*, **10**: 265; 92. (53) Benrath, *93*, **54**: 328; 07. (54) Berkeley and Appleby, *5*, **85**: 489; 11. (55) Biltz, *7*, **19**: 385; 96. (56) Biltz, *Practical Methods for Determining Molecular Weights*. Easton, 1899. (57) Biltz, *7*, **40**: 185; 02. (58) Biltz, *13*, **331**: 334; 04. (59) Biltz, *93*, **82**: 438; 13.

(60) Biltz and Clinch, *93*, **40**: 218; 04. (61) von Bosse, *Diss.*, Leipzig, 1911. (62) Bourion and Rouyer, *34*, **176**: 1708; 23. (63) Bourion and Rouyer, *34*, **178**: 1171; 24. (64) Brühl and Schröder, *25*, **37**: 2512; 04. (65) Bruner, *180*, **1901**: 464. (66) Bruni and Berti, *36*, **30 II**: 317; 00. (67) Bruni and Sala, *36*, **34 II**: 479; 04. (68) Buchanan, *174*, **39 II**: 529; 98. (69) Büchner, *64P*, **20**: 322; 17.

(70) Burt, *4*, **85**: 1339; 04. (71) Cann and Cheek, *45*, **17**: 512; 25. (72) Carlson, *Klason Festschrift*, **1910**: 251. (73) Carrara, *36*, **24 II**: 504; 94. (74) Donnan, Bassett and Fox, *4*, **81**: 939; 02. (75) Drucker, *7*, **74**: 612; 10. (76) Drucker and Weissbach, *7*, **117**: 209; 25. (77) E. I. du Pont de Nemours & Co., Wilmington, Del., *0*. (78) Dutoit and Friderich, *27*, **19**: 321; 98. (79) Dziewónski, *25*, **36**: 962; 03.

(80) Dziewónski and Leyko, *25*, **47**: 1679; 14. (81) Eijkman, *176*, **1**: 47; 03. (82) Ephraim, *93*, **58**: 338; 08. (83) Erdmann and Unruh, *93*, **32**: 413; 02. (84) Eremie-Popa, *Diss.*, Leipzig, 1903. (85) Fox and Gauge, *4*, **99**: 1075; 11. (86) Frankland and Farmer, *4*, **79**: 1356; 01. (87) Franklin and Kraus, *11*, **21**: 8; 99. (88) Gabel, *Diss.*, Leipzig, 1906. (89) Gerlach, *91*, **24**: 106; 85.

(90) Gerlach, *91*, **26**: 413; 87. (91) Gordon, Henderson and Harrington, *7*, **27**: 425; 98. (92) Griffiths, *410*, **18**: 89; 1825. (93) von Halban, *7*, **67**: 129; 09. (94) Hantzsch, *25*, **42**: 68; 09. (95) Hantzsch and Hofmann, *25*, **44**: 1776; 11. (96) Hantzsch and Shibata, *93*, **73**: 309; 12. (97) Haring, *Diss.*, Leipzig, 1910. (98) Helff, *7*, **12**: 196; 93. (99) Hellwig, *93*, **25**: 157; 00.

(100) Henderson and Heilbron, *4*, **99**: 1887; 11. (101-102) Herz and Schuftan, *7*, **101**: 269; 22. (103) Hite, *11*, **17**: 507; 95. (104) Hunter, *50*, **10**: 330;

06. (105) Innes, *4*, **79**: 261; 01. (106) Innes, *4*, **81**: 682; 02. (107) Isaachsen, *7*, **8**: 145; 91. (108) Jablczyński and Kon, *4*, **123**: 2953; 23. (109) Joannis, *34*, **115**: 820; 92.

(110) Johnston, *174*, **45 I**: 193; 06. (111) Johnston, *174*, **45 II**: 855; 08. (112) Jones, *11*, **19**: 581; 97. (113) Jones, *7*, **31**: 114; 99. (114) Jones, *11*, **27**: 16; 02. (115) Jones and Getman, *7*, **46**: 244; 03. (116) Jones and Getman, *11*, **31**: 303; 04. (117) Jones and Getman, *11*, **32**: 338; 04. (118) Jones and McMaster, *11*, **35**: 316; 06. (119) Jones and Mahin, *7*, **69**: 389; 09.

(120) Jüttner, *7*, **38**: 76; 01. (121) Junker, *Diss.*, Leipzig, 1907. (122) Kahlenberg, *50*, **5**: 339; 01. (123) Kahlenberg, *50*, **6**: 45; 02. (124) Kerler, *Diss.*, Erlangen, 1894. (125) Kirchhoff, *Diss.*, Leipzig, 1902. (126) Klopfer, *Diss.*, Leipzig, 1908. (127) Knecht and Batey, *290*, **25**: 194; 09. (128) Knecht and Batey, *4*, **101**: 1189; 12. (129) Kohler, *11*, **24**: 385; 00.

(130) Koppel and Blumenthal, *93*, **53**: 228; 07. (131) Koppel and Cahn, *93*, **60**: 53; 08. (132) Krafft, *25*, **32**: 1584; 99. (133) Krafft and Strutz, *25*, **29**: 1328; 96. (134) Krafft and Wiglow, *25*, **28**: 2573; 95. (135) Kreider and Jones, *11*, **45**: 282; 10. (136) Krüss and Thiele, *93*, **7**: 52; 94. (137) Kurilov, *7*, **24**: 697; 97. (138) Laing, *4*, **113**: 435; 18. (139) Landsberger, *93*, **17**: 422; 98.

(140) Langlet, *7*, **56**: 624; 06. (141) Legrand, *6*, **59**: 423; 35. (142) Lehner, *25*, **36**: 1105; 03. (143) Lespieau, *34*, **125**: 1094; 97. (144–145) Ley, *7*, **22**: 77; 97. (146) Ludlam, *4*, **81**: 1193; 02. (147) McBain and Coleman, *83*, **15**: 27; 19. (148) McBain and Taylor, *7*, **76**: 179; 11. (149) McIntosh and Archibald, *62*, **205**: 120; 05. *7*, **55**: 150; 06.

(150) Marckwald and Chwolles, *25*, **31**: 791; 98. (151) Mascarelli and Musatty, *36*, **41 I**: 73; 11. (152) Meldrum and Turner, *4*, **93**: 876; 08. (153) Meldrum and Turner, *4*, **97**: 1605; 10. (154) Meldrum and Turner, *4*, **97**: 1805; 10. (155) Meyer and Desamari, *25*, **42**: 2809; 09. (156) Meyer and Jaeger, *25*. **36**: 1555; 03. (157) Michael and Hibbert, *13*, **390**: 68; 12. (158) Moles, *132*, **10**: 30; 12. (159) Moles, *7*, **90**: 70; 15.

(160) Moles and Gomez, *7*, **90**: 594; 15. (161) Mulder, *Schiek. Verhandel. Rotterdam*, **1864**: 90. (162) Muthmann, *25*, **31**: 1829; 98. (163) Oddo, *36*, **29 II**: 330; 99. (164) Oddo, *36*, **31 II**: 222; 01. (165) Oddo, *36*, **32 II**: 107; 02. (166) Oddo, *36*, **32 II**: 123; 02. (167) Oddo and Serra, *36*, **29 II**: 318; 99. (168) Oddo and Serra, *36*, **29 II**: 343; 99. (169) Orndorff and Cameron, *11*, **17**: 517; 95.

(170) Orndorff and Terrasse, *11*, **18**: 173; 96. (171) Orndorff, Terrasse and Morton, *11*, **19**: 845; 97. (172) Oswald, *6*, **1**: 32; 14. (173) Pařizek and Šulc, *25*, **26**: 1408; 93. (174) Patrick, Hyden and Milan, *50*, **29**: 1004; 25. (175) Peddle and Turner, *4*, **99**: 685; 11. (176) Pfeiffer, *25*, **47**: 1580; 14. (177) Piccini, *93*, **8**: 115; 95. (178) Prideaux and Green, *50*, **28**: 1273; 24. (179) Raoult, *6*, **20**: 297; 90

(180) Riiber, *25*, **34**: 1060; 01. (181) Rimini and Olivari, *36*, **37 II**: 227; 07. (182) Rosenheim and Liebknecht, *13*, **308**: 40; 99. (183) Rosenheim, Schapiro and Italiener, *93*, **129**: 196; 23. (184) Rosenheim and Woge, *93*, **15**: 283; 97. (185) Rouyer, *34*, **180**: 1934; 25. (186) Rügheimer and Rudolfi, *13*, **339**: 311; 05. (187) Rupp, *7*, **53**: 693; 05. (188) Sakurai, *4*, **61**: 989; 92. (189) Salvadori, *36*, **26 I**: 237; 96.

(190) Schaefer and Hein, *93*, **100**: 249; 17. (191) van Scherpenberg, *70*, **35**. 346; 16. (192) Schlamp, *7*, **14**: 272; 94. (193) Scholl and Berblinger, *25*, **36**: 3427; 03. (194) Schroeder, *93*, **44**: 1; 05. (195) Schroeder and Steiner, *52*, **79**: 49; 09. (196) Sidgwick, *4*, **117**: 396; 20. (197) Skinner, *4*, **61**: 339; 92. (198) Sluiter, *64P*, **17**: 1036; 15. (199) Smits, *7*, **39**: 385; 01.

(200) Snethlage, *7*, **90**: 1; 15. (201) Speyers, *50*, **1**: 766; 96. (202) Steiner, *Diss.*, Giessen, 1906. (203) Stobbe and Posnjak, *13*, **371**: 287; 09. (204) Timofeev, *53*, **35**: 644; 03. (205) Tinkler, *4*, **95**: 921; 09. (206) Tollens, *25*, **48**: 489; 15. (207) Trautz and Anschütz, *7*, **56**: 236; 06. (208) Trilling, *Diss.*, Erlangen, 1895. (209) Turner, *4*, **97**: 1184; 10.

(210) Turner, *4*, **99**: 880; 11. (211) Turner and Bissett, *4*, **105**: 1777; 14. (212) Turner and English, *4*, **105**: 1786; 14. (213) Turner and Pollard, *182*, **29**: 349; 13. (214) Turner and Pollard, *4*, **105**: 1751; 14. (215) Vandenberghe, *93*, **10**: 47; 95. (216) Virtanen, *13*, **424**: 150; 21. (217) Waentig, *7*, **68**: 513; 09. (218) Waentig and Pescheck, *7*, **93**: 529; 19. (219) Walden, *25*, **32**: 2862; 99.

(220) Walden, *7*, **55**: 281; 06. (221) Walden, *25*, **39**: 658; 06. (222) Walden, *7*, **75**: 555; 10. (223) Walden, *134*, **8**: 1161; 14. (224) Walden, *134*, **9**: 233; 15. (225) Walden, *134*, **9**: 509; 15. (226) Walden, *134*, **9**: 1021; 15. (227) Walden, *134*, **9**: 1485; 15. (228) Walden, *7*, **94**: 295; 20. (229) Walden and Centnerszwer, *7*, **39**: 513; 02.

(230) Walden and Centnerszwer, *7*, **55**: 321; 06. (231) Walker and Lumsden, *4*, **73**: 502; 98. (232) Wallace, *4*, **7**: 77; 55. (233) Walther, *25*, **37**: 78; 04. (234) Washburn and Read, *1*, **41**: 729; 19. (235) Wedekind, *7*, **45**: 235; 03, (236) Weitz and Nelken, *13*, **425**: 187; 21. (237) Weitz, Roth and Nelken, *13*, **425**: 161; 21. (238) Werner, *93*, **15**: 1; 97. (239) Woelfer, *Diss.*, Halle, 1894. *8*, **57**: 91; 96.

(240) Zeisel and Stocket, *57*, **34**: 1327; 13. (241) Baker, *135*, **36**: 203; 77. (242) Brauner, *182*, **17**: 65; 01. (243) Bredig and Joyner, *9*, **24**: 285; 18. (244) Farmer, *4*, **83**: 1440; 03. (245) Hantzsch and Caldwell, *7*, **61**: 227; 07. (246) Herz and Knoch, *93*, **46**: 460; 05. (247) Hutchinson and Pollard, *4*, **69**: 212; 96. (248) Jost, *25*, **39**: 4327; 06. (249) Konovalov and Plotnikov, *53*, **31**: 1020; 99.

(250) Kremers, *8*, **99**: 25; 56. (250.5) Kurovski, *25*, **43**: 1078; 10. (251) Lobry de Bruyn and Jungius, *70*, **22**: 421; 03. (252) Matignon, *34*, **133**: 289; 01. (253) Muthmann and Nagel, *25*, **31**: 2009; 98. (254) Naumann, *25*, **43**: 313; 10. (255) Nernst and Hohmann, *7*, **11**: 352; 93. (256) Rosenheim and Levy, *25*, **40**: 2166; 07. (257) Rosenheim and Stadler, *93*, **49**: 1; 06. (259) Schlenk, *13*, **394**: 178; 12.

(261) Schmidlin, *25*, **45**: 3171; 12. (262) Stolba, *52*, **90**: 193; 63. (263) Strömholm, *7*, **44**: 63; 03. (263.5) Tanatar and Kurovski, *53*, **40**: 580; 08. (264) Timmermans, *28*, **20**: 16; 06. (265) Vandenberghe, *186*, **1899**: 657. (266) Vandenberghe, *186*, **1900**: 206. (267) Vandenberghe, *186*, **1903**: 908. (268) Vandenberghe, *186*, **1904**: 821. (269) Vorländer and Schilling, *25*, **32**: 1876; 99.

(270) Walden, *Molekulargrössen von Elektrolyten in nichtwässerigen Lösungsmitteln.* Dresden and Leipzig, Steinkopff, 1923. (271) Werner and Gubser, *25*, **34**: 1579; 01.

P-T-X RELATIONS FOR SYSTEMS OF TWO OR MORE COMPONENTS AND CONTAINING TWO OR MORE PHASES (L-V, L_I-L_{II}-V AND S-L-V SYSTEMS)

F. C. KRACEK

CONTENTS

ABBREVIATIONS AND SYMBOLS

L (resp. L_I, L_{II}) Liquid phase.

S Solid phase.
V Vapor phase.
M % Mole %.

C g B/100 g H_2O.
crit. Critical point.
max. Maximum.
x_B Mole fraction of B.

m Values in the metastable regions.
E Eutectic point.
U Transformation temperature or incongruent melting point.

† Saturated solution.

Bold-face values indicate triple points.

The crystal phases (Bodenkörper) are indicated on the central line and apply to all the succeeding values until a new phase is indicated.

MATIÈRES

ABRÉVIATIONS ET SYMBOLES

L (resp. L_I, L_{II}) Phase liquide.

S Phase solide.
V Phase vapeur.
M % Pourcentage moléculaire.

C g de B/100 g H_2O.
crit. Point critique.
max. Maximum.
x_B Fraction moléculaire de B.

m Valeurs dans les régions métastables.
E Point eutectique.
U Température de transformation ou point de fusion incongruent.

† Solution saturée.

Les chiffres en caractères gras sont des points triples.

Les phases cristallines (Bodenkörper) sont indiquées sur la ligne centrale et se rapportent à toutes les valeurs successives, jusqu'à ce qu'une nouvelle phase soit indiquée.

INHALTSVERZEICHNIS

ABKÜRZUNGEN UND ZEICHEN

L (bezw. L_I, L_{II}) Flüssigkeitsphase.

S Bodenkörper.
V Dampfphase.
M % Mole %.

C g B/100 g H_2O.
crit. Kritischer Punkt.
max. Maximum.
x_B Molenbruch B.

m Werte im metastabilen Gebiet.
E Eutektischer Punkt.
U Transformationstemperatur oder inkongruenter Schmelzpunkt.

† Gesättige Lösung.

Fettgedruckte Zahlen bedeuten Tripelpunkte.

Die Bodenkörper sind längst der Mitte angegeben und beziehen sich auf alle folgende Werte bis zur nächst angegebenen Phase.

INDICE PAGE

ABBREVIAZIONI E SIMBOLI

L (oppure L_I, L_{II}) Fase liquida.

S Fase solida.
V Fase gassosa.
M % Percento molecolare.

C g di B/100 g H_2O.
crit. Punto critico.
max. Massimo.
x_B Frazione molecolare di B.

m Valori nelle regioni metastabili.
E Punto eutettico.
U Temperatura di trasformazione oppure punto di fusione incongruente.

† Soluzione satura.

I numeri scritti in nero indicano i punti tripli.

Le composizioni delle fasi cristalline (Bodenkörper) sono riportate nella linea centrale, e ognuna si riferisce a tutti i valore che seguono fin dove si trova indicata una fase nuova.

TWO-COMPONENT SYSTEMS—NON-AQUEOUS

Standard Arrangement, *v.* p. viii

A = **Argon**; B = $\mathbf{O_2}$

t = 82.1°K (173)

M % A		p_{mm}		M % A		p_{mm}	
Liq.	Vap.	O_2	A	Liq.	Vap.	O_2	A
0	0	300	0	13.6	20.6	260.0	67.5
3.3	5.8	290.5	17	92.7*	97.8	9.0	411
5.6	9.2	283.5	28.5	**100**	**100**	0	**411**
10.2	16	269.8	51.4				

* Satd. soln., solid phase, Argon.

A = **Argon**; B = $\mathbf{N_2}$ (168, 169); *cf.* (128)

See also p. 284, 309

85.11°K, Isotherm

Wt. % B	p_{mm}		Wt. % B	p_{mm}	
in system	B. P.*	Dew pt.‡	in system	B. P.*	Dew pt.‡
0	602.8	602.8	65.3	1379	
10.0	747.5		74.05		1242
24.3		731.8	82.6	1562	
31.5	1005		100	1743	1743
52.8		968			

* Vapor space estimated as less than ⅓ % of total volume.
‡ Estimated from p-v diagram.

Isobars

Wt. % B	p_{mm} = 500	760	1000	1500
in system	B. P., °K			
0	83.45	87.26	89.93	94.18
10	81.42	85.25	87.98	92.32
31.5	78.65	82.40	85.06	89.29
65.3	75.86	79.41	81.95	85.97
82.6	74.82	78.30	80.76	84.70
99	73.94	77.35	79.78	83.64
100	73.87	77.28	79.71	83.57
	Dew points, °K			
24.3	81.79	85.46	88.04	92.15
52.8	79.41	82.97	85.40	89.33
74.05	77.22	80.66	83.08	86.93

A = $\mathbf{O_2}$; B = $\mathbf{N_2}$, *see also* Fig. 1 and p. 309 (219, 223, 297)

Critical region

M % A	t, °C	Liquid boundary		Vapor boundary	
		v, cm³/g	$p_{atm.}$	v, cm³/g	$p_{atm.}$
0	−147.13 crit.		33.49		
Air	−150.12		25.04		23.68
	−146.32	1.91	29.85		
	−144.35	1.98	32.5		
	−144.12		33.0		30.9

A = O_2; B = N_2, Critical region.—(*Continued*)

M % A	t, °C	Liquid boundary		Vapor boundary	
		v, cm³/g	$p_{atm.}$	v, cm³/g	$p_{atm.}$
Air	−143.35		34.0	5.32	32.0
	−143.14				32.3
	−142.35	2.17	35.3		33.5
	−142.0		35.7	4.61	34.1
	−141.35	2.28	36.5		35.3
	−141.0	2.63	36.9	3.95	36.1
	−140.9	2.67	37.1	3.82	36.4
	−140.8	2.76	37.2	3.78	36.6
	−140.73 crit.	2.86	37.25	3.64	36.9
	−140.63 max.			3.33	37.2
50.0	−140.95	0.00203*	30.1	0.00986*	27.7
	−138.02	.00225	34.2	.00842	32.0
	−135.95	.00245	37.4	.00735	35.0
	−134.50	.00266	39.5	.00645	37.6
50.0	−133.00	0.00314	41.5	0.00514	40.5
	−132.66 crit.	.00358	41.9	.0046	41.3
	−132.64			.00366	41.9
	−132.64			.00455	41.5
	−132.61			.00373	41.95
	−132.61			.0044	41.6
	−132.53 max.			.00404	41.9
75.0	−128	0.00244*	42.2	0.00609*	40.9
	−125.95	.00287	45.5	.00474	44.7
	−125.75	.00307	45.7	.00448	45.1
	−125.65	.00321	45.8	.00433	45.35
	−125.60 crit.	.00336	45.9	.00419	45.5
	−125.53 max.			.00375	45.85
100	−118.82 crit.		49.7		

* Volume of system referred to 0°C and 1 atm. as unity.

Values of p in atm. and of Mol % O_2 in coexisting liquid and vapor phases; C = Mol % O_2 in vapor (66, 67, 173); *cf.* (40, 128, 389)

	t, °C	M % O_2 in liquid											
		0	10	20	30	40	50	60	70	80	90	95	100
p	−198.68	0.702	0.6521	0.6015	0.5505	0.4994	0.4474	0.3937	0.3378	0.2775	0.2106		0.1380
C		0.0	2.68	5.48	8.54	12.04	16.26	21.65	29.02	40.06	58.98	74.79	100
p	−194.03	1.214	1.126	1.038	0.9535	0.8651	0.7777	0.6873	0.5934	0.4944	0.3868		0.2687
C		0.0	3.04	6.22	9.69	13.65	18.39	24.35	32.33	43.93	62.81	77.74	100.0
p	−182.63	3.689	3.439	3.186	2.931	2.674	2.414	2.152	1.886	1.613	1.331		1.033
C		0.0	3.86	7.98	12.50	17.61	23.60	30.90	40.18	52.69	70.80	83.44	100
p	−173.19	7.634	7.131	6.630	6.127	5.624	5.120	4.613	4.102	3.583	3.050		2.496
C		0.0	4.63	9.54	14.88	20.84	27.68	35.77	45.69	58.35	75.41	86.46	100
p	−163.08	14.58	13.62	12.68	11.76	10.86	9.96	9.066	8.172	7.271	6.357		5.415
C		0.0	5.64	11.43	17.54	24.17	31.55	40.02	50.09	62.47	78.40	88.30	100.0
p	−153.21	24.94	23.25	21.63	20.08	18.59	17.17	15.76	14.38	12.99	11.60		10.15
C		0.0	6.75	13.52	20.48	27.82	35.78	44.63	54.78	66.76	81.39	90.09	100
p	−148.13	31.94	29.75	27.69	25.73	23.88	22.10	20.35	18.65	16.95	15.24		13.47
C		0.0	7.53	14.85	22.20	29.81	37.91	46.79	56.81	68.47	82.49	90.71	100

A = O_2; B = CO_2, *see also* Fig. 2 (188, 189)
Critical region

M % A	t, °C	Liquid boundary		Vapor boundary	
		v*	$p_{atm.}$	v*	$p_{atm.}$
0	31.2 crit.		72.9		
10.53	17.6	0.00277	88.3	0.00796	66.2
	20.3	.00312	88.3	.00683	72.0
	22.0 crit.	.00363	86.8	.00599	76.4
	22.7			.00345	85.5
	22.7			.00554	78.7
	23.3 max.			.00469	82.8
20.03	9.6	0.00296	102.7	0.00881	65.3
	11.4	.00318	100.9	.00807	69.4
	12.5 crit.	.00337	99.7	.00752	72.25
	14.0			.00369	97.6
	14.0			.00681	76.8
	15.4			.00413	94.9
	15.4			.00602	82.1
	16.3 max.			.00498	89.2
100.0	−118.82 crit.		49.7		

* v = Volume of system referred to 20° and 1 atm. as unity.

A = O_2; B = Cu (132, 164, 339, 393, 421)

t, °C	O_2/2Cu in liq.*	p_{mm}
Cu + L_I		
1 083	0	
1 082	0.00036	
1 075	0.00516	
1 069	0.00779	
1 064	0.01516	
Cu_2O + L_I		
1 064	0.01560	
1 096	0.02098	
1 119.2		0.028
1 129	0.02817	
1 050.4		0.035
1 166	0.04037	
1 184.6		0.041

* Mole ratio.

t, °C	O_2/2Cu in liq.*	p_{mm}
Cu_2O + L_I + L_{II}‡		
1 195	0.0918	
1 195	0.4695	
Cu_2O + L_{II}		
1 235	0.500	0.6
1 231.3	{0.5162, 0.5256}	0.95
1 230.1		1.03
1 233.8		1.54
1 221.8		3.5
1 211.7		9.8
1 206.0	0.5544	
1 201.8	0.5616	
1 200.8		16.5
1 196.9		22.2
1 185.4		33
1 183.0	0.5743	
1 175.1		57.4
1 154.6		92.0
1 153.3		89.0
1 150.0		115.5
1 150.0	0.599	107
1 144.7		127.0
1 139.9		167.7
1 134.8		157.1
1 131.3		219.7
1 123.0		205.5
1 120.0	0.617	220
1 109.2		257
1 109.0	0.6271	

* Mole ratio.

t, °C	O_2/2Cu in liq.*	p_{mm}
Cu_2O + L_{II}		
1 100.3		302
1 096.5		314.5
1 091.9		344.5
1 090.1		387.5
1 088.5		353.5
1 085.5		393
1 085.3		361
1 084.2		373.5
1 081.2	0.6369	
Cu_2O + CuO + L_{II}		
1 080.2E	(0.638)	402.5
CuO + L_{II}		
1 083.8		450
1 088.7		512
1 089.5	0.6422	
1 092.6		601
1 096.4		671
1 097.2		722
1 105.7		939
1 107.8	0.6715	
1 119.0		1 258
1 120.0	0.675	1 320
1 120.5	0.678	
1 130.0		1 716
1 135.8		2 020
1 150.0	0.699	3 280
1 160.0	0.7245	
1 171.0		6 700
1 193.0	0.7345	

* Mole ratio.

A = O_2; B = **Cu**.—(*Continued*)

t, °C	O_2/2Cu in liq.*	p_{mm}
	$CuO + L_{II}$	
1 204.4		16 090
1 210.6		24 150
1 216.5	0.7585	
1 225.0	0.7705	
1 232.5		44 700

t, °C	O_2/2Cu in liq.*	p_{mm}
	Unsaturated solutions	
1 080.7	0.638	406.5
1 081.5	0.638	412
1 085.0	0.638	435
1 120	0.649	482
1 150	0.635	389
1 150	0.651	832
1 150	0.678	1 497

* Mole ratio.

‡ The composition of the immiscible liquids changes but slightly with temperature, the change being in direction toward increased mutual solubility as temp. increases. Two liquid layers persist above 1400°.

A = H_2; B = CO_2 (445): Critical region

Vol. % B	*t*, °C	Liquid boundary v*	Liquid boundary $p_{atm.}$	Vapor boundary v*	Vapor boundary $p_{atm.}$
4.99	15.3	0.00253	102.9	0.01105	57.2
	21.5	.00288	100.0	.00851	67.9
	26.8	.00381	93.2	.00582	81.75
	27.1 crit.	.00404	91.85	.00560	83.0
	27.3			.00425	90.5
	27.3			.00537	84.6
	27.5 max.			.00478	87.4
10.06	16.9			0.00940	67.8
	22.8			.00686	83.2
	24.2 crit.	0.00372	114.3	.00623	87.9
	25.0			.00410	108.4
	25.0			.00563	92.9
	26.45 max.			.00468	101
20.1	15.35			0.00877	79.1
	20.9			.00632	101.5
	22.2			.00595	106.4
	22.8 max.			.00498	120
0.0	31.2 crit.		72.9		
100.0	−239.9 crit.		12.8		

* v = Fraction of normal volume (0°C, 1 atm.).

A = Cl_2; B = I_2 (38, 324, 380, 431)

L + V, values of total vapor pressure, mm

Vapor composition: *t*, °C \ M % B	46.5	49.8	50.3	52.7	Liquid composition: M % B \ *t*, °C	30	64	80
10		13		14	59.6	52.0		
20		25	24	22.5	56.7	51.8		
25	43.5			31	51.1	50.7		
27.5	51		36.5		50.0	49.0		47.9
30		45	42.5	40	45.4		31.2	
40		72			45.3	35.2		
50		119			44.2	29.8		
60		191			38.6		11.4	
70		299						
80.3		454						
90.4		660						
96.6		808						

Saturated solutions

t, °C	M % B L	M % B Vap.	p_{mm}
	Cl_2 (crys.)		
−102	**0**	**0**	
	ICl_3 (crys.)		
+30	0.1		
42.5	0.7		
60.5	1.0		
75	2.1		
94	7.9		
101	**25.0**		12 170

t, °C	M % B L	M % B Vap.	p_{mm}
	ICl_3 (crys.)		
100			11 710
96	29.2		
95.4			8 140
90.4			5 190
89	33.1		
85.3			3 550
78.7			2 285

A = Cl_2; B = I_2: Saturated solutions.—(*Continued*)

t, °C	M % B L	M % B Vap.	p_{mm}
	ICl_3(Crys.)		
73.6	37.6	10.3	
70.1			1 185
64.1			773
60	39.2	12.5	571
50			296
40	42.2	19.2	147
30	44.2	29.8	72
25			49.5
22.7	45.7	36.4	42
20m	46.1		
	ICl_3 + α-ICl		
22.4E	46	36.5	40.5
	α-ICl		
25	47.4	40.8	41.5
26			41
27.2	**50.0**	**49.0**	**39**
27.1			36
26			31
24			27
22.5			24.5
20	54.4		21.0

t, °C	M % B L	M % B Vap.	p_{mm}
	α-ICl		
15	56.8	51.8	16.0
13.5			14.3
10	59.2		12
	α-ICl + I_2		
7.9E	60.3	52.1	11
	$_2$I		
10	60.6		11.2
20	64.9		15.0
25			20
30	67.1		25
40	68.9		43
50	71.4		63
70	78.1		
100	90.9		>100
114.3	**100.0**	**100**	**91**
	Iβ-Cl		
12.0m	47.6		
13.9m	**50.0**		
7.0m	54.3		
0.9m	58.1		

A = Cl_2; B = $COCl_2$ (303)

Vapor pressures of 71.7 Wt. % B solution

t, °C	−15	−10	−5	0	+5	10	15	20	25	30	35	40
p_{atm}	1	1.32	1.63	1.97	2.33	2.72	3.14	3.60	4.09	4.62	5.22	5.88

A = **HCl**; B = C_2H_6, Ethane (323)

Retrograde condensation of first kind takes place in region between critical point and point of max. temp. of each mixture. The form of the critical curve is analogous in all respects to that of system $N_2O + C_2H_6$ (*see* Fig. 9). The C_2H_6 employed showed a condensation range of 1.4 atm. at 21.4°C, owing to presence of unknown amount of impurities.

Critical region

M % A	*t*, °C	Liquid boundary v*	Liquid boundary $p_{atm.}$	Vapor boundary v*	Vapor boundary $p_{atm.}$
0	31.9 crit.	0.0065	48.9		
28.6	14.5	0.00345	44.5	0.0142	42.2
	21.3	.00385	51.1	.0112	49.0
	25.4	.00435	55.2	.0095	53.8
	27.4 {crit. max.	.0058	57	.0058	57
38.3	14.0	0.0033	45.5	0.0137	42.0
	21.3	.00355	53.1	.0106	51.6
	25.4	.0038	57.6	.0084	56.4
	27.3 {crit. max.	.0054	59.3	.0054	59.3
59.6	14.1	0.0028	46.9	0.0134	45.8
	21.2	.0031	54.0	.0107	53.4
	25.4	.0034	58.9	.0092	58.4
	30.2	.0042	65.1	.0062	64.8
	30.5 crit.	.0048	65.4		
	30.6 max.				65.3
86.8	13.7	0.0021	42.1	0.0173	40.4
	21.3	.0023	50.0	.0139	47.8
	25.4	.0024	54.4	.0123	52.7
	30.2	.0025	59.9	.0109	58.2
	41.5	.0031	75.3	.0072	74.2
	43.1 crit.	.0042	77.5		
	43.3 max.				77.3
100	51.3 crit.	0.0039	81.6		

* v = Volume referred to volume at 0° and 1 atm. as unity.

A = **HCl**; B = **C_2H_6O**, Methyl ether, critical phenomena (215)

A = **HCl**; B = **C_6H_7N**, Aniline

For vapor pressure of solutions saturated with the compound, AB(131 to 190°), *v.* (37, 232). For L-V isotherm 200°, *v.* (37).

A = **Br_2**; B = **I_2** (38, 210, 438)

t, °C	Atomic % B L	Atomic % B V	p_{mm}	*t*, °C	Atomic % B L	Atomic % B V	p_{mm}
Unsaturated solutions				151	70	48.5	770.1
50.2	25		331	159.4	80	50.3	757.8
	40		192	173.5	90	65.2	760.5
	50	8.2	86	187.5	100	100	771.7
	58	37.9	46	Solid solutions satd. with Br_2			
	100	100	3.5	19	32.5		83
92.8	50		372	23	35.9		85.8
	60	18.8	206.7	25	35.9		85
	70	27.7	160.5	31	43.6		79.5
	80	35.7	113	36	47.1		64.1
	100	100	30.7	40.4	50		48.2
58.7	0	0	771.2	Solid solutions satd. with I_2			
61.2	5		771.2	40.4	50.5		48.2
72.7	20	2.08	759.3	42	51.4		45.4
104.3	47.2	8.25	756.3	44.3	54.7		42.7
126	52	27.1	750	47.9	60.4		54.6
134.9	55		772.6	50	60.4		56.7
145.4	60	42.9	768.8	100	92.9		>200

A = **HBr**; B_1 = **SO_2**; B_2 = **H_2S**
L + V, 0 to 100% B, −30 to −80°C (426)

A = **I_2**; B_1 = **S**; B_2 = **Se**; B_3 = **Te** (175, 459)

A = **HI**; B = **H_2S**
L + V, 0 to 100% B, −30 to −80°C (426)

A = **SO_2**; B = **CO_2**, *see also* Fig. 3 and p. 285 (61, 85, 87, 88, 89, 90, 91)
L + V, critical region

Wt. % A	*t*, °C	Liquid boundary *v*, cm³/g	Liquid boundary $p_{atm.}$	Vapor boundary *v*, cm³/g	Vapor boundary $p_{atm.}$
0	31.2 crit.	2.24	72.9	2.24	72.9
10.35	26	1.621	61.4	8.658	45.2
	32	1.881	69.4	7.09	54.2
	37	2.055	74.6	5.357	63.5
	39 crit.	2.224	75.8	4.748	69.4
	40.4 max.				73.5
15.7	22	1.491	50.9	14.91	28.7
	27	1.506	56.3	12.53	33.6
	36.4	1.714	67	8.768	45.7
	46	1.963	76.5	5.988	60.4
	48.3 crit.	2.232	79.6	5.283	65.6
	49.8			5.034	67.4
	49.8			2.461	80.7
	52.1 max.				77
33.2	33.2	1.356	56.6	23.38	20.9
	44.5	1.455	69.5	14.21	31.2
	54.4	1.613	77.8	10.19	41.6
	65.3	1.982	87.8	7.023	56.4
	68 crit.	2.247	88.6	6.167	61.9
	70			5.738	66.2
	70			2.377	90
	72			5.244	70
	72			2.509	89.8
	74.2			4.420	78.2
	74.2			3.003	88
	75 max.				84
47.1	46.2	1.314	59.6	20.32	21.8
	56.8	1.495	68.9	14.09	30.2
	70.4	1.604	82.2	9.964	41.6
47.1	78.4	1.774	89.5	7.720	49.6
	83	2.002	92	6.851	57.2
	86 crit.	2.319	93	5.910	63.5
	88			5.530	68.4
	88			2.291	93.4
	89.6			4.897	71.8
	89.6			2.400	93.2
	91.4			4.500	75.1
	91.4			2.581	92.1
	93.4 max.				86
60.0	66.4	1.367	68.1	15.25	28.4
	70.8	1.402	70.0	13.68	30.8
	76.0	1.453	76	11.53	35.8
	81.0	1.510	81.4	10.11	40.5
	92	1.653	88.6	7.40	53.3
	98	1.831	92	6.114	61.4
	102	2.188	93.4	5.436	66.6
	106.5 crit.	2.509	94.2	4.794	73.6
	108.2			4.115	79.5
	108.2			2.688	93.1
	110			3.545	85.8
	110			3.188	89.6
	110.3 max.				87.5
70.9	61.5	1.232	55.6	21.59	20.4
	72.5	1.287	61.8	16.21	26.4
	81.4	1.311	68.6	12.71	32.4
	92.0	1.372	77.0	10.14	39.4
	102.8	1.511	84.0	7.514	51.2
	113.0	1.762	89.8	5.726	62.8
	119.5 crit.	2.489	90.8	4.331	73.4
	120.6			3.885	79.2
	120.6			2.553	90.4
	122.5 max.				85.5
81.4	71	1.123	48.8	19.10	21.4
	80	1.221	54.5	15.30	25.5
	94	1.319	63.2	10.85	34.6
	104	1.385	70.2	8.88	42.0
	114	1.418	77.4	7.05	51.2
	124	1.68	84.8	5.348	62.8
	132 crit.	2.204	86.6	3.907	75.8
	133.6			3.579	79.4
	133.6			2.466	86.0
	134.6 max.				84
91.1	81	1.125	40.4	18.40	21.4
	92	1.178	46.5	13.73	27.7
	102	1.216	52.2	10.98	33.8
	123.5	1.365	69.0	6.81	50.8
	133	1.483	75.2	4.94	62.3
	143	2.166	80.6	3.715	74.5
	145.4 crit.	2.192	81.4	3.20	78.0
	146.2 max.				80.4
100.0	157.2 crit.	2.07	78.2	2.07	78.2

A = **SO_2**; B = **C_2H_6**, Ethane, *see* Figs. 4 and 5 (282)

A = **SO_2**; B = **CH_3Cl**, Methyl chloride, *see also* Fig. 6 (86, 88, 89, 91, 92, 216)
Critical region

Vol. % A	*t*, °C	Liquid boundary *v*, cm³/g	Liquid boundary $p_{atm.}$	Vapor boundary *v*, cm³/g	Vapor boundary $p_{atm.}$
0	141.5		73.0		
25.0	100	1.562	33.0	12.42	31.3
	123	1.762	48.1	7.87	46.3
	127	1.808	51.6	7.17	49.0

A = SO_2; B = CH_3Cl: Critical region.—(*Continued*)

Vol. % A	t, °C	Liquid boundary v, cm³/g	Liquid boundary $p_{atm.}$	Vapor boundary v, cm³/g	Vapor boundary $p_{atm.}$
25.0	129	1.844	51.8	7.03	50.4
	136.8	1.950	59.0	5.48	57.8
	137.3	2.091	60.8	5.264	58.3
	141.5	2.232	64.5	4.206	61.4
	144.5 crit.	2.443	66.2	3.854	64.5
	145.8 max.				66
37.5	123	1.682	49	8.29	45.2
	135	1.760	58	5.87	54.8
	140	1.903	63.4	5.12	60.8
	145.5 max.			2.26	67.0
50.0	95.0	1.381	30.8	14.62	26.8
	110	1.468	39.4	10.72	36.0
	123.6	1.556	48.5	7.71	46.3
	132*	1.676	55.6	5.71	55.6
	138.8	1.820	61.2	5.25	59.6
	141	1.995	62.8	4.95	60.9
	144.4	2.054	66.4	4.66	64.0
	146 crit.	2.083	67.4	4.19	64.6
	147.2 max.				66.5
62.5	115.5	1.381	40.6	9.00	38.2
	128	1.481	48.5	6.93	47.4
	137.5	1.615	56.2	5.66	54.8
	145	1.782	63.2	4.52	62.2
	150 crit.	1.982	69.4	3.52	68.0
75.0	109	1.277	38.5	10.77	35.2
	122	1.332	45.4	7.73	44.5
	137	1.471	55.8	5.65	55
	143*	1.582	61.3	4.51	61.3
	146.5	1.692	66.2	3.71	65
	151	1.969	70.6	3.44	69
	152 crit.	2.025	71.4	3.41	70.2
	153 max.				71.4
87.5	112.4	1.296	40.3	9.14	36.5
	132	1.390	54	6.13	50.6
	144.5	1.547	64.7	4.62	61.4
	148	1.610	67.2	4.08	65.8
	155.5 {crit. max.	2.49	74.2	2.49	74.2
94.5	123	1.274	47.8	7.60	44.8
	136	1.375	58	5.57	55.2
	149	1.579	69.5	3.94	68.2
	152	1.680	71.8	3.28	70.8
	155.8 crit.	2.16	78.4		
100	157.2		78.2		

* Azeotropic indifferent point.

A = SO_2; B = Cu, System, L + V (387, 432)

A = H_2S; B = NH_3 (259, 349, 350, 353, 451)

t, °C	M % NH_3	$p_{atm.}$	t, °C	M % NH_3	$p_{atm.}$
$NH_4HS + L_I + V$			$NH_4HS + L_{II} + V$		
75.4	1.8		14.8		2.9
86.2	3.4*		<20.0	72.7	
87.7	3.8*		25		3.7
88.4	4.3		30		3.3
94.2		80.6	31.4		3.4
94.4	5.7		31.6		3.45
97.4	6.3*		31.7		3.5
101.1		89.7	35.7		4.6
102.4		91.9	39.6		4.3
103.0‡		93.9	39.7		4.4
			41.2	70.9	4.6
			41.4		4.6

A = H_2S; B = NH_3.—(*Continued*)

t, °C	M % NH_3	$p_{atm.}$	t, °C	M % NH_3	$p_{atm.}$
$NH_4HS + L_{II} + V$					
41.5		4.6	87.7		18.3
45.6		5.5	87.8		18.4
50.3		5.9	89.0		19.3
50.5		5.9	92.5		23
55		7.0	96		27
59.9		7.7	100		34
61.1		8.0	105		45
63.1		8.4	106.7		52
64.8		8.8	108.3	58.6	58
65		9	110.3		72
65.1		8.9	112.4		90
70.3		10.3	113.6		98
70.6		10.4	115.6		127
75		12	115.7	52.3	
77.8	66.7		116.5		172
79.4		13.7			
85		17			
85.7	65.6				

* These points lie near the three-phase line in L_I-V region.

‡ First critical endpoint.

A = H_2SO_4; B = NH_3

For diagrams and tables of melting and boiling points, *v.* (177).

A = N_2O_3; B = N_2O_4 (256)

Values of p_{mm}

t, °C \ Wt. % A	0	20	40	60	80	100
−24	70	110	170	268	460	865
−16	108	168	260	499	685	1250
− 8	172	262	398	623	1018	1785
0	266	400	600	925	1475	2480
+ 8	396	590	882	1331	2075	3360
16	598	860	1270	1857	2825	4430
20	684	1040	1520	2130	3260	5000

A = N_2O; B = CO_2, *see also* Figs. 7 and 8 (88, 93)

Critical region

Wt. % A	t, °C	Liquid boundary v, cm³/g	Liquid boundary $p_{atm.}$	Vapor boundary v, cm³/g	Vapor boundary $p_{atm.}$
0.0	31.2 crit.	2.24	72.9		
2.20	15.3	1.603	54.5	6.689	53.2
	19	1.658	58.7	5.933	57.9
	23.2*	1.712	64.1	5.055	64.1
	27.4	1.921	70.3	4.055	70.1
	30.8 crit.	2.33	74.3		74.1
	30.9 max.				74.2
4.08	16.5	1.553	55.6	6.458	54.7
	20.2	1.628	60.1	5.703	59.6
	23.3	1.704	64.3	5.024	63.6
	26.5*	1.817	68.7	4.232	68.7
	28.4	1.93	71.7	3.892	71.5
	30.7 crit.	2.356	74.5	3.213	74.3
	30.8 max.				74.4
7.42	16.2	1.591	54.9	6.60	53.8
	18.6	1.637	57.6	6.00	56.6
	21.4	1.684	61.6	5.53	60.8
	23	1.73	63.6	5.16	62.8
	26.6	1.823	69	4.42	68.7
	29*	1.962	72.2	3.77	72.2
	30.7 crit.	2.387	74.7	3.22	74.5
	30.8 max.				74.6
21.3	13.6	1.587	51.5	7.66	50.6
	15.3	1.630	53.8	6.70	52.8
	18.3	1.674	57.2	6.17	56.2
	23	1.761	63.4	5.26	62.6

A = N_2O; B = CO_2: Critical region.—(*Continued*)

Wt. % A	t, °C	Liquid boundary v, cm³/g	Liquid boundary $p_{atm.}$	Vapor boundary v, cm³/g	Vapor boundary $p_{atm.}$
21.3	25	1.805	66.1	4.78	65.8
	26.4	1.875	68.1	4.51	67.8
	29	2.006	72.0	3.90	71.7
	31.2 crit. max.	2.666	75.8	3.31	75.8
51.6	14.2	1.580	51.0	7.36	49.6
	17.1	1.595	54.3	6.70	53.1
	21.3	1.743	59.6	5.88	58.4
	24.2	1.773	64.0	5.22	62.8
	26	1.810	66.7	4.77	65.7
	28.4	1.869	69.9	4.33	69.0
	30.2	1.965	72.8	3.74	71.9
	32.2	2.135	75.7	3.11	75.0
	33 crit.	2.767	76.8		76.5
	33.1 max.				76.7
81.1	16.4	1.664	51.9	7.51	49.8
	18.8	1.711	54.4	6.94	52.5
	23.4	1.758	59.8	5.91	58.4
	26.4	1.805	64.1	5.15	63.0
	28.5	1.852	66.8	4.82	65.9
	30.8	1.947	69.8	4.30	69.2
	33.4	2.135	74.1	3.03	73.7
	34.4 crit.	2.89	75.8		75.5
	34.5 max.				75.6
91.9	16.5	1.578	51.0	7.56	48.9
	22	1.647	57.4	6.25	55.5
	25.1	1.667	61.0	5.72	59.2
	27.5	1.769	63.9	5.10	62.8
	30	1.884	67.1	4.64	65.9
	33.5	2.038	72.0	3.95	71.1
	35.2 crit.	2.268	74.5	3.34	73.6
	35.3 max.				74.3
100	36.0 crit.	2.39	71.9		

* Azeotropic indifferent point.

A = N_2O; B = C_2H_6, Ethane, *see also* Fig. 9 (212, 213, 214)
Critical region

Vol. % B	t, °C	Liquid boundary v*	Liquid boundary $p_{atm.}$	Vapor boundary v*	Vapor boundary $p_{atm.}$
0	36 crit.	0.0047	71.9		
18	2.85	0.00265	35.6	0.0205	35.3
	11.8	.0029	43.9	.0143	43.6
	19.1		51.8		51.5
	23	.0031	56.6	.0094	56.4
	29.8 max.			.0052	65.3
25	5.4	0.0027	38.1	0.0177	37.5
	13.2	.0029	45.6	.0131	45.1
	18.3	.0031	51.2	.0111	50.5
	22.2	.0032	55.6	.0094	55.1
	26.9	.0038	>61.4	.0066	<61.4
	27.6 crit.	.0043	>62.9	.0065	<62.9
	28.2 max.			.0046	63.4
43	9.8	0.0030		0.0150	40.6
	14.3		45.6	.0130	44.1
	20.5	.0035	52.3	.0096	51.8
	24.6	.0041	57.0	.0073	56.7
	26.05 crit. max.		58.4		
55	6.4	0.0036	36.9	0.0195	35.6
	11.35	.0038	41.1	.0164	40.0
	18.4	.0043	48.1	.0126	47
	25.4	.0050	55.5	.0084	54.9
	26.05 crit. max.	.0060	56.1	.0060	56.1

A = N_2O; B = C_2H_6, Ethane: Critical region.—(*Continued*)

Vol. % B	t, °C	Liquid boundary v*	Liquid boundary $p_{atm.}$	Vapor boundary v*	Vapor boundary $p_{atm.}$
76	5.25	0.0035	32.9	0.0217	31.3
	12.4	.0038	38.5	.0173	37
	18.4	.0041	44.0	.0140	42.2
	22	.0043	47.0	.0118	45.8
	26	.0048	51.1	.0092	50.3
	27.2	.0053	52.2	.0083	51.6
	27.9 crit. max.	.0066	52.6	.0066	52.6
100	32 crit.	.0064	48.8		

* v = Volume referred to 0°C and 1 atm. as unity.

A = NH_3; B = $(NH_2)_2$ (136, 244)

t, °C	Wt. % B	p_{mm}
	NH_3	
−77.6	**0**	**45.8**
−78		44.5
−79	8.5	41.2
	$NH_3 + (NH_2)_2$	
−80E	13.0	38.0
	$(NH_2)_2$	
−75	15.8	54
−70	19.5	76
−65	24.0	106
−60	28.9	146
−55	34.0	198
−50	39.5	253
−45	45.2	320
−40	51.1	397
−35	57.2	480
−30	63.3	562
−28	65.8	593
−26	68.3	617
−25	69.6	630
−24	70.8	641
−23	72.0	652
−22	73.3	661
−21	74.5	669
−20	75.7	676
−19	76.9	680
−18	78.1	683 max.
−17	79.3	683
−16	80.5	682
−15	81.6	679
−14	82.8	673
−13	84.0	665
−12	85.1	655
−11	86.2	640
−10	87.4	620
−8	89.6	575
−6	91.9	510
−4	94.0	420
−2	96.2	320
0	98.2	175
+1.8	**100.0**	**3.2**

A = NH_3; B = NH_4N_3 (75)

t, °C	Wt. % A	p_{mm}
	$NH_4N_3.2NH_3$	
−33	59.5	43.6
	NH_4N_3.(?)	
0	51	149.5

A = NH_3; B = NH_4NO_3
(130, 158, 190, 224)
Values of p_{mm}

M % B	0°	10°	20°
0	3221	4612	6429
19	1507		
20	1398		
21	1298		
22	1209		
23	1126		
24	1047	1591	
25	975	1489	
26	910	1395	
27	850	1309	
28	793	1226	
29	741	1151	
30	694	1080	1581
31	650	1015	1492
32	610	952	1408
33	574	897	1331
34	540	844	1259
35	507	795	1190
36	467	749	1126
37	449	707	1067
38	424	668	1011
39	400	632	959
40	377.5	599	911
41	357	568	865
42		540	823
43		514	783
44			745
45			709

t, °C	p_{mm}	M % B
	NH_4NO_3	
0	353.8	41.1
10	510.5	43.1
20	706	45.1

A = NH_3; B = NH_4Br (24, 31)

t, °C	p_{mm}	C
	$NH_4Br.3NH_3$	
8.7m	**1140**	**192**
	$NH_4Br.NH_3$	
−10m	405	208
−5 m	512	212
0 m	635	215
+5 m	780	218
	$NH_4Br.NH_3 + NH_4Br.3NH_3$	
6.5U	815	218.5
	$NH_4Br.NH_3$	
10	942	220
15	1130	226
20	1350	230
25	1590	235

A = NH_3; B = C_8H_{10}, *m*-Xylene
Values of *p* in atm. (99, 204, 329)

t, °C \ M % A	0	10	15	20	25	30	40	50
7.83	0.00303	2.05	2.96	3.64	4.17	4.56	5.07	5.38
9.82	0.00346	2.17	3.09	3.82	4.39	4.82	5.39	5.71
11.8	0.00397	2.24	3.20	3.99	4.60	5.07	5.70	6.06
13.8	0.00450	2.35	3.36	4.18	4.82	5.33	6.03	6.42
14.8	0.00480	2.40	3.43	4.29	4.96	5.49	6.17	6.58
16.8	0.00546	2.52	3.61	4.49	5.20	5.76	6.54	6.98
19.8	0.00663	2.66	3.82	4.79	5.57	6.19	7.08	7.61

t, °C \ M % A	60	70	80	90	92.5	95	97.5	100
7.83	5.50 (56.8–93.6%)*					5.51	5.55	5.63
9.82	5.87 (60.4–92.2%)*					5.89	5.94	6.03
11.8	6.23	6.26 (64.5–90.4%)*			6.27	6.29	6.35	6.46
13.8	6.62	6.68*‡		6.69	6.71	6.74	6.79	6.90
14.8	6.80	6.90	6.92	6.93	6.94	6.97	7.02	7.14
16.8	7.23	7.34	7.38	7.39	7.39	7.42	7.49	7.62
19.8	7.91	8.05	8.10	8.12	8.14	8.18	8.26	8.43

* Region of two liquid phases.
‡ 71–87.5 %.

Three phase, $L_I + L_{II} + V$

t, °C	$p_{atm.}$	M % A	
		L_I	L_{II}
−33.5	1	10	99.5
−20	1.8		
−10	2.8		
0	4.35		
+ 8	5.53	57.0	93.5
0	5.90	60.8	92.1
2	6.32	65.3	90.1
14	6.75	72.5	86.7
14.5*	6.86	81	

* Critical solution point.

A = NH_3; B = $C_2H_4(NH_2.HCl)_2$, Ethylenediamine hydrochloride (59)

A and B in equimolar proportions. The pressures correspond to $2NH_3 + C_2H_4(NH_2.HCl)_2 \leftrightarrows C_2H_4(NH_2)_2 + 2NH_4Cl$ + satd. soln. + V

t, °C	−23	−9.2	0	+12.4	16.8
p_{mm}	78–85	90–100	120–160	336	431

A = NH_3; B = NH_4CNS (69, 100, 129, 130, 131)
Values of p_{mm}

M % B	0°	10°	20°	M % B	0°	10°	20°
0	3 221	4 612	6 429	30	301.5	500	793
15	1 530			31	273	452.5	728
16	1 386			32	247	410	669
17	1 257			33	224.5	372.5	613
18	1 133			34	204	342	562
19	1 021	1 530		35	186.0	315.5	516
20	919	1 389		36	170.2	290.5	474
21	826	1 259		37	156.4	260.5	435.5
22	743	1 139		38	144.0	240.5	401.5
23	662	1 030	1 503	39	132.9	222.5	369.5
24	578	931	1 367	40	123.5	206.5	341
25	524	840	1 246	41	114.7	192.1	315
26	467	758	1 136	42	106.9	179.7	291.5
27	417.5	684	1 039	43		168.3	270
28	374	616	948	44			250.5
29	334.5	555	867				

M % B	30°	40°	M % B	30°	40°	M % B	30°	40°
0	8 749	11 658	39	575		44	395.5	593
35	789		40	533	790	45	368.5	554
36	726		41	494	735	46	344.5	518
37	672		42	457.5	683	47	322.5	485
38	622		43	425.5	636	48		456

t, °C	p_{mm}	M % B
	NH_4CNS	
0	105	42.3
10	165.2	43.3
20	235.3	44.9
30	322	47.0
40	407	49.8

A = NH_3; B = $Hg(CN)_2$
t = 0°C (71)

Wt. % NH_3	p_{mm}
20.72*	1067
20.93	1098
21.87	1200
22.36	1257
23.4	1362
24.33	1445
25.20	1536
26.10	1615
100.0	3221

* Satd. with $Hg(CN)_2.2NH_3$.

A = NH_3; B = $LiNO_3$ (100)

Wt. % B	t, °C	p_{mm}
	L + V	
63.66	15.5	487.5
	22.4	627.4
	30.05	818.1
	35.0	998.2
	$LiNO_3$	
	−13.0	239.3
	− 6.0	259.9
	+ 1.5	321.9
	8.5	382.9
63.66	9.5	392

A = NH_4Cl; B = $PbCl_2$, TlCl, $ZnCl_2$, $CdCl_2$, CuCl, $FeCl_3$ or LiCl (153)

A = CO_2; B = CaO (62, 420)

t, °C	p, mHg	Wt. % B*
	$CaCO_3$	
1240	30.0	9.2
1244.5	31.5	
1244.9	31.5	
1267.2	39.7	
1270.1	39.5	
1275.6	53.5	
1278.1	49.9	
	76.0	7.6
	83.6	7.8
	104.1	6.2
	92.7	4.6
	106.4	5.0
1296.0	107.3	
1296.9	106.2	
1304.8	108.3	
	109.4	4.0

A = CO_2; B = CaO.—(*Cont'd*)

t, °C	p, mHg	Wt. % B*
	$CaCO_3$	
1306.4	157.4	
1314.0	193.8	
1324.2	449.0	
1325.0	426.0	
1334.7	798.8	
1336.1	779.0	
1338.9	779.0	

* Free CaO.

A = $COCl_2$, Phosgene; B = $AlCl_3$ (143)

Wt. % B	p_{mm} 0°	25°
0	555	1406
5	540	1372
10	525	1335
15	508	1293
20	490	1243
25	462	1180
30	430	1107
35	394	1015
40	354	897
45	308	748
50	260	551
55		328

A = $COCl_2$, Phosgene; B = $CaAl_2Cl_8$ (144)

Wt. % B	p_{mm} 0°	25°
0	555	1405
5	551	1396
10	547	1387
15	542.5	1377
20	537.5	1364
25	529.5	1342
30	510.0	1301
35*	469.0	1212
t, °C	p_{mm}	Wt. % B
	$CaAl_2Cl_8.2COCl_2$ (?)	
0	493	32.5
25	1240	33.5

* Supersatd. solutions.

A = $COCl_2$, Phosgene; B = $SrAl_2Cl_8$ (142)
t = 25°C

Wt. % B	p_{mm}	Wt. % B	p_{mm}
0	1405	35	1350
5	1404	40	1287
10	1402	45	1185
15	1400	50	1140
20	1397	55*	867
25	1391	60*	664
30	1378		

* Supersatd. solutions.

A = $COCl_2$; B = $SrAl_2Cl_8$.—(*Continued*)

t, °C	p_{mm}	Wt. % B
$5SrAl_2Cl_8.9COCl_2$		
25	950	52.3

A = $COCl_2$, Phosgene; B = $BaAl_2Cl_8$ (142)

t, °C	p_{mm}	Wt. % B
$L_I + L_{II}$		
25	1402	50(L_{II})
$3BaAl_2Cl_8.8COCl_2$		
25	1340	55

A = $COCl_2$, Phosgene; B = $NaAlCl_4$ (142)

t = 25°C

Wt. % B	p_{mm}	Wt. % B	p_{mm}
0	1405	25	1379
5	1402	30	1354
10	1399	35	1308
15	1396	40*	1240
20	1391		

t, °C	p_{mm}	Wt. % B
$NaAlCl_4$		
25	1285	40

* Supersatd. solution.

For A = other C-compounds, *v.* the 𝕮-Table.

A = CuS; B = $CuSO_4$ (363)

A = Fe_2O_3; B = $FeCl_3$ (48, 428, 429)

t ± 2°C	$p_{atm.}$	t ± 2°C	$p_{atm.}$
$FeCl_3$ + FeOCl + V			
253	0.045	291	0.384
255	0.051	292	0.408
264	0.087	295	0.484
266	0.100	299	0.603
273	0.144	300	0.617
275	0.163	301	0.676
283	0.252		
FeOCl + L + V			
310	0.855	418	3.91
316	0.955	433	4.65
324	1.08	435	4.84
331	1.24	454	5.85
354	1.70	458	6.24
355	1.76	460	6.24
370	2.1	480	7.77
392	2.83	492	8.88
403	3.31	493	9.1
417	3.85		
FeOCl + Fe_2O_3 + V			
436	1.42	466	3.02
439	1.66	472	3.63
443	1.73	475	3.80
444	1.83	483	4.57
456	2.32	488	5.24
458	2.56	502	7.08
465	3.03	504	7.33

t ± 2°C	$p_{atm.}$
$FeCl_3$ + FeOCl + Fe_2O_3 + V	
110	5 × 10^{-8}
$FeCl_3$ + FeOCl (?) + L + V	
305	0.81
FeOCl + Fe_2O_3 + L + V	
525	11.7

𝕮-Table, The 𝕮-Arrangement

A = CCl_4, Carbon tetrachloride; B = C_2H_6O, Ethyl alcohol

Values of p_{mm} (377); *see also* p. 312

Wt. % A	34.8°	50°	60°	66°
0	173	312	446	544
2.57	221	413	601	741
7.02	225	428	630	780
15.75	226	430	637	788
23.31	223	427	637	789
28.32	220	427	630	782
41.75	206	403	600	752
51.14	193	381	571	716
56.13	187	369	554	700
60.94	179	355	534	677
72.87	156	317	487	614
79.98	142	292	453	576
89.77	122	257	404	520
100.0	103	223	354	462

A = CO_2; B = CH_3Cl, Methyl chloride (72, 84, 88, 89, 91, 160, 161, 211, 214); *see also* p. 286

This system resembles in all particulars the system CO_2—SO_2 (Fig. 3) and like the latter is characterized by very considerable pressure variation from the dew-point curve to the boiling-point curve within each constant total composition condensation loop. The critical points (crit.) and maximum temperatures (max.) are as follows:

Vol. % B	t, °C	$p_{atm.}$ L	$p_{atm.}$ V
0	31.2 crit.	72.9	
10.4	43 crit.	75.4	68
	45 max.		74
20.2	55.5 crit.	78	62
	60 max.		75.5
32.2	70.7 crit.	80	62
	74.5 max.		77
40.4	80 crit.	84.5	63.5
	84 max.		77.5
50.3	92.5 crit.	85	71.5
	94.8 max.		79
61.8	102.3 crit.	85	69
	105 max.		80
70.2	115 crit.	80	67
	117.5 max.		76
80	124 crit.	75.5	67
	126 max.		74
89.9	131 crit.	72	67
	133 max.		71
100	141.5 crit.	73	

A = CO_2; B = C_2H_2, Acetylene

Critical region (213, 214)

A = CO_2; B = C_2H_6, Ethane, *see also* Fig. 10 (213, 214, 221, 222)

Critical region

Vol. % B	t, °C	Liquid boundary v*	Liquid boundary $p_{atm.}$	Vapor boundary v*	Vapor boundary $p_{atm.}$
0	31.2 crit.	0.0044	72.9		
15	10.35	0.0028	49.45	0.0121	48.85
	16.0	.0030	56.32	.0098	55.72
	23.2 crit.	.0041	66.3	.0058	66.15
	23.35			.0046	66.52
	23.35			.0054	66.44
	23.4 max.			.0052	66.54
30	8.95	0.0031	49.07	0.0116	48.58
	14.95	.0035	56.28	.0087	55.82
	17.28	.0038	59.3	.0073	59.0
	18.68	.0045	61.2	.0058	61.1
	18.73	.0047	61.3	.0057	61.2
	18.8 {crit. max.			.0053	61.25
43	8.95	0.0034	48.45	0.0116	47.3
	14.95	.0039	55.3	.0084	54.5
	17.56	.0049	58.42	.0063	58.18
	17.62 {crit. max.			.0058	58.37
50	8.8	0.0035	47.5	0.0124	45.7
	9.1	.0035	47.7	.0122	45.95
	14.95	.0040	54.1	.0090	52.9
	17.55	.0049	57.2	.0068	56.6
	17.75	.0056	57.2	.0066	56.9
	17.85 crit.	.0061	57.15	.0065	57.0
	17.9 max.			.0063	57.1
100	32 crit.	0.0064	48.8		

* v = Volume referred to 0°C and 1 atm. as unity.

Solutions saturated with CO_2 (crys.)

t, °C	−80	−75	−70	−67	−65	−62.8
$p_{atm.}$	2.53	3.19	3.48	4.67	4.97	5.4
M % B				50		30

A = CO_2; B = $C_3H_7NO_2$, Urethane (196, 197, 198)

$L_I + L_{II}$ + V

Mixtures containing a suitable concentration of B (never exceeding 4%) exhibit (partial) liquid immiscibility up to the critical region.

t, °C	$p_{atm.}$	t, °C	$p_{atm.}$
26.0	63.1	33	73.4
27	64.5	34	75.0
28	65.85	35	76.6
29	67.3	36	78.25
30	68.75	37	80.0
31	70.3	37.3*	80.5
32	71.8		

* At this point the $L_I + L_{II}$ + V curve intersects the critical curve of the system; critical endpoint.

A = CO_2; B = $C_4H_{10}O$, Ethyl ether (348, 441, 442)

L + V (critical phenomena)

Liquid Wt. % A	Liquid $p_{atm.}$	Vapor Wt. % A	Vapor $p_{atm.}$
35°C			
14.6	7.7	82.9	6
25.9	15.5	88.7	9
36.6	27	91.1	23
46.6	43.6	93.8	31
50.2	48.4	95.9	57
54.2	58	97.9	60
59.2	70		
75*	74	75*	74
60°C			
14.6	15.5	82.9	9
25.8	23	88.7	15
32.8	48	91.1	46
37.6	58		
41.9	68		
44.4	77		
65*	85	65*	85

A = CO_2; B = $C_4H_{10}O$.—(*Continued*)

Liquid		Vapor	
Wt. % A	$p_{atm.}$	Wt. % A	$p_{atm.}$
100°C			
15.1	58	69.4	22
22.0	67	82.9	48
27.1	77	88.7	58
31.2	87		
36.6	94		
50*	94	50	94

* Critical point.

A = CO_2; B = C_5H_{12}, Isopentane
Critical phenomena (445)

A = CO_2; B = $C_6H_3N_3O_7$, Picric acid (139)

t, °C	$p_{atm.}$	t, °C	$p_{atm.}$
B (crys.)			
22.85	59.7	31.9*	73.2
25.5	63.1	98.4	212.7
28.3	67.2	98.9	192.6
29.6	69.4	99.9	173.9
30.4	70.5	101.1	155.9
30.8	71.2	102.9	135.3
31.2	71.8	104.9	117.8
31.4	72.3	106.5	101.8
31.6	72.6	108.1	90.2
31.8	72.9	121.5‡	

* First critical endpoint (pure CO_2 by same author 31.2°, 72.4 atm.); second critical endpoint unrealized.
‡ Triple point of B.

A = CO_2; B = $C_6H_5NO_2$, Nitrobenzene (198)

$L_I + L_{II} + V$, critical region

Two liquid phases exist in this system in the neighborhood of the critical point of A under conditions satisfying van der Waals' criteria for *double retrograde* condensation (van der Waals-Kohnstamm "Thermodynamik," Vol. 2, p. 382*ff.*). The phenomenon was not realized; approximate measurements are given for solutions up to 12.1 M % B. Between 9 and 12.1 M % B the three-phase ($L_I + L_{II} + V$) curve exhibits two critical points at *ca.* 29.9°, 67 atm. and 39.9°, 84 atm. respectively. The corresponding $L_{II} + V$ curve is established roughly to 40°, 101 atm.

A = CO_2; B = C_6H_7N, Aniline (359)

t, °C	$p_{atm.}$	t, °C	$p_{atm.}$
$AB + L_I + V$			
−0.6	33.3	12.8	46.5
+2.2	35.7	13.4	47.3
4.7	38.1	14.8	48.6
7.4	40.8	15.9	49.8
9.0	42.5	16.95	50.9
10.8	44.4	18	52

A = CO_2; B = C_6H_7N.—(*Continued*)

t, °C	$p_{atm.}$	t, °C	$p_{atm.}$
$AB + L_{II} + V$			
0	6	11.6	21.7
0.95	7.4	13.5	26.7
2	9	15.5	34.6
5	10.9	15.9	36.4
7	14	17.1	43.8
8.1	15	17.6	48.3
9.7	17.5	18	52
$L_I + L_{II} + V$			
Metastable		Stable	
8.7	41.8	19.7	54.1
9.85	42.8	20.7	55.4
10.0	43.2	21.5	56.3
10.9	43.9	25.15	61.1
11.5	44.8	26.3	62.7
11.85	45.1	30.25	68.4
13.25	46.6	33.9	74.0
13.95	47.4	35.8	77.1
16.0	49.7	37.15*	79.5
16.95	50.8		
17.8	51.8		
18	52		
$AB + L_I + L_{II}$			
18.0	52	18.2	80

* Critical solution point.

A = CO_2; B = C_7H_9N, Toluidines (359)

t, °C	$p_{atm.}$	t, °C	$p_{atm.}$
o-Toluidine			
$L_I + L_{II} + V$			
−7.5*	27.5	15.6	49.0
−2.1	31.5	19.4	53.5
+0.3	33.6	20.4	54.8
3.9	36.8	24.7	60.1
7.3	40.1	29.6	67.1
9.5	42.3	34.5	74.9
11.8	44.7	38.1**	80.8
m-Toluidine			
$AB + L_I + V$			
−3.4	30.8	2.9	36.2
−0.2	33.4	4.7	37.7
+1.9	35.3	5.7	38.6
$AB + L_{II} + V$			
−2.6	10.4	2.9	23.1
+0.6	16.5	5.0	31.5
$L_I + L_{II} + V$			
7.5	40.5	23.9	59.5
10.0	43.1	27.35	64.2
13.2	46.4	30.3	68.5
15.5	49.2	33.7	73.8
18.0	52.1	35.85	77.4
20.9	55.7	37.2**	79.6
$AB + L_I + L_{II} + V$			
6.3	39.2		
p-Toluidine			
$AB + L_I + V$			
−0.4	33.9	23.3	59.8
+5.1	39.1	25.6	62.4
9.6	43.6	27.0	64.3
13.1	47.6	29.7	67.7
17.5	52.7	30.8	69.0
19.8	55.5	31.5‡	70.0

A = CO_2; B = C_7H_9N.—(*Continued*)

t, °C	$p_{atm.}$	t, °C	$p_{atm.}$
$AB + L_{II} + V$			
29.7§	44	31.3	62.2
30.2	47.7	31.4	65.0
30.8	52.5	31.5‡	70.0
31.1	57.3		
$B + L_{II} + V$			
29.7§	44	34.0	32.5
30.3	43	36.2	26.8
32.0	38.2	44‖	0.0013
$L_I + L_{II} + V$			
31.5‡	70	35.05	75.7
32.8	72	37.75¶	80.4
33.9	73.9		

* Quadruple point.
** Critical solution point.
‡ $AB + L_I + L_{II} + V$.
§ $AB + B + L_{II} + V$.
‖ B, triple point.
¶ $L_I + L_{II} + V$, critical point.

A = CO_2; B = $C_{10}H_8$, Naphthalene (139)

t, °C	$p_{atm.}$	t, °C	$p_{atm.}$
$C_{10}H_8$			
25.2	62.1	31.7	71.4
27.7	65.4	31.95	71.9
29.5	68.1	32.2	72.3
30.3	69.3	32.4	72.7
30.9	70.3	32.8	73.7
31.4	70.9	33.0	74.1

A = CO_2; B = $C_{10}H_8$.—(*Continued*)

t, °C	$p_{atm.}$	t, °C	$p_{atm.}$
$C_{10}H_8$			
33.2	74.4	59.9	116
33.3*	74.6	61.3	103.3
58.5	201.7	63.5	88.5
58.8	184.0	65.1	79 2
59.1	164.0	66.5	67.9
59.3	146.0	68.3	58.3
59.7	131	79.7‡	0.0053

* First critical endpoint (pure CO_2, 31.2°, 72.4 atm., by same author); second critical endpoint unrealized.
‡ Triple point of B.

A = $CHCl_3$, Chloroform; B = $C_6H_4N_2O_4$, *m*-Dinitrobenzene (384.5, 423)

t, °C	p_{mm}	C
	m-$C_6H_4N_2O_4$	
23.5	157	
25.0		40.9
25.5	169.4	
27.9	185.3	
30.0		49.3
30.3	201.0	
33.5	224.6	
35.4	239.1	
38.4	262.8	
40		72.5
41	284.1	

A = CS_2; B = CH_4O, Methyl alcohol (79, 345)

t, °C	M % L_I	M % L_{II}	p_{mm}
$L_I + L_{II} + V$			
−15		81	*ca.* 70
0		76.8	154
+10	3.8	73.4	245
15	5.6	71.2	305
20	7.5	68.4	379
25	10.0	65.0	465
30	13.4	60.3	567
35	18.8	52.0	687
36	20.7	49	712
37	23.5	44	744
38	32	32	770

Isotherms—L + V

t, °C \ M % B	0	4.7	72.2	90.3	100
−10	78.4			80.5	
− 5	99.2			102	18.1
0	124.5			128	25.5
+ 5	156			160	35.5
10	193			199	48.9
15	237		303	246	65.8
20	290	373	375	303	88.5
25	353	458	460	371	117
30	424	557	561	451	152.2
35	510	676	680	545	198
40	609	813	819	656	254
45	723	976	979	785	322
50	857	1162	1168	935	406
55	1004	1375	1382	1108	506
60	1175			1305	627

A = CS_2; B = CH_4O: Isotherms—L + V.—(*Continued*)

t, °C \ M % B	11.7	19.4	26.4	30.7	52.9
30	563				
35	683				693
40	828	833	838	838	838
45	992	999	1002	1002	1002
50	1185	1193	1195	1195	1195
55	1405	1414	1416	1416	1416

A = $CHCl_3$, Chloroform; B = C_8H_9NO, Acetanilide (384.5, 423)

t, °C	p_{mm}	Wt. % B	t, °C	p_{mm}	Wt. % B
		C_8H_9NO			
20		10.7	45.2	390.5	
25.5	192.5		48.8	435.7	
30.0		14.5	50		23.7
32.8	255.2		51.1	465.0	
36.6	293.0		55.0	517.6	
40.0		18.7	55.1	519.5	
41.1	342.6		60		29.1

A = CH_4O, Methyl alcohol; B = C_2HCl_3O, Chloral, S-L-V (325)

A = CH_4O, Methyl alcohol; B = C_2H_6, Ethane
$L_I + L_{II}$ + V, critical vaporization-condensation region (220)

A = CH_4O, Methyl alcohol; B = C_3H_8, *n*-Propane
$L_I + L_{II}$ + V, critical vaporization-condensation region (217)

A = CH_4O, Methyl alcohol; B = C_4H_{10}, *n*-Butane
$L_I + L_{II}$ + V, critical vaporization-condensation region (218)

A = CH_4O, Methyl alcohol; B = C_5H_{12}, *n*- and *iso*-Pentane
$L_I + L_{II}$ + V, critical vaporization-condensation region (217, 218)

A = CH_4O, Methyl alcohol; B = C_6H_{14}, Hexane
$L_I + L_{II}$ + V, upper critical solution point 43.8°C, 550 mm, *p* approx. constant from 31 to 83% hexane (392), critical vaporization-condensation region (217). *See also* p. 287.

A = C_2HCl_3O, Chloral; B = C_2H_6O, Ethyl alcohol
For vapor pressure of solutions saturated with the compound AB (20 to 46°C) *v.* (37, 225, 231).

A = C_2H_2,* Acetylene; B = C_2H_6, Ethane (213, 214), *see also* Fig. 11

Vol. % B	t, °C	Liquid boundary v‡	Liquid boundary $p_{atm.}$	Vapor boundary v‡	Vapor boundary $p_{atm.}$
0	35.2		61		
27	7.6	0.0032	39.6	0.0162	38.25
	14.0	.0035	45.6	.0125	44.6
	22.2	.00425	54.6	.0083	53.9
	23.75	.0052	56.27	.0067	56.0
	23.8 crit.	.0056	56.25		
	23.85 max.			.0061	56.23
41	14.0	0.0038	48.2	0.0117	46.1
	19.35	.0044	53.7	.0091	52.0
	21	.0054	55.1	.0074	54.6
	21.05 crit.	.0055	55.1		
	21.15 max.			.0060	55.0
51	14.0	0.0039	50.5	0.0116	46.4
	19.4	.0050	55.0	.0080	53.3
	19.75	.0056	55.0	.0071	54.1
	19.85 crit.	.0059	54.9	.0070	54.2
	19.95 max.			.0064	54.6
61	14.0	0.0041	48.4	0.0123	44.6
	20.1	.0053	53.7	.0081	52.1
	20.55	.0057	53.7	.0077	52.6
	20.75 crit.	.0065	53.5	.0074	53.1
	20.8 max.			.0068	53.4
68	14.0	0.00405	45.3	0.0146	40.3

A = C_2H_2,* B = C_2H_6.—(*Continued*)

Vol. % B	t, °C	Liquid boundary v‡	Liquid boundary $p_{atm.}$	Vapor boundary v‡	Vapor boundary $p_{atm.}$
68	22.2	.0051	51.8	.0096	49.2
	23.05	.0055	52.35		
	23.15	.0056	52.4		
	23.4 crit.	.0063	52.3	.0080	51.2
	23.5			.0079	51.3
	23.6			.0065	52.3
	23.6			.0075	51.6
	23.75 max.			.0071	52.1
100	32.1 crit.	0.0067	48.8		

* The C_2H_6 employed contained small amounts of unknown impurities.
‡ *v* = Volume of system referred to volume at 0°C and 1 atm. as unity.

A = C_2H_4O, Acetaldehyde; B = **Paraldehyde** and **Metaldehyde**, for *p* = 760 mm (34, 410, 411, 412)
(*a*) A + B (Parald.) + satd. soln. + V, *ca.* −123°
(*b*) A + B (Metald.) (mix. crys.) + satd. soln. + V, −122.8°
(*c*) B (Parald.) + B (Metald.) (mix. crys.) + satd. soln. + V, +12.9°

A = C_2H_6, Ethane; B = C_2H_6O, Ethyl alcohol
$L_I + L_{II}$ + V, critical vaporization-condensation region (220)

A = C_2H_6, Ethane; B = C_3H_8O, *n*-Propyl alcohol
$L_I + L_{II}$ + V, critical vaporization-condensation region (220)

A = C_2H_6, Ethane; B = $C_4H_{10}O$, Butyl alcohol
$L_I + L_{II}$ + V, critical vaporization-condensation region (220)

A = C_2H_6, Ethane; B = $C_5H_{12}O$, Amyl alcohol
$L_I + L_{II}$ + V, critical vaporization-condensation region (220)

A = C_2H_6, Ethane; B = $C_{10}H_8$, Naphthalene (322)

t, °C	$p_{atm.}$
	$C_{10}H_8$
80.0	
62.1	47.8
58.4	59.3
55.1	70.4
55.5	78.2
55.7	86.0
56.3	97.1
57.4*	124.8

Critical vaporization curve, solutions rich in ethane

t, °C	$p_{atm.}$
32.3‡	48.1
37.4	51.7
39.4*	52.9

* Critical endpoint. ‡ Critical point of ethane.

A = C_2H_6O, Ethyl alcohol; B = $C_3H_8O_3$, Glycerol (5, 11, 329)

Wt. % A	p_{mm}	Wt. % A	p_{mm}	Wt. % A	p_{mm}
		t = 15°			
2	5.0	14	18.6	33.5	25.3
5	10.0	16.5	19.3	44.0	26.8
5.5	10.2	18.3	21.0	53.0	28.5
9.7	14.9	22.5	22.8	67.5	29.9
10	15.2	27.5	24.1	100	32.5

A = C_2H_6O; B = $C_4H_{10}O$, *v.* p. 361

A = C_2H_6O, Ethyl alcohol; B = C_6H_6, Benzene
Values of p_{mm} (377, 378); *cf.* (439, 440); *see also* p. 313

Wt. A	34.8°	50°	60°	66°
0	147	271	389	477
2.07	174	326	471	578
3.85	185	347	503	620
9.47	195	371	545	677
17.38	198	379	562	702
25.64	198	382	570	711
32.15	197	380	569	711
50.14	190	371	557	697
64.91	178	351	530	671
79.88	155	311	479	609
93.28	122	257	403	520
100	103	223	354	462

A = C_2H_6O, Ethyl alcohol; B = $C_4H_{10}O$, Ethyl ether
Values of p_{mm} (249); *see also* p. 288, 313

Wt. % B \ t,°C	0	5	10	15	20	25	30	35	40	45	50
0	12.4	17.3	24.3	33.2	44.4	59.7	79.3	103.1	134.6	173.3	221.1
10.04	43.3	54.6	70.1	89.2	112.4	140.7	174.8	217.3	266.3	327.5	400.5
20.07	70.9	90.2	114.4	144.5	174.0	214.2	262.9	318.5	386.5	467	558
30.09	93.7	118.1	147.2	182.1	224.8	274	334	403.5	486	582	693
40	111.8	139.5	175.0	215.5	268	324.5	395.5	476.5	571	679	804.5
50	126.7	158.5	197.9	248	302.5	368	446	536.5	641.5	762	903.5
60.07	141.1	178.1	221.7	271	333	405	491.5	590.5	708.5	843	995
68.54	151.7	190.5	236.8	293.5	359	436	529	632	758	901	1062.5
80.07	160.8	203.6	253.9	314.5	384.5	467.5	567	681.5	812	965	1136
90.03	172.0	217.0	271.7	335.5	411	499.5	604.5	726	866	1026	1208.5
100.0	185.3	233.2	291.7	360.5	442	537	647.5	775.5	921.5	1090	1276.5

A = $C_4H_{10}O$, Ethyl ether; B = $C_{14}H_8O_2$, Anthraquinone
Double retrograde condensation (406, 408, 417, 418)

A = $C_6H_4N_2O_4$, *m*-Dinitrobenzene; B = C_6H_6, Benzene (384.5, 423)

t, °C	p_{mm}	*C*	*t*, °C	p_{mm}	*C*
		m-$C_6H_4N_2O_4$			
20		35.1	32.2	108.5	
25	82.1	49.3	35.3	119.2	
28.1	92.5		38.4	134.5	
30.0		66.7	40		108
30.2	100.2		41	145.9	
30.3	100.9				

A = $C_6H_5NO_2$, Nitrobenzene; B = C_6H_{14}, *n*-Hexane (78, 199)
$L_I + L_{II} + V$

t, °C	p_{mm}	*t*, °C	p_{mm}	*t*, °C	p_{mm}
15.55	103.8	18.65	115.9	20.24	123.3
16.52	106.3	19.05	119.2	20.3	124.1
17.65	111.2	19.45	119.5	20.4*	125
18.22	115.0	19.85	121.8		

* Critical solution point.

A = C_6H_6, Benzene; B = $C_{20}H_{24}N_2O_2$, Quinine (174)
t = 25.8°C

Wt. % B	p_{mm}	Phases
79.7	77	AB + satd. soln. + V
80.0 83.0	62	AB + A_2B_3 + V
86.2 92.4	41	A_2B_3 + 94% B (mix. crys.) + V
94.9	33	Mix. crys. + V
95.1	33	
97.0	16	
100.0	*ca.* 0.0	Pure B

A = C_6H_6O, Phenol; B = C_6H_7N, Aniline, L + V diagram (208)

A = C_6H_7N, Aniline; B = C_6H_{12}, Cyclohexane (199)
$L_I + L_{II} + V$

t, °C	23.22	25.50	25.61	27.3	27.8	29.0	30.5	31.1*
p_{mm}	90.65	100.4	101.1	108.0	110.5	117.0	124	127

* Critical solution point.

A = C_6H_7N, Aniline; B = C_6H_{14}, *n*-Hexane (192, 199)
Wt. % B; *see also* p. 314

t, °C	L_I	L_{II}	p_{mm}
40.0	13.5	85.4	267

TWO-COMPONENT SYSTEMS—AQUEOUS

Standard Arrangement, *v.* p. viii

HCl, S + L + V (17)

HBr (17, 18, 20, 21, 22, 26, 27, 28)

t, °C	p_{mm}	*C*
	$HBr.2H_2O$	
−25	1	175.5
−21.8	10	
−18.9	30	188.5
−16.8	60	
−14.6	120	200.0
−13.0	220	
−12.4	280	
−12.0	340	213.8
−11.6	440	
−11.3	**525**	**224.4**
−11.5	760	235.2
−12	950	243.0
−12.6	1140	248.6
−13.3	1330	
−14.0	1520	263.8
−14.8	1710	
	$HBr.2H_2O + HBr.H_2O$	
−15.5E	1900	275.0
	$HBr.H_2O$	
−15.5	1900	275
−14.8	2090	
−14.0	2280	279
−11.0	3040	290
− 8.7	3800	300
− 7.2	4560	311
− 5.8	5320	325
− 4.7	6080	330
− 4.0		
− 3.3	8000	375

SO_2, S + L + V (17)

H_2S (258, 351, 352, 360, 361, 380)
$L_I + L_{II} + V$

t, °C	p_{mm}	*t*, °C	p_{mm}
	Metastable		
19.4	13 150	20.8	13 600
19.8	13 200	21.2	13 680
20.6	13 500	21.4	13 810

H_2S.—(*Continued*)

t, °C	p_{mm}	*t*, °C	p_{mm}
22.8	14 330	26.4	15 660
23.0	14 400	26.9	15 770
23.7	14 670	27.5	15 960
24.6	14 990	28.0	16 190
24.8	15 070	28.2	16 260
25.1	15 200	28.4	16 340
25.4	15 200	29.1	16 530
25.6	15 280	29.2	16 640
25.8	15 390		
	Stable		
30.3	17 060	32.0	17 780
31.0	17 400	32.7	18 090
31.2	17 400	33.2	18 240

t, °C	p_{mm}	M % H_2O in L
	$H_2S.6H_2O + L_I + V$	
0.0		0.4
10.0		0.55
17.4	12 620	0.8
21.2	13 780	1.0
26.0	15 500	1.2
29.5	16 850	1.6
	$H_2S.6H_2O + L_{II} + V$	
5.0		99.5
10.0		99.3
15.0		99.0
16.3	4 030	
17.9	4 790	
19.7	5 780	
20.0		98.6
21.0	6 540	
23.3	8 130	
24.8	9 800	
25.0		97.8
25.6	10 640	
27.4	13 000	97.2
28.5	14 820	96.8
29.2	16 190	96.45
29.5	16 850	96.3
	$H_2S.6H_2O + L_I + L_{II} + V$	
29.5	16 850	1.6 and 96.3

H_2SeO_3 (**264**)

t, °C	p_{mm}	C	t, °C	p_{mm}	C
H_2SeO_3					
22.0		535.6	36.8	19.0	
32	16.5		38.3	19.5	
35.4	18.0		39.5	21	
36.1	18.5		40.3	22	
			42		905.4

NH_3, *see also* Fig. 12 (**1, 81, 99, 114, 138, 151, 152, 245, 263, 277, 278, 285, 306, 307, 308, 309, 312, 315, 319, 326, 337, 343, 346, 347, 390, 415, 416, 448, 454, 456**); *v. also* p. 290

L + V system, values of p_{mm}

t, °C \ M % B	5	10	15	20	25	30
−70						1.4_0
−60						3.5_8
−50					4.65	9.1_5
−40					10.3	17.6
−30			6.9	12.5	21.1	35.0
−20			14.2	24.7	40.6	65.7
−10		15.40	27.2	46.2	73.8	88.0
0	14.6_1	28.7_9	49.5_5	81.7_5	127.5	195.8
+10	27.0_6	51.4_2	85.9_5	138.8	$209._5$	$317._5$
20	51.7_8	87.8	142.9	$224._7$	$335._5$	$494._5$
30	81.0	143.9	$228._7$	$351._6$	$515._3$	$745._0$
40	131.8	$227._5$	$353._5$	$543._0$	$766._9$	$1\ 143._5$
50	207.5	$348._0$	$530._2$	$783._5$	1 109	$1\ 554._5$
60	$316._5$	$517._2$	$772._5$	$1\ 123._5$	1 566	2 163
70	$468._7$	$748._0$	1 099	$1\ 571._4$	2 161	2 944
80	$676._9$	$1\ 057._7$	1 527	2 154	2 920	3 928
90	$955._4$	$1\ 462._3$	2 079	2 891	3 874	5 151
100	$1\ 321._0$	1 982	2 777	3 814	5 053	6 651
110	$1\ 790._4$	2 640	3 671	4 953	6 495	8 460
120	2 386	3 457	4 724	6 337	8 231	10 624
130	3 129	4 465	6 028	8 000	10 300	
140	4 042	5 683	7 592	9 978		
150	5 151	7 142	9 446			
160	6 487	8 881				
170	8 073	10 920				

t, °C \ M % B	35	40	45	50	55	60
−90	0.3_1					
−80	0.9_5	1.7_3	3.2_2		7.9_7	11.6_1
−70	2.5_8	4.5_3	8.0_1	12.2_7	18.8_1	26.8_0
−60	6.2_9	10.6_9	18.3_0	27.2_1	43.9_6	61.0_5
−50	14.0_6	23.1_2	38.3_5	55.5_5	80.8	110.4
−40	29.1	46.5	74.7	105.9	150.6	$201._9$
−30	56.2	87.3	136.6	189.8	$264._9$	$349._5$
−20	102.4	155.1	$236._5$	$323._3$	$442._3$	$575._2$
−10	176.9	$262._2$	$391._2$	$525._5$	$707._0$	$907._5$
0	$292._3$	$425._2$	$619._7$	$819._7$	1 087	1 379
+10	$463._0$	$660._4$	$947._0$	1 234	1 615	2 024
20	$708._5$	$992._6$	1 401	1 801	2 328	2 887
30	1 050	$1\ 448._6$	2 010	2 556	3 265	4 010
40	1 513	2 055	2 810	3 538	4 472	5 446
50	2 152	2 847	3 301	4 788	5 998	7 241
60	2 195	3 319	5 143	6 353	7 882	9 454
70	3 919	5 128	6 760	8 778	10 188	
80	5 170	6 703	8 737	10 616		
90	6 712	8 609	11 120			
100	8 580	10 899				
110	10 812					

t, °C \ M % B	65	70	75	80	85	90	95
−90				11.7_1			
−80			24.5_4	28.2_2	31.2_9	33.8_1	35.9_8
−70	36.0_4	45.4_4	54.0_5	61.7_5	68.3_0	73.5_5	78.1_2
−60	74.6_8	92.6_4	109.3	124.1	136.4	147.0	156.3
−50	143.3	175.9	$205._8$	$231._9$	$254._4$	$274._0$	$291._6$
−40	$258._9$	$314._1$	$364._2$	$409._0$	$447._3$	$480._8$	$511._5$
−30	$441._5$	$530._3$	$611._0$	$682._6$	$744._6$	$798._8$	$850._3$
−20	$718._7$	$854._5$	$978._5$	1 089	$1\ 185._7$	1 271	1 353
−10	1 120	1 322	$1\ 505._5$	1 669	1 812	1 942	2 066
0	1 685	1 974	2 235	2 469	2 677	2 685	3 048
+10	2 452	2 852	3 215	3 541	3 829	4 101	4 359
20	3 468	4 010	4 502	4 941	5 336	5 710	6 073
30	4 781	5 500	6 148	6 731	7 265	7 764	8 261
40	6 448	7 375	8 216	8 977	9 675		
50	8 522	9 703					

NH_3.—(*Continued*)

t, °C	M % B	p_{mm}	t, °C	M % B	p_{mm}
NH_3			$(NH_3).H_2O$		
−77.60	**100.0**	**45.8**	−82.0	55.0	6.6
−80.5	95.0	34.4	**−79.2**	**50.0**	**5.4**
−84.4	90.0	23.3	-81.8_5	45.0	2.7
−89.0	85.0	14.3	−89.0	40.0	0.6_7
			−99.9	35.0	0.09
$NH_3 + (NH_3)_2.H_2O$					
−93E	81.2	9.0_3			
$(NH_3)_2.H_2O$			$(NH_3).H_2O$ + Ice		
−91.2	80.0	10.5	−100.3E	34.6	0.08_3
-83.8_5	75.0	17.7	Ice		
−79.7	70.0	20.9	−68.7	30.0	1.6
−78.8	**66.66**	**20.2**	−46.0	25.0	6.4
−79	65.0	17.4	-31.2_5	20.0	11.4
-83.8_5	60.0	8.6	−20.1	15.0	14.1
			-11.9_5	10.0	13.5
$(NH_3)_2.H_2O + (NH_3).H_2O$			-5.3_5	5.0	10.3
-86.3_5E	58.5_5	6.5	**0.0**	**0.0**	**4.579**

NH_4NO_3 (**68, 120, 320, 321, 434**), *see further* p. 293

C	p_{mm}, 100°C	C	p_{mm}, 100°C
0	760.00	160	$469._2$
5	$745._9$	180	$447._6$
10	$732._2$	200	$427._9$
20	$706._0$	300	$350._6$
40	$658._9$	400	$296._9$
60	$617._5$	500	$257._4$
80	$580._6$	600	$227._1$
100	$548._3$	700	$203._1$
120	$519._1$	800	$183._8$
140	$492._9$	890†	$169._6$

t, °C	p_{mm}	C
NH_4NO_3 (R* IV)		
(10)	6.4_5	147.0
15	8.5_5	$165._5$
20	11.2_5	$187._0$
25	14.7	$212._5$
30	19.0	$242._5$
NH_4NO_3(R*IV) + NH_4NO_3 (R? III)		
32.1	21.0_5	256.9
NH_4NO_3 (R? III)		
40	29.2	$293._0$
50	42.9_5	352
60	61.1	421
70	84.9	498
80	115.4	580
NH_4NO_3 (R? III) + NH_4NO_3 (Tet.* II)		
84.2	$130._3$	614
NH_4NO_3 (Tet. II)		
90	$143._9$	716
95	$156._5$	803
100	$169._6$	890
(105)	$(183._4)$	(978)

* R = orthorhombic; Tet. = tetragonal.

NH_4Cl, *see further* p. 293

Values of p_{mm} (**120, 357, 384.5, 433, 434**)

t,°C \ C	0.0	10.0	20.0	30.0	40.0	50.0	60.0	70.0	80.0
0	4.579	4.3	4.0	(3.8)					
10	9.210	8.6	8.1	7.6					
20	17.539	16.4	15.5	14.5	Saturated solutions				
30	31.834	29.9	28.1	26.3	24.7				
40	55.34	51.9	48.9	45.8	42.9				
50	92.54	86.8	81.7	76.6	71.8	67.5			
60	149.46	$140._2$	$132._0$	$123._6$	$116._0$	109.0			
70	233.79	$219._3$	$206._5$	$193._4$	$181._4$	$170._5$	$160._6$		
80	355.47	$333._5$	$314._0$	$294._1$	$275._9$	$259._3$	$244._2$		
90	526.00	$493._5$	$464._6$	$435._2$	$408._2$	$383._6$	$361._4$	$341._1$	
100	760.00	$713._0$	$671._2$	$628._7$	$589._8$	$554._3$	$522._1$	$492._9$	
110	1074.5	1008	949	$888._9$	$833._8$	$783._7$	$738._2$	$696._8$	$659._2$

t, °C	p_{mm}	C	t, °C	p_{mm}	C
α-NH_4Cl			α-NH_4Cl + β-NH_4Cl		
20	13.9	37.2	845.1	403_2	$149._5$
25	18.5	39.3			
30	24.5	41.4	β-NH_4Cl		
160	247_1	$125._2$	190	443_1	$154._0$
170	303_9	$134._9$	195	492_4	$158._2$
180	370_3	$144._8$	200	539_6	$162._3$

NH_4Br, *see further* p. 293
Values of p_{mm} (**70, 358, 384.5, 394, 433, 434**)

t, °C \ C	0	10.0	20.0	40.0	60.0	80.0	100.0	120.0	140.0
0.0	4.579	4.4	4.3	4.0	3.7				
10.0	9.210	8.9	8.6	8.0	7.4				
20.0	17.539	17.0	16.4	15.3	14.2				
30.0	31.834	30.8	29.8	27.7	25.7				
40.0	55.34	53.6	51.7	48.2	44.7	41.5			
50.0	92.54	89.6	86.5	80.5	74.8	69.4			
60.0	149.46	144.7	139.7	130.0	120.8	112.1	103.9		
70.0	233.79	226.3	218.6	203.4	188.9	175.3	162.4		
80.0	355.47	344.1	332.3	309.3	287.3	266.5	247.0	228.8	
90.0	526.00	509.2	491.8	457.6	425.1	394.3	365.5	338.5	
100.0	760.00	735.7	710.5	661.2	614.2	569.8	528.1	489.0	452.0

t, °C	p_{mm}	C
	α-NH_4Br	
90	329.7	133.0
95	390.2	
100	459.4	144.0
105	538.1	
110	627.3	155.4
115	728.5	
116.53	760.0	
120	843	167.3
125	971	
130	1113	179.7
135	1272	

t, °C	p_{mm}	C
	α-NH_4Br + β-NH_4Br	
137.8	1369	189.2
	β-NH_4Br	
140	1450	191.8
145	1650	
150	1872	202.2
155	2117	
160	2385	212.8

$$\log x_\alpha = -\frac{372.7}{T} + 0.31978$$

$$\log x_\beta = -\frac{293.7}{T} + 0.12727$$

yield values about 0.7% lower than those reported by (**394**).

$(NH_4)_2SO_4$, *see further* p. 293
Values of p_{mm} (**120, 384.5, 433, 434**)

t, °C \ C	0	5	10	20	30	40	50	60	70	80	90	100
0	4.579	4.5+	4.5−	4.4	4.2	4.1	4.0	3.9	3.8			
10	9.210	9.1	9.0	8.7	8.5	8.3	8.0	7.8	7.6			
20	17.539	17.4	17.1	16.7	16.2	15.7	15.3	14.8	14.4			
30	31.834	31.5	31.1	30.3	29.4	28.6	27.7	26.9	26.2			
40	55.34	54.7	54.1	52.6	51.1	49.6	48.2	46.8	45.5	44.2		
50	92.54	91.5	90.4	87.9	85.5	83.0	80.6	78.3	76.1	73.9		
60	149.46	147.8	146.0	142.0	138.0	134.1	130.2	126.5	122.8	119.4		
70	233.79	231.2	228.4	222.2	215.9	209.7	203.7	197.8	192.2	186.7		
80	355.47	351.6	347.2	337.8	328.3	318.9	309.7	300.8	292.2	283.9	276.0	
90	526.00	520.2	513.8	499.9	485.8	471.8	458.2	445.0	432.3	420.1	408.3	
100	760.00	751.7	742.3	722.2	701.9	681.7	662.1	643.0	624.7	607.0	590.0	573.7
110	1074.5	1063	1050	1021	992.3	963.8	936.1	909	883	858	834	811

t, °C	p_{mm}	C
	$(NH_4)_2SO_4$	
0	3.8	70.7
10	7.5	73.0
20	14.2	75.45
22	16.0	75.95
24	18.1	76.45
26	20.3	77.00
28	22.8	77.50
30	25.6	78.05
40	44.1	81.05
50	73.0	84.40
60	116.7	88.00
70	180.7	91.60
80	271.9	95.30
90	398.0	99.15
100	568.5	103.3
110	793	108.15

$(NH_4)H_2PO_4$ (**77, 120**)

t	p_{mm}	C
	$(NH_4)H_2PO_4$	
19	15.31	Wt. % B = 18.0 + 0.455t
20	16.33	
21	17.41	
22	18.51	
23	19.66	
24	20.82	
25	22.09	
26	23.47	
27	24.88	
28	26.31	
29	27.88	
30	29.57	

CO_2, critical region (**220, 348**)

C_2H_6, Ethane (**220**)

$L_I + L_{II} + V$ in neighborhood of critical point of B; t = 15–32°C, p = 33–49 atm.

C_5H_{12} (mix. of *n*- and *iso*-Pentane) (**356**)

Two liquid phases: The three-phase pressure exceeds sum of vapor pressures of pure components.

t, °C	$p_{atm.}$	t, °C	$p_{atm.}$
150	22.4	180	38.8
160	27.0	187.1	44.1
170	32.4	crit.	

C_6H_6 (**356**)

Two liquid phases: The three-phase pressure exceeds the sum of the vapor pressures of the pure components.

t, °C	$p_{atm.}$	t, °C	$p_{atm.}$
150	10.6	220	42.9
160	13.2	230	50.9
170	16.4	240.1	60.4
180	20.1	250.2	70.7
190	24.6	260.1	82.2
200	29.8	267.8	92.7
210	35.9	crit.	

C_6H_{14}, *n*-Hexane, *see also* Fig. 13 (**354, 356**)

L_I-V region between the three-phase curve and the critical curve
Boiling-point values for $p_{atm.}$

t, °C \ M % A	0	2.3	5.2	8.6	11.8
170	10.69	14.45	18.05		
175		15.55	19.2		
180	12.70	16.65	20.35	22.8	
185		17.85	21.6	24.25	
190	14.97	19.1	22.9	25.8	
195		20.5	24.2	27.4	31.5
200	17.56	21.85	25.6	29.0	33.4
205		23.3	27.0	30.7	35.3
210	20.50	24.8	28.55	32.4	37.1
215		26.4	30.1	34.1	38.9
220	23.8	28.1	31.65	35.8	40.55
222		28.8	32.25	36.3	40.8
223					41.1
224				36.95	41.25
225		29.75	33.2	37.25	41.4
226				37.5	41.6
227			33.75	37.7	41.8
228			34.1	37.8	41.7
229			34.35	37.95	41.1
230		31.4	34.6	37.9	
231		31.8	34.75	37.5	
232		32.05	34.8		
233		32.25			
234.8	29.6				

C_6H_{14}.—Boiling-point values for $p_{atm.}$—(*Continued*)

t, °C \ M % A	15.3	18.9	22.8	25.7	27.7
210	40.8				
215	42.8				
220	44.3	48.0			
222	44.8	48.3	51.0	51.8	52.1
223	44.9	48.3	50.7	51.2	
224	45.0	48.15	49.9		
225	45.0	47.75			
226	44.85	46.7			
227	44.5				
228	43.2				

Dew-point values for $p_{atm.}$

t, °C \ M % A	0	2.3	5.2	8.6	11.8
234.8	29.6				
233		31.4			
232		30.8	32.9		
231		30.2	32.1	35.85	
230		29.6	31.4	34.8	
229		29.2	30.8	33.9	37.6
228		28.7	30.3	33.15	36.55
227		28.2	29.8	32.5	35.6
225				31.2	34.0
222					31.95
220	23.8				

t, °C \ M % A	15.3	18.9	22.8	25.7	27.7
228	40.3				
227	38.75				
226	37.5	41.75			
225	36.5	40.2	{47.5* / 46.5		
224		39.05	43.4		
223		38.1	42.0	46.3	
222	34.25	37.2	40.8	44.5	46.9
221			40.0	43.2	45.2
220	33.1	35.7	39.0	42.1	44.0
218					43.0

* *t-p* curve passes through a temperature maximum at 225.1°, p = 47.0 atm.

$L_I + L_{II} + V$

t, °C	M % B, L_I	$p_{atm.}$	t, °C	M % B, L_I	$p_{atm.}$
163.8	94.8	16.7	200		34.8
170		19.0	205		38.2
175		21.2	207.1	84.7	39.65
176.4	91.4	21.7	210		41.8
180		23.5	215.25	81.1	46.0
185		26.0	220		50.2
190		28.8	220.75	77.2	50.9
194.0	88.2	31.1	221.6	74.3	51.7
195		31.7	222.2*	72.3	52.1

* The ($L_I + L_{II}$ + V) three-phase curve and the curve of critical points intersect at this point, *i.e.*, critical phenomena are encountered before complete mixing takes place in mixtures containing less than 72.3 M % hexane.

C_6H_{14}.—The critical fold

M % A	Press. max. t, °C	Press. max. $p_{atm.}$	Temp. max. t, °C	Temp. max. $p_{atm.}$	Critical point t, °C	Critical point $p_{atm.}$
0.0	234.6	30.15	234.6	30.15	234.6	30.15
2.3	233.5	32.3	233.65	32.0	233.6	32.2
5.2	231.8	34.85	232.7	33.9	232.6	34.3
8.6	229.4	39.95	231.3	37.0	231.1	37.4
11.8	227.0	41.8	229.8	39.6	229.5	40.4
15.3	224.5	45.0	228.4	41.8	227.9	43.3
18.9	222.5	48.35	226.7	44.5	226.1	46.5
22.8	221.7	51.0	225.0	47.0	224.2	49.6
25.7			223.6	49.0	222.9	51.2
27.7			222.8	50.2	222.2	52.1
100.0					374	217.5

C_7H_8, Toluene (41)

Vapor phase compositions in contact with two liquid phases at *ca.* 760 mm.

CH_2O_2, Formic acid (98, 184, 186, 200, 226, 229, 336, 341)

% = Wt. % formic acid

Values of p_{mm}

t, °C	49.36 %	70.49 %	89.53 %
5			9.1
6			9.7
8			11.0
10			12.4
12			13.9
14	10.5	10.2	15.7
16	11.8	11.5	17.7
17	12.5	12.2	18.7
18	13.3	13.0	19.8
19	14.1	13.8	20.9
20	14.9	14.6	22.1
22	16.8	16.4	24.5
24	18.9	18.5	27.2
26	21.2	20.8	30.1
28	23.9	23.4	33.5
30	26.8	26.3	37.2
32	30.0	29.5	41.1
34	33.6	33.9	45.2
36	37.5	36.7	49.7
38	41.9	40.8	54.3
40	46.6	45.3	59.1
42		50.5	
43		53.2	
44		56.0	
105	760		
106.5			760
107.6		760	

CH_2O_2, Formic acid.—(*Continued*)

t, °C	22.66 %	Max. B. P. %	Max. B. P. p_{mm}	Max. B. P. B. P., °C
19	15.3	79.9	43	38
42	57.0	85.1	97	54
61	145.1	87.3	262	77
81	346.5	89.5	740	107.1
100	719.8	92.6	1830	135

t, °C	50.02 %	t, °C	79.8 %
17	12.0	18	12.8
32	29.5	42	50.6
43	53.8	60	122.5
55	98.4	61	128.3
70	195.5	81	294.4
81	310.5	100	595.1
91	459		
100	641		

$C_2H_2O_4$, Oxalic acid (384.5, 423)

t, °C	p_{mm}	C
	$H_2C_2O_4.2H_2O$	
40	52.5	21.52
50	85.9	31.46
60	135.8	44.32
70	208.1	61.08
80	310.7	84.5

B = **Various esters and ethers**

Values of p_{mm} for saturated solutions of the esters (328)

B	0°	10°	20°	30°
Methyl formate	186.7	296.3	451.7	729.8
Ethyl formate	74.6	125.4	202.1	312.8
Propyl formate	25.6	46.0	79.8	131.9
Methyl acetate	61.3	104.4	169.3	264.0
Ethyl acetate	28.4	49.9	85.4	140.2
Propyl acetate	12.0	22.9	41.8	72.5
Methyl propionate	25.5	46.2	79.3	132.0
Ethyl propionate	12.9	24.6	45.0	78.0
Propyl propionate	7.3	14.2	26.9	48.5
Ethyl ether	185.1	292.7	445.0	652.1
Ethyl sulfide	20.6	36.9	62.9	105.3

$C_3H_6O_2$, Methyl acetate (257); *v. also* p. 290

M_B/l	25°, p_{mm}		35°, p_{mm}	
	H_2O	$C_3H_6O_2$	H_2O	$C_3H_6O_2$
0.2542	24.0	22.5	42.1	38.3
0.5084	24.1	43.7	41.9	73.9
1.017	23.5	85.3	41.6	134.8
1.525	22.8	122.0	40.6	183.9
2.033	23.3	149.2	40.9	226.6

C_3H_8O, *n*-Propyl alcohol (222) *v. also* p. 290

t, °C	$p_{atm.}$	*t*, °C	$p_{atm.}$
2.5 Wt. % H_2O			
95.1	1.04	183.1	13.55
98.1	1.17	216.8	25.12
105.1	1.52	227.8	30.61
116.8	2.25	245.1	40.14
130.8	3.54	254.6	47.4
145.4	5.57	264.9*	55.9
160.2	7.99		
25 Wt. % H_2O			
166.9	11.20	241.4	48.0
179.1	14.56	250.2	56.2
182.7	15.76	261.8	67.3
215.7	30.57	275.9*	83.8
224.6	35.85		

* Critical point. The critical point of pure C_3H_8O was 264.0°C and 51.51 atm.

$C_4H_6O_4$, Succinic acid (384.5, 423)

t, °C	p_{mm} $C_4H_6O_4$	*C*
30	31.3	10.58
40	53.9	16.21
50	89.2	24.42
60	142.7	35.83
70	220.9	51.07
80	332.7	70.79
90	487.6	95.5

$C_4H_6O_6$, Tartaric acid (384.5, 422)

t, °C	p_{mm} $C_4H_6O_6$	*C*
20.0		139.4
22.7	18.4	
25.0		147.4
26.2	22.0	
29.1	25.4	
30.0		156.2
31.2	28.1	
34.6	33.3	
38.1	39.2	
40.0		176.0
41.7	46.6	
43.2	49.9	
46.3	57.6	
50.0		195.0

$C_4H_{10}O$, Ethyl ether, *see also* Fig. 14 (220, 249, 266, 355)
Wt. % H_2O

t, °C	L_I	L_{II}	$p_{atm.}$
0	1.0	88.4	0.247
5	1.05	89.8	.311
10	1.12	91.3	.388
15	1.15	92.4	.477
20	1.20	93.5	.585

$C_4H_{10}O$.—(*Continued*)
Wt. % H_2O

t, °C	L_I	L_{II}	$p_{atm.}$
25	1.26	94.3	0.710
30	1.32	94.9	.858
34.1			1.00
40	1.50	95.5	1.24
45			1.43
50	1.7	95.9	1.74
60	1.8	96.3	2.38
70	2.0	96.8	3.19
80	2.2	97.2	4.23
90			5.51
100			7.04
110			8.95
120			11.25
130			14.0
150			21.0
155	5.47		23.05
160			25.3
170			30.2
175	6.63		32.9
185	7.87		39.1
190	8.44		42.4
Critical curve			
193.9	0		36.1
194.0	0.59		37.3
194.1	1.29		38.6
194.85	3.15		41.9
196.4	5.47		45.3
197.6	6.63		47.1
199.35	7.87		48.9
200.1	8.44		49.7
200.8	9.35		50.4
201.0	9.44		50.65
201.9	10.10		51.55
202.2*	10.3		51.8
374‡	100		217.8

* First critical endpoint (intersection of three-phase curve with the critical curve).

‡ Second critical endpoint unknown; must lie near critical point of H_2O.

$C_4H_{10}O$, Isobutyl alcohol (200, 276)

t, °C	Wt. % B L_I	Wt. % B L_{II}	p_{mm}
−20	15.65	87.0	
−15	14.55	86.6	
−10	13.45	86.2	
− 5	12.45	85.8	
0	11.55	85.4	
+ 5	10.70	85.0	
10	9.95	84.55	
15	9.25	84.1	
20	8.70	83.7	28
25	8.20	83.2	
30	7.80	82.75	49
35	7.55	82.2	

$C_4H_{10}O$.—(*Continued*)

t, °C	Wt. % B L_I	Wt. % B L_{II}	p_{mm}
40	7.30	81.7	82
45	7.15	81.15	
50	7.05	80.5	135
55	7.05	79.8	174
60	7.00	79.1	219
65	7.00	78.3	>287
70	7.05	77.5	344
75	7.20	76.6	<437
80	7.45	75.6	529
85	7.85	74.5	651
90	8.30	73.3	794
95	8.85	71.95	962
100	9.55	70.5	1155
105	10.35	68.8	1375
110	11.40	67.0	1630
115	12.65	64.9	1925
120	14.25	62.3	2255
122	15.05	60.9	2410
124	15.90	59.2	2560
126	17.00	57.1	2720
128	18.35	54.6	2885
130	20.2	51.1	3055
131	21.5	48.8	
132	24.0	44.9	3220
132.5	26.0	40.5	
132.8*	33.0‡		3290

L_I increases in alcoholic content as *t* decreases from 60°C; presumably there is a lower critical solution point which has not been reached experimentally, unless the freezing-point curve, which is also unknown, intersects the L_I-L_{II} boundary.

* Critical solution point.

‡ Flat max. on the temperature-composition curve for the two-phase system extending over a range of *ca.* 6 % in composition.

$C_5H_8O_2$, Acetylacetone (392)
Critical solution isotherm, 91.2°C

Wt. % B	p_{mm}	Wt. % B	p_{mm}
0	550.2	51.60	647.2
11.77	637.0	59.22	649.2
19.56	638.4	74.14	648.0
24.12	642.2	80.08	646.0
39.14	648.0	100.0	186.3

C_6H_6O, Phenol (126, 227, 332, 371, 392, 413), *see also* Fig. 15 and p. 291

t, °C	Wt. % B L_I	Wt. % B L_{II}	Wt. % B V	p_{mm}
15	8.8	72.3		11.4
20	8.8	71.4	5.55	15.7
25	8.9	70.4		22.6
30	9.1	69.4	6.00	29.5
35	9.4	68.2		39.8
40	9.9	66.8	6.55	52.9
45	10.7	65.2		69.6
50	12.0	63.2	7.25	90.9
55	14.0	60.3		118

C_6H_6O.—(*Continued*)

t, °C	Wt. % B L_I	Wt. % B L_{II}	Wt. % B V	p_{mm}
60	17.1	56.2	8.15	150
65	21.9	49.2		189
68.5	33.5	33.5	9.20	220

$C_6H_6O_2$, Resorcinol (422)

t, °C	p_{mm} $C_6H_6O_2$	*C*
20.0	15.27	103
22.5	17.53	
25.0	20.04	117
27.5	22.84	
30.0	25.93	131
32.5	29.33	
35.0	33.07	
37.5	37.16	
40.0	41.58	161

$C_{12}H_{22}O_{11}$, Sucrose (252, 260, 305, 384.5)

t, °C	p_{mm} $C_{12}H_{22}O_{11}$	*C*
0	4.04	179.2
10	8.03	190.5
20	15.1	203.9
30	26.9	219.5
40	45.8	238.1
50	74.6	260.4
60	116.5	287.3
70	174	320.4

HCN (385)

x_B	p_{mm}, 18°C HCN	p_{mm}, 18°C H_2O
0.05	167.0	15.1
.10	283.4	14.7
.15	349.5	14.2
.20	381.0	13.8
.25	398.5	13.5
.30	409.1	13.3
.35	417.2	13.2
.40	421.3	12.9
.45	425.4	12.7
.50	430.6	12.4
.55	434.8	12.0
.60	442.0	11.6
.65	451.0	11.1
.70	462.0	10.4
.75	474.0	9.8
.80	488.0	9.0
.85	503.0	7.9
.90	521.0	6.4
.95	540.5	4.0
1.00	566.2	0

C_6H_7N, Aniline (3, 371)
Values of Wt. % B

t, °C	L_I	L_{II}	V
41	3.7	94.4	13.4
49.5	3.9	94.2	16.7
56.3	4.1	93.9	16.8*
64.5	4.4	93.4	17.5
75.0	5.0	92.75	18.3¶
82.0	5.4	92.2	19.7
90.0	6.0	91.5	19.8
100.0	6.9	90.5	
125	10.1	86.9	
150	17.5	79.1	
167	47		

C_6H_7N.—(*Continued*)

Values of Wt. % B.—(*Continued*)

56.3°C isotherm			75.0°C isotherm		
L_I	V	p_{mm}	L_I	V	p_{mm}
0	0	125.7	0	0	289.3
1.86	6.84	126	1.38	5.6	297
2.52	8.84		2.88	10.8	300
3.35	10.51		3.46	12.1	301
3.37	11.2		3.49	12.1	301
3.49	11.6		4.18	13.7	301
3.91	12.8		4.6	14.4	302
3.95			4.7	14.8	302
4.3‡	15.5		4.9	15.1	302
			5.2§	18.2	303

*127 mm. ¶ 303 mm. ‡ L_{II}, *ca.* 94.5 %. § L_{II} *ca.* 94 %.

$C_6H_{15}N$, Triethylamine (**225, 384.5**)

Values of p_{mm}

t, °C \ Wt. % B	0	1.35	4.40	10.95	23.34	41.69	84.84	93.88	100.0
6	7.018				24.15				
8		14.94			27.67			34.68	
10	9.209	16.48	21.58	28.07	31.69	33.26		38.57	37.4
12		18.25	25.05	33.25	36.3	37.9	43.4	42.85	40.4
14	11.99	20.55	29.1	38.7	41.55	43.0	48.15	47.65	44.0
16		23.15	33.8	45.0	47.55	48.65	53.55	53.0	48.1
18	15.48	26.1	39.25	52.25	54.2	54.95	59.25	58.95	52.8
20		29.4	45.6	60.3	61.3	62.2	65.6	65.5	58.0
22	19.88	33.15	52.95	68.8	69.2	69.8	72.9	72.9	63.7
24		37.4	61.5	76.9	77.8	77.8	80.8	80.5	70.0
26	25.21	42.2	71.3	85.7	87.2	86.5	89.3	88.9	76.8
28		47.7	81.4	95.0		96.0	98.6	98.3	84.1
30	31.82	54.0	93.9	105.2		106.2	108.6	108.5	92.1
32		61.0	107.8	116.3		117.5	119.6	119.7	100.7
34	39.90	68.8	123.2	128.6		129.8	131.7	131.8	109.9
36		77.5	140.2	141.9		143.2	144.8	144.9	119.8
38	49.69	87.1	156.5	156.1		157.4	159.2	159.0	130.6
40		97.8	172.7	171.5		172.6	174.8	174.2	142.1
42	61.50	109.6	189.7	188.3		188.7	191.6	190.6	154.6
44		122.3	207.8	206.3		206.4	209.5	208.4	168.0
46	75.65	132.0						227.7	182.4
48		150.9							197.9
50	92.51	167.2	← Two liquid phases →						214.4

$L_I + L_{II} + V$, boundary curve

t, °C	Wt. % B			p_{mm}
	L_I	L_{II}	V	
18.6	51.9			
20	20.9	92.9	94.1	64.6
21	14.8	94.0	93.9	67.9
22	10.3	95.0	93.6	70.1
25	7.3	95.2		
30	5.8	96.6		
35	4.6	96.5		
40	3.7	96.5		
50	2.9	96.4		

Change in critical-solution temperature with pressure

t, °C	18.3	18.45	19.63	19.95	20.0	21.2	21.3	21.3
p_{atm}	0	9.5	63	78	79	140	144	146

$C_8H_{11}N$, 2, 4, 6-Trimethylpyridine (γ-Collidine)

Values of p_{mm} (**225, 384.5**)

t, °C \ Wt. % B	0	6	52.9	58.68	85.74	95.8	98.7	100
10	9.21	9.1	9.8					2.7
15	12.79	12.7	13.0	13.1		10.4	7.9	3.3
20	17.54	18.2	17.6	17.9	17.5	14.3	10.9	4.1
25	23.75	24.6	24.2	24.1	24.4	19.3	15.1	5.2
			Two liquid phases					

$C_8H_{11}N$: Values of p_{mm}.—(*Continued*)

t, °C \ Wt. % B	0	6	52.9	58.68	85.74	95.8	98.7	100
30	31.82	33.1	32.3	32.3	32.9	26.6	20.8	6.3
35	42.18	44.2	43.4	42.9	43.2	36.1	28.7	7.7
40	55.32	57.7	56.3	56.5	57.0	49.0	38.1	9.4
45	71.88	74.8	74.1	73.6	74.8	65.6	50.5	11.7
50	92.51	96.4	95.2	95.0	96.0	85.8	67.2	14.8
55	118.04	122.3	120.9	121.9	124.0	111.5	87.4	18.9
60	149.38							23.8
65	187.54	Two liquid phases						31.0

NH_4HCO_3 (**67, 295, 437**)

With negligibly small vapor space, $\log_{10} p_{mm} = 2.55169 + 0.0499125t - 851.5 \times 10^{-6}t^2 + 10225.6 \times 10^{-9}t^3$.

CH_4N_2O, Urea (**120, 384.5**)

t, °C	p_{mm}	C
	CH_4N_2O	
19	13.37	
20	14.15	79.0
21	14.93	
22	15.73	
23	16.56	
24	17.44	
25	18.39	
26	19.39	
27	20.46	
28	21.61	
29	22.76	
30	23.93	93.0

Tl, Salts (**57**)

Salt	t at 1 atm.	C
TlCl	100.01	2.41†
Tl_2SO_4	100.32	18.45†

$TlNO_3$ (**10, 33, 384.5**)

t, °C	p_{mm}	C
	$TlNO_3$(R)*	
90	490.2	200
92	521.6	
94	554.6	
96	589.3	
98	625.7	
100	663.9	414
101	683.7	
102	703.9	
103	724.6	
104	745.7	
104.65	760.0	
105	767.4	594
106	789.6	
107	812.3	
108	835.4	
110	853.9	
196	760.0	

* R = rhombic.

$ZnCl_2$ (**237, 272, 281, 434**)

t, °C	p_{mm}	C
20	<2	
	$ZnCl_2$	
90	22	
100	35	615.0
110	57	
120	86	

$ZnCl_2$.—(*Continued*)

t, °C	p_{mm}	C
	$ZnCl_2$	
130	118	
140	145	
150	193	
160	258	

$ZnSO_4$ (**238, 382, 384.5, 434**)

t, °C	p_{mm}	C
20	15.3	†
105	760	85.7†

$Zn(NO_3)_2$ (**240**)

t, °C	p_{mm}
20	9.6†

$CdBr_2$ (**237, 434**)

t, °C	p_{mm}
10	6†
20	10†
30	16†
40	40†
68	122†
70	188†
80	279†

$CdSO_4$ (**82, 144.5**)

t, °C	p_{mm}	C
	$CdSO_4.\frac{8}{3}H_2O$	
0	3.94	75.6
	$CdSO_4.H_2O$	
75.87	279.3	76.3
80.03	334.4	68.7
90.04	500.3	63.1
100.0	729.8	60.8

$Cd(NO_3)_2$ (**239**)

t, °C	p_{mm}
20	10†

$CuCl_2$ (**103, 237, 384.5, 423**)

t, °C	p_{mm}	C
	$CuCl_2.2H_2O$	
20	11.94	77.0
22	13.49	
25	16.13	78.6
28	19.20	
30	21.52	80.3
35	28.4	
38	33.4	
41	39.1	83.8

$CuSO_4$ (82, 203, 271.5, 304, 382, 434)

t, °C	p_{mm}	C
	$CuSO_4.5H_2O$	
60	141.6	40.0
65	175.9	
70	216.9	
75	265.5	
80	322.7	
85	390.1	
90	468.1	
95	558.6	
	$CuSO_4.3H_2O$*	
100	662.8	75.4
104.2	760.0	
105	781.9	

* Reported values for the transition $5H_2O \Leftrightarrow 3H_2O$ vary between 55 and *ca.* 100°. The S-L-V curve and dissociation pressure curve intersect at 96.5°; direct determination yields 95.7 ± 0.2° for the transition, and a small heat effect at *ca.* 56°.

$AgNO_3$ (33)

t, °C	p_{mm}	C
	$AgNO_3$ (R)*	
133	760	1941
135	800	
150	960	
	$AgNO_3$ (R) + $AgNO_3$ (trig.)	
159.8		
	$AgNO_3$ (trig.)*	
160	1000	
167	1015	
170	1010	
185	900	
191	760	

* R = Rhombic; trig. = trigonal.

$MnCl_2$ (101, 335, 434)

t, °C	p_{mm}	C
	α-$MnCl_2.4H_2O$	
15.5	7.85	
20.0	9.45	
30.0	17.0	80.7
40.0	28.7	
50.0	46.3	98.1
57.8	62.9	
	α-$MnCl_2.4H_2O$ + $MnCl_2.2H_2O$	
58.10		105.7
	$MnCl_2.2H_2O$	
60	64.8	108.6
70.5	110.3	
80.5	172.1	112.8
90.0	262.0	

$MnBr_2$ (237, 467)

t, °C	p_{mm}	C
	$MnBr_2.4H_2O$	
20	5	59.4
60	40	
100	200	69.6

MnI_2 (237)

t, °C	p_{mm}
	$MnI_2.4H_2O$
20	3.5
50	7
60	13
80	42.5
100	104
	$MnI_2.2H_2O$
110	154
	$MnI_2.H_2O$
130	210

$MnSO_4$ (238)

t, °C	p_{mm}
	$MnSO_4.5H_2O$
20	11.3
	$MnSO_4.4H_2O$
60	162

$Mn(NO_3)_2$ (239, 467)

t, °C	p_{mm}	C
20	7.4	137
70	80	

$FeCl_3$ (32)

t = 15°C		Solid =
C	p_{mm}	Fe_2Cl_6+
43	6.0	$12H_2O$
116m	1.4	$12H_2O$
99.6m	2.3	$7H_2O$
121.0m	1.3	$5H_2O$
	1.8	$12H_2O$ + $7H_2O$*

* $S_I + S_{II}$ + V.

$CoCl_2$ (96, 103, 384.5, 434)

t, °C	p_{mm}	C
	$CoCl_2.6H_2O$ (red)	
25	15.3	52.7
30	19.7	
35	25.0	61.3
40	31.3	
45	38.5	
50	45.9	
	$CoCl_2.6H_2O$ + $CoCl_2.2H_2O$	
52.4	48.5	
	$CoCl_2.2H_2O$ (blue)	
55	55.4	
60	71.2	90.5
65	90.8	
70	114.8	
80	179.6	
90	273.6	
100	406.6	104.0

$CoSO_4$ (82, 384.5)

t, °C	p_{mm}	C
	$CoSO_4.7H_2O$ + $CoSO_4.6H_2O$	
45.3	67.0	
	$CoSO_4.6H_2O$	
50.2	84.9	55.3
55.3	107.7	
60.2	134.9	60.5
65.2	167.3	
70.2	207.3	65.8

$NiCl_2$ (103, 110, 384.5)

t, °C	p_{mm}	C
	$NiCl_2.6H_2O$	
19.8	9.6	64.0
24.1	12.0	
30.3	17.0	
31.0	17.5	69.5
35.1	21.5	
36.25	22.8	
	$NiCl_2.6H_2O$ + $NiCl_2.4H_2O$	
36.85	23.5	
	$NiCl_2.4H_2O$	
40.6	28.9	73.6
45.2	36.7	
48.3	42.6	
54.1	56.4	

$CrCl_2$ (193)

t, °C	p_{mm}	C
	$CrCl_2.3H_2O$ (?)	
49	27.6	
50	28.8	
51	30.3	
52	32.5	
55	39.7	
60	56.0	
65	78.4	

H_3BO_3 (236, 391, 434)

t, °C	p_{mm}	C
	H_3BO_3	
5	6	
10	7	3.5
15	12	
103.3	760	46.9

$(NH_4)_2Al_2(SO_4)_4$ (256)

t, °C	p_{mm}
	$(NH_4)_2Al_2(SO_4)_4.24H_2O$
60	141.8
65	177.0
70	218.5
75	266.4
80	319.8
85	376.9
90	421.7

$MgCl_2$ (103, 165, 185, 237, 247, 340, 384.5, 433, 434), *see further* p. 295.

C	p_{mm} 0°C	p_{mm} 100°C
0	4.579	760.00
1	4.55	756.3
2	4.53	754.6
3	4.51	749.3
4	4.48	745.7
5	4.45	741.9
6	4.42	737.7
8	4.36	728.7
10	4.29	718.5
15	4.07	688
20	3.80	652
25	3.49	609
30	3.16	561
35	2.80	511
40	2.44	460
45	2.08	408
50	1.73	358
55		309
60		264
65		223
70		186

$MgCl_2$.—(*Continued*)

t, °C	p_{mm}	C
	Ice	
0	4.579	0
−10	1.95	13.0
−20	0.77	20.0
−30	0.29	24.7
	Ice + $MgCl_2.12H_2O$	
−33.5	0.20	26.2
	$MgCl_2.12H_2O$	
−30	0.27	27.9
−20	0.53	36.5
−18	0.58	39.3
−17	0.59	41.3
−16.8	0.59	41.9
−16.6	0.58	42.6
−16.4	**0.56**	**44.05**
−16.6	0.52	46.0
	$MgCl_2.12H_2O$ + α-$MgCl_2.8H_2O$	
−16.8E	0.50	46.5
	$MgCl_2.12H_2O$ + β-$MgCl_2.8H_2O$	
−17.4mE	0.45	47.6
	$MgCl_2.12H_2O$ + $MgCl_2.6H_2O$	
−19.4mE	0.34	50.2
	α-$MgCl_2.8H_2O$	
−15	0.57	47.0
−10	0.82	48.8
− 5	1.10	51.0
	β-$MgCl_2.8H_2O$	
−15m	0.54	48.6
−10m	0.74	51.0
	β-$MgCl_2.8H_2O$ + $MgCl_2.6H_2O$	
− 9.6mU	0.76	51.3
	α-$MgCl_2.8H_2O$ + $MgCl_2.6H_2O$	
− 3.4U	1.22	51.9
	$MgCl_2.6H_2O$	
0	1.56	52.3
10	3.08	53.5
20	5.77	54.7
30	10.3	56.1
40	17.4	57.6
50	28.3	59.2
60	44.0	61.1
70	65.7	63.4
80	93.8	66.0
90	128.5	69.2
100	165.4	73.0
110	195.3	78.2
112	197.9	79.5
	max.	
114	196.4	81.3
116	186.4	83.8
	$MgCl_2.6H_2O$ + $MgCl_2.4H_2O$	
116.7U	175.5	85.5
	$MgCl_2.4H_2O$	
120	192	86.4
130	248	88.9
140	316	91.8

$MgCl_2$.—(*Continued*)

t, °C	p_{mm}	*C*
$MgCl_2.4H_2O$		
160	459	100.1
175	516	112
	max.	
180	470	121
$MgCl_2.4H_2O + MgCl_2.2H_2O$		
181.5U	427	126

$MgBr_2$ (384.5, 434)

t, °C	p_{mm}	*C*
108	760	75.0†

$CaCl_2$ (15, 16, 30, 31, 51, 52, 60, 107, 108, 119, 141, 159, 180, 181, 185, 187, 194, 234, 242, 248, 267, 268, 269, 302, 313, 317, 318, 344, 364, 386, 433, 434, 444, 460)

t, °C	p_{mm}	*C*
Ice + $CaCl_2.6H_2O$		
−50.3	0.03	44.0
$CaCl_2.6H_2O$		
0	2.08	60.0
+ 5	2.74	63.7
10	3.71	65.7
15	4.76	69.4
20	6.06	73.2
25	6.97	81.4
27	7.28	85.9
28.5	7.36	90.9
	max.	
29	7.33	93.2
29.5	7.22	96.1
$CaCl_2.6H_2O + \alpha\text{-}CaCl_2.4H_2O$		
29.93U	6.85	101.2
$CaCl_2.6H_2O$		
29.95m	**6.70**	**102.70**
$CaCl_2.6H_2O + \beta\text{-}CaCl_2.4H_2O$		
29.16mE	5.48	112.9
$CaCl_2.6H_2O + CaCl_2.2H_2O$		
27.6mE	4.27	123.6
$\alpha\text{-}CaCl_2.4H_2O$		
20m	4.18	91.0
25m	5.38	96
$\alpha\text{-}CaCl_2.4H_2O + CaCl_2.6H_2O$		
29.93U	6.85	101.2
$\alpha\text{-}CaCl_2.4H_2O$		
35	8.63	107.3
40	10.53	115.3
$\alpha\text{-}CaCl_2.4H_2O + CaCl_2.2H_2O$		
45.3U	12.06	130.2
$\beta\text{-}CaCl_2.4H_2O$		
20m	3.34	104.5
25m	4.41	108.8
$\beta\text{-}CaCl_2.4H_2O + CaCl_2.6H_2O$		
29.16mE	5.48	112.9
$\beta\text{-}CaCl_2.4H_2O$		
30m	5.71	113.9
35m	7.21	120.5
$\beta\text{-}CaCl_2.4H_2O + CaCl_2.2H_2O$		
38.4mU	8.19	127.5
$CaCl_2.2H_2O$		
30m	4.97	124.4
35m	6.72	126.2

$CaCl_2$.—(*Continued*)

t, °C	p_{mm}	*C*
$CaCl_2.2H_2O + \beta\text{-}CaCl_2.4H_2O$		
38.4mU	8.19	127.5
$CaCl_2.2H_2O$		
40m	8.97	128.1
$CaCl_2.2H_2O + \alpha\text{-}CaCl_2.4H_2O$		
45.3U	12.06	130.2
$CaCl_2.2H_2O$		
50	15.5	132.2
60	25.7	136.8
70	41.2	141.6
80	63.9	146.8
90	95.2	152.6
100	138	159
120	268	172
140	467.5	191
160	719	223
170	815	255
172	825	265
	max.	
$CaCl_2.2H_2O + CaCl_2.H_2O$		
175.5U	796	297
$CaCl_2.2H_2O$		
175.7m	**771**	**308**

$Ca(NO_3)_2$ (44, 45, 124, 125, 434, 436)

t, °C	p_{mm}	*C*
$\alpha\text{-}Ca(NO_3)_2.4H_2O$ + Ice		
−28.7E	0.32	75
$\alpha\text{-}Ca(NO_3)_2.4H_2O$		
0	2.7	102
5	3.9	108
10	5.2	115
15	6.9	122
20	9.4	129
25	12.0	138
30	14.9	151.3
35	17.7	166.7
37	18.9	174.3
39	19.5	183.8
40	19.7	189.7
	max.	
41	19.7	197.2
42	19.3	208.2
42.5	19.0	218.5
42.7	**18.6**	**227.65**
$\alpha\text{-}Ca(NO_3)_2.4H_2O + Ca(NO_3)_2.3H_2O$		
42.7E	18.0	242.5
$\alpha\text{-}Ca(NO_3)_2.4H_2O$		
42m	13.8	256
41m	12.3	272
$\alpha\text{-}Ca(NO_3)_2.4H_2O + Ca(NO_3)_2.2H_2O$		
40.0mE	11.0	289
$\alpha\text{-}Ca(NO_3)_2.4H_2O$		
38m	8.6	306
35m	6.4	335
$\alpha\text{-}Ca(NO_3)_2.4H_2O + Ca(NO_3)_2$		
32.7mE	4.5	357
$\alpha\text{-}Ca(NO_3)_2.4H_2O$		
30m	3.9	383
20m	1.5	
15m	1.2	

$Ca(NO_3)_2$.—(*Continued*)

t, °C	p_{mm}	*C*
$Ca(NO_3)_2.3H_2O$		
35m	13.3	
40m	16.2	237
$\alpha\text{-}Ca(NO_3)_2.4H_2O + Ca(NO_3)_2.3H_2O$		
42.7E	18.0	242.5
$Ca(NO_3)_2.3H_2O$		
44	18.8	247
46	19.8	255
48	20.5	264
49	20.6	271
	max.	
50	20.5	280
50.5	20.2	286
51.1	**19.0**	**303.55**
51	16.8	320
$Ca(NO_3)_2.3H_2O + Ca(NO_3)_2.2H_2O$		
50.6E	15.4	337
$Ca(NO_3)_2.3H_2O + Ca(NO_3)_2$		
49.8mE	14.3	357
$Ca(NO_3)_2.2H_2O$		
20m	4.25	
30m	7.1	
$\alpha\text{-}Ca(NO_3)_2.4H_2O + Ca(NO_3)_2.2H_2O$		
40.0mE	11.0	289
$Ca(NO_3)_2.2H_2O$		
45m	13.2	
48m	14.4	316
$Ca(NO_3)_2.3H_2O + Ca(NO_3)_2.2H_2O$		
50.6E	15.4	337
$Ca(NO_3)_2.2H_2O + Ca(NO_3)_2$		
51.9U	16.0	358
$Ca(NO_3)_2$		
30m	4.2	356
$\alpha\text{-}Ca(NO_3)_2.4H_2O + Ca(NO_3)_2$		
32.7mE	4.5	357
$Ca(NO_3)_2$		
35m	5.9	
40m	8.0	
45m	10.8	
48m	12.8	
$Ca(NO_3)_2.3H_2O + Ca(NO_3)_2$		
49.8mE	14.3	357.5
$Ca(NO_3)_2.2H_2O + Ca(NO_3)_2$		
51.9U	16.0	358
$Ca(NO_3)_2$		
55	19	
60	24.9	358
151	760.0	376

Values of p_{mm}*

C	20°	30°	40°	50°	60°
25.3	16.4	29.9	52.6	86.8	140.6
44.1	15.3	27.6	48.0	80.2	130.5
98.8	11.3	20.6	36.1	61.3	99.7
144.5	8.2	15.1	26.6	45.3	75.0
200	5.4	10.4	18.7	31.6	52.7
260	3.7	6.9	12.7	21.9	36.8
288	3.2	6.0	10.7	18.9	31.9
295	3.1	5.8	10.4	18.0	30.0
322	2.5	4.9	9.2	16.2	27.5
333	2.4	4.6	8.6	15.1	25.5
342	2.3	4.5	8.4	14.8	25.0

* *See also* p. 295.

$Ca(NO_3)_2$.—(*Continued*)

C	100°	*C*	100°
0	760.00	44.4	655.8
6.69	746.9	47.3	647.7
12.61	735.3	59.3	614.4
18.62	719.8	70.7	583.8
22.7	710.1	72.5	578.4
28.4	697.4	81.1	556.6
36.4	676.6	168.1	356.6

$SrCl_2$ (141, 384.5, 434)

t, °C	p_{mm}	*C*
116	760.0	105.9†

$Sr(NO_2)_2$ (301)

112.5	763	210†

$Sr(NO_3)_2$ (57)

106.79	760.0	113†

$Ba(OH)_2$ (46, 235, 434)

$Ba(OH)_2.3H_2O$		
100.0	520	
109	732	219

$BaCl_2$ (423, 434)

$BaCl_2.2H_2O$		
25	21.4	37
30	28.6	38.2
35	37.7	
40	49.3	40.7
45	63.8	
50	81.7	43.6
55	103.9	
100	660	58.8

$Ba(NO_2)_2$ (301)

114	769.5	450†

$Ba(NO_3)_2$ (384.5, 434)

101.5	760.0	36.2†

LiCl (63, 106, 171, 250, 384.5, 434, 443, 444)

$LiCl.3H_2O + LiCl.2H_2O$		
−16.5	0.43	
$LiCl.2H_2O$		
0.0	0.88	63.5
+10.0	1.32	72.3
$LiCl.2H_2O + LiCl.H_2O$		
12.5	1.44	74.6
$LiCl.H_2O$		
20	2.13	78.7
30	3.56	84.3
40	5.85	90.1
50	9.6	96.2
60	15.2	102.4
70	23.2	108.9
80	35	115.7
90	51	122.6
100	73	129.6
$LiCl.H_2O$ + LiCl		
100.5	74	129.9
LiCl		
110	131	131.7
120	240	133.9

LiBr, *see further* p. 296

Values of p_{mm} (63, 64, 65, 171, 207, 384.5, 434)

C \ t, °C	0	20	40	60	80	100
0	4.579	17.539	55.34	149.46	355.47	760.00
5	4.5	17.2	54.3	146.6	349	746
10	4.4	16.8	53.0	143.3	341	729
20	4.1	15.8	50.0	135.3	322	690
40	3.4	13.2	41.9	114.2	274	591
60	2.6	10.1	32.6	89.6	217	473
80	1.8	7.2	23.5	65.6	161.3	356.5
100	1.2	4.9	16.2	45.9	114.3	256.3
120	0.8	3.3	11.0	31.6	79.5	180.5
140	0.56	2.3	7.7	22.1	56.2	129.0
160		1.6	5.5	15.9	41.0	95.6
180			4.0	11.9	31.2	74.5
200			3.1	9.3	25.1	62.0
220				7.5	20.5	51.5
240					17.4	44.3
260						38.8

LiBr.—(*Continued*)

t, °C	p_{mm}	C
	$LiBr.3H_2O$	
(−20)	0.24	100.5
(−10)	0.36	122.0
0.0	0.5	146
	$LiBr.3H_2O + LiBr.2H_2O$	
+4.0	0.54	158
	$LiBr.2H_2O$	
10.0	0.73	166
20.0	1.2	178.5
30.0	1.9	191
40.0	2.9	204
	$LiBr.2H_2O + LiBr.H_2O$	
44.0	3.46	209
	$LiBr.H_2O$*	
50	4.6	214
60	7.2	224
70	11.1	234.5
80	16.8	245.5
90	25.2	256
100	37.3	266.5
110	54.3	277

* $LiBr.H_2O$ transforms into anhydrous LiBr at *ca.* 159°, *p* = *ca.* 228 mm.

LiI (144.5, 170, 384.5, 434), *see further* p. 296

C	p_{mm}, 100°C	C	p_{mm}, 100°C
0	760.0	140	246.3
5	750.3	160	184.9
10	739.6	180	139.8
20	715.2	200	107.1
40	648.6	250	58.7
60	578.9	300	35.0
80	494.0	350	22.4
100	406.7	400	15.1
120	323.6	450	10.7

LiI.—(*Continued*)

t	p_{mm}	C
	$LiI.3H_2O$	
0	0.4	152
10	0.8	158
20	1.5	164
30	2.6	171
40	4.4	179
50	7.1	189
60	11.2	201
70	15.0	222
72	15.3	230
	max.	
74	15.25	240
75.2	**15.0**	**247.7**
74	10.8	276
72	8.3	289
	$LiI.3H_2O + LiI.2H_2O$	
70.5E	7.1	297
	$LiI.2H_2O$	
72	7.2	305
74	7.4	315
	max.	
76	7.2	330
78.0	6.9	349
79.0	**6.1**	**371.5**
	$LiI.2H_2O + LiI.H_2O$	
78.2E	4.5	410
	$LiI.H_2O$	
90	6.7	444
100	8.7	481
110	11.0	525
120	12.6	588
	max.	
125	12.5	633
128	11.9	670
130.5	**9.4**	**743.1**
	$LiI.H_2O + LiI.½H_2O$	
129E	6.5	810
	$LiI.½H_2O$	
130	6.9	830
140	7.2	860

$LiNO_3$ (117, 243, 384.5, 434)

t	p_{mm}	C
	$LiNO_3.3H_2O$	
0	2.9	53.65
10	5.6	60.35
20	9.5	71.75
25	11.6	82.75
26	11.9	85.90
27	12.2	89.85
28	12.2	95.90
29	11.8	105.0
29.5	11.3	113.0
29.6	11.1	115.2
29.7	10.9	117.8
	max.	
29.8	10.6	121.2
29.87	**10.1**	**127.6**
29.8	9.5	132.5
29.7	9.3	135.3
29.6	9.1	137.3
	$LiNO_3.3H_2O + LiNO_3.½H_2O$	
29.55E	9.0	138.3
	$LiNO_3.½H_2O$	
30.0	9.2	138.9
35	11.8	142.9
40	14.8	148.9
50	22.6	160.5
60	32.3	177.4
	$LiNO_3.½H_2O + LiNO_3$	
61.1	33.1	180.6
	$LiNO_3$	
62	34.2	181.9
65	38.1	186.1
70	45.1	193.6
75	52.8	201.9

NaOH; *see also* p. 370

t, °C	p_{mm}	C
	$NaOH.4H_2O$	
0	2.3	42
	$NaOH.4H_2O + NaOH.3½H_2O$	
5	2.4	47.5
	$NaOH.3½H_2O$	
10	3.0	51.5
12.5	3.2	54.1
	max.	
15.0	2.9	61.5
15.5	**2.8**	**63.5**
15.0	2.3	67.1
12.5	1.4	74.6
10.0	1.0	78.4
5.0	0.54	83.5
	$NaOH.3½H_2O + NaOH.2H_2O$	
0.75E	0.35	
	$NaOH.2H_2O + NaOH.H_2O$	
12.0U	0.42	103
	$NaOH.H_2O$	
20	0.61	109
30	0.91	117.5
40	1.2	129
50	1.3	145
60	1.0	174
62.5	0.7	190.7
64.0	0.4	211
64.3	**0.3**	**222.3**
64.0	0.16	240
62.5	0.06	269

NaOH.—(*Continued*)

t, °C	p_{mm}	C
	$NaOH.H_2O$ + α-NaOH	
61.5U	0.025	295
	α-NaOH	
80	0.075	314
100	0.25	338
150	4.4	416
200	54	555
220	120	645
240	210	785
260	260	990
	max.	
280	195	1500
300	15	3350
	α-NaOH + β-NaOH	
303	0.8	4200
	β-NaOH	
310	0.04	6550
322	**0.00***	**∞**

* *p* given represents the partial pressure of H_2O vapor only. The total pressure at this point is the vapor pressure of NaOH, which is 0.03 ± 0.02 mm.

NaF (73, 434)

C	p_{mm}, 100°C	C	p_{mm}, 100°C
0.00	760.00	3.00	743.1
1.00	754.4	4.00	737.2
2.00	748.8	4.29†	735.4

NaCl; *see also* p. 370

t, °C	p_{mm}	Wt. % B
	NaCl	
0	3.5	26.25
10	6.9	26.30
20	13.2	26.40
30	23.9	26.50
40	41.6	26.65
50	69.5	26.85
60	112.0	27.05
70	175.0	27.30
80	265.2	27.60
90	391.6	27.85
100	564	28.15
108.67	760	28.40
110	795	28.45

$NaClO_3$; *see also* p. 370

t, °C	p_{mm}	C
	$NaClO_3$	
0	3.51	84.4
20	12.8	101.0
40	38.0	122.0
60	95.5	148.0
80	209.4	179
100	411.3	214
110	557.7	233
120	741.4	251
130	968.0	271
255	760.0	

NaOH (7, 8, 107, 141, 265, 283, 284, 316, 383, 430, 433, 434, 452); *see further* p. 296. Values of p_{mm}

C \ t, °C	20	40	60	80	100	120	160	200	250	300	350
0	17.539	55.34	149.46	355.47	760.0	1 488.9	4 633	11 647	29 771	64 290	123 660
5	16.9	53.2	143.5	341.5	730	1 430	4 450	11 200	28 600	61 800	118 900
10	16.0	50.6	137	325.5	697	1 365	4 260	10 750	27 500	59 300	114 100
20	13.9	44.2	120.5	288.5	621	1 225	3 860	9 800	25 300	54 700	105 400
30	11.3	36.6	101	246	537	1 070	3 460	8 950	23 300	50 800	98 000
40	8.7	28.7	81	202	450	920	3 090	8 150	21 500	47 200	91 600
50	6.3	20.7	62.5	160.5	368	770	2 690	7 400	19 900	44 100	85 800
60	4.4	15.5	47	124	294	635	2 340	6 750	18 400	41 200	80 700
70	3.0	10.9	34.5	94	231	515	2 030	6 100	17 100	38 700	76 000
80	2.0	7.6	24.5	70.5	179	415	1 740	5 500	15 800	36 300	71 900
90	1.3	5.2	17.5	53	138	330	1 490	5 000	14 700	34 200	68 100
100	0.9	3.6	12.5	38.5	105	262	1 300	4 500	13 650	32 200	64 600
120		1.7	6.3	20.5	61	164	915	3 650	11 800	28 800	58 600
140	C	0°C	3	11	35.5	102	765	2 980	10 300	25 900	53 400
160	0	4.579	1.5	6	20.5	63	470	2 430	8 960	23 300	49 000
180	5	4.4		3.5	12	40	340	1 980	7 830	21 200	45 100
200	10	4.2		2	7	25	245	1 620	6 870	19 200	41 800
250	20	3.6		0.5	2	8	110	985	5 000	15 400	35 000
300	30	2.9		0.1	0.5	2.7	50	610	3 690	12 500	29 800
350	40	2.2				0.9	23	380	2 750	10 300	25 700
400							11	240	2 080	8 600	22 400
500								100	1 210	6 100	17 500
700									440	3 300	11 500
1000										1 470	6 800
2000										150	1 760
4000											120
8000											7

NaCl (12, 13, 56, 57, 73, 76, 106, 108, 109, 121, 205, 233, 286, 384.5, 395, 397, 399, 402, 403, 405, 422, 424), *see further* p. 297

Values of p_{mm}

t, °C \ Wt. % B	0.0	2.5	5	7.5	10	12.5	15.0	17.5	20.0	22.5	25.0	27.5
0	4.579	4.5	4.4	4.4	4.3	4.2	4.1	4.0	3.8	3.7	3.5	
10	9.21	9.1	8.9	8.8	8.6	8.4	8.2	8.0	7.7	7.4	7.1	
20	17.54	17.3	17.0	16.7	16.4	16.1	15.7	15.3	14.8	14.2	13.6	
30	31.83	31.4	30.9	30.4	29.8	29.2	28.5	27.7	26.8	25.8	24.7	
40	55.34	54.5	53.6	52.7	51.7	50.7	49.5	48.1	46.6	44.9	43.0	
50	92.54	91.2	89.7	88.1	86.4	84.7	82.8	80.5	78.1	75.3	72.2	
60	149.46	147.2	144.8	142.3	139.7	136.8	133.7	130.0	126.0	121.7	116.8	
70	233.79	230.2	226.4	222.4	218.3	213.9	208.9	203.5	197.5	190.7	183.1	
80	355.47	350	344	338	332	325	318	309.5	300.5	290.2	278.9	266
90	526.00	517	509	500	491	481	470	458	445.1	430	414	395
100	760.00	748	736	723	710	695	680	665	643	622	599	572
110	1074.5	1057	1040	1022	1003	983	961	936	911	881	849	810
B. P., °C	100.0	100.44	100.90	101.40	101.93	102.51	103.16	103.89	104.72	105.68	106.78	108.12

$NaClO_3$ (33, 73, 206, 384.5, 433, 434), *see further* p. 297

Values of p_{mm}

C \ t, °C	0	20	40	60	80	100
0	4.579	17.539	55.34	149.46	355.47	760.0
5	4.51	17.3	54.6	147.4	350.5	749.4
10	4.45	17.0	53.7	145.1	345.1	737.9
20	4.30	16.5	52.0	140.5	334.2	714.4
40	4.03	15.4	48.7	131.6	313.0	669.1
60	3.78	14.5	45.7	123.4	293.5	627.4
80	3.47	13.6	42.9	115.9	275.7	589.5
100		12.8	40.4	109.2	259.7	555.1
120			38.2	103.1	245.1	524.1

C \ t, °C	0	20	40	60	80	100
140				97.5	232.0	495.9
160					220.0	470.3
180						447.0
200						425.6

NaBr (73, 333, 334, 384.5, 433, 434), *see further* p. 297

Values of p_{mm}

C \ t, °C	0	10	20	30	40	50	60	70	80	90	100	110
0	4.579	9.210	17.539	31.834	55.34	92.54	149.46	233.79	355.47	526.00	760.00	1074.5
5.0	4.5	9.1	17.25	31.3	54.4	91.0	147.0	230	349.5	517	747.4	1057
10.0	4.4	8.9	17.0	30.8	53.6	89.7	145.0	226.5	344.5	510	735.5	1041
20.0	4.3	8.6	16.3	29.6	51.5	86.1	139	217.5	331	489	707.2	1000
30.0	4.1	8.2	15.6	28.3	49.1	82.1	132.5	207.5	315.5	467	674.5	954
40.0	3.9	7.8	14.8	26.8	46.6	77.8	125.5	196.5	299	442	639.3	904
50.0	3.6	7.3	13.9	25.3	43.9	73.5	118.5	185.5	282	418	603.3	853
60.0	3.4	6.9	13.1	23.8	41.3	69.1	111.5	174.5	265.5	393	567.6	803
70.0	3.2	6.5	12.3	22.3	38.8	64.9	105	164	249.5	369	530.1	754
80.0		6.1	11.5	21.0	36.4	60.9	98.5	154	234	346	500.1	707
90.0			10.8	19.7	34.2	57.1	92	144	219.5	324.6	469.0	663
100.0					32.0	53.6	86.5	135.5	205.5	304.5	439.9	622
110.0						50.3	81	127	193	285.5	412.7	583
120.0										268	387.4	548
121.9											382.9 †	
125.0												531

NaI (73, 433, 434), *see further* p. 297

Values of p_{mm}

C \ t, °C	0	20	40	60	80	100	120	140
0	4.579	17.539	55.34	149.46	355.47	760.00	1488.9	2709.5
10	4.5	17.1	54.1	146.1	347	743	1455	2648
25	4.3	16.5	52.0	140.6	334.3	715	1400	2548
50	3.9	15.1	47.0	128.3	305.1	652	1278	2326
75	3.5	13.4	42.3	114.3	271.8	581	1138	2072
100	3.0	11.8	37.2	100.5	239.1	511	1001	1822
125	2.7	10.2	32.3	87.2	207.4	443.5	869	1581
150	2.3	8.8	27.9	75.4	179.3	383.5	751	1367
175		7.7	24.2	65.3	155.2	332	650	1183
200			21.0	56.7	134.8	288	565	1028
225				49.5	117.7	251.5	493	897
250				43.5	103.4	221	433	788
275					91.3	195.2	382	696
300						173.3	340	618
325								

t, °C	p_{mm}	C
	NaI	
100	174.4	303.4
141	760	

Na_2SO_4 (10, 49, 50, 56, 57, 73, 233, 271.5, 304, 381, 384.5, 419, 434, 455, 461), *see further* p. 297

Values of p_{mm} ± 1–4% from 0–100°C

t, °C \ Wt. % B	0.0	5.0	10.0	15.0	20.0	25.0	30.0
0.0	4.579	4.50	4.42	4.33	4.22	4.10	
10.0	9.21	9.05	8.88	8.70	8.52	8.25	
20.0	17.54	17.24	16.93	16.60	16.15	15.77	
30.0	31.83	31.34	30.79	30.22	29.54	28.79	27.02*
40.0	55.34	54.5	53.6	52.6	51.5	50.2	48.6
50.0	92.54	91.2	89.8	88.2	86.4	84.4	81.7
60.0	149.46	147.0	145.0	142.7	140.0	136.8	132.6
70.0	233.79	230.5	227.2	223.4	219.4	214.6	208.3
80.0	355.47	351	346	340.4	334.4	327.4	358.1
90.0	526.00	519	512	504	496	486	
100.0	760.00	751	741	730	718	704	

* Supersatd. solution.

Na_2SO_4.—(*Continued*)

t, °C	p_{mm}	Wt. % B	t, °C	p_{mm}	Wt. % B
	$Na_2SO_4.10H_2O$			α-Na_2SO_4	
(15)	12.3	11.78			
(17.5)	14.2	13.83	40	47.4	32.56
20	16.5	16.11	45	62.0	32.17
22.5	19.1	18.60	50	80.4	31.81
25	21.9	21.54	55	103.2	31.48
27.5	24.9	25.07	60	131.2	31.18
30	28.0	29.00	65	165.7	30.87
	$Na_2SO_4.10H_2O$ + α-Na_2SO_4		70	207.2	30.62
32.4	30.8	33.24	75	257.5	30.30
	α-Na_2SO_4 + $Na_2SO_4.7H_2O$		80	317.4	30.21
24.4m	19.1	34.07	85	386.9	30.04
	$Na_2SO_4.7H_2O$		90	472.5	29.90
(15)m	11.6	27.25	95	571.7	29.79
(17.5)m	13.1	29.13	100	686.4	29.68
20m	15.1	30.98	102.84	760.0	29.60
22.5m	17.3	32.78	110	974.7	29.54
26.0m	20.6	35.48	120	1 355	29.47
	α-Na_2SO_4		130	1 850	29.46
20m	14.4	34.53	140	2 480	29.51
25m	19.6	34.00	150	3 275	29.61
30m	26.8	33.49	160	4 260	29.74
35	35.9	33.00	170	5 465	29.89

Na_2SO_4.—(*Continued*)

t, °C	p_{mm}	Wt. % B
α-Na_2SO_4 + β-Na_2SO_4		
180 ± 20	6 925	30.08
β-Na_2SO_4		
190	8 680	30.43
200	10 750	30.74
210	13 200	31.07
220	16 000	31.38
230	19 350	31.70
β-Na_2SO_4 + γ-Na_2SO_4		
235 ± 5	21 200	31.86
γ-Na_2SO_4		
240	23 250	31.14
260	33 150	28.16
(280)	45 850	24.94
(300)	62 000	21.41
(320)	82 300	17.53

$Na_2S_2O_3$ (**423, 434, 463, 464, 465**)

t, °C	p_{mm}	*C*
$Na_2S_2O_3.5H_2O$		
0	3.95	50.2
10	7.66	59.6
20	14.0	70.0
30	24.0	82.9
40	37.6	103.1

$Na_2S_2O_3$.—(*Continued*)

t, °C	p_{mm}	*C*
$Na_2S_2O_3.5H_2O$		
43	41.7	113.4
45	43.5	124.0
46	43.9	130.7
47	43.7	139.8
48	41.3	156.0
$Na_2S_2O_3.5H_2O$ + $Na_2S_2O_3.2H_2O$		
48.15	40.6	159.7
$Na_2S_2O_3.2H_2O$		
50	43.4	163.5
55	50.8	175.7
60	57.2	191.7
65	60.6	213.8
66	60.8	219.0
$Na_2S_2O_3.2H_2O$ + $Na_2S_2O_3$		
66.45	60.9	221.3
$Na_2S_2O_3$		
70	69.7	223.9
80	99.6	231.6
90	138.2	239.5
100	186.2	248.0

$NaNO_2$ (**301**)

t, °C	p_{mm}	*C*
128	761.5	214†

$NaNO_3$ (**10, 56, 57, 73, 106, 120, 121, 243, 286, 384.5, 404, 407, 422, 433, 434**), *see further* p. 297

Values of p_{mm}

C \ *t*, °C	0	25	50	75	100	125
0	4.579	23.763	92.54	289.32	760.00	1740.5
5	4.50	23.34	90.9	284.1	746.3	1709
10	4.42	22.93	89.2	278.9	732.5	1677
20	4.28	22.14	86.1	268.8	705.6	1615
30	4.15	21.39	83.1	259.1	679.6	1554
40	4.04	20.69	79.6	249.9	654.8	1496
50	3.93	20.04	77.5	241.1	631.3	1442
60	3.83	19.42	74.9	232.9	609.0	1390
70	3.73	18.83	72.56	225.1	588.1	1341
80	3.64*	18.29	70.25	217.8	568.2	1294
90		17.77	68.1	210.8	549.4	1250
100		17.29*	66.1	204.3	531.6	1209
110			64.2	199.4	514.8	1170
120				192.1	498.9	1135
130				186.5	483.7	1097
140				181.2*	469.4	1064
150					455.7	1032
160					442.6	1002
170					430.1	973
180					418.3*	945
190						919
200						893
210						869
220						846
230						824

* Supersaturated

$NaNO_3$.—(*Continued*)

t, °C	p_{mm}	*C*	*t*, °C	p_{mm}	*C*
$NaNO_3$					
0	3.70	73.0	70	148.1	135.6
10	7.20	80.5	80	216.1	148.0
20	13.25	88.2	90	306.7	160.9
25	17.67	92.0	100	422.9	176.0
30	23.27	96.2	110	569.2	192.4
40	39.13	104.8	120	748.5	210.6
50	63.3	113.9	120.59	760.0	211.7
60	98.6	124.0	125	851.6	220.3

Na_2CO_3 (**49, 94, 95, 140, 384.5, 423, 433, 434, 457**), *see further* p. 29

Values of p_{mm} ±1% at 0° to *ca.* ±0.5% at 100°

t, °C \ Wt. % B	0.0	5.0	10.0	15.00	20.00	25.00	30.00
0.0	4.579	4.5					
10.0	9.210	9.0	8.8				
20.0	17.539	17.2	16.8	16.3			
30.0	31.834	31.2	30.4	29.6	28.8	27.75	26.4
40.0	55.34	54.2	53.0	51.6	50.2	48.4	46.1
50.0	92.54	90.7	88.7	86.5	84.1	81.2	77.5
60.0	149.46	146.5	143.5	139.9	136.1	131.6	125.7
70.0	239.79	235	230.5	225	219	211.5	202.5
80.0	355.47	348	342	334	325	315	301
90.0	526.00	516	506	494	482	467	447
100.0	760.00	746	731	715	697	676	648

* Supersaturated.

Na_2CO_3.—(*Continued*)

t, °C	p_{mm}	Wt. % B
$Na_2CO_3.10H_2O$		
15.0	12.3	14.10
20.0	16.9	17.70
25	21.4	22.15
27.5	24.0	25.00
30	26.8	28.15
31	27.9	29.70
32	28.8	31.35
$Na_2CO_3.10H_2O$ + $Na_2CO_3.H_2O$		
33.1m	29.5	33.30
$Na_2CO_3.H_2O$		
36.0	34.8	32.95
40	43.6	32.65
45	57.1	32.35
50	74.1	32.10
55	95.4	31.85
60	121.5	31.70
65	153.7	31.60
70	192.7	31.50
75	239.8	31.45
80	296.2	31.40
85	363.4	31.35
90	442.4	31.30
95	535.3	31.25
100	631.7	31.20
110m	915.7	31.10
$Na_2CO_3.7H_2O$		
(20)m	15.3	(24.7)
(25)m	20.3	(27.3)
(30)m	26.2	30.10
34	31.7	32.35
35	33.2	32.95
$Na_2CO_3.10H_2O$ + $Na_2CO_3.7H_2O$		
32.15	29.0	31.50

Na_2CO_3.—(*Continued*)

t, °C	p_{mm}	Wt. % B
$Na_2CO_3.H_2O$ + $Na_2CO_3.7H_2O$		
35.6	34.0	33.05
$Na_2CO_3.H_2O$ + Na_2CO_3		
105 ± 5	769.8	31.15

$NaCHO_2$, Formate (**384.5, 434**)

C	p_{mm}, 100°C	*C*	p_{mm}, 100°C
0	760.00	80	490
5	742	100	446
10	723	120	410
20	685	140	379
40	610	157.7†	355
60	545		

$NaCH_3COO$ (**141, 146, 434**)

t, °C	p_{mm}	*C*
$NaC_2H_3O_2$		
100	319	170 ± 2
123	760	193 ± 5

$Na_2C_4H_4O_6$, Tartrate (**141, 254, 298, 299, 300, 434**)

$Na_2C_4H_4O_6.2H_2O$		
0.0	4.4	24
5	6.2	28
10	8.6	32
15	11.9	36.5
20	16.2	41
25	21.7	45
30	28.8	50
35	37.9	54
40*	49.3	59
45	63.4	64
50	80.9	69
100	593	130
108 ± 0.5	760.0	146

* Dissociation pressures indicate a probable transition at *ca.* 40°.

KOH (51, 107, 123, 141, 302, 316, 331, 344, 383, 384.5, 395, 397, 434), *see further* p. 298

Values of p_{mm}

C \ t, °C	0	20	40	60	80	100
0	4.579	17.539	55.34	149.46	355.47	760.00
5	4.43	17.0	53.5	144.6	344	735
10	4.25	16.3	51.4	138.9	331	707
20	3.83	14.7	46.4	125.4	299	639
30	3.35	12.9	40.7	110.1	263	563
40	2.82	10.9	34.6	94	225	485
50	2.30	8.9	28.6	78.6	190	413
60	1.82	7.2	23.2	64.6	158	348
80	1.08	4.4	14.6	42.6	108	246
100		2.6	8.8	26.5	70.5	172
120			5.2	16.2	45.5	118
140				9.8	29	81
160						56
178						40†

K_2SO_4 (56, 57, 73, 121, 162, 233, 344, 384.5, 433, 434), *see further* p. 298

Values of p_{mm}

C \ t, °C	0	30	60	80	100
0	4.579	31.834	149.46	355.47	760.00
0.5	4.573				759.0
1	4.568	31.76	149.1	354.6	758.1
2	4.557	31.68	148.8	353.8	756.4
3	4.548	31.62	148.4	353.0	754.8
4	4.538	31.55	148.1	352.3	753.3
5	4.529	31.49	147.8	351.6	751.8
6	4.520	31.43	147.5	350.9	750.3
8		31.30	147.0	349.6	747.4
10		31.18	146.4	348.2	744.4
15			144.9	344.7	737.0
20				341.2	729.5

KOH.—(*Continued*)

t, °C	p_{mm}	C
	$KOH.2H_2O$	
0	0.7	97
10	1.2	103
20	1.8	112
25	2.2	
27.5	2.35	
29	2.4	
30	2.4	126
31	2.35	
32	2.25	
	$KOH.2H_2O + KOH.H_2O$	
32.5	2.2	135
	$KOH.H_2O$	
40	3.3	
50	5.5	140
60	9.1	
80	21	
100	40	178

KCl (56, 57, 73, 120, 233, 251, 253, 384.5, 422, 457)

t, °C	p_{mm}	C
	KCl	
20.0	15.5	34.0
25	20.5	35.5
30	26.9	37.0
35	35.1	
40	45.8	40.0
45	62.1	
50	74.8	42.6
55	93.0	
100	567.8	56.1
108.6	760.0	

$KClO_3$ (73, 141, 179, 187, 304, 384.5, 423, 434)

t, °C	p_{mm}	C
	$KClO_3$	
0	4.54	3.3
10	9.10	5.1

$KClO_3$.—(*Continued*)

t, °C	p_{mm}	C
	$KClO_3$	
20	17.23	7.4
30	31.07	10.2
35	41.03	11.9
40	53.57	14.0
45	69.23	16.3
50	88.59	18.9
55	112.4	21.6
60	141.3	24.5
65	176.5	27.6
70	217.8	31.1
75	267.3	34.6
80	325.7	38.4
85	393.5	42.6
90	472.4	47.0
95	563.5	51.4
100	668.1	56.1
103.9	760.0	59.9
290	11 700 max.	1×10^3
366	sec. B. P.	3×10^4

KBr (73, 106, 344, 384.5, 434)

t, °C	p_{mm}	C
	KBr	
0	3.95	53.5
100	526.5	105.3

KI (73, 106, 344, 384.5, 434)

t, °C	p_{mm}	C
	KI	
0	3.4	127.5
10	6.6	136
20	12.2	144
30	21.5	152
40	36.5	160
50	59.0	168
60	93.0	176
70	142.0	184
80	210.0	192
90	303	200
100	427	208
118.2	760.0	220

K_2SO_4.—(*Continued*)

t, °C	p_{mm}	C
	K_2SO_4	
0	4.51	7.38
10	8.98	
20	17.04	11.24
25	23.05	
30	30.8	13.08
35	40.7	
40	53.3	14.86
45	69.1	
50	88.8	16.58
60	142.7	18.28
80	340	21.40
100	723	24.19
101.4	760	24.4

KNO_2 (301)

t, °C	p_{mm}	C
132	758.5	475†

KNO_3 (33, 56, 57, 73, 120, 203, 304, 320, 338, 344, 384.5, 423)

t, °C	p_{mm}	C
	α-KNO_3 (Rhombic)	
−2.82	3.621	11.52
0	4.45	13.3
+10	6.86	20.9
20	16.52	31.6
25	22.10	37.3
30	29.20	45.8
35	38.11	
40	49.09	63.9
45	62.56	
50	78.88	85.5
55	98.53	
60	121.94	110.0
65	149.6	
70	181.8	138
75	219.3	
80	262.2	169
85	311.5	
90	366.9	202
95	429.3	
100	499.0	246
105	576	
110	660	295
115.5	760	330
120	852	365

KNO_3.—(*Continued*)

t, °C	p_{mm}	C
	α-KNO_3 (Rhombic)	
125	958	415
	α-KNO_3 + β-KNO_3	
129U	1048	
	α-KNO_3	
130m	1071	
135m	1189	
	β-KNO_3 (Rhombohedral)	
120m	837	
125m	950	
	β-KNO_3	
130	1074	?
135	1207	
140	1354	
150	1676	
160	2042	
180	2884	
200	3820	
220	4765	
240	5560	
250	5930	
260	5980	
265	5995 max.	
270	5970	
280	5750	
300	4740	
320	2670	
	Boiling points	
115.5	760	330
332	760	1×10^5

$K_2C_4H_4O_6$, Tartrate (141, 167, 254, 298, 299, 300, 434)

t	p_{mm}	C
	$K_2C_4H_4O_6.2H_2O$	
10	7.1	144
15	9.7	150
20	13.1	156
25	17.4	162
30*	23.0	168
35	30.0	174
40	38.8	180
45	49.5	168
100	458	241
115 ± 0.5	760	246

* Reported transition at 29.2° can not be established on basis of existing vapor-pressure data.

K_2CrO_4 (4, 201, 327, 434)

t, °C	p_{mm}	C
	K_2CrO_4	
0	4.10	57.2
20	15.4	62.4
40	47.8	67.9
60	126.7	73.9
80	295.8	80.3
100	622.0	86.9
105.9	760.0	88.9

$K_2Cr_2O_7$ (202, 233, 423)

t, °C	p_{mm}	C
	$K_2Cr_2O_7$	
20	17.20	12.2
25	23.20	
30	30.95	18.4
35	40.85	
40	53.30	26.3
45	68.95	
50	88.3	35.3
55	112.0	
60	140.9	45.1
80	323	68.7
100	649	98.5
104.9	760	108

$K_2Cr_2(SO_4)_4$ (241)

t, °C	p_{mm}
	$K_2Cr_2(SO_4)_4.24H_2O$
20	15.0

$K_2Al_2(SO_4)_4$ (256, 467)

t, °C	p_{mm}
	$K_2Al_2(SO_4)_4.24H_2O$
60	144.1
65	179.4
70	221.3
75	269.7
	$K_2Al_2(SO_4)_4.24H_2O$ + $K_2Al_2(SO_4)_4.18H_2O$ (?)
79.5*	317.3
	$K_2Al_2(SO_4)_4.18H_2O$ (?)
80	321.9
85	367.0
90	417.3

* Other determinations give transition at 84 to 91°.

$KNaC_4H_4O_6$, Rochelle salt (147, 166, 254, 298, 299, 300)

t, °C	p_{mm}	C
	$KNaC_4H_4O_6.4H_2O$	
0	4.0	27
10	8.0	40
20	15.2	56
30	27.1	76
40	46.2	106
	$KNaC_4H_4O_6.4H_2O$ + $Na_2C_4H_4O_6.2H_2O$	
41*	48.6	
44	54.3	
46	58.5	
48	62.9	
50	67.6	
52	72.6	
	$KNaC_4H_4O_6.4H_2O$ + $Na_2C_4H_4O_6.2H_2O$ + $K_2C_4H_4O_6.2H_2O$	
54	77.9	

* The salt becomes unstable with respect to its own saturated solution at 41 ± 1°C. The dissociation pressure curve of the 4-hydrate meets the S-L-V curve at *ca.* 54°C. The transition is reported between 54–59°; at this temp. the solution becomes saturated with both $Na_2C_4H_4O_6$ and $K_2C_4H_4O_6$, both present as dihydrates, and the double salt breaks up completely. No data exist on the corresponding ternary system. Solubility data refer to the *d*-double salt (Seignette's salt).

RbCl (57, 344, 384.5, 434)

t, °C	p_{mm}	C
	RbCl	
20	12.8	91.1
40	38.9	103.5
60	101.5	115.5
80	233.9	127.2
100	484.7	138.9
113.7	760	147

Rb_2SO_4 (57, 384.5, 434)

t, °C	p_{mm}	C
	Rb_2SO_4	
100	673	81.8
103.5	760	83.0

Cs salts (56, 57)

Salt	t at 1 atm.	C†
CsCl	119.92	290
Cs_2SO_4	109.96	225
$CsNO_3$	107.23	221
$Cs_2Al_2(SO_4)_4.24H_2O$	100.53	23

NON-AQUEOUS SYSTEMS CONTAINING THREE OR MORE COMPONENTS

Standard arrangement, *v.* p. viii

A = O_2; B = S; C = Cu (330)

A = (O_2 + N_2), Air; B = CO_2
Critical region (6, 80, 447)

A = SO_2; B = $HgBr_2$; C = HgI_2

Data with reference to the elevation of the critical temperature of SO_2 by addition of B and C. Temperature range, 157 to 255°C. No pressure data (287).

A = NH_3; B = NH_4NO_3; C = NH_4CNS (69, 129, 130, 131, 158, 190, 224)

t, °C	p_{mm}	M % B	M % C
	NH_4NO_3		
0	102.8	11.7	34.8
0	216.5	20.0	20.0
0	294.5	29.8	10.0
10	122.0	12.8	38.3
10	298.5	21.2	21.2
10	406.5	31.3	10.4
20	384	22.6	22.6
20	546	33.4	11.2
	NH_4CNS		
20	173	13.5	40.5
	NH_4NO_3 + NH_4CNS		
0	86.5	11.0	37.7
10	122	12.5	39.0
20	167	15.6	39.6

M % B + C \ Mole ratio	p_{mm} B/C = 1/3			B/C = 1			B/C = 3		
	0°	10°	20°	0°	10°	20°	0°	10°	20°
0	3221	4612	6429	3221	4612	6429	3221	4612	6429
16	1524								
17	1384			1521					
18	1253			1390			1519		
19	1136			1268			1398		
20	1030	1554		1161			1290		
21	933	1409		1063	1581		1191		
22	846	1284		972	1454		1100		
23	767	1170		888	1330		1015	1512	
24	696	1067	1521	830	1223		932	1400	
25	630	971	1398	740	1122		864	1293	
26	572	886	1285	678	1031	1551	799	1198	
27	520	809	1184	620	948	1434	736	1110	
28	473	739	1090	568	872	1328	680	1029	1553
29	429.5	676	1006	521	803	1231	630	956	1450
30	391.7	619	926	477.5	739	1141	582	888	1353
31	357	568	855	438	685	1058	538	826	1263
32	324.5	521	789	402.5	629	981	498.5	768	1181
33	296.0	479	729	370.5	580	908	462.5	716	1106
34	271	440	673	342	536	836	430	668	1035
35	248.5	405	622	315.5	496	769	400.5	624	971
36	227.8	373	584	290.5	460	709	374	584	909
37	209.5	344	532	269	427	654	349.5	547	853
38	193.0	317	493.5	249.5	397.5	607	328.5	513	801
39	178.1	293	457.5	231.5	371	565	308.5	481	754
40	164.9	270.5	424.5	216.5	347	527		452	709
41	152.4	250	394		325.5	492.5		425.5	668
42	141.3	231	366		306.4	462			630
43	131.2	214	340			435			595
44	122.2	198.6	316			410.5			562
45	116.1	184.7	294.5			388.5			
46	106.4	172.0	275						
47		160.9	258						
48		150.5	242						
49		141.4	227.5						
50	Satd.	133.2	214	Satd. soln.					
51	soln.	125.6	202.5						
52			191.6				Satd. soln.		
53			181.8						
54			173.2						

A = NH_3; B = CH_4O, Methyl alcohol; C = C_3H_6O, Acetone (102)

A = CO_2 (287, 288, 289, 290, 291, 292, 293, 294)

B =	SiO_2	SiO_2	SiO_2	TiO_2	TiO_2	TiO_2	CaO	CaO
C =	Na_2O	K_2O	CaO	CaO	Na_2O	K_2O	Na_2O	K_2O
D =			Na_2O	Na_2O				
E =			K_2O	K_2O				

A = CO_2; B = $C_6H_3N_3O_7$, Picric acid; C = $C_{10}H_8$ (139)

t, °C	$p_{atm.}$	t, °C	$p_{atm.}$	t, °C	$p_{atm.}$
BC		BC + C		BC + B	
23.4	60.7	28.0	66.0	23.45	60.4
25.9	64.0	29.4	68.1	25.4	62.9
29.1	68.9	31.1	70.7	26.8	65.0
29.5	69.8	31.3	70.9	28.2	67.3
29.9	70.4	31.6	71.4	29.1	68.5
30.6	71.2	31.9	72.0	29.9	69.8
30.9	71.9	32.2	72.4	30.55	70.9
31.1	72.2	32.4	72.6	30.9	71.6
31.3*	72.6	32.6	73.2	31.3	72.3
101.1	212.5	32.8	73.9	31.6*	72.9
102.1	193.6	33.0	74.0	89.5	195.9
103.7	175.4	32.2*	74.3	89.9	184.1
105.9	165.9	54.7	174.8	90.6	164.9
110.6	145.7	54.1	160.0	91.5	150.3
115.2	130.0	54.3	146.6	92.6	135.3
121.7	117.0	55.3	132.0	94.2	120.2
150.7		56.5	121.0	95.5	105.5
BC + C		58.1	107.0	97.6	91.0
22.6	58.4	59.3	94.5	98.9	78.8
24.6	61.0	77.1E		113.4E	
26.5	63.9				

* First critical endpoint; second critical endpoint unrealized. For comparison, crit. pt. CO_2 by same author 31.2°, 72.4 atm.

A = CCl_4; B = C_2H_5OH; C = C_6H_6 (377, 378, 379)

Wt. % B	Values of p_{mm} 34.8°	50°	60°	66°
Wt. Ratio A/C = 23/77				
0	153	281	407	500
2.05	191	353	515	632
8.11	201	380	559	692
17.50	204	390	580	721
26.50	204	392	585	729
40.13	199	385	577	722
50.57	193	376	564	709
59.43	186	363	546	688
72.23	167	334	508	642
82.38	148	301	462	589
89.96	130	270	421	542
100.0	103	223	354	462
Wt. Ratio A/C = 55.4/44.6				
0	163	295	426	521
2.71	203	380	551	678
5.33	208	391	575	710
12.72	212	406	599	744
22.20	212	408	603	753
33.40	208	400	598	746
55.17	190	372	560	703
70.77	167	335	508	643
81.02	147	301	465	589
89.25	128	266	417	539
100.0	103	223	354	462
Wt. Ratio A/C = 73.7/26.3				
0	166	303	435	533
2.48	207	387	561	687
6.10	215	408	600	744
12.01	218	414	612	763
22.81	216	414	615	767
Wt. Ratio A/C = 73.7/26.3				
30.80	213	410	608	762
43.90	203	393	588	740
56.11	187	370	559	703
66.30	173	343	522	663
80.79	144	297	459	584
94.35	115	244	387	501
100.0	103	223	354	462
Wt. Ratio A/C = 85.2/14.8				
0	170	307	441	541
11.60	221	422	625	777
20.98	219	420	624	778
30.92	215	414	615	769
47.56	199	389	583	733
59.64	184	361	543	687
70.48	163	325	497	631
84.28	137	280	437	560
100.0	103	223	354	462

Wt. % C	Values of p_{mm} 34.8°	50°	60°	66°
Wt. Ratio B/A = 23.3/76.7				
0	223	427	637	789
13.25	220	423	628	776
23.45	217	419	617	768
37.0	213	407	602	751
50.63	209	397	589	731
66.91	201	383	566	700
79.49	194	366	535	661
89.70	182	338	490	600
95.29	170	308	446	546
100.0	147	271	389	477

A = CCl_4; B = C_2H_5OH; C = C_6H_6.—(*Continued*)

Wt. % C	Values of p_{mm} 34.8°	50°	60°	66°
Wt. Ratio B/A = 56.13/43.87				
0	187	369	554	700
7.2	194	381	571	721
13.16	199	388	581	729
19.77	202	392	586	735
30.42	205	395	589	738
43.75	205	395	589	738
62.59	203	391	583	724
75.69	200	385	570	708
84.87	194	373	548	681
94.04	185	349	509	625
97.19	172	317	457	562
100.0	147	271	389	477

A = $CHCl_3$, Chloroform; B = $C_4H_{10}O$, Ethyl ether; C_1 = $C_6H_3N_3O_7$, Picric acid, C_2 = C_8H_9NO, Acetanilide, C_3 = $C_{10}H_8$, Naphthalene (275); *cf.* (115, 116, 150, 195, 409)

Values of p_{mm}

x_A in A + B	A + B saturated with: Nil, 13.60°	C_1, 12.75°	C_2, 12.20°	C_3, 12.35°
0	341	327	319	272
10	305	293	283	243.5
20	267	255	247.5	214.5
30	228	218.5	211	186
40	193	185	177.5	157
50	163	156	150	132.5
60	140	134	129.5	115
70	127	122.5	117.5	104
80	122	120	113	96.5
90	122	119	112.5	91.5
100	126.2	121	115.5	92

A = CS_2; B = C_3H_6O, Acetone; C_1 = $C_6H_3N_3O_7$, Picric acid, C_2 = C_8H_9NO, Acetanilide (275); *cf.* (342, 466)

Values of p_{mm}

x_A in A + B	A + B saturated with: Nil, 24.8°	C_1, 24.6°	C_2, 24.8°
0	231.5	170.5	208.5
10	321	250	280
20	379	324	331
30	414	375	368
40	435	406	398
50	448	423	415
60	453	429	422
70	455	431	426
80	453	432	428
90	439	420	419
100	358	357	358

A = CS_2; B = $C_3H_8O_2$, Methylal; C_1 = $C_6H_3N_3O_7$, Picric acid, C_2 = $C_{10}H_8$, Naphthalene (275); *cf.* (466)

x_A in A + B	A + B saturated with: Nil, 16.53°	C_1, 18.10°	C_2, 18.60°
0	265.5	236	252
10	292	278	267
20	313	309	280
30	329	332	289
40	338	346	294
50	341	353	295.5
60	340.5	355	293
70	335	355.5	286
80	325	350	273
90	304	327	253
100	263	275.5	126.5

A = CS_2; B = $C_4H_{10}O$, Ethyl ether; C_1 = $C_6H_3N_3O_7$, Picric acid, C_2 = $C_{10}H_8$, Naphthalene, C_3 = $C_{10}H_{16}O$, Camphor (275)

Values of p_{mm}

x_A in A + B	A + B saturated with: Nil, 20.5°	C_1, 18.2°	C_2, 22.2°	C_3, 20.3°	x_A in A + B	A + B saturated with: Nil, 20.5°	C_1, 18.2°	C_2, 22.2°	C_3, 20.3°
0	449	404	381	173	60	424	382	339	217
10	452	407	379	181	70	409	368	326	222
20	453	408	374	189	80	385	349	311	227
30	450	406	368	196	90	350	321	293	232
40	444	402	360	204	100	307	277	273	237
50	436	393	350	211					

SYSTEMS CONTAINING THREE OR MORE COMPONENTS—AQUEOUS

Standard Arrangement, *v.* p. viii

B = HCl; C = Cu_2Cl_2 (462)

p_{mm}	g C/100 g A	p_{mm}	g C/100 g A	p_{mm}	g C/100 g A
g B/100 g A = 22.4		g B/100 g A = 27.6		g B/100 g A = 31.1	
t = *ca.* 52°		70	13.8	133	29.0
55	0	66	27.6	131	33.6
55	6.9	64	34.7	126	41.5
55	12.8	64	37.4	g B/100 g A = 32	
55	25.5	61	40.8	*t* = *ca.* 91°	
55	37.9	g B/100 g A = 31.1			
55	43.6	*t* = *ca.* 85°		192	0
g B/100 g A = 27.6		150	0	187	7.35
t = *ca.* 65°		146	7.2	180	14.7
75.5	0	142	14.7	173	22.2
73	6.9	138	21.8	166	29.4

B = HCl; C = LiCl (462)

p_{mm}	g C/100 g A	p_{mm}	g C/100 g A	p_{mm}	g C/100 g A
g B/100 g A = 7.4		g B/100 g A = 18.2		g B/100 g A = 22.4	
t = *ca.* 52°		57	10.4	121	22.9
87	0	61	15.6	191.5	28.2
80.5	5.07	75	25.9	767	46.3
76.5	9.18	156	38.9	1490	
63.5	18.4	395	52.3	g B/100 g A = 28	
51	27.6	820	64.5	*t* = *ca.* 65°	
49.5	34.2	1500	79.5		
49.5	39.0	g B/100 g A = 22.4		79	0
68	51.0	*t* = *ca.* 52°		122	5.9
312	76.0			186	11.8
g B/100 g A = 18.2		55.5	0	312	17.6
t = *ca.* 52°		57	5.5	648	26.0
67.5	0	65	10.9	992	30.4
59	5.2	78.5	16.6	1344	36.8

B = I_2; C = HI (427)

B = H_2SO_4; C = As_2O_3 (384)

p_{As_2O} = *ca.* 0.00001 mm from a 0.015% As_2O_3 solution in H_2SO_4 (sp. gr. = 1.84) at 60°C.

B = NH_3; C = NH_4NO_3 (100)

t, °C	p_{mm}	*t*, °C	p_{mm}
18.82 Wt. % B; 33.7 Wt. % C			
−12.95	53.2	10.95	188.0
−7.25	73.5	18.8	272.5
+0.10	109.0	27.72	405.0
7.98	159.5	35.2	555.7

B = NH_3; C = NH_4Cl (310)

t, °C	p_{mm}	*t*, °C	p_{mm}
16.85 Wt. % B; 5.27 Wt. % C		12.90 Wt. % B; 10.26 Wt. % C	
19.01	182.1	23.1	158.5
26.0	251.1	30.9	230.5
32.9	343	38.3	319
39.2	449	45.4	429
49.3	667	51.2	543
57.8	913	58.1	708

B = NH_3; C = C_2H_6O, Ethyl alcohol (102)

B = NH_3; C = $C_6H_{14}O_6$, Mannitol (310)

t, °C	p_{mm}	*t*, °C	p_{mm}
12.27 Wt. % B; 4.56 Wt. % C			
22.9	143.8	42.7	349
29.8	197.7	50.6	479
36.8	271	57.8	630

B = NH_3; C = CH_4N_2O, Urea (145, 310)

t, °C	p_{mm}	*t*, °C	p_{mm}
16.36 Wt. % B; 10.43 Wt. % C		17.22 Wt. % B; 5.29 Wt. % C	
24.5	254.4	25.1	260.4
29.4	312	29.6	317
35.2	403	35.0	400
40.4	497	39.7	485
45.6	611	45.9	622
54.4	856	50.1	726
59.1	1014	54.5	857
		58.0	974

B = NH_3; C = NH_4CNS (100, 129)

Wt. % B	p_{mm}	Wt. % B	p_{mm}
Wt. ratio A/C = 1			
10°C		30°C	
16.64	97	16.67	252
23.24	177	20.98	371
30.44	344	25.34	550
35.90	554	29.20	755
39.68	766	32.02	956
42.98	978	34.52	1167
45.64	1175	36.72	1381
47.84	1358	38.10	1530
49.74	1526		
t = 20°C			
Wt. ratio A/C = 10/3			
9.37	64	34.52	757
14.89	137	37.47	950
20.63	235	40.33	1168
26.58	395	42.67	1368
30.90	565	44.62	1550
Wt. ratio A/C = 7/6			
8.47	66	36.76	928
13.10	107	38.99	1107
19.24	198	41.13	1291
26.71	394	42.83	1451
31.44	593	43.89	1559
34.55	773		
Wt. ratio A/C = 1/2			
9.53	77	34.63	775
16.79	154	37.61	970
22.78	270	40.2	1188
28.37	447	42.11	1370
31.83	614		
Wt. ratio A/C = 1/6.335			
17.51	159	36.20	898
22.74	268	37.91	1031
27.51	421	39.15	1136
30.69	564	40.56	1266
32.43	667	41.65	1377
34.09	769	42.51	1463

0.1865 g NH_4CNS per cm^3 of 22.16% NH_3 solution

t, °C	p_{mm}
−15.3	39.6
− 8.03	62.0
− 0.81	94.5
+ 6.78	143.9
10.16	170.8
17.19	237.6
23.0	314.1
30.3	433.1
35.7	543.1

B = NH_3; C = $CuSO_4$ (310)

t, °C	p_{mm}	*t*, °C	p_{mm}
14.65 Wt. % B; 2.68 Wt. % C		6.54 Wt. % B; 3.94 Wt. % C	
18.9	138.5	30.6	91.8
26.4	197.6	37.0	126.2
36.1	307	41.5	155.1
43.6	422	46.9	194.7
47.5	493	52.6	250.1
50.8	560	57.7	309
56.5	693		

B = NH_3; C = $CaCl_2$ (100)

t, °C	p_{mm}	*t*, °C	p_{mm}
22.9 Wt. % B; 12.9 Wt. % C			
−13.4	54.0	16.4	272.6
− 5.0	88.6	23.1	370.1
+ 1.8	129.8	29.8	498.2
2.5	136.5	35.6	640.3
9.3	193.1		

B = NH_3; C = $Ca(NO_3)_2$ (100)

t, °C	p_{mm}	*t*, °C	p_{mm}
19.18 Wt. % B; 22.48 Wt. % C		25.77 Wt. % B; 55.8 Wt. % C	
−14.5	34.8	−12.1	82.6
− 9.3	48.1	− 4.9	124.1
− 2.2	73.2	+ 3.97	202.3
+ 5.3	110.2	11.0	291.1
15.1	181.7	18.0	413.0
21.2	242.0	25.0	575.3
29.5	354.0	32.4	782.7
36.4	474.0		

B = NH_3; C = $LiNO_3$ (100)

t, °C	p_{mm}	*t*, °C	p_{mm}
18.0 Wt. % B; 45.7 Wt. % C		21.5 Wt. % B; 42.2 Wt. % C	
−13.5	16.7	−14.9	24.5
−12.2	19.6	− 7.0	41.6
− 4.2	31.9	0.0	63.8
+ 1.7	46.3	+ 7.0	95.3
8.5	66.8	14.0	136.4
14.4	91.1	20.4	188.4
21.6	131.0	27.1	257.0
28.7	183.2	35.2	371.1
35.2	246.9		
23.3 Wt. % B; 18.0 Wt. % C		26.2 Wt. % B; 30.1 Wt. % C	
−14.5	50.8	−15.4	52.9
− 8.1	73.7	− 7.8	84.4
+ 0.8	110.2	− 0.1	131.8
6.5	161.9	+ 8.4	203.1
13.4	225.2	15.2	283.4
20.0	308.0	21.0	369.7
28.0	441.8	27.5	491.5
35.1	598.1	35.1	683.1
38.4 Wt. % B; 55.5 Wt. % C			
−11.6	121.3	15.4	493.0
− 5.5	169.6	20.5	623.8
+ 1.0	242.1	27.6	862.7
8.2	345.4	34.4	1141

B = NH_3; C = NaI (100)

t, °C	p_{mm}	*t*, °C	p_{mm}
16.06 Wt. % B; 32.34 Wt. % C		26.9 Wt. % B; 64.9 Wt. % C	
−14.4	40.9	−14.6	87.5
− 8.0	61.1	−13.0	96.6
+ 1.2	90.4	− 9.6	120.3
3.15	116.3	− 8.0	143.0
10.7	170.8	− 0.9	190.3
17.9	242.4	+ 6.0	276.0
25.8	347.5	13.1	394.8
35.0	519.2	20.1	551.8
		26.9	753.8

B = NH_3; C = Na_2SO_4 (310)

t, °C	p_{mm}	t, °C	p_{mm}
16.73 Wt. % B; 4.23 Wt. % C		15.44 Wt. % B; 4.53 Wt. % C	
27.6	321.1	25.8	215.3
31.1	364.0	28.7	238.8
33.0	395.0	30.9	261.2
35.2	435.2	33.1	288.7
37.0	472	34.7	307.3
38.5	485.2	37.3	342.7
39.1	497.3	39.4	374.9
40.3	523.3	42.7	429.8
42.0	550.4	45.0	468.6
43.0	580.9	46.2	491.6
44.7	619.3		
46.5	666.5		
9.90 Wt. % B; 4.25 Wt. % C			
29.1	167.7	37.9	246.0
31.1	183.5	40.1	271.6
33.4	202.8	43.1	310.4
34.8	215.9	46.2	352.8
36.5	232.4		

B = NH_3; C = K_2SO_4 (310)

t, °C	p_{mm}	t, °C	p_{mm}
7.49 Wt. % B; 3.05 Wt. % C			
40.4	203.5	51.1	320.0
46.7	265.2	58.5	428

B = NH_4NO_3; C = $NaNO_3$ (279, 320, 384.5)

NH_4NO_3 + $NaNO_3$ crystals			
10	5.4	30	14.6
15	7.0	35	18.5
20	9.0	38	21.4
25	11.6	40*	31.2

* Unsaturated solution containing 68.4 g $NaNO_3$ and 150.4 g NH_4NO_3 per 100 g H_2O.

B = CO_2; C = Heavy-metal oxides at 18°C (156)

Oxide	Carbonate, g/l: p_{CO_2} 1 atm.	Carbonate, g/l: p_{CO_2} 56 atm.
PbO.....	0.14	0.15
ZnO.....	0.7	0.84
CuO.....	0.3	0.41
Ag_2O....	1.05	1.7
MnO....	0.4	0.8
FeO.....	0.72	0.77

B = NH_4Cl; C = KNO_3 (120, 384.5)

NH_4Cl + KNO_3			
19	11.99	25	16.92
20	12.73	26	17.82
21	13.51	27	18.80
22	14.31	28	19.77
23	15.15	29	20.78
24	16.03	30	21.83

B = CO_2; C = MgO (53, 122, 155, 182)

t = 18°C: p_{CO_2} atm.	$MgCO_3$, g/l	p_{CO_2} atm.	$MgCO_3$, g/l	t, °C	$MgCO_3$, g/l
$Mg(OH)_2$		$MgCO_3.3H_2O$		p_{CO_2} = 1 atm.	
0.0000	0.0126	2.5	35.4	3.5	35.6
0.0002	1.63	3.0	38.1	12	26.5
0.00025	1.87	3.5	40.4	18	22.1
0.00030	2.10	4.0	42.6	30	15.8
0.00035	2.31	4.5	44.3	40	11.8
$Mg(OH)_2$ +		5.0	46.0	50	9.5
$MgCO_3.3H_2O$		6.0	49.3	p_{CO_2} = 5 atm.	
0.00037	2.39	7.0	52.5	10	35.7
$MgCO_3.3H_2O$		8.0	55.1	15	32.8
0.0004	2.42	9.0	57.2	40	13.7
0.00045	2.47	10.0	59.2	p_{CO_2} = 34 atm.	
0.0005	2.51	16.0	70.5	0	85.8
0.001	3.11	$MgCO_3.3H_2O$ +		5	83.2
0.01	6.04	$Mg(HCO_3)_2$		10	79.3
0.1	12.2	18.2	74.9	18	74
0.5	20.6	$Mg(HCO_3)_2$		30	68.8
1.0	25.8	35.0	74.9	40	64.4
1.5	29.8	56.0	74.9	50	61.8
2.0	32.9			60	55.6

B = CO_2; C = SrO, t = 18°C (156)

p_{CO_2} atm.	$SrCO_3$, g/l
$SrCO_3$	
1	1.2
$Sr(HCO_3)_2$	
>35	3.8

B = CO_2; C = BaO, t = 18°C (156, 255)

p_{CO_2} atm.	$BaCO_3$, g/l
$BaCO_3$	
1	2.7
$Ba(HCO_3)_2$	
25.0	5.9

B = CO_2; C = CaO (122, 154, 182, 183, 255, 365, 366)

t = 16–18°C: p_{CO_2} atm.	$CaCO_3$, mg/l	p_{CO_2} atm.	$CaCO_3$, mg/l	t, °C	$CaCO_3$, mg/l
$Ca(OH)_2$		$CaCO_3$		p_{CO_2} = 56 atm.	
3.16×10^{-14}	2000	0.142	537	18	3930
$Ca(OH)_2$ + $CaCO_3$		0.254	668	25	4030
2.6×10^{-14}	2000	0.417	793	35	3800
$CaCO_3$		0.553	892	45	3390
2.80×10^{-10}	74	0.730	979	55	2550
9.78×10^{-9}	26	0.984	1094	p_{CO_2} = 3.2 × 10^{-4} atm.	
6.14×10^{-8}	18	1.0	1110		
2.19×10^{-7}	16	2	1400	0	81
3.73×10^{-7}	15.9	4	1820	5	75
3.85×10^{-7}	15.9	6	2110	10	70
6.07×10^{-7}	16	10	2500	15	65
7.62×10^{-6}	22	14	2830	20	60
7.63×10^{-5}	40	18	3070	25	56
2.15×10^{-4}	56	25	3420	30	52
5.04×10^{-4}	75.1	35	3890		
8.08×10^{-4}	85.6	$CaCO_3$ +			
3.33×10^{-3}	138.2	$Ca(HCO_3)_2$			
1.39×10^{-2}	224.7	36.5	3930		
2.82×10^{-2}	298.6	$Ca(HCO_3)_2$			
5.01×10^{-2}	362.5	56	3930		

B = C_6H_6, Benzene; C = C_2H_6O, Ethyl alcohol (42, 43)

760 mm isobar; *see also* p. 316

t, °C	Wt. % L_I: A	B	C	Wt. % L_{II}: A	B	C
69.0	0.3	0.04	99.66	97.0	2.7	0.3
68.0	0.3	0.4	99.3	92.8	6.8	0.4
67.0	0.4	1.2	98.4	88.1	11.4	0.5
66.0	0.5	2.8	96.7	81.8	17.6	0.6
65.5	0.7	5.2	94.1	77.3	22.0	0.7
65.0	1.0	9.1	89.9	65.6	32.4	2.0

B = C_2H_6O, Ethyl alcohol; C = $C_4H_{10}O$, Ethyl ether, *see also* Fig. 16 (104, 249, 296)

L + V, 0° isotherm, values of p_{mm}

Wt. % C	Wt. % B in A + B: 94.7	89.9	79.5	69.9	57.5	47.3	37.9	29.0	20.5	10.5
2				20.5	25.0		30.5		52	
4				29.5	39.5	47.0	52.5	61.0	91.5	60.5
6		32.0	33.0	37.2	52.0	62.0	71.0	86.5	124.0	91.0
8		38.0	39.8	45.0	63.5	75.0	87.0	109.0	146.5	126.5
10		44.5	46.5	52.5	73.0	87.0	100.5	129.5	159.0	170.0
12		50.5	53.0	59.8	81.5	96.5	112.5	144.0		
15	58.0	59.0	62.5	70.2	92.5	109.0	127.5	156.5		
20	71.5	72.5	77.0	86.0	107.5	125.5	145.5			
25	83.5	85.0	90.2	100.0	121.0	138.5	154.0			
30	95.0	96.3	101.8	112.0	132.0	148.5	159.0			
35	104.5	106.3	111.7	122.5	140.5	154.5				
40	113.0	115.0	121.0	131.5	148.0	158.5				
50	128.5	129.5	136.6	145.0	157.5					
60	141.5	142.7	148.8	155.5						
70	153.0	154.3	159.3	163.0						
80	162.0	163.3	167.3	169.0						
90	172.0	173.0	175.0	176.0						

Wt. % L_I: A	B	C	Wt. % L_{II}: A	B	C	p_{mm}
88.4	0	11.6	1.0	0	99.0	187.5
81.0	8.4	10.6	1.3	2.7	96.0	184.0
80.1	9.4	10.5				183.0
74.0	15.5	10.5	3.5	7.3	89.2	175.0
70.4	18.1	11.5				168.0
68.5	20.0	11.5	6.6	13.6	79.8	166.5

Continued on p. 378

B = C_2H_6O; C = $C_4H_{10}O$.—(*Continued*)

Isotherms, values of p_{mm}

Wt. % A	Wt. % B	Wt. % C	−20°	−10°	0°	+5°	10°	15°	20°	25°	30°	35°	40°	45°	50°
4.5	85.5	10	16	27	46	59	76	96	120						
4.0	76.0	20	26	44	70		110		170						
3.0	57.0	40	35	60	100	128	164	207	262						
2.0	38.0	60	48	80	131	166	210	264	327						
1.67	31.67	66.67			149	187	234	288	353	430	522	628	750	892	1053
1.43	27.14	71.43			155	195	244	300	366	446	541	651	777	924	1092
1.0	19.0	80	60	98	157	197	247	306	376						
3.3	30.0	66.7			150	189	236	292	359	435	530	636	760	903	1066
5.0	28.3	66.7			152	193	239	295	363	443	537	645	771	916	1082
6.6	26.7	66.7			155	194	243	300	368	447	543	654	780	929	1095
10.0	23.3	66.7			158	199	248	308	376	457	555	668	798	949	1120
13.3	20.0	66.7	2 liq. phases		165	207	259	320	392	476	577	695	829	984	1162
20.0	13.3	66.7			174	217	269	332	408	495	600	722	861	1022	1206
26.6	6.7	66.7			181	227	283	349	426	517	628	754	902	1069	1262
2.85	25.71	71.43			157	197	246	304	370	453	547	659	789	936	1106
4.29	24.28	71.43			160	200	249	306	374	457	554	666	796	946	1116
5.71	22.85	71.43			161	201	251	309	379	462	560	673	804	956	1129
8.57	20.0	71.43			164	205	255	316	387	473	574	690	823	977	1155
11.42	17.14	71.43	2 liq. phases		167	211	262	323	396	482	586	705	839	998	1179
17.14	11.42	71.43			175	218	272	336	412	501	607	730	870	1034	1221
22.85	5.71	71.43			182	227	283	350	429	521	632	757	903	1072	1264

B = C_2H_6O; C = $C_4H_{10}O$.—(*Continued from p. 377*)

Wt. % L_I			Wt. % L_{II}			
A	B	C	A	B	C	p_{mm}
60.2	23.4	16.4	14.2	22.0	63.8	161.0
			17.8	24.2	58.0	161.0
59.0	24.0	17.0				160.5
55.0	25.1	19.9	19.0	24.5	56.5	159.0
43.8	26.7	29.5				158.5
30.6	27.4	42.0				158.5

B = C_2H_6O, Ethyl alcohol; C = $C_4H_{10}O$, Ethyl ether; D = $C_{12}H_{11}N$, Diphenylamine (249)

Values of p_{mm}

t, °C	3.3 % A, 63.3 % B, 33.3 % C, 0 % D	3.3 % A, 63.3 % B, 33.2 % C, 0.1 % D	3.3 % A, 63.3 % B, 33.1 % C, 0.2 % D
0	102.2	100.1	99.3
5	127.4	124.5	
10	159	155.7	155.5
15	196	194	192
20	241	238	236
25	293	290	288
30	358	353	352
35	431	427	425
40	518	517	514
45	621	614	612
50	738	731	729

B = C_2H_6O, Ethyl alcohol; C = Na_2CO_3 (191, 203)

t, °C	p_{mm}	Wt. % L_I A	Wt. % L_I B	Wt. % L_I C	Wt. % L_{II} A	Wt. % L_{II} B	Wt. % L_{II} C
		$Na_2CO_3.7H_2O + Na_2CO_3.H_2O$					
34.6	87.5	36.4	63.3	0.3	66.5	1.0	32.5
		$Na_2CO_3.H_2O$					
36.0	94.5	37.7	62.0	0.3	66.8	1.1	32.1
40.0	117.0	38.6	61.0	0.4	66.9	1.2	31.9
49	186	38.6	61.0	0.4	67.3	1.2	31.5
68	442	43.3	55.8	0.9	68.9	2.3	28.8

B = C_2H_6O; C = Na_2CO_3.—(*Continued*)

t, °C	45	50	55	60	65	70	75	80	81.6
p_{mm}‡	151.5	195	249	313	390	482	601	719	760

‡ S + L_I + L_{II} + V; S = $Na_2CO_3.H_2O$.

B = C_3H_6O, Acetone; C = C_6H_6O, Phenol (370, 373, 374, 375, 376), *see also* Figs. 17 and 18

Conjugate solutions

t, °C	p_{mm}	L_I Wt. % A	L_I Wt. % B	L_{II} Wt. % A	L_{II} Wt. % B
50.0	92	88	0	37	0
	100	89.3	0.2	30.6	4.2
	150	89.9	4.2	21.0	21.0
	200	85.6	9.5	22.3	30.2
	250	80.2	14.4	25.8	37.9
	300	60.8	27.7	36.9	38.4
	310*	47.7	34.3	47.7	34.3
56.5	126	85.5	0	40	0
	150	87.9	0.5	29.4	6.6
	200	89.2	3.4	23.0	18.5
	250	84.2	10.0	21.8	27.6
	300	81.2	12.7	24	33.4
	350	72.4	19.5	29.4	37.4
	375	64.3	24.8	35.3	37.6
	386*	47.5	33.5	47.5	33.5
68.0	220	73	0	60	0
	250	81.4	0.6	34.6	6.4
	300	86.4	1.6	28.0	14.7
	350	87.0	4.6	26.1	20.6
	400	83.7	8.8	25.4	26.0
	450	81.0	11.2	26.5	30.4
	500	74	16.6	29.8	33.6
	550	63.7	23.1	37.9	33.4
	570*	50.6	29.4	50.6	29.4
75.0	315*	64.6	1.4	64.6	1.4
	350	78.6	1.4	34.5	9.5
	400	83.9	2.1	31.4	14.0
	450	85.4	5.6	29.2	22.2
	500	84.0	7.6	30.1	26.9

t, °C	p_{mm}	L_I Wt. % A	L_I Wt. % B	L_{II} Wt. % A	L_{II} Wt. % B
75.0	550	81.2	10.0	33.2	29.8
	600	75.9	14.1	39	30.2
	650	68.3	18.9	47.4	28.1
	685*	54.5	25.5	54.5	25.5
85.0	510*	61	5.0	61	5
	550	76.6	5.4	42.8	9.2
	600	79.5	5.9	39.1	12.9
	650	79.9	7.3	37.4	17.0
	700	78.6	9.0	37.4	20.5
	750	75.9	11.4	39.8	22.8
	800	72.6	13.6	45.2	23.1
	850	63.8	18.0	53.9	21.2
	857*	60.9	19.1	60.9	19.1
90.0	684*	59.6	8.4	59.6	8.4
	700	65.9	9.1	51.9	10.1
	750	69.3	9.7	48.1	12.5
	800	69.4	10.6	49.5	16.0

* Critical solution pressure.

t, °C	p_{mm}	L_I Wt. % A	L_I Wt. % B	L_{II} Wt. % A	L_{II} Wt. % B
90.0	850	67.7	12.3	55.7	15.3
	875*	63.5	13.5	63.5	13.5
92	825*	58.9	11.5	58.9	11.5

Wt. % composition and vapor pressure of the three coexistent phases ($L_I + L_{II} + V$) at 56.5°C

p_{mm}	L_I A	L_I B	L_{II} A	L_{II} B	Vapor A	Vapor B
126	85.5	0	40	0	92.2	0
180	89.0	3.5	24	16.5	72.2	25.4
220	88.5	5.5	22.5	23.5	55.9	43
260	85.2	8.8	23	29	28.1	71.2
300	80.3	13.5	25	32.5		
324					22.6	77
350	72.5	19.5	29.5	37		
380	59.3	27.7	37	37		
386*	48	33	48	33		

* Critical solution pressure.

Vapor pressure isotherms on the $L_I + L_{II}$ boundary

Wt. ratio A/B	50° Wt. % C	50° p_{mm}	56.5° Wt. % C	56.5° p_{mm}	68° Wt. % C	68° p_{mm}	75° Wt. % C	75° p_{mm}	85° Wt. % C	85° p_{mm}	90° Wt. % C	90° p_{mm}	92°
100.0/0.00	12	92	14.5	126	27	220							Critical solution
	63		60.0		40								point
91.96/8.04	5.0	179	6.0	236	7.8	370	8.8	481	13.0	638			Wt. % A = 58.9
	64.8	98	63.2	136	56.8	232	52.1	321	38.0	513			Wt. % B = 11.5
84.4/15.6	5.4	245	6.5	315	8.4	475	9.9	602	13.7	798	20.2	855	Wt. % C = 29.6
	65.5	103	63.8	141	58.8	245	55.6	340	47.2	537	37.5	699	p = 825
77.48/22.52	7.5	281	8.5	358	11.0	529	13.4	655	18.8	853	30.5	837	
	65.3	109	63.9	149	59.0	260	56	363	48.4	577	39.0	755	
68.18/31.82	11.8	301	13.0	382	15.6	562	20.1	673	29.3	822			
	64.0	115	62.4	160	58.0	287	54.3	405	45.4	654			
49.83/50.17	24	302	25.9	379	32.0	531							
	58	151	56.6	212	49.0	396							

Point of max. pressure on the $L_I + L_{II}$ surface 90.5 ± 0.5°C, p = 885 mm, Wt. % A = 63, B = 14.5, C = 22.5.

B = $C_3H_6O_2$, Methyl acetate; C = $C_{12}H_{22}O_{11}$, Sucrose, at 25 and 35°C [257]

B = $C_3H_8O_3$, Glycerol; C = **NaCl** [83]

Solutions saturated with NaCl, boiling points, °C

Wt. % B in A	p_{mm}; *see also* p. 316: 92.5	149.5	233.7	355.4	525.9	760.0
0	56.6	66.8	77.3	87.7	98.2	108.7
10	56.1	66.6	77.3	87.9	98.5	109.1
20	57	67.6	78.1	88.7	99.2	109.8
30	58.2	68.8	79.3	89.9	100.5	111.1
40	59.4	70.0	80.6	91.2	101.8	112.5
50	60.6	71.3	82.0	92.8	103.5	114.2
60	62.6	73.4	84.2	95.0	106.0	116.8
70	65.6	76.7	87.7	98.7	109.8	120.9
80	71.7	83.1	94.5	106.0	117.6	129.0
90	87.2	98.9	111.6	124.4	137.1	149.8
95.64	105.8	120.5	135.2	149.9	164.7	179.3

B = C_6H_6O, Phenol; C = C_6H_7N, Aniline [368, 369, 371]

Wt. % L_I, 56.3°C A	B	C	Wt. % L_{II}, 56.3°C A	B	C	Wt. % V, 56.3°C A	B	C
40	60	0	85.5	14.5	0	92.2*	7.83*	0*
26.5	65	8.5	92.5	6.6	0.9	90.6	6.05	3.4
17.1	62.2	20.7	93.7	4.7	1.6	88.9	4.89	6.2
15.4	53.3	31.3	94.6	3.4	2.0	87.4	3.81	8.8
11.1	44.6	44.3	95.0	2.6	2.4	86.7	2.26	11.0
5.5	0	94.5	95.7	0	4.3	84.5	0	15.5

* p = 126 mm.

B = $C_{12}H_{22}O_{11}$, Sucrose; C = **NaCl**, t = 25°C [367]

M_C*	M_B*	p_{H_2O}/p
	NaCl	
6.22	0.40	1.338
6.23	0.58	1.340
6.33	1.03	1.349
6.33	1.18	1.352
6.54	2.34	1.388
6.63	2.82	1.405
	$C_{12}H_{22}O_{11}$	
	6.18	1.1721
0.855	5.95	1.194
0.92	5.97	1.197
1.74	5.90	1.226
2.83	5.92	1.274
3.40	5.97	1.304
3.41	5.98	1.306
	$C_{12}H_{22}O_{11}.NaCl.2H_2O$	
5.02	5.01	1.304
5.16	4.75	1.304
5.98	3.51	1.323
6.49	3.17	1.382
	$C_{12}H_{22}O_{11} + C_{12}H_{22}O_{11}.NaCl.2H_2O$	
5.04	6.23	1.404

M_C*	M_B*	p_{H_2O}/p
	NaCl + $C_{12}H_{22}O_{11}.NaCl.2H_2O$	
6.79	3.08	1.419
	$C_{12}H_{22}O_{11}$ + NaCl	
7.3	6.72	1.563

* M_C, M_B = Moles/100 g H_2O.

B = SiO_2; C = K_2O, *see* Figs. 19 and 20

Locate the desired composition of solution in each figure, and interpolate the values of t and p. At these values the solution is saturated with respect to the phase within whose field the point falls, as indicated by the dotted boundary curves which appear as a background in Fig. 19.

Example: (Composition in Mol %).

50 % H_2O
25 % K_2SiO_3
25 % SiO_2
t = 360°C
p = *ca.* 45 atm.
Solid phase = $K_2Si_2O_5.H_2O$

For detailed data, *v.* [280]; *cf.* [294].

B = $CuCl_2$; C = KCl
(274, 446)

t, °C	p_{mm}
$K_2CuCl_4.2H_2O + CuCl_2.2H_2O$	
42.5	38.4
46.6	47.4
51.5	58.4
$K_2CuCl_4.2H_2O + CuCl_2.2H_2O + KCuCl_3$	
56.1	73.4
$KCuCl_3 + CuCl_2.2H_2O$	
59.1	84.5
63.6	101.8
65.5	109
70.5	133
74.6	158
81.4	200.5
89.2	268
92.6	306
95	330
97.1	355
$K_2CuCl_4.2H_2O + KCuCl_3$	
65.5	116
74.6	172
86.4	260
88.2	276
89.2	292
92.0	322
$K_2CuCl_4.2H_2O$ + KCl	
42.5	46.2
46.6	57
51.5	70.4
56.1	88.4
59.1	100.4
63.6	119.4
65.5	131.5
74.6	187
81.4	233
86.4	272
$K_2CuCl_4.2H_2O + KCuCl_3$ + KCl	
92.4	330
$KCuCl_3$ + KCl	
92.6	332
95	369.7
97.1	402.6
100	448

B = $CaSO_4$; C = NaCl (165)

t, °C	p_{mm}
NaCl + $CaSO_4$	
0	4.2
5	5.0
10	6.9
15	9.5
20	13.0
25	17.5
30	23.4
35	31.0
40	40.8
45	53.0
50	68.3
55	87.3
60	111
65	139
70	173

B = $CaSO_4$; C = NaCl.—
(Continued)

t, °C	p_{mm}
NaCl + $CaSO_4$	
75	214
80	263
90	462
95	557

B = LiOH; C = Li_2CO_3 (111, 133, 316, 434)

g B/100 g A*	p_{mm}, 100°C
Li_2CO_3	
0	760.00
1	747
2	730
3	713
4	696
5	679
6	662
10	542
15	604
LiOH + Li_2CO_3	
16.5‡	526

* Solutions saturated with C at all concentrations of B.
‡ Saturated with both B and C.

B = NaOH; C = NaCl
(7, 8, 265)

First and second boiling points and constitution diagrams

B = NaCl; C = KCl (233)

t, °C	p_{mm}
NaCl + KCl	
20	12.64
22	14.25
24	16.03
26	18.01
28	20.20
30	22.60
32	25.25

B = NaCl; C = $KClO_3$ (74)

M*	p_{mm}, 16.39°C
NaCl + $KClO_3$	
0	5.110
1.025	5.073
1.118	5.070
1.248	5.060
1.484	5.043
1.867	5.011
2.616	4.943
3.152	4.907
3.225	4.904
3.522	4.875
3.901	4.840
4.276	4.813
4.987	4.745
5.705	4.695
6.672	4.707
NaCl + $NaClO_3$ + $KClO_3$	
7.974	4.707

* M = Moles $NaClO_3$ per 1000 g H_2O in the solution.

M'‡	p_{mm}, 16.39°C
NaCl + $KClO_3$	
0	5.110
0.765	5.090
0.937	5.079

B = NaCl; C = $KClO_3$.—
(Continued)

M'‡	p_{mm}, 16.39°C
NaCl + $KClO_3$	
1.075	5.067
1.237	5.051
1.388	5.034
1.540	5.014
NaCl + KCl + $KClO_3$	
1.593	5.007

‡ M' = Moles KCl per 1000 g H_2O in the solution.

B = NaCl; C = KNO_3 (74)

M*	p_{mm},16.39°C
NaCl + KNO_3	
0	4.550
1.289	4.553

B = NaCl; C = KNO_3.—
(Continued)

M*	p_{mm}, 16.39°C
NaCl + KNO_3	
2.488	4.487
3.745	4.431
4.197	4.400
4.657	4.369
5.031	4.345
5.936	4.289
NaCl + KNO_3 + $NaNO_3$	
6.51	4.263
NaCl + KNO_3	
6.854‡	4.253

* M = Moles $NaNO_3$ per 1000 g H_2O in the solution.
‡ Supersaturated with $NaNO_3$.

LITERATURE

(For a key to the periodicals see end of volume)

(1) Abegg and Riesenfeld, *7*, **40**: 84; 02. (2) Adams, *1*, **37**: 481; 15. (3) Alexejew, *8*, **28**: 305; 86. (4) Alluard, *34*, **59**: 500; 64. (5) Anderson, *7*, **88**: 191; 14. (6) Andrews, *62*, **178**: 45; 87. (7) Antropoff, *9*, **30**: 457; 24. (8) Antropoff and Sommer, *7*, **123**: 161; 26. (9) Apfel, *Diss.*, Darmstadt, 1911.

(10) Applebey and Hughes, *4*, **107**: 1798; 15. (11) Bachmann, *93*, **100**: 1; 17. (12) Badger, *33*, **27**: 932; 22. (13) Badger and Baker, *33*, **23**: 569; 20. (14) Bagster, *4*, **111**: 494; 17. (15) Baker and Waite, *33*, **25**: 1137; 21. (16) Baker and Waite, *33*, **25**: 1174; 21. (17) Bakhuis Roozeboom, *70*, **3**: 29, 59, 73, 84; 84. (18) Bakhuis Roozeboom, *70*, **3**: 433; 84. (19) Bakhuis Roozeboom, *70*, **4**: 65; 85.

(20) Bakhuis Roozeboom, *70*, **4**: 102; 85. (21) Bakhuis Roozeboom, *70*, **4**: 108; 85. (22) Bakhuis Roozeboom, *70*, **4**: 331; 85. (23) Bakhuis Roozeboom, *70*, **4**: 361; 85. (24) Bakhuis Roozeboom, *70*, **4**: 379; 85. (25) Bakhuis Roozeboom, *70*, **4**: 381; 85. (26) Bakhuis Roozeboom, *70*, **5**: 323; 86. (27) Bakhuis Roozeboom, *70*, **5**: 351; 86. (28) Bakhuis Roozeboom, *70*, **5**: 363; 86. (29) Bakhuis Roozeboom, *70*, **5**: 387; 86.

(30) Bakhuis Roozeboom, *7*, **4**: 31; 89. (31) Bakhuis Roozeboom, *70*, **8**: 1; 89. (32) Bakhuis Roozeboom, *7*, **10**: 477; 92. (33) Bakhuis Roozeboom, *64P*, **4**: 371; 02. (34) Bakhuis Roozeboom, *64P*, **5**: 283; 02. (35) Bakhuis Roozeboom, *64P*, **6**: 63; 03. (36) Bakhuis Roozeboom, *64P*, **6**: 331; 03. (37) Bakhuis Roozeboom, *64P*, **9**: 99; 06. (38) Bakhuis Roozeboom, *64P*, **9**: 363; 06. (39) Bakhuis Roozeboom, *64P*, **6**: 599; 04.

(40) Baly, *3*, **49**: 517; 00. (41) Barbaudy, *34*, **176**: 1616; 23. (42) Barbaudy, *34*, **180**: 1924; 25. (43) Barbaudy, *42*, **24**: 1; 27. (44) Bassett and Taylor, *4*, **101**: 576; 12. (45) Bassett and Taylor, *4*, **105**: 1926; 14. (46) Bauer, *93*, **47**: 401; 05. (47) Baume and Robert, *34*, **169**: 969; 19. (48) Baur, *9*, **32**: 428; 26. (49) Baxter and Cooper, *1*, **46**: 923; 24.

(50) Baxter and Lansing, *1*, **42**: 419; 20. (51) Baxter and Starkweather, *1*, **38**: 2038; 16. (52) Baxter and Warren, *1*, **33**: 340; 11. (53) Beckurts, *293*, **18**: 429; 81. (54) Bergstrom, *50*, **26**: 358; 22. (55) Bergstrom, *50*, **26**: 876; 22. (56) Berkeley, *62*, **203**: 189; 04. (57) Berkeley and Applebey, *5*, **85**: 489; 11. (58) Berkeley and Hartley, *5*, **77**: 156; 06. (59) Bidet, *34*, **155**: 279; 12.

(60) Biltz, *7*, **40**: 185; 02. (61) Blümcke, *8*, **34**: 10; 88. (62) Boeke, *190*, **1912 I**: 91. (63) Bogorodskii, *53*, **25**: 316; 93. (64) Bogorodskii, *53*, **26**: 209; 94. (65) Bogorodskii, *53*, **29**: 179; 96. (66) Bokhorst, *Diss.*, Amsterdam, 1915. (67) Bonnier, *34*, **177**: 685; 23. (68) Bowen, *50*, **30**: 721; 26. (69) Bradley and Alexander, *1*, **34**: 15; 12.

(70) Bridgman, *65*, **52**: 91; 16. (71) Brinkley, *1*, **44**: 1210; 22. (72) Brinkmann, *Diss.*, Amsterdam, 1904. *427*, **60 II**: 667; 04. (73) Brönsted, *7*, **82**: 621; 13. (74) Brönsted, *137*, **1**: No. 5; 18. (75) Browne and Houlehan, *1*, **35**: 649; 13. (76) Buchanan, *174*, **39**: 529; 00. (77) Buchanan and Winner, *45*, **12**: 448; 20. (78) Büchner, *64P*, **20**: 322; 17. (79) Büchner and Prins, *64P*, **19**: 1232; 17.

(80) Cailletet, *51*, **9**: 192; 80. (81) Carius, *13*, **99**: 129; 56. (82) Carpenter and Jette, *1*, **45**: 578; 23. (83) Carr, Townsend and Badger, *45*, **17**: 643; 25. (84) Caubet, *34*, **130**: 167; 00. (85) Caubet, *34*, **130**: 828; 00. (86) Caubet, *34*, **131**: 108; 00. (87) Caubet, *34*, **131**: 1200; 00. (88) Caubet, *Thesis*, Paris, 1901. (89) Caubet, *Mém. soc. sci. phys. nat. Bordeaux*, **1**: 1; 01.

(90) Caubet, *34*, **132**: 128; 01. (91) Caubet, *7*, **40**: 257; 02. (92) Caubet, *7*, **43**: 115; 03. (93) Caubet, *7*, **49**: 101; 04. (94) Caven and Sand, *4*, **99**: 1359; 11. (95) Caven and Sand, *4*, **105**: 2752; 14. (96) Charpy, *34*, **113**: 794; 91. (97) Cohen, *7*, **14**: 53; 94. (98) de Coninck, *Rev. gén. chim. pure appliquée*, **19**: 68; 16. (99) Cragoe, Meyers and Taylor, *31*, No. **369**; 19.

(100) Davis, Olmsted and Lundstrum, *1*, **43**: 1575, 1580; 21. (101) Dawson and Williams, *7*, **31**: 59; 99. (102) Delépine, *49*, **25**: 496; 92. (103) Derby and Yngve, *1*, **38**: 1439; 16. (104) Desmaroux, *315*, **19**: 322; 22. (105) Dieterici, *8*, **38**: 1; 89. (106) Dieterici, *8*, **42**: 513; 91. (107) Dieterici, *8*, **50**: 47; 93. (108) Dieterici, *8*, **62**: 616; 97. (109) Dieterici, *8*, **67**: 859; 99.

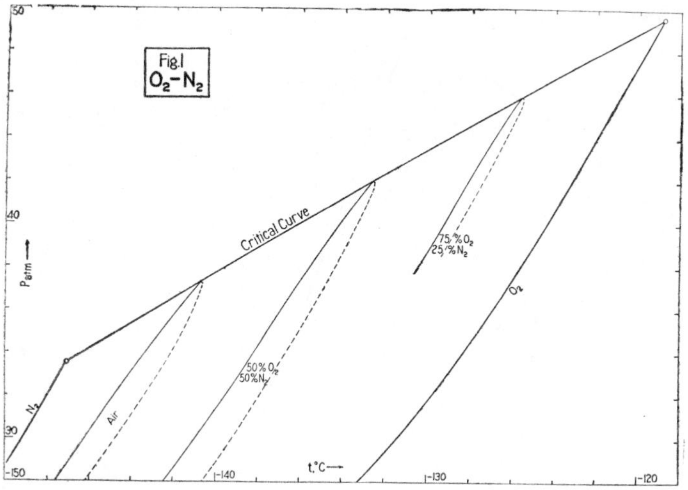
Fig.1
O_2-N_2
Critical Curve
75 % O_2
25 % N_2
50 % O_2
50 % N_2
Air
N_2
O_2
P_{atm}
t, °C
50
40
30
-150
-140
-130
-120

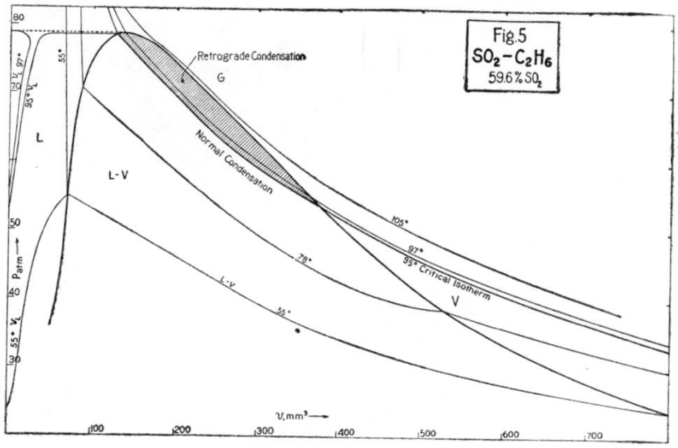
Fig.5
$SO_2-C_2H_6$
59.6 % SO_2
Retrograde Condensation
G
L
L-V
Normal Condensation
105°
97°
95° Critical Isomerm
78°
55°
V
P_{atm}
V, mm³
80
70
50
40
30
100
200
300
400
500
600
700

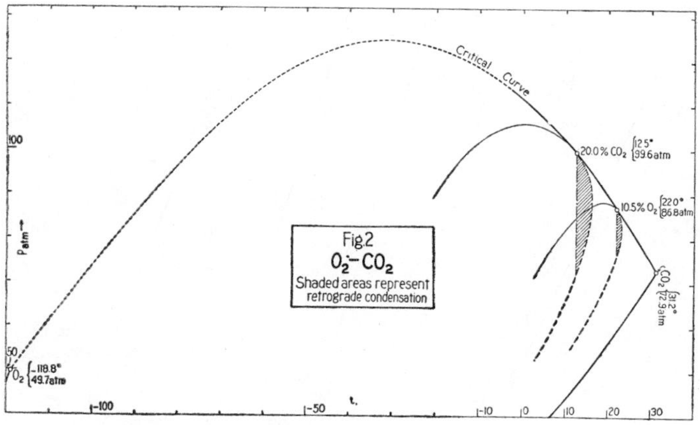
Fig2
O_2-CO_2
Shaded areas represent retrograde condensation
Critical Curve
20.0 % CO_2 12.5° 99.6 atm
10.5 % O_2 22.0° 86.8 atm
CO_2 31.2° 72.9 atm
O_2 -118.8° 49.7 atm
P_{atm}
t.
100
50
-100
-50
-10
0
10
20
30

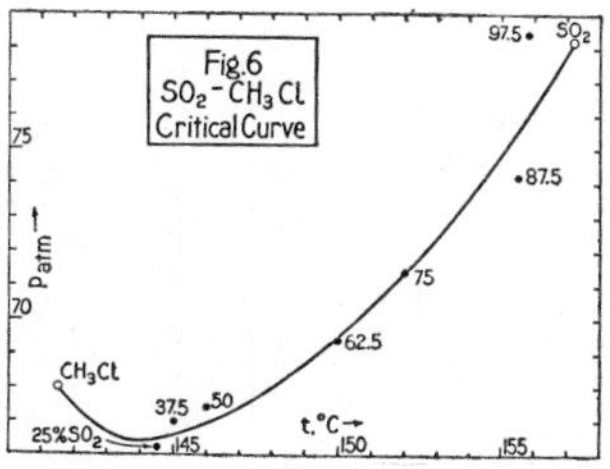
Fig.6
SO_2-CH_3Cl
Critical Curve
CH_3Cl
SO_2
97.5
87.5
75
62.5
50
37.5
25 % SO_2
12.5
P_{atm}
t, °C
75
70
145
150
155

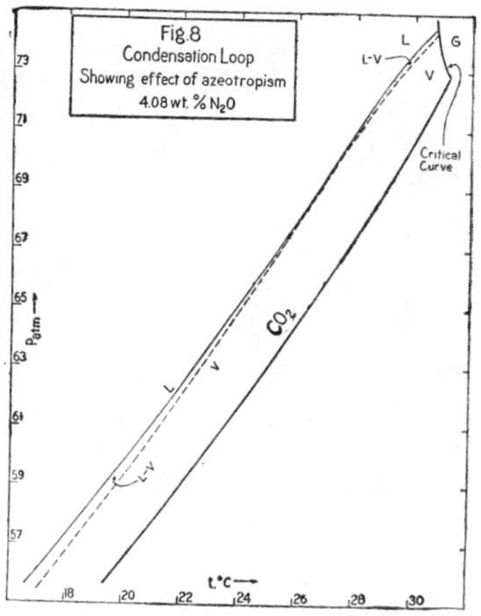
Fig.8
Condensation Loop
Showing effect of azeotropism
4.08 wt. % N_2O
L
G
L-V
V
Critical Curve
CO_2
P_{atm}
t, °C
73
71
69
67
65
63
61
59
57
18
20
22
24
26
28
30

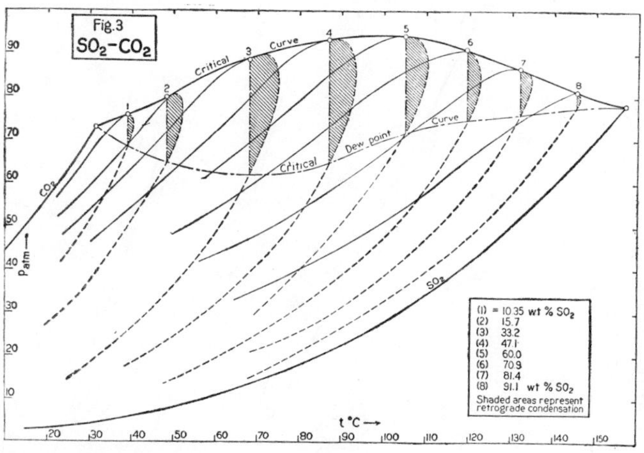
Fig.3
SO_2-CO_2
Critical Curve
Critical Dew point Curve
CO_2
SO_2
(1) = 10.35 wt % SO_2
(2) 15.7
(3) 33.2
(4) 47.1
(5) 60.0
(6) 70.9
(7) 81.4
(8) 91.1 wt % SO_2
Shaded areas represent retrograde condensation
P_{atm}
t °C
90
80
70
60
50
40
30
20
10
20
30
40
50
60
70
80
90
100
110
120
130
140
150

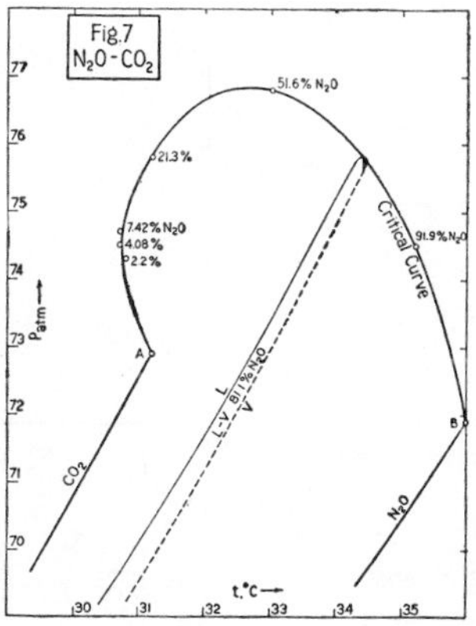
Fig.7
N_2O-CO_2
51.6 % N_2O
21.3 %
7.42 % N_2O
4.08 %
2.2 %
A
B
91.9 % N_2O
Critical Curve
L
L-V 81.1 % N_2O
V
CO_2
N_2O
P_{atm}
t, °C
77
76
75
74
73
72
71
70
30
31
32
33
34
35

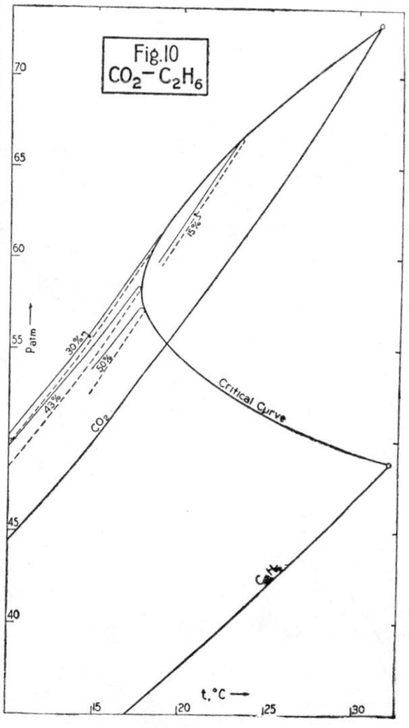
Fig.10
$CO_2-C_2H_6$
Critical Curve
CO_2
C_2H_6
30 %
43 %
58 %
85 %
P_{atm}
t, °C
70
65
60
55
45
40
15
20
25
30

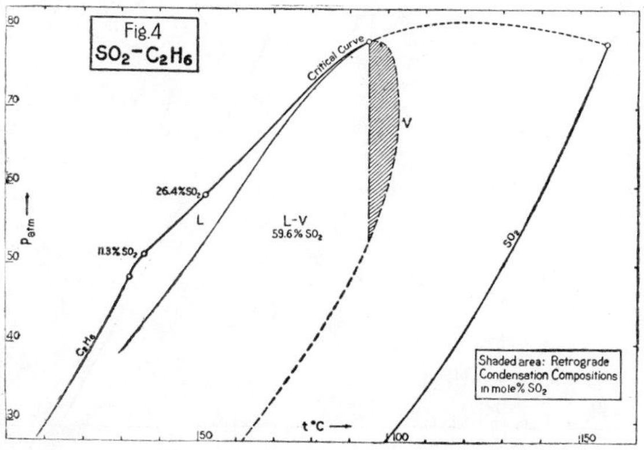
Fig.4
$SO_2-C_2H_6$
Critical Curve
26.4 % SO_2
11.3 % SO_2
L
L-V
59.6 % SO_2
V
SO_2
C_2H_6
Shaded area: Retrograde Condensation Compositions in mole % SO_2
P_{atm}
t °C
80
70
60
50
40
30
50
100
150

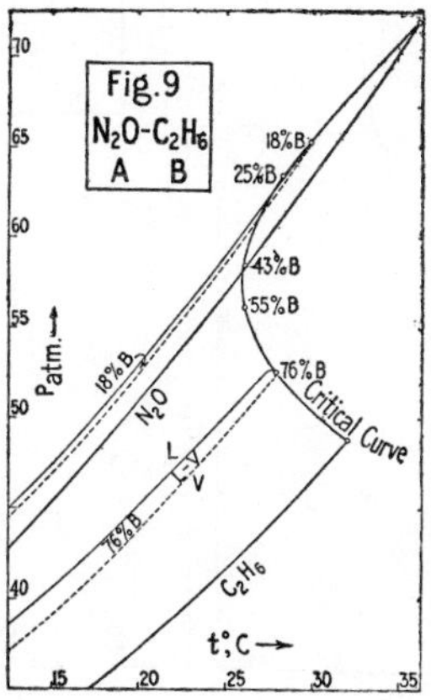
Fig.9
$N_2O-C_2H_6$
A B
18 % B
25 % B
43 % B
55 % B
76 % B
Critical Curve
18 % B
N_2O
L
L-V
V
76 % B
C_2H_6
$P_{atm.}$
t, °C
70
65
60
55
50
45
40
15
20
25
30
35

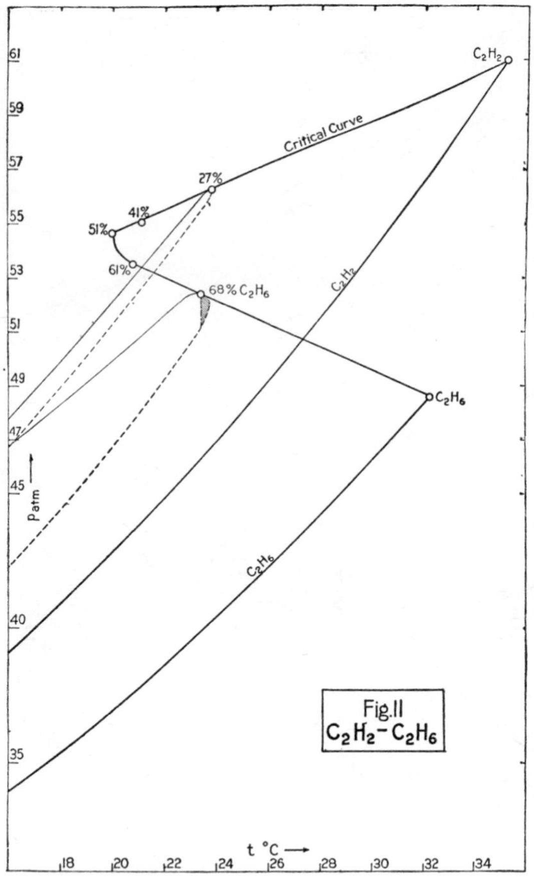

Fig. 11
$C_2H_2-C_2H_6$

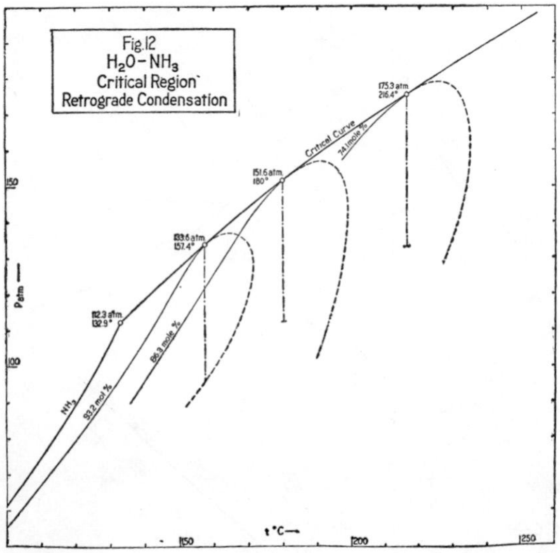

Fig. 12
H_2O-NH_3
Critical Region
Retrograde Condensation

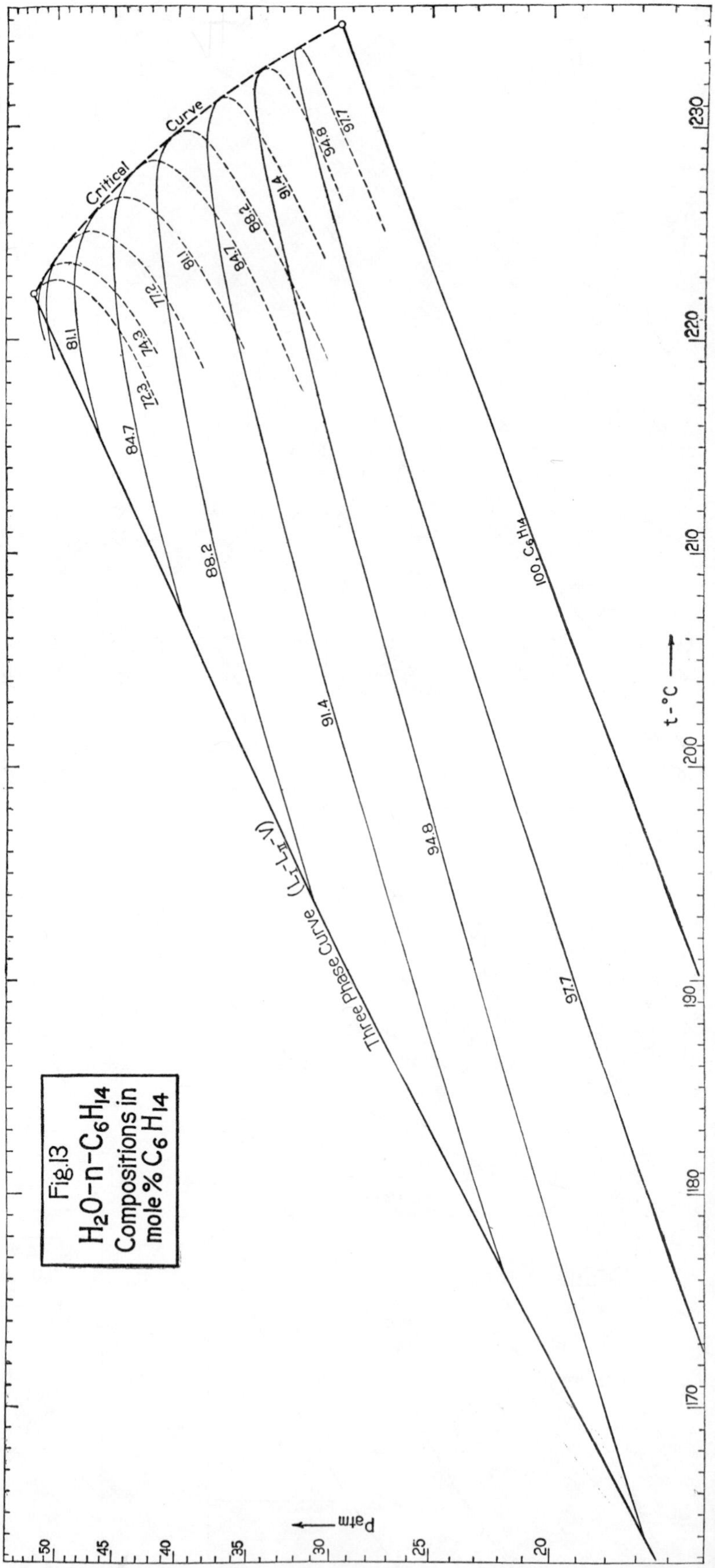

Fig. 13
$H_2O-n-C_6H_{14}$
Compositions in mole % C_6H_{14}

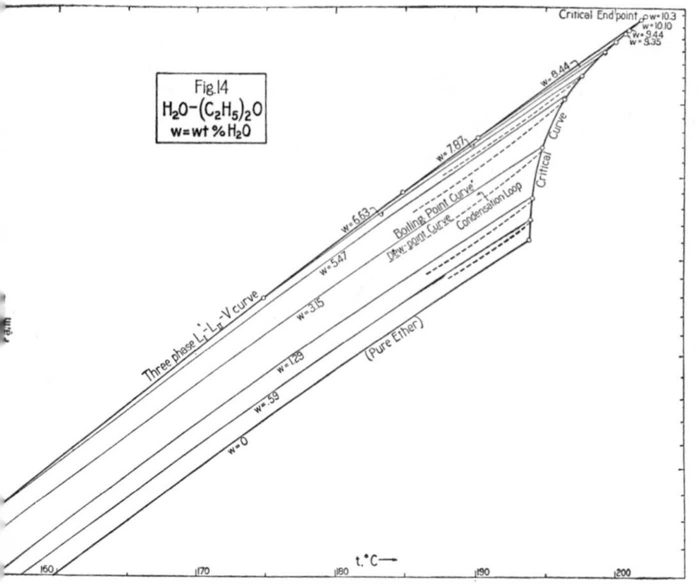

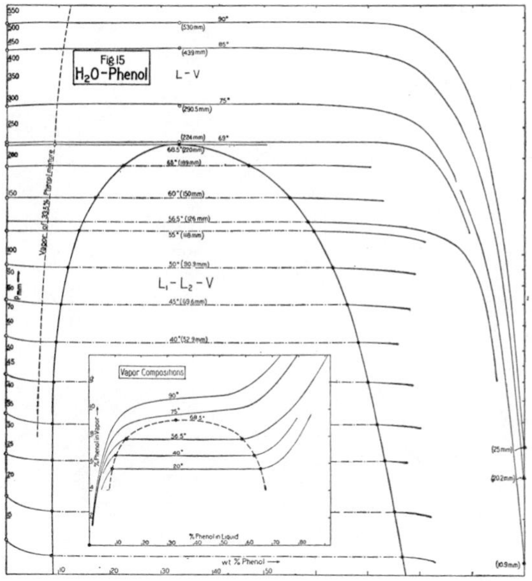

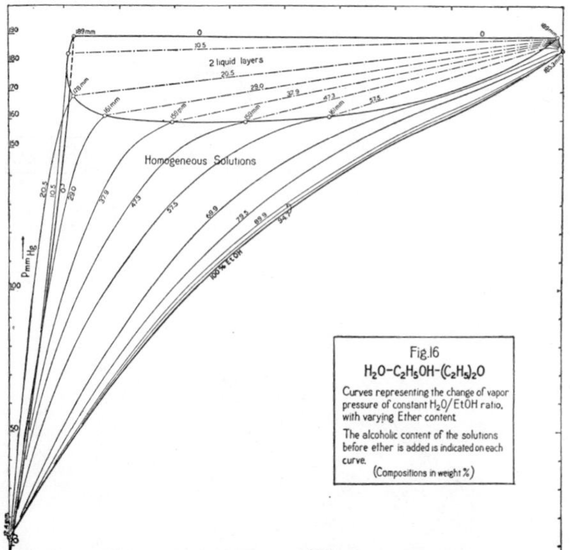

Fig.16
$H_2O-C_2H_5OH-(C_2H_5)_2O$
Curves representing the change of vapor pressure of constant H_2O/EtOH ratio, with varying Ether content
The alcoholic content of the solutions before ether is added is indicated on each curve.
(Compositions in weight %)

(110) Dieterici, *8*, **70**: 617; 23. (111) Dittmar, *54*, **7**: 730; 88. (112) Dodge and Davis, *1*, **49**: 610; 27. (113) Dodge and Dunbar, *1*, **49**: 591; 27. (114) Doijer, *7*, **6**: 481; 90. (115) Dolezalek and Schulze, *7*, **83**: 45; 13. (116) Dolezalek and Schulze, *7*, **98**: 395; 21. (117) Donnan and Burt, *4*, **83**: 335; 03. (118) Dorsman, *Diss.*, Amsterdam, 1908. (119) Drecker, *8*, **34**: 952, 88.

(120) Edgar and Swann, *1*, **44**: 570; 22. (121) Emden, *8*, **31**: 145; 87. (122) Engel, *6*, **13**: 344; 88. (123) Errera, *36*, **18**: 225; 88. (124) Ewing, *1*, **49**: 1963; 27. (125) Ewing, Krey, Law, and Lang, *1*, **49**: 1958; 27. (126) Ferguson, *50*, **31**: 757; 27. (127) Ferguson and Funnell, *69*, **18 III**: 122; 24. (128) Fischer, *97*, **7**: 527; 26. (129) Foote, *1*, **43**: 1031; 21.

(130) Foote and Brinkley, *1*, **43**: 1018; 21. (131) Foote and Hunter, *1*, **42**: 69; 20. (132) Foote and Smith, *1*, **30**: 1344; 08. (133) de Forcrand, *6*, **15**: 433; 08. (134) Fouard, *27*, **13**: 784; 13. (135) Frazer and Lovelace, *1*, **36**: 2439; 14. (136) Friedrichs, *93*, **127**: 221; 23. (137) Funk, *25*, **33**: 3696; 00. (138) Gaus, *Diss.*, Breslau, 1900. *93*, **25**: 236; 00. (139) de Gee, *Thesis*, Amsterdam, 1916.

(140) Gerasimov, *53*, **45**: 1655; 13. (141) Gerlach, *91*, **26**: 413; 87. (142) Germann and Birosel, *50*, **29**: 1469; 25. (143) Germann and McIntyre, *50*, **29**: 102; 25. (144) Germann and Timpany, *50*, **29**: 1423; 25. (144.5) Gmelin-Kraut, *B50*. (145) Goldschmidt, *93*, **28**: 97; 01. (146) Green, *50*, **12**: 655; 08. (147) Greenish and Smith, *347*, **66**: 774; 01. (148) Groschuff, *25*, **36**: 1783; 03. (149) Groschuff, *25*, **36**: 4351; 03.

(150) Grünzweig, *Diss.*, Darmstadt, 1913. (151) Guthrie, *3*, **18**: 22; 84. (152) Guthrie, *3*, **18**: 105; 84. (153) Hachmeister, *93*, **109**: 145; 19. (154) Haehnel, *52*, **107**: 165; 24. (155) Haehnel, *52*, **108**: 61; 24. (156) Haehnel, *52*, **108**: 187; 24. (157) Hall and Harkins, *1*, **38**: 2658; 16. (158) Halla and Hirschko, *93*, **127**: 137; 22. (159) Hammerl, *75*, **78 II**: 59; 79.

(160) Hartman, *64V*, **8**: 106; 98. *168*, No. **43.** (161) Hartman, *64V*, **9**: 60; 00. *168*, No. **56.** (162) Hartung, *83*, **15 III**: 150; 20. (163) Hausrath, *8*, **9**: 522; 02. (164) Heyn, *93*, **39**: 1; 04. (165) van't Hoff, Armstrong, Hinrichsen, Weigert and Just, *7*, **45**: 257; 03. (166) van't Hoff and Goldschmidt, *7*, **17**: 505; 95. (167) van't Hoff and Müller, *25*, **32**: 857; 99. (168) Holst and Hamburger, *64P*, **18**: 872; 16. (169) Holst and Hamburger, *7*, **91**: 573; 16.

(170) Hüttig and Pohle, *93*, **138**: 1; 24. (171) Hüttig and Reuscher, *93*, **137**: 155; 24. (172) Inglis, *Proc. Phys. Soc. Camb.*, **20**: 640; 02. (173) Inglis, *3*, **11**: 640; 06. (174) van Iterson-Rotgans, *176*, **10**: 920; 13. *7*, **87**: 305; 14. (175) Jaeger and Menke, *93*, **77**: 320; 12. (176) Jänecke, *Gesättigte Salzlösungen vom Standpunkt der Phasenlehre.* Halle, W. Knapp, 1908. (177) Jänecke, *92*, **33**: 279; 20. (178) Jänecke, *70*, **42**: 740; 23. (179) Jahn, *7*, **59**: 31; 07.

(180) Johnston, *174*, **45**: 193; 07. (181) Johnston, *174*, **45**: 855; 07. (182) Johnston, *1*, **37**: 2001; 15. (183) Johnston and Williamson, *1*, **38**: 975; 16. (184) Jones, *54*, **38**: 362T; 19. (185) Jones and Getman, *7*, **49**: 385; 04. (186) Kahlbaum and Schröter, *7*, **13**: 14; 94. (187) Kahlenberg, *50*, **5**: 339; 01. (188) Keesom, *Diss.*, Leiden, 1904. *427*, **60 II**: 668; 04. (189) Keesom, *64P*, **6**: 532; 04. *168*, No. **88.**

(190) Kendall and Davidson, *1*, **42**: 1141; 20. (191) Ketner, *7*, **39**: 641; 02. (192) Keyes and Hildebrand, *1*, **39**: 2126; 17. (193) Knight and Rich, *4*, **99**: 87; 11. (194) Koch, *148*, **29**: 37; 22. (195) Kohnstamm and van Dalfsen, *64V*, **10**: 167; 01. (196) Kohnstamm and Reeders, *64P*, **11**: 913; 09. (197) Kohnstamm and Reeders, *18*, **15**: 161; 10. (198) Kohnstamm and Reeders, *64P*, **14**: 270; 12. (199) Kohnstamm and Timmermans, *64P*, **13**: 865; 11.

(200) Konovalov, *8*, **14**: 34; 81. (201) Koppell, in *B21*, **IV**: I_2, 347. (202) Koppell, in *B21*, **IV**: I_2, 353. (203) Kracek, *0*. (204) Kraus and Zeitfuchs, *1*, **44**: 1249, 2714; 22. (205) Krauskopf, *50*, **14**: 489; 10. (206) Kremers, *8*, **97**: 1; 56. (207) Kremers, *8*, **103**: 57; 58. (208) Krulla, *136*, **35**: 471; 11. (209) Kruyt and Helderman, *64P*, **19**: 439; 16.

(210) Kruyt and Helderman, *7*, **93**: 89; 19. (211) Kuenen, *7*, **11**: 38; 93. (212) Kuenen, *3*, **40**: 173; 95. (213) Kuenen, *3*, **44**: 174; 97. (214) Kuenen, *7*, **24**: 667; 97. (215) Kuenen, *7*, **37**: 485; 01. (216) Kuenen, *7*, **41**: 43; 02. (217) Kuenen, *3*, **6**: 637; 03. (218) Kuenen, *64P*, **14**: 644; 11. *168*, No. **125.** (219) Kuenen and Clark, *64P*, **19**: 1088; 17.

(220) Kuenen and Robson, *3*, **48**: 180; 99. *7*, **28**: 342; 99. (221) Kuenen and Robson, *3*, **3**: 149, 622; 02. (222) Kuenen and Robson, *3*, **4**: 116; 02. (223) Kuenen, Verschoyle and van Urk, *64P*, **26**: 49; 23. *168*, No. **161.** (224) Kurilov, *7*, **25**: 107; 98. (225) Lattey, *4*, **91**: 1959; 07. (226) Lecat, *La tension de vapeur des mélanges de liquides. L'azéotropisme.* Brussels, H. Lamertin, 1918. (227) van der Lee, *7*, **33**: 622; 00. (228) de Leeuw, *7*, **77**: 284; 11. (229) Leonard, Smith and Richmond, *173*, **22**: 92; 97.

(230) Leopold, *7*, **65**: 428; 09. (231) Leopold, *7*, **66**: 359; 09. (232) Leopold, *7*, **71**: 59; 10. (233) Leopold and Johnston, *1*, **49**: 1974; 27. (234) Lescoeur, *34*, **92**: 1158; 81. (235) Lescoeur, *34*, **96**: 1578; 83. (236) Lescoeur, *6*, **19**: 35; 90. (237) Lescoeur, *6*, **2**: 78; 94. (238) Lescoeur, *6*, **4**: 213; 95. (239) Lescoeur, *6*, **7**: 416; 96.

(240) Lescoeur, *6*, **9**: 537; 96. (241) Lescoeur and Mathurin, *27*, **50**: 33; 88. (242) Lidbury, *7*, **39**: 453; 02. (243) Lincoln and Klein, *50*, **11**: 318; 07. (244) Lobry de Bruyn and Dito, *64P*, **5**: 171; 02. (245) Locke and Forssall, *11*, **31**: 268; 04. (246) Loomis, *8*, **51**: 500; 94. (247) Loomis, *8*, **57**: 495; 96. (248) Loomis, *8*, **60**: 523; 97. (249) Louder, Briggs and Browne, *45*, **16**: 932; 24.

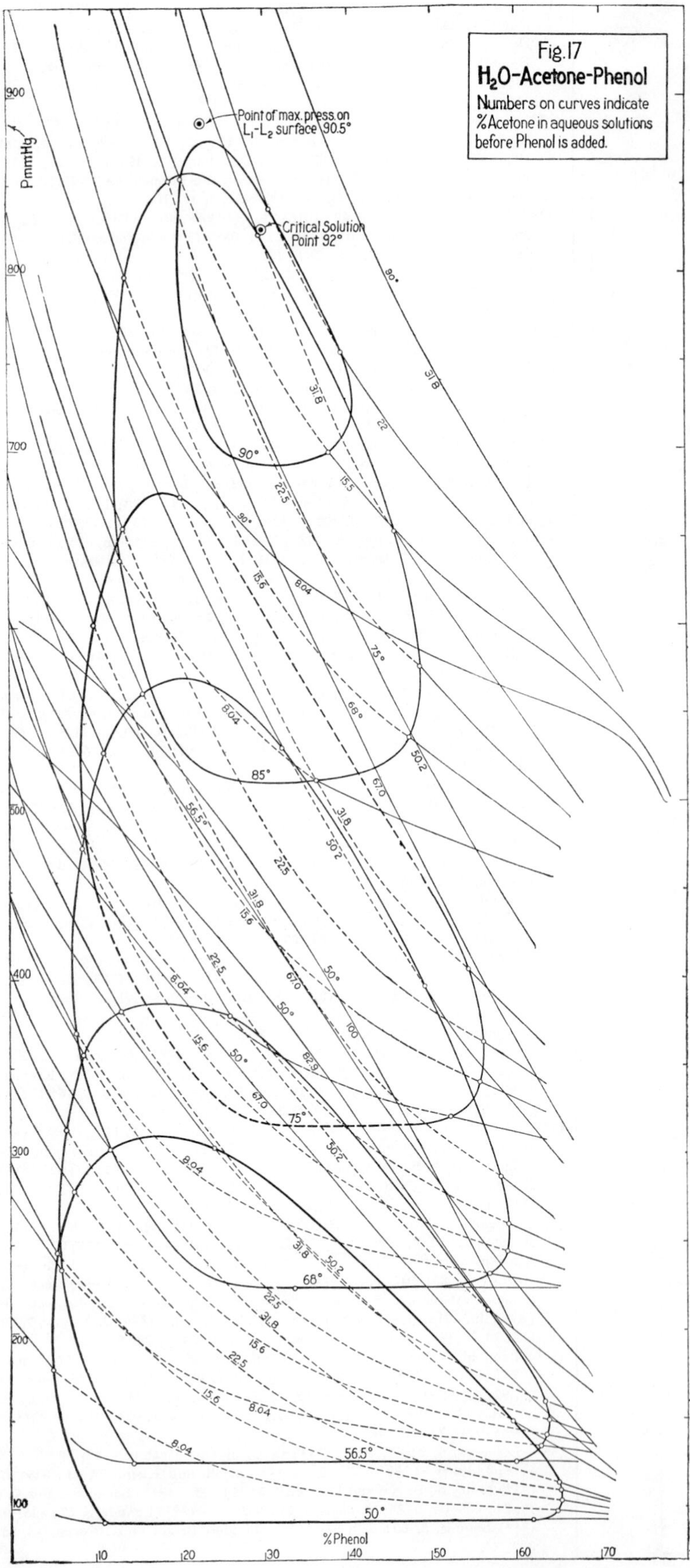

Fig. 17
H_2O-Acetone-Phenol
Numbers on curves indicate % Acetone in aqueous solutions before Phenol is added.

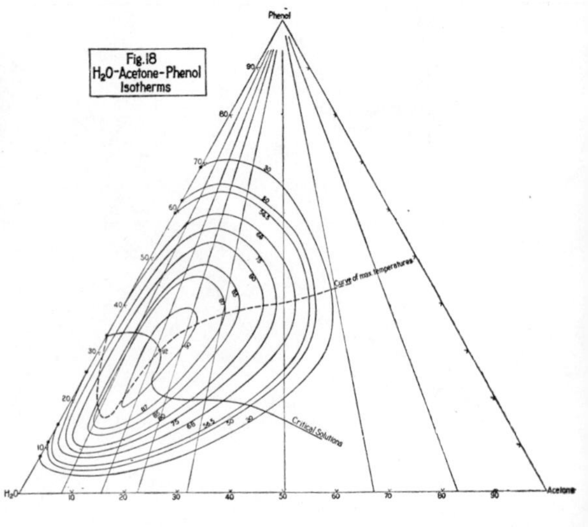

Fig. 18
H_2O-Acetone-Phenol
Isotherms

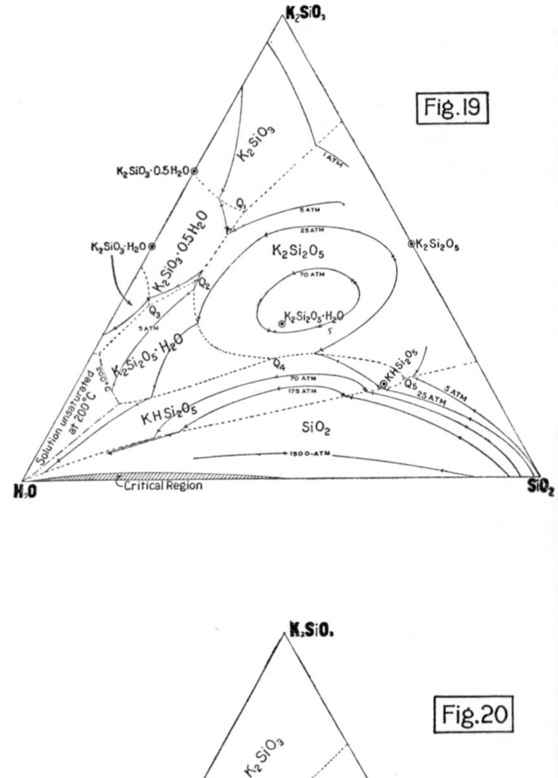

Fig. 19

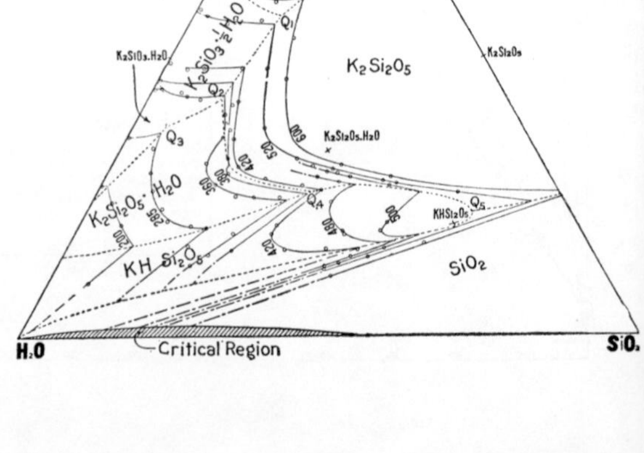

Fig. 20

(250) Lovelace, Bahlke and Frazer, *1*, **45**: 2930. (251) Lovelace, Frazer and Miller, *1*, **38**: 515; 16. (252) Lovelace, Frazer and Rogers, *1*, **42**: 1793; 20. (253) Lovelace, Frazer and Sease, *1*, **43**: 102; 21. (254) Lowry and Morgan, *1*, **46**: 2192; 24. (255) McCoy and Smith, *1*, **33**: 468; 11. (256) Macisevskii, *53*, **48**: 1917; 16. (257) McKeown and Stowell, *4*, **1927**: 97. (258) McLauchlan, *7*, **44**: 600; 03. (259) Magnusson, *50*, **11**: 21; 07.

(260) Maier, *8*, **31**: 423; 10. (261) Makovetzkii, *53*, **40**: 216; 08. (262) Makovetzkii, *53*, **40**: 752; 08. (263) Mallet, *11*, **19**: 804; 97. (264) Manchot and Ortner, *93*, **120**: 300; 22. (265) Marcan, *Diss.*, Karlsruhe, 1923. (266) Marchis, *34*, **116**: 388; 93. (267) Marden and Elliot, *45*, **7**: 320; 15. (268) Marignac, *149*, **55**: 113; 76. (269) Marignac, *6*, **8**: 410; 76.

(270) Marshall, *182*, **29**: 157; 13. (271) Marshall and Peace, *4*, **103**: 298; 16. (271.5) Mellor, *B71*. (272) Menzies and Boving, *172*, **8 XXII**: 219; 12. (273) Meyer, *9*, **19**: 833; 13. (274) Meyerhoffer, *7*, **5**: 97; 90. (275) Michaud, *8*, **6**: 223; 16. *Thesis*, Paris, 1916. (276) Michels, *64V*, **31**: 53; 23. (277) Mittasch, Kuss and Schlueter, *93*. **159**: 1; 26. (278) Mollier, *414*, No. **63**: 85; 09. (279) Mondain-Monval, *14*, **3**: 121; 25.

(280) Morey, *1*, **39**: 1173; 17. (281) Moser, *8*, **14**: 62; 81. (282) Mund and Herrent, *42*, **21**: 51; 24. (283) von Muralt, *Diss.*, Zurich, 1919. (284) Mylius and Funk, *25*, **33**: 3686; 00. (285) Neunausen and Patrick, *50*, **25**: 693; 22. (286) Nicol, *3*, **22**: 502; 86. (287) Niggli, *93*, **75**: 161; 12. (288) Niggli, *93*, **77**: 321; 12. (289) Niggli, *93*, **84**: 229; 13.

(290) Niggli, *9*, **20**: 156; 14. (291) Niggli, *190*, **1914 II**: 69. (292) Niggli, *93*, **98**: 241; 16. (293) Niggli, *93*, **106**: 126; 19. (294) Niggli, *Die Leichtflüchtigen Bestandteile im Magna.* Leipzig, Teubner, 1920. (295) Nishizawa, *142*, **23**: 830; 20. (296) Olmer, *27*, **29**: 382; 21. (297) Onnes, Dorsman and Holst, *64P*, **17**: 950; 15. **18**: 409; 16. *168*, No. **145b**. (298) Osann, *509*, **3**: 204; 1824. (299) Osann, *509*, **3**: 369; 1824.

(300) Osann, *509*, **5**: 107; 1825. (301) Oswald, *14*, **1**: 32; 14. (302) Paranjpe, *318*, **2**: 59; 18. (303) Paternò and Mazzucchelli, *36*, **50**: 30; 20. (304) Pavlovich, *7*, **84**: 169; 13. (305) Pearce and Snow, *50*, **31**: 231; 27. (306) Perman, *4*, **67**: 868; 95. (307) Perman, *4*, **67**: 983; 95. (308) Perman, *4*, **73**: 511; 98. (309) Perman, *4*, **79**: 718; 01.

(310) Perman, *4*, **79**: 725; 01. (311) Perman, *4*, **81**: 480; 02. (312) Perman, *4*, **83**: 1168; 03. (313) Perman, *83*: **8**: 68; 12. (314) Perman and Saunders, *83*, **19**: 112; 23. (315) Pickering, *4*, **63**: 141; 93. (316) Pickering, *4*, **63**: 890; 93. (317) Pickering, *25*, **26**: 2766; 93. (318) Pickering, *25*, **27**: 67; 94. (319) Postma, *70*, **39**: 515; 20.

(320) Prideaux, *54*, **39**: 182T; 20. (321) Prideaux and Caven, *54*, **38**: 353T; 19. (322) Prins, *64P*, **17**: 1095; 15. (323) Quint Gzn, *7*, **39**: 14; 01. (324) Ramsay and Young, *4*, **49**: 453; 86. (325) Ramsay and Young, *62*, **117**: 71; 87. (326) Raoult, *6*, **1**: 262; 74. (327) Raoult, *34*, **87**: 167; 78. (328) Rayman, *Diss.*, Budapest, 1906. (329) von Rechenberg, *Einfache und fraktionierte Destillation.* Leipzig, Schimmel, 1923.

(330) Reinders and Goudriaan, *93*, **126**: 85; 23. (331) Rey, *92*, **1890**: 510. (332) Rhodes, Wells and Murray, *45*, **17**: 1199; 25. (333) Richards and Churchill, *7*, **28**: 313; 99. (334) Richards and Wells, *7*, **56**: 348; 06. (335) Richards and Wrede, *7*, **61**: 313; 07. (336) Richmond, *173*, **33**: 305; 08. (337) Riesenfeld, *7*, **45**: 461; 03. (338) Rivett, *7*, **80**: 537; 12. (339) Roberts and Smyth, *1*, **43**: 1061; 21.

(340) Rodebush, *1*, **40**: 1204; 18. (341) Roloff, *7*, **11**: 7; 93. (342) Rosanoff and Easley, *1*, **31**: 953; 09. (343) Roscoe and Dittmar, *13*, **112**: 327; 59. (344) Roth, *B3*, p. 1436. (345) Rothmund, *7*, **26**: 433; 98. (346) Rupert, *1*, **31**: 866; 09. (347) Rupert, *1*, **32**: 748; 10. (348) Sander, *7*, **78**: 513; 12. (349) Scheffer, *7*, **71**: 214; 10.

(350) Scheffer, *7*, **71**: 671; 10. (351) Scheffer, *64P*, **13**: 829; 11. (352) Scheffer, *64P*, **14**: 195; 11. (353) Scheffer, *7*, **76**: 161; 11. (354) Scheffer, *64P*, **16**: 404; 13. (355) Scheffer, *7*, **84**: 728; 13. (356) Scheffer, *64P*, **17**: 834; 14. (357) Scheffer, *64P*, **18**: 446; 16. (358) Scheffer, *64P*, **19**: 798; 17. (359) Scheffer, *64P*, **21**: 665; 19.

(360) Scheffer and Meyer, *64P*, **21**: 1204; 19. (361) Scheffer and Meyer, *64P*, **21**: 1338; 19. (362) Scheffer and Treub, *7*, **81**: 308; 12. (363) Schenck and Hemplemann, *187*, **10**: 283; 12. (364) Schlamp, *7*, **14**: 272; 94. (365) Schloesing, *34*, **74**: 1552; 72. (366) Schloesing, *34*, **75**: 70; 72. (367) Schoorl, *70*, **42**: 790; 23. (368) Schreinemakers, *7*, **29**: 577; 99. (369) Schreinemakers, *7*, **30**: 460; 99.

(370) Schreinemakers, *7*, **33**: 78; 00. (371) Schreinemakers, *7*, **35**: 459; 00. (372) Schreinemakers, *64P*, **3**: 1; 01. (373) Schreinemakers, *7*, **39**: 485; 02. (374) Schreinemakers, *7*, **40**: 440; 02. (375) Schreinemakers, *7*, **41**: 331; 02. (376) Schreinemakers, *18*, **8**: 1; 03. (377) Schreinemakers, *7*, **47**: 445; 04. (378) Schreinemakers, *7*, **48**: 257; 04. (379) Schreinemakers, *7*, **50**: 169; 04.

(380) Schreinemakers, *7*, **82**: 59; 13. (381) Schrumb, *1*, **45**: 342; 23. (382) Schüller, *Wiss. Beil. zur Jahresb. d. K. Karl Gym., Aachen*, **1890**. *427*, **1890 II**: 360. (383) Schüller, *Wiss. Beil. zur Jahresb. d. K. Karl Gym., Aachen*, **1892**, No. 420. *427*, **1892 II**: 340. (384) Schwers, *54*, **39**: 33T; 26. (384.5) Seidell, *B51*. (385) Shirado, *41B*, **2**: 85; 27. (386) Sidgwick and Ewbank, *4*, **125**: 2268; 24. (387) Sieverts and Bergner, *7*, **82**: 257; 13. (388) Sieverts and Oehme, *25*, **46**: 1238; 13. (389) Simons, *45*, **19**: 482; 27.

(390) Sims, *13*, **118**: 333; 1861. (391) Skirrow, *7*, **37**: 84; 01. (392) Shükarev, *7*, **71**: 90; 10. (393) Slade and Farrow, *5*, **87**: 524; 12. (394) Smith and Eastlack, *1*, **38**: 1261; 16. (395) Smits, *64V*, **5**: 292; 97. (396) Smits, *18*. **1**: 97; 98. (397) Smits, *64P*, **2**: 88; 00. (398) Smits, *64P*, **2**: 469; 00. (399) Smits, *64P*, **2**: 635; 00.

(400) Smits, *64P*, **3**: 86; 01. (401) Smits, *64P*, **3**: 133; 01. (402) Smits, *64P*, **3**: 503; 01. (403) Smits, *64P*, **3**: 507; 01. (404) Smits, *64P*, **3**: 717; 01. (405) Smits, *64P*, **4**: 163; 02. (406) Smits, *64P*, **6**: 171; 03. (407) Smits, *64P*, **6**: 628; 04. (408) Smits, *64P*, **12**: 231; 09. (409) Smits and Berckmans, *64P*, **21**: 401; 19.

(410) Smits and de Leeuw, *64P*, **13**: 318; 10. (411) Smits and de Leeuw, *64P*, **13**: 229; 10. (412) Smits and de Leeuw, *7*, **77**: 269; 11. (413) Smits and Maarse, *64P*, **14**: 192; 11. (414) Smits and de Mooy, *64P*, **13**: 339; 10. (415) Smits and Postma, *64P*, **12**: 186; 09. (416) Smits and Postma, *64P*, **17**: 182; 14. (417) Smits and Treub, *64P*, **14**: 183; 11. (418) Smits and Treub, *64P*, **14**: 189; 11. (419) Smits and Wuite, *64P*, **12**: 244; 09.

(420) Smyth and Adams, *1*, **45**: 1167; 23. (421) Smyth and Roberts, *1*, **42**: 2582; 20. (422) Speranskii, *7*, **70**: 519; 10. (423) Speranskii, *7*, **78**: 86; 11. (424) Speranskii, *7*, **84**: 160; 13. (425) Speranskii, *7*, **85**: 623; 13. (426) Steele and Bagster, *4*, **97**: 2607; 10. (427) Stegmüller, *9*, **16**: 85; 10. (428) Stirnemann, *190B*, **52**: 334; 25. (429) Stirnemann, *190B*, **53**: 59; 26.

(430) Stock and Seelig, *25*, **52**: 672; 19. (431) Stortenbeker, *7*, **3**: 11; 89. (432) Stubbs, *4*, **103**: 1445; 13. (433) Tammann, *8*, **24**: 523; 85. (434) Tammann, *Mém. Acad. Sci. St. Petersburg*, **35**: No. 9; 87. (435) Tammann, *8*, **33**: 322; 88. (436) Taylor and Henderson, *1*, **37**: 1688; 15. (437) Terres and Weiser, *9*, **27**: 177; 21. (438) Terwogt, *93*, **47**: 203; 05. (439) Thayer, *50*, **2**: 382; 98.

(440) Thayer, *50*, **3**: 36; 99. (441) Thiel and Caspar, *7*, **86**: 257; 14. (442) Thiel and Schulte, *7*, **96**: 312; 20. (443) Tower, *1*, **30**: 1219; 08. (444) Tucker, *62*, **215**: 319; 15. (445) Verschaffelt, *64V*, **7**: 281, 389; 99. **8**: 651; 00. (446) Vriens, *7*, **7**: 194; 91. (447) van der Waals, *Die Kontinuität des gasförmigen und flüssigen Zustandes.* Leipzig, Berth, 1881. (448) Wachsmuth, *293*, **8**: 510; 76. (449) Wade, *5*, **61**: 285; 97.

(450) Walker, *7*, **2**: 602; 88. (451) Walker, *4*, **71**: 428; 97. (452) Wartenberg and Albrecht, *9*, **27**: 162; 21. (453) Washburn and Heuse, *1*, **37**: 309; 15. (454) Watts, *13 Suppl.*, **3**: 227; 64. (455) Wilson, *1*, **43**: 704; 21. (456) Wilson, *86*, No. **146**; 25. (457) Woitaschewsky, *7*, **78**: 110; 12. (458) Wood, *83*, **11**: 29; 15. (459) Wright, *4*, **107**: 1527; 15.

(460) Wüllner, *8*, **110**: 564; 60. (461) Wuite, *7*, **86**: 349; 14. (462) Yannakis, *27*, **37**: 253; 25. (463) Young and Burke, *1*, **26**: 1413; 04. (464) Young and Burke, *1*, **28**: 315; 06. (465) Young and Mitchell, *1*, **26**: 1389; 04. (466) Zawidzki, *7*, **35**: 129, 722; 00. (467) Abegg, *B21*.

RELATIVE EFFICIENCIES OF DRYING AGENTS

MARTIN SHEPHERD

VALUES OF MG RESIDUAL H_2O PER LITER OF GAS DRIED AT 25°C

Drying agent	mg H_2O	Lit.
A filter at −194°	1.6×10^{-23}	
P_2O_5	$<2 \times 10^{-5}$	(6)
$Mg(ClO_4)_2$	$<5 \times 10^{-4}$	(7)
$Mg(ClO_4)_2.3H_2O$	$<2 \times 10^{-3}$	(7)
KOH (fused)	0.002	(1, 3)
Al_2O_3	0.003	(3, 4)
H_2SO_4	0.003	(1, 2)
MgO	0.008	(3)
NaOH (fused)	0.16	(1)
$CaBr_2$	0.2	(1)
CaO	0.2	(3)
$CaCl_2$ (gran.)	0.14 to 0.25	(5)
H_2SO_4, 95.1%	0.3	(3)
$CaCl_2$ (fused)	0.36	(1, 2)
$ZnCl_2$	0.8	(1, 2)
$ZnBr_2$	1.1	(1)
$CuSO_4$	1.4	(3)

LITERATURE

(For a key to the periodicals see end of volume)

(1) Baxter and Starkweather, *1*, **38**: 2038; 16. (2) Baxter and Warren, *1*, **33**: 340; 11. (3) Dover and Marden, *1*, **39**: 1609; 17. (4) Johnson, *1*, **34**: 911; 12. (5) McPherson, *1*, **39**: 1317; 17. (6) Morley, *1*, **26**: 1171; 04. (7) Willard and Smith, *1*, **44**: 2255; 22.

PHASE-EQUILIBRIUM DATA

* Including also systems of two liquid phases in the presence of the vapor phase but in most cases without determination of the pressure or composition of the vapor.

SOLUBILITIES OF LIQUIDS IN LIQUIDS. TWO-COMPONENT SYSTEMS*

Arthur E. Hill

Contents	Matières	Inhaltsverzeichnis	Indice	Page

Abbreviations and Conventions

Compositions are in Wt. % unless otherwise noted.

In nearly all cases the experiments were performed in sealed tubes, consequently, for values at room temperature, the pressure equalled one atmosphere; was greater than one atm. at higher temperatures and less than one atm. at lower temperatures.

Q_x quadruple point with the substance X present as crystalline phase.

m metastable.

* Including some systems in which one phase is a natural or commercial oil.

Abréviations et conventions

Les compositions sont exprimées en % poids à moins d'une autre indication.

Dans presque tous les cas, les expériences ont été effectuées dans des tubes scellés, par conséquent pour les valeurs à la température de la chambre, la pression égale une atmosphére; cette pression sera supérieure à une atm. pour des températures plus élevées et moindre qu'une atm. pour des températures plus basses.

Q_x point quadruple avec la substance X présente comme phase cristalline.

m métastable.

* Sont inclus quelques systèmes dans lesquels une phase est une huile naturelle ou de commerce.

Abkürzungen und Festlegungen

Die Zusammensetzungen sind, wenn nichts anderes bemerkt, in Gewichts-Prozenten (Wt. %) angegeben.

In beinahe allen Fällen wurden die Experimente in zugeschmolzenen Röhren ausgeführt. Es gilt deshalb der Wert für Zimmertemperatur und dem Druck von einer Atmosphäre. Er war grösser als eine Atmosphäre bei höherer, kleiner bei tieferer Temperatur.

Q_x Quadrupel-Punkt mit der Substanz X als kristalline Phase.

m metastabil.

* Enthält einige Systeme in welchen eine Phase ein vegetabilisches oder ein sonst in Verwendung befindliches Öl ist.

Abbreviazioni e convenzioni

Le composizioni, salvo i casi in cui è indicato diversamente, sono indicate in percentuale in peso.

In quasi tutti i casi le esperienze sono state esegute in tubi chiusi, e perciò a temperatura ordinaria la pressione era quella di una atmosfera, mentre, a temperature superiori, era maggiore di una atmosfera, e, a temperature inferiori, minore.

Q_x punto quadruplo in presenza della sostanza X allo stato di fase cristallina.

m metastabile.

* Sono compresi alcuni sistemi nei quali una delle fasi è un olio naturale o commerciale.

Sec. 1. The A-component is H_2O. The B-component, Br_2, is given first and the remaining B-components follow in the ℭ-arrangement (*v.* p. viii).

Br_2 (5, 11, 21, 23, 62, 63, 101, 157, 159)

°C	% B	
0	4.03	
5	3.73	
10	3.58	
15	3.48	
20	3.41	
22		99.954
25	3.34	(159)
30	3.29	
35	3.27	
40	3.30	
45	3.35	
50	3.40	

CClN, Cyanogen chloride (102)

8	7–8

CCl_3NO_2, Chloropicrin (138)

°C	% B	% A
0	0.2268	
25	0.1620	
32		0.1001
36		0.1184
41		0.1241
48		0.1645
50.8		0.1851
55		0.2262
75	0.1140	

CCl_4 (18, 105)

0	0.097	
10	0.083	
20	0.080	
24		0.010
28.5		0.013
30	0.085	

CS_2 (15, 16, 18, 50, 105)

°C	% B	
0	0.242	
10	0.230	
20	0.210	
22		99.24†
30	0.185	
40	(0.111)*	
49	(0.014)*	

* Data from (15).
† According to (18, 50, 105).

$CHCl_3$ (16, 18, 50, 54, 105)

0	0.98	
1.45Q*		
10	0.86	
20	0.80	
30	0.76	
40†	0.735	
50	0.745	
55	0.77	

* Solid = B hydrate.
† The figures for composition of the organic phase are too irregular to permit averaging; the percentage of water at temperatures between 0 and 40° is 0.1 ± 0.05.

CH_2Br_2, Methylene bromide (105)

°C	% B	
0	1.15	
10	1.13	
20	1.13	
30	1.16	

CH_2Cl_2, Methylene chloride (105)

0	2.30	
10	2.08	
20	1.96	
30	1.93	

CH_3I, Methyl iodide (105)

0	1.54	
10	1.42	
20	1.40	
30	1.41	

CH_3NO_2, Nitromethane (143)

ca. 103*	*ca.* 65

* Consolute temp.

C_2HCl_3O, Chloral (109)

172.5	92.5	
174.6	89.1	
179.8	84.5	

$C_2H_3Br_3O_2$, Bromal hydrate (146)

Consolute temp. = 103.4°C

$C_2H_4Cl_2$, 1, 1-Dichloroethane (105)

°C	% B	
0	0.652	
10	0.591	
20	0.547	
30	0.537	

$C_2H_4Cl_2$, Ethylene chloride (105)

0	0.914	
10	0.875	
20	0.861	
30	0.885	

$C_2H_4O_2$, Methyl formate (103)

0	21.13	
10	22.24	
20	23.29	
30	24.53	

C_2H_5Br, Ethyl bromide (105)

0	1.055	
10	0.956	
20	0.906	
30	0.888	

C_2H_5Cl, Ethyl chloride (61)

ca. 11	0.2

C_2H_5I, Ethyl iodide (105)

0	0.339	
10	0.412	
20	0.401	
30	0.413	

C_3H_4O, Acrolein (10, 10.5)
Stabilized by 0.4% hydroquinol

°C	% B	
0	20	95
20	21.6	92.8
40	23.6	90.4
50	25.8	87.8
60	29.1	84.3
70	33.2	79.8
80	40.4	72.4
85	46.8	65.8
88	56.2	

C_3H_5N, Propionitrile (110)

40	10.7	92.1
50	11.6	90.5
60	12.7	88.5
70	13.2	86.1
80	14.9	83.4
90	17.6	80.2
95	19.6	78.0
100	22.4	75.5
105	26.0	72.1
110	32.0	66.5
113.1	48.3	

C_3H_5ClO, Epichlorohydrin (77)

0	6.48	98.91
10	6.52	98.74
20	6.58	98.53
30	6.66	98.30
40	6.95	97.93
50	7.42	97.44
60	8.18	96.82
70	9.12	95.84
80	10.44	94.30

C_3H_6O, Propionaldehyde (152)

22	16

$C_3H_6O_2$, Ethyl formate (103, 148)

0	9.34	
10	9.07	
20	8.58	
30	7.34	

$C_3H_6O_2$, Methyl acetate (56.5, 103)

− 6.55Q$_A$	25.5	93.8
0	25.0	93.6
+10	24.6	93.0
20	24.2	91.8
25	24.1	91.3
30	24.0	90.8
40	24.2	89.4
50	24.6	87.7
60	25.1	85.9
80	27.5	80.6
90	30.2	77.3
100	35.2	71.8
105	40.3	66.0
108	52.5	

C_3H_7Br, *n*-Propyl bromide (105)

0	0.297	
10	0.262	
20	0.244	
30	0.246	

C_3H_7Br, Isopropyl bromide (105)

°C	% B	
0	0.416	
10	0.364	
20	0.317	
30	0.317	

C_3H_7Cl, *n*-Propyl chloride (105)

0	0.375	
10	0.322	
20	0.271	
30	0.276	

C_3H_7Cl, Isopropyl chloride (105)

0	0.438	
10	0.361	
20	0.304	
30	0.303	

C_3H_7I, *n*-Propyl iodide (105)

0	0.114	
10	0.103	
20	0.107	
30	0.103	

C_3H_7I, Isopropyl iodide (105)

0	0.167	
10	0.143	
20	0.140	
30	0.134	

$C_4H_4N_2$, Succinonitrile (115, 143)

18.5Q$_B$	10.2	92.0
20	11.0	91.5
25	11.5	90.4
30	13.2	89.1
35	15.0	87.4
40	18.4	84.1
45	22.0	80.0
50	28.2	74.0
55	42.5	59.5
55.5	(51.1)	

$C_4H_6O_3$, Acetic anhydride (81)

15	10.25	26

C_4H_8O, *n*-Butyraldehyde (152)

20	3.0

C_4H_8O, Isobutyraldehyde (152)

20	8.0

C_4H_8O, Methyl ethyl ketone (110) *v. also* p. 393

−20	40.1	89.4
0	30.6	89.6
+20	22.6	90.1
40	18.6	89.6
60	16.5	88.2
80	15.7	85.8
100	16.4	82.6
120	18.6	77.3
140	26.4	65.5
150	45	

H_2O.—(*Continued*)

$C_4H_8O_2$,* *n*-Butyric acid (34, 143)

°C	% B	
−7		60.6
−6		58.1
−5	24.6	55.3
−4	27.8	51.4
−3.5	30.8	48.6
−3	39.5	

* The two-liquid system is metastable throughout.

$C_4H_8O_2$, Isobutyric acid (27, 34, 42, 110, 135, 150)

−5	15.3	
0	15.8	80
+5	16.5	74.5
10	17.7	68.9
15	19.4	63.9
20	22.5	58.3
21	23.3	56.6
22	24.6	54.3
23	26.4	51.5
24	29.4	46.6
24.5	38	

$C_4H_8O_2$, Ethyl acetate (31, 32, 53, 83, 90, 103, 121)

0	10.08	97.72
5	9.49	97.56
10	8.88	97.39
15	8.40	97.18
20	7.94	96.99
25	7.56	96.76
30	7.22	96.53
35	7.01	96.27
40	6.86	96.00
45	6.76	95.75
50	6.70	95.47
55	6.66	95.19
60		94.90

$C_4H_8O_2$, Methyl propionate (103, 148)

0	7.80
10	6.80
20	6.10
30	5.60

$C_4H_8O_2$, Propyl formate (103, 148)

0	3.39
10	3.00
20	2.79
30	2.70

$C_4H_{10}O$, *n*-Butyl alcohol (56)

−2.95Q_A		
+5	80.38	9.55
10	80.33	8.91
15	80.14	8.21
20	79.93	7.81
25	79.73	7.35
30	79.38	7.08
35	78.94	6.83
40	78.59	6.60
50	77.58	6.46
60	76.38	6.52
70	74.79	6.73

$C_4H_{10}O$.—(*Continued*)

°C	% B	
80	73.53	6.89
90	69.9	7.9
100	66.2	9.2
110	62.4	10.5
115	59.0	12.8
120	54.0	16.1
125.15	32.5	

$C_4H_{10}O$, Isobutyl alcohol (3, 154)

30	7.75	82.9
40	7.25	81.8
50	7.1	80.6
60	7.1	79.2
70	7.2	77.6
80	7.55	75.6
90	8.2	73.5
100	9.35	70.2
105	10.3	68.9
110	11.3	67.0
115	12.3	64.75
120	14.85	61.7
125	18.0	57.47
130	23.6	51.25
(132)	36.8	

$C_4H_{10}O$, *sec.*-Butyl alcohol (3, 24, 143, 145)

−10	25.2	
0	25.0	61.8
+10	23.4	61.7
20	20.1	63.7
30	17.2	65.0
40	15.0	65.5
50	14.0	65.7
60	13.3	65.7
70	13.2	65.4
80	13.7	64.5
90	14.9	63.3
100	17.4	59.3
110	22.3	52.4
113.1	(35.7)	

$C_4H_{10}O$, Ethyl ether (1, 8, 25, 41, 50, 52, 57, 64, 67, 79, 80, 94, 96, 97, 98, 103, 113, 118, 141, 142, 147, 156)

°C	% A	% B (156)
−20	0.747	
−3.8 to +35 Q_A	*	†
40	1.50	4.50
50	1.66	4.04
60	1.72	3.60
70	2.00	3.10
80	2.17	2.75
90	2.33	

* % A = $0.9828 + 0.0130_2t$ (52).
† % B = $11.60 - 0.299_8t + 0.00301_6t^2$ (52).

$C_4H_{10}S$, Ethyl sulfide (103)

°C	% B
0	0.394
10	0.347
20	0.310
30	0.296

$C_4H_{11}N$, Diethylamine (3, 47, 74)

°C	% B	
143.5	37.5	
144	30	45
145	27.6	49
150	23.6	55.4
155	21.7	58.5

$C_5H_4O_2$, Furfural (82, 110)
p: varying

10	7.9	96.1
20	8.3	95.2
30	8.8	94.3
40	9.1	93.4
50	9.8	92.6
60	10.8	91.6
70	12.4	90.4
80	14.2	88.8
90	16.2	86.5
100	19.2	83.5
110	24	78.5
115	28	74.6
120	34.4	68.1
122.7	51	

$C_5H_8O_2$, Acetylacetone (110)

30	15.4	95.1
40	17.4	93.8
50	20.0	92.0
60	23.1	89.4
70	27.0	85.8
75	30.0	83.1
80	34.0	78.8
87.7	56.5	

$C_5H_{10}N_2O$, Nitrosopiperidine (36)

40		93.6
60		91.3
80	8.4	88.8
100	9.1	86.2
120	10.7	81.8
140	20.4	70.7
145	26	64.8
150.3	45	

$C_5H_{10}O$, Diethyl ketone (110, 148)

20	4.6	
40	3.4	97.4
60	3.0	96.2
80	3.2	94.9
100	3.7	93.1
120	4.0	90.2
140	4.7	87.0
160	6.1	83.3

$C_5H_{10}O_2$, Valeric acid (78)

16	3.5	90.4

$C_5H_{10}O_2$, Ethyl propionate (103, 148)

0	3.41
10	2.78
20	2.32
30	2.02

$C_5H_{10}O_2$, Methyl butyrate (148)

22	1.7

$C_5H_{10}O_2$, Isobutyl formate (148)

°C	% B
22	1.0

$C_5H_{10}O_2$, Propyl acetate (103, 148)

0	3.35
10	2.57
20	2.30
30	2.05

$C_5H_{12}O$, Isoamyl alcohol* (3, 6, 40, 50, 64, 153, 158, 160)

0	3.6	91.6
10	3.15	91.0
20	2.75	90.4
30	2.45	90.0
40	2.2	89.4
50	2.2	88.8
60	2.2	88.1
70	2.3	87.4
80	2.4	86.3
90	2.7	85.2
100	2.8	83.8
120	3.4	80.8
140	4.9	76.4
160	7.4	69.8
170	9.9	64.8
180	12.0	57.5
185	19.0	50.0
187.5	36.6	

* The isoamyl alcohol contained varying amounts of active amyl alcohol; the amount present in the most heavily weighted curve was 16 %.

$C_6H_4N_2O_5$, 2, 3-Dinitrophenol (125)

94.5m	6.74	
95Q_B		
108.2	10.90	
116.7		60.44
120.1	20.83	
120.4		52.15
122.2	35.13	
122.5	(36)	

$C_6H_4N_2O_5$, 2, 4-Dinitrophenol (125)

100.5m		99.02
104.2Q_B		
109.6	1.95	
117.6		98.24
121.7		97.70
126.1	2.98	
131.2		97.14
137.7	3.81	
156.0		93.35
170.5	8.99	
182.5*	12.98	

* Consolute point above 200°.

$C_6H_4N_2O_5$, 2, 5-Dinitrophenol (125)

92.4m		97.50
97.5Q_B		
113.5		96.72
124.7	2.33	
135.8	2.97	

$C_6H_4N_2O_5$.—(*Continued*)

°C	% B	
146.4	3.91	94.51
162.1	5.69	
172.2		91.73
194.5*	12.24	

* Consolute point above 200°.

$C_6H_4N_2O_5$, 2, 6-Dinitrophenol (125)

59.2Q_B		
71.1	0.703	
84.5		98.42
89.5	1.00	
102.6		97.80
117.6	1.87	
138.3		95.96
139.7	3.24	
147.9	3.97	
158		93.44
192.5*	12.26	

* Consolute point above 200°.

$C_6H_4N_2O_5$, 3, 4-Dinitrophenol (125)

48m		74.91
52.5Q_B		
73.8		70.23
82	6.05	
97.5	12.79	
101.6		55.40
104.6	23.28	
105.2	36.5	

C_6H_5ClO, *o*-Chlorophenol (134)

− 0.3Q_A		86.5
+82.9	3.76	
91.5		85.9
106.3	5.12	
118.9		82.82
156.6		70.62
159.1	13.58	
165.8	16.95	
166.2		60.72
170.1		54.95
170.7	22.59	
172.9		45.04
173	33	

C_6H_5ClO, *m*-Chlorophenol (134)

−0.4mQ_A		83.4
+3.2Q_B		(83.3)
11.8		82.9
23.1		82.3
85.25	5.12	
109.8		71.23
123.0	13.56	
127.5	17.84	
129.1		55.65
130.5		46.12
130.7		38.89
130.8	32.02	

C_6H_5ClO, *p*-Chlorophenol (134)

−0.3Q_B		86.5
+5.5		86.19

C_6H_5ClO.—(*Continued*)

°C	% B	
17.0		85.42
35.5		84.02
65.0	3.91	
97.0		74.03
107.7		69.36
113.8	10.66	
115.5		65.05
122.4		59.62
125	20.50	
125.8		53.49
128.2	29.16	
128.7		42.57
129	(38)	

$C_6H_5NO_2$, Nitrobenzene (14, 22)

10		99.82
20	0.19†	99.78
30	0.22†	99.73
55	0.27†	99.47
100	0.80	98.60
120*	1.6	
130*	2.1	
140*	2.7	
160*	4.0	93.0
180*	5.2	92.0
200*	8.2	88.0
220*	15.8	82.0
230*	24.0	74.0
235*	49	

* Data from (14).
† Data from (22).

$C_6H_5NO_3$, *o*-Nitrophenol (133)

43.5Q_B	0.35	99.48
60	0.46	99.24
80	0.69	98.80
100	1.08	98.22
120	1.59	97.40
140	2.32	96.40
160	3.75	95.00
180	6.80	93.12
200*	(10.5)	(89.5)

* Consolute temp. above 200°.

$C_6H_5NO_3$, *m*-Nitrophenol (133)

41.5Q_B	3.16	74.0
50	3.7	72.7
60	4.5	70.7
70	5.75	68.3
80	7.85	64.6
90	11.7	58.8
95	15.6	53.0
98.7	(33)	

$C_6H_5NO_3$, *p*-Nitrophenol (133, 143)

39.6Q_B	3.26	71.2
50	4.37	68.5
60	5.46	65.8
70	7.8	63.0
80	11.2	59.4
85	15.5	55.7
90	25.7	45.9
91.6	35.8	

C_6H_6, Benzene (18, 45, 48, 50, 52, 59, 60, 93)

°C	% A
5.4Q_B	0.0335
10	0.041
20	0.057
30	0.082
40	0.114
50	0.155
60	0.205
70	0.270
°C	% B
0	0.08
25	0.15
100*	0.176
150*	0.525
200*	1.81
250*	6.04
285*	8.53
300*	11.4

* Data from (59, 60).

$C_6H_6N_2O_2$, *o*-Nitroaniline (132)

°C	% B	
63Q_B		97.5
68		97.23
91		96.16
128.4	2.95	
142		92.06
160		89.5
164.5	7.19	
178.5	10.74	
188.5		81.88
194.2	17.50	
206.2		66.89
208.6	36.71	
210.3		52.30
211	48.4	

$C_6H_6N_2O_2$, *m*-Nitroaniline (132)

99Q_B		93.5
125		90.02
136.5	6.04	
159.9		83.60
164.2	13.08	
169.3		79.82
176.7		75.77
180.5	25.39	
185.2	36.94	
185.8		57.55
186.1	50.57	
187.5	(48.5)	

$C_6H_6N_2O_2$, *p*-Nitroaniline (132)

115.5Q_B		90.0
123.5	5.16	
124.2		92.52
129.2		86.82
141.5	9.29	
148.6		81.27
167.8		68.19
169.5	28.82	
170.4		62.58
172	39.49	51.07
172.5	(47)	

C_6H_6O, Phenol (3, 28, 42, 56, 76, 106, 110, 112, 117, 136, 143)

°C	% B	
0m	7.2	75.4
1.66mQ_B	7.3	75.2
10m	7.7	73.85
12.2Q*	7.8	73.5
15	7.95	73.0
20	8.2	72.1
25	8.45	71.05
30	8.75	69.9
35	9.1	68.5
40	9.6	66.8
45	10.45	65.0
50	11.8	62.6
55	13.8	59.2
60	16.8	55.1
65	23.9	45.8
66.0	34.0	

* Solid = B_2A.

C_6H_7N, Aniline (2, 3, 50, 55, 68, 107, 117, 131, 151)

− 0.62Q_A	3.28	95.64
+10	3.38	95.18
15	3.43	95.06
20	3.49	94.93
25	3.55	94.77
30	3.63	94.62
40	3.83	94.29
50	4.05	93.86
60	4.40	93.4
70	4.91	92.75
80	5.59	91.95
90	6.36	91.0
100	7.18	89.7
110	7.95	88.05
120	9.15	86.0
130	11.05	83.6
140	13.6	80.6
150	17.0	76.4
160	23.9	69.1
165	(30.6)	(61.8)
167.5	(46.16)	

C_6H_7N, β-Picoline (36)

49.4	26.4	
51.4		35.5
53.7		42.3
54.5	16.4	
61.0	12.7	
63.3		52.3
83.5		59.7
125.7	12.7	
133.3		59.7
140.0	16.4	
146.5		52.3
151		42.3
152		35.5
152.5	26.4	

$C_6H_8N_2$, Phenylhydrazine (7)

19.8	11.6	60.1
55.2	33.6	

H_2O.—(*Continued*)

$C_6H_{10}O_3$, Ethyl acetoacetate (79)

°C	Wt. B/l soln.
16–16.5	12.5

$C_6H_{12}O_2$, Isoamyl formate (148)

°C	% B
22	0.3

$C_6H_{12}O_2$, Isobutyl acetate (148)

°C	% B
22	0.5

$C_6H_{12}O_2$, Ethyl butyrate (148)

°C	% B
22	0.5

$C_6H_{12}O_2$, Propyl propionate (103)

°C	% B	
0	1.05	
10	0.84	
20	0.68	
30	0.60	

$C_6H_{12}O_3$, Paraldehyde (100)

°C	% B	
10	12.9	99.15
20	10.4	98.9
30	8.75	98.7
40	7.65	98.45
50	6.85	98.1
60	6.30	97.7
70	5.95	97.3
80		96.8

$C_6H_{13}N$, 1-Methylpiperidine (35)

°C	% B	
48.3	16.7	
48.5		21.3
48.7	13	26.9
49.5		37.2
50.3	10.3	
51.2		46.3
54.1	8.0	
55		55.9
61.5		65.3
63.6	6.4	
69.5	5.8	
70.0		74.2
77	5.3	
85.5		83.4
112		89.6
176		89.6
178	5.3	
196	8.8	
230		83.4
236	13.5	

$C_6H_{13}N$, 2-Methylpiperidine (37)

°C	% B	
79.3	19.4	
79.8	13.8	
80.4	10.6	
81		24.0
82.4	9.5	
83		29.2
86.5	8.6	
87		39.7
87.2		33.7
88.8		47.0

$C_6H_{13}N$.—(*Continued*)

°C	% B	
92.4	7.8	
94		52.4
112		64.7
165		72.3
171	8.2	
188	9.7	
220	15.0	
221		60.4
225		52.4
227	20–28	

$C_6H_{13}N$, 3-Methylpiperidine (36)

°C	% B	
56.9	19.2	
57.5		29.2
58.1	9.9	
59.9		38.1
69.8		50.5
80	4.8	
82		58.2
115		70.1
142.2		74.8
143	4.8	
184		74.8
197	9.9	
204		70.1
226.5		58.2
228.5	19.2	
232		50.5
234		38.1
235	29.2	

$C_6H_{13}N$, 4-Methylpiperidine (36)

°C	% B	
84.9	23.7	
85.1	16	
85.9		30
87.6	11.6	
88.8		36.2
94.2	8.9	
95.5		42.4
106.9		49.4
122.7		55.0
133.0		57.5
146.0	8.9	
157.8	11.6	
168.5		57.5
178.0	16.0	
183.6		49.4
186.2	23.7	
187.5		42.4
188.8		30.0
189.5	36.2	

$C_6H_{14}O_2$, Acetal (95, 137)

°C	% B
25	4.4

$C_6H_{14}O_2$, Ethylene glycol mono-*n*-butyl ether (19)

°C	% B	
49.1	24.8	
50	18.2	34.4
52	14.4	41.5
55	12.5	47.2
60	10.9	51.6
70	9.4	56.2
80	9.2	58.0
100	10.2	57.3

$C_6H_{14}O_2$.—(*Continued*)

°C	% B	
110	11.7	55.2
120	14.7	48.5
125	17.8	40.6
127	20.2	32.6
128	24.8	

$C_6H_{14}O_2$, Ethylene glycol monoisobutyl ether (19)

°C	% B	
24.5	24.6	
26	16.5	40.4
28	14.3	50.0
30	12.8	53.4
35	10.4	58.8
40	8.8	62.4
50	7.6	67.2
80	7.4	70.8
100	7.6	70.0
120	8.8	66.3
130	10.5	63.0
140	13.8	58.0
145	16.7	53.3
148	20.0	47.5
150.4	28	

$C_6H_{14}O_2$, 1, 2-Propylene glycol 1-propyl ether (19.5)

°C	% B	
34.4	37	
36	24.7	52.4
40	19.6	61.2
50	14.8	70.0
60	12.6	73.0
80	10.5	75.0
100	10.4	75.2
120	10.5	74.3
140	12.3	71.0
150	14.0	67.9
160	17.0	62.0
165	19.5	58.0
171.8	37	

$C_6H_{14}O_2$, 1, 2-Propylene glycol 2-propyl ether (19.5)

°C	% B	
42.6	35	
45	22.8	51.2
50	18.2	61.8
60	14.3	67.9
80	12.0	71.0
100	11.8	70.8
120	12.0	70.0
140	14.1	65.4
150	17.0	60.8
155	19.2	57.3
160	23.8	48.4
162	35	

$C_6H_{15}N$, Triethylamine (3, 46, 110, 143)

°C	% B	
18.7	(50)	
20	14.0	81.0
25	7.15	95.4
30	5.55	
40	4.0	95.5
50	3.0	95.6
60	2.0	95.7
70	1.75	96

$C_7H_4N_2O_6$, 3, 5-Dinitrobenzoic acid (38)

°C	% B	
87m	4.4	
96m		80.2
111.4m	10	
114m		67.4
120m		60
122Q_B	19.8	
122.6		50
123.6		40
123.8	30	

$C_7H_5ClO_2$, *o*-Chlorobenzoic acid (38)

°C	% B	
97m	5.5	
104.3Q_B		
115.2		62.9
125.9	19.3	
126.0		48.7
126.2	34.9	

$C_7H_5ClO_2$, *m*-Chlorobenzoic acid (38)

°C	% B	
116m		75.8
122m	4.2	
123.7Q_B		
136		60.2
142	18.9	
142.6		51.3
142.8	34.3	

$C_7H_5NO_3$, *o*-Nitrobenzaldehyde (128)

°C	% B	
39.7Q_B		99.9
63.8		99.0
66.9	0.70	
103.1	1.53	
113.5		96.49
145.1		94.80
161.7		93.56
166.0	4.75	

$C_7H_5NO_3$, *m*-Nitrobenzaldehyde (128)

°C	% B	
51Q_B		99.6
60		99.2
80	1.2	98.2
100	1.65	97.1
120	2.1	96.0
140	3.2	94.3
160	5.4	91.6
180	10.2	86.4
200	18.4	74.8
210	31	62.0
212	(46)	

$C_7H_5NO_3$, *p*-Nitrobenzaldehyde (128)

°C	% B	
97.1Q		98.2
132.4	2.91	
134.2		96.70
164.6		92.74
172.6		90.65
176.5	8.78	
205.4	20.67	
213.4		63.19
215.5	37.77	
216	(47.5)	

$C_7H_5NO_4$,* o-Nitrobenzoic acid (38)

°C	% B	
46.2	10	
51.6	20	49.5
52.0	29.8	39.4

$C_7H_5NO_4$, m-Nitrobenzoic acid (3, 38, 129)

76.7Q_B	5.0	69.75
80	5.3	69.0
85	5.8	67.6
90	6.8	65.5
95	8.1	62.5
100	10.6	58.8
105	16.0	52.7
108.3	(34)	

C_7H_6O, Benzaldehyde (39)

Room	0.3

$C_7H_6O_2$, Benzoic acid (3, 129)

64m	3.04	
75m	3.9	
80m	4.2	(79.7)
85m	4.8	(78)
95Q_B	7.0	72.8
100	7.8	69.0
105	9.2	64.0
110	13.2	57.2
115	23.6	45.2
116.2	34	

$C_7H_6O_2$, o-Hydroxybenzaldehyde (126)

67.4		97.13
85.8	1.68	
118.3		93.20
136.5	3.59	
146.3		90 56
154.0	5.34	

$C_7H_6O_2$, m-Hydroxybenzaldehyde (126)

(59)Q_B	(11.2)	(60.0)
62 4		53.9
63.5	19.2	
65.6		43.4
66.0	29.2	
66.1	31.9	
66.2	(35)	

$C_7H_6O_2$, p-Hydroxybenzaldehyde (126)

52.8m	13.2	
60.5m	20.7	
61.8m		49.8
62.4m	26.6	
62.8Q_B	27.4	46.2
63.8		42.2
64.4	(36.5)	

$C_7H_6O_3$,* o-Hydroxybenzoic acid (salicylic acid) (3, 38, 129)

65	5.1	65.9
70	6.0	63.9
75	7.1	61.6
80	8.7	58.1
85	13.0	52.0
89.1	(32)	

* The two-liquid system is metastable throughout.

$C_7H_7NO_2$,* o-Aminobenzoic acid (38)

°C	% B	
62.4	9.9	
73.0		67.0
74.6	13.5	
75.8		59.4
78	30.6	49.4
78+	38	

* The two-liquid system is metastable throughout.

$C_7H_7NO_2$, o-Nitrotoluene (14)

138		97.79
164	2.17	
197		91.90
205	5.97	
222		85.36
230	13.33	
231		82.05
237		77.21
238	20.77	
242	29.93	
243		69.21
245	(51)	

C_7H_8, Toluene (60)

150	0.174
200	0.605
250	2.38
300	10.1

C_7H_8O, o-Cresol (133)

8Q_B	2.5	87.0
20	2.7	86.4
30	2.9	85.9
40	3.1	85.4
50	3.25	84.85
60	3.4	84.4
70	3.75	83.8
80	4.25	83.0
90	4.6	82.1
100	5.1	80.95
110	5.7	79.6
120	6.3	78.0
130	7.0	76.0
140	9.5	72.2
150	14.9	65.5
160	26.5	52
162.8	(39.2)	

C_7H_8O, m-Cresol (133)

0.0	2.2	88.6
10	2.3	87.8
20	2.35	87.0
30	2.4	86.2
40	2.55	85.4
50	2.7	84.5
60	2.95	83.5
70	3.35	82.3
80	3.8	80.95
90	4.4	79.6
100	5.1	77.4
110	5.9	75.2
120	7.0	72.0
130	8.8	68.3
140	12.2	62.0
145	22.0	50.2
147	35.5	

C_7H_8O, p-Cresol (133)

°C	% B	
8.7Q_B	2.0	85.85
20		85.0
30		84.25
40	2.25	83.4
50	2.4	83.0
60	2.70	81.5
70	3.05	80.3
80	3.50	79.1
90	4.1	77.4
100	4.85	75.0
110	5.70	72.3
120	6.75	69.0
130	8.60	64.2
140	16.0	53.8
142	20.8	49.4
143.5	(34)	

C_7H_9N, 2, 6-Dimethylpyridine (36)

45.3	27.2	
50	16.3	46.0
60	11.4	55.2
70	9.8	60.9
80	9.3	64.2
100	9.4	67.2
120	10.5	67.2
130	11.7	66.9
140	13.4	65.1
150	16.5	60.8
155	18.9	56.7
160	21.2	49.7
164.9	33.8	

C_7H_9N, p-Toluidine (156)

44	1.775
57.5	2.04
69	2.345

C_7H_{12}, Heptine (49)

17	0.211
40	0.038

$C_7H_{14}O$, Heptaldehyde (49)

0	0.303
20	0.234
40	0.188

$C_7H_{14}O_2$, Heptylic acid (49)

20	0.29

$C_7H_{15}N$, 1-Ethylpiperidine (35)

7.45	30	
8	14.2	47.0
9	11.8	52.0
10	10.5	57.0
15	7.4	73.4
20	5.8	82.3
30	4.0	90.1
40	2.9	92.9
50	2.2	93.9
60	1.8	94.8
70		95.4

$C_8H_6O_2$, o-Phthalic aldehyde (120)

45.4Q_B	4.94	86.85
57.0		88.16
60.0	4.54	

$C_8H_6O_3$,* o-Aldehydobenzoic acid (127)

°C	% B	
21.1	9.38	
39.2		59.48
43.3	20.0	
44		40.83
45.75	29.2	

* The two-liquid system is metastable throughout.

$C_8H_8N_2O_3$, o-Nitroacetanilide (132)

81.0Q_B		96.0
99.0		94.54
110.2		93.65
120.0	3.97	
157.6	8.04	
173.1		83.47
179.2	11.97	
188.0		76.28
191.2	24.06	
195		65.04
197	41.16	
198	(49.2)	

$C_8H_8N_2O_3$, m-Nitroacetanilide (132)

118.5Q_B		90.0
130.0	5.21	
149.2		81.18
163.5	14.52	
166.4		73.74
175.7		66.03
176.9	31.13	
180	(45.6)	

$C_8H_8N_2O_3$, p-Nitroacetanilide (132)

161.5Q_B		80
164.2	14.36	
171.7		65.84
172.8	25.62	
176.6		54.93
177.4	42.65	

$C_8H_8O_2$, Phenylacetic acid (129)

45.5Q_B		
84.7	5.65	
94.8		61.94
106.8		39.69
108.0	20.00	

$C_8H_8O_2$, o-Toluic acid (38, 133)

94Q_B	2.5	91.2
100	2.8	90.0
110	3.8	87.5
120	5.4	84.9
130	6.9	81.2
140	9.2	76.1
150	13.5	67.6
155	18.7	59.6
157.5	23.8	54.8
160.7	(37.6)	

H_2O.—(*Continued*)

$C_8H_8O_2$, *m*-Toluic acid (38, 133)

°C	% B	
92.5QB	1.6	90.4
100	2.0	88.3
110	2.6	85.4
120	3.2	82.5
130	4.0	79.5
140	5.9	75.0
150	8.0	68.3
160	18.8	52.7
161.9	(35)	

$C_8H_8O_2$, *p*-Toluic acid (38, 133)

142.5QB	5.0	73.8
145	6.2	70.9
150	9.4	64.8
155	15.1	57.5
157	18.8	51.4
158.9	35	

$C_8H_8O_2$, 4-Hydroxytoluene-3-aldehyde (126)

87.7		96.09
99.1	2.52	
137.1		92.73
156.5	5.47	

$C_8H_8O_2$, 6-Hydroxytoluene-3-aldehyde (126)

79.5QB	3.0	(59.9)
87.2		56.0
99.3	5.45	
127	16.5	52.5
133.5	23.5	
136.8	35.4	

$C_8H_8O_2$, 5-Hydroxytoluene-2-aldehyde (126)

69.1QB	6.9	50.6
78.8		50.3
85.8	7.95	
116.3	14.3	
121.1		48.5
124.5		44.6
125	34	

$C_8H_8O_3$,* *p*-Methoxybenzoic acid (38)

136	19.7	
137		50
137.6	30	
138.2	40	

* The two-liquid system is metastable throughout.

$C_8H_8O_3$, Methyl salicylate (121)

15–30	0.1	

$C_8H_8O_3$, 2-Hydroxytoluene-3-carboxylic acid (129)

120.3		69.52
129.2QB		
131.8	5.07	
143.0		59.73
149.3	10.18	
151.3		50.51
153.3	29.81	
153.5	(31.5)	

$C_8H_8O_3$, 3-Hydroxytoluene-4-carboxylic acid (129)

°C	% B	
125.3	5.53	
131QB		
138.4	9.75	
139.4		54.40
144.6	19.89	41.46
145.2	(30.2)	

$C_8H_8O_3$, 4-Hydroxytoluene-3-carboxylic acid (129)

106.8	3.16	
107.8QB		
117.5	4.53	
117.7		69.29
120.2		67.91
131.5		59.85
135.6		55.16
138.5	10.21	
142.0		38.85
142.5	24.55	
142.8	(30)	

C_8H_9NO, Acetanilide (114)

83.2QB	5.2	87
86	5.4	
87		84.4
88		83.4
90	5.8	
91.5		81.9
95	6.1	
96		80.5
97.5	6.6	
118		80
127.5		75
134	20	
142	30	60
143.5	50	50
144	40	

C_8H_{10}, Xylene (60)

150	0.088	
200	0.307	
250	0.958	

$C_8H_{11}N$, 2, 4, 6-Trimethylpyridine (110)

5.7	17.2	
10	7.82	41.66
20	3.42	54.92
30	2.51	62.80
40	1.93	70.03
60	1.78	80.19
80	1.73	86.12
100	1.78	87.07
120	1.82	88.98
140	2.19	89.10
160	2.93	87.2
180	3.67	

$C_8H_{17}N$, 1-Propylpiperidine (35)

−3.0	3.2	
+0.5	2.7	
9.5		97.4
11	1.4	
15.5		97.9
30		98.4
32	0.6	

$C_9H_8O_2$, Allocinnamic acid (91, 92)

°C	Wt. B/l soln.
18	13.63
25	14.43
35	16.05
45	18.11
55	20.50
65	23.43
75	27.69

$C_9H_8O_4$,* Acetylsalicylic acid (aspirin) (38)

°C	% B	
25	4.8	
50	7.0	
60	8.5	
70	9.7	67.5
80	13.8	60.0
85	18.5	52.5
87.4	20.0	50.0
89+	34	

* The two-liquid system is metastable throughout.

$C_9H_{10}O_2$, Hydratropic acid (129)

34QB		
101.5		80.30
119.9	5.00	
143.5		60.16
149.2	19.31	
150	39.31	

$C_{10}H_{14}N_2$, Nicotine (58, 146, 149)

For vapor pressure, *v.* (124.5).

60.8	29	
65	14.8	51.2
70	12.1	63.0
75	10.3	70.9
80	9.0	75.9
85	8.1	79.1
90	7.4	80.5
100	7.1	81.2
125	7.5	81.3
150	8.0	81.2
175	10.0	77.0
190	12.9	68.4
200	16.3	56.5
205	20.4	48.0
208	32	

$C_{10}H_{18}O$, Cineole (30)

1.5	0.64	
7.5	0.57	
10	0.54	
21	0.35	
40	0.21	
50	0.19	

$C_{12}H_{11}N$, Diphenylamine (14)

150		97.3
175		95.5
200		93.2
230	1.5	90.0
250	2.0	88.0
270	4.4	85.6
290	11.6	77.2
300	22	66.2
303	44	

$C_{12}H_{13}NO$, Phenylammonium phenolate (3)

°C	% B	
40	4.0	91.1
50	4.5	89.2
60	5.2	87.4
70	5.9	85.6
80	6.6	83.8
90	7.3	82.1
100	8.0	80.3
110	9.5	77.7
120	12.7	73.2
130	18.4	65.3
135	24.2	58.6
140	41.2	

$C_{12}H_{17}NO_4.H_2O$, 3, 5-Dimethoxyacetophenetide (9)

35.6	4.13	
45.6	3.55	
58.1	3.28	
68.5	3.28	
84.3	3.55	
87QB		
99.8	4.16	
111.1	4.92	
118.4	5.50	
129.2	6.68	
173.6	22.89	

Ligroin (50)

d = 0.6646

22	0.227	99.50

Gasolene (18)

d = 0.70; B. P. = 40–145°C

°C	%A
25	0.0098
35	0.0141
37.5	0.0160

Kerosene (American) (45)

d_{20}^{20} = 0.792; B. P. = 190–250°C

− 2	0.0012
+18	0.005
23	0.007
30	0.008
36	0.012
53	0.026
59	0.031
61	0.035
66	0.043
79	0.063
85	0.075
94	0.097

Paraffin oil (45)

d_{18}^{18} = 0.883; B. P. = 200–300°C at 10 mm.

16	0.003
50	0.013
65	0.022
73	0.030
77	0.035
94	0.055

Variation of the Critical Solution Temperature (°C) with Pressure (146)

B-component	°C	kg/cm²	Δt/Δp
CH_3NO_2, Nitromethane	103.3	1–150	−0.008
C_3H_5N, Propionitrile	111.0	5–165	−0.02
$C_3H_8O_2$, Methylal	160.3	20– 64	−0.21
$C_4H_4N_2$, Succinonitrile	52.3	10–160	−0.003

C_4H_8O, Methyl ethyl ketone

Lower *t*

°C	kg/cm²	Δt/Δp	°C	kg/cm²	Δt/Δp
−13.8	78.2		37.3	700	0.071
− 6.1	150	0.107	44.1	800	0.068
− 0.7	225	0.091	51.3	900	0.072
+ 7.8	300	0.095	61.6	1000	0.103
16.05	400	0.083	66.9	1050	0.106
23.2	500	0.072	80	1085	
30.2	600	0.070			

Upper *t*

°C	141	136.8	132.8	86.5
kg/cm²	10	78.2	150	1075
Δt/Δp		−0.062	−0.052	−0.050

B-component	°C	kg/cm²	Δt/Δp
$C_4H_8O_2$, Isobutyric acid	26.4	1–525	−0.055
$C_4H_{10}O$, Isobutyl alcohol	134.2	10–180	−0.03
$C_4H_{10}O$, *sec.*-Butyl alcohol	113.8	1–800	−0.07
$C_5H_{10}O_2$, Isovaleric acid	95.0	5–60	−0.05
$C_6H_5NO_3$, *p*-Nitrophenol	94.3	1–120	+0.01
C_6H_6O, Phenol	66.09	10–1000	0.00456
C_6H_7N, Aniline	165	10–210	0.009
$C_6H_8N_2$, Phenylhydrazine	75.5 (sic)	5–155	−0.009
$C_6H_{15}N$, Triethylamine	18.35	5	
	22.36	200	+0.205
	29.19	600	0.171
	34.26	1000	0.127
	39.40	1500	0.103
	43.45	2000	0.080
$C_7H_4N_2O_6$, Dinitrobenzoic acid	123.3	10–110	0.006
$C_7H_5NO_4$, *m*-Nitrobenzoic acid	107.3	5–125	0.008
$C_7H_6O_2$, Benzoic acid	118.5	5–200	0.0025
$C_8H_{11}N$, 2, 4, 6-Trimethylpyridine	1.3	1–200	0.0045
$C_{10}H_{14}N_2$, Nicotine	61.3	1–200	0.01

Sec. 2. The key-formula of neither component begins with 16. Standard arrangement (*v.* p. viii).

O_2

B = O_3 (108, 119)

°C	% A	
−158	Consolute temp.	
−183		30

SO_2

B = KI (155)

°C	% B	
77.3	12	
78	8.5	15.0
80	6.8	17.6
84	4.5	21.1
88Q_B	2.7	24.0

NH_3

B = Na (70, 111)

°C	% B	
−72		16.6*
−65		13.6*
−60	2.15	10.9
−55	2.5	10.0
−50	3.0	8.9
−46	3.6	7.8
−42	4.7	6.2
−41.6	5.4	

* According to (111).

NH_4Cl

B = $AlCl_3$ (65)

°C	% A	
192.5Q†	0.08	94

NH_4Br

B = $AlBr_3$ (65)

98Q†	>0.092	9.0
159.5		8.7
160.5	0.093	
236.5	0.30	

$SbCl_3$

B = $SnCl_2$ (65)

°C	% B	
243.1Q†	1.2	89.6

B = $SnCl_4$‡ (65)

62.9	39.1	
63.0		67.9
64.5		64.4
65.4		56.4
65.9	48.7	

$SnCl_2$

B = $AlCl_3$ (65)

°C	% A	
192.0Q†	2.1	19.1

$SnBr_2$

B = $AlBr_3$ (65)

161.0 Q_{AB_2}	1.9	14.7
169.1	2.2	
185.4		13.7
187.3	3.5	
198.0	4.9	
201.4		11.1
202.4		10.7
204.5	8.7	

$PbBr_2$

B = $AlBr_3$ (65)

210.4Q_{AB_2}	1.1	21.0

TlCl

B = $AlCl_3$ (65)

192.0Q†	2.1	23.6

TlBr

B = $AlBr_3$ (65)

103.9Q†	>0.64	23.9
118	0.64	23.5
260		22.5

HgBr

B = $AlBr_3$ (65)

238.1Q_{AB}	1.9	34.9
275.5	3.5	

† Solid = double compound.

‡ The two-liquid system is metastable throughout.

Cu

B = Cu_2S (43)

°C	% A	
1150	3.7	94.8
1200	4.7	91.3
1300	7.2	91.0
1425	8.1	81.7
1485	7.2	79.9

Ag

B = AgCl (104)

1000	0.1

AgCl

B = $AlCl_3$ (65)

192.9Q*	0.75	18.6

AgBr

B = $AlBr_3$ (65)

105.9Q_{AB_2}	1.2	12.6
120.4	2.2	
139.7		12.0
156.3	3.2	
159.7		10.8
161.9	3.6	
173.0		9.8
183.6	5.5	
186.0	7.1	

$AlCl_3$

B = $BaCl_2$ (65)

°C	% B	
191.5Q_{A_2B}	3.1	18.9

B = NaCl

193.5Q*	0.09	8.8

B = KCl

193Q*	0.22	11.1

$AlBr_3$

B = $CaBr_2$ (65)

208.8Q*	0.6	10.9

B = $BaBr_2$

269.4Q_{A_2B}	1.0	17.5

B = NaBr

95.4Q*	1.0	7.0
110.9	1.2	
125.6		6.5
166.4	1.6	
166.9		6.1
202.7		5.4
222.1	2.2	
230		4.3
231.9	3.2	
232	3.25	

B = KBr

98.1Q*	0.18	11.2
189.6		9.7
265.9	0.39	

* Solid = double compound.

Sec. 3. The A-component key-formula does not begin with 16. The B-component key-formula begins with 16. A-components in standard arrangement; B-components in ℭ-arrangement (*v.* p. viii).

S

B = C_4H_5NS, Mustard oil (3)

°C	% B	
80		73.4
90	10.5	69.8
100	13.0	66.0
110	16.8	60.8
120	23.6	51.4
125	36.5	

B = C_6H_5Cl, Chlorobenzene

67		81.2
90	15	69.6
100	20.5	63.6
110	27.3	55.7
117	42	

B = C_6H_6, Benzene

86		78.5
100	8.0	74.5
110	10.0	71.2
120	11.8	68.0
130	13.6	64
140	15.6	59.7
150	18.0	53.9
160	25.9	43.7
162.8	34.8	

B = C_6H_7N, Aniline

72		85.9
100	6.0	76
110	8.6	71.2
120	11.3	64.7
130	15.4	54.5
135	20.3	45.2
138	31	

B = C_7H_8, Toluene

°C	% A	
50	22	
100	30	94.0
110	31.6	93.0
120	33.6	91.8
130	35.8	90.5
140	38.8	88.7
150	43.5	86.4
160	49.0	83.7
170	56.0	80.2
179.5	70	

SO_2

B = C_6H_{12}, Cyclohexane (69)

$-17Q_A$	9.0	96.0
−10	11.5	94.0
− 5	13.7	92.8
0	16.7	91.0
+ 5	22.7	87.2
10	31.7	78.4
12	38.5	72.1
13.5	55.6	

B = C_6H_{14}, *n*-Hexane (123)

$-73.5Q_A$		99.2
−60		99.0
−30	11.3	97.2

B = C_6H_{14}.—(*Continued*)

°C	% A	
−20	15.5	96.7
−10	20.7	96.1
0	27.3	95.6
+ 5	34.2	95.4
8	42.0	94.0
10.1	71	

B = C_8H_{18}, *n*-Octane (162)

B = $C_{16}H_{32}$, Cetene (124)

$- 2.2Q_B$	12.0	97.1
0.0	13.6	97.0
+10.0	21.2	96.7
20.0	30.4	96.0
30.0	39.8	94.0
35.0	44.7	92.0
40.0	52.8	87.8
42.0	59.0	84.0
42.7	72.0	

NH_3

B = C_8H_{10}, *m*-Xylene (71)

°C	% A		$p_{atm.}$
−33.5	1.73	96.61	1.0
+ 8	17.36	70.09	5.5
10	19.63	65.46	5.8
12	22.04	60.43	6.2
14	29.00	52.89	6.7
14.7	41.23		6.85

P_4

B = CS_2 (51)

°C	% A	
−7.8	9.4	
−6.7	46.1	85.2
−6.6	50.3	82.3
−6.5	55.6	77.9
−6.4	62.0	70.3
−6.38*	65.7	

* −6.5° (51).

B = $C_2H_4Br_2$, Ethylene bromide (51)

151.7	77.9
162.0	52.9
163.0	36.9
165.0	34.2
165.5	45.6
169.6	31.4

Consolute temp. *ca.* 165°.

B = $C_6H_4Br_2$, *p*-Dibromobenzene (51)

154.3	26.7	
159	33.1	55.3
161	36.4	52.3
163	45.1	

B = $C_6H_4Cl_2$
p-Dichlorobenzene (51)
Consolute temp. = 163°C

B = C_6H_5Cl
Chlorobenzene (51)
Consolute temp. = 264°C

B = $C_{10}H_8$, Naphthalene (51)

°C	% A	
132.8	25.4	
190.0	44.2	79.7
195.0	47.6	78.0
200	52.8	75.0
202.7	64.3	

B = $C_{10}H_{22}$, Decane (51)
Consolute temp. = >300°C

B = $C_{14}H_{10}$, Phenanthrene (51)

°C	% A	
198		74.7
199.1		66.6
199.2	47.4	
199.5	49.5	
200	56.7	

$SbBr_3$

B = C_6H_{12}, Cyclohexane (89)

92.5	17.4	97.6
110	25.8	96.5
130	36.4	95.0
150	47.8	92.7
170	62.3	86.3
175	74.0	

$SbCl_3$

C_6H_{12}, Cyclohexane (88, 89)

70	13.7	97
80	19.5	96.1
100	32.3	92.7
120	57.1	83.2
124	58.9	76.7
125.5	68	

$MgBr_2$

B = $C_4H_{10}O$, Ethyl ether (87)

°C	% B	
−10	58	98.2
0	59	97.7
+10	59.9	97.2
20	60.7	96.7
22.8Q*		
30	61.3	96.2
40	61.8	95.7
50	62.2	95.3
60	62.4	94.9
70	62.4	94.6
80	62.3	94.4
90	62.1	94.3

MgI_2

B = $C_4H_{10}O$, Ethyl ether (87)

14.8	64.5	
18.6		86.43
20.0	64.2	
23.6Q*		
24.4		85.4
28.4	64.5	
32.4		84.18
33.0	64.3	
37.3		80.6
38.0	67.2	
38.5	72.5	

* Solid = AB_2.

Variation of the Critical Solution Temperature (°C) with Pressure (146)

Components	°C	kg/cm²	$\frac{\Delta t}{\Delta p}$
S			
B = C_6H_5Cl, Chlorobenzene	117	5–85	−0.025
SO_2			
B = C_6H_{14}, Hexane	11.9	10–130	−0.023
B = $C_{10}H_{22}$, Diisoamyl	34.1	10–130	+0.03

Sec. 4. Both A- and B-component key-formulae begin with 16. ℭ-arrangement for both components (*v.* p. viii).

CCl_4

B = CH_2O_2, Formic acid (44)

°C	% A	
25	6.5	96.7

CS_2

B = CH_2O_2, Formic acid (44)

25	4.45	98.7

B = CH_4O, Methyl alcohol (26, 86, 110)

−73.6	18.7	
−38.7	28.8	
−18.85		99.64
− 4.43	41.3	
+ 6.46		98.74
10	47.7	98.4
15	50.2	97.9

B = CH_4O.—(*Continued*)

°C	% A	
20	53.3	97.2
25	57.3	96.0
30	62.7	94.0
35	72.7	88.9
36.5	80.8	

B = C_2H_6O, Ethyl alcohol (47, 72, 86)

−108.04		99.09
−100	32.0	99
− 80	38.5	98.7
− 60	46.7	98.0
− 40	57.4	96.1
− 30	67.1	93.0
− 25	76.3	87.6
− 24.3	82.3	

$CHBr_3$

B = CH_2O_2, Formic acid (44)

°C	% A	
25	20.2	97.8

CH_2O_2

Formic acid

B = C_6H_6, Benzene (33)

°C	% B	
3.8	10.2	
25	14.1	90.4
30	15.1	89.6
40	17.8	87.0
50	21.0	83.4
60	25.7	77.9
70	35.1	68.6
73.2	51.8	
	(44)	
25	13.1	87.3

B = C_7H_8, Toluene (44)

°C	% A	
25	9.9	91.6

B = C_8H_{10}, Xylene (44)

25	8.04	93.2

B = Kerosene (44)

25	0.89	98.4

B = Cottonseed oil (44)

°C	%B	
25	0.76	92.0

CH_3I

Methyl iodide

B = C_5H_5N, Pyridine (4)

°C	% A	
78.4m	32.17	
79m	29.23	
80.4m	23.92	
81.0Q*		
86.6	16.94	
87.0		37.31
117.0		42.90

* Solid = AB.

CH_4O

Methyl alcohol

B = C_6H_{12}, Cyclohexane (75, 92.5)

°C	% B	
16	31	
21.8		95.9
29.0	38.3	
38.5		91.0
39.9	50.6	
47.0		81.3
47.2	62.7	
48.2		77.6
49.1	71	

B = C_6H_{14}, Hexane (110)

10	26.5	96.8
20	31.6	95.9
25	34.7	95.1
30	38.3	93.7
35	43.6	91.2
40	52.7	85.5
42.6	68.9	

B = Cottonseed oil (44)

°C	% B	
25	7.79	95.0

$C_2H_4O_2$

Acetic acid

B = Kerosene (44)

°C	% A	
25	17.8	88.8

B = Cottonseed oil (44)

°C	% B	
25	5.3	64.2

C_2H_6O

Ethyl alcohol

B = $C_4H_4N_2$, Succinonitrile (116)

°C	% A	
$13.4Q_B$	20.2	
13.5		87.5
19.3	25.0	
20.0		84.0
24.6		80.1
28.2		75.1
29.2	39.8	
30.8	51.1	
31.2	59.2	

B = $C_4H_8Cl_2S$, Di-(2-chloroethyl) sulfide (mustard gas) (139)

°C	% B	
6	45.3	
7	46.6	
8	48.3	
9	50.4	
10	52.9	
11	56.0	
12	59.7	
13	64.1	
14	69.1	94.2
15	75.9	90.1
15.6	83.5	

B = C_4H_{10}, *n*-Butane (73)
Consolute temp. = 37.5°C

B = C_5H_{12}, Isopentane (73)
Consolute temp. = −30°C

B = $C_7H_5N_5O_8$, 2, 4, 6,-Trinitrophenylmethylnitramine (20.1)
Consolute temp. = 105°C

B = $C_7H_5N_3O_6$
Trinitrotoluene (20)
Consolute temp. = 96.5°C

B = Cottonseed oil (161)

°C	% B	
25	8.45	81.3

$C_2H_6O_4S$

Dimethyl sulfate

B = Turpentine oil (29)

°C	% A	
25.2	2.80	
38.0		93.99
50.3	5.28	

B = Turpentine oil.—(*Continued*)

°C	% A	
74.0	10.16	88.53
94.8	19.50	
95.3		80.54
101.9	27.79	
104.4		68.90
105.6	33.89	
107.9		57.44
108.2	50.22	

C_3H_6O

Acetone

B = $C_3H_8O_3$, Glycerol (84)

10	10.9	
20	12.3	
30	13.7	
40	15.1	89.6
50	16.8	88.6
60	19.0	86.4
70	21.3	83.0
80	25.1	78.0
90	34.0	69.8
95	44.0	59.5
95.7	51.7	

$C_3H_8O_3$

Glycerol

B = C_4H_8O

Ethyl methyl ketone (84)

°C	% B	
40	4.0	
50	4.5	92.2
60	5.2	91.8
80	6.8	90.2
100	8.6	89.4
120	9.8	88.0
130	11.4	84.0
140	13.6	80.4
150	17.0	78.6
160	32.0	64.4
164.5	48.4	

B = $C_5H_{12}O$, Isoamyl alcohol (84)

20	2.6	81.8
30	4.7	78.5
40	6.8	75.2
50	8.9	70.7
60	11.0	63.8
70	17.2	53.2
74.2	34	

B = C_7H_6O, Benzaldehyde (85)

67.5	4.5	
85.5		97.0
90	5.2	96.6
100	7.2	95.6
110	9.0	94.1
120	11.6	92.1
130	16.2	89.2
140	21.1	85.3
150	27.7	79.5
155	33.9	73.7
160	48.0	60.0
160.7	54.1	

B = $C_7H_6O_2$, Salicylaldehyde (85)

°C	% A	
100		92.8
110	3.2	90.8
120	4.7	88.7
130	6.3	86.6
140	8.0	84.2
150	10.0	81.3
160	13.6	77.0
170	22.2	68.0
175	30.0	59.8
176.6	44.8	

B = C_7H_8O, Anisole (85)

°C	% B	
160	5.6	
180	10.1	
200	14.6	
220	19.2	
240	24.2	87.7
260	31.5	80.7
270	38.2	73.8
275.5	56	

B = $C_7H_8O_2$, Guaiacol (85)

°C	% A	
39.5	44	
40	37.2	52.0
45	28.5	66.6
50	25.2	69.5
55	23.7	70.4
60	23.5	70.7
65	24.1	70.4
70	25.6	69.4
75	28.3	67.3
80	32.5	61.8
82	35.7	54.0
83.5	43	

B = C_7H_9N, Methylaniline (99)

190		85.5
200	11.2	84.3
210	15.4	79.9
215	19.5	75.3
220	26.5	67.4
224.5	46	

B = C_7H_9N, *o*-Toluidine (99)

100	7.8	87.6
110	8.8	86.8
120	10.7	85.2
130	13.9	82.2
140	18.4	77.2
150	26.6	69.7
154.4	47.2	

B = C_7H_9N, *m*-Toluidine (99)

6.7	46	
10	28.0	69.5
20	19.5	84.4
30	16.6	86.7
40	16.0	87.2
50	16.0	87.6
60	16.0	87.0
70	16.0	86.0
80	16.2	84.3
90	17.0	81.7

$C_3H_8O_3$.—(*Continued*)

B = C_7H_9N.—(*Continued*)

°C	% A	
100	19.8	77.8
110	25.4	71.2
115	29.5	66.2
120.5	47	

B = C_7H_9NO, *o*-Anisidine (99)

°C	% B	
141.0	34.25	
142.5		73.09
143.0	43.57	
144.5	51.69	
145.0	61.25	

B = C_8H_8O, Acetophenone (84)

90		97.2
100	4.7	96.4
110	5.6	95.6
120	6.7	94.3
130	8.0	92.6
140	9.7	90.4
150	11.8	87.9
160	14.6	84.5
170	18.4	79.3
180	26.3	70.2
185.5	48	

B = $C_8H_{10}O_2$, Monoethyl pyrocatechol (99)

172.5	20.0	
175	21.1	
180	23.8	82.6
185	27.6	76.3
190	33.5	68.0
192.9	49.5	

B = $C_8H_{11}N$, Dimethylaniline (99)

°C	% A	
200	8.0	
220	10.6	90.6
240	13.3	87.7
260	16.2	84.4
270	20.1	80.3
280	29.0	71.4
285	38.3	61.8
287	50	

B = $C_9H_{13}N$

Ethylbenzylamine (99)

°C	% B	
50	34	
60	5.8	72.8
80	3.6	86.8
100	3.5	88.8
140	4.4	88.2
180	6.5	86.2
220	11.6	84.2
260	21.5	81.5
270	26.5	79.2
275	31.0	77.5
281	56	

$C_4H_8Cl_2S$

Di-(2-chloroethyl) sulfide (mustard gas)

B = **Ligroin** (140)

B. P. = >100°C; d^{24}_{24} = 0.6677

°C	% A	
9.0Q_A	(31.5)	86.4
9.6		84.5
10.3	32.5	
12		82.6
14		80.9
14.5	39.3	
16	43.7	
17.22		76.1
17.5	49.4	
18.3	56.8	
19	(66)	

B = **Gasolene** (140)

B. P. = 60–180°C

4.2	30.08	
4.5	30.14	
7.3		87.34
7.8		87.17
9.0	36.46	
9.5	36.51	
13.5	46.21	
14	46.32	
18		77.53
18.7	53.49	
20.4	66.02	

B = **Kerosene** (140)

B. P. = 130–260°C

8.9		91.88
9.5	33.13	
14.2	39.79	
14.3		89.68
21.9		84.93
24.3		81.42
25	68.67	
25.6	75	

B = **Railroad light oil** (140)

B. P. = 160–300°C

9.3	21.64	
14.5	24.33	
20.9	29.88	
23.6	38.49	
25.0		90.78
28.0		88.74
31.3		86.58
33.0	47.95	
35	54.48	
37	63.8	

$C_4H_{10}O$

Ethyl ether

B = $C_{18}H_{12}$, Chrysene (12, 144, 145)

Consolute temp. = 207–218°C with 21% B in solution

Chlorinated mustard oil

B. P., 112° at 17 mm; d^{20}_{20} = 1.355

B = **Railroad light oil** (140)

B. P. = 160–300°C

°C	% A	
−1	36	88.5
0	36.5	88
+1	37	87.5
2	38	87
3	39.5	86.5
4	42	85
5	44	84
6	48	82.5
7	55	80.5
8	(65)	(77)
8.3	(72.5)	

C_5H_{10}

Amylene

B = C_6H_7N, Aniline (69)

°C	% A	
−0.15	18.5	
+3.9		79.8
10.1		71.8
10.7	28.5	
14.15	39.6	
14.3		52.3
14.5	48.4	

C_5H_{12}

Isopentane

B = $C_6H_5NO_2$

Nitrobenzene (144, 145, 146)

Consolute temp. = 32.6°C, with 50.37% B in solution

B = C_6H_6O, Phenol (14)

°C	% B	
17.55	12.41	
26.60		91.87
29.35	16.95	
39.15		86.10
49.20	24.58	
54.95	28.46	
55.85		73.86
60.75	35.70	
62.25	45.33	
62.55		61.92
63.25		52.15
63.5	51.0	

B = $C_{12}H_{11}N$, Diphenylamine (13)

°C	% A	
15m	13.0	87.0
20m	16.4	84.7
25m	19.4	81.7
30m	22.5	80.2
35m	26.8	77.9
40m	33.8	72.0
41.9Q_B	37.2	68.9
42.5	40.3	67.4
44.9	54.2	

$C_6H_5NO_2$

Nitrobenzene

B = C_6H_{14}, Hexane (143, 145)

°C	% B	
−0.2	17.76	
+5.0		80.08
5.8	19.47	
14.0		70.94

B = C_6H_{14}.—(*Continued*)

°C	% B	
15.5	29.72	
16.1		67.21
17.7	34.21	
18.7		57.29
21.02	48.43	

C_6H_6

Benzene

B = $C_6H_6O_2$, Resorcinol (110)

°C	% A	
40m	16.60	
50m	18.16	
60m	20.04	95.41
70m	22.46	93.36
80m	25.51	90.73
90m	29.02	87.20
95.5Q_B		
100	34.17	81.30
108.9	58.1	

B = $C_6H_8N_2$, *m*-Phenylenediamine (130)

53.8Q_B	25.00	
54.7	25.16	
55.5	25.44	
58.8	27.86	
59.8		80.64
60.0	28.96	
64.2	34.09	
66.5	38.40	
68.8	49.09	
69.0	60.96	

B = $C_8H_{10}N_2O$, *m*-Monoacetylphenylenediamine (130)

°C	% B	
184.9Q_B		77.5
188.4		76.86
193.4		76.16
201.9		74.65
227.8		68.90
228.5	22.75	
257.6		57.03
263.4	39.10	
265.1		49.23
265.5	44.31	
266	(46.4)	

B = $C_8H_{10}N_2O$, *p*-Monoacetylphenylenediamine (130)

146.8Q_B		74.0
147.1		72.71
150.1		71.05
155.9		67.66
163.5		63.07
170.0		59.95
180.8	17.36	
181.3		51.70
186.3		41.23
187.8	30.12	
188	(35.3)	

C_6H_6O

Phenol

B = C_6H_{14}, Hexane (14)

14.40	17.58	
20.75		88.57

B = C_6H_{14}.—(*Continued*)

°C	% B	
29.20		83.94
31.70	26.11	
34.20	29.98	
37.00		68.78
37.65	40.20	64.96
38.65	41.64	
42.15	50.14	
42.5	51	
B = C_7H_{16}, Heptane (14)		
13.20	23.81	
14.45		79.36
17.95		74.02
20.05		65.41
22.05	33.31	
23.40	43.69	
23.50	45.8	
B = C_8H_{18}, Octane (14)		
19.65	14.0	
22.6	15.1	86.7
25	16.0	85.3
30	17.8	82.4
35	20.2	79.2
40	23.6	74.3
45	29.4	66.8
48	36.5	58.4
49.5	47	

$C_6H_6O_2$

Resorcinol

B = **C_8H_{10}**, *m*-Xylene (13)

°C	% A	
60m	2.95	88.2
70m	3.80	87.1
80m	4.77	85.5
90m	6.35	83.9
100m	7.75	82.3
100.3QA	8.1	81.8
110	10.1	80.2
120	12.9	77.3
130	16.5	73.9
135	19.2	71.4
140	22.3	67.6
145	28.4	59.7
148.7	43.6	

C_6H_7N

Aniline

B = **C_5H_{10}**, Cyclopentane (17)
Consolute temp. = 18°C

B = **C_5H_{12}**, Pentane (17)
Consolute temp. = 72°C

C_5H_{12}, Isopentane (17)
Consolute temp. = 77°C

B = **C_6H_{12}**
Methylcyclopentane (17)
Consolute temp. = 35°C

B = **C_6H_{14}**, Hexane (17, 26, 66)

°C	% A	
20	7.2	
30	10.0	89.6
40	14.0	86.8
50	23.1	80.6
55	29.0	74.8
58	37.6	68.0
59.6*	52	

B = **C_6H_{14}**, Isohexane (17)
Consolute temp. = 73.8°C

B = **C_7H_{14}**
Dimethylcyclopentane (17)
Consolute temp. = 45°C

B = **C_7H_{14}**
Methylcyclohexane (17, 146)
Consolute temp. = 35°C

B = **C_7H_{16}**, Heptane (17)
Consolute temp. = 70°C

B = **C_7H_{16}**, Isoheptane (17)
Consolute temp. = 72.8°C

B = **C_8H_{16}**
Dimethylcyclohexane (17)
Consolute temp. = 49°C

B = **C_8H_{18}**, Octane (17)
Consolute temp. = 72°C

B = **C_8H_{18}**, Isooctane (17)
Consolute temp. = 74°C

$C_{10}H_7NO_2$

Nitronaphthalene

B = **Paraffin** (14)

°C	% B	
43.4	11.65	
54.0		94.52
59.0	16.65	
72.0		92.01
75.0	25.01	
76.0		91.32
90.0	36.10	
98.5	45.38	
99.0		83.97
101.0		74.33
102.0	54.54	
103.0	65.5	

* 69° (17); p = ?.

Variation of the Critical Solution Temperature (°C) with Pressure

Components	°C	kg/cm²	$\frac{\Delta t}{\Delta p}$
CO_2 (146)			
B = **$C_6H_5NO_3$**, *o*-Nitrophenol	24.8	83–1275	0.33
CS_2 (146)			
B = **CH_4O**, Methyl alcohol	48.5	5–85	0.015
B = **C_3H_6O**, Acetone	−39.5	10–110	0.01
CH_2O_2, Formic acid (146)			
B = **C_6H_5Cl**, Chlorobenzene	106.6	5–65	0.035
B = **C_6H_6**, Benzene	82	5–65	0.03
CH_2I_2, Methylene iodide (146)			
B = **C_2H_6O**, Ethyl alcohol	93.8	5–75	−0.004
B = **C_3H_8O**, Propyl alcohol	75.7	1–100	+0.006
B = **C_3H_8O**, Isopropyl alcohol	93.2	1–200	0.012
B = **$C_4H_{10}O$**, Isobutyl alcohol	77.5	1–80	0.012
B = **C_6H_{12}**, Cyclohexane	34.5	5–120	0.01
B = **C_6H_{14}**, Hexane	105.4	5–155	−0.02
B = **$C_{10}H_{22}$**, Diisoamyl	119.5	5–65	−0.015
CH_4O, Methyl alcohol			
B = **C_4H_{10}**, *n*-Butane (73, 146)	16.6	20–150	+0.007
B = **C_4H_{10}**, Isobutane (146)	20.1	10–140	0.004
B = **C_6H_{12}**, Cyclohexane (146)	59.5	50–1000	0.0227
B = **C_6H_{14}**, Hexane (146)	42.2	1–105	0.032
B = **$C_{10}H_7Br$**, Bromonaphthalene (146)	62	5–195	−0.025
B = **$C_{10}H_{22}$**, Diisoamyl (146)	86.8	10–150	+0.04
$C_2H_4O_2$, Acetic acid			
B = **$C_{10}H_7Br$**, Bromonaphthalene (146)	42	5–210	0.025
C_2H_6O, Ethyl alcohol			
B = **$C_4H_4N_2$**, Succinonitrile (146)	24.3	10–160	−0.005
C_3H_5N, Propionitrile			
B = **$C_{10}H_{22}$**, Diisoamyl (146)	55.1	1–150	+0.016
C_3H_6O, Acetone			
B = **$C_{10}H_{22}$**, Diisoamyl (146)	18	1–90	0.01
$C_4H_4N_2$, Ethylene cyanide			
B = **$C_4H_{10}O$**, Isobutyl alcohol (146)	67.0	5–155	−0.004
C_4H_{10}, *n*-Butane (146)			
B = **$C_6H_5NO_2$**, Nitrobenzene	28.3	15–150	−0.04
B = **C_6H_7N**, Aniline	83	15–90	−0.08
$C_4H_{10}O$, Isobutyl alcohol			
B = **$C_{10}H_7Br$**, Bromonaphthalene (146)	8.6	1–180	−0.01
C_5H_{10}, Amylene			
B = **C_6H_7N**, Aniline (146)	21.8	1–165	−0.02
C_5H_{12}, Isopentane			
B = **$C_6H_5NO_2$**, Nitrobenzene (144, 146)	32.6	1–300	−0.026
$C_6H_5NO_2$, Nitrobenzene			
B = **C_6H_{14}**, Hexane (143, 146)	20.81	1–825	−0.008
	20.8	1–825	−0.01
B = **$C_{10}H_{22}$**, Diisoamyl (146)	28.37	1–1225	−0.0011
B = **Petroleum** (146)	13.95	1–725	+0.0014
C_6H_6, Benzene			
B = **$C_6H_6O_2$**, Resorcinol (146)	109.1	10–170	−0.03
$C_6H_6O_2$, Resorcinol			
B = **C_8H_{10}**, Ethylbenzene (146)	151.5	5–65	−0.025
C_6H_7N, Aniline			
B = **C_6H_{12}**, Cyclohexane (17, 146)	32.37	1.8–250	+0.0068
B = **C_7H_{14}**, Methylcyclohexane (146)	41.3	1–140	0.003
B = **$C_{10}H_{22}$**, Diisoamyl (146)	82	5–180	−0.001
C_7H_9N, *m*-Toluidine			
B = **$C_{10}H_{22}$**, Diisoamyl (146)	38.5	10–75	−0.003

LITERATURE

(For a key to the periodicals see end of volume)

(1) Aignan, *34*, **124**: 1013; 97. (2) Aignan and Dugas, *34*, **129**: 643; 99. (3) Alekseev, *8*, **28**: 305; 86. (4) Aten, *7*, **54**: 124; 06. (5) Bakhuis Roozeboom, *70*, **3**: 73; 84. (6) Balbiano, *25*, **9**: 1437; 76. (7) Blanksma, *176*, **7**: 417; 10. (8) Bödtker, *7*, **22**: 505; 97. (9) Bogert and Ehrlich, *1*, **41**: 741; 19.

(10) Boutaric, *42*, **18**: 126; 20. (10.5) Boutaric and Corbet, *34*, **183**: 42; 26. (11) Bray, *1*, **32**: 932; 10. (12) Bückner, *7*, **54**: 665; 06. (13) Campetti, *23*, **52**: 114; 17. (14) Campetti and Delgrosso, *Mem. R. Accad. Sci. Torino*, **61**: 187; 11. *10*, **2**: 433; 13. (15) Chancel and Parmentier, *34*, **99**: 892; 84. (16) Chancel and Parmentier, *34*, **100**: 773; 85. (17) Chavanne and Simon, *34*, **168**: 1111; 19. (18) Clifford, *45*, **13**: 631; 21. (19) Cox and Cretcher, *1*, **48**: 451; 26. (19.5) Cox, Nelson and Cretcher, *1*, **49**: 1080; 27.

(20) Crismer, *28*, **29**: 28; 20. (20.1) Crismer and Timmermans, *28*, **29**: 34; 20. (21) Dancer, *4*, **15**: 477; 62. (22) Davis, *1*, **38**: 1166; 16. (23) Dietz, *487*, **43**: 290; 98. (24) Dolgolenko, *7*, **62**: 499; 08. (25) Draper, *135*, **35**: 87; 77. (26) Drucker, *70*, **42**: 552; 23. (27) Drucker and Moles, *7*, **75**: 405; 10. (28) Dubrisay and Toquet, *27*, **25**: 354; 19. (29) Dubroca, *42*, **5**: 463; 07.

(30) Earle, *54*, **37**: 274T; 18. (31) Euler, *7*, **31**: 360; 99. (32) Euler and Svanberg, *19*, **6**: No. 14; 17. (33) Ewins, *4*, **105**: 350; 14. (34) Faucon, *6*, **19**: 70; 10. (35) Flaschner, *7*, **62**: 493; 08. (36) Flaschner, *4*, **95**: 668; 09. (37) Flaschner and McEwen, *4*, **93**: 1000; 08. (38) Flaschner and Rankin, *57*, **31**: 23; 10. (39) Flückinger, *293*, **7**: 103; 75.

(40) Fontein, *7*, **73**: 212; 10. (41) Forbes and Coolidge, *1*, **41**: 150; 19. (42) Friedländer, *7*, **38**: 385; 01. (43) Friedrich and Wachlert, *187*, **10**: 976; 13. (44) Gordon and Reid, *50*, **26**: 773; 22. (45) Groschuff, *9*, **17**: 348; 11. (46) Guthrie, *3*, **18**: 22; 84. (47) Guthrie, *3*, **18**: 495; 84. (48) Hantzsch and Sebalt, *7*, **30**: 258; 99. (49) Harkins and Cheng, *1*, **43**: 35; 21.

(50) Herz, *25*, **31**: 2669; 98. (51) Hildebrand and Buehrer, *1*, **42**: 2213; 20. (52) Hill, *1*, **45**: 1143; 23. (53) Hill and Attisani, *0*. (54) Hill and Brunhuber, *0*. (55) Hill and Macy, *1*, **46**: 1132; 23. (56) Hill and Malisoff, *1*, **48**: 918; 26. (56.5) Hill and Morrow, *0*. (57) Horiba, *41*, **31**: 922; 10. (58) Hudson, *7*, **47**: 113; 04. (59) Jaeger, *416*, **4**: 17; 23.

(60) Jaeger, *416*, **4**: 259; 23. (61) Jenkin and Shorthose, *B67*. (62) Jones, *4*, **99**: 392; 11. (63) Jones and Hartman, *78*, **30**: 295; 16. (64) Kablukov and Malischeva, *1*, **47**: 1553; 25. (65) Kendall, Crittenden and Miller, *1*, **45**: 963; 23. (66) Keyes and Hildebrand, *1*, **39**: 2126; 17. (67) Klobbie, *7*, **24**: 615; 97. (68) Kolthoff, *176*, **14**: 1081; 17. (69) Konowalow, *8*, **10**: 360; 03.

(70) Kraus and Lucasse, *1*, **44**: 1949; 22. (71) Kraus and Zeitfuchs, *1*, **44**: 1249; 22. (72) Kuenen, *3*, **6**: 637; 03. (73) Kuenen, *64P*, **14**: 644; 12. (74) Lattey, *3*, **10**: 397; 05. (75) Lecat, *Thesis*, Brussels, 1909. (76) Leone and Angelescu, *36*, **52 II**: 61; 22. (77) Leone and Benelli, *36*, **52 II**: 75; 22. (78) Lieben and Rossi, *13*, **159**: 58; 71. (79) Linde, *19*, **6**: No. 20; 17.

(80) Linebarger, *135*, **70**: 52; 94. (81) Lumière and Barbier, *27*, **33**: 783; 05. (82) Mains, *33*, **26**: 779; 22. (83) Marsson, *293*, **74**: 290; 53. (84) McEwen, *4*, **123**: 2279; 23. (85) McEwen, *4*, **123**: 2284; 23. (86) McKelvy and Simpson, *1*, **44**: 105; 21. (87) Menschutkin, *93*, **49**: 34; 06. (88) Menschutkin, *496*, **13**: 1, 263, 411, 565; 10. (89) Menschutkin, *496*, **14**: 251; 11.

(90) Merriman, *4*, **103**: 1774; 13. (91) Meyer, *25*, **44**: 2966; 11. (92) Meyer, *9*, **17**: 976; 11. (92.5) Mondain-Monval, *34*, **183**: 1104; 26. (93) Moore and Roaf, *5*, **77**: 86; 05. (94) Nernst, *7*, **6**: 16; 90. (95) Orton and Jones, *4*, **101**: 1708, 1720; 12. (96) Osaka, *58*, **84**: 248; 10. (97) Osaka, *41*, **31**: 221; 10. (98) Osaka, *172*, **4 A I**: 308; 09. *10*, **2**: 432; 13. (99) Parvatiker and McEwen, *4*, **125**: 1484; 24.

(100) Pascal and Dupuy, *27*, **27**: 353; 20. (101) Pearce and O'Leary, *453*, **30**: 379; 23. (102) Price and Green, *54*, **39**: 98; 20. (103) Rayman, *Diss.* Budapest, 1906. (104) Reinders, *7*, **77**: 213; 11. (105) Rex, *7*, **55**: 355; 06. (106) Rhodes and Markley, *50*, **25**: 527; 21. (107) Riedel, *7*, **56**: 243; 06. (108) Riesenfeld and Schwab, *25*, **55**: 2088; 22. (109) van Rossem, *7*, **62**: 681; 08.

(110) Rothmund, *7*, **26**: 433; 98. (111) Ruff and Ledner, *25*, **41**: 1948; 08. (112) Scarpa, *42*, **2**: 447; 04. (113) Scheiffer, *64P*, **15**: 380; 12. (114) Schoorl and de Weerd, *70*, **41**: 15; 22. (115) Schreinemakers, *7*, **23**: 417; 97. (116) Schreinemakers, *7*, **27**: 95; 98. (117) Schreinemakers, *7*, **29**: 577; 99. (118) Schuncke, *7*, **14**: 331; 94. (119) Schwab, *7*, **110**: 599; 24.

(120) Seekles, *70*, **42**: 706; 23. (121) Seidell, *464*, No. **67**: 10. (122) Seyer and Dunbar, *69*, **16**: 307; 22. (123) Seyer and Gill, *69*, **18 III**: 209; 24. (124) Seyer and Hugget, *69*, **18 III**: 213; 24. (124.5) Shükarev, *7*, **71**: 90; 10. (125) Sidgwick and Aldous, *4*, **119**: 1001; 21. (126) Sidgwick and Allot, *4*, **123**: 2819; 23. (127) Sidgwick and Clayton, *4*, **121**: 2263; 22. (128) Sidgwick and Dash, *4*, **121**: 2586; 22. (129) Sidgwick and Ewbank, *4*, **119**: 979; 21.

(130) Sidgwick and Neill, *4*, **123**: 2813; 23. (131) Sidgwick, Pickford and Wilsdon, *4*, **99**: 1122; 11. (132) Sidgwick and Rubie, *4*, **113**: 1013; 21. (133) Sidgwick, Spurrell and Davies, *4*, **107**: 1202; 15. (134) Sidgwick and Turner, *4*, **121**: 2256; 22. (135) Smirnoff, *7*, **58**: 667; 07. (136) Smits and Maarse, *64P*, **14**: 192; 11. (137) Stas, *14*, **19**: 146; 47. (138) Thompson and Black, *45*, **12**: 1066; 20. (139) Thompson, Black and Sohl, *1*, **43**: 877; 21.

(140) Thompson and Odeen, *45*, **12**: 1057; 20. (141) Thorin, *7*, **89**: 685; 15. (142) Thorne, *4*, **119**: 262; 21. (143) Timmermans, *7*, **58**: 129; 07. (144) Timmermans, *64P*, **13**: 507; 10. (145) Timmermans, *Thesis*, Brussels, 1911. (146) Timmermans, *42*, **20**: 491; 23. (147) Tolloczko, *7*, **20**: 389; 96. (148) Traube, *25*, **17**: 2294; 84. (149) Tsakalotos, *27*, **5**: 397; 09.

(150) Tsakalotos, *7*, **68**: 32; 10. (151) Vaubel, *52*, **52**: 72; 95. (152) Vaubel, *52*, **59**: 30; 99. (153) Verschaffelt, *7*, **15**: 437; 94. (154) Verschaffelt, *70*, **42**: 683; 23. (155) Walden and Centnerszwer, *7*, **42**: 432; 02. (156) Walker, *7*, **5**: 193; 90. (157) Wildermann, *7*, **11**: 407; 93. (158) Wilson, *1*, **43**: 704; 21. (159) Winkler, *136*, **23**: 687; 99.

(160) Wittstein, *495*, **11**: 567; 62. (161) Wroth and Reed, *1*, **38**: 2316; 16. (162) Seyer and Gallaugher, *69*, **20**: 343; 26.

PHASE EQUILIBRIA FOR THREE-COMPONENT SYSTEMS CONTAINING TWO LIQUID PHASES, THE COMPLETE COMPOSITION OF AT LEAST ONE OF WHICH IS KNOWN

A. S. Coolidge

Explanation of Diagrams and Tables

The data are presented by means of isothermal triangular diagrams with compositions in weight per cent (%).

For each of the two layers into which the system divides, a line can be drawn giving the composition of all mixtures capable of existing as such a layer. These lines may have various shapes. In the very common case that A and B are liquids of limited mutual solubility, but both soluble in all proportions in C, and supposing A to be denser than B, then the lower layer will give such a line as ab, Fig. 1, and the upper layer such a line as cd. If continued, the lines meet each other with a common tangent at the plait-point, o (*see* below). In another common case, in which A and B are completely miscible liquids and C is a solid very soluble in A but nearly insoluble in B, the two lines start together at the plait-point p, and run similar to pf and pg. In this case, they do not extend as far as the side, BC, of the diagram, but are terminated by the impossibility of producing solutions sufficiently rich in C. However, supersaturation with regard to C may occur, without knowledge on the part of the experimenter, so that in many of the graphs representing systems of this class, points near f and g may not represent the most stable condition of the system. This can be settled in any case by consulting the section of I. C. T. dealing with equilibrium between solid and liquid phases in three-component systems. In a few cases, the binodal lines have different courses, running entirely separate across the diagram without plait-points, or forming closed curves with two plait-points.

Every point upon the line ab represents a solution in equilibrium with another solution, which must lie somewhere upon the line cd. This relation can be expressed graphically by plotting any one of the three triangular coordinates of the point on the line ab against any one of the coordinates of the corresponding point on the line cd. Practically, that coordinate is chosen, the lines representing which cut the binodal most nearly at right angles. Thus, in systems having binodals of the type abodc, the % A in the lower layer is plotted against the % B in the upper layer. The plot is made on the same diagram, which must be extended downwards, and gives the curve hko. The sides of the lower triangle are numbered downwards, the right side giving % A in lower layer, and the left % B in the upper layer. Thus h, the beginning of the conjugation curve, has the coordinates 92% A, 95% B, meaning that a solution of the lower layer containing 92% of A is in equilibrium with one of the upper layer with 95% of B, or, graphically, that points a and c of the binodals are conjugate. The conjugation curve crosses the binodals at the plait-point, o, where the two layers become identical. By plotting % A in the upper layer against % B in the lower layer, on the same diagram, a continuation of the conjugation curve, olm, is obtained above the binodal. This has the advantage of locating the plait-point by an interpolation, instead of the customary extrapolation.

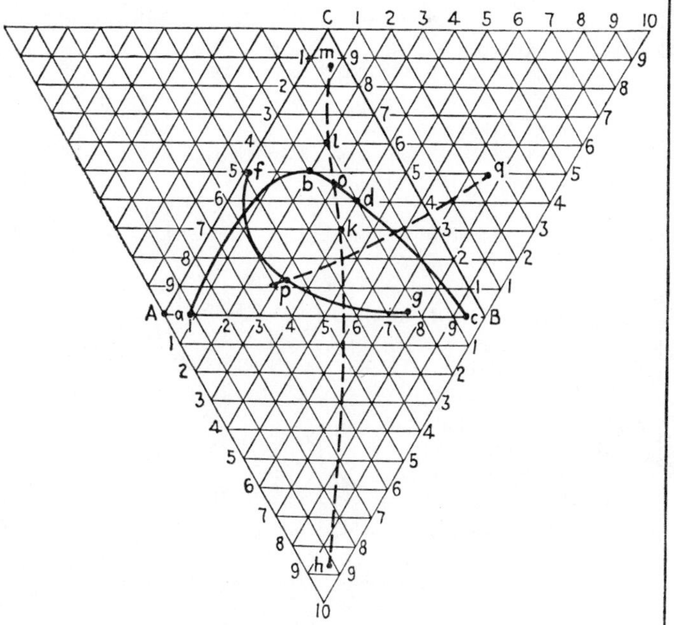

FIG. 1.

By the aid of the three lines just described, complete information can be read at once from the diagram, concerning composition of both phases, when a single datum (other than the temperature) is given. Thus, let it be required to find the equilibrium given that the lower layer contains 20% of B. Running up from 2 on the lower scale of the upper triangle, and parallel to AC, we strike the binodal at b, and read at once A = 30%, C = 50%. Now running parallel to BC, we strike the conjugation line at k, from which, again running parallel to AC, we find the point d representing the solution of the upper layer in equilibrium, namely, 20% A, 40% B, 40% C. Or, having found b, we can run up to l, then down to d, finding, of course, the same result.

In the case of systems having binodals like fpg, the conjugate line is constructed by plotting % C in the layer rich in C against % B in the layer rich in B, and has the general course of the line pq.

This method has several advantages over the customary one of drawing in numerous "tie-lines." First, it enables the phenomenon of conjugation to be represented as a continuous curve, from the smoothness of which the accuracy of the experimental data can be judged. It is found that in systems which have been accurately investigated, the conjugation line has only gentle curvature. Second, it makes possible the direct reading of any pair of conjugate points, without the necessity of interpolating between tie-lines, a matter of considerable difficulty and uncertainty when the tie-lines have changing slopes. Finally, it greatly reduces the number of lines necessary to represent a given system, so that several systems may be shown together without risk of confusion. While either the long or the short branch of the conjugation curve is sufficient to determine all possible equilibria, readings can be made more accurately from the long branch, particularly when the initial parts of the binodals run nearly parallel to the sides of the triangle. However, in the majority of cases, the experimental data are so meager or unreliable that they can be expressed without further loss of accuracy by the short portion; this is therefore done, in order to save space. Where several systems are shown on the same diagram, the binodals are in general shown solid and the conjugation lines dashed, both being suitably labelled. Since all but a very few of the systems graphed belong to one or the other of the two classes illustrated in Fig. 1, there will be no difficulty in interpreting these graphs. In two or three cases where the binodals have different courses, conjugation is indicated by the customary tie-lines.

Temperature effects are generally small, and can be most practically represented by superposing on the same diagram, isotherms for a series of temperatures covering the (generally narrow) range for which data are available. In some cases, however, the range of temperatures investigated greatly exceeds that of compositions. In such cases the graphs show temperature directly as a function of concentration, under some other limiting condition explained on the graphs themselves. Such graphs do not show conjugation.

Where a graph of the largest permissible size would not give the data with sufficient accuracy, tables, interpolated from large graphs, are presented. In these tables the argument is usually the percentage of the predominant component in each layer, and the entries show the percentage of one other component in the same layer, and where known, of the predominant component of the conjugate layer. For example, the system given by lines abodc and hkolm in Fig. 1, would be thus tabulated.

% A	% C	% $(B)_C$	% B	% C
30	50	40	40	40
.	.	.	.	.
.	.	.	.	.
.	.	.	.	.
92	0	95	95	0

Here, the first two columns give the compositions of solutions of the lower layer, the fourth and fifth, those of the upper layer; while the third, $(B)_C$, gives the percentage of B in the upper layer conjugate with each point of the lower layer. (In general, the entries under $(B)_C$ will not be round numbers, and will not coincide with those under B in the second part of the table.) In many cases, the effect of temperature has been roughly determined, but a complete series of data is not available for more than one temperature. In such cases, approximate values for the temperature coefficient are appended. Thus, suppose that point b, A = 30%, B = 20%, C = 50%, is a point on the 20° binodal, but that at 30°C the binodal passes through A = 30%, B = 22%, C = 48%. This would be expressed in the statement $dC/dT = -0.2$ for A = 30%.

Wherever possible, the accuracy of the data has been estimated, and a value assigned to the probable error. In the graphs, the probable error is indicated by a single value, giving, in the scale of the diagram, the distance from the lines as drawn, within which the true lines probably lie. The estimate is made for the most sharply curved portions of the binodals, which are the most susceptible to errors. The straighter portions, especially when they lie close to the sides of the basic triangle, may generally be credited with a somewhat higher accuracy. In some cases where particular parts of the curves are affected by errors greater than those assigned to the curve as a whole, they are drawn as wide bands, within which the true points probably lie.

The data on metallic systems require special discussion. They were made by a very rough method, and show great irregularities. In particular, the binodals often appear convex toward each other, with humps near the plait-point. In the domain of aqueous systems, such convexities and humps never appear in careful work. Bailey (4) states that their appearance is a delicate test for impurities. In the two or three aqueous systems in which they appear, they have, therefore, been eliminated in the graphs, and a large error has been assigned. However, it does not seem justifiable to carry this generalization over to the domain of metallic systems. The graphs have, therefore, been drawn as well as possible through the experimental points, but no attempt to estimate the reliability has been made.

METALLIC SYSTEMS

Sb-Bi-Zn, Fig. 2 (121)
Sb-Bi-Al, Fig. 3 (122)
Sb-Pb-Zn, Fig. 4 (121)
Sb-Pb-Al, Fig. 3 (122)
Bi-Sn-Zn, Fig. 2 (119, 125)
Bi-Sn-Al, Fig. 5 (120)
Bi-Zn-Cd, Fig. 2 (121)
Bi-Zn-Ag, Fig. 2 (119, 125)
Bi-Ag-Al, Fig. 5 (120)
Sn-Pb-Zn, Fig. 4 (119, 123, 124, 125)
Sn-Pb-Al, Fig. 5 (120)
Sn-Cd-Al, Fig. 3 (122)
Pb-Zn-Cd, Fig. 4 (121)
Pb-Zn-Ag, Fig. 4 (119, 124)
Pb-Ag-Al, Fig. 5 (120)

AQUEOUS SYSTEMS

A-B-Table

H_2O

B = HCl

C = Br_2, Table 1 (83)
C = $C_4H_{10}O$, *n*-Butyl alcohol (85)
C = $C_4H_{10}O$, Ethyl ether, Fig. 14 (33, 99); *v. also* p. 419
C = C_6H_6O, Phenol, Fig. 35 (36, 37)
C = $C_{10}H_{14}N_2$, Nicotine, Fig. 6 (36, 37)

B = Br_2

C = HBr, Table 1 (10, 83, 116)
C = H_2SO_4 (116)
C = $CdBr_2$ (116)
C = $HgBr_2$, Table 1 (54)
C = $SrBr_2$, Table 1 (87)
C = NaCl, Table 1 (83)
C = Na_2SO_4, Table 1 (62)
C = $NaNO_3$, Table 1 (62)
C = KBr, Table 1 (10, 64, 116, 118)
C = K_2SO_4, Table 1 (62)

B = HBr

C = SO_2, Table 2 (3)

B = H_2SO_4

C = $C_4H_{10}O$, *n*-Butyl alcohol (85)
C = $C_4H_{10}O$, Ethyl ether (41)
C = C_6H_6O, Phenol, Fig. 8 (36, 37, 53)
C = $C_6H_{12}O_3$, Paraldehyde (86)

B = NH_3

C = K_2CO_3, Figs. 6 and 7 (82)

B = HNO_3

C = $C_4H_{10}O$, *n*-Butyl alcohol (85)
C = $C_4H_{10}O$, Ethyl ether (41)
C = $C_6H_5NO_2$, Nitrobenzene (42)

B = NH_4NO_3

C = C_2H_6O, Ethyl alcohol (46)
C = $C_4H_{10}O$, Ethyl ether (106)

B = NH_4Cl

C = C_3H_6O, Acetone, Fig. 9 (11, 61)
C = C_3H_8O, *n*-Propyl alcohol (108)

B = $(NH_4)_2SO_4$

C = C_2H_6O, Ethyl alcohol, Table 3 (17, 74, 110)
C = C_3H_6O, Acetone, Fig. 10 (61, 74)
C = C_3H_8O, *n*-Propyl alcohol (74)
C = $C_{11}H_{12}N_2O$, Antipyrine (26)

B = K_2CO_3

C = $KC_{11}H_{19}O_4$, Potassium ethyl dipropylmalonate, Fig. 7 (75)

C-Table

The B-components are in the C-arrangement. The C-components are of three types as follows: (*a*) carbon compounds in the C-arrangement; followed by (*b*) organic natural or commercial oils, etc., in alphabetical arrangement; followed by (*c*) the inorganic compounds, in standard arrangement (*v.* p. viii).

H_2O

B = CCl_4

C = CH_4O, Methyl alcohol, Fig. 11 (12)
C = C_2H_6O, Ethyl alcohol, Fig. 11 (12, 31); *v. also* p. 424
C = C_3H_8O, *n*-Propyl alcohol, Fig. 11 (12)

B = CS_2

C = CH_4O, Methyl alcohol (34)
C = $C_2H_4O_2$, Acetic acid (63)
C = C_2H_6O, Ethyl alcohol, Fig. 12 (57, 90, 111); *v. also* p. 424
C = C_3H_8O, *n*-Propyl alcohol (57)
C = $C_4H_{10}O$, Isobutyl alcohol (57)

B = $CHCl_3$, Chloroform

C = CH_4O, Methyl alcohol, Fig. 13 (5, 12)
C = $C_2H_4O_2$, Acetic acid, Fig. 14 (101, 126); *v. also* p. 424
C = C_2H_6O, Ethyl alcohol, Fig. 13 (5, 11, 12, 79, 90)
C = C_3H_6O, Acetone, Fig. 13 (5, 12); *v. also* p. 425
C = $C_3H_6O_2$, Propionic acid, Fig. 14 (101)
C = C_3H_8O, *n*-Propyl alcohol, Fig. 13 (12)

B = CH_2O_2, Formic acid

C = $C_4H_{10}O$, Ethyl ether, Fig. 14 (101); *v. also* p. 422
C = C_6H_6, Benzene, Fig. 14 (44); *v. also* p. 422

B = CH_3I, Methyl iodide

C = CH_4O, Methyl alcohol (57)
C = C_2H_6O, Ethyl alcohol (57)
C = C_3H_8O, Propyl alcohol (57)
C = $C_4H_{10}O$, Isobutyl alcohol (57)

B = CH_3NO_2, Nitromethane

C = CdI_2 (108)

B = CH_4O, Methyl alcohol

C = C_2H_5Br, Ethyl bromide, Fig. 16 (12)
C = $C_4H_8O_2$, Ethyl acetate, Fig. 15 (6)
C = $C_4H_{10}O$, Ethyl ether, Fig. 15 (6)
C = $C_5H_{12}O$, *n*-Amyl alcohol (57)
C = $C_5H_{12}O$, Isoamyl alcohol, Fig. 17 (47)
C = C_6H_5Br, Bromobenzene, Fig. 16 (12)
C = C_6H_6, Benzene, Fig. 15 (5, 7.5, 57)
C = C_6H_7N, Aniline (57)
C = C_6H_{14}, Hexane, Fig. 18 (12)
C = C_7H_{16}, Heptane, Fig. 18 (12)
C = Gasolene (28)
C = Paraffin (28)
C = K_2CO_3, Table 4 (17, 51, 74)

B = $C_2H_4Cl_2$, Ethylene chloride

C = C_2H_6O, Ethyl alcohol, Fig. 19 (12)

B = $C_2H_4Cl_2$, 1, 1-Dichloroethane

C = C_2H_6O, Ethyl alcohol, Fig. 19 (12)

B = $C_2H_4O_2$, Acetic acid

C = C_3H_5ClO, α-Epichlorohydrin, Fig. 20 (71)
C = $C_4H_{10}O$, Ethyl ether, Fig. 14 (101); *v. also* p. 424
C = $C_6H_4ClNO_2$, Chloronitrobenzene (63)
C = C_6H_5Br, Bromobenzene (84)
C = $C_6H_5NO_2$, Nitrobenzene (63)
C = C_6H_6, Benzene, Table 5, Fig. 14 (63, 72, 84, 101, 114); *v. also* p. 424
C = C_6H_7N, Aniline, Figs. 37, 38 (1.5)
C = C_6H_{12}, Cyclohexane (63)
C = C_7H_7Br, Bromotoluene (84)
C = $C_7H_7NO_2$, Nitrotoluene (63)
C = C_7H_8, Toluene, Fig. 37 (84, 117)
C = C_8H_{10}, *m*-Xylene (84)
C = $C_9H_{11}Br$, Bromomesitylene (63)
C = Petroleum (63)

B = C_2H_5Br, Ethyl bromide

C = C_2H_6O, Ethyl alcohol, Fig. 16 (12)
C = C_3H_8O, Propyl alcohol, Fig. 21 (12)

B = C_2H_6O, Ethyl alcohol

C = C_3H_7Br, Propyl bromide, Fig. 19 (12)
C = $C_4H_4N_2$, Succinonitrile, Fig. 22 (92)
C = $C_4H_5Cl_3O_2$, Ethyl trichloroacetate, Fig. 12 (88)
C = $C_4H_6Cl_2O_2$, Ethyl dichloroacetate, Fig. 12 (88)
C = $C_4H_7ClO_2$, Ethyl chloroacetate, Fig. 12 (88)

C = C_4H_8O, Methyl ethyl ketone, Fig. 6 (19)

C = $C_4H_8O_2$, Ethyl acetate, Fig. 24 (6, 12, 79, 88, 100)

C = $C_4H_8O_2$, Methyl propionate, Fig. 25 (88)

C = $C_4H_8O_2$, Propyl formate, Fig. 26 (88)

C = C_4H_9Br, Isobutyl bromide, Fig. 19 (12)

C = $C_4H_{10}O$, *n*-Butyl alcohol, Fig. 21 (11, 33.5)

C = $C_4H_{10}O$, Isobutyl alcohol, Fig. 21 (12, 17.5)

C = $C_4H_{10}O$, Ethyl ether, Table 6 (6, 12, 16, 22, 32, 59, 68, 79)

C = $C_5H_{10}O$, Diethyl ketone, Fig. 27 (12)

C = $C_5H_{10}O_2$, Ethyl propionate, Fig. 25 (12, 88)

C = $C_5H_{10}O_2$, *n*-Butyl formate, Fig. 26 (88)

C = $C_5H_{10}O_2$, Methyl butyrate, Fig. 28 (88)

C = $C_5H_{10}O_2$, Propyl acetate, Fig. 24 (88)

C = $C_5H_{11}Br$, Isoamyl bromide, Fig. 19 (12)

C = $C_5H_{12}O$, Amyl alcohol (57)

C = $C_5H_{12}O$, Isoamyl alcohol, Table 7 (12, 38, 47, 88)

C = C_6H_5Br, Bromobenzene, Fig. 16 (12)

C = $C_6H_5NO_2$, Nitrobenzene, Fig. 21 (12, 35, 39)

C = C_6H_6, Benzene, Table 5 (5, 7.1, 11, 12, 57, 72, 81, 103, 105); *v. also* p. 424

C = C_6H_6O, Phenol, Fig. 35 (93)

C = C_6H_7N, Aniline (35, 39, 57)

C = $C_6H_{12}O_2$, Butyl acetate, Fig. 24 (88)

C = $C_6H_{12}O_2$, Ethyl butyrate, Fig. 28 (7, 12, 88)

C = $C_6H_{12}O_2$, Isoamyl formate, Fig. 26 (88)

C = $C_6H_{12}O_2$, Methyl isovalerate, Fig. 26 (88)

C = $C_6H_{12}O_2$, Propyl propionate, Fig. 25 (88)

C = C_6H_{14}, Hexane, Fig. 18 (12)

C = $C_6H_{15}N$, Triethylamine, Fig. 27 (76)

C = C_7H_6O, Benzaldehyde, Fig. 27 (12)

C = C_7H_7Br, Bromotoluene, Fig. 16 (12)

C = $C_7H_7NO_2$, *p*-Nitrotoluene, Fig. 21 (12)

C = C_7H_8, Toluene, Fig. 18 (12, 30)

C = C_7H_8O, Benzyl alcohol, Fig. 21 (12)

C = C_7H_9N, Methylaniline, Fig. 27 (12)

C = C_7H_9N, *o*-Toluidine, Fig. 21 (12)

C = $C_7H_{14}O_2$, Ethyl isovalerate, Fig. 26 (7, 88)

C = $C_7H_{14}O_2$, Isoamyl acetate, Fig. 24 (7, 88)

C = $C_7H_{14}O_2$, Propyl butyrate, Fig. 28 (88)

C = C_7H_{16}, Heptane, Fig. 18 (12)

C = $C_8H_8O_3$, Methyl salicylate, Fig. 24 (100)

C = C_8H_{10}, *o*-, *m*- or *p*-Xylene, Fig. 27 (12, 58)

C = $C_8H_{10}O$, Phenetole, Fig. 21 (12)

C = $C_9H_{10}O_2$, Benzyl acetate, Fig. 24 (12)

C = C_9H_{12}, Mesitylene, Fig. 27 (12)

C = $C_9H_{12}O$, Benzyl ethyl ether, Fig. 18 (12)

C = $C_{10}H_7Br$, *α*-Bromonaphthalene, Table 8 (65)

C = $C_{10}H_{12}O$, Anethole (56.5)

C = $C_{10}H_{12}O$, Methylchavicol (56.5)

C = $C_{10}H_{12}O_2$, Eugenol (56.5)

C = $C_{10}H_{16}$, Pinene, Fig. 27 (12)

C = $C_{10}H_{18}O$, Cineole (23)

C = $C_{10}H_{22}O$, Isoamyl ether, Fig. 18 (12)

C = $C_{13}H_{10}O$, Benzophenone, Fig. 29 (8)

C = $C_{16}H_{32}O_2$, Palmitic acid (24)

C = $C_{18}H_{34}O_2$, Oleic acid, Fig. 12 (24, 100)

C = Anise oil (56.5)

C = Arachis oil (23)

C = Axunge oil (23)

C = Beef marrow (23)

C = Beeswax (23)

C = Bergamot extract (24)

C = Butterfat (2, 23, 25, 112)

C = Cajaput oil (56.5)

C = Carnauba wax (24)

C = Castor oil (23)

C = Ceresine (23)

C = Cherrylaurel oil (56.5)

C = Cinnamon oil (56.5)

C = Citron extract (24)

C = Citron oil (56.5)

C = Clove extract (24)

C = Clove oil (56.5)

C = Cocoa butter (23)

C = Coconut oil (23)

C = Cod-liver oil (23)

C = Colza oil (23)

C = Cottonseed oil (23)

C = Eucalyptus oil (23)

C = Fennel oil (56.5)

C = Gasolene (23)

C = Hempseed oil (23)

C = Juniper extract (24)

C = Lavender oil (56.5)

C = Lemon extract (24)

C = Linseed oil (24)

C = Mace oil (56.5)

C = Margarin (2, 23, 25)

C = Mozambique wax (24)

C = Mustard oil (56.5)

C = Mutton tallow (23)

C = Oleomargarin (2, 23)

C = Olive oil (23)

C = Orange oil (56.5)

C = Palm butter (23)

C = Paraffin (23, 28)

C = Peppermint extract (24)

C = Peppermint oil (56.5)

C = Petroleum ether (27, 28, 112)

C = *Pinus pumilio* extract (24)

C = *Pinus sylvestris* extract (24)

C = Poppy oil (23)

C = Rosemary oil (56.5)

C = Sandalwood extract (24)

C = Sandalwood oil (56.5)

C = Sesame oil (23)

C = Sperm oil (23)

C = Sweet almond oil (23)

C = Turpentine (23, 56.5, 113)

C = Walnut oil (23)

C = "Wyte spirite" (24)

C = $MnSO_4$, Table 3 (29, 74, 97)

C = Na_2SO_4, Table 3 (17)

C = Na_2CO_3, Table 3 (21, 66, 74)

C = KF, Table 3 (51)

C = K_2CO_3, Table 3 (8, 17, 29, 51, 74)

B = **$C_2H_8N_2O_4$**, Ammonium oxalate

C = $C_4H_{10}O$, Ethyl ether (106)

B = **C_3H_4O**, Acrolein

C = $C_6H_6O_2$, Hydroquinol (14)

C = $C_7H_6O_5$, Gallic acid (14)

B = **$C_3H_4O_4$**, Malonic acid

C = $C_4H_{10}O$, Ethyl ether, Fig. 17 (67)

B = **C_3H_6O**, Allyl alcohol

C = NaCl, Table 9 (52)

C = Na_2CO_3, Table 9 (52)

C = KF, Table 9 (52)

C = K_2CO_3, Table 9 (52)

B = **C_3H_6O**, Acetone

C = $C_4H_8O_2$, Ethyl acetate, Fig. 30 (6)

C = $C_5H_{12}O$, Amyl alcohol, Fig. 30 (61)

C = C_6H_5Br, Bromobenzene, Fig. 16 (12)

C = C_6H_6, Benzene, Fig. 30 (5, 11, 61); *v. also* p. 425

C = C_6H_6O, Phenol, Fig. 31 (95.5, 96)

C = C_6H_7N, Aniline, Fig. 30 (61)

C = $C_6H_{12}O_6$, Dextrose, Table 10 (69)

C = C_7H_8, Toluene, Table 11 (61, 115)

C = $C_{10}H_8$, Naphthalene, Fig. 29 (8, 20)

C = $C_{10}H_{12}O$, *p*-Anethole, Fig. 29 (8)

C = $C_{12}H_{22}O_{11}(H_2O)$, Maltose, Table 10 (69)

C = $C_{12}H_{22}O_{11}$, Sucrose, Table 10 (8, 69)

C = $C_{13}H_{10}O$, Benzophenone, Fig. 29 (8)

C = $MnSO_4$ (74)

C = $CaCl_2$, Fig. 10 (49, 61)

C = Li_2SO_4, Fig. 9 (61)

C = NaCl, Fig. 10 (49, 61)

C = Na_2SO_4, Fig. 10 (61)

C = $NaNO_3$, Fig. 10 (61)

C = Na_2CO_3, Table 12 (8)

C = KF, Table 12 (49)

C = KCl, Fig. 9 (104)

C = K_2CO_3, Table 12 (8, 49, 74)

B = **$C_3H_6O_2$**, Propionic acid

C = $C_4H_{10}O$, Ethyl ether, Fig. 14 (101)

C = C_6H_6, Benzene, Fig. 14 (101); *v. also* p. 425

B = **C_3H_8O**, *n*-Propyl alcohol

C = $C_4H_{10}O$, *n*-Butyl alcohol, Fig. 21 (11)

C = $C_5H_{12}O$, Amyl alcohol (57)

C = C_6H_5Br, Bromobenzene, Fig. 16 (12)

C = C_6H_6, Benzene (57)

C = C_6H_7N, Aniline (57)

C = C_7H_7Br, Bromotoluene, Fig. 18 (12)

C = Paraffin (28)

C = $AgNO_3$ (108)

C = $MnSO_4$ (74)

C = $CaCl_2$ (108)

C = $BaCl_2$ (108)

C = LiCl (108)

C = NaCl, Table 13 (51, 108)

C = Na_2SO_4 (74, 108)

C = Na_2CO_3, Table 13 (52, 74)

C = KF, Table 13 (51)

C = KCl (108)

C = KBr (108)

C = KNO_3 (108)

C = K_2CO_3, Table 13 (51, 74, 108)

B = **C_3H_8O**, Isopropyl alcohol

C = $C_4H_{10}O$, *n*-Butyl alcohol, Fig. 21 (11)

C = KF, Table 14 (52)

C = K_2CO_3, Table 14 (52)

B = **$C_4H_4N_2$**, Succinonitrile

C = $C_4H_{10}O$, Ethyl ether (127); Vol. IV, *v.* p. 413

C = $C_6H_{14}O_6$, Mannitol (108)

C = $C_7H_6O_2$, Benzoic acid (128); *v.* Vol. IV, p. 413

B = $C_4H_4N_2$.—(*Continued*)
C = $C_{10}H_8$, Naphthalene (108)
C = $C_{10}H_{16}O$, Camphor (108)
C = $C_{12}H_{10}N_2$, Azobenzene (108)
C = $C_{12}H_{22}O_{11}$, Sucrose (108)
C = $C_{14}H_{10}O_2$, Benzil (108)
C = $AgNO_3$, Fig. 32 (78)
C = NaCl, Fig. 32 (91)

B = **$C_4H_6O_4$**, Succinic acid
C = $C_4H_{10}O$, Ethyl ether, Table 15 (48)
C = C_6H_6O, Phenol (108)

B = **$C_4H_6O_6$**, Tartaric acid
C = C_6H_6O, Phenol, Figs. 7 and 8 (95)

B = **C_4H_8O**, Methyl ethyl ketone
C = NaCl, Table 16 (50)
C = KF, Table 16 (50)

B = **$C_4H_8O_2$**, Butyric acid
C = $C_6H_{14}O_6$, Mannitol (108)
C = $C_{10}H_8$, Naphthalene (108)
C = $C_{12}H_{10}N_2$, Azobenzene (108)
C = $C_{12}H_{22}O_{11}$, Sucrose (108)
C = $C_{13}H_{10}O$, Benzophenone (108)
C = $Ba(NO_3)_2$, (108)
C = NaCl (108)
C = K_2SO_4 (108)

B = **$C_4H_8O_2$**, Ethyl acetate
C = $C_6H_8N_2O_3$, Aniline nitrate (42)
C = $ZnSO_4$ (40)
C = $MgSO_4$ (40)
C = NaCl (40, 73)
C = $Na_2S_2O_3$ (40)
C = $NaNO_3$ (73)
C = KCl (40)
C = KNO_3 (40)

B = **$C_4H_{10}O$**, *n*-Butyl alcohol
C = C_6H_6, Benzene, Fig. 15 (11)

B = **$C_4H_{10}O$**, Isobutyl alcohol
C = $C_5H_{12}O$, Isoamyl alcohol, Fig. 37 (18)
C = C_6H_6, Benzene (57)

B = **$C_4H_{10}O$**, *sec.*-Butyl alcohol
C = $C_6H_6O_2$, Hydroquinol (108)

B = **$C_4H_{10}O$**, *tert.*-Butyl alcohol
C = KCl (108)

B = **$C_4H_{10}O$**, Ethyl ether
C = $C_6H_{14}O_6$, Mannitol (41)
C = $C_6H_{15}N$, Triethylamine, Fig. 34 (76)
C = $Hg(CN)_2$ (106)
C = $FeCl_3$ (106)
C = $FeSO_4$ (106)
C = $Al_2(SO_4)_3$ (106)
C = LiCl (41)
C = NaOH (41)
C = NaF (106)
C = NaCl, Table 15 (9, 41, 73, 106, 107)
C = NaBr (106)
C = NaI (106)
C = Na_2SO_4 (41, 106)
C = Na_3PO_4 (106)
C = Na_3AsO_4 (106)
C = Na_2CO_3 (41)
C = $NaC_2H_3O_2$, Acetate, Table 15 (42, 73, 106)
C = $NaC_3H_5O_3$, Lactate (73)
C = NaC_6H_5O, Phenolate (73)
C = $NaC_7H_5O_2$, Benzoate (106)
C = $NaC_7H_5O_3$, Salicylate (106)
C = $NaC_9H_7O_2$, Cinnamate (106)
C = $Na_2C_4H_2O_4$, Maleate (73)
C = $Na_2C_4H_4O_4$, Succinate (106)
C = $Na_2C_4H_4O_6$, Tartrate (106)
C = $Na_2C_8H_4O_4$, Phthalate (106)
C = $Na_3C_6H_5O_7$, Citrate (106)
C = $NaC_6H_5O_3S$, Benzenesulfonate (106)
C = $NaC_6H_2N_3O_7$, Picrate (73)
C = Na_2CrO_4 (106)
C = $Na_2Cr_2O_7$ (106)
C = Na_2MoO_4 (106)
C = Na_2WO_4 (106)
C = KCl (41)
C = KI (41)
C = KNO_3 (41)

B = **C_5H_5N**, Pyridine
C = C_6H_6, Benzene, Fig. 37 (117.5)
C = $MgSO_4$ (108)
C = $CaCl_2$ (108)
C = LiCl (108)
C = KCl (108)
C = KBr (108)
C = K_2CO_3 (26, 108)

B = **$C_5H_{12}O$**, Isoamyl alcohol
C = NaCl, Table 17 (47)

B = **$C_6H_5NO_2$**, Nitrobenzene
C = C_6H_6O, Phenol (15)
C = $C_6H_8N_2O_3$, Aniline nitrate (42)
C = $C_6H_8N_2O_3$, Picoline nitrate (42)
C = $C_7H_9NO_2$, Ammonium benzoate (42)
C = $NaC_4H_7O_2$, Butyrate (42)
C = $NaC_5H_9O_2$, Isovalerate (42)
C = $NaC_6H_2N_3O_7$, Picrate (42)
C = $Na_2C_8H_4O_4$, Phthalate (42)
C = $KC_5H_9O_2$, Isovalerate (42)

B = **$C_6H_5NO_3$**, *o*- or *p*-Nitrophenol
C = C_6H_6O, Phenol (56)

B = **C_6H_6**, Benzene
C = C_6H_6O, Phenol, Fig. 15 (60); *v. also* p. 428
C = $AgClO_4$, Fig. 7 (129)

B = **C_6H_6O**, Phenol
C = $C_6H_6O_2$, *o*-Dihydroxybenzene (Pyrocatechol) Fig. 33 (70)
C = $C_6H_6O_2$, Hydroquinol, Fig. 33 (70)
C = $C_6H_6O_2$, Resorcinol, Fig. 33 (70)
C = $C_6H_6O_3$, Pyrogallol, Fig. 33 (4)
C = C_6H_7N, Aniline, Fig. 23 (1, 93)
C = $C_6H_{15}N$, Triethylamine, Fig. 34 (76)
C = $C_7H_6O_2$, Benzoic acid (108)
C = $C_7H_6O_3$, Salicylic acid (108)
C = $C_{10}H_8$, Naphthalene, Fig. 7 (15, 108)
C = $C_{10}H_9N$, Naphthylamine (15)
C = $C_{10}H_{16}O$, Camphor (108)
C = $C_{12}H_{10}N_2$, Azobenzene (108)
C = $C_{13}H_{10}O$, Benzophenone (108)
C = $C_{13}H_{10}O_3$, Salol (15)
C = $C_{14}H_8O_2$, Anthraquinone (15, 108)
C = $C_{14}H_{10}O_2$, Benzil (108)
C = $C_{18}H_{18}O_{12}$, Hexamethyl mellitate (108)
C = $Hg(CN)_2$ (108)
C = $MgCl_2$ (98)
C = $MgSO_4$ (108)
C = $Ca(OH)_2$, Fig. 35 (36, 37, 77)
C = $CaCl_2$ (98)
C = $Sr(OH)_2$ (77)
C = $SrCl_2$ (98)
C = $Ba(OH)_2$, Fig. 35 (36, 37, 77)
C = $BaCl_2$ (98)
C = $Ba(NO_3)_2$ (108)
C = LiOH (77)
C = LiCl (98)
C = NaOH, Fig. 8 (36, 37, 77)
C = NaF (98)
C = NaCl, Figs. 7 and 35 (36, 37, 94, 98, 108)
C = NaBr (98)
C = Na_2SO_4, Fig. 8 (36)
C = $NaNO_3$ (98)
C = $NaCHO_2$, Formate (98)
C = $NaC_2H_3O_2$, Acetate (98)
C = $NaC_3H_5O_3$, Lactate (98)
C = $NaC_7H_5O_2$, Benzoate (98)
C = $NaC_7H_5O_3$, Salicylate (98)
C = $NaC_{18}H_{33}O_2$, Oleate, Fig. 33 (4, 108)
C = $Na_2C_4H_4O_4$, Succinate (98)
C = $Na_2C_4H_4O_5$, Malate (98)
C = $Na_2C_4H_4O_6$, Tartrate (98)
C = $Na_3C_6H_5O_7$, Citrate (98)
C = $NaC_2H_2ClO_2$, Chloroacetate (98)
C = $NaC_2HCl_2O_2$, Dichloroacetate (98)
C = $NaCCl_3O_2$, Trichloroacetate (98)
C = NaCNS (98)
C = KOH (77)
C = KCl (98, 108)
C = KBr (108)
C = K_2SO_4 (108)
C = KNO_2 (108)

B = **C_6H_7N**, Aniline
C = C_6H_8ClN, Aniline hydrochloride, Fig. 36; Table 18 (41, 102)
C = $C_6H_8N_2O_3$, Aniline nitrate, Table 18 (41)
C = C_6H_{14}, Hexane (34)
C = $C_7H_9NO_2$, Ammonium benzoate (42)
C = $AgClO_4$ (55)
C = $CaCl_2$ (41)
C = LiCl (41)
C = NaOH (41)
C = NaCl (41)
C = $NaC_2H_3O_2$, Acetate (42)
C = $NaC_4H_7O_2$, Butyrate (42)
C = $NaC_5H_9O_2$, Isovalerate (42)
C = $NaC_7H_5O_2$, Benzoate (42)
C = $NaC_7H_5O_3$, Salicylate (42)
C = KCl (41)
C = $KC_5H_9O_2$, Isovalerate (42)

B = **$C_6H_{10}O_3$**, Ethyl acetoacetate
C = NaCl, Table 19 (73)
C = $NaNO_3$, Table 19 (73)

B = **$C_6H_{12}O_6$**, Dextrose (108)
C = $C_6H_{15}N$, Triethylamine

B = **$C_6H_{14}O_6$**, Mannitol (108)
C = $C_6H_{15}N$, Triethylamine

B = **$C_6H_{15}N$**, Triethylamine
C = $C_{10}H_8$, Naphthalene (108)
C = $C_{10}H_{16}O$, Camphor (108)
C = $C_{12}H_{10}N_2$, Azobenzene (108)
C = $C_{12}H_{22}O_{11}$, Sucrose (108)
C = $C_{14}H_{10}O_2$, Benzil (108)
C = $BaCl_2$ (108)
C = KCl (108)
C = K_2SO_4 (108)
C = K_2CO_3 (108)
C = KCNS (108)

B = **$C_7H_5BrO_2$**, *p*-Bromobenzoic acid
C = $C_{10}H_8$, Naphthalene (45)

B = **$C_7H_5ClO_2$**, *p*-Chlorobenzoic acid
C = $C_{10}H_8$, Naphthalene (45)

B = **$C_7H_5IO_2$**, *p*-Iodobenzoic acid
C = $C_{10}H_8$, Naphthalene (45)

B = **$C_7H_5NO_4$**, *p*-Nitrobenzoic acid
C = $C_{13}H_{10}O$, Benzophenone (45)

B = **$C_7H_7NO_2$**, *m*-Aminobenzoic acid
C = $C_{10}H_{16}O$, Camphor (45)

C = $C_{13}H_{10}O$, Benzophenone (45)
B = **$C_7H_7NO_2$**, *p*-Aminobenzoic acid
C = $C_{10}H_8$, Naphthalene (45)
C = $C_{10}H_{16}O$, Camphor (45)
C = $C_{13}H_{10}O$, Benzophenone (45)
C = $C_{14}H_{10}O_2$, Benzil (45)
B = **C_7H_8**, Toluene
C = $AgClO_4$ (130)
B = **$C_7H_8N_2O$**, Phenylurea
C = $CaCl_2$ (106)
C = LiCl (106)
C = NaBr (106)
C = NaI (106)
B = **C_7H_8O**, *o*-, *m*-, or *p*-Cresol
C = $NaC_{18}H_{33}O_2$, Oleate, Fig. 33 (4)

B = **$C_{10}H_{14}N_2$**, Nicotine
C = NaOH, Fig. 6 (36, 37)
C = Na_2SO_4, Fig. 6 (36, 37)

B = **$C_{11}H_{12}N_2O$**, Antipyrine
C = $Na_2S_2O_3$ (26)
C = K_2CO_3 (26)

NON-AQUEOUS SYSTEMS

SO_2 (80)

B = **C_5H_{10}**, Amylene
C = C_5H_{12}, Pentane
B = **C_5H_{12}**, Pentane
C = C_6H_6, Benzene
C = C_6H_{12}, Butylethylene
B = **C_6H_6**, Benzene
C = C_6H_{12}, Cyclohexane
C = C_6H_{12}, Butylethylene
C = C_6H_{14}, Hexane
B = **C_6H_{12}**, Cyclohexane
C = C_9H_{20}, Nonane
B = **C_6H_{12}**, Butylethylene
C = C_6H_{14}, Hexane
B = **C_7H_8**, Toluene
C = C_8H_{18}, Octane
C = Kerosene
B = **C_8H_{10}**, Xylene
C = Naphthene
B = **C_8H_{16}**, Octylene
C = Naphthene
B = **Gasolene**
C = Naphthene

ℭ-Table

The ℭ-arrangement (*v.* p. viii)

Natural and commercial oils, etc., are placed last in alphabetical order.

CS_2 (34)

B = **CH_4N_2O**, Urea
C = CH_4O, Methyl alcohol
B = **CH_4O**, Methyl alcohol
C = $C_4H_6O_4$, Succinic acid
C = $C_{12}H_{11}N$, Diphenylamine
C = $HgCl_2$
C = $BaCl_2$
C = NaI
C = KCl
C = KBr

C_2H_6O

Ethyl alcohol

B = **$C_3H_6O_3$**, Methyl carbonate
C = Gasolene (89)
B = **C_3H_8O**, Isopropyl alcohol
C = Gasolene (89)
B = **$C_3H_8O_3$**, Glycerol
C = Ethereal oils (13)
B = **$C_4H_{10}O$**, *n*-Butyl alcohol
C = Gasolene (89)
B = **$C_4H_{10}O$**, Isobutyl alcohol
C = Gasolene (89)
B = **$C_4H_{10}O$**, Ethyl ether
C = Gasolene (89)
B = **$C_5H_{12}O$**, Amyl alcohol
C = Gasolene (89)
B = **C_6H_6**, Benzene
C = Gasolene (89)
B = **$C_6H_{12}O$**, Cyclohexanol
C = Gasolene (89)
B = **$C_{10}H_{18}O$**, Terpineol
C = Gasolene (89)
B = **$C_{11}H_{16}O$**, Butylcresol
C = Gasolene (89)
B = **Butter fat**
C = Coconut oil (43)
B = **Castor oil**
C = Gasolene (89)

$C_3H_7NO_2$

Urethane

B = **C_6H_7N**, Aniline
C = C_6H_{14}, Hexane (34)

$C_6H_4N_2O_4$

m-Dinitrobenzene

B = **$C_6H_5NO_2$**, Nitrobenzene
C = C_6H_{14}, Hexane (108)

$C_6H_5NO_2$

Nitrobenzene (108)

B = **$C_6H_5NO_3$**, *p*-Nitrophenol
C = C_6H_{14}, Hexane
B = **$C_6H_6O_2$**, Hydroquinol
C = C_6H_{14}, Hexane
B = **$C_6H_6O_2$**, Resorcinol
C = C_6H_{14}, Hexane
B = **$C_6H_6O_3$**, Pyrogallol
C = C_6H_{14}, Hexane
B = **C_6H_{14}**, Hexane
C = $C_7H_5NO_3$, *p*-Nitrobenzaldehyde
C = $C_7H_5NO_4$, *m*-Nitrobenzoic acid

C_6H_6

Benzene (109)

B = **C_6H_7N**, Aniline
C = C_6H_{12}, Cyclohexane
C = C_7H_{16}, Heptane
C = Gasolene

C_6H_7N

Aniline

B = **C_6H_{14}**, Hexane
C = C_7H_7NO, Benzamide (34)
C = $C_{13}H_{12}N_2S$, 1, 2-Diphenylthiourea (34)
C = $C_{14}H_{10}O_2$, Benzil (34)
B = **C_7H_8**, Toluene
C = Gasolene (109)
B = **C_8H_{10}**, Xylene
C = Gasolene (109)

SPECIAL TABLES

Table 1.—H_2O; Br_2; Electrolytes

Moles per l; $HgBr_2$, t = 25°C

$HgBr_2$	0.00	0.05	0.10	0.15	0.20	
Br_2	0.216	0.220	0.222	0.223	0.223	±0.0005

With other salts, the solubility of bromine is best expressed as the ratio of the excess bromine dissolved (concentration of bromine in the salt solution minus that in pure water at same temperature) to salt concentration. This ratio has the values tabulated under the corresponding salt formulae.

M_{salt}/l	Ratio, KBr		Ratio, $SrBr_2$
	t = 0°C	t = 25°C	t = 25°C
0.001	0.7 ±0.1		
0.01	1.0 ±0.04		1.4±0.2
0.02	1.06±0.02		1.6±0.1
0.05	1.14±0.02	1.0 ±0.05	1.9±0.1
0.1	1.17±0.02	1.04±0.05	2.2±0.1
0.2	1.20±0.05	1.08±0.05	2.5±0.1
0.5	1.25±0.05	1.15±0.05	3.0±0.2
1	1.30±0.05	1.20±0.05	
2	1.45±0.1	1.30±0.1	

M_{salt}/l	Ratio, t = 20.8°C		
	HBr	HCl	NaCl
0.05	1.10±0.02		
0.1	1.12±0.02		
0.2	1.13±0.02		
0.5	1.14±0.02		
1	1.17±0.02	0.26±0.005	0.15±0.01
2	1.21±0.03	0.28±0.005	0.16±0.01
3		0.30±0.005	0.18±0.01

Ratio	M_{salt}/l, t = 25°C	
	0.05	1.0
$NaNO_3$	−0.033±0.002	−0.033±0.001
Na_2SO_4, K_2SO_4	−0.056±0.002	−0.056±0.001

Table 2.—H_2O; HBr; SO_2

At −33.5°C, the number of moles of HBr which dissolve in SO_2 containing about 1 mole of water per 1000 g, is equal, within 1%, to the number of moles of water present.

Table 3.—H_2O(A); C_2H_6O(B), Ethyl Alcohol; Salts (C)

C = $(NH_4)_2SO_4$

% B	% C, 15°	% C, 30°	% (C)c ±1, 33°	% C, 50°
15	25.3*	24.5*		23.9*
20	20.3*	20.0*		19.5*
25	16.0*	16.0*		15.7*
30	12.5*	12.8*		12.8*
40	6.7†	7.2†		7.4†
45			28	
50	3.1†	3.8†	31	4.2†
60		1.8†	36	
65			38	

TABLE 3.—(*Continued*)

% C \ t, °C	%B ± 0.5, 15	30	60
30	10.8	10.2	9.7
35	7.6	7.0	6.5
40		4.5	

* ±0.5.
† ±0.3.

C = $MnSO_4$; t = 30°C

% B	% C	% (C)$_C$ ± 0.5	% C	% B ± 0.3
30	9.3 ± 0.3	21.0	20	17.3
35	6.2 ± 0.3	24.5	25	12.3
40	4.0 ± 0.3	27.5	30	8.7
45	2.5 ± 0.3	30.0	35	6.3
50	1.7 ± 0.2	32.5		
55	1.0 ± 0.2	35.0		

Plait-point ±1: A = 62 %; B = 23 %; C = 15 % at 30°C.
Temperature coefficients: dC/dT = *ca.* −0.06 for B = 35 %; dB/dT = −0.1 for C = 20 or 35 %.

C = Na_2SO_4; t = 35°C

% B	% C ± 0.5	% (C)$_C$ ± 1	% C	% B ± 0.5
20	11.7	21	20	10.7
25	8.4	25	25	6.0
30	6.0		30	3.9
35	4.2			

Plait-point ±1: A = 69 %; B = 15 %; C = 16 % at 35°C.
Temperature coefficients: dC/dT = 0.1 for B = 25 %; dB/dT = 0.0 for C = 25 %; $d(C)_C/dT$ = *ca.* −0.2 for B = 25 %.

C = Na_2CO_3; t = 30°C

% B	% C	% C	% B ± 0.3
10	17.0 ± 0.3	20	7.0
15	12.8 ± 0.3	25	3.4
20	9.4 ± 0.3	30	1.5
30	4.8 ± 0.3		
40	2.1 ± 0.2		
50	0.6 ± 0.2		
60	0.4 ± 0.1		

C_1 = KF; C_2 = K_2CO_3; t = 25°C

% B	% C_1*	% (C_1)$_C$ ± 0.5	% C_2	% (C_2)$_C$ ± 0.5
10	22.0		22.0*	6.0
15	18.7	6.0	18.0*	10.0
20	16.4	8.0	14.6*	14.0
30	12.7	11.0	9.0†	19.0
40	9.0	15.0	5.0†	23.5
50	6.2	18.5	2.5†	27.0
60	4.0	22.0	1.0†	31.0
70	2.2		0.45‡	36.0
80	1.4		0.13§	42.0
90	1.2	43.0	0.10§	

% Salt (25°C)	20	25	30	35	40	45
% B for C_1*	13.0	7.0	4.0	2.2	1.4	0.7
% B for C_2	12.5*	7.2*	4.0*	2.2†	1.1†	0.7‡

Plait-points ±1 at 25°C: A = 57 %; B = 31 %, C_1 = 12 %; A = 65 %; B = 20.5 %; C_2 = 14.5 %.

Temperature coefficient of carbonates, negligible; but K_2CO_3 in conjugated layer is 1 % less at 40 than at 25°C.

* ±0.2. ‡ ±0.05.
† ±0.1. § ±0.03.

TABLE 4.—H_2O(A); CH_4O(B), METHYL ALCOHOL; K_2CO_3(C)
t = 22°C

% B	% C	% (C_C) ± 0.5	dC/dT
10.0±0.5	40		
6.5±0.5	45		
5.0±0.5	50		
15	34.5±0.5		−0.06
20	31.0±0.5		−0.05
30	23.5±0.5	26.0	−0.05
40	17.5±0.5	32.0	−0.04
50	12.0±0.5		−0.04
60	8.0±0.5		−0.04
70	5.5±1	49.0	−0.04

Plait-point ±0.5: A = 46.7 %, B = 28.5 %, C = 24.8 %.

TABLE 5.—H_2O(A); C_2H_6O(B), ETHYL ALCOHOL; C_6H_6(C), BENZENE

% C	% B ± 0.5, 0°C	% B ± 0.2, 25°C	% (A)$_C$ ± 0.5, 25°C	% B ± 0.5, 60°C	% (A)$_C$ ± 1, 65°C
20	56.5	52.3	3.2	46.0	8
30	53.5	49.5	5.0	44.2	14
40	48.3	44.8	6.5	40.5	19
50	41.5	39.0	9.0	36.0	25
60	33.9	32.5	13.5	30.5	31
70	26.0	25.4	21.0	24.2	40
80		17.7	34.0	17.0	54
90		9.2	53.0		
95		4.8	65.5 ± 1		
98			78.0 ± 1		
% A					
30	56.7	52.5		45.5	
35	55.5	52.2		46.0	
40	53.4	50.8		45.2	
50	47.0	45.6		42.0	
60		38.7		36.0	
70		29.6			
80		19.9			

Intermediate temperatures can be found by linear interpolation.
Plait-points ± 0.5 at 25°C: A = 9.8 %, B = 37.2 %, C = 53.0 %; ±1 at 65°C: A = 19.5 %, B = 39.5 %, C = 41.0 %.

H_2O(A); $C_2H_4O_2$(B), Acetic acid; C_6H_6(C), Benzene

% C	t = 25°C, % (A)$_C$ ± 0.5	t = 25°C, % B ± 0.2	t = 35°C, % (A)$_C$ ± 1	t = 35°C, % B ± 0.2
15	2.0	65.5	2	64.4*
20	3.0	64.1	3	63.1
30	5.7	59.0	7	58.3
40	8.5	52.5	10	51.8
50	12.0	45.0	15	44.4
60	15.2	36.9	19	36.4
70	20.5	28.3	25	
80	29.0		34	
90	46.0		50	
95	63.0		65	

% A	25	30	40	50	60
% B, 25°C	65.2†	62.8†	56.2†	48.2†	39.0†
% B, 35°C	64.0*	62.0*	55.6†	47.9†	38.8†

Plait-point ±1 % at 25°C: A = 8.0 %; B = 53.5 %; C = 38.5 %.
* ±0.3.
† ±0.2.

TABLE 6.—H_2O(A); C_2H_6O(B), ETHYL ALCOHOL; $C_4H_{10}O$(C), ETHYL ETHER

% C	0°C % (A)c ± 0.5	0°C % B ± 0.2	25°C % (A)c ± 0.5	25°C % B ± 0.2
40	41.7	27.6	47.0	28.2
45	46.2	27.3	51.5	27.8
50	50.0	26.3	55.2	26.8
55	54.0	25.3	59.0	25.7
60	57.5	23.5	62.5	24.0
65	60.5	21.5	65.0	22.0
70	63.0	19.2	67.5	19.6
75	65.2	16.5	70.0	16.8
80	67.5	13.4	72.5	13.5
85	71.0	10.2	76.2	10.2
90	74.5	6.8	80.5	6.6
95	79.5	3.2	87.0	2.9
98.7			94.0	0.0
99	88.4	0.0		

% A	% B 0°C	% B 25°C
40	27.7 ± 0.2	28.3 ± 0.3
45	27.6 ± 0.2	28.2 ± 0.3
50	26.9 ± 0.2	27.5 ± 0.3
55	25.9 ± 0.2	26.7 ± 0.3
60	24.2 ± 0.2	25.2 ± 0.3
65	22.1 ± 0.2	23.2 ± 0.5
70	18.9 ± 0.3	20.4 ± 0.5
75	14.5 ± 0.3	16.8 ± 0.5
80	9.4 ± 0.3	13.0 ± 0.5
85	4.0 ± 0.3	8.8 ± 0.5
88.4	0.0	
90		3.8 ± 0.5
94		0.0

Plait-points ±0.5

	0°C	25°C
% A	37.0	40.0
% B	27.7	28.3
% C	35.3	31.7

TABLE 7.—H_2O(A); C_2H_6O(B), ETHYL ALCOHOL; $C_5H_{12}O$(C), ISOAMYL ALCOHOL

Probable error, 0.2% below 100°C; 0.5% above; % B for various temperatures

°C \ % C	40	45	50	55	60
0	29.4	27.7	25.7	23.7	21.3
15	27.5	26.4	24.6	22.6	20.3
25	26.4	25.3	23.8	21.8	19.5
40	24.7	23.7	22.5	20.5	18.4
55	23.0	22.3	21.2	19.2	17.1
70	21.2	20.7	19.5	17.7	15.7
85	19.1	18.8	17.7	16.0	14.1
100	17.0	16.6	15.7	14.0	12.4
120		13.3	12.6	11.3	9.9
140			9.5	8.2	6.8
160			5.3	4.7	3.6

°C \ % C	65	70	75	80	85
0	18.5	15.6	12.4	8.6	4.9
15	17.6	14.8	11.6	8.1	4.5
25	17.0	14.1	11.0	7.6	4.0
40	15.9	13.0	10.2	6.8	3.3
55	14.8	12.1	9.2	6.0	2.6
70	13.6	11.1	8.0	5.1	1.7
85	12.2	9.7	6.7	4.0	0.4
100	10.6	8.1	5.4	2.3	
120	8.0	5.7	3.2	0.4	
140	5.3	3.1	0.7		
160	2.0				

TABLE 7.—(*Continued*)

°C \ % A	40	45	50	55	60
0	30.5	30.2	29.7	29.1	28.4
15	28.2	28.0	27.5	26.8	26.0
25	26.8	26.6	26.1	25.4	24.5
40	25.0	24.8	24.3	23.6	22.8
55	23.3	23.2	22.7	22.0	21.1
70	21.4	21.4	20.9	20.2	19.3
85		19.0	18.9	18.5	17.9
100		17.0	16.8	16.3	15.7
120		13.5	13.5	13.2	12.8
140		10.0	10.1	10.0	9.7
160			6.1	6.1	6.0

°C \ % A	65	70	75	80	85
0	27.4	25.2	21.5	17.0	12.0
15	24.8	23.2	20.6	16.8	12.1
25	23.5	22.0	19.8	16.5	12.1
40	21.8	20.5	18.5	16.0	12.0
55	20.3	19.0	17.3	15.0	11.7
70	18.5	17.5	16.0	14.0	11.1
85	17.0	16.2	14.8	13.0	10.2
100	15.0	14.2	13.2	11.7	9.2
120	12.3	11.7	11.0	10.0	8.0
140	9.2	8.7	8.0	7.1	5.7
160	5.9	5.5	5.0	4.5	3.4

°C	90% A	95% A
0	6.5	1.3
15	7.2	2.0
25	7.3	2.4
40	7.4	2.5
55	7.3	2.6
70	7.0	2.5
85	6.4	2.3
100	5.8	2.0
120	4.9	1.0
140	3.4	0.1
160	1.5	

% A	% C in conjugate layer; error, ±0.5% 15.5°C	28°C
40	11.0	9.5
45	14.0	12.5
50	18.0	16.0
55	22.0	20.0
60	27.0	25.0
65	33.0	30.5
70	40.0	37.5
75	48.5	45.5
80	60.5	57.0
85	71.0	68.0
90	80.5	78.5
95	88.0	86.5

Plait-points ±0.5%

	15.5°C	28°C
% A	52.8	55.0
% B	27.0	25.0
% C	20.2	20.0

TABLE 8.—H_2O(A); C_2H_6O(B), ETHYL ALCOHOL; $C_{10}H_7Br$(C), α-BROMONAPHTHALENE

x g of C are mixed with 100 g aqueous B, and the temperature determined at which the mixture becomes opaque. Table 8 shows percentage by weight of B in original aqueous solution. Probable error, 0.03%.

°C \ x	0.3163	0.4074	0.5015	0.6310
30			9.04	7.56
28			8.76	7.30
26		10.26	8.48	7.05
24		9.96	8.22	6.81
22		9.68	7.97	6 58

TABLE 8.—(*Continued*)

°C \ x	0.3163	0.4074	0.5015	0.6310
20		9.41	7.73	6.35
18		9.17	7.51	6.14
16		8.92	7.29	5.93
14		8.69	7.08	5.73
12	10.36	8.47	6.88	5.55
10	10.12	8.27	6.70	5.37
8	9.89	8.05	6.51	5.19
6	9.68	7.86	6.33	5.03
4	9.48	7.68	6.16	4.88
+ 2	9.28	7.51	6.00	4.73
0	9.09	7.34	5.85	4.59
− 2	8.91	7.18	5.71	4.46
− 4	8.73	7.03	5.58	4.33
− 6	8.58	6.88	5.45	4.23
− 8	8.42	6.75	5.33	4.13
−10	8.29	6.64	5.22	4.04

°C \ x	0.7945	1.000	1.260	1.585
30	6.40	5.48	4.81	4.42
28	6.15	5.23	4.58	4.19
26	5.90	5.00	4.35	3.98
24	5.67	4.77	4.14	3.77
22	5.44	4.54	3.93	3.57
20	5.22	4.34	3.74	3.39
18	5.01	4.14	3.55	3.20
16	4.81	3.95	3.39	3.02
14	4.61	3.77	3.20	2.86
12	4.43	3.60	3.04	2.70
10	4.27	3.45	2.87	2.55
8	4.11	3.30	2.74	2.41
6	3.96	3.16	2.60	2.27
4	3.82	3.03	2.47	2.14
+ 2	3.69	2.90	2.34	2.02
0	3.56	2.78	2.23	1.91
− 2	3.45	2.67	2.13	1.80
− 4	3.34	2.57	2.03	1.70
− 6	3.24	2.48	1.94	1.61
− 8	3.15	2.40	1.86	1.53
−10	3.07	2.32	1.78	1.46

TABLE 9.—H_2O(A); C_3H_6O(B), ALLYL ALCOHOL; SALTS (C)

% B	NaCl = C; Na_2CO_3 = C_1; KF = C_2; K_2CO_3 = C_3; t = 20°C; error, ±0.2 unless otherwise indicated			
	% C	% C_1	% C_2	% C_3
10			14.8*	16.0
15	16.3*	10.0	11.8	12.9
20	14.1	8.0	9.8	10.5
30	11.0	4.6	7.5	7.0
40	8.7	2.5	5.5	4.9
50	6.5	1.1†	4.0†	2.6
60	4.7	0.4†	2.2†	1.1
70	3.0		1.3†	0.5†
80				0.1

* ±0.3.
† ±0.1

TABLE 9.—(*Continued*)

% salt	% B	
	C_2	C_3
20	5.8*	6.8
25	4.0	4.0
30	2.0	2.0

TABLE 10.—H_2O(A); C_3H_6O(B), ACETONE; SUGARS (C)
Grams acetone soluble in 100 g of aqueous solvent originally containing tabulated percentage of the sugar named; probable error, 0.1 % of amount of acetone

Sugar \ % sugar		10	20	30	40	50
Dextrose	15°C......	736.7	255.3	157.5	86.95	36.16
	25°C......	747.9	247.7	149.8	79.57	33.02
	35°C......	761.5	240.8	142.5	74.03	31.18
Maltose	15°C......	353.6	185.4	119.9	78.35	46.17
	25°C......	348.1	181.2	116.0	74.73	42.95
	35°C......	342.0	176.9	112.4	70.53	39.82
Sucrose	15°C.....	597.2	272.5	172.4		
	25°C.....	581.8	263.2	162.5		
	35°C.....	574.8	251.8	150.6		

% sucrose	20°C	25°C	30°C
40	96.44	92.76	89.84
45	71.92	68.81	65.72
50	50.83	48.13	45.85
55	35.78	33.81	32.54
60	25.17	24.18	23.35
65	18.33	17.68	17.09
70	13.22	12.82	12.53

TABLE 11.—H_2O(A); C_3H_6O(B), ACETONE; C_7H_8(C), TOLUENE
Probable error, 0.2 %

% A	% B		
	0°C	20°C	30°C
0.5	29.2	23.5	
1.0	39.0	33.1	
1.5	45.2	40.0	37.0
2.0	49.4	44.4	41.9
2.5	52.6	48.1	45.9
3.0	55.4	51.1	48.5
4.0	59.2	55.4	52.9
5.0	61.8	58.4	56.4
7.0	64.9	62.4	60.7
10.0	67.0	65.0	64.0
15.0	67.5	66.0	65.3
20.0	66.4	65.1	64.5
25.0	64.9	63.5	62.8
30.0	62.9	61.5	
% C	**0°C**	**20°C**	**30°C**
0.4			28.1
0.5	38.5	34.3	31.2
1.0	45.5	42.0	39.6
1.5	49.7	46.4	44.1
2.0	52.4	49.7	47.2
3.0	56.0	53.2	51.0
4.0	58.8	55.5	53.9
5.0	60.4	57.4	56.0
6.0		59.0	
7.0			58.7
10.0			61.3

Fig. 2 Isotherms
Alloys
Probable error -- see introduction

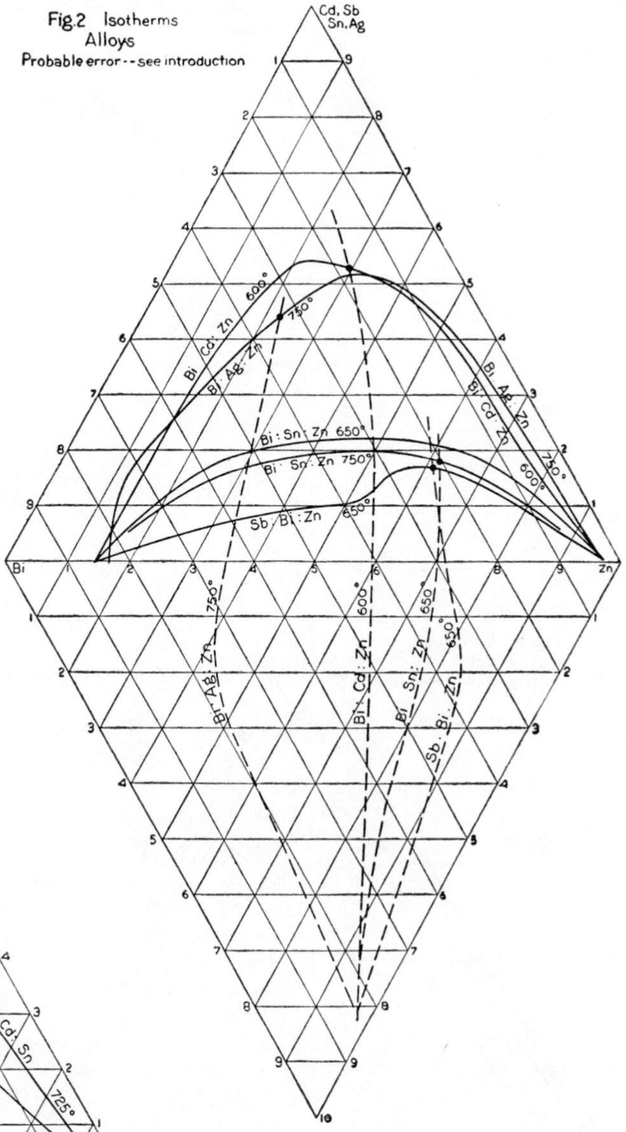

Fig. 3 Isotherms
Alloys
Probable error -- see introduction

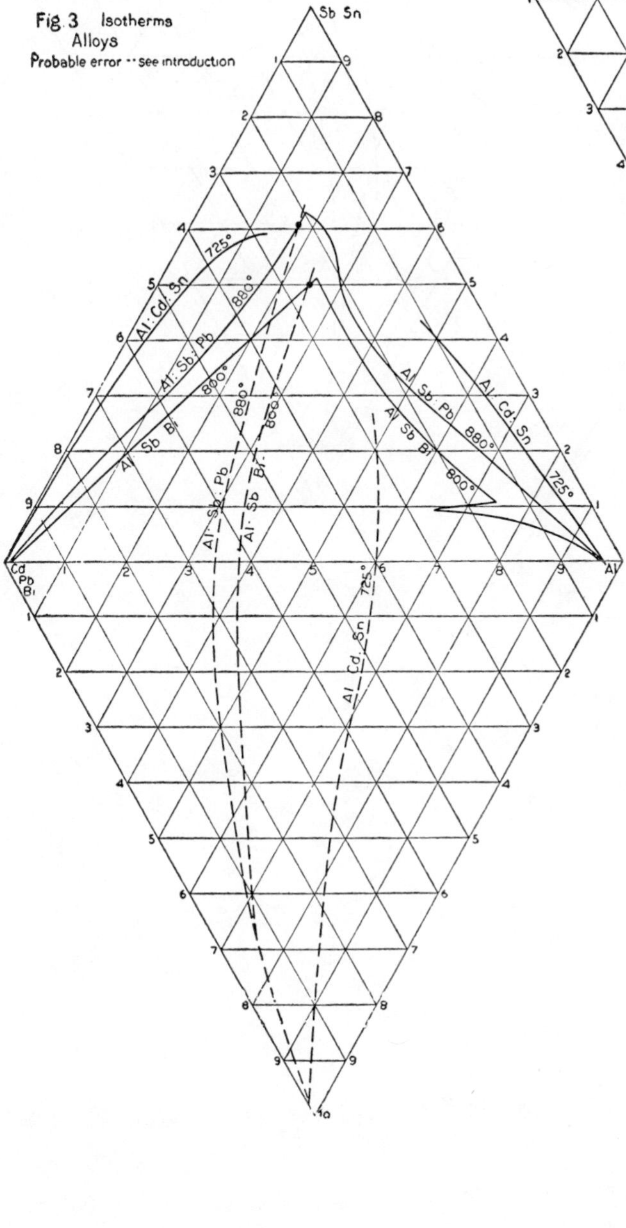

Fig. 4 Isotherms
Alloys
Probable error -- see introduction

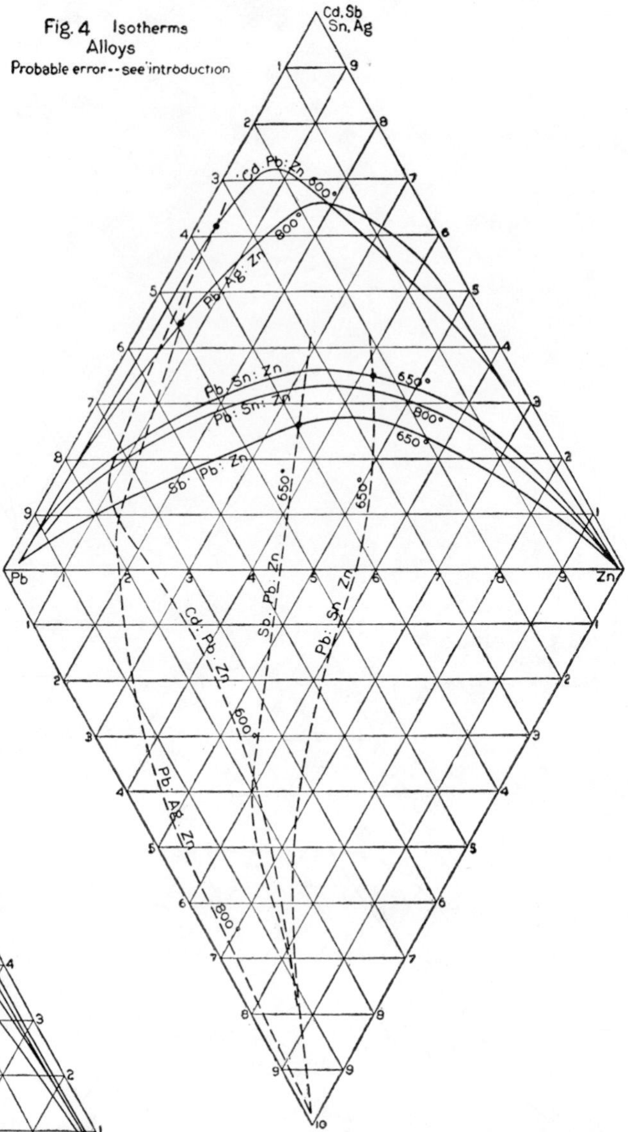

Fig. 5 Isotherms
Alloys
Probable error -- see introduction

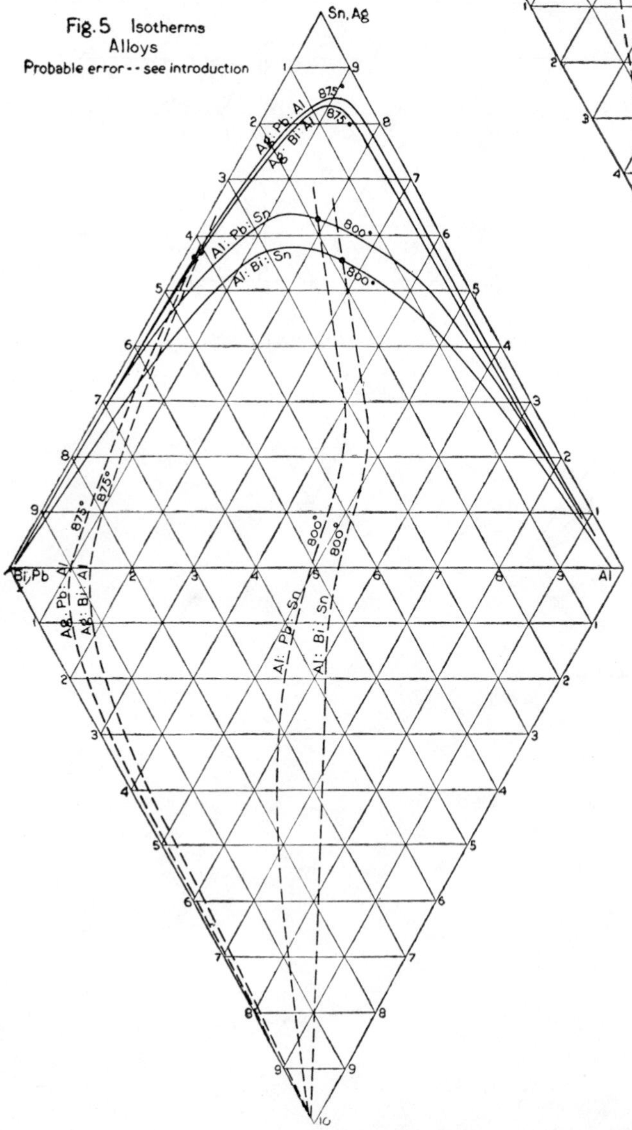

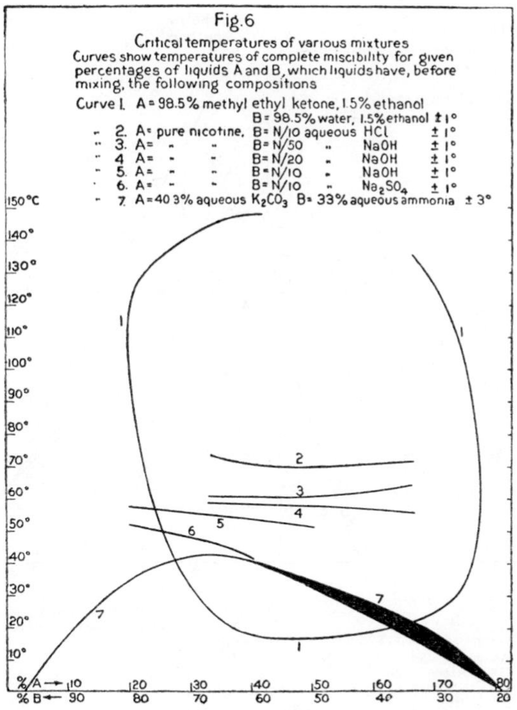

Fig. 6
Critical temperatures of various mixtures
Curves show temperatures of complete miscibility for given percentages of liquids A and B, which liquids have, before mixing, the following compositions

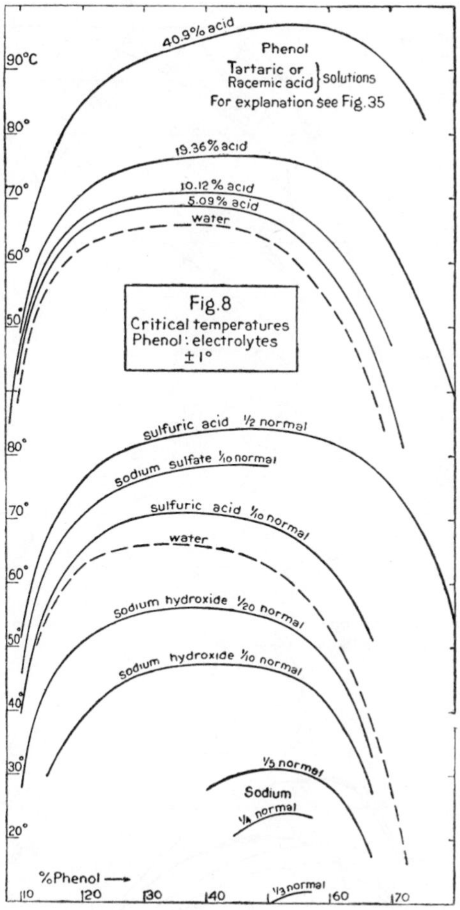

Fig. 8
Critical temperatures
Phenol: electrolytes
± 1°

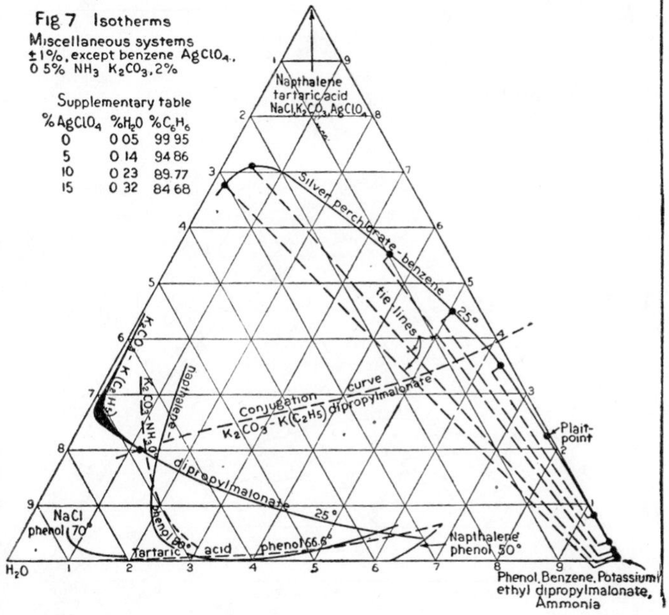

Fig. 7 Isotherms

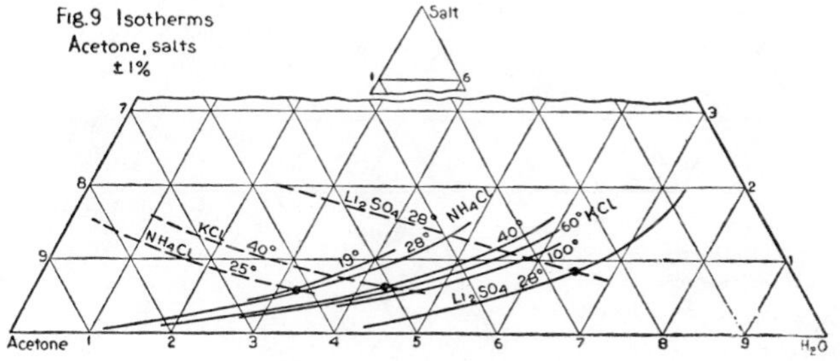

Fig. 9 Isotherms
Acetone, salts
± 1%

TABLE 12.—H_2O(A); C_3H_6O(B), ACETONE; SALTS (C)

C = Na_2CO_3; t = 25°C; probable error, 0.2%

% B	2.8	5	10	15	20	30
% C	20	17.0	12.5	9.4	6.7	2.8

C = KF; C_1 = K_2CO_3; error, 0.2% unless otherwise indicated

% B	t = 20°C				t = 25°C
	% C	% (C)c ± 0.5	% C_1	% $(C_1)_c$	% C_1
5	21.5*			1.5	
10	15.9		17.2	4.5	16.4
15	12.7		13.5	7.8	13.0
20	10.5		10.5	10.3	10.3

* ± 0.3.

Continued on p. 413

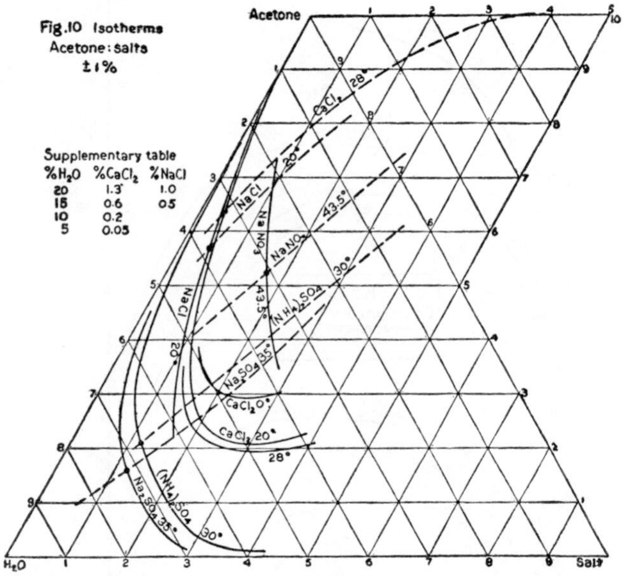

Fig. 10 Isotherms
Acetone: salts
±1%

Supplementary table

%H_2O	%$CaCl_2$	%NaCl
20	1.3	1.0
15	0.6	0.5
10	0.2	
5	0.05	

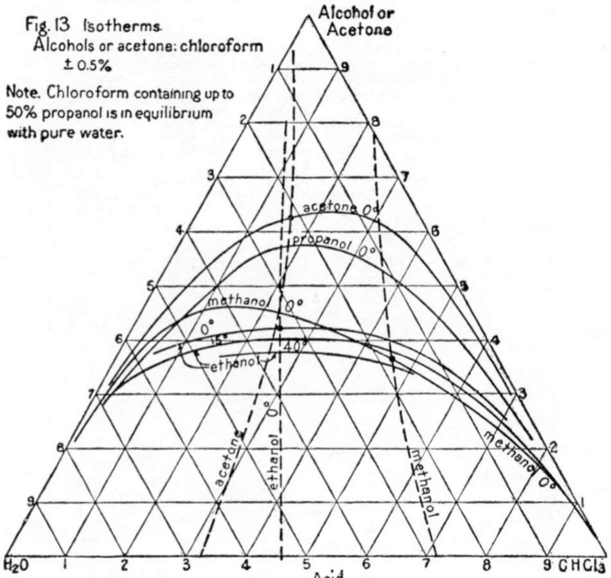

Fig. 13 Isotherms.
Alcohols or acetone: chloroform
± 0.5%

Note. Chloroform containing up to 50% propanol is in equilibrium with pure water.

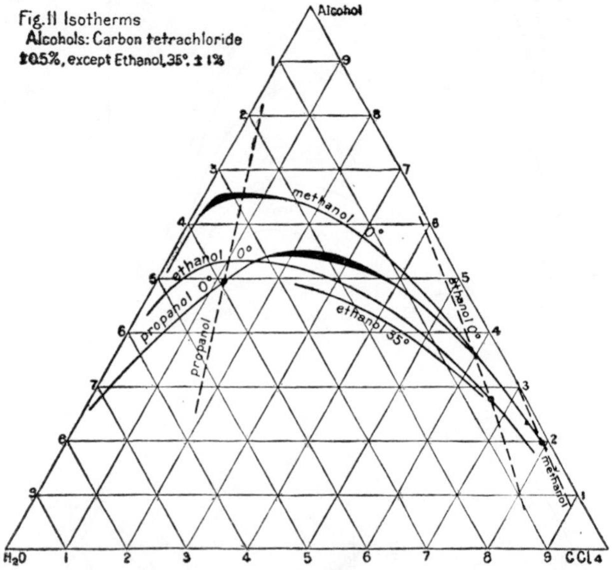

Fig. 11 Isotherms
Alcohols: Carbon tetrachloride
±0.5%, except Ethanol, 35°, ± 1%

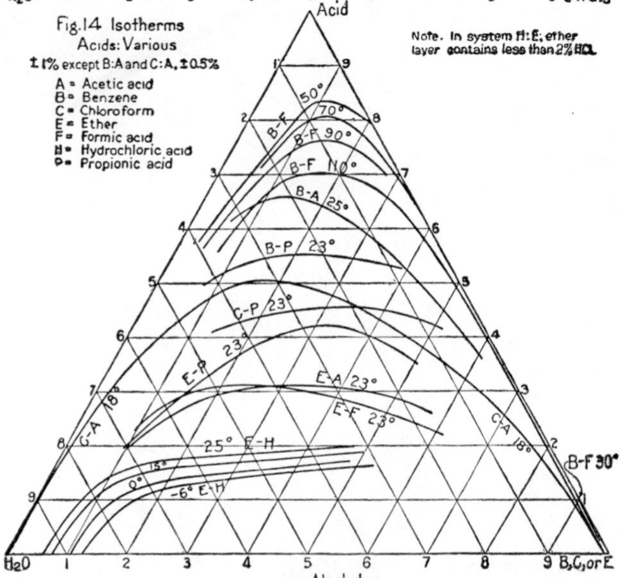

Fig. 14 Isotherms
Acids: Various
± 1% except B:A and C:A, ± 0.5%
A = Acetic acid
B = Benzene
C = Chloroform
E = Ether
F = Formic acid
H = Hydrochloric acid
P = Propionic acid

Note. In system H:E; ether layer contains less than 2% HCl.

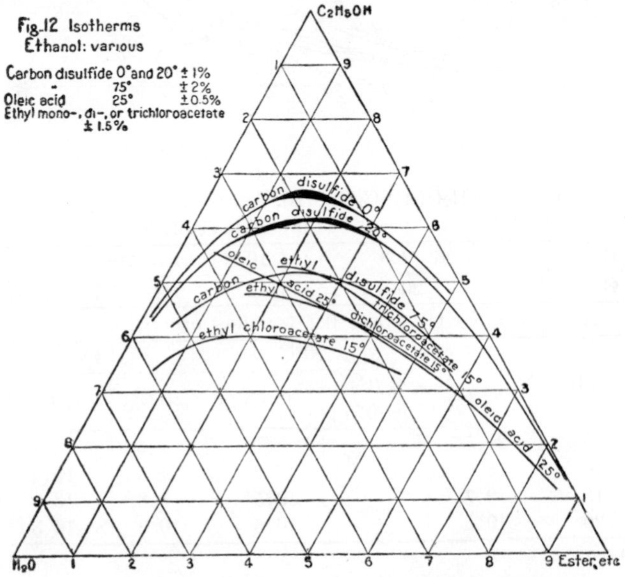

Fig. 12 Isotherms
Ethanol: various

Carbon disulfide 0° and 20° ± 1%
" 75° ± 2%
Oleic acid 25° ± 0.5%
Ethyl mono-, di-, or trichloroacetate ± 1.5%

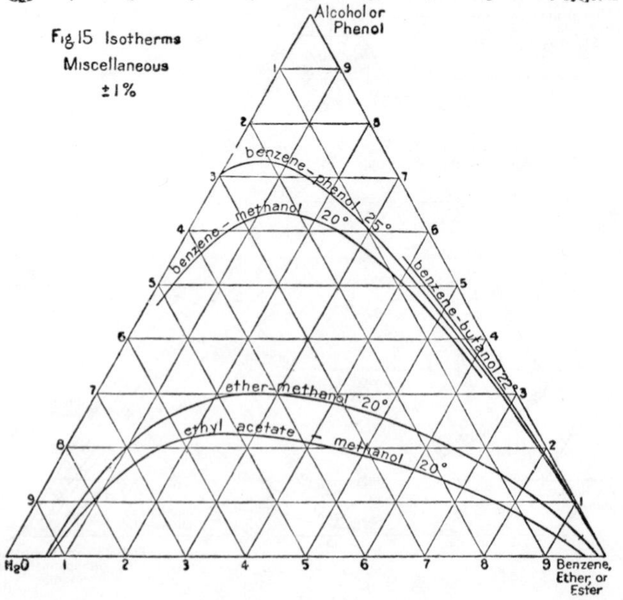

Fig. 15 Isotherms
Miscellaneous
± 1%

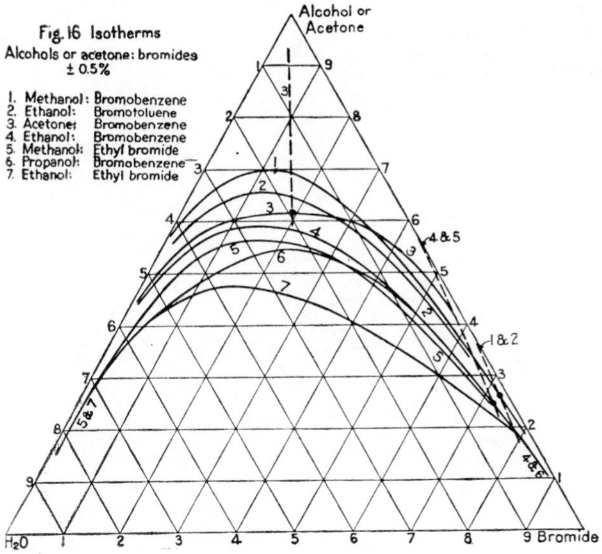

Fig. 16 Isotherms
Alcohols or acetone: bromides
± 0.5%

1. Methanol: Bromobenzene
2. Ethanol: Bromotoluene
3. Acetone: Bromobenzene
4. Ethanol: Bromobenzene
5. Methanol: Ethyl bromide
6. Propanol: Bromobenzene
7. Ethanol: Ethyl bromide

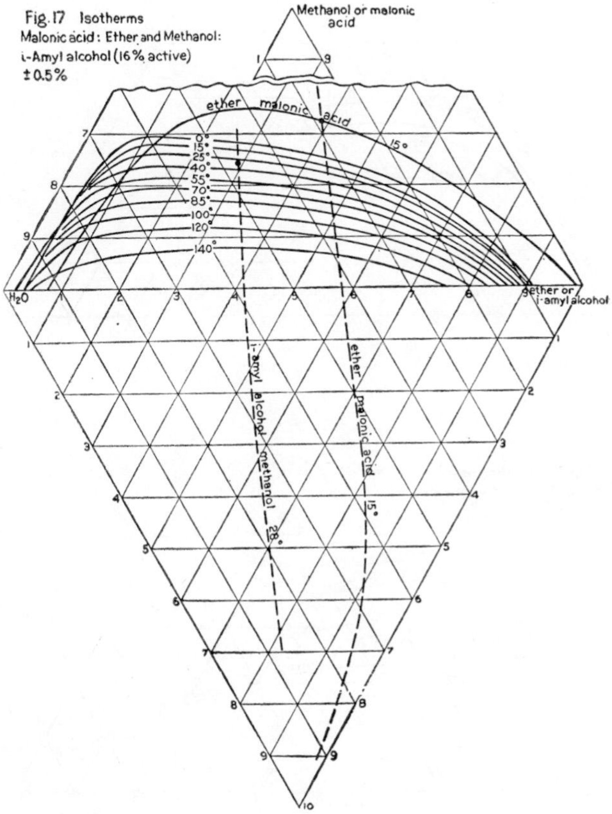

Fig. 17 Isotherms
Malonic acid: Ether and Methanol:
i-Amyl alcohol (16% active)
±0.5%

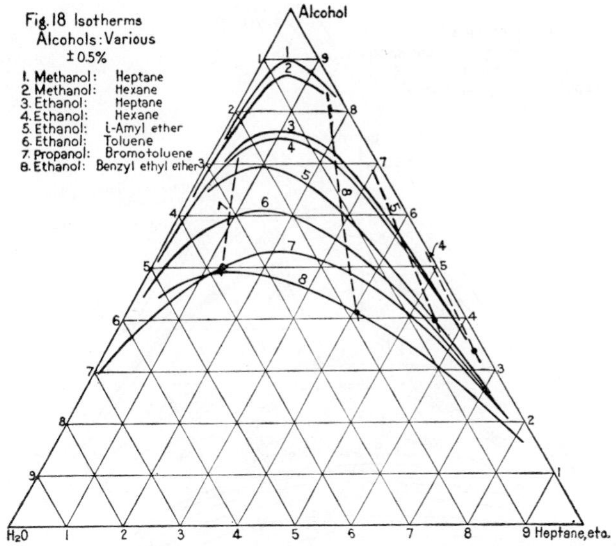

Fig. 18 Isotherms
Alcohols: Various
±0.5%

1. Methanol: Heptane
2. Methanol: Hexane
3. Ethanol: Heptane
4. Ethanol: Hexane
5. Ethanol: i-Amyl ether
6. Ethanol: Toluene
7. Propanol: Bromotoluene
8. Ethanol: Benzyl ethyl ether

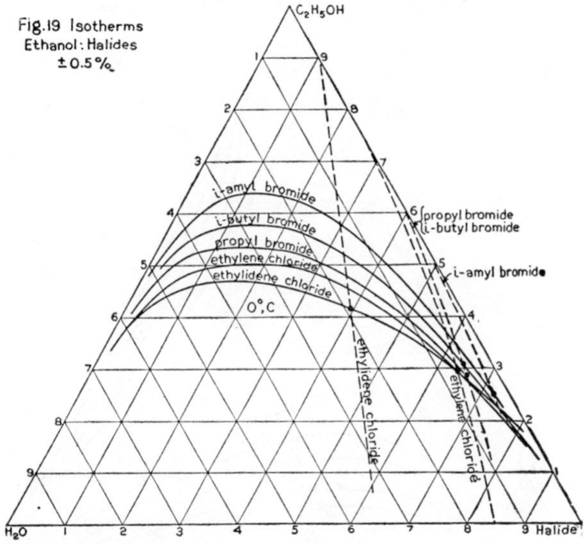

Fig. 19 Isotherms
Ethanol: Halides
±0.5%

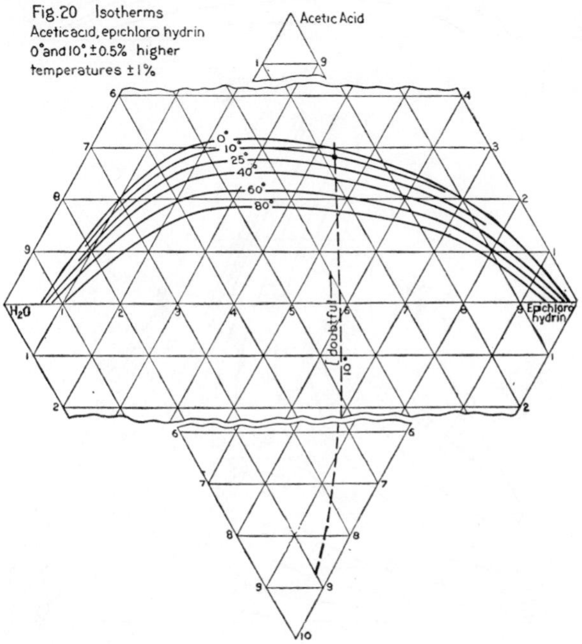

Fig. 20 Isotherms
Acetic acid, epichloro hydrin
0° and 10°, ±0.5% higher
temperatures ±1%

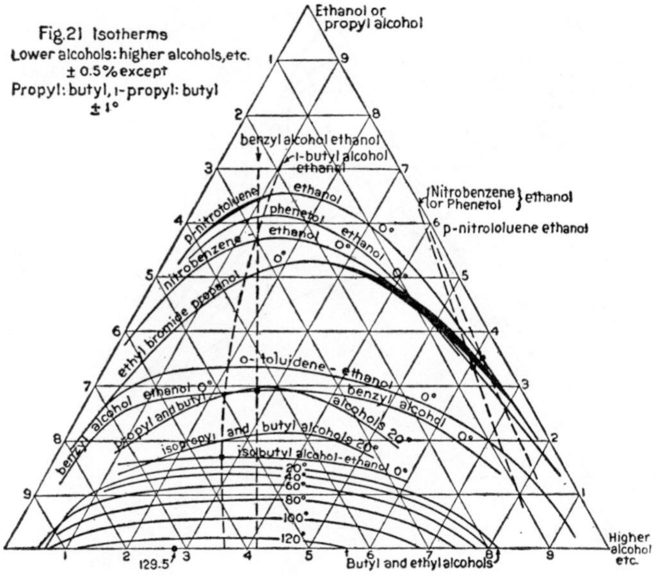

Fig. 21 Isotherms
Lower alcohols: higher alcohols, etc.
± 0.5% except
Propyl: butyl, i-propyl: butyl
± 1°

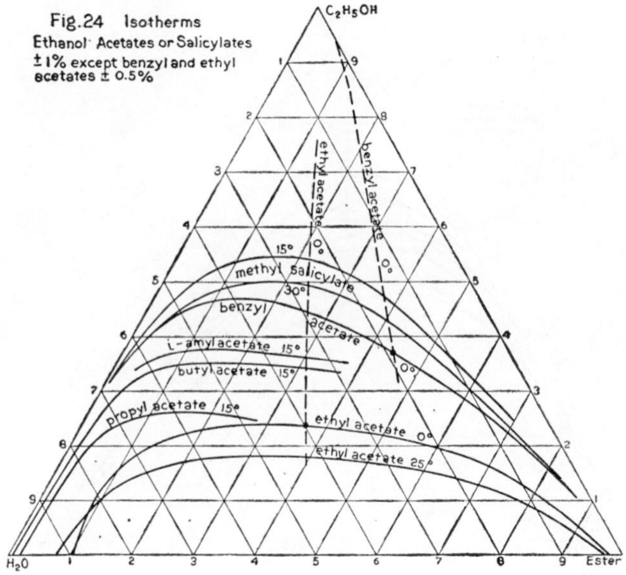

Fig. 24 Isotherms
Ethanol: Acetates or Salicylates
± 1% except benzyl and ethyl acetates ± 0.5%

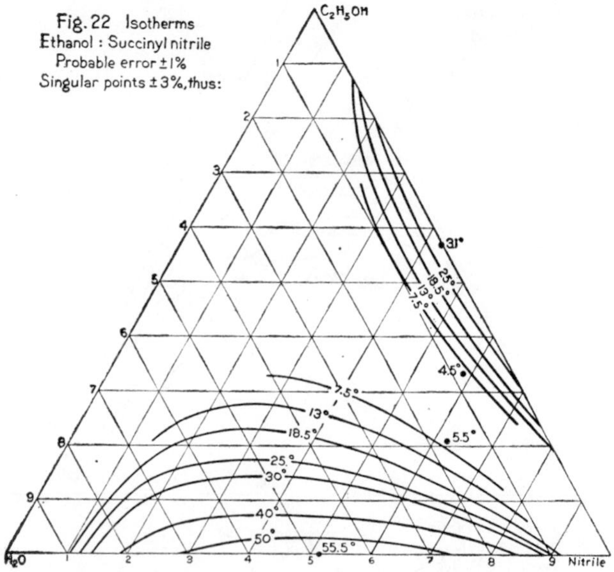

Fig. 22 Isotherms
Ethanol : Succinyl nitrile
Probable error ± 1%
Singular points ± 3%, thus:

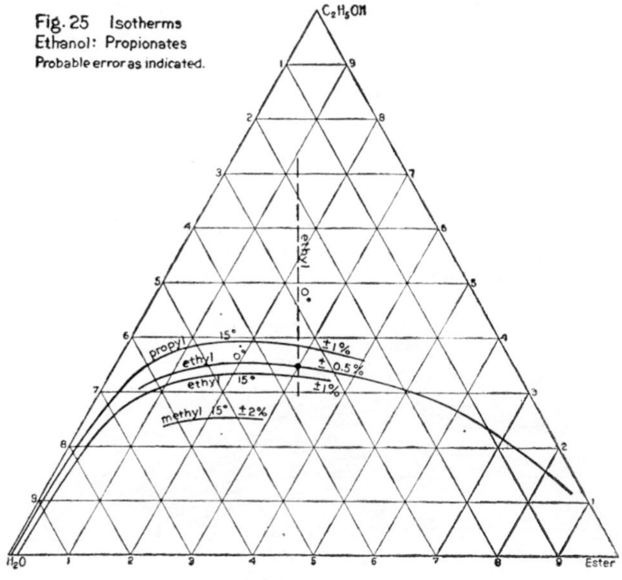

Fig. 25 Isotherms
Ethanol: Propionates
Probable error as indicated.

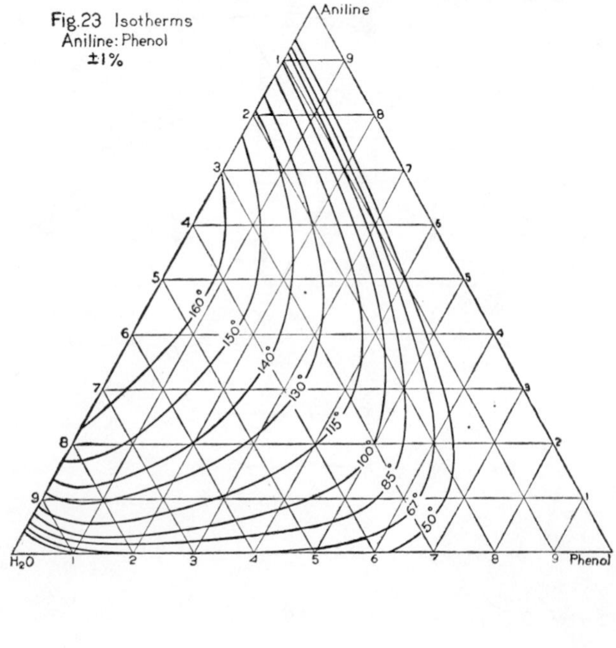

Fig. 23 Isotherms
Aniline: Phenol
± 1%

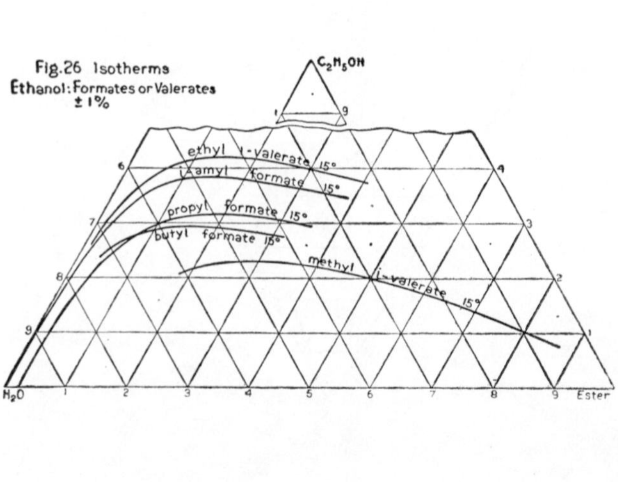

Fig. 26 Isotherms
Ethanol: Formates or Valerates
± 1%

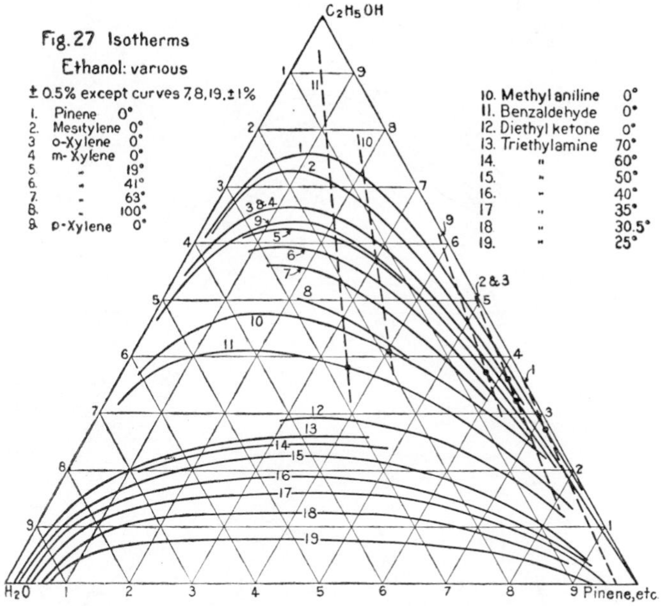

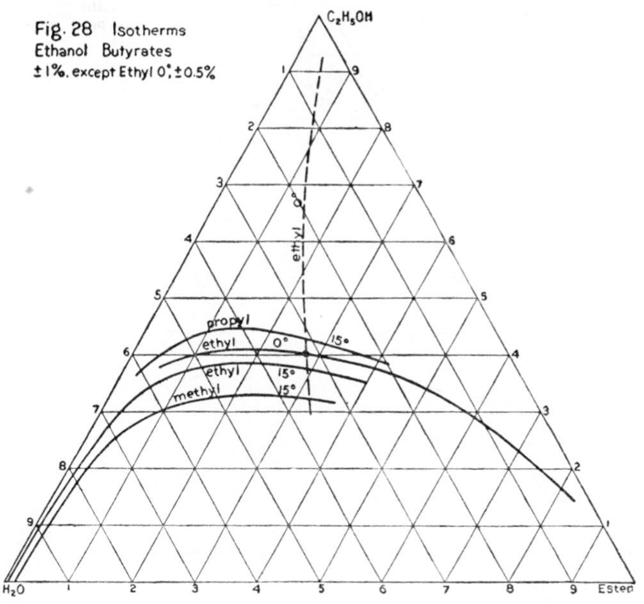

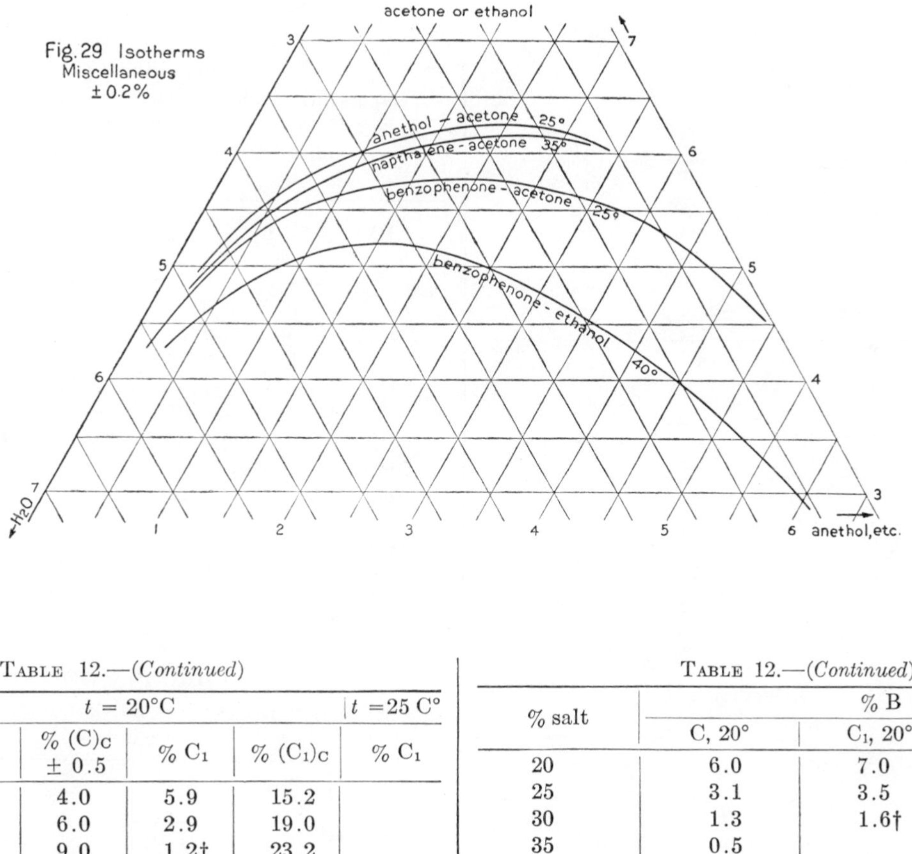

TABLE 12.—(*Continued*)

% B	t = 20°C				t = 25 C°
	% C	% (C)$_C$ ± 0.5	% C_1	% (C_1)$_C$	% C_1
30	7.2	4.0	5.9	15.2	
40	4.7	6.0	2.9	19.0	
50	2.7	9.0	1.2†	23.2	
60	1.2†	12.0	0.5†		
70	0.5†	15.5			
96.4			0.0†	52.4	
98	0.0†	46.3			

TABLE 12.—(*Continued*)

% salt	% B		
	C, 20°	C_1, 20°	C_1, 25°
20	6.0	7.0	6.2
25	3.1	3.5	3.2
30	1.3	1.6†	1.4†
35	0.5		
45	0.3		
46.3	0.0		
52.4		Tr.	

* ±0.3. † ±0.1.

Plait-points, t = 20°C: A = 57.5%; B = 37%; C = 5.5% ± 1%. A = 69.7%; B = 20.0%; C_1 = 10.3% ± 0.5%.

Temperature coefficients: dC/dT = −0.06 for 15% B; dC/dT = −0.02 for 30% B.

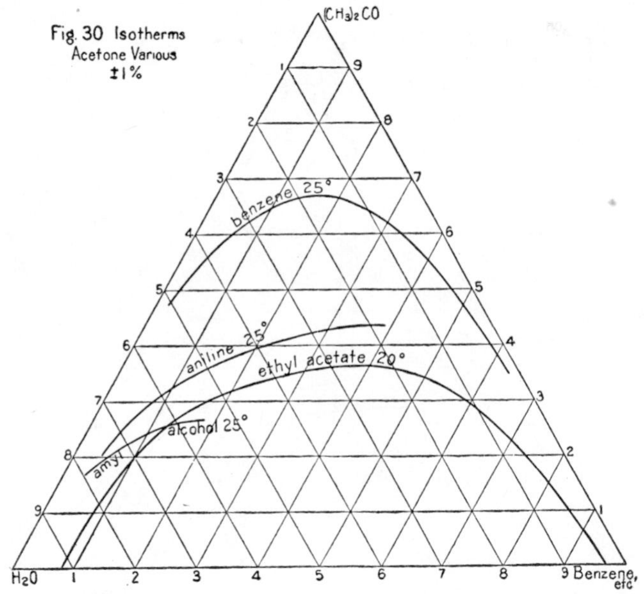

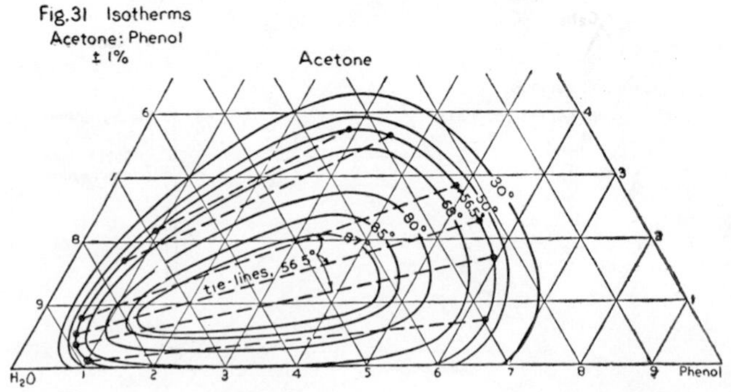

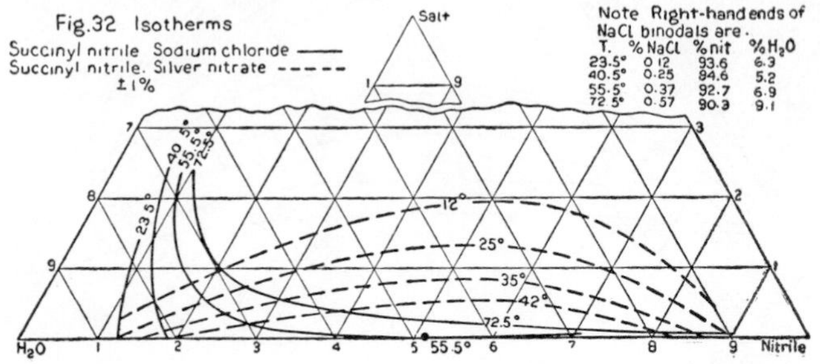

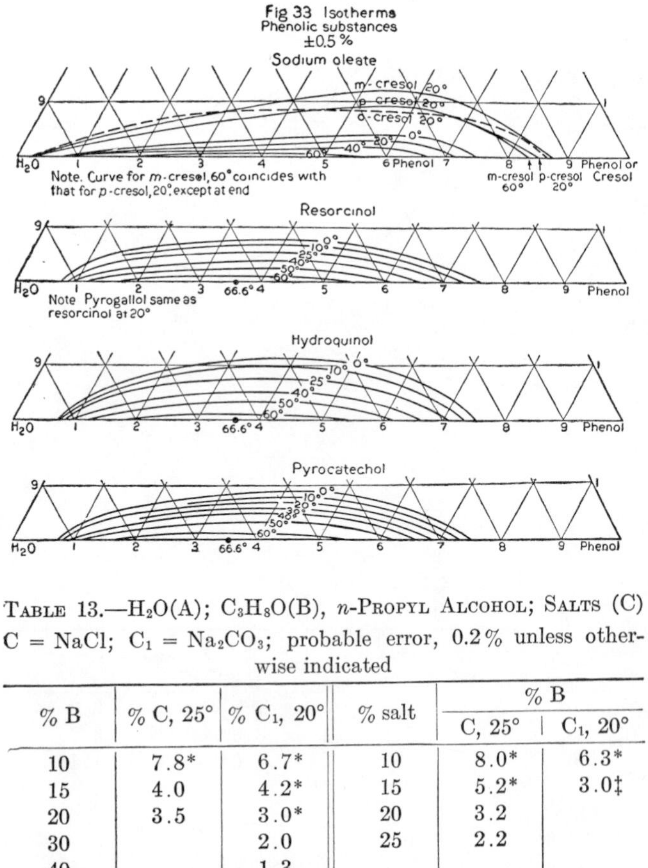

TABLE 13.—H_2O(A); C_3H_8O(B), *n*-PROPYL ALCOHOL; SALTS (C)

C = NaCl; C_1 = Na_2CO_3; probable error, 0.2% unless otherwise indicated

% B	% C, 25°	% C_1, 20°	% salt	% B C, 25°	% B C_1, 20°
10	7.8*	6.7*	10	8.0*	6.3*
15	4.0	4.2*	15	5.2*	3.0‡
20	3.5	3.0*	20	3.2	
30		2.0	25	2.2	
40		1.3			
50	2.3	0.7†			
60		0.3†			
70		0.2†			
80	0.8				

* ±0.3. † ±0.1. ‡ ±0.5.

TABLE 13.—(*Continued*)

Temperature coefficient; $dB/dT = -0.08$ for 9% C.

C = KF; C_1 = K_2CO_3; t = 25°C; probable error, ±0.2% unless otherwise indicated; solutions marked (a), (a); (b), (b); (c), (c) are conjugate

% B	% C	% C_1	% salt	% B C	% B C_1
10	5.7	6.7	10	5.7 (b)	6.8†
15	3.3	3.8	15	3.1	3.8
20	2.4	2.7	20	1.6	2.0
30	1.9	2.1*	25	1.0*	1.0*
40	1.6*	1.6*	30	0.5*	0.5*
50	1.1*	1.0*	40	0.2*	0.2*
60	0.8*	0.5*	47.6	0.04 (c)	
70	0.5*		53		0.02 (a)
80	0.3*(b)				
95.8		0.02 (a)			
96.8	0.2*(c)				

* ±0.1.
† ±0.3.

Temperature coefficient: $dB/dT = -0.02$ for C = 15%.

TABLE 14.—H_2O(A); C_3H_8O(B), ISOPROPYL ALCOHOL; SALTS (C)

C = KF; C_1 = K_2CO_3; t = 20°C; error, ±0.2% unless otherwise indicated

% B	% C	% C_1	% salt	% B C	% B C_1
10	15.5*	17.0‡	20	5.0*	7.0
15	12.8*	13.7	25	2.5*	4.0
20	10.7*	12.0	30	1.5*	2.1
30	7.5†	9.0‡			
40	6.0†	6.2			
50	4.5†	4.0			
60	4.0*				
80	1.8				

* ±0.5. † ±1.0. ‡ ±0.3.

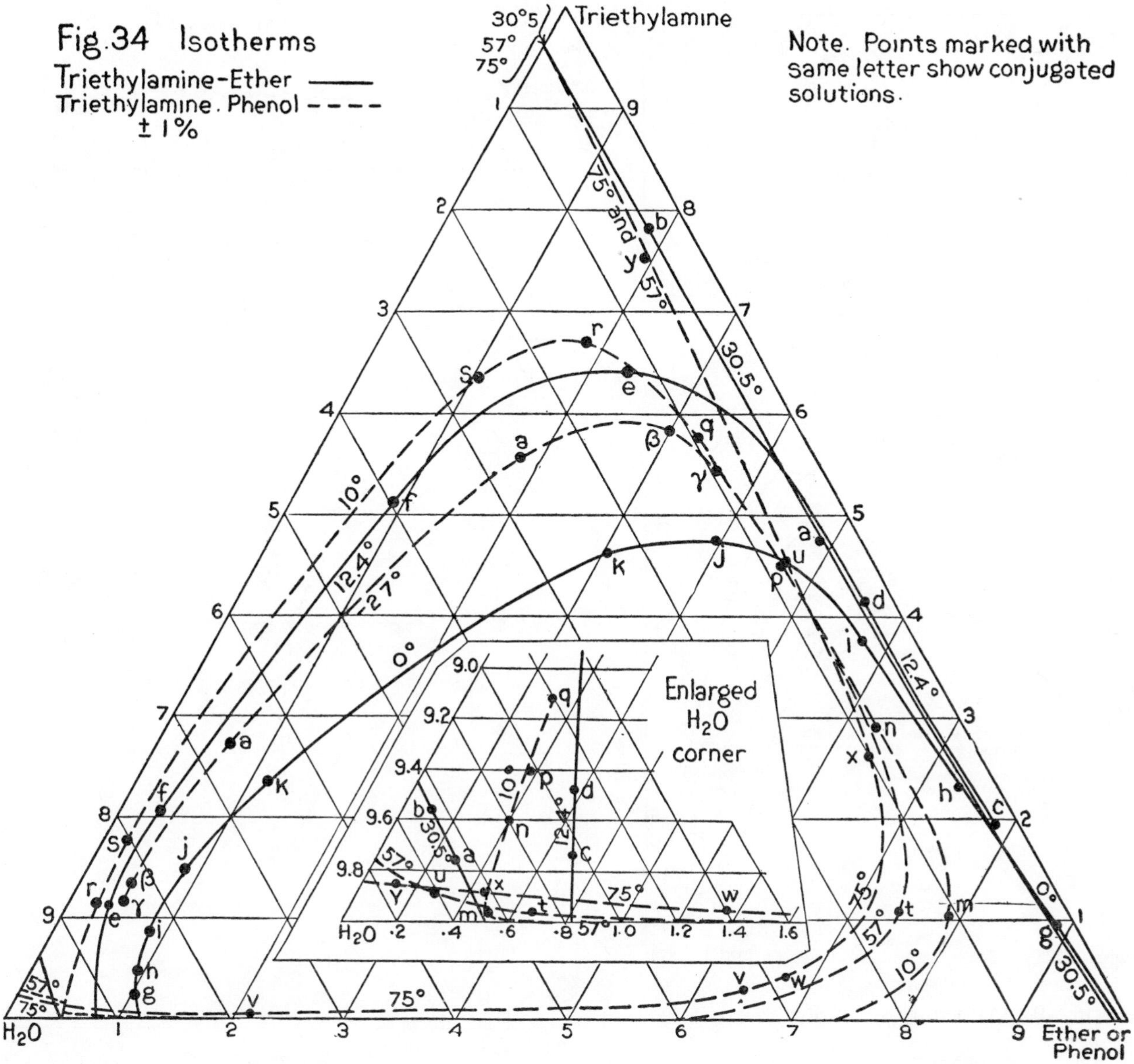

TABLE 15.—H_2O(A); $C_4H_6O_4$(B), SUCCINIC ACID; $C_4H_{10}O$(C), ETHYL ETHER

% B	% C		
	15°	20°	25°
0	7.80	6.87	6.00 ± 0.05
2	8.00	6.97	6.10 ± 0.05
4	8.11	7.07	6.20 ± 0.05
6		7.17	6.35 ± 0.05
8			6.50 ± 0.05

Mutually saturated solns. of A, B, and C in %, ±0.05.

	Upper			Lower		
°C	A	B	C	A	B	C
15	1.40	1.29	97.31	86.10	5.68	8.22
20	1.53	1.47	97.00	85.67	7.10	7.23
25	1.66	1.69	96.35	84.68	8.76	6.56

Solubility of water in ether containing less than above amounts of acid is given by linear interpolation between above values and those for pure ether: (1.18 % at 15°; 1.24 % at 20°; 1.31 % at 25°).

TABLE 15.—(*Continued*)

Ratio of % acid in water layer to % acid in ether layer from about 1 % in water layer to saturation, is given, to ±0.01, by

$R = 4.65 - 0.043a$, at 15°
$R = 5.15 - 0.046a$, at 20°
$R = 5.65 - 0.052a$, at 25°
where a = % in water layer

H_2O(A); $C_4H_{10}O$(B), Ethyl ether; Salts (C)

C = NaCl; C_1 = $NaC_2H_3O_2$; error, ±0.2 % unless otherwise indicated

% salt	% B		
	C, 15°	C, 25°	C_1, 18°
0	7.8*	6.0*	7.2*
2	6.6*	5.1*	5.9*
4	5.5*	4.2*	4.7*
6	4.3*	3.4*	3.9*
8	3.5	2.6	3.2*
10	2.8	2.0	
15	1.5	1.1	
20	0.8	0.6	
25	0.3		

* ±0.1.

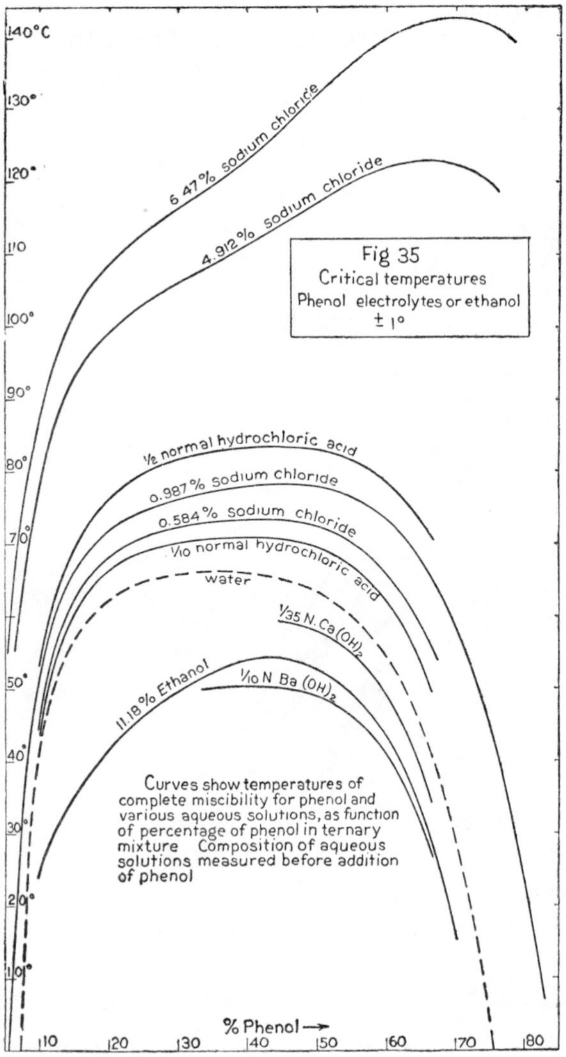

Fig 35
Critical temperatures
Phenol electrolytes or ethanol
± 1°

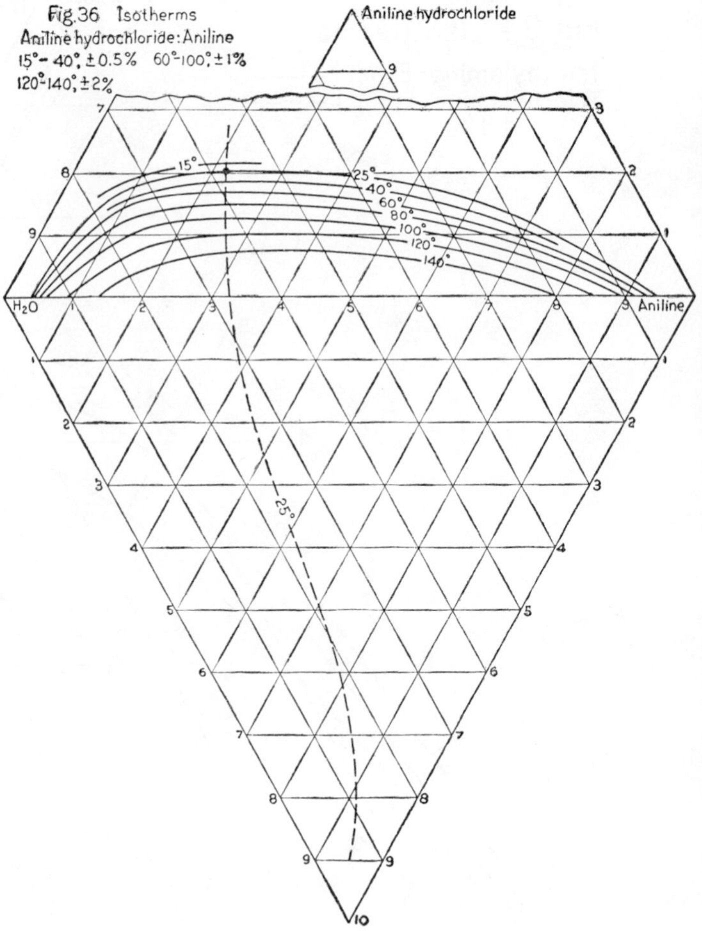

Fig. 36 Isotherms
Aniline hydrochloride: Aniline
15°–40°, ±0.5% 60°–100°, ±1%
120°–140°, ±2%

Table 16.—H_2O(A); C_4H_8O(B), Methyl Ethyl Ketone; Salts (C)
C = NaCl; C_1 = KF; t = 20°C

% B	% C ± 0.5	% C	% B
10	7.5	10	8.0 ± 0.5
15	3.0	15	4.5 ± 1
20	0.7	20	2.5 ± 1
% B	**% C_1 ± 0.2**	**% C_1**	**% B**
10	5.5	10	5.1 ± 0.2
15	2.7	15	2.5 ± 0.2
20	1.0	20	1.0 ± 0.2
		25	0.4

Table 17.—H_2O(A); $C_5H_{12}O$(B), Isoamyl Alcohol;* NaCl(C)
Systems conjugated at 28°C

Upper		Lower	
% C	% B	% C	% A
0	2.3 ± 0.1	0	9.8 ± 0.1
5	1.65 ± 0.1		8.7 ± 0.1
10	1.05 ± 0.1		7.7 ± 0.1

Table 17.—(*Continued*)

Upper		Lower	
% C	% B	% C	% A
15	0.6 ± 0.1		6.7 ± 0.1
20	0.35 ± 0.05		5.7 ± 0.1
26.36	0.22 ± 0.05	0.05	4.5

* Isoamyl alcohol contained 16 % active isomer.

Table 18.—H_2O(A); C_6H_7N(B), Aniline; Aniline Salts (C)

100 cm³ of aqueous solution of aniline hydrochloride or nitrate, containing given number of moles per l, dissolves tabulated weight of B at given temperature; values may be 0.5 g too high.

M_{salt}/l	0.5	0.75	1.00	1.25	1.50	2.00
g B, 18°C	4.6	4.9	5.3	5.9	8.0	20.5
g B, 24°C	4.9	5.3	5.7	6.4	8.7	

Table 19.—H_2O(A); $C_6H_{10}O_3$(B), Ethyl Acetoacetate; Salts (C)
t = 18°C; probable error, 0.2 %

% NaCl	0	2	4	6
% B	11.1	9.2	8.0	7.3
% $NaNO_3$	0	4	8	
% B	11.1	10.3	9.6	

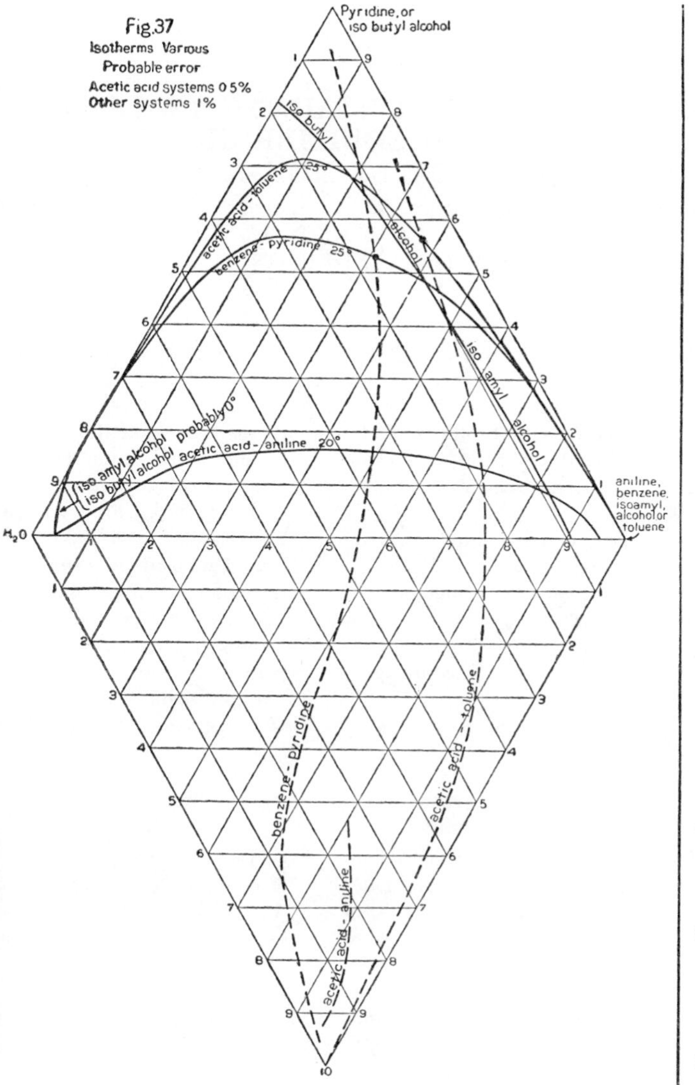

Fig. 37
Isotherms Various
Probable error
Acetic acid systems 0.5%
Other systems 1%

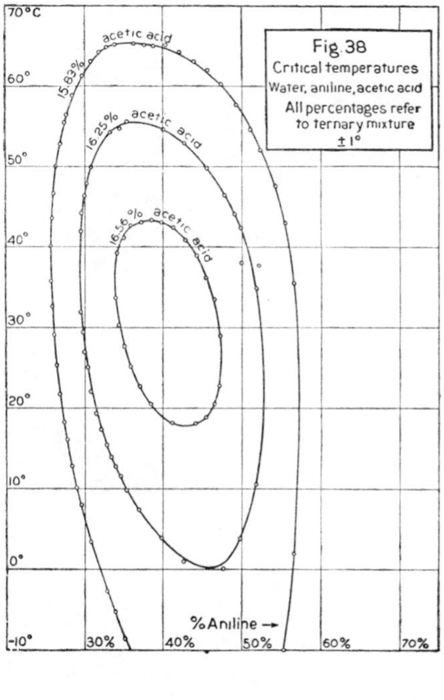

Fig. 38
Critical temperatures
Water, aniline, acetic acid
All percentages refer to ternary mixture
±1°

LITERATURE

(For a key to the periodicals see end of volume)

(1) Aleksěev, *8*, **28**: 305; 86. (1.5) Angelescu and Mirescu, *Bull. soc. chim. Romania*, **7**: 11; 25. (2) Asboth, *136*, **20**: 685; 96. (3) Bagster and Cooling, *4*, **117**: 693; 20. (4) Bailey, *4*, **123**: 2579; 23. (5) Bancroft, *2*, **3**: 21; 95. (6) Bancroft, *2*, **3**: 114; 95. (7) Bancroft, *2*, **3**: 193; 95. (7.1) Barbaudy, *70*, **45**: 207; 13. (7.5) Barbaudy, *34*, **182**: 1279; 26. (8) Bell, *50*, **9**: 531; 05. (9) Bennett, *347*, **89**: 146; 12.

(10) Boericke, *9*, **11**: 57; 05. (11) Bogin, *45*, **16**: 380; 24. (12) Bonner, *50*, **14**: 738; 10. (13) Böttger, *Jahresb. phys. Verein. Frankfurt*, **1870**: 13. (14) Boutaric, *42*, **18**: 126; 20. (15) Boutaric and Nabot, *34*, **176**: 1618; 23. (16) Boutin and Sanfourche, *27*, **25**: 458; 19. (17) de Bruijn, *7*, **32**: 63; 00. (17.5) Brun, *34*, **180**: 1745; 25. (18) Brun, *34*, **183**: 207; 26. (19) Bruni, *22*, **8 II**: 141; 99.

(20) Cady, *50*, **2**: 168; 98. (21) Cocheret, *Diss.*, Leiden, 1911. *10*, **2**: 439; 13. (22) Corliss, *50*, **18**: 681; 14. (23) Crismer, *186*, **30**: 97; 95. (24) Crismer, *28*, **9**: 145; 95. (25) Crismer, *28*, **10**: 312; 96. (26) Crismer, *Mém. acad. Belg.*, *Mém. Couronn.* (8° ed.) **58**: No. 4; 98. (27) Crismer, *28*, **16**: 83; 02. (28) Crismer, *28*, **18**: 18; 04. (29) Cuno, *8*, **25**: 356; 08.

(30) Curtis, *50*, **2**: 371; 98. (31) Curtis and Titus, *50*, **19**: 738; 15. (32) Desmaroux, *315*, **19**: 322; 22. (33) Draper, *135*, **35**: 87; 77. (33.5) Drauilon, *42*, **22**: 149; 25. (34) Drucker, *70*, **42**: 552; 23. (35) Duboux and Dutoit, *342*, **13**: 4; 08. (36) Dubrisay, *6*, **17**: 222; 22. (37) Dubrisay and Toquet, *27*, **25**: 354; 19. (38) Duclaux, *6*, **7**: 264; 76. (39) Duperthuis and Phillippe, *Mitt. Gebiet Lebensmitteluntersuch. Hyg.*, **1**: 188; 10.

(40) Euler, *7*, **31**: 360; 99. (41) Euler, *7*, **49**: 303; 04. (42) Euler and Suanberge, *9*, **23**: 192; 17. (43) Ewers, *352*, **6**: 155; 12. *10*, **1**: 378; 12. (44) Ewins, *4*, **105**: 350; 14. (45) Flaschner and Rankin, *57*, **31**: 23; 10. (46) Fleckenstein, *Diss.*, Erlangen, 1904. (47) Fontein, *7*, **73**: 212; 10. (48) Forbes and Coolidge, *1*, **41**: 150; 19. (49) Frankforter and Cohen, *1*, **36**: 1103; 14.

(50) Frankforter and Cohen, *1*, **38**: 1136; 16. (51) Frankforter and Frary, *50*, **17**: 402; 12. (52) Frankforter and Temple, *1*, **37**: 2697; 15. (53) Hatcher and Skirrow, *1*, **39**: 1939; 17. (54) Herz and Paul, *93*, **85**: 214; 14. (55) Hill and Macy, *1*, **46**: 1132; 24. (56) Hoeflake, *70*, **36**: 24; 16. (56.5) Hofman, *233*, **57**: 651; 20. *233*, **60**: 1034; 33. (57) Holmes, *4*, **113**: 263; 18. (58) Holt and Bell, *4*, **105**: 633; 14. (59) Horiba, *479*, **3**: 63; 11.

(60) Horiba, *429*, **1**: 49; 14. (61) Jacobs, *Thesis*, Leiden, 1914. (62) Jakovkin, *7*, **20**: 19; 96. (63) Jones, *4*, **123**: 1374; 23. (64) Jones and Hartmann, *78*, **30**: 295; 16. (65) Jones and Lapworth, *4*, **105**: 1804; 14. (66) Ketner, *7*, **39**: 641; 02. (67) Klobbie, *7*, **24**: 615; 97. (68) Kono, *41*, **44**: 406; 23. (69) Krug and McElroy, *320*, **6**: 153, 184; 92.

(70) Leone and Angelescu, *36*, **52 II**: 61; 22. (71) Leone and Benelli, *36*, **52 II**: 75; 22. (72) Lincoln, *50*, **4**: 161; 00. (73) Linde, *19*, **6**: No. 20; 17. (74) Linebarger, *11*, **14**: 380; 92. (75) McDavid, *68*, **30**: 440; 10. (76) Meerburg, *7*, **40**: 641; 02. (77) van Neurs, *Diss.*, Leiden, 1913. *10*, **4**: 761; 21. (78) Middleberg, *7*, **43**: 305; 03. (79) Miller and McPherson, *50*, **12**: 706; 08.

(80) Moore, Morrell and Egloff, *33*, **18**: 396; 18. (81) Mossler and Markus, *452*, **47**: 291; 14. (82) Newth, *4*, **77**: 775; 00. (83) Oliveri-Mandalà, *36*, **50 II**: 89; 20. (84) Orton and Jones, *4*, **115**: 1055; 19. (85) Orton and Jones, *4*, **115**: 1194; 19. (86) Pascal and Dupuy, *27*, **27**: 353; 20. (87) Pearce and O'Leary, *453*, **30**: 379; 23. (88) Pfeiffer, *7*, **9**: 444; 92. (89) Rothen and Boutier, *478*, **40**: 7, 268; 23. *378*, Spec. No., 733; 23.

(90) Schoorl and Regenbogen, *70*, **41**: 1, 125; 22. (91) Schreinemakers, *7*, **23**: 417; 97. (92) Schreinemakers, *7*, **27**: 95; 98. (93) Schreinemakers, *7*, **29**: 577; 99. (94) Schreinemakers, *7*, **30**: 460; 99. (95) Schreinemakers, *7*, **33**: 74; 00. (95.5) Schreinemakers, *7*, **33**: 78; 00. (96) Schreinemakers, *7*, **39**: 485; 02. (97) Schreinemakers and Deuss, *7*, **79**: 554; 12. (98) Schryver, *5B*, **83**: 96; 10. (99) Schuncke, *7*, **14**: 331; 94.

(100) Seidell, *464*, No. **67**: 14, 53, 69; 10. (101) Shilov and Lepin, *7*, **101**: 353; 22. (102) Sidgwick, Pickford and Wilsdon, *4*, **99**: 1122; 11. (103) Sidgwick and Spurrell, *4*, **117**: 1397; 20. (104) Snell, *50*, **2**: 457; 98. (105) Taylor, *50*, **1**: 301; 97. (106) Thorin, *7*, **89**: 685; 15. (107) Thorne, *4*, **119**: 262; 21. (108) Timmermans, *7*, **58**: 129; 07. (109) Tizard and Marshall, *54*, **40**: 20T; 21.

(110) Traube and Neuberg, *7*, **1**: 509; 87. (111) Tuchschmidt and Follenius, *25*, **4**: 583; 71. (112) Vandam, *28*, **20**: 374; 06. (113) Vezes and Mouline, *27*, **31**: 1043; 04. (114) Waddell, *50*, **2**: 233; 98. (115) Walton and Jenkins, *1*, **45**: 2555; 23. (116) Wildermann, *7*, **11**: 407; 93. (117) Woodman, *50*, **30**: 1283; 26. (117.5) Woodman and Corbet, *4*, **127**: 2461; 25. (118) Worley, *4*, **87**: 1107; 05. (119) Wright, *5*, **50**: 372; 92.

(120) Wright, *5*, **52**: 11; 93. (121) Wright, *5*, **52**: 530; 93. (122) Wright, *5*, **55**: 130; 94. (123) Wright and Thompson, *5*, **45**: 461; 89. (124) Wright and Thompson, *5*, **48**: 25; 90. (125) Wright and Thompson, *5*, **49**: 156; 91. (126) Wright, Thompson and Leon, *5*, **49**: 174; 91. (127) Schreinemakers, *7*, **25**: 543; 98. (128) Schreinemakers, *7*, **26**: 237; 98. (129) Hill, *1*, **44**: 1163; 22.

(130) Hill and Miller, *1*, **47**: 2702; 25.

PHASE-EQUILIBRIUM DATA FOR CONDENSED SYSTEMS CONTAINING TWO LIQUID PHASES WITH A THIRD COMPONENT IN DISTRIBUTION EQUILIBRIUM BETWEEN THEM, THE TWO LIQUID PHASES BEING PRACTICALLY NON-MISCIBLE; DISTRIBUTION COEFFICIENTS

George Shannon Forbes and Gaylord West Anderson

Symbols, Units and Conventions

$[A]_B$ (resp. $[A]_C$) Equilibrium concentration of the distributed component, A, in gram-formula-weights per liter of the solution (A + B), (resp. the solution (A + C)).

M_A/l_B (resp. M_A/l_C) Gram-formula-weights of A per l of B (resp. C).

g A/l_B Grams of A per l of solution (A + B).

g A/l_C Grams of A per l of solution (A + C).

g A/kg B Grams of A per 1000 g of B.

K Distribution ratio at *t*, °C = $[A]_C/[A]_B$.

K′ Distribution ratio at *t*, °C = 1/K.

The pressure is atmospheric throughout.

Where no limits are given under °C, the constancy of temperature is not known.

Symboles, unités et conventions

$[A]_B$ (resp. $[A]_C$) Concentration d'équilibre du constituant distribué, A, exprimée en mol. gr. par litre de solution (A + B), (resp. de solution (A + C)).

M_A/l_B (resp. M_A/l_C) Mol. gr. de A par litre de B (resp. C).

g A/l_B Grammes de A par litre de solution (A + B).

g A/l_C Grammes de A par litre de solution (A + C).

g A/kg B Grammes de A par 1000 g de B.

K Rapport de distribution à *t*, °C = $[A]_C/[A]_B$.

K′ Rapport de distribution à *t*, °C = 1/K.

La pression est partout la pression atmosphérique.

Lorsqu'aucunes limites ne sont données sous °C, la constance de la température n'est pas connue.

Zeichen, Einheiten und Festlegungen

$[A]_B$ (bezw. $[A]_C$) Die Gleichgewichtskonzentration der verteilten Komponente A, in Grammformelgewicht pro Liter der Lösung (A + B) (bezw. der Lösung (A + C)).

M_A/l_B (bezw. M_A/l_C) Grammformelgewicht von A pro Liter von B (bezw. C).

g A/l_B Gramme von A pro Liter der Lösung von (A + B).

g A/l_C Gramme von A pro Liter der Lösung (A + C).

g A/kg B Gramme von A auf 1000 g von B.

K Das Verteilungsverhältnis bei der Temperatur *t*, °C = $[A]_C/[A]_B$.

K′ Das Verteilungsverhältnis bei der Temperatur *t*, °C = 1/K.

Drucke immer ein Atmosphäre.

Wo keine Grenzangaben unter °C sich vorfinden, ist die Konstanz der Temperatur unbekannt.

Simboli, unità e convenzioni

$[A]_B$ (o $[A]_C$) Concentrazione di equilibrio del componente A ripartito, espressa in numero di grammiformula per litro di soluzione (A + B) (o soluzione (A + C)).

M_A/l_B (o M_A/l_C) Numero di grammiformula di A per l di B (o di C).

g A/l_B Grammi di A per l di soluzione (A + B).

g A/l_C Grammi di A per l di soluzione (A + C).

g A/kg B Grammi di A per 1000 g di B.

K Coefficiente di ripartizione a *t*, °C = $[A]_C/[A]_B$.

K′ Coefficiente di ripartizione a *t*, °C = 1/K.

Si suppone sempre che la pressione è quella atmosferica.

Quando non vengono indicati limiti sotto la notazione °C, significa che non si conosce se la temperatura era mantenuta costante o no.

𝔄-𝔅 TABLE

Aqueous Systems

The C-component is H_2O in all cases

The A-component (the distributed component) is an elementary substance or a compound whose key formula does not begin with 16; 𝔄-𝔅-Table, standard arrangement. The B-components are compounds whose key formulae begin with 16 and are in the ℭ-arrangement under the respective A-components. The D-component, where given, is a solute in the aqueous layer.

Systèmes aqueux

Le constituant C est H_2O dans tous les cas

Le constituant A (le constituant distribué) est une substance élémentaire ou un composé dont la formule clé ne commence pas par 16; Table 𝔄-𝔅, arrangement type. Les constituants B sont des composés dont la formule clé commence par 16 et ils sont disposés suivant l'arrangement ℭ sous les composés A respectifs. Le constituant D, représente, lorsqu'il est donné, un corps dissout dans la couche aqueuse.

Systeme mit Wasser

In allen Fällen is H_2O die C-Komponente

Die A-Komponente (die verteilte Komponente) ist ein elementarer Stoff oder eine Verbindung dessen Schlüsselformel nicht mit 16 beginnt; 𝔄-𝔅-Tafel, Standardanordnung. Die B-Komponente ist eine Verbindung deren Schlüsselformel mit 16 beginnt, sie steht unter der entsprechenden A-Komponente in der ℭ-Anordnung. Eine D-Komponente ist, wenn angegeben, ein gelöster Stoff in der wässrigen Schichte.

Sistemi acquosi

Il componente C è sempre l'acqua

Il componente A (cioè componente distribuito tra i due liquidi) è un elemento, o un composto di cui la formula chiave non comincia con 16; Tabella 𝔄-𝔅 dell'ordinamento standard. I componenti B sono composti di cui le formule chiavi cominciano con 16; essi si trovano nell'ordinamento ℭ sotto i rispettivi componenti A. Il componente D, dove è indicato, è una sostanza disciolta nello strato acquoso.

H_2O_2

B = $CHCl_3$, Chloroform (14, 173)

B = CH_3I, Methyl iodide (173)

B = $C_4H_8O_2$, Ethyl acetate (173); *cf.* (14); at 25°C, K = 4.0 ± 0.1 for $[A]_B$ = 0.50–0.72

B = $C_4H_8O_2$, Propyl formate (14, 173)

B = $C_4H_{10}O$, Isobutyl alcohol (14, 173)

B = $C_4H_{10}O$, Ethyl ether (173); *cf.* (91, 120)

t = 25°C

$[A]_B$	K ± 0.1
0.161	9.1
0.252	8.8
0.345	8.2

B = $C_5H_{12}O$, Amyl alcohol (20, 85, 106)

$[A]_B$	K
t = 0°C	
0.0115–0.0281	6.88 ± 0.05
0.199 –0.749	6.65 ± 0.1
t = 25°C	
0.094 –0.912	7.0 ± 0.1

B = $C_5H_{12}O$, Amyl alcohol (20, 85, 106)

D = Aqueous solutions of NaOH; $Na_2B_4O_7$; $K_2B_2O_4$

B = $C_6H_5NO_2$, Nitrobenzene (14, 173)

B = C_6H_6, Benzene (14, 173)

B = C_6H_6O, Phenol (173)

B = C_6H_7N, Aniline (173); at 25°C, K = 4.09 ± 0.05 for $[A]_B$ = 0.062 – 0.114

B = C_7H_9N, *m*-Toluidine (173)

B = $C_7H_{14}O_2$, Amyl acetate (14, 173); at 25°C, K = 13.1 ± 0.2 for $[A]_B$ = 0.182 – 0.295

B = $C_7H_{14}O_2$, Ethyl isovalerate (14, 173)

B = $C_7H_{14}O_2$, Propyl butyrate (14, 173)

B = C_8H_8O, Acetophenone (14, 173)

B = $C_8H_{16}O_2$, Isoamyl propionate (14, 173)

B = $C_8H_{16}O_2$, Isobutyl butyrate (14, 173)

B = C_9H_7N, Quinoline (173)

Cl_2

B = CCl_4 (83)

t = 0°C

$[A]_C$	K*
0.050	0.195
.1	.141
.2	.117
.3	.0935
.6	.0775
.9	.0705

* Partial hydrolysis.

ClO_2

B = CCl_4 (15)

$[A]_C$	K′
t = 0°C	
0.164	1.27 ± 0.02
0.046	1.21 ± 0.02
0.0016	1.17 ± 0.02
t = 25°C	
0.121	1.69 ± 0.03
0.035	1.66 ± 0.03
0.0030	1.60 ± 0.03

B = CCl_4 (15)

D = Aqueous solutions of H_2SO_4; KCl; $KClO_3$

HCl

B = $C_4H_{10}O$, Ethyl ether (86); *see* p. 400

B = C_6H_6, Benzene (165.5, 170.5, 180)

Br_2

B = CCl_4 (81, 82, 84, 95, 122); *cf.* (72)

$[A]_B$	K′ ± 0.05*
t = 0°C	
0.1	20.85
0.5	22.05
1.0	23.52
1.5	25.00
2.0	26.45

B = CCl_4: *t* = 0°C.—(*Continued*)

$[A]_B$	K′ ± 0.2†
t = 25°C	
0.04	26.8
0.1	27.2
0.5	29.0
1.0	30.4
1.5	31.9
2.0	33.4
2.5	35.0
3.0	36.5
3.5	38.1

t = 40°C

$[A]_B$	K′ ± 2†
0.1	30
0.5	31

* No hydrolysis.

† Partial hydrolysis. At 25°C M_A/kg C ÷ mole fraction of A in B at infinite dilution = 0.371 ± 0.001.

B = CCl_4 (68, 75, 82, 95, 169)

D = Aqueous solutions of HBr; $HgBr_2$; $HgBr_2$ + KBr; $CdBr_2$; $CdBr_2$ + KBr; $CaBr_2$; $BaBr_2$; Na_2SO_4; $NaNO_3$; KCl; K_2SO_4

B = CCl_4 + CS_2 (mixtures) (67, 72)

B = CS_2 (72, 81); *cf.* (8)

t = 25°C

$[A]_B$	K′ ± 2*
0.25	78
0.50	79
1.0	80
1.5	81
2.0	82

* Partial hydrolysis.

B = CS_2 (82, 136)

D = Aqueous solution of KBr

t = 25°C

KBr = 1/16 M

$[A]_B$	K ± 0.005*
0.005	0.0696
0.02	0.0651
0.03	0.0621

B = CS_2; D = KBr *t* = 25°C.—(*Continued*)

KBr = 1/8 M

$[A]_B$	K ± 0.001*
0.005	0.1055
0.02	0.099
0.03	0.094
0.04	0.090
0.05	0.086

KBr = 1/4 M

$[A]_B$	K ± 0.001*
0.005	0.1735
0.02	0.167
0.03	0.163
0.04	0.159
0.05	0.155
0.06	0.151

KBr = 1/2 M

$[A]_B$	K ± 0.002*
0.02	0.303
0.03	0.298
0.04	0.293
0.05	0.288
0.06	0.283
0.095	0.271

* Partial hydrolysis.

B = $CHBr_3$, Bromoform (81)

t = 25°C

$[A]_B$	K′ ± 0.2*
0.125	64.7
0.25	65.5
0.5	66.7
0.75	67.6
1.0	68.2
1.5	68.7
2.0	68.8
2.5	68.9

* Partial hydrolysis.

B = C_2HCl_5, Pentachloroethane (76)

B = $C_2H_2Cl_4$, Tetrachloroethane (76)

I_2

$B = CCl_4$ (31, 32, 81, 99, 175)

$t = 25°C$

$[A]_B$	$K' \pm 0.5$*
0.02	85.1
0.04	85.2
0.06	85.4
0.08	86.0
0.09	86.4
0.10	87.5

* $K' \pm 0.5 = 82.8$ for $[A]_B = 0.034 - 0.044$ at $18 \pm 0.02°C$; = 56.7 for g A/kg B = 0.023 − 0.051 at 25°C.

$B = CCl_4$ (31, 68, 75, 101, 169)
D = Aqueous solutions of $HgCl_2$; $HgBr_2$; $HgI_2 + KI$; CaI_2; BaI_2; SrI_2; KI + starch; $K_2C_2O_4$

$B = CCl_4$ (32)
D = Aqueous solution of KI; at $18 \pm 0.02°C$, $K' = 0.00115 \pm 0.00001$ for $[A]_B = 0.03$

$B = CCl_4 + C_7H_8$ (mixtures) (29)
D = Aqueous solution of KI

$B = CS_2$ (29, 31, 37, 81); *cf.* (8)

$t = 25°C$

$[A]_B$	$K' \pm 5$*
0.1	586
0.2	590
0.3	601
0.4	614
0.5	629
0.6	646

* Partial hydrolysis.

$B = CS_2$ (82, 119, 169)
D = Aqueous solutions of ZnI_2; $ZnI_2 + KI$; $CdI_2 + KI$; NiI_2; LaI_3; SrI_2; Na_2SO_4; $NaNO_3$; C_2H_5OH

$B = CS_2$ (82); *cf.* (27)
D = Aqueous solution of KI

$t = 25°C$

KI = 1/32 M

$[A]_B$	$K \pm 0.0003$*
0.1	0.0364
0.2	0.0323
0.3	0.0290
0.4	0.0264
0.5	0.0242
0.6	0.0224

KI = 1/16 M

$[A]_B$	$K \pm 0.0005$*
0.05	0.0750
0.1	0.0703
0.2	0.0626
0.3	0.0564
0.4	0.0513
0.5	0.0472
0.6	0.0437

$B = CS_2$; D = KI
$t = 25°C$.—(*Continued*)

KI = 1/8 M

$[A]_B$	$K \pm 0.001$*
0.02	0.153
0.05	0.148
0.1	0.139
0.2	0.124
0.3	0.112
0.4	0.102
0.5	0.094
0.6	0.087
0.7	0.080

KI = 1/4 M

$[A]_B$	$K \pm 0.002$*
0.02	0.300
0.05	0.291
0.1	0.276
0.2	0.249

* Partial hydrolysis.

$B = CS_2 + CCl_4$ (mixtures) (67, 71)

$B = CS_2 + CCl_4$ (mixtures) (29, 67, 72)
D = Aqueous solutions of BaI_2; KI

$B = CS_2 + CHCl_3$ (mixtures) (29)
D = Aqueous solution of KI

$B = CS_2 + C_6H_6$ (mixtures) (29)
D = Aqueous solution of KI

$B = CS_2 + C_7H_8$ (mixtures) (29)
D = Aqueous solution of KI

$B = CS_2$ + Petroleum ether, B. P., 83–85° (mixtures) (29)
D = Aqueous solution of KI

$B = CHBr_3$, Bromoform (81)

$t = 25°C$

g A/l_B	$K' \pm 5$*
30	434
60	467
90	493
120	510
150	532

* Partial hydrolysis.

$B = CHCl_3$, Chloroform
D = $C_3H_8O_3$, Glycerol + H_2O (mixtures) (63, 67, 72)

$B = CHCl_3$, Chloroform (72); at 25°C, $K' = 131 \pm 2$ for $[A]_B = 0.02$–0.17, with partial hydrolysis

$B = CHCl_3 + C_6H_6$ (mixtures) (29)
D = Aqueous solution of KI

$B = C_2Cl_4$, Tetrachloroethylene (76)

$B = C_2HCl_3$, Trichloroethylene (76)

$B = C_2HCl_5$, Pentachloroethane (76)

$B = C_2H_2Cl_4$, Tetrachloroethane (76)

$B = C_4H_8O_2$, Ethyl acetate (35)
D = Aqueous solution of KI

$B = C_5H_{12}O$, Amyl alcohol (69); at 25°C, $K' = 230 \pm 20$ for $[A]_B = 0.00127 - 0.00278$, with partial hydrolysis

$B = C_5H_{12}O$, Amyl alcohol (69)
D = Aqueous solution of KI

$B = C_6H_5NO_2$, Nitrobenzene (32); at $18 \pm 0.02°C$, $K' = 173 \pm 3$ for $[A]_B = 0.033 - 0.333$

$B = C_6H_5NO_2$, Nitrobenzene (33)
D = Aqueous solution of KI

$B = C_6H_6 + C_7H_8$ (mixtures) (29)
D = Aqueous solution of KI

$B = C_6H_6$ + Petroleum ether, B. P., 83–85° (mixtures) (29)
D = Aqueous solution of KI

$B = C_{10}H_{12}$, Tetralin (77)

$t = 25°C$

$[A]_B$	$K' \pm 10$
0.1	370
0.2	347
0.3	335
0.4	325

$B = C_{10}H_{18}$, Decahydronaphthalene (77)

$t = 25°C$

$[A]_B$	$K' \pm 0.5$
0.03	67.0
0.04	62.2
0.05	59.6

SO_2

$B = CHCl_3$, Chloroform (42, 96, 102)

$[A]_B$	$K \pm 0.05$
$t = 0°C$*	
0.05	1.42
0.1	1.12
0.2	1.05
0.4	1.00
0.7	0.98
$t = 20°C$	
0.05	1.39
0.1	1.20
0.2	1.06
0.4	0.98
0.7	0.94
1.1	0.92

* At 0°C, $K = 5.7 \pm 0.2$ for $[A]_B = 0.000932$.

$B = C_6H_6$, Benzene (46)
D = Aqueous solutions of NaOH; KOH

H_2S

$B = C_6H_6$, Benzene (56); at 25°C, $K = 0.167 \pm 0.005$ for $[A]_B = 0.072$–0.108

H_2S + HCN (mixtures)

$B = C_6H_6$, Benzene (56)

H_2SO_4

$B = C_5H_{12}O$, Amyl alcohol (117)

$t = 25°C$

$[A]_B$	$K' \pm 0.0001$
0.0001	0.0052
0.0003	0.0062
0.0006	0.0072
0.0012	0.0084
0.0017	0.00915

$TeCl_4$

$B = C_4H_{10}O$, Ethyl ether (113)

N_2O_3

$B = CHCl_3$, Chloroform (142)

$t = 0°C$

$[A]_B$	$K \pm 0.1$
0.0265	0.9
0.0125	1.0
0.0055	1.3

NH_3

$B = CCl_4$ (74, 155, 158)

$t = 25°C$

$[A]_B$	$K' \pm 0.0001$
0.01	0.0047
0.03	0.0059
0.05	0.00715
0.07	0.00835

$B = CHBr_3$, Bromoform (74, 155, 158)

$t = 25°C$

$[A]_B$	$K' \pm 0.001$
0.05	0.026
0.2	0.035
0.3	0.041
0.4	0.047

$B = CHCl_3$, Chloroform (1, 7, 30, 36, 37, 62, 109, 148, 155)

$t = 25°C$

$[A]_B$	$K \pm 0.2$*
0.01	24.5
0.05	23.1
0.1	21.8
0.2	19.7
0.4	16.6
0.6	14.2
0.8	12.40
1.0	11.10
1.2	10.15

* At 2°C, $K = 38.5 \pm 1$ for $[A]_B/l_B$ cf. = 0.017; at 18°C, $K = 28.0 \pm 0.5$ for $[A]_B = 0.0015$.

K from 15 – 35°C for solns. *ca.* 0.01 molal is given by the equation: $K_t = 28.2 - 0.37\,(t - 15)$.

$B = CHCl_3$ (1, 30, 36, 37, 38, 62, 148)
D = Aqueous solutions of various salts

$B = CHCl_3 + C_5H_{12}O$, Amyl alcohol (mixtures) (67, 71)

$B = C_4H_{10}O$, Ethyl ether (100); *cf.* (8)

B = $C_4H_{10}O$.—(*Continued*)

t = 20°C

$[A]_C$	K ± 2
0.01	160
0.005	204

B = $C_5H_{12}O$, Amyl alcohol (69); *cf.* (158); at 20°C, K′ = 0.145 ± 0.005 for $[A]_B$ = 0.0122–0.455

N_2H_4, Hydrazine

B = C_6H_6, Benzene (58); from 13 - 15°C, K = 75 ± 5 for $[A]_B$ = 0.011–0.057

HNO_3

B = $C_4H_{10}O$, Ethyl ether (12, 13, 86, 149); *cf.* (165)

t = 25°C

$[A]_B$	K
0.0005	80 ± 2
0.001	66 ± 2
0.002	53 ± 1
0.005	35 ± 1
0.01	28.5 ± 0.5
0.03	17.0 ± 0.5
0.05	13.5 ± 0.2
0.07	11.6 ± 0.2
0.09	11.0 ± 0.2

B = $C_4H_{10}O$, Ethyl ether (165)
D = Aqueous solutions of various nitrates alone and with the addition of HCl, H_2SO_4 and H_3PO_4

$SbCl_3$

B = $C_4H_{10}O$, Ethyl ether (113)
D = HCl

$AsCl_3$

B = $C_4H_{10}O$, Ethyl ether (113)
D = HCl

As_2O_3

B = $C_5H_{12}O$, Amyl alcohol (4); at 25°C, K = 5.49 ± 0.05 for $[A]_B$ = 0.0083–0.0324

B = $C_5H_{12}O$, Amyl alcohol (4)
D = Aqueous solution of H_3BO_3

As_2S_3 (colloidal) (22)

B = $C_4H_{10}O$, Ethyl ether

For **HCN** and other compounds of carbon, *see* p. 422.

$SnCl_4$

B = $C_4H_{10}O$, Ethyl ether (113)
D = HCl

B = C_8H_{10}, Xylene (153, 154)

°C	Wt. % Cl in	K
	($A.5H_2O$ + B)	
66	0.08	504 ± 10
80	0.17	228 ± 10
97.5	0.33	122 ± 5
111	0.68	59 ± 5
	($A.4H_2O$ + B)	
66	0.92	45 ± 2

B = C_8H_{10}.—(*Continued*)

°C	Wt. % Cl in	K
	($A.4H_2O$ + B).—(*Continued*)	
80	1.55	27 ± 2
100	2.51	17 ± 1
111	3.23	13 ± 1
	($A.3H_2O$ + B)	
80	9.95	4.3 ± 0.1
94	9.32	4.6 ± 0.1
100	10.56	4.1 ± 0.1
111	10.03	4.2 ± 0.1

$GaCl_3$

B = $C_4H_{10}O$, Ethyl ether (160.5)
D = HCl

t = 20.0°C

M_D/l	K′*
2.0	0.035 ± 0.003
3.0	0.21 ± 0.01
4.0	8.5 ± 0.1
5.0	57 ± 2
5.45	75 ± 3
6.0	42 ± 2
7.0	10.0 ± 0.3
8.0	2.0 ± 0.1

* 100 mg Ga as $GaCl_3$ in 50 cm³ HCl of varying concentration and 50 cm³ ether.

$ZnCl_2$

B = $C_4H_{10}O$, Ethyl ether
D = HCl (113)

$CdCl_2$

B = $C_5H_{12}O$, Amyl alcohol (74)

CdI_2

B = $C_4H_{10}O$, Ethyl ether (39)

t = 30°C

$[A]_B$	K ± 0.1
0.01	6.1
0.02	5.8
0.05	5.3
0.10	4.9
0.15	4.65*
0.20	4.49*

* ± 0.05.

B = $C_5H_{12}O$, Amyl alcohol (39, 74)

t = 25°C

$[A]_B$	K ± 0.05
0.03	1.36
0.05	1.21
0.1	1.09
0.2	1.03
0.5	1.05*
1.0	1.2*
1.5	1.3*

t = 30°C

$[A]_B$	K ± 0.02
0.03	1.70
0.05	1.53
0.1	1.39
0.2	1.24†
0.5	1.13†
1.0	1.11†

* ± 0.1. † ± 0.01.

$HgCl_2$

B = $CHCl_3$, Chloroform (62)

B = $C_4H_{10}O$, Ethyl ether (62, 159, 160); *cf.* (113, 152); from 0–25°C, K = 0.42 ± 0.02 for $[A]_B/l_B$ = 0.01–0.02; 0–17°C, K = 0.30 ± 0.05 for $[A]_B$ = 0.3–0.5

B = $C_4H_{10}O$, Ethyl ether (113)
D = HCl

B = C_6H_6, Benzene (97); *cf.* (62)

t = 25°C

$[A]_B$	K ± 0.05
0.001	11.97
0.005	12.31
0.010	12.73
0.015	13.16
0.020	13.58
0.025	14.01
	t = 40°C
0.001	10.82
0.005	11.16
0.010	11.61
0.015	12.05
0.020	12.49
0.025	13.03

B = C_6H_6 (98, 147)
D = Aqueous solutions of NaCl; KCl

B = C_7H_8, Toluene (43, 63, 111); *cf.* (16, 62, 97)

t = 25°C

$[A]_B$	K ± 0.2*
0.001	10.8
0.005	11.2
0.01	11.4
0.02	11.5
0.31	12.7

* From 0–50°C, K = 11.6 ± 0.3 for $[A]_B$ = 0.005.

B = C_7H_8, Toluene (43, 111)
D = Aqueous solutions of $ZnCl_2$; $Hg(NO_3)_2$

B = $C_{10}H_{12}$, Tetralin (77)

$HgBr_2$

B = C_6H_6, Benzene (147); at 25°C, K = 0.89 ± 0.01 for $[A]_B$ = 0.0035–0.194

B = C_6H_6, Benzene (147)
D = Aqueous solution of KBr

HgI_2

B = C_6H_6, Benzene (147)
D = Aqueous solution of KI

$Hg(CN)_2$

B = $C_4H_{10}O$, Ethyl ether (147)
D = Aqueous solution of KCN

$CuCl_2$

B = $C_4H_{10}O$, Ethyl ether (113)
D = HCl

$AgClO_4$

B = C_6H_6, Benzene (78); at 25°C, K = 46000 ± 5000 for $[A]_B$ = <0.0000506

$AgNO_3$

B = C_6H_7N, Aniline (54.5)

t = 16 ± 1°C

$[A]_B$	K′
0.05	71 ± 5
0.10	90 ± 3
0.20	106 ± 2
0.90	173 ± 2

$HAuCl_4$

B = $C_4H_{10}O$, Ethyl ether (113); 40 Wt. % of A in C removed by single extraction with B

B = $C_4H_{10}O$, Ethyl ether (113)
D = HCl; 98 Wt. % of A removed by single extraction from 10% D

$IrCl_4$

B = $C_4H_{10}O$, Ethyl ether (113)

B = $C_4H_{10}O$, Ethyl ether (113)
D = HCl

$PtCl_4$

B = $C_4H_{10}O$, Ethyl ether (113)

B = $C_4H_{10}O$, Ethyl ether (113)
D = HCl

$PdCl_2$

B = $C_4H_{10}O$, Ethyl ether (113)

B = $C_4H_{10}O$, Ethyl ether (113)
D = HCl

$FeCl_3$

B = $C_4H_{10}O$, Ethyl ether (113)
D = HCl

$Fe(CNS)_3$ (63); *cf.* (62)

B = $C_4H_{10}O$, Ethyl ether

°C	$[A]_B$	K
0	0.0167	0.53*
10	0.0128	0.99*
20	0.0091	1.8†
25	0.00025	13.9‡
	0.001	6.9§
	0.002	4.8‖
	0.005	2.7‖
	0.01	1.8‖
30	0.0059	3.3¶
35	0.0048	4.3§

* ± 0.05.
† ± 0.2.
‡ ± 1.0.
§ ± 0.5.
‖ ± 0.1.
¶ ± 0.3.

B = $C_4H_{10}O$, Ethyl ether (63)
D = HNO_3

$NiCl_2$

B = $C_4H_{10}O$, Ethyl ether (113)
D = HCl

$Cr(CNS)_3$

B = $C_4H_{10}O$, Ethyl ether (63)

°C	$[A]_B$	K
0	0.0092	0.77*
8	0.0085	0.91*
20	0.0072	1.24†
30	0.0059	1.72†

* ± 0.02.
† ± 0.05.

$Cr(CNS)_3.3H_2O$, Chromitrihydrotrithiocyanate
B = $C_4H_{10}O$, Ethyl ether (10)

$Cr(CNS)_4.2H_2O$, Chromidihydrotetrathiocyanate
B = $C_4H_{10}O$, Ethyl ether (10)

$Cr(CNS)_5.H_2O$, Chromihydropentathiocyanate
B = $C_4H_{10}O$, Ethyl ether (10)

H_3BO_3
B = $CS_2 + C_5H_{12}O$, Amyl alcohol (mixtures) (67, 72)
B = $C_5H_{12}O$, Amyl alcohol (112); *cf.* (2); at 15°C, K = 3.37 ± 0.02 for $[A]_B$ = 0.085–0.264; at 25°C, K = 3.34 ± 0.05 for $[A]_B$ = 0.008–0.086; at 35°C, K = 3.31 ± 0.05 for $[A]_B$ = 0.044
B = $C_5H_{12}O$, Amyl alcohol (2)
D = Aqueous solution of KF

$AlBr_3$
B = C_6H_6, Benzene (105.5)
B = C_7H_8, Toluene (105.5)

LiCl
B = $C_5H_{12}O$, Amyl alcohol (39, 41)
t = 25–30°C

$[A]_B$	K
0.003	216 ±5
0.01	162 ±5
0.02	119 ±3
0.03	98 ±3
0.05	67 ±2
0.1	45 ±2
0.2	28.5±1
0.3	20.5±1
0.5	13.5±1
1.0	9.0±0.5
1.5	7.5±0.5

B = $C_5H_{12}O$.—(*Continued*)
t = 24.90°C (20.5)

$[A]_B$	10^3 K′
0.00015	3.0±0.05
0.00030	3.1±0.05
0.00045	3.2±0.1
0.00060	3.3±0.1

NaOH
B = $C_4H_{10}O$, Isobutyl alcohol (177)
t = 25°C

$[OH^-]_C$	K′ ± 0.0_53
0.000076	0.000019
0.000152	0.000025

NaCl
B = $C_4H_{10}O$, Ethyl ether (88)
D = Aqueous solution of acetic acid

$NaC_2H_3O_2$
B = $C_4H_{10}O$ (88)
D = Aqueous solution of acetic acid

$NaC_7H_5O_3$, Salicylate
B = Olive oil (64); at 15°R, K′ = 0.1 ± ? for g A/l_B = 1.56

KOH
B = $C_4H_{10}O$, Isobutyl alcohol (177); at 25°C and $[OH^-]_C$ = 0.000146, K′ = 0.0_438 ± 0.0_55

KI
B = $C_6H_5NO_2$, Nitrobenzene (32); at 25°C, K = 5450 ± 100 for $[A]_B$ = 0.00111
B = C_6H_6O, Phenol (134); at 18°C, K = 13 ± 1 for g A/100 cm³ = 0.52–2.09

$K_2CO(CNS)_4$
B = C_2H_6O, Ethyl alcohol (3.1)

ℭ-TABLE

The A-components (the distributed substances) are compounds whose key formulae begin with 16; the ℭ-arrangement. Under each A-component the B-components are likewise in the ℭ-arrangement, liquids of indefinite composition (oils, etc.) being placed at the end in alphabetical order. The C-component is H_2O.

The D-component, where given, is a solute in the aqueous layer.

Les constituants A (les substances distribuées) sont des composés dont la formule clé commence par 16; arrangement ℭ. Sous chaque constituant A, les constituants B sont de même disposés suivant l'arrangement ℭ; les liquides de composition non définie (huiles, etc.) étant placés à la fin dans l'ordre alphabétique. Le constituant C est H_2O.

Le constituant D, représente, lorsqu'il est mentionné, un corps dissout dans la couche aqueuse.

Die A-Komponente (die verteilte Komponente) ist eine Verbindung, deren Schlüsselformel mit 16 beginnt; die ℭ-Anordnung. Unter jeder A-Komponente steht, gleichfalls in der ℭ-Anordnung, die B-Komponente. Flüssigkeiten unbestimmter Zusammensetzung (Öle, etc.) befinden sich am Ende in alphabetischer Reihenfolge. Die C-Komponente ist H_2O.

Eine D-Komponente ist, wenn angegeben, der gelöste Stoff in der wässrigen Schichte.

I componenti A (le sostanze distribuite tra i due liquidi) sono composti di cui la formula chiave comincia con 16; ordinamento ℭ. Sotto ciascun componente A i componenti B sono disposti pure secondo l'ordinamento ℭ; i liquidi di composizione non definita (olii, etc.) sono messi alla fine in ordine alfabetico. Il componente C è l'acqua.

Il componente D, quando è indicato, è una sostanza disciolta nello strato acquoso.

HCN
B = C_6H_6, Benzene (62, 63); *cf.* (56)

°C	10^3 M_A/l_B	K
6	3.25	1.92†
7	14.8*	3.9‡
10	3.55	1.72†
16	3.63	1.63†
20	15.4*	3.7‡
25	3.75	1.55†

* 10^3 $[A]_B$. † ± 0.05. ‡ ± 0.2.

$CHCl_3$
B = Olive Oil (25, 121); K = ∞

CH_2O, Formaldehyde
B = $CHCl_3$, Chloroform (74)
t = 25°C

$[A]_B$	K′ ± 0.001
0.05	0.025
0.1	0.031
0.3	0.054
0.5	0.073
0.7	0.089

B = $C_4H_{10}O$, Ethyl ether (63)

°C	10^3 $[A]_B$	K ± 0.3
0	6.8	8.5
10	6.3	9.2
20	6.3	9.2

B = $C_5H_{12}O$, Amyl alcohol (74)
t = 25°C

$[A]_B$	K′ ± 0.1
1.0	3.05
3.0	2.05
5.0	1.5
8.0	1.2

CH_2O_2, Formic acid
B = CCl_4 (59)
B = CS_2 (59)
B = $CHBr_3$, Bromoform (59)
B = $CHCl_3$, Chloroform (155); *cf.* (149); at 25 ± 0.5°C, K′ = 0.031 ± 0.001 for $[A]_B$ = 0.001
B = $C_4H_{10}O$, Ethyl ether (5, 156); *cf.* (26, 53, 129, 135, 149); *see also* p. 400

B = $C_4H_{10}O$.—(*Continued*)
t = 15.0°C (129.5)

$[A]_B$	K′
0.05	0.40 ± 0.02
0.10	0.41 ± 0.02
0.20	0.43 ± 0.015
0.30	0.44 ± 0.015
0.40	0.45 ± 0.01
0.50	0.46 ± 0.01

t = 18 ± 0.02°C

$[A]_B$	K′ ± 0.005
0.02	0.374
0.05	0.383
0.10	0.393
0.20	0.406
0.40	0.427
0.60	0.446

t = 25 ± 0.5°C

$[A]_B$	K′ ± 0.01
0.002	0.35
0.005	0.38
0.009	0.41
0.013	0.44

B = $C_4H_{10}O$.—(*Continued*)
t = 26.3°C (129.5)

$[A]_B$	K′
0.05	0.35 ± 0.01
0.10	0.36 ± 0.01
0.20	0.37 ± 0.01
0.30	0.374 ± 0.005
0.40	0.384 ± 0.005
0.50	0.393 ± 0.005

B = C_6H_6, Benzene (17); *cf.* (57, 59, 87, 94); *see also* p. 400
t = 25 ± 0.03°C

$[A]_B$	K ± 5
0.012	286
0.015	267
0.020	245
0.025	226
0.035	195

B = C_7H_8, Toluene (59)
B = C_8H_{10}, Xylene (59)
B = Cottonseed oil (59)
B = Kerosene (59)

CH_4O, Methyl alcohol
B = Olive oil; K′ = 0.02 (25)
B = Cottonseed oil (179)

CH_5N, Methylamine

B = $CHCl_3$, Chloroform (**109**); *cf.* (**155**)

°C	$10^3[A]_B$	K ± 0.05
18*	9.53	8.49
25	15.7	7.98
32.35	19.7	5.99

* ± 0.005.

B = $C_4H_{10}O$, Ethyl ether (**156**); at 25 ± 0.5°C, K′ = 0.113 ± 0.003 for $[A]_B$ = 0.0006 – 0.0039

B = $C_5H_{12}O$, Amyl alcohol (**69**)

B = C_8H_{10}, Xylene (**155**)

$C_2HCl_3O_2$, Trichloroacetic acid

B = $C_4H_{10}O$, Ethyl ether (**156**)

t = 25 ± 0.5°C

$[A]_B$	K′ ± 0.05
0.001	0.48
0.005	1.05
0.010	1.48
0.015	1.81

B = C_5H_{10}, Amylene (**115, 149**)

B = C_6H_6, Benzene (**42, 115, 149**)

$[A]_B$	K
t = 18°C	
0.0005	107 ± 2
0.0007	91 ± 2
0.0012	75 ± 1
0.0018	64 ± 1
0.003	52.0 ± 0.5
0.007	35.0 ± 0.3
0.015	24.2 ± 0.3
0.04	15.5 ± 0.2
0.10	9.6 ± 0.1
0.15	7.5 ± 0.1
t = 22°C	
0.015	22 ± 1
0.04	14.8 ± 0.5
0.10	9.2 ± 0.5
0.15	7.0 ± 0.2
0.25	5.1 ± 0.2
0.40	4.3 ± 0.2

$C_2H_2Cl_2O_2$ Dichloroacetic acid

B = $C_4H_{10}O$, Ethyl ether (**156**)

t = 25 ± 0.5°C

$[A]_B$	K′
0.002	1.04 ± 0.04
0.005	1.49 ± 0.04
0.01	1.99 ± 0.08
0.015	2.32 ± 0.08
0.025	2.68 ± 0.08

B = C_6H_6, Benzene (**42, 58**)

$[A]_B$	K
t = 13–15°C	
0.03	22 ± 2
0.06	19 ± 2
0.09	18 ± 2
t = 18 ± 0.05°C	
0.0005	66 ± 1
0.001	51.5 ± 1
0.002	43 ± 1
0.005	34.3 ± 0.5
0.01	27.2 ± 0.5

$C_2H_2O_4$, Oxalic acid

B = $C_4H_{10}O$, Ethyl ether (**21, 127, 155**); *cf.* (**8, 49, 149, 156**)

$[A]_B$	K
t = 15°C	
0.0041	17 ± 2
0.01	14 ± 1
0.02	12.6 ± 0.5
0.03	11.8 ± 0.5
t = 25 ± 0.01°C	
0.0_454	100 ± 5
0.0_3168	61 ± 2
0.0_3465	42 ± 1
0.0041	21.7 ± 0.5
0.01	16.8 ± 0.2
0.02	14.9 ± 0.2
0.03	13.9 ± 0.2
t = 27°C	
0.0023	19 ± 3
0.01	17 ± 1
0.02	14.9 ± 0.5
0.03	13.8 ± 0.5
0.04	13.1 ± 0.5
0.06	12.1 ± 0.5

B = $C_4H_{10}O$, Ethyl ether + $C_5H_{12}O$, Amyl alcohol (mixtures) (**71**)

B = $C_4H_{10}O$, Ethyl ether (**49, 127**)

D = Aqueous solutions of H_2SO_4; NH_4Cl; $(NH_4)_2C_2O_4$; $Na_2C_2O_4$

B = $C_5H_{12}O$, Amyl alcohol (**69, 158**)

t = 20°C

$[A]_B$	K′ ± 0.007
0.01	0.231
0.025	0.281
0.05	0.326
0.15	0.403
0.225	0.423

$C_2H_3BrO_2$, Bromoacetic acid

B = $CHCl_3$, Chloroform (**155**)

B = $C_4H_{10}O$, Ethyl ether (**156**)

B = C_8H_{10}, Xylene (**155**)

$C_2H_3ClO_2$ Chloroacetic acid

B = CCl_4 (**73, 155**)

t = 25°C

$[A]_B$	K′ ± 0.01
0.2	0.20
0.4	0.36
0.6	0.52

B = CS_2 (**73**)

t = 25°C

$[A]_B$	$10^3K'$
0.05	7.1±0.2
0.10	9.7±0.2
0.15	13.1±0.3
0.20	17.8±0.3

B = $CHBr_3$, Bromoform (**73, 155**)

t = 25°C

B = $CHBr_3$.—(*Continued*)

$[A]_B$	$10^2K'$
0.15	3.1±0.3
0.4	5.2±0.3
0.8	8.7±0.5
1.2	12.4±0.5

B = $CHCl_3$, Chloroform (**73, 155, 156**)

t = 25°C

$10^3[A]_B$	$10^3K'$
0.625	14.6±0.7
1.25	18.3±0.7
2	20.4±0.7
4	25.0±0.7
6	29.0±0.7
25	50.5±1
50	57 ±1
100	63 ±3
200	68 ±3
300	70 ±3
500	77 ±3
750	101 ±3

B = $C_4H_{10}O$, Ethyl ether (**63, 143, 156**)

$[A]_B$	K′
t = 18°C	
0.02	1.99
0.05	2.18
0.1	2.32
0.3	2.57
0.6	2.70
1.2	2.81
t = 25°C	
0.002	1.16 ± 0.05
0.005	1.40 ± 0.05
0.01	1.6 ± 0.1
0.015	1.7 ± 0.1
0.02	1.8 ± 0.1

B = $C_4H_{10}O$, Ethyl ether (**63, 143**)

D = Aqueous solutions of H_2SO_4; $NaC_2H_2ClO_2$

B = C_6H_6, Benzene (**58, 70, 155**)

$[A]_B$	K′ ± 0.001
t = 13–15°C	
0.02	0.025
0.03	0.0255
0.04	0.027
0.05	0.028
t = 25°C	
0.02	0.026
0.03	0.029
0.04	0.0305
0.05	0.032
0.1	0.036
0.2	0.039
0.3	0.0425
0.4	0.051

B = C_7H_8, Toluene (**70, 155**)

t = 25°C

$[A]_B$	$10^3K'$
0.01	19.4 ± 0.4
0.05	25.7 ± 0.4
0.1	27.8 ± 0.4
0.2	32.8 ± 0.5
0.3	39.0 ± 0.5
0.5	55.0 ± 0.5

(B = C_7H_8.—(*Continued*); t = 25°C.—(*Continued*))

$C_2H_3Br_3O_2$, Bromal hydrate (**6, 108**)

B = Olive oil at room temp., K′ = 0.67 ± 0.05

$C_2H_3Cl_3O_2$, Chloral hydrate

B = $C_4H_{10}O$, Ethyl ether (**63**)

°C	$[A]_B$	K ± 0.002
0	0.764	0.233
10	0.764	0.233
20	0.766	0.235
30	0.766	0.236

B = C_6H_6, Benzene (**18**)

B = C_7H_8, Toluene (**63**)

°C	$[A]_B$	K ± 1
0	0.011	74.5
10	0.011	64.5
20	0.015	58.0

B = Olive oil (**6, 107, 108, 118**)

°C	g A/kg B	$10^2K'$
3	0.8	5.3 ± 0.5
Room		22 ± 2
30	2.7	24 ± 2

$C_2H_4Cl_2$, Ethylene chloride

B = Olive oil (**25**); at room temp., K′ = 60 ± 5

C_2H_4OS, Thioacetic acid

B = $C_4H_{10}O$, Ethyl ether (**156**)

$C_2H_4O_2$, Acetic acid

B = CCl_4 (**73, 145, 155**); *cf.* (**171**)

t = 25°C

$[A]_B$	K′ ± 0.003
0.25	0.060
1.0	0.106
2.0	0.172
3.0	0.243
4.0	0.315

B = CCl_4 + CS_2 (mixtures) (**67, 71**)

B = CS_2 (**73, 145**); *cf.* (**171**)

t = 25°C

$[A]_B$	K′ ± 0.001
0.5	0.043
0.6	0.049
0.7	0.055
0.8	0.061
0.9	0.0675
1.0	0.0735

B = $CHBr_3$, Bromoform (**73, 145, 155**)

t = 25°C

$[A]_B$	K′
0.5	0.103 ± 0.003
1.0	0.132 ± 0.003
2.0	0.198 ± 0.005
3.0	0.270 ± 0.005
4.0	0.35 ± 0.01

$C_2H_4O_2$.—(*Continued*)

B = $CHCl_3$, Chloroform (**34, 73, 139, 145, 155**); *cf.* (**28, 149, 171**)

t = 20°C

$[A]_B$	K
0.002	36.2 ± 0.2
0.004	31.2 ± 0.2
0.006	27.7 ± 0.2
0.008	25.25 ± 0.1
0.010	23.5 ± 0.1
0.012	22.1 ± 0.1
0.02	18.55 ± 0.1
0.04	14.05 ± 0.1
0.06	11.95 ± 0.05
0.08	10.60 ± 0.05
0.10	9.68 ± 0.05
0.12	8.94 ± 0.05
0.14	8.36 ± 0.05
0.16	7.84 ± 0.03
0.18	7.43 ± 0.03
0.20	7.10 ± 0.03
0.22	6.82 ± 0.03

t = 25°C

$[A]_B$	K
0.03	15.92 ± 0.05
0.04	14.36 ± 0.05
0.06	12.33 ± 0.05
0.08	10.98 ± 0.05
0.10	10.02 ± 0.05
0.12	9.32 ± 0.04
0.14	8.77 ± 0.04
0.16	8.29 ± 0.04
0.18	7.86 ± 0.03
0.20	7.50 ± 0.03
0.22	7.19 ± 0.03
0.24	6.94 ± 0.03
0.26	6.73 ± 0.03
0.4	5.55 ± 0.05
0.7	4.45 ± 0.1
1.0	3.8 ± 0.1
1.5	3.2 ± 0.1
2.0	2.8 ± 0.1
2.5	2.6 ± 0.1
3.0	2.4 ± 0.1
3.5	2.25 ± 0.1
4.0	2.2 ± 0.1

B = $CHCl_3$, Chloroform (**34, 45, 139**)
D = Aqueous solutions of HCl; H_2SO_4; HNO_3; NH_4NO_3; $Ba(NO_3)_2$; $LiNO_3$; NaCl; $NaC_2H_3O_2$; KCl; $KClO_3$; $KClO_4$; K_2SO_4; NaOH, and the following acids separately: citric, malic, succinic, tartaric

B = $C_4H_8O_2$, Ethyl acetate (**171**)

B = $C_4H_{10}O$, Ethyl ether (**62, 88, 100, 103**); *cf.* (**8, 55, 63, 110, 127, 149, 156, 171**); *v. also* p. 400

B = $C_4H_{10}O$.—(*Continued*)

$[A]_B$*	K ± 0.02 0°C†	K ± 0.02 5°C†
0.02	1.85	1.90
0.05	1.82	1.87
0.10	1.79	1.83
0.20	1.72	1.76
0.40	1.61	1.64
0.60	1.52	1.55
0.80	1.45	1.47

$[A]_B$	K ± 0.01 10°C	K ± 0.01 15°C
0.02	1.99	2.055
0.05	1.955	2.015
0.10	1.91	1.965
0.20	1.83	1.89
0.40	1.72	1.775
0.60	1.62	1.675
0.80	1.53	1.59
	20°C	**25°C**
0.02	2.10	2.15
0.05	2.055	2.12
0.10	2.005	2.06
0.20	1.93	1.985
0.40	1.81	1.87
0.60	1.71	1.77
0.80	1.62	1.675

t = 18°C

$[A]_B$	K ± 0.01
0.05	2.03
0.10	1.98
0.25	1.87
0.50	1.735
0.75	1.625
1.0	1.53
1.5	1.385
2.0	1.29
2.5	1.21
3.0	1.15
3.5	1.10
4.0	1.06
4.5	1.03

°C	$[A]_B$	K ± 0.02
7.5	0.918	1.45
12	0.881	1.52
13	0.345	1.76
27	0.325	1.94

* At 0 ± 0.2°C, K = 2.03 ± 0.02 for $[A]_B$ in M/l of solvent = 0.000709; at 25°C, K = 2.21 ± 0.02, for $[A]_B$ in M/l of solvent = 0.000665.

† At 0 and 5°C, probable error, ± 1–2°C.

B = $C_4H_{10}O$, Ethyl ether (**88, 89, 90, 100, 103**); *cf.* (**63**)
D = Aqueous solutions of ethyl alcohol; $MgCl_2$; $MgSO_4$; $BaCl_2$; NaCl; NaBr; Na_2SO_4; $NaNO_3$; KCl; KBr; KI; K_2SO_4; KNO_3; acetates of the following: NH_4, Pb^+, Zn, Cd, Hg^{++}, Ag, Cu^{++}, Fe^{++}, Fe^{+++}, Co, Ni, Cr^{+++}, Al, La, Mg, Na, K

B = $C_5H_{12}O$, Amyl alcohol (**69, 145, 158**); *cf.* (**171**)

B = $C_5H_{12}O$.—(*Continued*)

°C	$[A]_B$	K′ ± 0.01
20	0.6	0.92
25	0.8	0.93

B = $C_6H_5NO_2$, Nitrobenzene (**171**)

B = C_6H_6, Benzene (**17, 62, 70, 92, 145**); *cf.* (**18, 47, 87, 94, 114, 149, 171**); *v. also* p. 400

t = 15–16°C

$[A]_B$	K
0.184	14.3 ± 0.1
0.050	23.8 ± 0.2
0.0041	55.1 ± 0.3
0.0018	60.7 ± 0.8
0.00042	80.1 ± 1

t = 25 ± 0.03°C

$[A]_B$	K
3.11	3.580 ± 0.005
2.69	4.016 ± 0.005
1.46	5.95 ± 0.01

t = 25°C

$[A]_B$	K
1.09	6.93 ± 0.01
0.739	8.26 ± 0.01
0.614	8.87 ± 0.01
0.486	9.76 ± 0.03
0.256	12.9 ± 0.03
0.224	13.29 ± 0.05
0.158	16.4 ± 0.05
0.1015	18.30 ± 0.05
0.0714	21.15 ± 0.1
0.0443	25.9 ± 0.1
0.0165	38.4 ± 0.2
0.0125	42.5 ± 0.2

At 6°C, K = 59.5 ± 1, for $[A]_B$ in moles per l of solvent = 0.000032; at 18.5°C, K = 54.5 ± 1, for $[A]_B$ in moles per l of solvent = 0.000036.

B = C_6H_6, Benzene (**47**)
D = Aqueous solution of $NaC_2H_3O_2$

B = C_7H_6O Benzaldehyde (**171**)

B = C_7H_8, Toluene (**70, 145, 155**); *cf.* (**171**)

t = 25°C

$[A]_B$	$10^2K'$
0.01	2.00 ± 0.02
0.1	4.40 ± 0.05
0.3	7.02 ± 0.08
0.5	8.7 ± 0.1
0.7	10.1 ± 0.1
1.0	11.95 ± 0.1
1.3	13.6 ± 0.1

B = C_8H_{10}, *o*-Xylene (**70, 145**)

t = 25°C

$[A]_B$	K′
0.1	0.048 ± 0.001
0.3	0.066 ± 0.001
0.6	0.088 ± 0.003
1.0	0.114 ± 0.003
1.5	0.146 ± 0.005
2.0	0.173 ± 0.005
2.5	0.200 ± 0.005

B = C_8H_{10}, *m*-Xylene (**70, 145**)

t = 25°C

$[A]_B$	K′
0.02	0.0222 ± 0.0005
0.1	0.041 ± 0.001
0.2	0.053 ± 0.001
0.3	0.062 ± 0.001
0.4	0.069 ± 0.001
0.6	0.083 ± 0.001
0.8	0.095 ± 0.001
1.0	0.106 ± 0.001

B = C_8H_{10}, *p*-Xylene (**70, 145**)

t = 25°C

$[A]_B$	K′
0.1	0.0550 ± 0.0005
0.5	0.078 ± 0.001
1.0	0.109 ± 0.001
1.5	0.141 ± 0.001
2.0	0.172 ± 0.001
2.3	0.191 ± 0.001

B = $C_{10}H_{12}$, Tetralin (**77**)

t = 25°C

$[A]_B$	K
0.04	48 ± 2
0.1	36 ± 2
0.2	28 ± 1
0.4	19.9 ± 0.5
0.7	14.5 ± 0.5
1.0	12.0 ± 0.5

B = $C_{10}H_{18}$, Decalin (**77**)

t = 25°C

$[A]_B$	K
0.05	106 ± 2
0.10	81 ± 2
0.15	66 ± 1
0.20	56 ± 1
0.25	49 ± 1

B = Cottonseed oil (**59**)

B = Kerosene (**59**)

B = Kerosene (**24**)
D = Aqueous solutions of $CaCl_2$; KCl

B = Petroleum ether (**171**)

$C_2H_4O_3$, Glycollic acid

B = $C_4H_{10}O$, Ethyl ether (**129**); at 15°C, K = 32 ± 1; at 26°C, K = 38 ± 1

C_2H_6O, Ethyl alcohol

B = CCl_4 (**19**); *v. also* p. 400; at 25°C, K′ = 0.0244 ± 0.0005, for $[A]_B$ = 0.0097–0.0553

B = CS_2 (**19**); *v. also* p. 400; at 25°C, K′ = 0.0143 ± 0.0005 for $[A]_B$ = 0.0059–0.222

B = $C_4H_{10}O$, Ethyl ether; *v.* p. 401

B = C_6H_5Br, Bromobenzene (**19**); *v.* p. 401

B = C_6H_6, Benzene (**110**); *cf.* (**18**); *v. also* p. 401

B = C_6H_6.—(*Continued*)

t = 25°C

g A/l_B	K ± 0.05
50	1.02
100	1.14
150	1.26
200	1.37

B = Cottonseed oil (179)

B = Olive oil (107, 108, 121)

°C	g C/kg A + B	K′ ±0.005
3	0.8	0.026
30	1.4	0.047

C_2H_7N, Ethylamine

B = $CHCl_3$, Chloroform (155)

t = 25 ± 0.5°C

$[A]_B$	K′ ± 0.05
0.0015	0.35
0.005	0.50
0.01	0.62
0.02	0.77

B = $C_4H_{10}O$, Ethyl ether (156); at 25 ± 0.5°C, K′ = 0.172 ± 0.005 for $[A]_B$ = 0.00045–0.0025

B = C_7H_8, Toluene (109)

°C ± 0.005	$[A]_B$	K ± 0.05
18	0.00295	26.09
25	0.00565	19.13
32.35	0.0127	14.77

B = C_8H_{10}, Xylene (155)

C_2H_7N, Dimethylamine

B = $CHCl_3$, Chloroform (155)

B = $C_4H_{10}O$, Ethyl ether (156); at 25 ± 0.5°C, K′ = 0.231 for $[A]_B$ = 0.00033–0.00305

B = C_7H_8, Toluene (109)

°C ± 0.005	$[A]_B$	K ± 1
18	0.0037	23
25	0.0058	19
32.35	0.0077	13

B = C_8H_{10}, Xylene (155)

C_2H_8ClN, Dimethylamine hydrochloride

B = $CHCl_3$, Chloroform (74)

$C_3H_3NO_2$, Cyanoacetic acid

B = $C_4H_{10}O$, Ethyl ether (62)

°C	$[A]_B$/l solvent	K
0	0.00050	1.66 ± 0.03
10	0.00042	2.16 ± 0.03
21	0.00035	2.73 ± 0.05
30	0.00033	3.16 ± 0.05

B = C_6H_6, Benzene (62)

°C	$[A]_B$/l solvent	K ± 1
6	0.00023	59
25	0.00022	69

$C_3H_4Br_2O_2$, 1, 2-Dibromopropionic acid

B = $CHCl_3$, Chloroform (155)

B = $C_4H_{10}O$, Ethyl ether (156)

B = C_8H_{10}, Xylene (155)

$C_3H_4O_3$, Pyruvic acid

B = $CHCl_3$, Chloroform (155)

B = $C_4H_{10}O$, Ethyl ether (156)

B = C_8H_{10}, Xylene (155)

$C_3H_4O_4$, Malonic acid

B = $C_4H_{10}O$, Ethyl ether (21, 155); *cf.* (140, 156)

t = 25 ± 0.01°C

$[A]_B$	K ± 0.2
0.003	12.1
0.005	11.7
0.010	11.1
0.013	10.9

$C_3H_5BrO_2$, 1-Bromopropionic acid

B = $CHCl_3$, Chloroform (155)

B = $C_4H_{10}O$, Ethyl ether (156)

B = C_8H_{10}, Xylene (155)

$C_3H_5IO_2$, 2-Iodopropionic acid

B = $CHCl_3$, Chloroform (155)

B = $C_4H_{10}O$, Ethyl ether (156)

B = C_8H_{10}, Xylene (155)

C_3H_6O, Acetone

B = CCl_4 (74, 76, 158)

t = 25°C

$[A]_B$	K′ ± 0.01
0.1	0.45
0.5	0.52
1.0	0.59
1.5	0.66
2.0	0.72

B = $CHCl_3$, Chloroform (74, 76); *v. also* p. 400

t = 25°C

$[A]_B$	K′ ± 0.2
0.2	5.2
1.0	4.6
2.0	3.8
3.0	3.1

B = C_2Cl_4, Tetrachloroethylene (76)

B = C_2HCl_3, Trichloroethylene (76)

B = C_2HCl_5, Pentachloroethane (76)

B = $C_2H_2Cl_4$, Tetrachloroethane (76)

B = C_6H_6, Benzene (70, 158); *cf.* (124); *v. also* p. 401

t = 25°C

$[A]_B$	K′ ± 0.02
0.4	0.94
0.7	0.96
1.2	1.00
1.6	1.03
2.0	1.06
2.4	1.09

B = C_6H_6, Benzene (124)

D = Aqueous solutions of LiCl; NaCl; KCl

B = C_7H_8, Toluene (63); *v. also* p. 401

B = C_7H_8.—(*Continued*)

°C	$[A]_B$	K ± 0.1
0	0.0173	2.1
10	0.0165	2.1
20	0.0165	2.05
30	0.0165	1.95

B = Olive oil (107); *cf.* (25); at 3°C, K′ = 0.145 ± 0.01 for g A/l_B = 5.0–6.1; at 30°C, K′ = 0.23 ± 0.02 for g A/l_B = 7.2–8.7

$C_3H_6O_2$, Propionic acid

B = $CHCl_3$, Chloroform (155); *cf.* (149)

t = 25 ± 0.5°C

$[A]_B$	K′ ± 0.005
0.0005	0.141
0.0010	0.159
0.0015	0.171
0.0020	0.182

B = $C_4H_{10}O$, Ethyl ether (156); *cf.* (149); *v. also* p. 401

t = 25 ± 0.5°C

$[A]_B$	K′ ± 0.04
0.001	1.31
0.002	1.38
0.005	1.47
0.008	1.52

B = $C_4H_{10}O$, Ethyl ether (88, 89)

D = Aqueous solutions of $MgCl_2$; NaCl; KNO_3; K propionate

B = C_6H_6, Benzene (17); *cf.* (87, 149); *v. also* p. 401

t = 25 ± 0.03°C

$[A]_B$	K
0.0223	6.91 ± 0.03
0.0343	5.57 ± 0.03
0.0778	3.98 ± 0.02
0.128	3.25 ± 0.02
0.276	2.34 ± 0.01
0.644	1.646 ± 0.005
1.002	1.398 ± 0.005
2.710	1.033 ± 0.003
3.556	1.002 ± 0.003

B = C_8H_{10}, Xylene (155)

B = Cottonseed oil (59)

$C_3H_6O_2$, Ethyl formate

B = Olive oil; K′ = 4 ± 1 (121)

$C_3H_6O_3$, Lactic acid

B = $CHCl_3$, Chloroform (155)

t = 25 ± 0.5°C

$[A]_B$	K′ ± 0.0007
0.0005	0.0168
0.0007	0.0185
0.0010	0.0203
0.0015	0.0219
0.0018	0.0226

B = $C_4H_{10}O$, Ethyl ether (127, 129, 156)

B = $C_4H_{10}O$.—(*Continued*)

t = 15–27.5°C (127)

$[A]_B$	K±?
0.01	12.2
0.05	11.3
0.10	10.6
0.15	10.0
0.20	9.4
t = 25 ± 0.5°C (156)	
0.001	6.1
0.005	5.6

C_3H_7N, Allylamine (155)

B = C_8H_{10}, Xylene

$C_3H_7NO_2$, Urethane

B = Olive oil (6, 108, 118); *cf.* (121); at room temp., K′ = 0.135 ± 0.01 for g A/l_B = 3.9

C_3H_8O, *n*-Propyl alcohol

B = Cottonseed oil (179)

B = Olive oil; K′ = 0.1 (121)

C_3H_8O, Isopropyl alcohol

B = Olive oil; K′ = 0.36 ± 0.03 (25)

C_3H_9N, Propylamine

B = C_7H_8, Toluene (109)

°C ± 0.005	$[A]_B$	K ± 0.05
18	0.0174	5.44
25	0.0091	4.47
32.35	0.0178	3.31

B = C_8H_{10}, Xylene (155)

C_3H_9N, Trimethylamine

B = $CHCl_3$, Chloroform (155)

B = $C_4H_{10}O$, Ethyl ether (63, 156)

t = 0°C

$[A]_B$	K′ ± 0.02
0.0082	0.15
t = 10°C	
0.0124	0.25
t = 20°C	
0.0178	0.40
t = 25 ± 0.5°C	
0.001	0.66
0.003	0.67
0.005	0.68
0.010	0.71
t = 30°C	
0.023	0.57

B = C_6H_6, Benzene (70, 155); at 25°C, K′ = 0.50 ± 0.02 for $[A]_B$ = 0.03–0.59

B = C_7H_8, Toluene (63, 109); *cf.* (62)

t = 25°C

$[A]_B$	K
0.0002	4.7 ± 0.3
0.0005	3.5 ± 0.3
0.001	3.1 ± 0.2
0.002	2.6 ± 0.1
0.005	2.4 ± 0.1
0.01	2.35 ± 0.1
0.02	2.3 ± 0.1
0.04	2.25 ± 0.1

C_3H_9N.—(*Continued*)

B = C_7H_8.—(*Continued*)

°C	K
10	4.5 ± 0.15
20	2.9 ± 0.1
30	1.95 ± 0.1
40	1.35 ± 0.05
60	0.76 ± 0.03
90	0.47 ± 0.03

B = C_8H_{10}, Xylene (155)

$C_4H_4Br_2O_4$, 1, 2-Dibromosuccinic acid

B = $C_4H_{10}O$, Ethyl ether (21); at 25 ± 0.01°C, K = 0.059 ± 0.001 for $[A]_B$ = 0.531

$C_4H_4N_2$, Succinonitrile

B = $CHCl_3$, Chloroform (63)

B = $CHCl_3$, Chloroform (63)

D = Aqueous solutions of HCl; KOH; KCl

$C_4H_4O_4$, Fumaric acid

B = $C_4H_{10}O$, Ethyl ether (21, 156); *cf.* (140)

t = 25 ± 0.5°C

$[A]_B$	K
0.001	1.7 ± 0.1
0.002	1.4 ± 0.1

t = 25 ± 0.01°C

$[A]_B$	K
0.005	1.1 ± 0.1
0.01	0.90 ± 0.05
0.02	0.82 ± 0.05
0.03	0.79 ± 0.05

$C_4H_4O_4$, Maleic acid

B = $C_4H_{10}O$, Ethyl ether (21, 155); *cf.* (140, 156)

t = 25 ± 0.01°C

$[A]_B$	K
0.00023	23.7 ± 0.5
0.00057	17.8 ± 0.5
0.001	15.5 ± 0.2
0.003	11.9 ± 0.2
0.005	10.9 ± 0.1
0.01	9.65 ± 0.1

$C_4H_5BrO_4$, Bromosuccinic acid

B = $C_4H_{10}O$, Ethyl ether (21, 156)

B = C_8H_{10}, Xylene (155)

$C_4H_5Cl_3O_2$, Trichlorobutyric acid

B = C_5H_{10}, Amylene (115, 149)

B = C_6H_6, Benzene (42, 115, 149)

$C_4H_6O_2$, α-Crotonic acid

B = $CHCl_3$, Chloroform (155)

B = $C_4H_{10}O$, Ethyl ether (156)

B = C_8H_{10}, Xylene (155)

$C_4H_6O_4$, Succinic acid

B = $CHCl_3$, Chloroform (155)

t = 25 ± 0.5°C

$[A]_B$	K′ ± 0.0005
0.00015	0.0110
0.0003	0.0143
0.0006	0.0176
0.0010	0.0201

B = $C_4H_{10}O$, Ethyl ether (21, 51, 127, 155, 156); *cf.* (8, 140, 149)

t = 0 ± 0.01°C

$[A]_B$	K ± 0.05
0.001	4.83
0.002	4.71
0.003	4.62
0.005	4.52
0.015	4.44

t = 15°C

$[A]_B$	K ± 0.03
0.015	6.30
0.03	6.23
0.05	6.14
0.08	6.02

t = 20°C

$[A]_B$	K
0.015	6.98
0.03	6.92
0.05	6.84
0.08	6.74
0.10	6.67

t = 25 ± 0.01°C

$[A]_B$	K
0.0005	8.49*
0.001	8.13*
0.002	7.87*
0.003	7.80*

t = 25°C

$[A]_B$	K
0.015	7.74
0.03	7.67
0.05	7.57
0.08	7.45
0.10	7.36

* ± 0.08.

B = $C_5H_{12}O$, Amyl alcohol (69, 158)

t = 20°C

$[A]_B$	K′ ± 0.015
0.035	0.690
0.2	0.650
0.35	0.615

B = $C_{10}H_{22}O$, Amyl ether (149)

$C_4H_6O_5$, Malic acid

B = $C_4H_{10}O$, Ethyl ether (127); *cf.* (8); at 15°C, K = 63 ± 2 for $[A]_B$ = 0.009–0.016; at 25.5°C, K = 71 ± 2 for $[A]_B$ = 0.002–0.017

$C_4H_6O_6$, Tartaric acid

B = $C_4H_{10}O$, Ethyl ether (127); *cf.* (8, 149, 156)

$[A]_B$	K ± 5	
	15°C	27°C
0.002	216	266
0.004	209	253
0.007	198	234

$C_4H_7Cl_3O_2$, 1, 1, 2-Trichlorobutyraldehyde hydrate

B = Olive oil; at room temp., K′ = 1.6 ± 0 1 (6, 108)

C_4H_8O, Methyl ethyl ketone

B = Olive oil (25); K′ = 2.3 ± 0.2

$C_4H_8O_2$, *n*-Butyric acid

B = $CHCl_3$, Chloroform (155)

t = 25 ± 0.5°C

$[A]_B$	K′ ± 0.02
0.0005	0.47
0.0007	0.50
0.0010	0.53
0.0015	0.55
0.0022	0.56

B = $C_4H_{10}O$, Ethyl ether (156)

t = 25 ± 0.5°C

$[A]_B$	K′ ± 0.2
0.0015	4.2
0.003	4.5
0.006	4.9
0.010	5.1
0.014	5.3

B = $C_4H_{10}O$, Ethyl ether (89)

D = Aqueous solution of NaCl

B = C_6H_6, Benzene (17, 57); *cf.* (87, 94)

t = 13–15°C

$[A]_B$	K
0.15	0.77 ± 0.03
0.20	0.68 ± 0.03
0.25	0.61 ± 0.03
0.30	0.56 ± 0.03

t = 25 ± 0.03°C

$[A]_B$	K
0.025	1.725 ± 0.01
0.05	1.235 ± 0.01
0.10	0.930 ± 0.005
0.15	0.788 ± 0.005
0.20	0.697 ± 0.003
0.25	0.635 ± 0.003
0.30	0.591 ± 0.003
0.50	0.473 ± 0.003
1.0	0.388 ± 0.003
2.0	0.33 ± 0.02
3.0	0.31 ± 0.02
4.0	0.34 ± 0.02

B = C_8H_{10}, Xylene (155); at 25 ± 0.5°C, K′ = 0.158 ± 0.005 for $[A]_B$ = 0.0007–0.0013

B = Cottonseed oil (59)

B = Kerosene (24)

D = Aqueous solutions of $CaCl_2$; KCl

$C_4H_8O_2$, Isobutyric acid

B = CCl_4 (158)

B = $CHCl_3$, Chloroform (149, 155)

B = $C_4H_{10}O$, Ethyl ether (156)

B = C_6H_6, Benzene (87, 94, 149, 158)

B = C_7H_8, Toluene (158)

B = C_8H_{10}, Xylene (155)

$C_4H_8O_2$, Ethyl acetate

B = C_6H_6, Benzene (124); at 20°C, K′ = 12.20 ± 0.05 for g A/l_C = 0.8–2.5

B = C_6H_6, Benzene (124, 125)

D = Aqueous solutions of NH_4Cl; NH_4NO_3; $(NH_4)_2SO_4$; $MgSO_4$; LiCl; Li_2SO_4; NaCl; Na_2SO_4; $NaNO_3$; KCl; K_2SO_4; KNO_3; Glycerol; Dextrose; Sucrose

B = Olive oil (25); at room temp., K′ = 1.8 ± 0.2

B = Petroleum ether, B. P., 90–110° (124)

B = Petroleum ether, B. P., 90–110° (124)

D = Aqueous solutions of NaCl; Sucrose

$C_4H_8O_3$, 1 (2)-Hydroxybutyric acid

B = $C_4H_{10}O$, Ethyl ether (156)

$C_4H_8O_5$, 3, 4, 5-Trihydroxybutyric acid

B = Olive oil (11); at 25°C, K′ = 0.025 ± 0.002, calculated from separate solubilities

$C_4H_9NO_2$, Methylurethane

B = Olive oil (6, 108); at room temp., K′ = 0.04 ± 0.01

$C_4H_{10}O$, Isobutyl alcohol

B = Cottonseed oil (179)

B = Olive oil (121); K′ = 6 ± 1

$C_4H_{10}O$, *tert.*-Butyl alcohol

B = Olive oil (6); at room temp., K′ = 0.175 ± 0.01

$C_4H_{11}N$, *n*-Butylamine

B = $C_4H_{10}O$, Ethyl ether (156)

t = 25 ± 0.5°C

$[A]_B$	K′ ± 0.03
0.001	0.90
0.002	1.00
0.003	1.07

B = C_8H_{10}, Xylene (155)

t = 25 ± 0.5°C

$[A]_B$	K′ ± 0.02
0.0005	0.52
0.001	0.61
0.002	0.70
0.003	0.75
0.004	0.78

$C_4H_{11}N$, Isobutylamine

B = C_8H_{10}, Xylene (155)

$C_4H_{11}N$, Diethylamine

B = CCl_4 (158)

B = $CHCl_3$, Chloroform (155)

t = 25 ± 0.5°C

$[A]_B$	K′ ± 0.08
0.001	2.18
0.002	2.50
0.005	3.09
0.01	3.61
0.02	4.23

B = $C_2H_4Cl_2$, Ethylene chloride (158)

B = C_4H_9Br, *n*-Butyl bromide (158)

B = $C_4H_{10}O$, *n*-Butyl alcohol (158)

B = $C_4H_{10}O$, Isobutyl alcohol (158)

B = $C_4H_{10}O$, Ethyl ether (156); at 25 ± 0.5°C, K′ = 0.71 ± 0.02 for $[A]_B$ = 0.00044–0.0063

B = $C_5H_{12}O$, Amylalcohol (158)

B = $C_6H_3Cl_3$, 1, 3, 4-Trichlorobenzene (158)

B = $C_6H_4Cl_2$, *o*-Dichlorobenzene (158)

B = C_6H_5Br, Bromobenzene (158)

B = C_6H_6, Benzene (158)

t = 25 ± 0.5°C

$[A]_B$	K′ ± 0.02
0.002	0.61
0.005	0.69
0.009	0.76

B = C_7H_8, Toluene (109)

°C ± 0.005	$[A]_B$	K ± 0.005
18	0.0230	2.141
25	0.0223	1.596
32.35	0.1104	1.094

B = C_8H_{10}, Xylene (155)

t = 25 ± 0.5°C

$[A]_B$	K′ ± 0.02
0.0005	0.37
0.001	0.43
0.002	0.50
0.004	0.56
0.008	0.59

B = $C_8H_{18}O$, *n*-Butylether (158)

B = $C_8H_{18}O$, *sec.*-Octyl alcohol (158)

B = $C_{11}H_{16}O$, Isoamyl phenyl ether (158)

B = Paraffin oil (158)

B = Petroleum ether, B. P., 145–155° (158)

C_5H_5N, Pyridine

B = $CHCl_3$, Chloroform (155)

t = 25 ± 0.5°C

$[A]_B$	K′ ± 0.3
0.0013	5.6
0.003	8.1
0.005	9.2
0.010	10.6
0.017	11.2

B = C_6H_6, Benzene (62, 155, 178.5); *cf.* (58)

t = 25°C

M_A/l_B	K
0.000271	0.41 ± 0.02
0.000546	0.38 ± 0.02
0.001	0.35 ± 0.01
0.002	0.34 ± 0.01
0.004	0.34 ± 0.01

B = C_7H_8, Toluene (63, 155); *cf.* (149)

t = 25°C

$[A]_B$	K
0.001	0.70 ± 0.08
0.006	0.56 ± 0.04

B = C_7H_8: 25°C.—(*Continued*)

$[A]_B$	K
0.011	0.51 ± 0.02
0.025	0.48 ± 0.01
0.08	0.461 ± 0.005
0.12	0.456 ± 0.005

B = C_8H_{10}, Xylene (155); at 25 ± 0.5°C, K′ = 1.92 ± 0.06 for $[A]_B$ = 0.0019–0.019

$C_5H_6O_4$, Itaconic acid

B = $C_4H_{10}O$, Ethyl ether (21)

$C_5H_8O_3$, Levulinic acid

B = $CHCl_3$, Chloroform (155)

B = $C_4H_{10}O$, Ethyl ether (156)

B = C_8H_{10}, Xylene (155)

$C_5H_8O_4$, Glutaric acid

B = $CHCl_3$, Chloroform (155)

B = $C_4H_{10}O$, Ethyl ether (21, 155, 156)

$C_5H_{10}O_2$, Valeric acid

B = $CHCl_3$, Chloroform (155)

t = 25 ± 0.5°C

$[A]_B$	K′ ± 0.08
0.001	1.93
0.002	2.23
0.003	2.39
0.005	2.55

B = $C_4H_{10}O$, Ethyl ether (156); at 25 ± 0.5°C, K′ = 13.5 ± 0.5 for $[A]_B$ = 0.001–0.0057

B = C_6H_6, Benzene (17)

t = 25 ± 0.03°C

$[A]_B$	K ± 0.003
0.0292	0.466
0.0481	0.370
0.08	0.295
0.2	0.196*
0.3	0.164*
0.445	0.137*
0.929	0.0989†
1.4	0.0821†
1.848	0.0734†

* ± 0.001.
† ± 0.0005.

B = C_8H_{10}, Xylene (155)

t = 25 ± 0.5°C

$[A]_B$	K′ ± 0.03
0.001	0.63
0.003	0.89
0.007	1.18
0.012	1.39

$C_5H_{10}O_2$, Isovaleric acid

B = $CHCl_3$, Chloroform (155)

B = $C_4H_{10}O$, Ethyl ether (156)

B = $C_4H_{10}O$, Ethyl ether
D = Aqueous solution of NaCl (89)

B = C_6H_6, Benzene (87)

B = C_8H_{10}, Xylene (155)

$C_5H_{10}O_4$, Monacetin

B = Olive oil (6, 107, 108)

°C	g A/kg B	K′ ± 0.02
3	0.023	0.1
Room		0.06
36	0.016	0.07

$C_5H_{12}ClN$, ε-Chloroamylamine

B = $C_2H_2Cl_4$, Tetrachloroethane (54)

B = $C_6H_5NO_2$, Nitrobenzene (54)

B = C_6H_6, Benzene (54)

$C_5H_{11}N$, Piperidine

B = $CHCl_3$, Chloroform (155)

t = 25 ± 0.5°C

$[A]_B$	K′ ± 0.1
0.0008	2.0
0.0015	2.35
0.003	2.9
0.004	3.1
0.005	3.35
0.006	3.55

B = $C_4H_{10}O$, Ethyl ether (156)

t = 25 ± 0.5°C

$[A]_B$	K′ ± 0.015
0.002	0.66
0.005	0.70
0.008	0.73
0.012	0.765
0.018	0.79

B = C_6H_6, Benzene (62); *cf.* (58)

t = 25°C

$[A]_B/l_B$	K ± 0.1
0.0001	2.55
0.0002	1.9
0.0003	1.7
0.0005	1.45
0.0008	1.30*
0.0012	1.20*
0.002	1.10*
0.003	1.05*

* ± 0.05.

B = C_6H_6, Benzene (62)
D = Aqueous solutions of NaOH; NaCl; Piperidine hydrochloride

B = C_8H_{10}, Xylene (155)

t = 25 ± 0.5°C

$[A]_B$	K′ ± 0.01
0.0005	0.37
0.001	0.44
0.002	0.53
0.003	0.56
0.004	0.57

$C_5H_{11}NO$, Valeramide

B = Olive oil (64); at 15°R, K′ = 0.31 ± 0.03 for g A/l_B = 2.41

$C_5H_{12}O$, Isoamyl alcohol

B = Cottonseed oil (179)

$C_5H_{12}O$, Amylene hydrate

B = Olive oil (6); at room temp., K′ = 1.0 ± 0.1 for g A/l_B = 33

$C_5H_{12}O_4S_2$, Diethylsulfonmethane

B = Olive oil (6); at room temp., K′ = 0.15 ± 0.01 for g A/l_B = 0.68

$C_5H_{12}O_4S_2$, Dimethylsulfondimethylmethane

B = Olive oil (6); at room temp., K′ = 0.11 ± 0.01 for g A/l_B = 0.12–0.62

$C_5H_{13}N$, *n*-Amylamine

B = $CHCl_3$, Chloroform (155)

t = 25 ± 0.5°C

$[A]_B$	K′ ± 0.3
0.0007	5.9
0.001	7.3
0.0015	9.1
0.002	10.6
0.0025	12.0

B = C_8H_{10}, Xylene (155)

$C_5H_{13}N$, Isoamylamine

B = $C_4H_{10}O$, Ethyl ether (156); at 25 ± 0.5°C, K′ = 1.9 ± 0.1 for $[A]_B$ = 0.00039–0.00184

B = C_8H_{10}, Xylene (155)

$C_6H_3N_3O_7$, Picric acid

B = $CHBr_3$, Bromoform (73, 155)

t = 25°C

$[A]_B$	K′ ± 0.03
0.4	1.18
0.6	1.34
0.8	1.48
1.0	1.60

B = $CHCl_3$, Chloroform (73, 155)

t = 25°C

$[A]_B$	K′ ± 0.03
0.3	1.30
0.6	1.73
0.9	2.05
1.2	2.33
1.5	2.58

B = $CHCl_3$, Chloroform + $C_4H_{10}O$, Ethyl ether (mixtures) (71)

B = $C_4H_{10}O$, Ethyl ether (151)

B = $C_5H_{12}O$, Amyl alcohol (69, 158); *cf.* (151)

t = 25°C

$[A]_B$	K′ ± 0.07
0.005	1.75
0.02	2.14
0.05	2.71
0.10	3.29
0.20	3.82
0.26	3.98

B = C_6H_6, Benzene (92, 138, 158, 172); *cf.* (170.5)

t = 15–18°C

$[A]_B$	K′
0.000932	2.23 ± 0.02
0.00225	1.45 ± 0.01
0.01	0.705 ± 0.005
0.02	0.505 ± 0.005
0.05	0.320 ± 0.005
0.10	0.240 ± 0.005
0.18	0.187 ± 0.002

$C_6H_3N_3O_7$.—(*Continued*)

B = C_7H_8, Toluene (70); *cf.* (149, 151)

t = 25°C

$[A]_B$	K′
0.01	1.7 ± 0.2
0.05	3.0 ± 0.2
0.1	4.1 ± 0.2
0.2	5.6 ± 0.1
0.3	6.8 ± 0.1
0.5	8.7 ± 0.1

B = $C_{10}H_{12}$, Tetralin (77)

t = 25°C

$[A]_B$	K
0.02	0.45 ± 0.02
0.03	0.37 ± 0.02
0.05	0.30 ± 0.01
0.10	0.22 ± 0.01

C_6H_6BrN, *m*-Bromoaniline

B = C_6H_6, Benzene (50)

C_6H_6BrN, *p*-Bromoaniline

B = C_6H_6, Benzene (48); *cf.* (50); at 25°C, K′ = 132 ± 2 for g A/l_B = 2.4

C_6H_6ClN, *m*-Chloroaniline

B = C_6H_6, Benzene (50)

C_6H_6ClN, *p*-Chloroaniline

B = C_6H_6, Benzene (48); *cf.* (50); at 25°C, K′ = 83 ± 3 for g A/l_B = 14.3–28.4

$C_6H_6N_2O_2$, *o*-Nitroaniline

B = C_6H_6, Benzene (48)

t = 25°C

$[A]_B$	K′ ± 1.0
0.05	61.5
0.10	64.0
0.15	65.3

$C_6H_6N_2O_2$, *m*-Nitroaniline

B = C_6H_6, Benzene (48)

t = 25°C

$[A]_B$	K′ ± 1.0
0.05	23.0
0.10	25.0

$C_6H_6N_2O_2$, *p*-Nitroaniline

B = C_6H_6, Benzene (48)

t = 25°C

$[A]_B$	K′ ± 0.5
0.01	8.6
0.03	9.3

C_6H_6O, Phenol

B = CCl_4 (74, 76, 155); *cf.* (170)

t = 25°C

$[A]_C$	K′
0.05	0.40 ± 0.02
0.1	0.44 ± 0.02
0.2	0.625 ± 0.02
0.3	0.91 ± 0.05
0.4	1.45 ± 0.05
0.49	3.05 ± ?

B = CS_2 (74)

t = 25°C

$[A]_B$	K′
0.05	0.62 ± 0.02
0.2	0.80 ± 0.02

B = CS_2: 25°C.—(*Continued*)

$[A]_B$	K′
0.5	1.45 ± 0.05
1.0	2.47 ± 0.05
2.0	4.45 ± 0.1
4.0	8.0 ± 0.1

B = $CHBr_3$, Bromoform (74, 155)

t = 25°C

$[A]_B$	K′ ± 0.2
0.2	2.7
1.0	4.4
3.0	7.9
5.0	10.5
7.0	12.3

B = $CHCl_3$, Chloroform (74, 76, 155)

t = 25°C

$[A]_B$	K′ ± 0.1
0.25	3.45
1.0	5.35
2.0	7.7
3.0	9.65
4.0	11.1
5.0	12.2

B = C_2Cl_4, Tetrachloroethylene (76)

B = C_2HCl_3, Trichloroethylene (76)

B = C_2HCl_5, Pentachloroethane (76)

B = $C_2H_2Cl_4$, Tetrachloroethane (76)

B = $C_5H_{12}O$, Amyl alcohol (69); *cf.* (158)

t = 25°C

$[A]_B$	K′
0.075–0.26	16.5 ± 1
55	14.3 ± 0.5

B = C_6H_6, Benzene (139, 155); *cf.* (114, 124, 170); *see also* p. 402

t = 25°C

$[A]_B$	10^2K
0.06	43.8 ± 0.2
0.13	41.2 ± 0.2
0.28	36.3 ± 0.2
0.64	28.5 ± 0.1
1.5	18.6 ± 0.1
3.0	12.23 ± 0.05
5.0	9.00 ± 0.05
6.0	8.30 ± 0.05

B = C_6H_6, Benzene (124, 139)
D = Aqueous solutions of LiCl; NaCl; KCl; K_2SO_4

B = C_7H_8, Toluene (70, 155)

t = 25°C

$[A]_B$	K′
0.4	2.05 ± 0.05
2.0	3.6 ± 0.1
4.0	5.5 ± 0.2
6.0	7.1 ± 0.2
8.0	8.6 ± 0.2

B = C_8H_{10}, *m*-Xylene (70)

t = 25°C

$[A]_B$	K′
0.2	1.55 ± 0.5
2.0	3.05 ± 0.5
4.0	4.7 ± 0.1
6.0	6.3 ± 0.1
8.0	7.9 ± 0.2

B = Olive oil (11); *cf.* (130); at 25°C, K′ = 10 ± 1

B = Olive oil (130)
D = Aqueous solution of NaCl

$C_6H_6O_2$, Hydroquinol

B = $C_4H_{10}O$, Ethyl ether (126); at 15°C, K′ = 2.7 ± 0.5

$C_6H_6O_2$, Resorcinol

B = CCl_4 (170)

B = $C_4H_{10}O$, Ethyl ether (170); K′ = 4.2 ± 0.4

B = C_6H_6, Benzene (170); K = 2.6 ± 0.3

B = Olive oil (11); at 25°C, K′ = 0.04 ± 0.005 calculated from separate solubilities

C_6H_7N, Aniline

B = CCl_4 (170)

B = $C_3H_6O_3$, Lactic acid (3.5)

B = $C_4H_{10}O$, Ethyl ether (170)

B = C_6H_6, Benzene (48); at 25°C, K′ = 10.1 ± 0.3 for g A/l_B = 1.83 – 0.914

B = C_7H_8, Toluene (133)

t = 25°C

$[A]_B$	K′ ± 0.2
0.22*	12.3*
0.1	7.8
1.0	10.2
2.0	12.8
3.0	15.5
4.0	18.2
t = 48°C	
2.24	13.3

* t = 1°C.

B = C_7H_8, Toluene (133)
D = Aqueous solutions of $Ca(OH)_2$; $Ba(OH)_2$; $Sr(OH)_2$; K_2SO_4; $K_2B_2O_4$

B = C_8H_{10}, Xylene (155)

t = 25 ± 0.5°C

$[A]_B$	K′ ± 0.1
0.0005	2.95
0.0007	3.4
0.0010	3.95
0.0015	4.65
0.002	5.3

C_6H_8ClN, Aniline hydrochloride

B = C_6H_7N, Aniline (150)

$C_6H_8N_2$, Phenylenediamine

B = C_6H_6, Benzene (48); at 25°C, K′ = 0.549 ± 0.005 for g A/l_B = 0.55 – 4.1 (ortho); K′ = 0.179 ± 0.002 for g A/l_B = 0.9 – 1.6 (meta)

$C_6H_8O_7$, Citric acid

B = $C_4H_{10}O$, Ethyl ether (127); *cf.* (129)

t = 15°C

$[A]_B$	K ± 2
0.0015	129
0.004	128

t = 25.5°C

$[A]_B$	K ± 3
0.0015	158
0.004	150
0.007	142

$C_6H_{11}BrN_2O_2$, Bromural

B = Olive oil (118); from 17–20°C, K′ = 1.3 ± 0.1

$C_6H_{12}O_2$, *n*-Caproic acid

B = $CHCl_3$, Chloroform (155)

t = 25 ± 0.5°C

$[A]_B$	K′ ± 0.3
0.0005	5.2
0.0008	5.7
0.0012	6.1

B = C_8H_{10}, Xylene (155)

$C_6H_{12}O_2$, Isocaproic acid

B = $CHCl_3$, Chloroform (155)

B = C_8H_{10}, Xylene (155)

$C_6H_{12}O_2$, Hexoic acid

B = C_6H_6, Benzene (17)

t = 25 ± 0.03°C

$[A]_B$	K ± 0.0005
0.2	0.0444
0.3	0.0368
0.4	0.0318
0.6	0.0267

$C_6H_{12}O_2S_4$, Ethylxanthic acid

B = CS_2 (61)

B = CS_2 (61)
D = Aqueous solution of $MgSO_4$

B = $CHCl_3$, Chloroform (61)

B = $C_5H_{12}O$, Amyl alcohol (61)

B = $C_5H_{12}O$, Amyl alcohol (61)
D = Aqueous solution of $MgSO_4$

B = $C_6H_5NO_2$, Nitrobenzene (61)

B = C_7H_8O, Benzyl alcohol (61)

B = C_7H_8O, Benzyl alcohol (61)
D = Aqueous solution of $MgSO_4$

B = Ligroin (61)

$C_6H_{12}O_3$, 1-Hydroxyisocaproic acid

B = CCl_4 (80); at 25°C, K = 0.49 ± 0.03 for $[A]_B$ = 0.065–0.415

B = CCl_4 (80)
D = Aqueous solutions of NaCl; $K_2C_2O_4$

$C_6H_{13}N$, 1-Methylpiperidine
B = $C_4H_{10}O$, Ethyl ether (156)
B = C_8H_{10}, Xylene (155)

$C_6H_{15}N$, Dipropylamine
B = $C_4H_{10}O$, Ethyl ether (156)
B = C_7H_8, Toluene (109)
B = C_8H_{10}, Xylene (155)

$C_6H_{15}N$, Triethylamine
B = $CHCl_3$, Chloroform (155)
t = 25 ± 0.5°C

$[A]_B$	K′ ± 0.6
0.001	16.1
0.003	19.0
0.006	21.1
0.01	22.6

B = $C_5H_{12}O$, Amyl alcohol (69, 158)
B = C_7H_8, Toluene (63, 109); *cf.* (62)
t = 25°C

$[A]_B$	K ± 0.02
0.0011	0.76*
0.0026	0.69
0.0052	0.44
0.01	0.31
0.02	0.23†
0.07	0.15†
0.13	0.11†

$[A]_B$ = 0.5

°C	K
0	0.47 ± 0.02
10	0.290 ± 0.015
20	0.22 ± 0.01
40	0.145 ± 0.008
60	0.110 ± 0.005
90	0.087 ± 0.005

* ± 0.03.
† ± 0.01.

B = C_8H_{10}, Xylene (155)
t = 25 ± 0.5°C

$[A]_B$	K′ ± 0.2
0.001	3.2
0.004	4.6
0.006	5.2
0.011	6.1
0.015	6.6

$C_6H_{15}N$, *n*-Hexylamine
B = C_8H_{10}, Xylene (155)
t = 25 ± 0.1°C

$[A]_B$	K′ ± 0.1
0.001	3.0
0.003	4.2
0.005	4.9
0.01	5.8
0.017	6.2

$C_7H_3N_3O_8$, 2, 4, 6-Trinitrobenzoic acid
B = $C_4H_{10}O$, Ethyl ether (156)

$C_7H_4N_2O_6$, 2, 4-Dinitrobenzoic acid
B = $CHCl_3$, Chloroform (155)
B = $C_4H_{10}O$, Ethyl ether (156)
B = C_8H_{10}, Xylene (155)

$C_7H_4N_2O_6$, 3, 5-Dinitrobenzoic acid
B = $CHCl_3$, Chloroform (155, 162)
B = $C_4H_{10}O$, Ethyl ether (156)
B = C_6H_6, Benzene (164)
B = C_8H_{10}, Xylene (155)

$C_7H_5ClO_2$, *o*-Chlorobenzoic acid
B = $CHCl_3$, Chloroform (155)
B = $C_4H_{10}O$, Ethyl ether (156)
B = C_8H_{10}, Xylene (155)

$C_7H_5IO_2$, *o*-Iodobenzoic acid
B = $CHCl_3$, Chloroform (155)
B = $C_4H_{10}O$, Ethyl ether (156)
B = C_8H_{10}, Xylene (155)

$C_7H_5NO_3S$, Saccharin
B = $C_4H_{10}O$, Ethyl ether (104)
D = HCl; at 25 ± 0.1°C, K = 0.062 ± 0.001 for g A/l_B = 1.3–3.15
B = $C_7H_{14}O_2$, Amyl acetate
D = HCl (104); at 25 ± 0.1°C, K = 0.0314 ± 0.0005 for g A/l_B = 1.4–3.45

$C_7H_5NO_4$, *o*-Nitrobenzoic acid
B = $CHCl_3$, Chloroform (155)
t = 25 ± 0.5°C

$[A]_B$	K′ ± 0.01
0.0006	0.18
0.001	0.23
0.0015	0.27
0.003	0.37

B = $C_4H_{10}O$, Ethyl ether (156)
B = C_6H_6, Benzene (164)
t = 25°C

[A]/kg B	K′ ± 0.005
0.005	0.330
0.01	0.420
0.02	0.540
0.03	0.625

t = 40°C

[A]/kg B	K′ ± 0.005
0.005	0.390
0.01	0.465
0.02	0.570
0.03	0.645
0.04	0.715
0.06	0.820

B = C_8H_{10}, Xylene (155)
t = 25 ± 0.5°C

$[A]_B$	K′ ± 0.002
0.0005	0.101
0.0007	0.091
0.0009	0.087

$C_7H_5NO_4$, *m*-Nitrobenzoic acid
B = $CHCl_3$, Chloroform (155)
t = 25 ± 0.5°C

$[A]_B$	K′ ± 0.02
0.0006	1.23
0.001	1.45
0.0015	1.66

B = $C_4H_{10}O$, Ethyl ether (156)
B = C_6H_6, Benzene (164)

B = C_6H_6.—(*Continued*)
t = 25°C

[A]/kg B	K′ ± 0.05
0.005	1.60
0.02	2.60
0.05	3.85
0.10	5.25
0.15	6.35

t = 40°C

[A]/kg B	K′ ± 0.05
0.005	1.60
0.02	2.45
0.05	3.43
0.10	4.57
0.15	5.50
0.25	6.95

B = C_8H_{10}, Xylene (155)
t = 25 ± 0.5°C

$[A]_B$	K′ ± 0.02
0.001	0.82
0.002	0.94
0.003	1.07

$C_7H_5NO_4$, *p*-Nitrobenzoic acid
B = $CHCl_3$, Chloroform (155)
t = 25 ± 0.5°C

$[A]_B$	K′ ± 0.02
0.0006	1.26
0.001	1.49
0.0015	1.71

B = C_8H_{10}, Xylene (155)
t = 25 ± 0.5°C

$[A]_B$	K′ ± 0.02
0.0002	0.48
0.0005	0.67
0.0009	0.84

$C_7H_6O_2$, Benzoic acid
B = CCl_4 (144)
B = $CHCl_3$, Chloroform (65, 149, 155)
t = 25 ± 0.5°C

$[A]_B$	K ± 0.01
0.001	0.38
0.002	0.32
0.005	0.24

t = 10°C

g A/kg B	K ± 0.001
1	0.215
2	0.156
5	0.106
10	0.076
15	0.0599*
20	0.0510*

t = 40°C

g A/kg B	K ± 0.001
1	0.277
2	0.213
5	0.141
10	0.108
15	0.0890*
20	0.0767*

* ± 0.0005.

B = $C_4H_{10}O$, Ethyl ether (156); *cf.* (8, 149)
t = 25 ± 0.5°C

$[A]_B$	K′ ± 1
0.001	24
0.005	29
0.010	34
0.014	38

B = C_6H_6, Benzene (23, 47, 114, 158); *cf.* (65, 149)
t = 6 ± 0.1°C

$[A]_B$	K ± 0.001
0.01	0.253
0.02	0.185
0.03	0.151
0.04	0.130
0.05	0.115
0.07	0.096
0.10	0.0808*
0.15	0.0661*
0.20	0.0580*

t = 20°C

$[A]_B$	K ± 0.001
0.01	0.228†
0.02	0.17†
0.03	0.144‡
0.04	0.129‡
0.05	0.117‡
0.07	0.101‡
0.10	0.085
0.15	0.071
0.20	0.062
0.40	0.0433*
0.60	0.0342*

t = 25°C

$[A]_B$	K ± 0.001
0.0015	0.572†
0.005	0.326†
0.01	0.251‡
0.02	0.187‡
0.03	0.156‡
0.04	0.132‡
0.05	0.117‡
0.07	0.097‡
0.10	0.084‡
0.15	0.072‡
0.20	0.064‡

* ± 0.0005.
† ± 0.005.
‡ ± 0.002.

B = C_6H_6, Benzene (47, 161)
D = Aqueous solutions of NaCl; K benzoate
B = C_7H_8, Toluene (149)
B = C_7H_8O, Phenyl methyl ether (149)
B = C_8H_{10}, Xylene (155); *cf.* (149)
t = 25 ± 0.5°C

$[A]_B$	K′
0.001	1.09 ± 0.05
0.003	1.87 ± 0.01
0.006	2.68 ± 0.01
0.010	3.43 ± 0.02
0.017	4.12 ± 0.02

B = $C_8H_{10}O$, Phenetole (149)
B = $C_{10}H_{22}O$, Amyl ether (149)
B = Benzine (149)
B = Olive oil (11); at 25°C, K′ = 12.5 ± 1, calculated from separate solubilities

$C_7H_6O_3$, Hydroxybenzoic acid
B = Olive oil (11); at 25°C, K′, calculated from separate solubilities = 0.4 ± 0.1 for *m*-A; = 0.6 ± 0.1 for *p*-A

$C_7H_6O_3$, p-Hydroxybenzoic acid
B = $C_4H_{10}O$, Ethyl ether (156)

$C_7H_6O_3$, Salicylic acid
B = $CHCl_3$, Chloroform (65, 149, 155)

t = 10°C

g A/kg B	K
0.5	0.635 ± 0.01
1.0	0.47 ± 0.01
2.0	0.344 ± 0.007
3.0	0.286 ± 0.007
5.0	0.225 ± 0.005
6.0	0.202 ± 0.005

t = 25 ± 0.5°C

$[A]_B$	K
0.0006	0.92 ± 0.03
0.001	0.76 ± 0.03
0.002	0.60 ± 0.02
0.004	0.465 ± 0.015
0.006	0.407 ± 0.015

t = 40°C

g A/kg B	K
0.5	0.695 ± 0.01
1.0	0.555 ± 0.01
2.0	0.445 ± 0.007
3.0	0.380 ± 0.007
5.0	0.310 ± 0.005
6.0	0.282 ± 0.005
10.0	0.222 ± 0.002
15.0	0.187 ± 0.002
18.0	0.172 ± 0.002

B = $C_4H_{10}O$, Ethyl ether (156)

t = 25 ± 0.5°C

$[A]_B$	K′ ± 2
0.002	26
0.003	29
0.005	34
0.010	43
0.014	49

B = C_6H_6, Benzene (65, 114, 149)

t = 10°C

g A/kg B	K
0.5	0.63 ± 0.01
1.0	0.49 ± 0.01
2.0	0.375 ± 0.007
3.0	0.325 ± 0.007
4.0	0.292 ± 0.007
5.0	0.268 ± 0.005

t = 18°C

g A/kg B	K
0.5	0.70 ± 0.02
1.0	0.51 ± 0.02
2 0	0.36 ± 0.02
3.0	0.32 ± 0.02
4.0	0.29 ± 0.01
5.0	0.27 ± 0.01
6.0	0.25 ± 0.01
8.0	0.21 ± 0.01

t = 40°C

g A/kg B	K
0.5	0.61 ± 0.01
1.0	0.50 ± 0.01
2.0	0.410 ± 0.007
3.0	0.363 ± 0.007

B = C_6H_6: 40°C.—(*Continued*)

g A/kg B	K
4.0	0.331 ± 0.007
5.0	0.307 ± 0.005
6.0	0.287 ± 0.005
8.0	0.260 ± 0.005

B = C_6H_6, Benzene (161, 163)
D = Aqueous solutions of NaCl; KCl
B = C_8H_{10}, Xylene (155)

t = 25 ± 0.5°C

$[A]_B$	K′ ± 0.03
0.001	0.65
0.002	0.84
0.003	0.99
0.005	1.18

B = C_6H_6O, Phenol (5.5)

t = 25.0°C

$[A]_B$	K′
0.1	14.7 ± 0.4
0.2	15.5 ± 0.3
0.3	16.2 ± 0.2
0.5	17.3 ± 0.2

B = Olive oil (11); K′ = 12 ± 1, calculated from separate solubilities

$C_7H_6O_4$, Dihydroxybenzoic acid
B = Olive oil (11); at 25°C, K′, calculated from separate solubilities = 1.0 ± 0.1 for 2, 4-A; = 0.3 ± 0.1 for 2, 5-A; = 0.05 ± 0.01 for 3, 4-A

$C_7H_6O_4$, Gentisic acid
B = $CHCl_3$, Chloroform (155)
B = $C_4H_{10}O$, Ethyl ether (156)
B = C_8H_{10}, Xylene (155)

$C_7H_6O_4$, Resorcylic acid
B = $C_4H_{10}O$, Ethyl ether (156)
B = C_8H_{10}, Xylene (155)

$C_7H_6O_5$, Gallic acid
B = $C_4H_{10}O$, Ethyl ether (156); at 25 ± 0.5°C, K′ = 0.45 ± 0.01 for $[A]_B$ = 0.00013–0.027

C_7H_7NO, Benzamide
B = Codliver oil (9)
B = Olive oil (107); *cf.* (108)

°C	g A/l_B	K′
3	7.05	0.66 ± 0.03
36	5.33	0.43 ± 0.02

$C_7H_7NO_2$, o-Aminobenzoic acid
B = $CHCl_3$, Chloroform (155)

t = 25 ± 0.5°C

$[A]_B$	K′ ± 0.005
0.0006	0.133
0.001	0.144
0.002	0.165
0.003	0.180

B = $C_4H_{10}O$, Ethyl ether (156); at 25 ± 0.5°C, K′ = 1.11 ± 0.04 for $[A]_B$ = 0.00056–0.0068
B = C_6H_6, Benzene (48)

$C_7H_7NO_2$, Salicylamide
B = Codliver oil (9)
B = Olive oil (107)

°C	g A/l_B	K′ ± 1
3	1.27	22
36	1.07	14

$C_7H_8N_2O$, p-Nitrosomethylaniline
B = C_6H_6, Benzene (48); at 6°C, K′ = 3.0 ± 0.1 for g A/l_B = 3.0–3.9; at 25°C, K′ = 3.3 ± 0.1 for g A/l_B = 0.54–0.92

$C_7H_8N_4O_2$, Theobromine
B = Olive oil (3)

°C	K′ ± 0.1
16	1.4
17	1.7

$C_7H_8N_4O_2$, Theophylline
B = Olive oil (3); at 18°C, K′ = 1.6 ± 0.2

C_7H_8O, m-Cresol
B = $C_4H_{10}O$, Ethyl ether (170)

C_7H_9N, Benzylamine
B = $CHCl_3$, Chloroform (155)

t = 25 ± 0.5°C

$[A]_B$	K′ ± 0.5
0.004	12.9
0.007	14.0
0.01	14.8
0.015	15.7
0.02	16.3

B = $C_4H_{10}O$, Ethyl ether (156); at 25 ± 0.5°C, K′ = 2.05 ± 0.1 for $[A]_B$ = 0.0013–0.0096
B = C_8H_{10}, Xylene (155)

t = 25 ± 0.5°C

$[A]_B$	K′ ± 0.08
0.002	1.53
0.005	1.88
0.009	2.09
0.014	2.16

C_7H_9N, Methylaniline
B = C_8H_{10}, Xylene (155)

C_7H_9N, Toluidine
B = C_6H_6, Benzene (48); *cf.* (50); at 25°C, K′ = 13.4 ± 0.2 for g A/l_B = 1.2–2.0 (ortho); K′ = 19.1 ± 0.3 for g A/l_B = 1.4–2.5 (meta); K′ = 24.1 ± 0.5 for g A/l_B = 1.4–2.9 (para)

C_7H_9N, o-Toluidine
B = $C_2H_4O_2$, Acetic acid (3.5)

C_7H_9N, p-Toluidine
B = CCl_4 (170)

C_7H_9NO, p-Anisidine
B = C_6H_6, Benzene (48); at 25°C, K′ = 6.0 ± 0.1 for g A/l_B = 4.35–9.01

$C_7H_{12}O_4$, Pimelic acid
B = $C_4H_{10}O$, Ethyl ether (21, 155); at 25 ± 0.01°C, K = 0.72 ± 0.01 for $[A]_B$ = 0.0025–0.014

$C_7H_{12}O_5$, Diacetin
B = Olive oil (6, 108); at room temp., K′ = 0.23 ± 0.02

$C_7H_{14}O_2$, Isoamylacetic acid
B = C_8H_{10}, Xylene (155)

$C_7H_{15}NO$, Valerdimethylamide
B = Olive oil (64); at 15°R, K′ = 0.42 ± 0.05 for g A/l_B = 3.8

$C_7H_{15}NO$, Valerethylamide
B = Olive oil (64); at 15°R, K′ = 0.25 ± 0.02 for g A/l_B = 2.6

$C_7H_{15}NO_2$, Lactdiethylamide
B = Olive oil (64); at 15°R, K′ = 0.15 ± 0.01 for g A/l_B = 1.94

$C_7H_{16}O_4S_2$, Sulfonal
B = Olive oil (6, 108); *cf.* (121); at room temp., K′ = 1.1 ± 0.1 for g A/l_B = 0.7–1.1

$C_7H_{15}NO_2$, Isobutylurethane
B = Codliver oil (9)

$C_7H_{17}N$, n-Heptylamine
B = $C_4H_{10}O$, Ethyl ether (156)

t = 25 ± 0.5°C

$[A]_B$	K′ ± 0.5
0.002	13.1
0.004	17.1
0.006	19.7
0.008	20.8

B = C_8H_{10}, Xylene (155)

t = 25 ± 0.5°C

$[A]_B$	K′ ± 0.5
0.001	11.1
0.004	14.4
0.007	18.2
0.01	22.3

$C_8H_6O_4$, Phthalic acid
B = $C_4H_{10}O$, Ethyl ether (21, 156)

t = 25 ± 0.5°C

$[A]_B$	K
0.001	1.36 ± 0.05
0.003	1.14 ± 0.05
0.005	1.05 ± 0.05
0.01	0.92 ± 0.03
0.02	0.84 ± 0.03
0.03	0.81 ± 0.03

B = C_8H_{10}, Xylene (155)
B = Olive oil (11); at 25°C, K′ = 0.01 ± 0.001, calculated from separate solubilities

$C_8H_6O_4$, Isophthalic acid
B = $C_4H_{10}O$, Ethyl ether (21); at 25 ± 0.01°C, K = 0.0945 ± 0.001 for $[A]_B$ = 0.0028

$C_8H_6O_4$, Piperonylic acid
B = $CHCl_3$, Chloroform (155)
B = C_8H_{10}, Xylene (155)

$C_8H_6O_4$, Terephthalic acid
B = Olive oil (11); at 25°C, $K' = 9 \pm 1$, calculated from separate solubilities

$C_8H_8O_2$, Phenylacetic acid
B = $CHCl_3$, Chloroform (155)
$t = 25 \pm 0.5$°C

$[A]_B$	$K' \pm 0.05$
0.0005	1.71
0.0010	1.94
0.0015	2.14

B = $C_4H_{10}O$, Ethyl ether (156); at 25 ± 0.5°C, $K' = 15.2 \pm 0.5$ for $[A]_B = 0.0012$–0.016
B = C_8H_{10}, Xylene (155)
$t = 25 \pm 0.5$°C

$[A]_B$	$K' \pm 0.02$
0.001	0.52
0.003	0.77
0.005	1.00

$C_8H_8O_2$, Toluic acid
B = Olive oil (11); at 25°C, K', calculated from separate solubilities = 40 ± 4 for *o*-A; 21 ± 2 for *m*-A; and 29 ± 3 for *p*-A

$C_8H_8O_3$, *p*-Methoxybenzoic acid
B = $CHCl_3$, Chloroform (155)
$t = 25 \pm 0.5$°C

$[A]_B$	$K' \pm 0.1$
0.0007	5.15
0.001	5.6
0.0014	6.0
0.0018	6.4

B = C_8H_{10}, Xylene (155)
B = Olive oil (11); at 25°C, $K' = 12 \pm 1$, calculated from separate solubilities

$C_8H_8O_3$, Mandelic acid
B = $C_4H_{10}O$, Ethyl ether (156)
B = C_6H_6, Benzene (149); at 19°C, $K = 89.5 \pm 1$ for g $A/l_B = 0.16$–0.75
B = C_7H_8O, Phenyl methyl ether (149)

$C_8H_8O_3$, Vanillin
B = $C_4H_{10}O$, Ethyl ether (104); at 25 ± 0.1°C, $K = 0.107 \pm 0.003$ for g $A/l_B = 1.3$–3.3

$C_8H_8O_4$, Guaiacyl acid carbonate
B = Olive oil (11); at 25°C, $K' = 3.7 \pm 0.3$

C_8H_9NO, Acetanilide
B = $CHCl_3$, Chloroform (104); at 25 ± 0.1°C, $K = 0.129 \pm 0.003$ for g $A/l_B = 1.25$–3.7
B = $C_4H_{10}O$, Ethyl ether (104); at 25 ± 0.1°C, $K = 0.335 \pm 0.01$ for g $A/l_B = 0.9$–3.4
B = C_6H_6, Benzene (48); at 25°C, $K = 0.605 \pm 0.005$ for g $A/l_B = 5.8$

$C_8H_{10}N_2O$, *p*-Nitrosodimethylaniline
B = C_6H_6, Benzene (48); at 6°C, $K' = 37.3 \pm 0.5$ for g $A/l_B = 3.7$–5.5; at 25°C, $K' = 51 \pm 1$ for g $A/l_B = 11.4$–13.8

$C_8H_{10}N_4O_2$, Caffeine
B = $CHCl_3$, Chloroform (104); at 25 ± 0.1°C, $K = 0.047 \pm 0.003$ for g $A/l_B = 1.88$–5.90

g A/l_B	K
$t = 19.5$°C (45.5)	
10	19.2 ± 0.4
20	15.4 ± 0.2
40	11.0 ± 0.2
80	7.0 ± 0.1
$t = 25.0$°C (45.5)	
10	17.9 ± 0.4
20	14.7 ± 0.2
40	11.2 ± 0.2
80	6.9 ± 0.1

B = $CHCl_3$, Chloroform (45.5)
D = Aqueous solutions of H_2SO_4; C_2H_6O, Ethyl alcohol (1%); Na benzoate; Na salicylate; KBr

g A/l_B	K'
D = H_2SO_4 (1*N*)	
$t = 19.5$°C	
10	9.2 ± 0.3
20	8.2 ± 0.2
40	6.5 ± 0.1
80	4.5 ± 0.1
$t = 25.0$°C	
10	8.6 ± 0.3
20	7.7 ± 0.2
40	6.4 ± 0.2
80	4.5 ± 0.1
D = C_2H_6O (1%)	
$t = 19.5$°C	
10	23.4 ± 0.4
20	18.7 ± 0.4
40	12.8 ± 0.3
80	7.4 ± 0.2
D = $NaC_7H_5O_2$ (0.1*N*)	
$t = 19.5$°C	
10	10.7 ± 0.3
20	9.4 ± 0.3
40	7.3 ± 0.2
80	4.9 ± 0.1
D = $NaC_7H_5O_3$ (0.1*N*)	
10	5.1 ± 0.2
20	4.7 ± 0.2
40	4.1 ± 0.1
80	3.2 ± 0.1
D = KBr (1*N*)	
10	19.4 ± 0.4
20	15.6 ± 0.4
40	11.3 ± 0.3
80	7.0 ± 0.2

B = $C_4H_{10}O$, Ethyl ether (128, 129); at 25°C, $K' = 7.2 \pm 0.2$

B = Olive oil (3)

°C	g A/l_B	$K' \pm 0.05$
15	3.49	0.53
16	3.05	0.44
17	2.75	0.37

B = Sesame oil (174)

$C_8H_{11}N$, Benzylmethylamine
B = $C_4H_{10}O$, Ethyl ether (156)
B = C_8H_{10}, Xylene (155)

$C_8H_{11}N$, 2, 3, 4-Trimethylpyridine
B = C_7H_8, Toluene (63)

°C	$[A]_B$	$K \pm 0.002$
0	0.0580	0.060
10	0.0587	0.044
20	0.0588	0.037*
30	0.0594	0.034*
50	0.0596	0.0285*
70	0.0597	0.025*
90	0.0598	0.022*

* ± 0.001.

$C_8H_{11}N$, 3, 4-Dimethylaniline
B = C_8H_{10}, Xylene (155)

$C_8H_{11}N$, Phenylethylamine
B = C_8H_{10}, Xylene (155)

$C_8H_{12}N_2O_3$, Veronal
B = Olive oil (118); at 17–20°C, $K' = 0.115 \pm 0.01$ for g A/kg (A + B) = 0.26

$C_8H_{14}O_4$, Suberic acid
B = $C_4H_{10}O$, Ethyl ether (21, 155)

$C_8H_{14}O_6$, Diethyl tartrate
B = $C_2H_4Br_2$, Ethylene bromide (178)
B = C_6H_6, Benzene (178)
$t = 20$°C

g A/kg (A + B)	K'
10	5.4 ± 0.3
20	4.2 ± 0.1
30	3.6 ± 0.1

$C_8H_{17}N$, Coniine
B = $C_4H_{10}O$, Ethyl ether (156); *cf.* (105); at 25 ± 0.5°C, $K' \pm 0.3 = 5.6$ for $[A]_B = 0.0011$–0.0019; = 7.0 for $[A]_B = 0.0037$–0.0074
B = C_8H_{10}, Xylene (155)
$t = 25 \pm 0.5$°C

$[A]_B$	$K' \pm 0.3$
0.001	6.0
0.005	7.8
0.01	10.1

B = Sesame oil (174)

$C_8H_{18}O_4S_2$, Trional
B = Olive oil (6, 108, 118); *cf.* (121); at 17–20°C, $K' = 4.5 \pm 0.4$ for g $A/l_B = 1.6$–3.4

C_9H_7N, Quinoline
B = C_8H_{10}, Xylene (155); at 25 ± 0.5°C, $K' = 17 \pm 2$ for $[A]_B = 0.0018$–0.0094

C_9H_7NO, 8-Hydroxyquinoline
B = C_6H_6, Benzene (52)

$C_9H_8O_2$, Cinnamic acid
B = C_8H_{10}, Xylene (155)
$t = 25 \pm 0.5$°C

$[A]_B$	$K' \pm 0.1$
0.0005	3.0
0.001	4.5
0.0015	5.8
0.002	7.0

$C_9H_8O_4$, *o*-Acetylsalicylic acid (Aspirin)
B = $C_4H_{10}O$, Ethyl ether (156)
$t = 25 \pm 0.5$° C

$[A]_B$	$K' \pm 0.1$
0.001	4.7
0.002	5.3
0.003	5.7
0.005	6.15
0.007	6.45
0.009	6.7

B = C_8H_{10}, Xylene (155)
$t = 25 \pm 0.5$°C

$[A]_B$	$K' \pm 0.01$
0.001	0.235*
0.002	0.280*
0.003	0.31
0.005	0.365
0.007	0.41

* ± 0.005.

$C_9H_8O_4$, Homophthalic acid
B = $C_4H_{10}O$, Ethyl ether (40)

$C_9H_9NO_3$, Hippuric acid
B = $C_4H_{10}O$, Ethyl ether (156)
$t = 25 \pm 0.5$°C

$[A]_B$	$K' \pm 0.01$
0.0005	0.40
0.001	0.38
0.002	0.36
0.003	0.35

$C_9H_{10}O_2$, Hydrocinnamic acid
B = $CHCl_3$, Chloroform (155)
$t = 25 \pm 0.5$°C

$[A]_B$	$K' \pm 0.2$
0.0007	7.5
0.0010	8.4
0.0013	9.1
0.0018	10.0

B = C_8H_{10}, Xylene (155)
$t = 25 \pm 0.5$°C

$[A]_B$	$K' \pm 0.1$
0.0015	3.0
0.003	3.9
0.005	4.3

$C_9H_{11}NO$, Aceto-*o*-toluidine
B = C_6H_6, Benzene (48)

$C_9H_{11}NO_2$, Phenylurethane
B = Olive oil (121); $K' = 190 \pm 20$, calculated from separate solubilities

$C_9H_{13}N$, Benzylethylamine
B = $C_4H_{10}O$, Ethyl ether (156)
B = C_8H_{10}, Xylene (155)

$C_9H_{14}O_6$, Triacetin
B = Olive oil (6, 108); at room temp., K′ = 0.3 ± 0.05

$C_9H_{16}O_4$, Azelaic acid
B = $C_4H_{10}O$, Ethyl ether (21, 155)

$C_9H_{17}NO_3$, Detonal
B = Olive oil (118); at 17–20°C, K′ = 1.75 ± 0.1 for g A/kg B = 2.13–5.48

$C_9H_{19}NO$, Valerdiethylamide
B = Olive oil (64); at 15°R, K′ = 5.8 ± 0.6 for g A/l_B = 13.4

$C_9H_{20}O_4S_2$, Tetronal
B = Olive oil (6, 108); at room temp., K′ = 4.0 ± 0.4

$C_9H_{21}N$, Tripropylamine
B = C_7H_8, Toluene (109); at 18 ± 0.005°C, K = 0.003 ± 0.0005 for $[A]_B$ = 0.1

$C_{10}H_8O$, β-Naphthol
B = C_6H_6, Benzene (92); at 29 ± 0.5°C, K′ = 67 ± 5 for g A/l_B = 9.2–30.3

$C_{10}H_9N$, Naphthylamine
B = C_6H_6, Benzene (48); at 25°C, K′ = 252 ± 10 for g α-A/l_B = 15.6–31.7; = 279 ± 10 for g β-A/l_B = 15.9–25.4

$C_{10}H_{11}NO_3$, p-Acetoxyacetanilide
B = $CHCl_3$, Chloroform (45.5)
t = 25.0°C

g A/l_B	K′ ± 0.3
5	9.8
10	11.0
20	12.8
30	14.5

$C_{10}H_{14}N_2$, Nicotine
B = Sesame oil (174)

$C_{10}H_{14}N_4O_3$, Ethoxycaffeine
B = Olive oil (3); at room temp., K′ = 1.75 ± 0.05 for g A/l_B = 19.1

$C_{10}H_{14}O$, Thymol
B = Castor oil (146)
B = Codliver oil (146)
B = Cottonseed oil (146)
B = Linseed oil (146)
B = Olive oil (146); K′ ± 20 = 450 for g A/l_B = 45–450, at 25 ± 0.05°C; = 406 for g A/l_B = 46–460, at 37.2°C
B = Peanut oil (146)
B = Petrolatum (liquid) (146)

$C_{10}H_{16}O_4$, Camphoric acid
B = $CHCl_3$, Chloroform (155)
B = $C_4H_{10}O$, Ethyl ether (21, 166, 167); at 25 ± 0.01°C, K = 0.0353 ± 0.0005 for $[A]_B$ = 0.041–0.065
B = C_8H_{10}, Xylene (155)

$C_{10}H_{18}O_4$, Sebacic acid
B = $C_4H_{10}O$, Ethyl ether (21)

$C_{10}H_{19}N$, Bornylamine
B = C_8H_{10}, Xylene (155)

$C_{10}H_{19}N$, Camphylamine
B = C_8H_{10}, Xylene (155)

$C_{10}H_{19}NO_3$, Epronal
B = Olive oil (118); at 17–20°C, K′ = 3.3 ± 0.1 for g A/kg (A + B) = 2.57

$C_{11}H_{12}N_2O$, Antipyrine
B = $CHCl_3$, Chloroform (45.5)
t = 25.0°C

g A/l_B	K′
10	17.6 ± 0.3
20	15.6 ± 0.3
40	12.4 ± 0.2
80	8.2 ± 0.2

B = $CHCl_3$, Chloroform (45.5)
D = Aqueous solutions of H_2SO_4; Na salicylate
t = 25.5°C

g A/l_B	K′
D = H_2SO_4 (1N)	
10	1.14 ± 0.02
25	1.16 ± 0.02
50	1.19 ± 0.02
D = $NaC_7H_5O_3$(0.1N)	
10	16.0 ± 0.3
20	14.0 ± 0.3
40	11.5 ± 0.3
80	7.6 ± 0.2

$C_{11}H_{16}N_2O_2$, Pilocarpine
B = Sesame oil (174)

$C_{12}H_{11}N_3$, p-Aminoazobenzene
B = C_6H_6, Benzene (48); at 25°C, K′ = 3170 ± 100 for g A/l_B = 28.4–36.6

$C_{12}H_{12}O_5$, α-Keto-γ-phenyladipic acid
B = $C_4H_{10}O$, Ethyl ether (40)

$C_{13}H_{20}N_2O_2$, Novocaine
B = Sesame oil (174)

$C_{14}H_{12}O_3$, Benzilic acid
B = $CHCl_3$, Chloroform (155)
t = 25 ± 0.5°C

$[A]_B$	K′ ± 0.06
0.0003	1.27
0.0006	1.70
0.001	2.11
0.0015	2.54
0.0018	2.77

B = $C_4H_{10}O$, Ethyl ether (156)
t = 25 ± 0.5°C

$[A]_B$	K′ ± 1
0.001	17.5
0.003	24.3
0.005	27.5
0.007	29.5
0.009	30.5

B = C_8H_{10}, Xylene (155)
t = 25 ± 0.5°C

$[A]_B$	K′ ± 0.02
0.0001	0.27
0.0004	0.49
0.0007	0.65
0.001	0.80

$C_{15}H_{22}ClNO_2$, β-Eucaine hydrochloride
B = Sesame oil (174)

$C_{17}H_{19}NO_3$, Morphine
B = $CHCl_3$, Chloroform (116)
D = Aqueous C_2H_6O, Ethyl alcohol; mixture of 0.08 g morphine hydrochloride, C cm³ of H_2O, D cm³ of alcohol and 10cm³ of $CHCl_3$ were shaken together, after which the layers were nearly equal in volume

C	D	K
20	0	75
17.5	2.5	4
15	5	1
12.5	7.5	0.5
10	10	0.2

B = $CHCl_3$ + CH_4O, Methyl alcohol (mixtures) (105)
D = Aqueous solution of K_2CO_3; equal parts $CHCl_3$ and CH_4O; 40g K_2CO_3/50 cm³ H_2O; at 25 ± 0.1°C, K = 0.15 ± 0.02 for g A/l_B = 1.2–3.6
B = $CHCl_3$ + C_2H_6O, Ethyl alcohol (mixtures) (105)
D = Aqueous NaCl; $CHCl_3$, 2 parts; C_2H_5OH, 1 part; NaCl, 35 g/100 cm³ H_2O; at 25 ± 0.1°C, K = 0.53 ± 0.05 for g A/l_B = 0.40–0.97
B = Sesame oil (174)

$C_{17}H_{19}NO_3.HCl$, Morphine hydrochloride
B = $CHCl_3$ + $C_5H_{12}O$ (mixture: chloroform, 3 vols. + amyl alcohol, 1 vol.) (105)
D = Aqueous solution of NH_4OH; at 25 ± 0.1°C, K′ = 0.345 ± 0.03 for g A/l_B = 0.70–1.42

$C_{17}H_{21}NO_4$, Cocaine
B = Sesame oil (174)

$C_{17}H_{22}BrN$, Methylpropylphenylbenzylammonium bromide
B = $CHCl_3$, Chloroform (176)

$C_{17}H_{23}NO_3$, Atropine
B = $CHCl_3$, Chloroform (144); cf. (105)
t = 25°C

g A*	K′ ± 1
0.01	8.0†
0.05	17
0.10	23
0.20	30
0.40	37
0.60	39

* Per 15 cm³ soln. (A + B).
† ± 0.5

B = Sesame oil (174)

$C_{18}H_{21}N_3O$, Codeine
B = $CHCl_3$ (105)
D = Aqueous solution of NH_4OH; at 25 ± 0.1°C, K = 0.0067 ± 0.0003 for g A/l_B = 2.40–5.63
B = $C_4H_{10}O$, Ethyl ether (105)
D = Aqueous solution of NH_4OH; at 25 ± 0.1°C, K = 0.94 ± 0.04 for g A/l_B = 0.47–1.45
B = Sesame oil (174)

$C_{18}H_{34}O_2$, Oleic acid
B = Benzine (79)
D = Aqueous solution of C_2H_6O, Ethyl alcohol

$C_{19}H_{24}ClNO_3(2H_2O)$, Dionine
B = Sesame oil (174)

$C_{20}H_{14}O_4$, Phenolphthalein
B = C_6H_6, Benzene (137); K′ = 13.1 ± 0.2

$C_{20}H_{20}ClN_3$, Fuchsin (131, 132)
B = $C_4H_{10}O$, Isobutyl alcohol
t = 25°C

g A/l_B	K′ ± ?
0.018	24.0
0.103	4.3
0.620	1.94

B = $C_4H_{10}O$, Isobutyl alcohol (131, 132)
D = HCl, 7 M per l
t = 25°C

g A/l_B	K′ ± ?
0.042	8.0
0.232	9.3
1.108	7.9

$C_{22}H_{24}ClN_3$, Fuchsin new (Höchst)
B = $C_4H_{10}O$, Isobutyl alcohol (131, 132)
t = 25°C

g A/l_B	K′ ± ?
0.0125	6.5
0.600	2.1
5.700	1.8

$C_{20}H_{24}N_2O_2$, Quinine
B = $CHCl_3$, Chloroform (105)
D = Aqueous solution of NH_4OH; at 25°C, K is "very small"

B = $C_4H_{10}O$, Ethyl ether (168)
t = 0°C

g A/l$_B$	K ± 0.05
5	0.66
10	0.53
15	0.40

B = Sesame oil (174)

$C_{21}H_{22}N_2O_2$, Strychnine
B = $CHCl_3$, Chloroform (144)
t = 25°C

g A/l$_B$	K′ ± 1
1.7	25
8.7	61
41.5	64

B = Sesame oil (174)

$C_{21}H_{23}N_3O_5$, Strychnine nitrate
B = $CHCl_3$, Chloroform (144)
t = 25°C

g A/l$_B$	K ± 0.1
0.28	5.3
1.62	4.2
11.3	2.0

$C_{21}H_{24}N_2O_6S$, Strychnine sulfate
B = $CHCl_3$, Chloroform (105)
D = Aqueous solution of NH_4OH; at 25 ± 0.1°C, K = 0.003 ± 0.001 for g A/l$_B$ = 1.65–4.7
B = $CHCl_3$ + $C_4H_{10}O$ (Ethyl ether) (mixtures) (105)
D = Aqueous solution of NH_4OH; at 25 ± 0.1°C, K = 0.087 ± 0.002 for g A/l$_B$ = 1.4–3.3

$C_{22}H_{23}NO_7$, Narcotine
B = Sesame oil (174)

$C_{22}H_{24}BrN$, Tribenzylmethylammonium bromide
B = $CHBr_3$, Bromoform (44)
B = $CHCl_3$, Chloroform (44)

$C_{22}H_{24}ClN$, Tribenzylmethylammonium chloride
B = $CHBr_3$, Bromoform (44)

$C_{22}H_{25}NO_6$, Colchicine
B = Sesame oil (174)

$C_{23}H_{26}N_2O_4$, Brucine
B = Sesame oil (174)

$C_{32}H_{49}NO_9$, Veratrine
B = Sesame oil (174); at 20°C, K′ = 12 ± 1 for g A/l$_B$ = 13.9, calculated from separate solubilities

$C_{34}H_{47}NO_{11}$, Aconitine
B = $CHCl_3$, Chloroform (105)
D = Aqueous solution of NH_4OH; at 25 ± 0.1°C, K = 0.017 ± 0.002 for g A/l$_B$ = 3.2–5.6
B = $C_4H_{10}O$, Ethyl ether (105)
D = Aqueous solution of NH_4OH; at 25 ± 0.1°C, K = 0.140 ± 0.005 for g A/l$_B$ = 1.2–3.1

MISCELLANEOUS TABLE

The A-component (the distributed component) is a dyestuff or a material of unknown or indefinite composition.

Alphabetical arrangement

Le constituant A (le constituant distribué) est une teinture ou une matière de composition inconnue ou non définie.

Arrangement alphabétique.

Die A- Komponente (der verteilte Stoff) ist ein Farbstoff oder ein Stoff unbekannter oder unbestimmter Zusammensetzung.

Alphabetische Anordnung.

Il componente A (ripartito tra i due liquidi) è una sostanza colorante o un prodotto di composizione sconosciuta o non definita.

Ordine alfabetico.

Alcohols
B = Fats (141)

Aliphatic acids, mixtures of
B = $C_4H_{10}O$, Ethyl ether (103)
B = Wines (103)

Alkali Blue 6 B (Bayer)
B = $C_4H_{10}O$, Isobutyl alcohol (131, 132)
t = 25°C

g A/l$_B$	K′ ± ?
0.105	13.3
0.212	14.0
0.425	14.1

Congo Red (Bayer)
B = $C_4H_{10}O$, Isobutyl alcohol (131, 132)
t = 25°C

g A/l$_B$	K′ ± ?
0.0022	0.24
0.012	0.13
0.042	0.09

B = $C_4H_{10}O$, Isobutyl alcohol (131, 132)
D = 4M KOH/l
t = 25°C

g A/l$_B$	K′ ± ?
0.0024	0.36
0.010	0.23
0.060	0.13

Erythrosine A (Höchst)
B = $C_4H_{10}O$, Isobutyl alcohol (131, 132)
t = 25°C

g A/l$_B$	K′ ± ?
0.011	7.9
0.0234	2.2
0.063	0.14

Fuchsin, *v.* p. 432

Methylene Blue
B = C_6H_7N, Aniline (123)

Methylene Blue, D
B = $C_4H_{10}O$, Isobutyl alcohol (131, 132)
t = 25°C

g A/l$_B$	K′ ± ?
0.0052	0.76
0.054	0.30
0.108	0.24

B = $C_4H_{10}O$, Isobutyl alcohol (131, 132)
D = HCl (2N)
t = 25°C

g A/l$_B$	K′ ± ?
0.0075	1.07
0.0224	0.60
0.192	0.44

Methylene Blue, G (Conc.) (Basel)
B = $C_4H_{10}O$, Isobutyl alcohol (131, 132)
t = 25°C

g A/l$_B$	K′ ± ?
0.0043	2.7
0.050	0.64
0.156	0.34

B = $C_4H_{10}O$, Isobutyl alcohol (131, 132)
t = 25°C
D = HCl (0.33N)

g A/l$_B$	K′ ± ?
0.00227	7.1
0.043	1.45
0.268	0.88

D = KOH (0.003N)

g A/l$_B$	K′ ± ?
0.018	4.5
0.070	2.8
0.500	1.67

Patent Blue (Höchst)
B = $C_4H_{10}O$, Isobutyl alcohol (131, 132)
t = 25°C

g A/l$_B$	K′ ± ?
0.0010	0.24
0.375	0.17

Phenolphthalein, *v.* p. 432

Ponceau Crystal
B = $C_4H_{10}O$, Isobutyl alcohol (131, 132)
t = 25°C

g A/l$_B$	K′ ± ?
0.001	0.05
0.006	0.03
0.015	0.03

B = $C_5H_{12}O$, Amyl alcohol (151)

Quinoline Yellow (Bayer)
B = $C_4H_{10}O$, Isobutyl alcohol (131, 132)
t = 25°C

g A/l$_B$	K′ ± ?
0.018	1.6
0.200	1.7
0.964	1.5

B = $C_4H_{10}O$, Isobutyl alcohol (131, 132)
t = 25°C
D = HCl (10N)

g A/l$_B$	K′ ± ?
0.036	5.5
0.390	6.4
2.030	6.4

D = KOH (10N)

g A/l$_B$	K′ ± ?
0.017	1.4
0.160	1.14
0.800	1.11

Rocelline (Basel)
B = $C_4H_{10}O$, Isobutyl alcohol (131, 132)
t = 25°C

g A/l$_B$	K′ ± ?
0.0118	7.3
0.0736	2.4
0.300	1.7

Violet Crystal (Basel)
B = $C_4H_{10}O$, Isobutyl alcohol (131, 132)
t = 25°C

g A/l$_B$	K′ ± ?
0.017	19
0.104	5.3
0.820	3.35

NON-AQUEOUS SYSTEMS

A = I_2
B = CCl_4, Carbon tetrachloride
C = $CHCl_3$, Chloroform (93)
B = CCl_4, Carbon tetrachloride
C = $C_3H_8O_3$, Glycerol (93)
B = $CHCl_3$, Chloroform
C = $C_3H_8O_3$, Glycerol (63, 72)
B = $C_4H_{10}O$, Ethyl ether
C = $C_2H_6O_2$, Glycol (93)
B = $C_4H_{10}O$, Ethyl ether
C = $C_3H_8O_3$, Glycerol (63)
B = C_6H_6, Benzene
C = CCl_4, Carbon tetrachloride (93)
B = C_6H_6, Benzene
C = $C_3H_8O_3$, Glycerol (93)

A = CH_2O_2, Formic acid
B = $C_4H_{10}O$, Ethyl ether
C = H_2SO_4 (5); also H_2SO_4+ NaCl

A = $C_2H_4O_2$, Acetic acid
B = $CHCl_3$, Chloroform
C = $C_3H_8O_3$, Glycerol (74)
B = $C_4H_{10}O$, Ethyl ether (110)
C = Fused salts; $CaCl_2.6H_2O$; $LiNO_3.3H_2O$

A = C_2H_6O, Ethyl alcohol
B = $C_4H_{10}O$, Ethyl ether (110)
C = $CaCl_2.6H_2O$ (fused)
B = C_6H_6, Benzene (110)
C = $CaCl_2.6H_2O$ (fused)

A = $C_5H_{10}O_2$, Valeric acid
B = Benzine
C = H_2SO_4 (60)

A = $C_8H_{14}O_6$, Diethyl tartrate (178)
B = $C_2H_4Br_2$, Ethylene bromide
C = CH_3NO, Formamide

A = $C_{10}H_{16}O$, Citral
B = C_2H_6O, Ethyl alcohol
C = Lemon oil (105); at 25 ± 0.1°C, K_B = 0.07 ± 0.01 for g A/l_B = 27.5–33.4

A = H_3BO_3
B = $C_5H_{12}O$, Amyl alcohol
C = $C_3H_8O_3$, Glycerol (74)

The B-component is Acetone. The C-component is Glycerol (157).
CH_2O_2, Formic acid
$C_2HCl_3O_2$, Trichloroacetic acid
$C_2H_3BrO_2$, Bromoacetic acid
$C_2H_2Cl_2O_2$, Dichloroacetic acid
$C_2H_3ClO_2$, Chloroacetic acid
$C_2H_4O_2$, Acetic acid
C_2H_4OS, Thioacetic acid
C_2H_7N, Ethylamine
C_2H_7N, Dimethylamine
$C_3H_4O_4$, Malonic acid
$C_3H_5BrO_2$, 1-Bromopropionic acid
$C_3H_6O_2$, Propionic acid
$C_4H_4O_4$, Fumaric acid
$C_4H_4O_4$, Maleic acid
$C_4H_5BrO_4$, Bromosuccinic acid
$C_4H_6O_4$, Succinic acid
$C_4H_6O_5$, Malic acid
$C_4H_6O_6$, Tartaric acid
$C_4H_8O_2$, *n*-Butyric acid
$C_4H_8O_2$, Isobutyric acid
$C_4H_{11}N$, Diethylamine
$C_5H_8O_4$, Glutaric acid
$C_5H_{10}O_2$, Isovaleric acid
$C_5H_{11}N$, Piperidine
$C_6H_{13}N$, *n*-Methylpiperidine
$C_6H_{15}N$, Dipropylamine
$C_6H_{15}N$, Triethylamine
$C_7H_6O_5$, Gallic acid
$C_7H_7NO_2$, Anthranilic acid
$C_8H_6O_4$, Phthalic acid
$C_8H_8O_3$, Mandelic acid
$C_9H_9NO_3$, Hippuric acid
Acid phthalates of C_2H_7N, Dimethylamine; C_3H_9N, Trimethylamine; $C_4H_{11}N$, Diethylamine; $C_5H_{11}N$, Piperidine; $C_6H_{13}N$, *n*-Methylpiperidine; $C_6H_{15}N$, Dipropylamine and Triethylamine; $C_9H_{13}N$, Benzylethylamine; $C_8H_{19}N$, Diisobutylamine; $C_9H_{21}N$, Tripropylamine; $C_{10}H_{23}N$, Diisoamylamine

LITERATURE

(For a key to the periodicals see end of volume)

(1) Abbott and Bray, *1*, **31**: 729; 09. (2) Abegg, Fox and Herz, *93*, **35**:129; 03. (3) Aiello, *205*, **124**: 192; 21. (3.1) Allen and Middleton, *Proc. Indiana Acad. Sci.* **32**: 153; 22. (3.5) Angelescu, *Bull. soc. chim. România*, **7**: 72; 25. (4) Auerbach, *93*, **37**: 353; 03. (5) Auerbach and Zeglin, *7*, **103**: 200; 23. (5.5) Bailey, *4*, **127**: 1951; 25. (6) Baum, *277*, **42**: 119; 99. (7) Bell and Feild, *1*, **33**: 940; 11. (8) Berthelot and Jungfleisch, *6*, **26**: 396; 72. (9) Bierich, *278*, **174**: 202; 19.

(10) Bjerrum, *93*, **118**: 131; 21. **119**: 39; 21. *137*, **7**: 66; 15. (11) Böeseken and Waterman, *64P*, **14**: 608; 12. (12) Bogdan, *9*, **11**: 824; 05. (13) Bogdan, *9*, **12**: 489; 06. (14) Brann, *Diss.*, Wisconsin, 1914. (15) Bray, *7*, **54**: 569; 06. (16) Brown, *50*, **2**: 51; 98. (17) Brown and Bury, *4*, **123**: 2430; 23. (18) Bubanovic, *147*, **2**: No. **33**: 13. (19) Bugarszky, *7*, **71**: 705; 10.

(20) Calvert, *7*, **38**: 513; 01. (20.5) Cavanagh, *5*, **106**: 243; 24. (21) Chandler, *1*, **30**: 694; 08. (22) Corliss, *50*, **18**: 681; 14. (23) Creighton, *143*, **180**: 63; 15. (24) Crowell, *1*, **40**: 453; 18. (25) Cushny, *289*, **40**: 17; 10. (26) Dakin, Janney and Wakeman, *141*, **14**: 341; 13. (27) Dawson, *4*, **79**: 238; 01. (28) Dawson, *4*, **81**: 521; 02. (29) Dawson, *4*, **81**: 1086; 02.

(30) Dawson, *4*, **89**: 1666; 06. (31) Dawson, *7*, **56**: 605; 06. (32) Dawson, *4*, **93**: 1308; 08. (33) Dawson and Gawler, *4*, **81**: 524; 02. (34) Dawson and Grant, *4*, **81**: 512; 02. (35) Dawson and Leslie, *4*, **99**: 1601; 11. (36) Dawson and McCrae, *4*, **77**: 1239; 00. (37) Dawson and McCrae, *4*, **79**: 493; 01. (38) Dawson and McCrae, *93*, **26**: 94; 01. (39) Dhar and Datta, *9*, **19**: 583; 13.

(40) Dieckmann and Hardt, *25*, **52**: 1134; 19. (41) Donnan and Garner, *4*, **115**: 1313; 19. (42) Drucker, *7*, **49**: 563; 04. (43) Drucker, *9*, **18**: 236; 12. (44) Drucker, *9*, **18**: 562; 12. (45) Dubrisay, *34*, **154**: 431; 12. (45.5) Emery and Wright, *1*, **43**: 2323; 21. (46) Ephraim and Aellig, *37*, **6**: 37; 23. (47) Farmer, *4*, **83**: 1440; 03. (48) Farmer and Warth, *4*, **85**: 1713; 04. (49) Fedorov, *53*, **35**: 639; 03.

(50) Flürscheim, *4*, **97**: 84; 10. (51) Forbes and Coolidge, *1*, **41**: 150; 19. (52) Fox, *4*, **97**: 119; 10. (53) Fresenius and Grünhut, *91*, **60**: 457; 21. (54) Freundlich and Richards, *7*, **79**: 681; 12. (54.5) Frumkin and Kulvarskaja, *93*, **138**: 278; 24. (55) Garraud, *Thèse de Pharmacie*, Bordeaux, 1897. (56) Gellert, *Diss.*, Budapest, 1914. *10*, **4**: 820; 22. (57) Georgievics, *7*, **84**: 353; 13. (58) Georgievics, *7*, **90**: 47; 15. (59) Gordon and Reid, *50*, **26**: 773; 22.

(60) Gurvich, *53*, **46**: 401; 14. *7*, **87**: 323; 14. (61) Halban and Hecht, *9*, **24**: 65; 18. (62) Hantzsch and Sebaldt, *7*, **30**: 258; 99. (63) Hantzsch and Vagt, *7*, **38**: 705; 01. (64) Harrass, *Arch. intern. pharmacodynamie*, **11**: 431; 03. (65) Hendrixson, *93*, **13**: 73; 97. (66) Herz, *196*, **15**: 1; 09. (67) Herz, *B13*, 190; 12. (68) Herz and Bulla, *93*, **71**: 254; 11. (69) Herz and Fischer, *25*, **37**: 4746; 04.

(70) Herz and Fischer, *25*, **38**: 1138; 05. (71) Herz and Kurzer, *9*, **16**: 240; 10. (72) Herz and Kurzer, *9*, **16**: 869; 10. (73) Herz and Lewy, *9*, **11**: 818; 05. (74) Herz and Lewy, *Jahresber. Schles. Ges. vaterl. Kultur, Naturw. Sekt.*, **1906**: 1. (75) Herz and Paul, *93*, **85**: 214; 14. (76) Herz and Rathmann, *9*, **19**: 552; 13. (77) Herz and Schuftan, *7*, **101**: 269; 22. (78) Hill, *1*, **43**: 254; 21. (79) Holde, *9*, **16**: 436; 10.

(80) Isobe, *Diss.*, Rigakushi. (81) Jakovkin, *7*, **18**: 585; 95. (82) Jakovkin, *7*, **20**: 19; 296. (83) Jakovkin, *7*, **29**: 613; 99. (84) Jones and Hartmann, *78*, **30**: 295; 16. (85) Joyner, *93*, **77**: 103; 12. (86) Jüttner, *7*, **38**: 56; 01. (87) Keane and Narracott, *173*, **34**: 436; 09. (88) Kolosovskii, *28*, **25**: 183; 11. (89) Kolosovskii, *28*, **25**: 334; 11.

(90) Kolosovskii, *27*, **9**: 632; 11. (91) Kolosovskii, *28*, **28**: 257; 14. (92) Kurilov, *7*, **25**: 419; 98. (93) Landau, *53*, **42**: 377; 10. *7*, **73**: 200; 10. (94) Lasserre, *Ann. inst. Pasteur*, **21**: 829; 07. (95) Lewis and Storch, *1*, **39**: 2544; 17. (96) Lindner, *57*, **33**: 613; 12. (97) Linhart, *1*, **37**: 258; 15. (98) Linhart, *1*, **38**: 1272; 16. (99) Linhart, *1*, **40**: 158; 18.

(100) Löfman, *93*, **107**: 241; 19. (101) Lottermoser, *9*, **27**: 496; 21. (102) McCrae and Wilson, *93*, **35**: 11; 03. (103) Malvezin, *27*, **5**: 332; 09. (104) Marden, *45*, **6**: 315; 14. (105) Marden and Elliott, *45*, **6**: 928; 14. (105.5) Menshutkin, *53*, **41**: 1089; 09. (106) Menzel, *7*, **105**: 402; 23. (107) Meyer, *277*, **46**: 338; 01. (108) Meyer, *172*, 7th, **A2**: 37; 09. (109) Moore and Winmill, *4*, **101**: 1635; 12.

(110) Morgan and Benson, *1*, **29**: 1176; 07. (111) Morse, *7*, **41**: 709; 02. (112) Müller and Abegg, *7*, **57**: 513; 07. (113) Mylius, *93*, **70**: 203; 11. (114) Nernst, *7*, **8**: 110; 91. (115) Nernst and Hohmann, *7*, **11**: 352; 93. (116) Nicholls, *173*, **47**: 506; 22. (117) Noyes and Stewart, *1*, **32**: 1133; 10. (118) Odaira, *429*, **1**: 319; 16. (119) Osaka, *479*, **1**: 93; 05.

(120) Osipov and Popov, *53*, **35**: 637; 03. (121) Overton, *Studien über die Narkose.* Jena, Fischer, 1901. (122) Pecsi, *Diss.*, Budapest, 1914. *10*, **4**: 818; 22. (123) Pelet-Jolivet, *Rev. gén. mat. col.*, **13**: 249; 09. (124) Philip and Bramley, *4*, **107**: 377; 15. (125) Philip and Bramley, *4*, **107**: 1831; 15. (126) Pinnow, *91*, **50**: 154; 11. (127) Pinnow, *91*, **54**: 321; 15. (128) Pinnow, *279*, **32**: 257; 16. (129) Pinnow, *279*, **37**: 49; 19. (129.5) Pinnow, *279*, **44**: 204; 22.

(130) Reichel, *205*, **22**: 149; 09. (131) Reinders, *55*, **13**: 96; 13. (132) Reinders and Lely, *64P*, **15**: 482; 12. (133) Riedel, *7*, **56**: 243; 06. (134) Riesenfeld, *7*, **41**: 346; 02. (135) Riesser, *202*, **96**: 355; 16. (136) Roloff, *7*, **13**: 327; 94. (137) Rosenstein and Adams, *1*, **35**: 1883; 13. (138) Rothmund and Drucker, *7*, **46**: 827; 03. (139) Rothmund and Wilsmore, *7*, **40**: 611; 02.

(140) Sabalitschka, *25*, **53**: 1383; 20. (141) Salzmann, *277*, **70**: 233; 12. (142) Sapozhnikov, *53*, **32**: 375; 00. (143) Schreiner, *93*, **122**: 201; 22. (144) Seidell, *Proc. Am. Pharm. Assoc.*, **58**: 1031; 10. (145) Seidell, *464*, No. 67; 10. (146) Seidell, *11*, **48**: 453; 12. (147) Sherrill, *7*, **43**: 705; 03. (148) Sherrill, *1*, **29**: 1641; 07. (149) Shilov and Lepin, *7*, **101**: 353; 22.

(150) Sidgwick, Pickford and Wilsdon, *4*, **99**: 1122; 11. (151) Sisley, *27*, **27**: 901; 02. (152) Skinner, *4*, **61**: 339; 92. (153) Smirnov, *53*, **38**: 1172; 06. (154) Smirnov, *7*, **58**: 373; 07. (155) Smith, *50*, **25**: 204; 21. (156) Smith, *50*, **25**: 605, 616; 21. (157) Smith, *50*, **25**: 721; 21. (158) Smith, *50*, **26**: 256; 22. (159) Strömholm, *52*, **66**: 423; 02.

(160) Strömholm, *7*, **44**: 63; 03. (160.5) Swift, *1*, **46**: 2375; 24. (161) de Sziszkovski, *147*, **2**: No. 41; 12. (162) de Sziszkovski, *147*, **3**: No. 3; 14. (163) de Sziszkovski, *147*, **3**: No. 5; 14. (164) de Sziszkovski, *147*, **3**: No. 10; 15. (165) Tanret, *27*, **17**: 497; 97. (165.5) Taylor, *50*, **29**: 995; 25. (166) Thoms and Runze, *25*, **50**: 1217; 17. (167) Thoms and Zehrfeld, *25*, **50**: 1221; 17. (168) Treadwell, *37*, **6**: 744; 23. (169) Van Name and Brown, *12*, **44**: 105; 17.
(170) Vaubel, *52*, **67**: 473; 03. (170.5) Voznesenskii and Chmutov, *53*, **57**: 343; 25. (171) Waentig and Pescheck, *7*, **93**: 529; 19. (172) Walden, *25*, **34**: 4185; 01. (173) Walton and Lewis, *1*, **38**: 633; 16. (174) Wámossy, *Magyar Orvosi Arch.*, **14**: 384; 13. *10*, **4**: 824; 22. (175) Washburn and Strachan, *1*, **35**: 681; 13. (176) Wedekind and Paschke, *7*, **73**: 118; 10. (177) Winther, *7*, **56**: 719; 06. (178) Winther, *7*, **60**: 563; 07. (178.5) Woodman and Corbet, *4*, **127**: 2461; 25. (179) Wroth and Reid, *1*, **38**: 2316; 16.
(180) Knight and Hinshelwood, *4*, **1927**: 466.

P-V-T RELATIONS IN THE GASEOUS STATE FOR SUBSTANCES WHICH ARE LIQUID OR SOLID AT 0° AND 1 ATMOSPHERE

F. G. KEYES

VALUES OF *pv*

Pressure in atmospheres, volume in liters per gram, unless otherwise indicated

A-Tables.—Elementary Substances

As, Arsenic (5, 7, 22, 28)

$p_{atm.}$	600°C	700°C	800°C	900°C	1000°C	1100°C	1200°C
0.020	0.275	0.363	0.420	0.492			
0.035	0.272	0.340	0.394	0.458	0.593		
0.050	0.269	0.325	0.376	0.437	0.549	0.712	0.900
0.100	0.259	0.298	0.342	0.393	0.496	0.613	0.777
0.200	0.242	0.284	0.324	0.357	0.434	0.534	0.674
0.300	0.231	0.278	0.316	0.347	0.411	0.498	0.626
0.400	0.223	0.273	0.310	0.340	0.399	0.474	0.596
0.500		0.268	0.304	0.335	0.389	0.457	0.576
0.600		0.263	0.300	0.332	0.382	0.444	0.558
0.700		0.258	0.296	0.330	0.376	0.434	0.539
0.800		0.256	0.294	0.328	0.373	0.426	0.522
0.900			0.292	0.327	0.371	0.421	0.507
1.000				0.326	0.370	0.418	0.494
1.100					0.369	0.414	0.484

$p_{atm.}$	500°C	800°C	900°C	1000°C	1100°C	1200°C
1.200				0.4857	0.5806	0.6906
1.300					0.5752	0.6835
1.400						0.6770
1.500						0.6735
1.600						0.6700

Br, Bromine (11, 15, 18, 19, 20, 21)

$p_{atm.}$	700°C	800°C	900°C	1000°C	1100°C	1200°C	1300°C
0.500	0.4987						
0.600	0.4987	0.5532	0.6119				
0.700	0.4987	0.5530	0.6115	0.6795			
0.800	0.4987	0.5528	0.6112	0.6779	0.7560		
0.900		0.5524	0.6108	0.6763	0.7530	0.8487	
1.000		0.5520	0.6105	0.6747	0.7509	0.8423	0.9639
1.1000			0.6101	0.6731	0.7492	0.8382	0.9574
1.2000				0.6715	0.7476	0.8360	0.9533
1.3000					0.7461	0.8343	
1.4000						0.8329	

P, Phosphorus (7, 14, 22, 28, 30)

$p_{atm.}$	500°C	600°C	700°C	800°C	900°C	1000°C	1100°C	1200°C
0.050	0.586	0.638	0.787	0.860				
0.100	0.562	0.612	0.701	0.818	1.012	1.340	1.754	2.210
0.200	0.536	0.597	0.674	0.774	0.914	1.156	1.486	1.946
0.300	0.524	0.590	0.664	0.760	0.881	1.084	1.354	1.799
0.400	0.516	0.585	0.658	0.749	0.866	1.044	1.288	1.704
0.500		0.582	0.653	0.740	0.856	1.020	1.248	1.632
0.600			0.649	0.732	0.847	1.004	1.212	1.572
0.700					0.838	0.988	1.194	1.520
0.800							1.160	1.478
0.900							1.140	1.440
1.000							1.122	1.407
1.100								1.378

I, Iodine (4, 12, 13, 17, 29, 31, 33, 34)

$p_{atm.}$	500°C	800°C	900°C	1000°C	1100°C	1200°C
0.400	0.2495	0.3725				
0.500	0.2495	0.3718	0.4339			
0.600	0.2495	0.3709	0.4313	0.5135		
0.700		0.3698	0.4288	0.5083	0.6119	
0.800		0.3684	0.4263	0.5034	0.6046	0.7240
0.900		0.3665	0.4237	0.4987	0.5979	0.7151
1.000			0.4212	0.4942	0.5918	0.7065
1.100				0.4899	0.5862	0.6983

S, Sulfur (6, 7, 8, 9, 10, 17, 23, 28, 32, 34, 35)

$p_{atm.}$	250°C	300°C	350°C	400°C	450°C	500°C
0.01	0.1835	0.2095	0.2560			0.735
0.015	0.1798	0.2071	0.2419	0.3220	0.475	0.731
0.020		0.2056	0.2355	0.3080	0.474	0.716
0.050			0.2304	0.2748	0.376	0.587
0.100			0.2283	0.2639	0.328	0.473
0.150			0.2276	0.2609	0.314	0.422
0.200				0.2590	0.306	0.393
0.300				0.2561	0.299	0.370
0.400				0.2532	0.295	0.360
0.500				0.2507	0.291	0.352
0.600					0.286	0.344
0.700					0.284	0.336
0.800						0.329
0.900						0.322
1.000						0.316
1.100						0.311

$p_{atm.}$	550°C	600°C	650°C	850°C	950°C	1020°C
0.050	0.954	1.127	1.216	1.519		
0.100	0.781	1.042	1.169	1.498	1.623	1.701
0.150	0.674	0.964	1.128	1.481	1.612	1.694
0.200	0.604	0.893	1.092	1.467	1.604	1.688

S.—(*Continued*)

$p_{atm.}$	550°C	600°C	650°C	850°C	950°C	1020°C
0.300	0.528	0.787	1.037	1.447	1.584	1.675
0.400	0.489	0.719	0.996	1.434	1.574	1.664
0.500	0.464	0.674	0.960	1.426	1.566	1.657
0.600	0.448	0.639	0.925	1.420		
0.700	0.433	0.610	0.892	1.416		
0.800	0.421	0.587	0.858			
0.900	0.409	0.566	0.826			
1.000	0.400	0.549	0.798			
1.100	0.389	0.532	0.771			
1.200	0.380	0.516	0.750			
1.300			0.734			

Se, Selenium (**5, 22, 28, 35**)

$p_{atm.}$	500°C	550°C	600°C	650°C	700°C	750°C	800°C	850°C	900°C
0.010	0.206	0.251							
0.015	0.197	0.248	0.327	0.404	0.455				
0.020	0.190	0.245	0.328	0.406	0.459	0.504			
0.035	0.179	0.234	0.326	0.408	0.466	0.510	0.538	0.576	0.598
0.050	0.172	0.223	0.314	0.407	0.471	0.516	0.542	0.578	0.601
0.100		0.188	0.254	0.366	0.464	0.520	0.552	0.582	0.608
0.200			0.216	0.288	0.386	0.481	0.538	0.572	0.604
0.300				0.258	0.331	0.442	0.514	0.556	0.592
0.400				0.246	0.300	0.410	0.498	0.548	0.584
0.500					0.284	0.385	0.483	0.539	0.580
0.600					0.278	0.373	0.472	0.532	0.578
0.700					0.272	0.364	0.460	0.523	0.575
0.800						0.355	0.450	0.515	0.572
0.900						0.347	0.440	0.507	0.567
1.000							0.418	0.496	0.562
1.100								0.490	0.557

𝔅-Tables.—Chemical Compounds

H_2O, Superheated steam (**1, 2, 16, 16.5**)

$p_{atm.}$	110°C	120°C	130°C	140°C	150°C
1.00	1.723	1.772	1.819	1.866	1.912
1.1	1.720	1.769	1.817	1.864	1.910
1.2	1.717	1.767	1.815	1.863	1.909
1.3	1.713	1.764	1.813	1.861	1.907
1.4	1.710	1.761	1.811	1.859	1.906
1.5		1.759	1.809	1.857	1.904
1.6		1.756	1.807	1.855	1.902
1.7		1.754	1.805	1.854	1.901
1.8		1.751	1.803	1.852	1.899
1.9		1.748	1.800	1.850	1.898
2.0	**160°C**	**170°C**	1.798	1.848	1.896
2.5	1.936	1.987	1.786	1.838	1.887
3.0	1.929	1.979		1.828	1.878
3.5	1.922	1.972		1.816	1.869
4.0	1.914	1.965			1.859
4.5	1.906	1.957			1.849
5.0	1.897	1.949			
5.5	1.887	1.941			
6.0	1.878	1.933			
6.5		1.924	**180°C**		
7.0		1.916	1.970		
7.5		1.906	1.962	**185°C**	
8.0			1.954	1.981	
8.5			1.946	1.973	
9.0			1.937	1.966	
9.5			1.927	1.957	
10.0				1.947	
10.5				1.937	
11.0				1.925	

CH_4O, Methyl alcohol (**26**) ✓

Volume in decaliters (10 l) per gram

$p_{atm.}$	120°C	160°C	180°C	200°C	230°C	240°C
2	0.0991	0.1107	0.0933*	0.1204	0.1291	0.1313
4	0.0944	0.1082		0.1192	0.1286	0.1309
6	0.0883	0.1057		0.1179	0.1279	0.1305
8		0.1031		0.1164	0.1272	0.1299
10	0.0900†	0.1003	0.1089	0.1149	0.1263	0.1292
12		0.0969	0.1064	0.1134	0.1253	0.1283
14		0.0931	0.1037	0.1118	0.1242	0.1273
16		0.0883	0.1010	0.1101	0.1229	0.1262
18		0.08213	0.0986	0.1082	0.1216	0.1249
20			0.0947	0.1062	0.1201	0.1236
22			0.0911	0.1041	0.1185	0.1221
24	**220°C**		0.0872	0.1018	0.1169	0.1206
26	0.1098	**225°C**	0.0831	0.0994	0.1151	0.1189
28	0.1078	0.1101		0.0968	0.1132	0.1173
30	0.1057	0.1082		0.0939	0.1113	0.1157
32	0.1037	0.1062		0.0908	0.1092	0.1140
34	0.1016	0.1042		0.0874	0.1072	0.1123
36	0.0993	0.1022		0.0834	0.1051	0.1105
38	0.0969	0.1001		0.0794	0.1029	0.1087
40	0.0944	0.0978			0.1007	0.1069
42	0.0918	0.0954			0.0983	0.1051
44	0.0891	0.0929			0.0959	0.1032
46	0.0859	0.0903				0.1014
48	0.0827	0.0876				0.0998
50	0.0789	0.0847				0.0974
52	0.0747	0.0816				0.0953
54	0.0697	0.0781				0.0931
56	0.0639	0.0746				0.0908
58		0.0695				0.0883
60		0.0635				0.0858
62						0.0830
64						0.0801
66						0.0770
68						0.0736
70						0.0699
72						0.0656
74						0.0605
76						0.0540
78						0.0443

$p_{atm.}$	232°C	234°C	236°C	238°C	239°C	239.5°C
28	0.1136	0.1146	0.1154	0.1162	0.1166	
30	0.1119	0.1128	0.1137	0.1146	0.1149	
32	0.1101	0.1111	0.1121	0.1129	0.1133	
34	0.1082	0.1093	0.1104	0.1112	0.1116	
36	0.1064	0.1074	0.1086	0.1094	0.1099	
38	0.1044	0.1054	0.1068	0.1076	0.1081	
40	0.1023	0.1035	0.1049	0.1057	0.1062	
42	0.1002	0.1014	0.1029	0.1038	0.1044	
44	0.0980	0.0993	0.1009	0.1018	0.1024	
46	0.0957	0.0971	0.0987	0.0998	0.1003	
48	0.0933	0.0947	0.0966	0.0977	0.0982	
50	0.0908	0.0923	0.0942	0.0954	0.0960	
52	0.0882	0.0898	0.0918	0.0932	0.0938	
54	0.0854	0.0872	0.0893	0.0907	0.0914	
56	0.0825	0.0844	0.0867	0.0882	0.0890	
58	0.0794	0.0816	0.0839	0.0856	0.0865	
60	0.0760	0.0785	0.0808	0.0828	0.0838	
62	0.0723	0.0752	0.0778	0.0799	0.0812	
64	0.0680	0.0716	0.0742	0.0767	0.0783	0.0793
66	0.0628	0.0675	0.0704	0.0734	0.0752	0.0762
68	0.0562	0.0626	0.0662	0.0698	0.0717	0.0728

* At 100°C. † At 140°C.

$p_{atm.}$	232°C	234°C	236°C	238°C	239°C	239.5°C
70		0.0552	0.0611	0.0657	0.0679	0.0690
72			0.0543	0.0609	0.0634	0.0647
74				0 0543	0.0579	0.0593
76					0.0500	0.0523
78						0.0407

$C_2H_4O_2$, Acetic acid (24)

$p_{atm.}$	92°C	105.1°C	118°C	132.9°C	147.6°C	162.5°C	184.1°C
0.04	0.377	0.426	0.474				
0.06	0.363	0.414	0.463				
0.08	0.354	0.404	0.453				
0.10	0.346	0.395	0.444				
0.12	0.340	0.387	0.436		0.525	0.565	0.605
0.14	0.335	0.380	0.429	0.478	0.517	0.561	0.602
0.16	0.330	0.373	0.422	0.471	0.510	0.557	0.599
0.18	0.326	0.368	0.416	0.465	0.504	0.553	0.596
0.20	0.322	0.362	0.410	0.459	0.498	0.550	0.594
0.22	0.318	0.357	0.405	0.453	0.493	0.546	0.592
0.24	0.315	0.353	0.400	0.448	0.488	0.543	0.590
0.26	0.312	0.350	0.395	0.444	0.484	0.540	0.588
0.28	0.308	0.346	0.391	0.439	0.480	0.537	0.586
0.30	0.305	0.343	0.386	0.435	0.477	0.534	0.584
0.32	0.302	0.340	0.382	0.431	0.474	0.531	0.582
0.34	0.300	0.338	0.379	0.428	0.470	0.529	0.581
0.36	0.297	0.335	0.375	0.424	0.467	0.526	0.579
0.38	0.294	0.332	0.372	0.420	0.464	0.523	0.578
0.40		0.330	0.369	0.417	0.461	0.520	0.576
0.42		0.327	0.366	0.414	0.459	0.518	0.575
0.44		0.325	0.364	0.411	0.456	0.516	0.574
0.46		0.323	0.361	0.408	0.454	0.513	0.572
0.48		0.320	0.359	0.405	0.451	0.511	0.571
0.50		0.318	0.356	0.402	0.449	0.508	0.569
0.52		0.316	0.354	0.400	0.447	0.506	0.568
0.54		0.313	0.352	0.397	0.445	0.504	0.566
0.56		0.311	0.350	0.395	0.442	0.501	0.565
0.58		0.308	0.348	0.392	0.440	0.499	0.564
0.60		0.306	0.346	0.390	0.438	0.497	0.562
0.62		0.304	0.345	0.388	0.436	0.495	0.561
0.64		0.302	0.343	0.386	0.434	0.492	0.559
0.66			0.341	0.384	0.432	0.490	0.558
0.68			0.339	0.382	0.431	0.488	0.556
0.70			0.338	0.380	0.429	0.486	0.555
0.72			0.336	0.379	0.427	0.484	0.554
0.74			0.335	0.377	0.425	0.482	0.552
0.76			0.333	0.376	0.423	0.480	0.551
0.78			0.332	0.374	0.421	0.478	0.549
0.80			0.330	0.373	0.420	0.476	0.548
0.82			0.329	0.371	0.418	0.474	0.546
0.84			0.328	0.370	0.416	0.472	0.545
0.86			0.327	0.369	0.415	0.470	0.543
0.88			0.325	0.367	0.413	0.468	0.542
0.90			0.324	0.366	0.411	0.466	0.540
0.92			0.323	0.365	0.409	0.464	0.539
0.94			0.322	0.363	0.408	0.462	
0.96				0.362	0.406	0.460	
0.98				0.361	0.404		
1.00				0.360	0.402		

$p_{atm.}$	50°C	78.4°C	$p_{atm.}$	78.4°C	$p_{atm.}$	78.4°C
0.02	0.268		0.10	0.307	0.18	0.289
0.04	0.246	0.341	0.12	0.302	0.20	0.286
0.06	0.235	0.325	0.14	0.296	0.22	0.283
0.08		0.315	0.16	0.293	0.24	0.281

$p_{atm.}$	162.5°C	183.75°C	200°C	240°C	280°C	$p_{atm.}$	280°C
2	0.397					18	0.527
3	0.357	0.437	0.487	0.607		19	0.517
4		0.407	0.459	0.587	0.683	20	0.506
5		0.379	0.435	0.568	0.671	21	0.496
6			0.413	0.550	0.659	22	0.485
7			0.393	0.533	0.648	23	0.474
8				0.518	0.636	24	0.464
9				0.503	0.624	25	0.453

$p_{atm.}$	162.5°C	183.75°C	200°C	240°C	280°C	$p_{atm.}$	280°C
10				0.486	0.613	26	0.443
11				0.471	0.602	27	0.432
12				0.456	0.591	28	0.421
13				0.442	0.580	29	0.409
14				0.428	0.569	30	0.396
15				0 413	0.558	31	0.381
16					0.548	32	0.364
17					0.538		

C_2H_6O, Ethyl alcohol (25)

$p_{atm.}$	130°C	140°C	150°C	160°C	170°C	180°C	190°C
4	0.6843	0.708	0.7343	0.7567	0.7783	0.7973	
5	0.666	0.695	0.722	0.746	0.768	0.7887	0.8157
6	0.633	0.6797	0.7097	0.735	0.758	0.7803	0.808
7		0.661	0.6963	0.7233	0.7473	0.7717	0.800
8			0.681	0.7117	0.737	0.7627	0.7917
9			0.6617	0.699	0.726	0.7537	0.7833
10			0.633	0.6857	0.715	0.7443	0.7747
11				0.671	0.7033	0.7347	0.766
12				0.6523	0.6917	0.7243	0.7567
13					0.679	0.7137	0.747
14					0.6645	0.7025	0.7373
15					0.6463	0.6907	0.727

t, °C	$p_{atm.}$		$p_{atm.}$	180°C	190°C	$p_{atm.}$	190°C
	2	3					
100	0.646		16	0.6777	0.7167	21	0.654
110	0.6707	0.648	17	0.663	0.705	22	0.6387
	4		18	0.646	0.6935	23	0.6217
120	0.655		19	0.625	0.681	24	0.602
			20		0.668		

$p_{atm.}$	200°C	210°C	220°C	225°C	230°C	232°C	234°C
5	0.834	0.851	0.8583	0.8653	0.875	0.8833	0.8997
6	0.827	0.845	0.853	0.8607	0.8707	0.879	0.8955
7	0.8197	0.839	0.8473	0.8557	0.866	0.874	0.891
8	0.8123	0.833	0.8415	0.8503	0.861	0.869	0.8867
9	0.8047	0.826	0.8357	0.845	0.856	0.864	0.882
10	0.797	0.8195	0.8293	0.839	0.8507	0.859	0.8767
11	0.789	0.8127	0.823	0.833	0.845	0.8533	0.871
12	0.7813	0.8057	0.8163	0.827	0.8393	0.8473	0.8653
13	0.773	0.7983	0.8093	0.8203	0.8333	0.8413	0.8595
14	0.765	0.7907	0.8027	0.8137	0.827	0.8353	0.8533
15	0.756	0.783	0.7953	0.807	0.8207	0.829	0.847
16	0.747	0.775	0.788	0.800	0.8143	0.8225	0.840
17	0.7377	0.7667	0.7807	0.793	0.8077	0.8157	0.8337
18	0.728	0.758	0.773	0.786	0.8007	0.809	0.8267
19	0.718	0.7495	0.7653	0.7783	0.7947	0.802	0.820
20	0.7077	0.7407	0.7573	0.771	0.7863	0.795	0.8127
21	0.6967	0.7317	0.7493	0.763	0.779	0.7875	0.8057
22	0.6853	0.7223	0.741	0.7553	0.7713	0.780	0.798
23	0.6735	0.713	0.7327	0.7473	0.764	0.7723	0.7907
24	0.6607	0.703	0.7243	0.7393	0.756	0.7647	0.783
25	0.647	0.693	0.7157	0.731	0.748	0.757	0.7753
26	0.632	0.683	0.707	0.7227	0.740	0.749	0.767
27	0.616	0.6723	0.698	0.7143	0.7317	0.741	0.759
28	0.5977	0.661	0.689	0.7055	0.7233	0.7327	0.751
29	0.577	0.649	0.6797	0.6967	0.715	0.7243	0.743
30		0.6365	0.670	0.6877	0.7063	0.716	0.735
31		0.6227	0.660	0.6787	0.6973	0.7073	0.7265
32		0.6077	0.6495	0.6693	0.6885	0.6985	0.718
33		0.5915	0.6387	0.660	0.6797	0.6897	0.7097
34		0.573	0.6275	0.650	0.6703	0.681	0.701

C_2H_6O.—(*Continued*)

$p_{atm.}$	200°C	210°C	220°C	225°C	230°C	232°C	234°C
35		0.551	0.615	0.640	0.661	0.672	0.692$_7$
36			0.602$_3$	0.630	0.651$_7$	0.662$_7$	0.684
37			0.588$_7$	0.619$_3$	0.642	0.653	0.675
38			0.573$_7$	0.608$_3$	0.632	0.643$_5$	0.666
39			0.557	0.597	0.622	0.633$_7$	0.657
40				0.585	0.612	0.623$_7$	0.647$_3$
41				0.572	0.601$_7$	0.613$_7$	0.637$_5$
42				0.557$_7$	0.590$_7$	0.603	0.627$_3$
43				0.542	0.579$_3$	0.592$_5$	0.617
44				0.523$_3$	0.567$_3$	0.581$_3$	0.606
45				0.500	0.554$_7$	0.569$_5$	0.594$_3$
46				0.469$_5$	0.541	0.556$_7$	0.582$_3$
47					0.525$_3$	0.543	0.569$_7$
48					0.506	0.527$_7$	0.556
49					0.482	0.510	0.541$_5$
50					0.445	0.488	0.525$_3$
51						0.456	0.506$_7$
52							0.483$_5$
53							0.452

$p_{atm.}$	236°C	237°C	238°C	239°C	240°C	241°C	242°C
5	0.903	0.904$_7$	0.906$_3$	0.908$_3$	0.910	0.911	0.912
6	0.899	0.901	0.903	0.905	0.907	0.908	0.909$_3$
7	0.895	0.897$_3$	0.899$_3$	0.901$_3$	0.903$_3$	0.904$_7$	0.906$_3$
8	0.890$_7$	0.893	0.895$_3$	0.897$_5$	0.899$_7$	0.901	0.902$_7$
9	0.886	0.888$_5$	0.891	0.893	0.895	0.897	0.898$_7$
10	0.881$_3$	0.883$_7$	0.886	0.888$_3$	0.890$_7$	0.892$_3$	0.894
11	0.876	0.878$_7$	0.881	0.883$_3$	0.885$_7$	0.887$_3$	0.889
12	0.870$_7$	0.873	0.875$_7$	0.878	0.880$_3$	0.882	0.884
13	0.865	0.867$_3$	0.870	0.872$_3$	0.875	0.876$_3$	0.878$_3$
14	0.859	0.861$_3$	0.864	0.866$_7$	0.869	0.870$_7$	0.872$_7$
15	0.852$_7$	0.855$_3$	0.858	0.860$_7$	0.863	0.865	0.866$_7$
16	0.846$_3$	0.849	0.852	0.854$_7$	0.857	0.859	0.860$_7$
17	0.840	0.842$_7$	0.845$_3$	0.848$_3$	0.850$_7$	0.852$_7$	0.854$_7$
18	0.833$_3$	0.836	0.839	0.842	0.844$_7$	0.846$_5$	0.848$_3$
19	0.826$_7$	0.829$_5$	0.832$_7$	0.835$_7$	0.838	0.840$_3$	0.842
20	0.820	0.823	0.826	0.829	0.831$_7$	0.834	0.836
21	0.813	0.816	0.819	0.822	0.825	0.827$_3$	0.829$_3$
22	0.806	0.809	0.812$_3$	0.815$_3$	0.818$_7$	0.820$_7$	0.823$_0$
23	0.799	0.802	0.805$_7$	0.808$_5$	0.812	0.814	0.816$_3$
24	0.791$_7$	0.795	0.792$_5$	0.801$_7$	0.805	0.807$_3$	0.809$_7$
25	0.784	0.787$_7$	0.791$_5$	0.794$_5$	0.798$_3$	0.800$_3$	0.803
26	0.776$_7$	0.780$_3$	0.784	0.787$_3$	0.791$_3$	0.793$_5$	0.796
27	0.769	0.773	0.777	0.780$_3$	0.784	0.786$_5$	0.789
28	0.761$_7$	0.765$_3$	0.769$_5$	0.773	0.777	0.779$_3$	0.782
29	0.754	0.758	0.762	0.765$_7$	0.769$_7$	0.772	0.774$_7$
30	0.746	0.750	0.754$_3$	0.758	0.762$_3$	0.765	0.767$_3$
31	0.738	0.742	0.746$_3$	0.750$_3$	0.755	0.757$_7$	0.760
32	0.730	0.734	0.738$_7$	0.743	0.747$_7$	0.750	0.753
33	0.721$_7$	0.726	0.730$_7$	0.735	0.739$_7$	0.742$_5$	0.745$_3$
34	0.713$_3$	0.719	0.722$_3$	0.727	0.732	0.735	0.737$_7$
35	0.705	0.709$_3$	0.714	0.718$_7$	0.724	0.727	0.730
36	0.696	0.700$_7$	0.705$_7$	0.710$_3$	0.716	0.719	0.722
37	0.687$_7$	0.692	0.697	0.702	0.707$_7$	0.711	0.714
38	0.678$_7$	0.683$_3$	0.688$_5$	0.693$_5$	0.699	0.702$_7$	0.706
39	0.669$_7$	0.674$_3$	0.679$_7$	0.684$_8$	0.690	0.694	0.698
40	0.660	0.665	0.670$_3$	0.676	0.681$_3$	0.685$_7$	0.689
41	0.650$_7$	0.656	0.661	0.666$_7$	0.672$_3$	0.676$_7$	0.681
42	0.640$_7$	0.646	0.651$_3$	0.657$_3$	0.663	0.667$_7$	0.672
43	0.630$_3$	0.636	0.641$_7$	0.647$_7$	0.653$_7$	0.658$_5$	0.663
44	0.619$_7$	0.625$_3$	0.631$_3$	0.637$_9$	0.643$_7$	0.649	0.654
45	0.608$_5$	0.614$_7$	0.620$_7$	0.627$_3$	0.633$_7$	0.639$_5$	0.644$_7$
46	0.597	0.603	0.609$_7$	0.616$_5$	0.623$_2$	0.629$_3$	0.635
47	0.584$_5$	0.591	0.598	0.605$_5$	0.612$_7$	0.619	0.625
48	0.571$_5$	0.578$_5$	0.585$_7$	0.593$_7$	0.602	0.608$_3$	0.614$_3$
49	0.557$_7$	0.564$_7$	0.573	0.581$_7$	0.590$_5$	0.597$_3$	0.603$_3$
50	0.543	0.550$_3$	0.559	0.568$_7$	0.578$_7$	0.585$_3$	0.592
51	0.526$_7$	0.534	0.545	0.555$_3$	0.566	0.573	0.580
52	0.508$_3$	0.516$_5$	0.529	0.541	0.552$_7$	0.560	0.567
53	0.487	0.497	0.512	0.525$_7$	0.538	0.545$_5$	0.553$_3$
54	0.460	0.475	0.492$_3$	0.508$_3$	0.522	0.530	0.538
55	0.425	0.449	0.470	0.489	0.504$_3$	0.513$_3$	0.521$_7$
56			0.443$_5$	0.467	0.485$_3$	0.495	0.504
57			0.412$_5$	0.443	0.465	0.475$_5$	0.485$_3$
58				0.418$_5$	0.444$_5$	0.454$_3$	0.465$_3$

$p_{atm.}$	243.1°C	244.35°C	246°C	$p_{atm.}$	243.1°C	244.35°C	246°C
5	0.914	0.916$_7$	0.920	32	0.757	0.761$_3$	0.769$_7$
6	0.911$_5$	0.914	0.918	33	0.749$_7$	0.754	0.762$_3$
7	0.908$_7$	0.911	0.915	34	0.742	0.746$_7$	0.755
8	0.905	0.907	0.912	35	0.734$_7$	0.739	0.747$_7$
9	0.901	0.904	0.908$_7$	36	0.727	0.731$_3$	0.740
10	0.897	0.900	0.904$_7$	37	0.719$_3$	0.724	0.732
11	0.892	0.895$_7$	0.900$_5$	38	0.711$_7$	0.716	0.724$_3$
12	0.887	0.891	0.896	39	0.703$_7$	0.708	0.716$_7$
13	0.881$_7$	0.885$_7$	0.891	40	0.695$_7$	0.700	0.708$_7$
14	0.876	0.880	0.886	41	0.687$_7$	0.692$_3$	0.700$_3$
15	0.870	0.874$_3$	0.880$_3$	42	0.679$_3$	0.684	0.692$_3$
16	0.864$_3$	0.868$_7$	0.875	43	0.670$_7$	0.675$_7$	0.684
17	0.858	0.862$_7$	0.869	44	0.662	0.667	0.675$_3$
18	0.852	0.856$_7$	0.863	45	0.653	0.658$_7$	0.666$_7$
19	0.846	0.850$_3$	0.857	46	0.644	0.649$_7$	0.658
20	0.839$_5$	0.844	0.851	47	0.634$_3$	0.640$_3$	0.648$_7$
21	0.833	0.838	0.844$_7$	48	0.624$_3$	0.631	0.639
22	0.826$_7$	0.831$_5$	0.838$_3$	49	0.614	0.621	0.629$_3$
23	0.820	0.825	0.832	50	0.603$_3$	0.611	0.619
24	0.813$_3$	0.818	0.825$_3$	51	0.592	0.600$_3$	0.608$_7$
25	0.806$_7$	0.811$_3$	0.818$_7$	52	0.579$_7$	0.589	0.597
26	0.800	0.804$_7$	0.812	53	0.566$_7$	0.577	0.585$_7$
27	0.793	0.797$_7$	0.805	54	0.552$_3$	0.564	0.573
28	0.786	0.790$_3$	0.798	55	0.536$_7$	0.550	0.560
29	0.779	0.783$_3$	0.791$_3$	56	0.520	0.535$_3$	0.546
30	0.771$_7$	0.776	0.784	57	0.501$_3$	0.519$_7$	0.531$_3$
31	0.764$_3$	0.768$_7$	0.777	58	0.481	0.502$_3$	0.515$_5$

C_3H_8O, Propyl alcohol (27)

$p_{atm.}$	180°C	200°C	220°C	230°C	240°C	260°C	280°C
3	0.585						
4	0.576	0.607	0.639	0.655	0.670	0.699	0.726
5	0.566	0.599	0.632	0.649	0.663	0.693	0.722
6	0.555	0.590	0.624	0.642	0.657	0.688	0.718
7	0.545	0.582	0.617	0.635	0.651	0.682	0.713
8	0.533	0.573	0.610	0.628	0.645	0.677	0.708
9	0.521	0.564	0.602	0.621	0.638	0.671	0.704
10	0.509	0.555	0.594	0.614	0.632	0.666	0.699
11		0.545	0.586	0.606	0.625	0.660	0.694
12		0.535	0.578	0.599	0.618	0.654	0.689
13		0.524	0.570	0.591	0.611	0.649	0.684
14		0.512	0.562	0.583	0.604	0.643	0.679
15		0.500	0.553	0.575	0.597	0.637	0.674
16			0.544	0.566	0.589	0.631	0.669
17			0.535	0.558	0.582	0.625	0.663
18			0.526	0.549	0.574	0.619	0.650
19			0.516	0.540	0.566	0.612	0.653

$p_{atm.}$	220°C	230°C	240°C	250°C	260°C	270°C	280°C
20	0.505	0.531	0.558	0.582	0.606		0.647
21	0.493	0.522	0.549	0.575	0.599	0.623	0.642
22	0.481	0.512	0.541	0.567	0.593	0.617	0.636

$p_{atm.}$	220°C	230°C	240°C	250°C	260°C	270°C	280°C
23	0.468	0.501	0.532	0.559	0.586	0.611	0.630
24	0.453	0.490	0.523	0.551	0.579	0.604	0.625
25		0.479	0.514	0.543	0.572	0.598	0.619
26		0.466	0.504	0.534	0.565	0.591	0.613
27		0.452	0.494	0.525	0.557	0.585	0.607
28		0.437	0.483	0.517	0.550	0.578	0.601
29		0.419	0.472	0.507	0.542	0.571	0.595
30			0.460	0.498	0.534	0.564	0.589
31			0.447	0.488	0.525	0.556	0.583
32			0.432	0.477	0.516	0.549	0.576
33			0.416	0.466	0.507	0.541	0.570
34			0.396	0.455	0.498	0.534	0.563
35				0.443	0.488	0.525	0.556
36				0.429	0.478	0.517	0.549
37				0.415	0.468	0.509	0.542
38				0.399	0.457	0.500	0.535
39				0.380	0.446	0.490	0.527
40					0.434	0.481	0.520
41					0.420	0.471	0.512
42			263.64°C		0.406	0.461	0.504
43			0.412		0.390	0.450	0.496
44			0.399		0.372	0.439	0.487
45			0.385		0.352	0.427	0.478
46			0.369		0.328	0.415	0.469
47			0.351		0.298	0.401	0.459
48			0.328			0.388	0.449
49			0.298			0.373	0.439
50			0.260			0.357	0.428
51						0.338	0.418
52						0.318	0.406
53						0.293	0.395
54						0.264	0.383
55							0.370
56							0.356
57							0.341
58							0.325
59							0.309
60							0.291
61							0.273
62							0.254
63							0.235

$p_{atm.}$	130°C	150°C
2	0.519	
3	0.498	0.537
4		0.524
5		0.508

$C_4H_{10}O$, Ethyl ether ([3])

Volume in cm³ per gram; the last figure given has relative significance only

$p_{atm.}$	200°C	225°C	250°C	275°C	300°C	375°C
15	444.45	483.32	521.19	556.27	591.71	625.09
20	412.56	457.37	499.39	537.59	576.22	612.29
25	375.89	429.21	476.38	519.35	560.50	599.31
30	268.54	398.24	452.19	500.04	544.48	586.17
35	273.62	364.00	426.91	480.15	528.25	572.95
40		325.61	400.43	459.80	511.82	559.63
45		283.25	373.05	439.12	495.44	546.31
50		236.96	345.66	418.65	479.40	533.14
55			319.08	398.80	463.85	520.19
60			293.91	380.10	449.08	508.39
65				362.86	435.09	497.03
70				352.92	420.07	486.33
75				335.62	410.35	476.29
80					399.46	467.31
85					389.59	458.84
90						451.18

$p_{atm.}$	150°C	175°C
15	356.96	403.05
20		361.47
25		308.13

LITERATURE

(For a key to the periodicals see end of volume)

(1) Battelli, *6*, **26:** 394; 92. (2) Battelli, *6*, **3:** 408; 94. (3) Beattie, *1*, **46:** 342; 24. (4) Biltz, *7*, **2:** 920; 88. (5) Biltz, *7*, **19:** 385; 96. (6) Biltz, *25*, **34:** 2490; 01. (7) Biltz and Meyer, *7*, **4:** 249; 89. (8) Biltz and Preuner, *57*, **22:** 627; 01. (9) Bleier and Kohn, *25*, **33:** 50; 00.
(10) Bleier and Kohn, *57*, **21:** 575; 00. (11) Bodenstein and Cramer, *9*, **22:** 327; 16. (12) Crafts and Meier, *25*, **13:** 851; 80. (13) Crafts and Meier, *34*, **90:** 690; 80. (14) Hittorf, *8*, **126:** 193; 65. (15) Jahn, *25*, **15:** 1238; 82. (16) Jakob, *98*, **56:** 1980; 12. (16.5) Knoblauch, Linde and Klebe, *414*, No. **21:** 33; 05. (17) Krause and Meyer, *7*, **6:** 5; 90. (18) Meyer, *25*, **13:** 394; 80. (19) Meyer and Pzüblin, *25*, **13:** 405; 80.
(20) Perman, *5*, **48:** 45; 90. (21) Perman and Atkinson, *5*, **66:** 10; 00. *7*, **33:** 215, 577; 00. (22) Preuner and Brockmöller, *7*, **81:** 129; 12. (23) Preuner and Schupp, *7*, **68:** 129; 09. (24) Ramsay and Young, *4*, **49:** 790; 86. (25) Ramsay and Young, *62*, **177:** 123; 86. (26) Ramsay and Young, *62*, **178:** 314; 87. (27) Ramsay and Young, *62*, **180:** 137; 89. (28) Sainte-Claire Deville and Troost, *34*, **56:** 891; 63. (29) Starck and Bodenstein, *9*, **16:** 961; 10.
(30) Stock, Gibson and Stamm, *25*, **45:** 3527; 12. (31) Thiele, *93*, **1:** 277; 92. (32) Troost, *34*, **86:** 1394; 78. (33) Troost, *34*, **91:** 54; 80. (34) Troost, *34*, **95:** 30; 82. (35) Wartenberg, *93*, **56:** 320; 07.

COMPRESSIBILITY OF SOLUTIONS

L. H. Adams

The fragmentary nature of the recorded data makes it impossible to reconcile conflicting values, or to calculate true compressibility coefficients. The information is therefore given merely in the form of literature references.

AQUEOUS SOLUTIONS

Solute	*P*, range megabaryes	*t*, range °C	Lit.
	𝔅-Table		
HBr	1– 8	18	(21)
HCl	1– 8	15–20	(21, 22)
H_2SO_4	1– 8	17–22	(21, 22)
NH_4OH	1	18	(23)
HNO_3	1– 8	15–18	(21, 22)
NH_4NO_3	1	18	(23)
NH_4Cl	1– 8	0–22	(2, 21, 22, 23)
NH_4Br	1– 8	18	(21)
NH_4I	1– 8	18	(21)
$(NH_4)_2SO_4$	1– 300	18–20	(10, 16, 21, 24)
$ZnSO_4$	1– 750	15	(22, 26)
$Fe_2(SO_4)_3$	1– 8	15–18	(21, 22)
$MgSO_4$	1– 850	15	(24, 26)
$CaCl_2$	1– 10	0–20	(7, 23)
$SrCl_2$	1	0–20	(23)
$BaCl_2$	1– 300	0–20	(22, 23, 24)
LiOH	1– 8	18	(21)
LiCl	1– 9	14–18	(16, 21)
LiBr	1– 9	14–18	(16, 21)
LiI	1– 8	18	(21)
Li_2SO_4	1	18	(23)

Solute	P, range megabaryes	t, range °C	Lit.
$LiNO_3$	1– 9	14–18	(16, 21)
NaOH	1– 950	15–18	(23, 26)
NaCl	1– 300	0–20	(10, 16, 21, 23, 24)
NaBr	1– 9	14–18	(16, 20)
NaI	1	18	(23)
Na_2SO_4	1– 8	19	(21, 22)
$NaNO_3$	1– 300	14–20	(10, 16)
Na_2CO_3	1– 900	15–20	(10, 21, 26)
KOH	1– 900	15–20	(21, 22, 26)
KCl	1– 300	0–20	(7, 10, 16, 21, 23)
$KClO_3$	1	17	(22)
KBr	1– 9	14–18	(16, 21)
KI	1– 300	18–20	(10, 21)
K_2SO_3	1	18	(23)
K_2SO_4	1	18	(23)
KNO_3	1– 9	14–18	(16, 21)
$K_4Fe(CN)_6$	1– 300		(24)
$K_2Cr_2O_7$	1	17	(22)
RbCl	1– 9	14	(16)
CsCl	1– 9	14	(16)
Sea water	*v. infra*		(9, 24)

ℭ-Table

Solute	P, range megabaryes	t, range °C	Lit.
C_2H_5OH	1–1500	0–70	(11, 13, 14)
$(C_2H_5)_2O$	100– 300	20	(18)
CH_3COOCH_3	100– 300	20	(18)
CH_3COOH	1– 275	25–35	(8)
$CH_2ClCOOH$	1– 300	25	(8)
$CHCl_2COOH$	1– 290	25	(8)
CCl_3COOH	1– 270	25	(8)
Sucrose	1–1500	0–30	(1, 4, 5, 11, 17, 24, 25)
Urethane	100– 300	20	(19)
α-Methyl glucoside	1– 70	0–30	(1)
Casein	100– 300	20	(15)
Peptone	100– 300	20	(15)

NON-AQUEOUS SOLUTIONS

ℭ-Table

A	B	P, range megabaryes	t, range °C	Lit.
CCl_4	C_6H_6	1– 600	25	(6)
CS_2	$CHCl_3$	1– 10	25	(7)
CS_2	C_2H_5OH	1– 10	25	(7)
CS_2	CH_3COCH_3	1– 430	25	(20)
$CHCl_3$	CH_3COOH	1– 500	25	(20)
$CHCl_3$	C_2H_5OH	1– 10	25	(7)
$CHCl_3$	CH_3COCH_3	1– 480	25	(20)
$CHCl_3$	$(C_2H_5)_2O$	1– 600	25	(6)
$C_2H_4Cl_2$	C_6H_6	1– 600	25	(6)
CH_3COOH	C_6H_6	1– 450	25	(20)
CH_3COOH	$C_6H_5CH_3$	1– 450	25	(20)
C_2H_5OH	C_6H_6	1– 480	25	(20)
C_2H_5OH	Resorcinol	1– 250	188–242	(10)
CH_3COCH_3	$C_5H_{11}OH$	1–1000	16– 26	(3)
$(C_2H_5)_2O$	C_6H_5COOH	1– 250	150–212	(10)
$C_5H_{11}OH$	C_6H_6	1–1000	16– 26	(3)
$C_6H_5NO_2$	C_6H_6	1– 360	25	(20)
$C_6H_5NO_2$	$C_6H_5CH_3$	1– 430	25	(20)
$C_6H_5NH_2$	C_6H_6	1– 520	25	(20)
$C_6H_5NH_2$	C_6H_{14}		40	(12)
$C_6H_5NH_2$	$C_6H_5CH_3$	1– 550	25	(20)

Relative Volumes of Sea Water for Different Temperatures and Pressures (13, 19)

See also Heck and Service, U. S. Coast and Geodetic Survey, Spec. Publ. No. 108

Salinity: 31.130 parts per mille by weight

P	0°C	4.97°C	9.97°C	14.96°C	19.96°C
0	0.97560	0.97595	0.97660	0.97749	0.97862
200	.96672	.96731	.96815	.96919	.97042
400	.95840	.95919	.96019	.96136	.96270
600	.95056	.95153	.95268	.95397	.95539
Salinity: 38.525 parts per mille					
0	0.96996	0.97041	0.97113	0.97209	0.97326
200	.96130	.96196	.96286	.96396	.96523
400	.95317	.95403	.95508	.95629	.95766
600	.94551	.94654	.94772	.94904	.95049

Volume and Compressibility, $\beta = \left(\frac{1}{v_0}\frac{dv}{dP}\right)$ of Sea Water at 0°C and $35.\frac{0}{00}$ Salinity

P, megabarye	v, cm^3/g (?)	$10^6\beta$
0	0.97264	46.4
100	.96819	45.0
200	.96388	43.6
300	.95970	42.3
400	.95566	41.0
500	.95173	39.8
600	.94791	38.7
700	.94421	37.6
800	.94060	36.6
900	.93709	35.6
1000	.93367	34.7

LITERATURE

(For a key to the periodicals see end of volume)

(1) Berkeley, Hartley and Burton, *62*, **218**: 295; 19. (2) Braun, *8*, **31**: 331; 87. (3) Carnazzi, *59*, **9**: 161; 05. (4) Cohen and de Boer, *7*, **84**: 41; 13. (5) Cohen and Valeton, *7*, **92**: 433; 17. (6) Dolezalek and Speidel, *7*, **94**: 72; 20. (7) Drecker, *8*, **20**: 870; 83. (8) Drucker, *7*, **52**: 641; 05. (9) Ekman, *Die Zusammendruckbarkeit des Meerwassers, etc.* Conseil permanent international pour l'exploration de la mer. Publications de circonstance No. **43.** Copenhagen, 1908.

(10) Gilbaut, *7*, **24**: 385; 97. (11) Guinchant, *34*, **132**: 469; 01. (12) Keyes and Hildebrand, *1*, **39**: 2126; 17. (13) Moesveld, *7*, **105**: 450; 23. (14) Pagliani, *22*, **5 I**: 777, 885, 937; 89. (15) Palitzsch, *1*, **41**: 346; 19. (16) Pohl, *Diss.*, Bonn, 1906. (17) Quincke, *8*, **41**: 669; 90. (18) Richards and Chadwell, *1*, **47**: 2283; 25. (19) Richards and Palitzsch, *1*, **41**: 59; 19.

(20) Ritzel, *7*, **60**: 319; 07. (21) Roentgen and Schneider, *8*, **29**: 165; 86. **34**: 531; 88. (22) Schmidt, *75*, **114 IIa**: 945; 05. (23) Schumann, *8*, **31**: 14; 87. (24) Tait, *68*, **20**: 141; 95. (25) Valeton, *Diss.*, Utrecht, 1914. (26) Watson, *68*, **33**: 282; 13.

LITERATURE REFERENCES

LITERATURE REFERENCES

In all literature references cited in International Critical Tables the name of the journal or publication is indicated by means of a *Key Number* corresponding to the list given below. The numbers which follow this key number in a literature citation are, in the order named: (1) the volume, (2) the page, and (3) the last two figures of the year. Thus *64V*, **31**: 253; 22, indicates Verslag Koninklijke Akademie van Wetenschappen te Amsterdam, Vol. 31, page 253, 1922. Series numbers are not given. Key Numbers referring to books and other non-serial publications are preceded by the letter *B*, and the volume number is given in Roman numerals. Thus *B10*, **IV**: 191; 18, indicates Doelter, Handbuch der Mineralchemie, page 191 of Vol. 4 of the 1918 edition. The Key Number *O* is used to indicate "private communication from."

DAS LITERATURVERZEICHNIS

In allen Literaturstellen, die in I. C. T. verzeichnet sind, ist der Name der Zeitschrift oder der Publikation mit Hilfe einer *Schlüsselnummer*, entsprechend der unten folgenden Liste, angegeben. Die Zahlen, welche diesen Schlüsselnummern bei einem Literaturzitat folgen, bedeuten der Reihe nach: (1) der Band, (2) die Seite und (3), die letzten zwei Zahlen des Jahrganges. So bedeutet z. B. *64V*, **31**: 253; 22, Verslag Koninklijke Akademie van Wetenschappen te Amsterdam, Band 31, Seite 253, 1922. Serien-Nummern werden nicht angegeben. Der Schlüsselzahl wird ein *B* vorausgesetzt, wenn sie Bücher, oder eine andre nicht periodische Veröffentlichung bezeichnet. Die Bandnummer wird durch römische Ziffern angegeben. Es bedeutet z. B. also *B10*, **IV**: 191; 18, Doelter, Handbuch der Mineralchemie, Seite 191, des 4 Bandes, der Auflage des Jahres 1918. Die Schlüsselzahl *O* wird gebraucht, um anzuzeigen, dass es eine "private Mitteilung" ist.

RÉFÉRENCES BIBLIOGRAPHIQUES

Le nom du journal ou de la publication de toutes les références bibliographiques citées dans les Tables Critiques Internationales est indiqué au moyen d'un *nombre-clé* correspondant à la liste donnée ci-dessous. Les nombres qui suivent ce nombre-clé dans un renvoi bibliographique indiquent dans l'ordre suivant: (1) le volume, (2) la page, et (3) les deux derniers chiffres de l'année. Ainsi *64V*, **31**: 253; 22, indique Verslag Koninklijke Akademie van Wetenschappen te Amsterdam, Vol. 31, page 253, 1922. Les numéros des séries ne sont pas donnés. Les nombres-clés se rapportant à des livres ou à des publications non périodiques sont précédés de la lettre *B* et le numéro du volume est donné en chiffres romains. Ainsi *B10*, **IV**: 191; 18, indique Doelter, Handbuch der Mineralchemie, page 191 du volume 4 de l'édition de 1918. Le nombre-clé *O* est employé pour indiquer "communication privée de."

INDICAZIONI BIBLIOGRAFICHE

In tutte le indicazioni bibliografiche che si incontrano nelle "Tabelle Critiche Internazionali" il nome del giornale o della pubblicazione è espresso con un *numero chiave* riportato nell'elenco dato più oltre. I numeri che, nella citazione, vengono dopo il numero chiave sono disposti con l'ordine seguente: (1) il volume, (2) la pagina, e (3) le ultime due cifre del millesimo. Cosi *64V*, **31**: 253; 22, indica la Verslag Koninklijke Akademie van Wetenschappen te Amsterdam, Vol. 31, pagina 253, 1922. I numeri di serie non vengono dati. Quando un numero chiave è preceduto dalla lettera *B* si riferisce a libri o ad altre pubblicazioni non periodiche, e il numero del volume viene allora scritto in cifre romane. Cosi *B10*, **IV**: 191; 18, indica Doelter, Handbuch der Mineralchemie, pagina 191 del IV° volume dell'edizione 1918. Il numero chiave *O* indica "Comunicazione privata da . . . "

KEY TO THE PERIODICALS

Data regarding the libraries which receive many of these periodicals may be found through the following sources:

United States and Canada: "Periodicals Abstracted by Chemical Abstracts, 1926" (Chemical Abstracts, Ohio State Univ., Columbus, Ohio); "Union List of Serials in the Libraries of the United States and Canada, 1925–1927" (H. W. Wilson & Co., New York City); "A Catalogue of Scientific Periodicals in Canadian Libraries, 1924" (McGill Univ., Montreal, Canada).

Great Britain: "A World List of Scientific Periodicals Published in the Years 1900–1921" (Oxford Univ. Press, London, 1925–).

Holland: "Chemisch Jaarboekje tevens Jaarboekje der Nederlandsche Chemische Vereeniging, Vol. 3." (Amsterdam, D. B. Centen, 1920.)

1. Journal of the American Chemical Society.
2. Physical Review.
3. London, Edinburgh and Dublin Philosophical Magazine and Journal of Science.
4. Journal of the Chemical Society, London. (Memoirs of the Chemical Society; *continued as* Quarterly Journal; *later* Journal.)
5. Proceedings of the Royal Society (London). A. Mathematical and Physical Sciences.

5B. Proceedings of the Royal Society (London). B. Biological Sciences.

6. Annales de chimie et de physique. (*Divided into* Nos. 14 and 16 *in 1914.*)
7. Zeitschrift für physikalische Chemie, Stöchiometrie und Verwandtschaftslehre.
8. Annalen der Physik. [Journal der Physik, 1790–1794. Neues Journal der Physik, 1795–1796. Annalen der Physik, 1799–1819; Annalen der Physik und der physikalische Chemie, 1819–1824 (Gilbert). Annalen der Physik und Chemie, 1824–1899 (Poggendorff, Wiedemann). Annalen der Physik, 1900– (Drude, Wien and Planck).]
9. Zeitschrift für Elektrochemie und angewandte physikalische Chemie.
10. Tables annuelles internationales de constantes et données numériques.
11. American Chemical Journal. (*Combined with* No. 1 *in 1914.*)
12. American Journal of Science. (American Journal of Science and Arts, 1820–79; *known also as* Silliman's Journal of Science.)

13. Annalen der Chemie, Justus Liebig's.
14. Annales de chimie.
16. Annales de physique.
18. Archives néerlandaises des sciences exactes et naturelles. Series IIIA (Sciences exactes).
19. Arkiv för Kemi, Mineralogi och Geologi.
22. Atti della reale accademia nazionale dei Lincei. (Rendiconti classe di scienze fisiche, matematiche e naturali.)
23. Atti della reale accademia delle scienze di Torino.
24. Atti del reale istituto Veneto di scienze, lettere ed arti.
25. Berichte der deutschen chemischen Gesellschaft.
26. Berichte der deutschen physikalischen Gesellschaft. *See also* No. 96.
27. Bulletin de la société chimique de France. (*Before 1908 was* Bulletin de la société chimique de Paris.)
28. Bulletin de la société chimique de Belgique. (*Before 1904 was* Bulletin de l'association belge des chimistes.)
29. Bureau of Mines, Bulletins.
30. Bureau of Mines, Technical Papers.
31. Bureau of Standards, Scientific Papers.
31A. Bureau of Standards, Bulletin.
33. Chemical and Metallurgical Engineering. (*Name changed July, 1918 from* Metallurgical and Chemical Engineering.)
34. Comptes rendus hebdomadaires des séances de l'académie des sciences, de l'institut de France.
35. Elektrochemische Zeitschrift.
36. Gazzetta chimica italiana.
37. Helvetica Chimica Acta.
38. Journal of the American Ceramic Society.
40. Journal of the American Institute of Metals. (Transactions of the American Brass Founders' Association, 1908–11; Transactions of the American Institute of Metals, 1912–16; Journal of the American Institute of Metals, 1917–18; *discontinued in 1918 and incorporated with* Bulletin of the American Institute of Mining Engineers; *with No. 148, 1919, this Bulletin became* Bulletin of the American Institute of Mining and Metallurgical Engineers; *with No. 154, 1919, name changed again to* Mining and Metallurgy.)
41. Journal of the Chemical Society of Japan (Nippon Kwagaku Kwai Shi). (*Name changed in Jan., 1921 from* Journal of the Tokyo Chemical Society.)
41B. Bulletin of the Chemical Society of Japan.
42. Journal de chimie physique.
45. Industrial and Engineering Chemistry. (*Name changed Jan., 1923 from* Journal of Industrial and Engineering Chemistry.)
49. Journal de pharmacie et de chimie.
50. Journal of Physical Chemistry.
51. Journal de physique et le radium. (*Formed from* Le radium *and* Journal de physique, théorique et appliquée.)
52. Journal für praktische Chemie.
53. Journal of the Russian Physico-Chemical Society. (Chemical part.)
54. Journal of the Society of Chemical Industry.
55. Kolloid-Zeitschrift. (*Formerly* Zeitschrift für Chemie und Industrie der Kolloide.)
56. Mechanical Engineering. (*Formerly* No. 122.)
57. Monatshefte für Chemie und verwandte Teile anderer Wissenschaften.
58. Nature, London.
59. Nuovo Cimento.
60. Översikt av Finska Vetenskaps-Societetens Förhandlingar. (*Discontinued with* Vol. 64, 1921–22.)
62. Philosophical Transactions of the Royal Society of London, Series A, Physical and Mathematical.
63. Physikalische Zeitschrift, vereinigt mit dem Jahrbuch der Radioaktivität und Elektronik.
64P. Proceedings of the Royal Academy of Sciences of Amsterdam.
64V. Verslag koninklijke Akademie van Wetenschappen te Amsterdam.
65. Proceedings of the American Academy of Arts and Sciences.
67. Proceedings of the Physical Society of London.
68. Proceedings of the Royal Society of Edinburgh.
69. Proceedings and Transactions of the Royal Society of Canada.
70. Recueil des travaux chimiques des Pays-Bas.
72. Rendiconti reale istituto Lombardo di scienze e lettere.
75. Sitzungsberichte Akademie der Wissenschaften in Wien, mathematisch-naturwissenschaftliche Klasse.
76. Sitzungsberichte der preussischen Akademie der Wissenschaften.
78. Transactions of the American Electrochemical Society.
79. Transactions of the American Institute of Chemical Engineers.
80. Transactions of the American Institute of Mining and Metallurgical Engineers.
82. Transactions of the Ceramic Society (England).
83. Transactions of the Faraday Society.
86. University of Illinois, Engineering Experiment Station, Bulletins.
87. Verhandelingen der koninklijke Akademie van Wetenschappen te Amsterdam.
88. Verhandlungen der physikalischen Gesellschaft zu Berlin. *See also* No. 96.
89. Wissenschaftliche Abhandlungen der physikalisch-technischen Reichsanstalt.
90. Wissenschaftliche Abhandlungen der Kaiserlichen Normal-Eichungs-Kommission. (*Now* Reichsanstalt für Mass und Gewicht.)
91. Zeitschrift für analytische Chemie.
92. Zeitschrift für angewandte Chemie.
93. Zeitschrift für anorganische und allgemeine Chemie. (*Name changed in 1915 from* Zeitschrift für anorganische Chemie.)
94. Zeitschrift für Krystallographie. (*Name changed in 1921 from* Zeitschrift für Krystallographie und Mineralogie.)
96. Zeitschrift für Physik. (Verhandlungen der physikalischen Gesellschaft zu Berlin, 1882–1898; Verhandlungen der deutschen physikalischen Gesellschaft, 1899–1902; Berichte der deutschen physikalischen Gesellschaft, 1903–1919; Zeitschrift für Physik, 1920– .)
97. Zeitschrift für technische Physik.
98. Zeitschrift des Vereines deutscher Ingenieure.
112. Dinglers polytechnisches Journal.
117. Scientific Proceedings of the Royal Dublin Society.
122. Journal of the American Society of Mechanical Engineers. *See* No. 56.
128. Journal of the Washington Academy of Sciences.
132. Anales de la sociedad española de fisica y quimica.
133. British Association for the Advancement of Science, Reports.
134. Bulletin de l'académie des sciences de l'union des républiques soviétiques socialistes. (*Formerly* Bulletin de l'académie impérial des sciences de St. Pétersbourg; *name changed in 1917 to* Bulletin de l'académie des sciences de Russie; *present name dates from 1925.*)
135. Chemical News and Journal of Industrial Science. (*Name changed in 1921 from* Chemical News and Journal of Physical Science.)
136. Chemiker-Zeitung.
137. Kongelige Danske Videnskabernes Selskab, Mathematisk-fysiske Meddelelser.
138. Societas scientiarum fennica. Commentationes physico-mathematicae.

139. Ferrum.
140. Journal of the Iron and Steel Institute, London.
141. Journal of Biological Chemistry.
142. Journal of the Society of Chemical Industry, Japan. (*Formerly* Journal of Chemical Industry, Japan.)
143. Journal of the Franklin Institute.
144. Mathematikai ès Természettudomanyi Ertesitö, Budapest.
147. Meddelanden från K. Vetenskapakademiens Nobelinstitut.
148. Zeitschrift für die gesamte Kälte-Industrie.
149. Archives des sciences physiques et naturelles. (Bibliothèque britannique, 1796–1815; Bibliothèque universelle des sciences, belles-lettres et arts, 1816–1835; Bibliothèque universelle de Genève, 1836–1845; Supplément à la bibliothèque universelle de Genève. Archives des sciences physiques et naturelles, 1846–1847; Bibliothèque universelle de Genève. Archives des sciences physiques et naturelles, 1848–1857; Bibliothèque universelle, revue suisse et étrangère. Archives des sciences physiques et naturelles, 1858–1861; Bibliothèque universelle et revue suisse. Archives des sciences physiques et naturelles, 1862–1877; Bibliothèque universelle. Archives des sciences physiques et naturelles, 1878– .)
151. Mémoires de l'académie royale des sciences de l'institut de France.
152. Carnegie Institution of Washington, Publications.
157. U. S. Department of Agriculture, Bulletin.
159. Science Reports of the Tôhoku Imperial University. Series I, Mathematics, Physics and Chemistry.
165. Bulletin internationale de l'académie des sciences de Cracovie. *Name changed to* Bulletin internationale de l'académie Polonaise des sciences et des lettres.
167. Jahresbericht über die Fortschritte der Chemie und verwandte Theile anderer Wissenschaften.
168. Communications from the Physical Laboratory at the University of Leiden.
169. Annales de l'Institut Polytechnique Pierre-le-Grand, Pétrograd.
170. Memorie della reale accademia nazionale dei Lincei.
172. International Congress of Applied Chemistry.
173. Analyst, London.
174. Transactions of the Royal Society of Edinburgh.
175. Annales academiae scientiarum Fennicae.
176. Chemisch Weekblad, Amsterdam.
180. Anzeiger der Akademie der Wissenschaften, Krakau.
181. Travaux de la société de physique et de chimie de Kharkoff.
182. Proceedings of the Chemical Society, London.
185. Chemisches Centralblatt.
186. Bulletin de la classe des sciences, académie royale de Belgique.
187. Metall und Erz, Zeitschrift für Metalhüttenwesen und Erzbergbau, einschl. Aufbereitung.
188. Nachrichten von der königlichen Gesellschaft der Wissenschaften zu Göttingen. Geschaftliche Mitteilungen; mathematisch-physikalische Klasse.
190. Neues Jahrbuch für Mineralogie, Geologie und Paläontologie.
190B. Neues Jahrbuch für Mineralogie, Geologie und Paläontologie, Beilage Band.
192. Metallurgie. (*Divided into* Nos. 139 and 187.)
196. Sammlung chemischer und chemisch-technischer Vorträge.
197. Proceedings of the National Academy of Sciences.
199. Le Radium. (*Merged into* No. 51 *in 1920.*)
201. Proceedings of the Cambridge Philosophical Society.
202. Zeitschrift für physiologische Chemie.
203. Archiv für Anatomie und Physiologie. Physiologische Abteilung. *Merged with* No. 278.
205. Biochemische Zeitschrift.
208. Physica, Nederlandsch Tijdschrift voor Natuurkunde.
213. Sitzungsberichte der mathematisch-physikalischen Klasse der Bayerischen Akademie der Wissenschaften zu München.
218. Naturwissenschaften.
221. Berichte über die Verhandlungen der sächsischen Akademie der Wissenschaften zu Leipzig. Mathematisch-physikalische Klasse.
233. Pharmaceutisch Weekblad.
238. Travaux et mémoires du bureau international des poids et mésures.
245. Zeitschrift für das gesamte Schiess- und Sprengstoffwesen.
250. Bulletin de la société française de physique.
271. Revue scientifique.
273. Berichte der deutschen pharmazeutischen Gesellschaft. *See also* No. 293.
277. Proceedings of the Society for Experimental Biology and Medicine.
278. Archiv für die gesamte Physiologie des Menschen und der Tiere. (Pflüger.)
279. Zeitschrift für Untersuchung der Nahrungs- und Genussmittel sowie der Gebrauchsgegenstande. Zeitschrift für Untersuchung der Lebensmittel.
284. Journal of the American Pharmaceutical Association.
285. Journal of Mathematics and Physics.
287. Kolloidchemische Beihefte.
289. Journal of Physiology.
290. Journal of the Society of Dyers and Colourists.
291. Arbeiten aus dem Reichsgesundheitsamte.
292. Proceedings and Transactions of the Nova Scotian Institute of Science.
293. Archiv der Pharmazie. (*Combined with* No. 273 *in 1924 to form* Archiv der Pharmazie und Berichte der deutschen pharmazeutischen Gesellschaft.)
294. Mémoires de l'académie de Belgique.
302. Smithsonian Institution Publications. Miscellaneous Collection.
315. Mémorial des poudres. (*Formerly* Mémorial des poudres et salpétres.)
316. Journal and Proceedings of the Royal Society of New South Wales.
317. Chemische Industrie. (*Combined with* No. 92 *in 1921; separated again in 1923.*)
318. Journal of the Indian Institute of Science.
319. Die deutsche pharmazeutische Zeitung.
320. Journal of Analytical and Applied Chemistry. *Merged into* No. 1 *in 1893.*
322. Schriften der Dorpater Naturforscher-Gesellschaft an der Universität.
324. Canadian Chemistry and Metallurgy.
325. Proceedings of the Royal Institution of Great Britain.
342. Annales de chimie analytique et de chimie appliquée et revue de chimie analytique réunies.
347. Pharmaceutical Journal and Pharmacist.
352. Milchwirtschaftliche Zentralblatt. (*Name changed in 1912 from* Milch-Zeitung.)
365. Bureau of Standards, Circulars.
373. Chemisch-technisches Repertorium. (*Supplement to* No. 136.)
378. Chimie et industrie.
382. Refrigerating Engineering. (Transactions of the American Society of Refrigerating Engineers, 1905–13; American Society of Refrigerating Engineers Journal; *present name dates from July, 1922.*)
388. Översigt av Förhandlingar kongl. Svenska Vetenkaps-Akademien.
397. Gas- und Wasserfach. (*Name changed Jan., 1922 from* Journal für Gasbeleuchtung und verwandte Beleuchtungsarten sowie für Wasserversorgung.)

406. Monthly Weather Review.
410. Edinburgh Philosophical Journal, 1819–26; Edinburgh New Philosophical Journal, 1826–64; Quarterly Journal of Science, 1864–70; Quarterly Journal of Science and Annals of Mining, Metallurgy, Engineering, Industrial Arts, Manufactures and Technology, 1871–79; Monthly Journal of Science and Annals of Astronomy, Biology, Geology, Industrial Arts, Manufactures and Technology, 1879–85.
414. Mitteilungen über Forschungsarbeiten auf den Gebiete des Ingenieurwesens hrsg. vom Vereine deutscher Ingenieure.
416. Brennstoff-Chemie.
426. Acta Societatis Fennicae. (1839–1842, Commentationes Societatis Fennicae.)
427. Physikalische Berichte. (Beiblätter zu den Annalen der Physik und Chemie; Beiblätter *united with* Fortschritte der Physik *and* Halbmonatliches Literaturverzeichnis *to form* Physikalische Berichte.)
428. Repertorium für Experimental-Physik für physikalische Technik für mathematische und astronomische Instrumentenkunde (*Before 1867 was* Repertorium für physikalische Technik für mathematische und astronomische Instrumentenkunde; *also known as* Carl's Repertorium.)
429. Memoirs of the College of Science, Kyoto Imperial University. (*Before 1914 was part of* Memoirs of the College of Science and Engineering, Kyoto Imperial University.)
448. Proceedings of the Fourth International Congress of Refrigeration.
451. Memoirs of the College of Engineering, Kyoto Imperial University. *See* No. 429.
452. Die oesterreichische pharmazeutische Post.
453. Proceedings of the Iowa Academy of Science.
461. Proceedings of the Royal Society of New South Wales.
462. Bulletin institut international du froid.
463. Société de physique et d'histoire naturelle de Genève. Mémoires.
464. United States Public Health Service. Hygienic Laboratory Bulletins.
465. Zeitschrift der deutschen Öl- und Fett-Industrie.
466. Repertorium der analytischen Chemie (Organ des Vereins analytischer Chemiker). *See also* No. 92.
467. Zeitschrift für Chemie. Leipzig.
468. Kungliga Svenska Vetenskapsakademiens. Handlingar.
472. Papier-Fabrikant.
474. Zeitschrift für komprimierte und flüssige Gase.
475. Bulletin institut international du froid.
478. Bulletin de l'association des chimistes de sucrerie et de distillerie de France et des colonies.
479. Memoirs of the College of Science and Engineering, Kyoto Imperial University. *Divided in 1914 into* Nos. 429 and 451.
485. Teknisk Tidskrift. Upplaga C. Kemi och Bergsvetenskap.
487. Die deutsche pharmazeutische Zeitung.
491. Wochenblatt für Papierfabrikation.
495. Vierteljahresschrift für präktische Pharmazie. *Combined in 1923 with* No. 293.
496. Mémoires de l'institut polytechnique, Pierre-le-Grand, Pétrograd.
497. Archiv for Pharmaci og Chemi.
498. Pharmazeutische Zeitschrift für Russland.
499. Archiv für Mineralogie, Geognosie, Bergbau und Hüttenkunde (Karstens).
500. Zeitschrift für das Berg-, Hütten- und Salinenwesen in dem preussischen Staate.
501. Mémoires couronnés et autres mémoires publiés par l'Académie Royale des sciences, des lettres et des beaux-arts de Belgique. Collection in 8vo.
502. Archives du Musée Teyler (Harlem).
503. Quarterly Journal of Science, Literature and the Arts.
504. Mémoires de l'académie des sciences de Russie.
505. Technology Reports of the Tôhoku Imperial University.
509. Archiv für Chemie und Meterologie. A section of "Archiv für die gesammte Naturlehre (Kastners Archiv)."

B3. Landolt-Börnstein, Physikalisch-chemische Tabellen. 5th ed. Berlin, Springer, 1923.
B12. Friese, Das Porzellan als Isolier- und Konstruktions-Material in der Elektrotechnik. Klosterlausnitz, 1904.
B13. Nernst Festschrift, 1912.
B21. Abegg, Handbuch der anorganische Chemie. Leipzig, Hirzel, 1905– .
B40. Shorthose, Thermal Properties of Methyl Chloride. Dept. of Scientific and Industrial Research, Food Investigation Board, Report No. 19, 1924.
B50. Gmelin-Kraut's Handbuch der anorganischen Chemie. Heidelberg, Winter, 1906– .
B51. Seidell, Solubilities of Inorganic and Organic Substances. New York, Van Nostrand, 1919.
B57. Tammann, Krystallizieren und Schmelzen. Leipzig, Barth, 1903.
B60. Fourth International Congress of Refrigeration Reports, Papers presented by the President. Leiden, Ijdo, 1924.
B67. Jenkins and Shorthose, Thermal Properties of Ethyl Chloride. Dept. of Scientific and Industrial Research, Food Investigation Board, Special Report No. 14, 1923.
B71. Mellor, Treatise on Inorganic and Theoretical Chemistry. London, Longmans, 1922- .
B72. Bunsen Gasometrische Methoden. 2nd ed. Braunschweig, 1877.
B81. Great Britain Challenger Office: Report of Scientific Results. Voyage H. M. S. Challenger, Physics and Chemistry.
B82. Lunge and Berl, Chemisch-technische Untersuchungsmethoden. Berlin, Springer, 1910.